SIXTH CANADIAN EDITION

UNDERSTANDING HUMAN SEXUALITY

Janet Shibley Hyde
University of Wisconsin—Madison

John D. DeLamater
University of Wisconsin—Madison

E. Sandra Byers
University of New Brunswick

Understanding Human Sexuality
Sixth Canadian Edition

ISBN-13: 978-1-25-902476-4
ISBN-10: 1-25-902476-8

2 3 4 5 6 7 8 9 0 TCP 1 9 8 7 6 5

Printed and bound in Canada

Director of Product Management: *Rhondda McNabb*
Product Manager: *Jason Chih*
Senior Marketing Manager: *Margaret Greenfield*
Product Developer: *Katherine Goodes*
Senior Product Team Associate: *Marina Seguin*
Supervising Editor: *Cathy Biribauer*
Photo/Permissions Researcher: *Monika Schurmann*
Copy Editor: *Dawn Hunter*
Plant Production Coordinator: *Sheryl MacAdam*
Manufacturing Production Coordinator: *Emily Hickey*
Cover and Interior Design: *Dave Murphy*
Composition: *Laserwords Private Limited*
Cover Photo: *Masterfile/Royalty Free*
Printer: *Transcontinental Printing Group*

Library and Archives Canada Cataloguing in Publication Data

Hyde, Janet Shibley, author
    Understanding human sexuality / Janet Shibley Hyde, University of Wisconsin-Madison, John D. DeLamater, University of Wisconsin-Madison, E. Sandra Byers, University of New Brunswick. — Sixth Canadian edition.
    Includes bibliographical references and index.
    ISBN 978-1-25-902476-4 (pbk.)

    1. Sex—Textbooks. I. DeLamater, John D., author II. Byers, E. Sandra, 1951-, author III. Title.

HQ12.H92 2014   306.7   C2014-904959-5

Author Biographies

Janet Shibley Hyde, the Helen Thompson Woolley Professor of Psychology and Women's Studies at the University of Wisconsin–Madison, received her education at Oberlin College and the University of California, Berkeley. She has taught a course in human sexuality since 1974, first at Bowling Green State University, then at Denison University, and now at the University of Wisconsin. Her research interests are in gender differences and gender-role development in childhood and adolescence. Author of the textbook *Half the Human Experience: The Psychology of Women,* she is a past president of the Society for the Scientific Study of Sexuality and is a Fellow of the American Psychological Association and the American Association for the Advancement of Science. She has received many other honours, including an award for excellence in teaching at Bowling Green State University, the Chancellor's Award for teaching at the University of Wisconsin, and the Kinsey Award from the Society for the Scientific Study of Sexuality for her contributions to sex research. In 2000–2001 she served as one of the three scientific editors for U.S. Surgeon General David Satcher's report *Promoting Sexual Health and Responsible Sexual Behavior.* She is married to John DeLamater.

John D. DeLamater, Professor of Sociology at the University of Wisconsin–Madison, received his education at the University of California, Santa Barbara, and the University of Michigan. He created the human sexuality course at the University of Wisconsin in 1975 and has since taught it regularly. His current research and writing are focused on the effects of life-course transitions on sexuality. He has published papers on the effects of having a child, of dual-career couples, and of divorce, and is studying the effects of menopause and later-life transitions on sexual attitudes and behaviour. He is the co-author of the textbook *Social Psychology.* He is a Fellow of the Society for the Scientific Study of Sexuality and the 2002 recipient of the Kinsey Award from the Society for Career Contributions to Sex Research. He has received awards for excellence in teaching from the Department of Sociology and Interfraternity Council-Panhellenic Association, and is a Fellow and past Chair of the Teaching Academy at the University of Wisconsin. He regularly teaches a seminar for graduate students on teaching undergraduate courses. He is married to Janet Hyde.

E. Sandra Byers is a Professor and Chair of the Department of Psychology at the University of New Brunswick (UNB). She was honoured by UNB with a University Research Scholar Award in 2008. Dr. Byers grew up in Montreal and received her university education at the University of Rochester and West Virginia University. She created the human sexuality course at the University of New Brunswick in 1979 and has taught it annually since then. She is the author or co-author of more than 125 journal articles and book chapters, and has supervised 49 honours, masters, and doctoral theses. Much (but not all) of her research has been in the areas of sexual satisfaction, sexual communication, sexual violence, and attitudes toward sexual health education. She also has a private practice in clinical psychology specializing in the treatment of sexual problems and concerns, and she regularly teaches a graduate seminar on sex therapy. She has won several awards, most recently the Kinsey Award from the Society for the Scientific Study of Sexuality in 2013, the Distinguished Scientific Contributions Award from the Society for the Scientific Study of Sexuality in 2009, and the Distinguished Contributions to Psychology as a Profession Award from the Canadian Psychological Association in 2010. She is a past president of the Canadian Sex Research Forum, a Fellow of the Canadian Psychological Association and the Society for the Scientific Study of Sexuality, a member of the Advisory Board of the Sex Information and Education Council of Canada, an editorial board member of four sexuality journals, and the founding director of the Muriel McQueen Fergusson Centre for Family Violence Research. Dr. Byers has given more than 150 invited addresses and workshops, and has been interviewed about sexual issues by numerous radio and television stations, magazines, and newspapers. As a sexuality educator, researcher, and therapist in Canada, Dr. Byers is uniquely placed to provide a Canadian perspective on human sexuality. She has been married to Dr. Larry Heinlein, who is also a clinical psychologist, for 41 years, and has two daughters, Krista and Alyssa. To learn more about Dr. Byers and her research, you can visit her website at http://www.unb.ca/fredericton/arts/departments/psychology/people/byers.html.

Contents in Brief

Contents

Preface

Continuing a Research-Based Tradition in Sexuality

Since its conception, *Understanding Human Sexuality* has achieved distinction and success by following the science of human sexuality. The first of the modern sexuality textbooks, *Understanding Human Sexuality* introduced this topic to students through the science that has uncovered what we know about the field. Groundbreaking when it first appeared, this research-based tradition continues to result in a contemporary, balanced introduction to human sexuality in an integrated learning system that engages students in learning about the content of the course, about others, and about themselves.

Our goal in creating the Sixth Canadian Edition of *Understanding Human Sexuality* was to maintain the best features of the highly regarded American textbook while providing a truly Canadian focus. Over the past two decades, *Understanding Human Sexuality* has been widely recognized for its comprehensive and multidisciplinary coverage of a broad range of topics, its commitment to excellent scholarship, and its appeal and accessibility to students. The Sixth Canadian Edition retains these strengths while incorporating the latest information about a range of sexual topics, including Internet issues related to sexuality, adolescent sexual behaviour, transgender individuals, the causes and treatment of sexual disorders, and legal decisions related to sex work.

Following the Science to Understand Human Sexuality

Understanding Human Sexuality is grounded in science and the research that informs science. This foundation, drawn from several perspectives, is reflected by us, as the authors. We bring these different perspectives to our introduction to human sexuality. The importance we place on science comes from the desire to provide students with an understanding of human sexuality based on the best available research and also on what we see and do as researchers ourselves.

The quality of sex research is highly variable. One of our responsibilities as authors is to sift through available studies and present only those of the best quality and the greatest relevance to this course. We are thrilled to observe that the quality of sex research improves every decade. In this edition, recent studies of excellent quality in terms of sampling, research design, and measurements have been added.

A Book for Students

First and foremost, we have kept in mind that students want to learn about sexuality and that our job as writers is to help them learn. We have covered topics completely, with as clear a presentation as possible, and have made a special effort to use language that will enlighten rather than intimidate. In the selection and preparation of illustrations for the book, our goal has always been to convey as much information as possible, simply and clearly.

The book assumes no prior university or college courses in biology, psychology, or sociology. It is designed as an introduction following the four major objectives of our own courses in human sexuality:

1. To provide students with an understanding of the methods and results of research that has contributed to our scientific knowledge about human sexuality, as well as the tools to read research reports and evaluate claims critically and intelligently

2. To provide practical information needed for everyday living, such as information about sexual anatomy, contraception, sexually transmitted infections, and ways to deal with problems in sexual functioning

3. To help students appreciate the fabulous diversity of human sexuality along many dimensions, including age, sexual orientation and identity, ethnicity within Canada, and culture around the world

4. To help students feel more comfortable with thinking and talking about sex, both to minimize their own personal discomfort and to help them become responsible decision makers in a vital aspect of their personal lives and in their roles as citizens and voters

All of the above information is supported by research so that students feel confident in what they are learning and applying to their lives.

What Is Unique About the Sixth Canadian Edition of *Understanding Human Sexuality*?
A Commitment to Canadian Content

First is the Canadian content. There are many ways in which sexuality in Canada is different from sexuality in the United States or Europe—whether it's rates of breastfeeding, teenage pregnancy, and STIs; attitude toward same-sex relationships; or laws regulating sexuality. These differences are reflected throughout the text—every chapter has significant Canadian content. Thus, students are provided with information that is relevant to their own lives, their own experiences, and their own communities. In keeping with the substantial amount of excellent sexuality research being conducted in Canada, the textbook also highlights Canadian sexuality research and researchers. Professors who reviewed the Sixth Canadian Edition were extremely positive about the inclusion of Canadian content, enthusiastically praising both the extent and the relevance of Canadian information compared with other texts available.

A Focus on Diversity and an Inclusive Approach

Second, in the Sixth Canadian Edition we have continued to pay special attention to making the text more inclusive. In keeping with the diversity within Canadian society, we use inclusive language that respects diversity and does not assume any particular lifestyle or life choices. Thus, for example, we use "partner" rather than "spouse," and language that applies equally to gay, lesbian, bisexual, and heterosexual students. We have also highlighted sexuality in Canadian ethnocultural communities, including the Chinese, South Asian, Caribbean, and First Nations communities, as well as regional differences, such as between Canadians living in Quebec and those living in other provinces.

Canadian Legal Information in Every Chapter

Third, students will find discussion of Canadian laws and Canadian legal issues in each chapter. This includes laws related to same-sex relationships, sexual assault, child sexual abuse, contraception and abortion, pornography, and prostitution, among others. We have provided a complete list of the sexually related statutes in the *Criminal Code of Canada*, as well as a history of the evolution of some of these statutes.

Relevant, Engaging Pedagogy

Fourth, to understand human sexuality fully, one must recognize one's own sexuality, as well as the diversity of others' sexuality. We highlight research and issues of particular interest to Canadian students in each chapter and provide support for student understanding of personal sexuality in several ways:

- The presentation of information helps students feel more at ease with thinking and talking about sex, increasing their comfort with a tension-causing topic and helping them make responsible decisions.

- **First Person** boxes share how sexuality may be experienced on the personal level. They provide practical information needed for everyday living, such as information about sexual anatomy, contraception, and sexually transmitted infections, and for dealing with problems in sexual functioning, such as early ejaculation or the inability to have an orgasm.

- **A Sexually Diverse World** boxes present an appreciation of the fabulous diversity of human sexuality along many dimensions, including age, sexual orientation and identity, ethnicity within Canada (a multiethnic perspective), and culture around the world (a multicultural perspective).

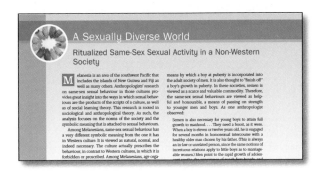

- **Milestones in Sex Research** boxes provide students with an extended look at classic and new studies that influence our understanding of human sexuality.

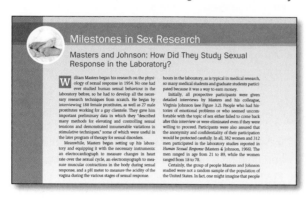

Milestones in Sex Research

Masters and Johnson: How Did They Study Sexual Response in the Laboratory?

William Masters began his research on the physiology of sexual response in 1954. No one had ever studied human sexual behaviour in the laboratory before, so he had to develop all the necessary research techniques from scratch. He began by interviewing 188 female prostitutes, as well as 27 male prostitutes working for a gay clientele. They gave him important preliminary data in which they "described many methods for elevating and controlling sexual tensions and demonstrated innumerable variations in stimulative techniques," some of which were useful in the later program of therapy for sexual disorders.

Meanwhile, Masters began setting up his laboratory and equipping it with the necessary instruments: an electrocardiograph to measure changes in heart rate over the sexual cycle, an electromyograph to measure muscular contractions in the body during sexual response, and a pH meter to measure the acidity of the vagina during the various stages of sexual response.

hours in the laboratory, as is typical in medical research, so many medical students and graduate students participated because it was a way to earn money.

Initially, all prospective participants were given detailed interviews by Masters and his colleague, Virginia Johnson (see Figure 3.2). People who had histories of emotional problems or who seemed uncomfortable with the topic of sex either failed to come back after this interview or were eliminated even if they were willing to proceed. Participants were also assured that the anonymity and confidentiality of their participation would be protected carefully. In all, 382 women and 312 men participated in the laboratory studies reported in *Human Sexual Response* (Masters & Johnson, 1966). The men ranged in age from 21 to 89, while the women ranged from 18 to 78.

Certainly, the group of people Masters and Johnson studied were not a random sample of the population of the United States. In fact, one might imagine that people

- **Learning Objectives** at the beginning of each chapter provide a preview of topics to help students prepare for reading and studying.

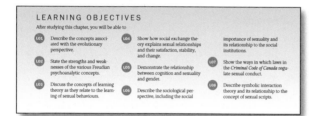

LEARNING OBJECTIVES

After studying this chapter, you will be able to

L01 Describe the concepts associated with the evolutionary perspective.

L02 State the strengths and weaknesses of the various Freudian psychoanalytic concepts.

L03 Discuss the concepts of learning theory as they relate to the learning of sexual behaviours.

L04 Show how social exchange theory explains sexual relationships and their satisfaction, stability, and change.

L05 Demonstrate the relationship between cognition and sexuality and gender.

L06 Describe the sociological perspective, including the social

importance of sexuality and its relationship to the social institutions.

L07 Show the ways in which laws in the *Criminal Code of Canada* regulate sexual conduct.

L08 Describe symbolic interaction theory and its relationship to the concept of sexual scripts.

- **Key terms** are defined and placed at the bottom of the page close to where the term is introduced. In addition, all key terms are included in the online Glossary.

example, university students who watch soap operas are more likely than nonviewing students to overestimate the incidence of divorce. The second influence is **agenda-setting**. News reporters select what to report and what to ignore and, within the stories they report, what to emphasize. For example, in 1998 the U.S. media chose to highlight the sexual dalliances of President Bill Clinton, suggesting to the public that these matters were important. In contrast, the Canadian media have rarely focused on the sexual activities of Canadian politicians. The media in many ways tell us what agenda to pay attention to. The third influence is **social learning**, a theory

Cultivation: In communications theory, the view that exposure to the mass media makes people think that what they see there represents the mainstream of what really occurs.

Agenda-setting: In communications theory, the idea that the media define what is important and what is not by which stories they report.

Social learning: In communications theory, the idea that the media provide role models whom we imitate.

excellent information about sexuality and promote sexual health. At the same time, a well-sampled study of youth between the ages of 10 and 17 who use the Internet regularly indicated that approximately 20 percent had received at least one sexual solicitation or approach over the Internet in the last year, and 3 percent had received an aggressive sexual solicitation in which the initiator asked to meet the recipient somewhere or sent him or her money or gifts (Finkelhor et al., 2000).

In the chapters that follow, we will examine the content of the media and the Internet on numerous sexual issues, and we will consider what effects exposure to this media content might have on viewers.

Let us now consider the perspectives on sexuality that are provided by scientific observations of humans in a wide variety of societies.

- **End-of-chapter study and review tools** in each chapter include a chapter summary and questions for thought, discussion, and debate.

SUMMARY

Theories provide explanations for sexual phenomena. Sociobiologists view human sexual behaviours as the product of natural selection in evolution, and thus view these behavioural patterns as being genetically controlled. Contemporary evolutionary theorists view behaviour as the result of an interaction between evolved mechanisms and environmental influence.

Among the psychological theories, Freud's psychoanalytic theory views the sex energy, or libido, as a major influence on personality and behaviour. Freud introduced the concepts of erogenous zones and psychosexual stages of development. Learning theory emphasizes how sexual behaviour is learned and modified through reinforcements and punishments according to principles of operant conditioning. Behaviour therapy

Social learning theory adds the concepts of imitation, identification, and self-efficacy to learning theory. Social exchange theory highlights the role of rewards and costs in relationships. Cognitive psychologists focus on people's thoughts and perceptions—whether positive or negative—and how these influence sexuality.

Sociologists study the ways in which society influences our sexual expression. At the macro level of analysis, sociologists investigate the ways in which institutions such as religion, the economy, the family, medicine, and the law influence sexuality. Symbolic interaction theory draws attention to processes of communication and interaction. Sexual scripts provide us with guidelines for behaviour in many situations. Reiss's sociological theory argues that all societies

QUESTIONS FOR THOUGHT, DISCUSSION, AND DEBATE

1. Compare and contrast how a sociobiologist, a psychoanalyst, and a sociologist would explain why people engage in premarital intercourse.

2. You are visiting your married sister and her family for the holidays. Her six-year-old asks you a question: "Why do mommies stay home with kids?" Drawing on the knowledge you gained from Chapter 2, how would you answer this question? Which ideas about parental investment, social learning, or social norms and scripts would you use to explain why, in most cultures, women perform the child-rearing activities?

3. From a sociologist's point of view, how have social institutions controlled female sexuality?

4. Could script theory explain the pattern of same-sex and mixed-sex sexual behaviour of Melanesian males described in the Sexually Diverse World box? Explain your answer.

5. Find out more about a recent decision by the Supreme Court of Canada with respect to a sex law. Do you agree or disagree with the decision? To what extent does the decision reflect current Canadian social norms?

Our own courses are surveys, designed to provide students with a broad range of information about sexuality. Reflecting that approach, this book is intended to be complete and balanced in its coverage. For instructors who lack the time or resources to cover the entire book, or for those who prefer to rearrange the order of topics, we have written all the chapters to be fairly independent of one another.

What's New in the Sixth Canadian Edition?

Building on the first five editions, this new edition provides Canadian data wherever reliable figures are available, features Canadian research and researchers, describes sexuality in the major Canadian ethnocultural communities, highlights issues important to Canadian students, and ensures that inclusive language and visuals appear throughout. Some of the major content changes and additions to the Sixth Canadian Edition are as follows:

Chapter 1 Sexuality in Perspective

- Added Are You Curious? questions
- Updated statistics throughout the chapter
- Expanded the coverage of sex with same-sex partners
- Added new information on the regional differences in sexuality
- Revised Table 1.2: Comparison of Sexuality in Quebec to Sexuality in Canada Overall
- Added new content on Aboriginal peoples and sexuality
- Updated Table 1.3: Percentage of Canadians and Americans Who Approve of Various Issues

Chapter 2 Theoretical Perspectives on Sexuality

- Added Are You Curious? questions
- Updated the law section to reflect recent court cases

- Expanded the coverage on gender schema theory
- Introduced new content on evolutionary perspectives
- Added material in evolutionary psychology and psychoanalytic theory
- Updated Table 2.1: What Are the Sexual Offences in the *Criminal Code of Canada* in 2010?
- Expanded the discussion on sexual scripts

Chapter 3 Sex Research
- Added Are You Curious? questions
- Revised feature: Where Can I Go in Canada to Become a Sex Researcher?
- Added content on the recent studies that use an MRI scanner to image sex
- Introduced new content related to measuring sex
- Included new material on purposeful distortion
- Added a new feature: Masters and Johnson: How Did They Study Sexual Response in the Laboratory?
- Enhanced coverage on the causes of cancer

Chapter 4 Sexual Anatomy
- Added Are You Curious? questions
- Broadened the discussion on hymen reconstruction
- Updated research on ovarian cancer
- Added content on the ten breast cancer subtypes
- Added trends to remove pubic hair
- Added information about race and prostate cancer rates
- Expanded coverage on cancer of the sex organs

Chapter 5 Sex Hormones, Sexual Differentiation, and Menstruation
- Added Are You Curious? questions
- Added new content on alternative therapies for PMS
- Added content from *DSM*-5
- Included new material on alternative therapies for menstrual problems
- Added new figure depicting hypospadias
- Increased discussion on endocrine disrupters
- Revised features: Is Environmental Pollution Affecting the Endocrine System? and Can Gender Be Assigned?
- Updated Table 5.1: homologous and analogous organs of the male and female reproductive systems
- Introduced new statistics on first menstruation
- Added material on innovative research on fluctuations in sex drive

Chapter 6 Conception, Pregnancy, and Childbirth
- Added Are You Curious? questions
- Updated statistics throughout the chapter
- Added new content on gender selection in Asian families
- Added new feature: Planning a Pregnancy?
- Introduced new research in the development of the conceptus
- Revised the discussion on home pregnancy tests
- Expanded the discussion of a father's experience in pregnancy
- Added content on the first stage of labour
- Added new and revised content on home birth versus hospital birth
- Broadened the discussion of in vitro fertilization
- Added a new section on prenatal genetic diagnosis

Chapter 7 Contraception and Abortion
- Added Are You Curious? questions
- Updated statistics throughout the chapter
- Revised the discussion of the vaginal ring and Depo-Provera injections
- Added a new feature: History of the Development of Sophisticated Methods of Contraception
- Revised Table 7.1: Contraception Around the World, Reported by Women Ages 15–44
- Added content on side effects of the pill
- Introduced material on medical abortions

Chapter 8 Sexually Transmitted Infections
- Added Are You Curious? questions
- Updated statistics throughout the chapter
- Revised discussion of the recent progress in HIV/AIDS research
- Mentioned the significant variations regarding STI rates
- Introduced new material on chlamydia
- Added new content on the HPV vaccine
- Revised discussion of genital herpes
- Added innovative information on preventing STIs
- Included new research on the other infections

Chapter 9 Sexual Response
- Added Are You Curious? questions
- Expanded discussion of the sexual response cycle

- Added new feature: Sex Toys and Physical Disability
- Updated visuals to demonstrate two-person sex
- Added new content on orgasm
- Included new material on neurochemical influences on sexual response

Chapter 10 Sexuality and the Life Cycle: Childhood and Adolescence

- Added Are You Curious? questions
- Thoroughly revised, reorganized, and updated the entire chapter
- Updated statistics throughout the chapter
- Updated research on same-sex and mixed-sex sexual behaviour
- Revised feature: What Impact Do the Mass Media Have on Adolescent Sexuality?

Chapter 11 Sexuality and the Life Cycle: Adulthood

- Added Are You Curious? questions
- Updated the law on polygamy
- Clarified the distinction between polyamory and polygamy
- Added new content on online dating and how adults are now meeting on the Internet
- Added new content on Internet infidelity
- Added a definition of singleism
- Added new research on sex and the two-career family
- Added innovative content on nonmonogamous relationships and extradyadic sex
- Expanded the discussion on sexuality and menopause
- Revised material on sexual behaviour

Chapter 12 Attraction, Love, and Communication

- Added Are You Curious? questions
- Updated statistics throughout the chapter
- Revised feature: Why I Chose to Have an Arranged Marriage
- Increased the discussion of the role of communication in relationships
- Added new material on the science of online dating
- Expanded coverage on moving from the laboratory to real life
- Revised section on attraction online
- Updated research and content on intimacy

- Added content on the biology of love
- Included new material on relationship education

Chapter 13 Gender and Sexuality

- Added Are You Curious? questions
- Added new feature: Sex, Gender, and Sexual Orientation in Samoa
- Updated content on gender-reassignment surgery
- Added new content in the attitudes about casual sex and cultural factors sections
- Included new research on socialization
- Expanded discussion on gender roles and ethnicity
- Added new material on gender differences in psychological functioning
- Updated research on attitudes about casual sex
- Added content on sex drive
- Expanded material on cultural factors
- Added new information on what causes a person to be transgender

Chapter 14 Sexual Orientation and Identity: Gay, Lesbian, Bi, Straight, or Asexual?

- Added Are You Curious? questions
- Updated content on attitudes toward gay men, lesbians, and bisexuals
- Clarified information on the Metropolitan Community Church
- Revised LGBs and the law section
- Added innovative content on LGB development
- Revised Table 14.1: The NSFG and CCHS Statistics on Same-Sex Behaviour, Identity, and Attraction
- Added new feature: Sexual Fluidity and Questioning
- Added content on brain factors

Chapter 15 Variations in Sexual Behaviour

- Added Are You Curious? questions
- Introduced toucherism and sexsomnia to the chapter
- Updated research on the sexual compulsivity scale
- Added new content on transvestism and hypersexuality
- Revised online sexual activity use and abuse section
- Expanded the discussion of medical treatments
- Updated content in prevention of paraphilic and nonparaphilic disorder section
- Updated content on paraphilias to reflect the *DSM*-5

Chapter 16 Sexual Coercion

- Added Are You Curious? questions
- Included information about child advocacy centres
- Updated information and statistics related to sexual assault
- Added material on partner sexual assault of women and men
- Revised feature: What Should I Do After a Sexual Assault?
- Included new information on sexual assault resistance and sexual assault prevention programs
- Added new content on child sexual abuse
- Revised Table 16.2: Categories of People Who Were Accused of Child Sexual Offences in 2009
- Added new feature: What Causes Pedophilia?

Chapter 17 Sex for Sale

- Added Are You Curious? questions
- Included the recent Supreme Court decision on the prostitution laws
- Revised feature: Behind the Scenes: Making X-Rated Videos
- Added a study showing content analysis of music videos
- Introduced a Canadian study to the sex workers' well-being section
- Added new discussion of escort services
- Added original content on the role of third parties
- Heavily revised the customers section
- Added new content in the types of pornography section
- Added innovative research in the effects of pornography section

Chapter 18 Sexual Disorders and Sex Therapy

- Added Are You Curious? questions
- Updated statistics throughout the chapter
- Reordered content within the chapter
- Added new content in the sexual disorders section
- Revised male hypoactive sexual desire disorder section
- Added research in erectile disorder and premature ejaculation sections

- Introduced content on female sexual interest/arousal disorder
- Added new feature: A Case of Female Orgasmic Disorder
- Added new material on research on cannabis
- Updated diagnostic categories to reflect the *DSM-*5

Chapter 19 Sexuality Education

- Added Are You Curious? questions
- Updated research on sexual diversity
- Added new content on homophobic bullying
- Added content on the attitudes toward school-based sexuality education
- Updated research on purposes of sexuality education
- Revised the discussion of sexual diversity
- Added information on home-based sexuality education
- Added new content on sex education by health care professionals
- Revised features: Talking to Your Children About Sex and Sex Education for Persons with Developmental Disabilities

Chapter 20 Ethics, Religion, and Sexuality

- Added Are You Curious? questions
- Revised Table 20.1: Number and Percentage of Canadian Population Affiliated with Each of the Major Religions
- Updated Table 20.2: Canadians' Attitudes Toward Abortion
- Added new content on current trends and humanism
- Revised feature: Religious Position Statements on Abortion: Pro-Life Versus Pro-Choice
- Updated research on homosexuality

Additional Resources from McGraw-Hill Education

Innovative teaching and learning tools have been carefully developed to support readers, inside and outside the classroom. Please contact your McGraw-Hill Education representative for more information

CONNECT

Mc Graw Hill Education connect®

McGraw-Hill Connect™ is a web-based assignment and assessment platform that gives students the means to better connect with their coursework, with their instructors, and with the important concepts that they will need to know for success now and in the future.

With Connect, instructors can deliver assignments, quizzes and tests online. Instructors can edit existing questions and author entirely new problems. Track individual student performance—by question, assignment or in relation to the class overall—with detailed grade reports. Integrate grade reports easily with Learning Management Systems (LMS). And much more.

By choosing Connect, instructors are providing their students with a powerful tool for improving academic performance and truly mastering course material. Connect allows students to practise important skills at their own pace and on their own schedule. Importantly, students' assessment results and instructors' feedback are all saved online—so students can continually review their progress and plot their course to success.

Connect also provides 24/7 online access to an eBook—an online edition of the text—to aid them in successfully completing their work, wherever and whenever they choose.

Key Features

Simple Assignment Management
With Connect, creating assignments is easier than ever, so you can spend more time teaching and less time managing.
- Create and deliver assignments and test bank material easily to assign online.
- Streamline lesson planning, student progress reporting, and assignment grading to make classroom management more efficient than ever.
- Go paperless with the eBook and online submission and grading of student assignments.

Smart Grading
When it comes to studying, time is precious. Connect helps students learn more efficiently by providing feedback and practice material when they need it, where they need it.
- Automatically score assignments, giving students immediate feedback on their work and side-by-side comparisons with correct answers.

- Access and review each response; manually change grades or leave comments for students to review.
- Reinforce classroom concepts with practice tests and instant quizzes.

Instructor Library
The Connect Instructor Library is your course creation hub. It provides all the critical resources you'll need to build your course just how you want to teach it.
- Assign eBook readings and draw from a rich collection of textbook-specific assignments.
- Access instructor resources, including ready-made PowerPoint presentations and media to use in your lectures.
- View assignments and resources created for past sections.
- Post your own resources for students to use.

eBook
Connect reinvents the textbook learning experience for the modern student. Every Connect subject area is seamlessly integrated with Connect eBooks, which are designed to keep students focused on the concepts key to their success.
- Provide students with a Connect eBook, allowing for anytime, anywhere access to the textbook.
- Merge media, animation, and assessments with the text's narrative to engage students and improve learning and retention.
- Pinpoint and connect key concepts in a snap using the powerful eBook search engine.
- Manage notes, highlights, and bookmarks in one place for simple, comprehensive review.

LearnSmart

Mc Graw Hill Education | LEARNSMART®

No two students are alike. Why should their learning paths be? LearnSmart uses revolutionary adaptive technology to build a learning experience unique to each student's individual needs. It starts by identifying the topics a student knows and does not know. As the student progresses, LearnSmart adapts and adjusts the content based on his or her individual strengths, weaknesses, and confidence, ensuring that every minute spent studying with LearnSmart is the most efficient and productive study time possible.

SmartBook

SMARTBOOK™

As the first and only adaptive reading experience, Smartbook is changing the way students read and learn. Smartbook creates a personalized reading experience by highlighting the most important concepts a student needs to learn at that moment in time. As a student engages with Smartbook, the reading experience continuously adapts by highlighting content based on what each student knows and doesn't know. This ensures that he or she is focused on the content needed to close specific knowledge gaps, while it simultaneously promotes long-term learning.

Instructor Supplements

Connect is a one-stop shop for instructor resources, including:

- Instructor's Manual (by Carolyn Ensley, Wilfrid Laurier University): Each chapter in the Instructor's Manual contains key learning points, lecture ideas, class discussion topics, and more.
- Computerized Test Bank (by Heather Stewart and Ruth Martin, Durham College): The Test Bank provides a variety of questions, including multiple choice, true/false, and short answer. The multiple-choice and true/false questions include the answer as well as the page number in the main text where the material appears.
- Microsoft® PowerPoint® Presentations (by Heather Stewart and Ruth Martin, Durham College): These visual presentations, crafted for each chapter, include useful outlines, summaries, and visuals.

Annual Editions—Human Sexuality

This McGraw-Hill publication offers articles on topics related to the latest research and thinking in human sexuality from more than 300 public press sources. These editions are updated annually and contain helpful features, such as a topic guide, an annotated table of contents, unit overviews, and a topical index. An Instructor's Guide containing testing materials is also available.

Taking Sides: Clashing Views on Controversial Issues in Human Sexuality

This debate-style reader carefully examines issues with pro and con essays representing the arguments of leading scholars and commentators. An Instructor's Guide with testing materials is also available.

Student Supplements
Connect for Students

By choosing Connect, instructors are providing their students with a powerful tool for improving academic performance and truly mastering course material. Hyde Connect allows students to study and practice important skills at their own pace and on their own schedule with pre- and post-tests, additional quizzing material, videos relating to human sexuality, and an eBook for easy reference. Pre- and post-practice tests are tied to learning objectives and allow students to continually review their progress and plot their course to success. Online access to Connect with eBook is included with all Connect printed textbooks—no extra charge to the student.

Superior Learning Solutions and Support

The McGraw-Hill Ryerson team is ready to help you assess and integrate any of our products, technology, and services into your course for optimal teaching and learning performance. Whether it's helping your students improve their grades, or putting your entire course online, the McGraw-Hill Ryerson team is here to help you do it. Contact your Learning Solutions Consultant today to learn how to maximize all of McGraw-Hill Ryerson's resources!

For more information on the latest technology and Learning Solutions offered by McGraw-Hill Ryerson and its partners, please visit us online: www.mheducation.com.

Acknowledgements

I am extremely fortunate to have been able to call on a wide network of Canadian scholars in preparing the Canadian editions of *Understanding Human Sexuality*. Many of my colleagues and friends have been as generous with their time and expertise as I prepared this Sixth Canadian Edition as they were for the previous editions. I appreciate their contributions enormously. I am also appreciative that so many people were willing to provide me with copies of their scholarly work—their work is cited throughout this book. I have also benefited from the students in my classes. They keep me up to date on what university students are thinking and wondering about sexuality.

I am extremely indebted to the current and former members of my sexuality research group at the University of New Brunswick who provided input for one or more of the six editions. Thank you especially to Shannon Archibald, Marvin Claybourn, Jacqueline Cohen, Lyndsay Foster, Kaitlyn Goldsmith, Miranda Fudge, Cindy Letts, Christie Little, Sheila MacNeil, Sarah McAulay, Lorna Scott, Krystelle Shaughnessy, Deanne Simms, Sara Thornton, Jennifer Thurlow, Sarah Vannier, Ashley Thompson, and Angela Weaver. I am indebted to the various people who helped me identify the individuals whose life experiences are highlighted in the First Person boxes. These individuals often wrote or edited these stories themselves. Others willingly wrote Milestones in Sex Research boxes reflecting their expertise. This includes Lori Brotto, Freda Burdett, Jacqueline Cohen, Lyndsay Foster, Peggy Kleinplatz, Gayle MacDonald, Dana Menard, Krystelle Shaughnessy, Cory Silverberg, and Kris Wells. I am particularly grateful to the people (all Canadians) who agreed to share their own experiences in these boxes, including Cheryl Dobinson, William Fisher, Trevor Jacques, Trish McCourt, Kim McKay-McNab, Fran Odette, Faizal Suhukhan, Ayesha Suhukhan, and Richard Wassersung, as well as the people who chose to remain anonymous. Thank you also to James Cantor, Kaleigh Trace, Paul Vasey, and Richard Wassersug who contributed the new boxed content, reflecting their areas of expertise, for this edition.

I am also enormously grateful to Susan Voyer, who has served as my research assistant for the last four Canadian editions. She was not only relentless in tracking down information, regardless of how obscure, but also was proactive in bringing new developments and new sources to my attention. Her organizational skills are without equal. I relied heavily on her wise advice. This book would be noticeably poorer without her contributions.

The Sixth Canadian Edition of *Understanding Human Sexuality* has benefited from the careful reviews and valuable feedback of the following instructors:

Anne Almey, Concordia University

Cynthia Clarke, University of Guelph

Shaniff Esmail, University of Alberta

Derek Fisher, Mount Saint Vincent University

Elena Hannah, Memorial University of Newfoundland

Lisa Henry, University of Ottawa

Carla Labella, Mohawk College

Anick Legault, Dawson College

Dawn More, Algonquin College

Hiliary Rose, Concordia University

Kim Regehr, Conestoga College

Kate Salters, Simon Fraser University

Renu Sharma-Persaud, University of Windsor

Brandy Wiebe, University of British Columbia

I also owe many thanks to the editors and staff at McGraw-Hill Ryerson: Kim Brewster, group product manager; Jason Chih, project manager; Katherine Goodes, project developer; Cathy Biribauer, supervising editor; Scott Morrison, production coordinator; Dawn Hunter, copy editor; and Robyn Craig, photo researcher and permissions editor.

Finally, I could not have written this book without the enthusiastic support of my family. The love and gratitude I feel toward my husband, Larry, and our daughters, Krista and Alyssa, are immeasurable.

E. Sandra Byers

Are YOU Curious?

1. Do people in other cultures have sex the same way as people do in Canada?
2. Is Quebec a distinct society sexually speaking?
3. Is same-sex sexual behaviour found in other species?

Read this chapter to find out.

Sexuality in Perspective

LEARNING OBJECTIVES

After studying this chapter, you will be able to

L01 Identify some of the issues surrounding the terms sex and gender.

L02 Show the influences on sexuality of religion, science, the media, and the Internet.

L03 Describe the contributions of the major sex researchers to sex research and education.

L04 Differentiate between sexual attitudes and behaviours in Canada and in other cultures.

L05 Identify the influences of social class, gender, ethnicity, and geographic region in the sexual behaviour of Canadians.

L06 Compare sexual behaviour in humans and other species.

L07 Explain the principles of the sexual health and sexual rights perspectives.

Y ou're so beautiful," he whispered. "I want a picture of you just like this with your face flushed and your lips wet and shiny." . . . He tore open a foil packet he'd retrieved from his pocket. Mesmerized, she watched him sheath himself, amazed at how hard he was. She reached out to touch him, but he moved back, made sure she was ready, and then slid neatly inside her, so deeply she gasped. She contracted her muscles around him, and he closed his eyes and groaned, the sound so primal, it made her skin tingle.*

Human sexual behaviour is a diverse phenomenon. It occurs in different physical locations and social contexts, consists of a wide range of specific activities, and is perceived differently by different people. An individual engages in sexual activity on the basis of a complex set of motivations and organizes that activity on the basis of numerous external factors and influences. Thus, it is unlikely that the tools and concepts from any single scientific discipline will suffice to answer all or even most of the questions one might ask about sexual behaviour.[†]

Having children and healthy families are important goals to most Canadians, but some people cannot reach those goals without help. If there are technologies that can be used to help, a caring society should provide these. But there are misuses and harms, as well as benefits, that may come from use of the technologies—harms to both individuals and society.[‡]

---

* Debbi Rawlins. (2003). *Anything goes.* New York, NY: Harlequin Blaze.
† Laumann et al. (1994).
‡ Royal Commission on New Reproductive Technologies (1993).

Strikingly different though they may seem, all of the above quotations are talking about the same thing—sex. The first quotation is from a romance novel. It is intended to stimulate the reader's fantasies and arousal. The second is from a scholarly book about sex. It aims to stimulate the brain but not the genitals. The third is from a Royal Commission on the treatment of infertility. It points out the complexity of many sexual issues. From reading these brief excerpts, we can quickly see that the topic of sexuality is diverse, complex, and fascinating.

Why study sex? Most people are curious about sex, particularly because exchanging sexual information is somewhat taboo in our culture, so curiosity motivates us to study sex. Sex is an important force in many people's lives, so we have practical reasons for wanting to learn about it. Finally, most of us at various times experience concerns about our sexual functioning or wish that we could function better, and we hope that learning more about sex will help us. This book is designed to address all these needs. We'll consider several perspectives on sexuality: the effects of religion, science, the media, and culture on our understanding of sexuality, as well as a sexual health perspective. These perspectives make it clear that the study of sexuality is not confined to one

discipline but rather is multidisciplinary. However, first we must draw an important distinction between *sex* and *gender*.

 LO1

Sex and Gender

Sometimes the word *sex* is used ambiguously. In some cases sex refers to being male or female, and sometimes it refers to sexual behaviour or reproduction. In most cases, of course, the meaning is clear from the context. If you are filling out a job application form and one item says "Sex," you don't write, "I like it" or "As often as possible." It is clear that your prospective employer wants to know whether you are a male or a female. In other cases, though, the meaning may be ambiguous. For example, when a book has the title *Sex and Temperament in Three Primitive Societies*, what is it about? Is it about the sexual practices of primitive people and whether having sex frequently gives them pleasant temperaments? Or is it about the kinds of personalities that males and females are expected to have in those societies? Not only does this use of the word sex create ambiguities, but it also clouds our thinking about some important issues.

To remove—or at least reduce—this ambiguity, the term *sex* will be used in this book in contexts referring to sexual anatomy and sexual behaviour, and the term **gender** will be used to refer to the state of being male or female.

This is a book about sex, not gender; it is about sexual behaviour and the biological, psychological, and social forces that influence it. Of course, although we are arguing that sex and gender are conceptually different, we would not try to argue that they are totally independent of each other. Certainly, gender roles—the ways in which males and females are expected to behave—exert a powerful influence on the way people behave sexually, and so one chapter will be devoted to gender roles and their connection to sexuality.

How should we define sex, aside from saying that it is different from gender? A biologist might define sexual behaviour as "any behavior that increases the likelihood of gametic union [union of sperm and egg]" (Bermant & Davidson, 1974). This definition emphasizes the reproductive function of sex. However, medical advances, such as the birth control pill, have allowed us to separate reproduction from sex. Most Canadians now have sex not only for procreation but also for pleasure and intimacy.[1]

Noted sex researcher Alfred Kinsey defined sex as behaviour that leads to orgasm. Although this definition has some merits (it does not imply that sex must be associated with reproduction), it also presents some problems. If one person has intercourse with another person but does not have an orgasm, was that not sexual behaviour for her or him? If an individual has an orgasm through oral–genital stimulation, is that sex? Indeed, researchers in Canada have shown that undergraduate students have a very narrow definition of the term sex. Whereas almost everybody thought that penile–vaginal, and penile–anal intercourse constituted having sex, only about one-quarter of participants thought that oral sex resulting in orgasm would be defined as sex (Byers et al., 2009; Randall & Byers, 2003; Trotter & Alderson,

---

[1] Actually, even in former times sex was not always associated with reproduction. For example, a man in 1850 might have fathered 10 children; using a very conservative estimate that he engaged in sexual intercourse 1500 times during his adult life (once a week for the 30 years from age 20 to age 50), only 10 in 1500 of those acts, or fewer than 1 percent, resulted in reproduction.

[2] This definition, though an improvement over some, still has its problems. For example, consider a woman who feels no arousal at all during intercourse. According to the definition, intercourse would not be sexual behaviour for her. However, intercourse would generally be something we would want to classify as sexual behaviour. It should be clear that defining sexual behaviour is difficult.

2007). Our definition in this textbook includes much more than that, though.

To try to avoid some of these problems, **sexual behaviour** will be defined in this book as *behaviour that produces arousal and increases the chance of orgasm.*[2]

L02

Influences on Sexuality

Religion

Religion is a source of values and ethics regarding sexuality and, as such, is a powerful influence on the sexual attitudes and behaviour of many individuals. The moral code for each religion is unique—each religion has different views on what is right and what is wrong with respect to sexuality. Throughout most of recorded history, at least until about 100 years ago, religion (and rumour) provided most of the information that people had about sexuality, and in some cultures it still does. Here are a few historical examples of how different religions understood sexuality.

The ancient Greeks openly acknowledged both heterosexuality and homosexuality in their society and explained the existence of the two in a myth in which the original humans were double creatures with twice the normal number of limbs and organs; some were double males, some were double females, and some were half male and half female (LeVay, 1996). The gods, fearing the power of these creatures, split them in half, and forever after each one continued to search for its missing half. Heterosexuals were thought to have resulted from the splitting of the half male, half female; male homosexuals, from the splitting of the double male; and female homosexuals, from the splitting of the double female. It was through this mythology that the ancient Greeks understood sexual orientation and sexual desire.

Fifteenth-century Christians believed that "wet dreams" (nocturnal emissions) resulted from intercourse with tiny spiritual creatures called *incubi* and *succubi*, a notion put forth in a papal bull (an official document) of 1484 and a companion book, the *Malleus Maleficarum* ("witch's hammer"). The *Malleus* became the official manual of the Inquisition, in which people, particularly women, were tried as witches. Wet dreams, sexual dysfunction, and sexual lust were seen to be caused by witchcraft (Hergenhahn, 2001).

Over the centuries, Muslims have believed that sexual intercourse is one of the finest pleasures of life, reflecting the teachings of the great prophet Muhammad. Sexuality is regarded primarily as a source of pleasure and only secondarily as a means

Gender: The state of being male or female.
Sexual behaviour: Behaviour that produces arousal and increases the chance of orgasm.

First Person

Paul: The Story of a Gay Anglican Priest

P aul was born in 1950, the second of two children, to upper-middle-class parents in Nova Scotia. His parents stressed the importance of education, and there was no question that Paul would go to university, something his parents had not done. Paul described his parents as old-fashioned—more like parents were in the 1930s than like parents in the 1950s.

By the age of five, Paul realized two things about how he was different than other children. First, he wasn't interested in typical childhood activities, such as sports. Second, he was attracted to boys, not girls. As a result, he was a loner and turned to reading, art, music, and painting. It also became very important to Paul to receive the approval of adults. Growing up, Paul's parents attended the Anglican Church every week, but religion was not emphasized in his home. Nonetheless, Paul was drawn to religion, especially the ritual, music, and artistic forms that were part of it.

Paul's parents never talked to him about sex. Indeed, he never heard his father mention anything sexual. He did hear his mother whisper and giggle about sexual issues with her friends. This lack of communication made him realize that his parents couldn't handle sexuality issues. Sexuality also was never mentioned by

anyone connected with the Anglican Church, although Paul got the impression that "it was seen as an unpleasantness." He played sex games, such as "You show me yours and I'll show you mine" with other boys, but he had no interest in playing these games with girls. He did not have bad feelings about his sexual orientation but sensed that this was something he should definitely not discuss with either his parents or his priest. The fact that he could not be open about his sexual orientation made him feel increasingly lonely as a teenager.

Paul's first sexual experimentation occurred in university with "no strings attached, conveniently available" partners. He found the opportunity to express his sexuality fulfilling. He fell in love three times but says he "got hurt every time." When he was 37, he became engaged to a woman who had been kind to him when he had been ill and wanted to marry him even though she knew that he was gay. In the end, he realized that he was confusing kindness with love and that he could never be faithful to her, so he called the engagement off.

At first Paul fought the idea of entering the ministry. However, in his 20s he realized that "he had no choice" but to study for the priesthood. According to Paul, his

of reproduction, although the way the laws of the Quran are carried out has varied considerably from country to country (Boonstra, 2001; Ilkkaracan, 2001).

People of different religions hold different understandings of human sexuality, and these religious views often influence behaviour profoundly. The impact of religion on Canadians is particularly apparent in the discussion of homosexuality and abortion. For example, conservative Christians often use their interpretation of the Bible, an interpretation that is not shared by other Christian denominations, to justify their opposition to same-sex sexual behaviour and same-sex marriage. Other Canadians feel that these arguments have more to do with anti-gay prejudice and homophobia than with religion. A detailed discussion of religion and sexuality is provided in Chapter 20 online at Connect™ (also see the First Person box).

Science

It was against this background of religious understandings of sexuality that the scientific study of sex began in the nineteenth century; although, of course, religious notions continue to influence our ideas about sexuality. In addition, the groundwork for an understanding of the biological aspects of sexuality had already been laid by the research of physicians and biologists. Dutch microscopist Anton van Leeuwenhoek (1632–1723) had discovered sperm swimming in human semen. In 1875 Oskar Hertwig (1849–1922) first observed the fertilization of the egg by the sperm in sea urchins, although the ovum in humans was not directly observed until the twentieth century.

A major advance in the scientific understanding of the psychological aspects of human sexuality came with the work of Viennese physician Sigmund Freud sexuality went underground as a result because he was aware that being gay was not something the Anglican Church would tolerate. When he was ordained as a priest at age 26, he resigned himself to never living in a loving, long-term relationship with another man. At the time, he felt that he could accept this because he had "married the church." Nonetheless, he continued to have uncommitted sex (celibacy is not required of Anglican priests).

Paul feels that because he was not married to a woman, the Church hierarchy assumed he was gay. However, they were careful to "never ask the question so that they would not have to deal with the answer." Nonetheless, he feels that his career in the church was clearly impeded by his sexual orientation. For example, in contrast to married priests, he was not given the opportunity to move to other diocese to take on new challenges or to assume positions of leadership. He believes that the people in his parish also assumed he was gay. He heard reports of criticism of his sexual orientation by some of his parishioners, but these complaints did not go anywhere because there was never proof that he was gay. Nonetheless, the secrecy and lack of acceptance took their toll on Paul, and he developed an addiction to alcohol. Paul knew other gay priests, including a gay bishop who was a good friend and lover, who also were forced to hide their sexual orientation. Through it all, Paul never wavered in his commitment to his religion.

According to Paul, the official policy of the Anglican Church of Canada with respect to sexual orientation is that "heterosexual sex may be exercised within the confines of heterosexual marriage. Homosexuals must be celibate. Human rights do not enter the issue." However, Paul feels that the actual reception that homosexual church members get depends on whom they talk to. Whereas some clergy are open and welcoming to people of all sexual orientations, others appear to be "waging a vendetta against anyone who is not heterosexual."

Paul retired from the church at the age of 44 because of illness, although he remains a priest. Since that time, he has been more open about his sexuality. He has taken on the task of promoting the rights of nonheterosexuals within the church, trying to make the church more inclusive. This task was something he did not feel he could do when he was a parish priest. He would like the church to provide a safe environment in which people find spiritual sustenance and give support to one another without fear of reprisal.

Source: Based on an interview by Sandra Byers.

(1856–1939; see Figure 1.1), founder of psychiatry and psychoanalysis. His ideas will be discussed in detail in Chapter 2.

It is important to recognize the cultural context in which Freud and the other early sex researchers crafted their research and writing. They began their work in the Victorian era, the late nineteenth century, both in North America and in Europe. Norms about sexuality were extraordinarily rigid and oppressive (see Figure 1.2). Historian Peter Gay (1984) characterized this repressive aspect of Victorian cultural norms as

a devious and insincere world in which middle class husbands slaked their lust by keeping mistresses, frequenting prostitutes, or molesting children, while their wives, timid, dutiful, obedient, were sexually anesthetic and poured all their capacity for love into their housekeeping and their child-rearing. (p. 6)

Yet at the same time the sexual behaviour of Victorians was sometimes in violation of societal norms and expectations. Dr. Clelia Mosher was a physician who spent 30 years conducting a sex survey of Victorian women in the United States. Although the sample was small (47 women) and nonrandom, her results provide an alternative description of female sexuality during this period. For example, despite the Victorian stereotype that women felt no sexual desire, 80 percent of women who answered the question said that they felt a desire for sexual intercourse. Similarly, 72 percent of women indicated that they experienced orgasm. One woman commented that sex had been unpleasant for her for years because of her "slow reaction" but "orgasm [occurs] if time is taken." In his history of sexuality in the Victorian era, Gay (1984) documented the story of Mabel Loomis Todd, who, though married, carried on a lengthy affair

Figure 1.1   Two important early sex researchers. *(a)* Sigmund Freud. *(b)* Henry Havelock Ellis.

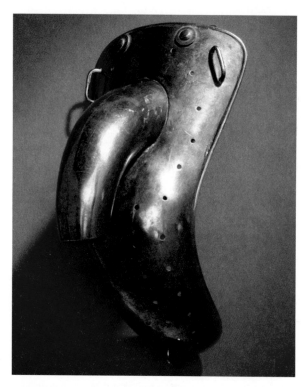

Figure 1.2   The Victorian era, from which Freud and Ellis emerged, was characterized by extreme sexual repression. Here is an apparatus that was sold to prevent *onanism* (masturbation).

with Austin Dickinson, a community leader in Amherst, Massachusetts. Many people knew about the "secret" affair, yet Mrs. Loomis did not become an outcast.

An equally great—though not so well known—early contributor to the scientific study of sex was Henry Havelock Ellis (1859–1939; see Figure 1.1). A physician in Victorian England, he compiled a vast collection of information on sexuality—including medical and anthropological findings and case histories—which was published in a series of volumes entitled *Studies in the Psychology of Sex* beginning in 1896. Havelock Ellis was a remarkably objective and tolerant scholar, particularly for his era. He believed that women, like men, are sexual creatures. A sexual reformer, he believed that sexual deviations from the norm are often harmless, and he urged society to accept them. In his desire to collect information about human sexuality rather than to make judgments about it, he can be considered the forerunner of modern sex research (for his autobiography, see Ellis, 1939; numerous biographies exist).

Another important figure in nineteenth-century sex research was German psychiatrist Richard von Krafft-Ebing (1840–1902) (Oosterhuis, 2000). His special interest was so-called pathological sexuality. He managed to collect more than 200 case histories of "pathological" individuals, which appeared in his book entitled *Psychopathia Sexualis*. His work tended to be neither objective nor tolerant. Nonetheless, it has had a lasting impact. He created the concepts of sadism, masochism, and pedophilia. The terms *heterosexuality* and *homosexuality* entered the English language in the 1892 translation of his book (Oosterhuis, 2000). One of his case histories is presented in Chapter 15.

One other early contributor to the scientific understanding of sexuality deserves mention: German

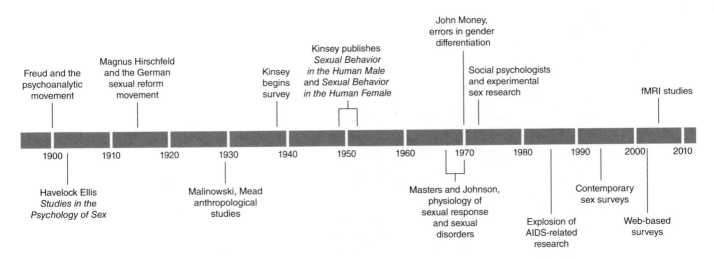

Figure 1.3 The history of scientific research on sex.

physician Magnus Hirschfeld (1868–1935). He founded the first sex research institute and administered the first large-scale sex survey, obtaining data from 10 000 people on a 130-item questionnaire. Unfortunately, most of the information he amassed was destroyed by the Nazis. Hirschfeld also established the first journal devoted to the study of sexuality, established a marriage counselling service, worked for legal reforms, and gave advice on contraception and sex problems. His special interest, however, was homosexuality. He made important contributions as a pioneer sex researcher (Bullough, 1994).

In the twentieth century, major breakthroughs in the scientific understanding of sex came with the massive surveys of human sexual behaviour in the United States conducted by Alfred Kinsey and his colleagues in the 1940s and with William Masters and Virginia Johnson's investigations of sexual disorders and the physiology of sexual response. These studies changed how people thought about sex and led to more open public discussion of sexuality (Connell & Hunt, 2006). At about the same time that the Kinsey research was being conducted, some anthropologists—most notably Margaret Mead and Bronislaw Malinowski—were beginning to collect data on sexual behaviour in other cultures. The 1990s saw a significant increase in research on sexuality in close relationships (Christopher & Sprecher, 2000).

A major national survey of the sexual behaviour of Canadians has never been conducted. However, Statistics Canada has included some questions about sexuality in several national surveys, such as the Canadian Community Health Survey, the National Population Health Survey, the General Social Survey, and the National Longitudinal Survey of Children and Youth. Canadian researchers have also conducted a large

number of smaller investigations that have provided important information on a rich array of sexual topics (see Chapter 3 for a description of the work of some of these researchers).

The scientific study of sexuality has not emerged as a separate, unified academic discipline like biology or psychology or sociology, although some researchers do call themselves sexologists. Rather, it tends to be interdisciplinary—a joint effort by biologists, psychologists, sociologists, anthropologists, and physicians (see Figure 1.3). This approach to understanding sexuality gives us a better view of humans in all their sexual complexity.

The Media

In terms of potency of influence, the mass media in North America today may play the same role that religion did in previous centuries. Canadians are influenced both by Canadian programs and, perhaps more so, by American prime-time television. Across a typical week in 2005, 35 percent of programs showed some sexual behaviour—ranging from kissing to intercourse—up from 23 percent in 1998 (Kunkel et al., 2005). References to safer sex—for prevention of both sexually transmitted infections (STIs) and pregnancy—are rare. Only 2 percent of sexual scenes portray any sexual precautions (Kunkel et al., 2005). Nonetheless, references to safer sex are increasing (Kaiser Family Foundation, 2003). Many, but not most, Canadians (47 percent) think there is too much sexually explicit programming on prime-time TV (*Maclean's*/Global Poll, 2000; see Figure 1.4).

In short, the average Canadian's views about sexuality are likely to be much more influenced by the mass media than by scientific findings. Communications theorists believe that the media can have three

Figure 1.4 Sexual portrayals in the media have become much more explicit, as in this scene from *Twilight*.

types of influence (Brown, 2002; Kunkel et al., 2007). The first, called **cultivation**, refers to the notion that people begin to think that what they see on television and in other media really represents the mainstream of what happens in our culture (Gerbner et al., 2002). For example, university students who watch soap operas are more likely than nonviewing students to overestimate the incidence of divorce. The second influence is **agenda-setting**. News reporters select what to report and what to ignore and, within the stories they report, what to emphasize. For example, in 1998 the U.S. media chose to highlight the sexual dalliances of President Bill Clinton, suggesting to the public that these matters were important. In contrast, the Canadian media have rarely focused on the sexual activities of Canadian politicians. The media in many ways tell us what agenda to pay attention to. The third influence is **social learning**, a theory

Cultivation: In communications theory, the view that exposure to the mass media makes people think that what they see there represents the mainstream of what really occurs.
Agenda-setting: In communications theory, the idea that the media define what is important and what is not by which stories they cover.
Social learning: In communications theory, the idea that the media provide role models whom we imitate.

we will take up in detail in Chapter 2. The contention here is that characters on television, in the movies, or in romance novels may serve as models whom we imitate, perhaps without even realizing it. Research has found, for example, that teens who watch more sexy television engage in first intercourse earlier than do other teens (Brown, 2002).

The Internet

The Internet is the newest, and perhaps most powerful, mass media influence. Computer and Internet use is spreading more rapidly than any previous technology, and most North American homes with children have Internet access. In 2009, 80 percent of Canadian adults were online, for personal nonbusiness reasons (Statistics Canada, 2010); use of social networking sites, such as Facebook, and the viewing of videos on YouTube are especially common among youth. Many individuals engage in sexual activity online. For example, research in New Brunswick found that 86 percent of male students and 39 percent of female students had viewed erotic pictures or videos on the Internet; 25 percent of the men and 13 percent of the women had engaged in sexual activity with a partner online (Shaughnessy et al., 2011). Thus, people, and especially young people, are not only accessing sexual material that is posted on the Internet by other people but also sharing explicit information and pictures of themselves through webcams, instant messaging, and smartphones (i.e., sexting); engaging in sexual activity with known and anonymous partners; and engaging in sexual activity through virtual worlds, such as Second Life.

As we will discuss in later chapters, the Internet has the potential for both positive and negative effects on sexual health. A number of sites, such as that for the Society of Obstetricians and Gynaecologists of Canada (see www.sexualityandu.ca), provide excellent information about sexuality and promote sexual health. At the same time, a well-sampled study of youth between the ages of 10 and 17 who use the Internet regularly indicated that approximately 20 percent had received at least one sexual solicitation or approach over the Internet in the last year, and 3 percent had received an aggressive sexual solicitation in which the initiator asked to meet the recipient somewhere or sent him or her money or gifts (Finkelhor et al., 2000).

In the chapters that follow, we will examine the content of the media and the Internet on numerous sexual issues, and we will consider what effects exposure to this media content might have on viewers.

Let us now consider the perspectives on sexuality that are provided by scientific observations of humans in a wide variety of societies.

LO4

Cross-Cultural Perspectives on Sexuality

Humans are a cultural species (Heine & Norenzayan, 2006). Although some other species are capable of learning from others, humans are unique in the way that cultural learning accumulates over time. What do anthropologists mean by the term *culture?* Generally, **culture** refers to traditional (that is, passed down from generation to generation) ideas and values transmitted to members of the group by symbols (such as language). These ideas and values then serve as the basis for patterns of behaviour observed in the group (S. Frayser, personal communication, 2004; Kroeber & Kluckhohn, 1963).

Ethnocentrism tends to influence people's understanding of human sexual behaviour. Most of us have had experience with sexuality in only one culture—Canada, for example—and we tend to view our sexual behaviour as the only pattern in existence and certainly as the only "natural" pattern. But anthropologists have discovered wide variations in sexual behaviour and attitudes from one culture to the next. There are even significant differences between Canada and the United States. For example, Canadians tend to have more permissive attitudes toward sexuality than Americans do. Some of these differences are summarized later in the chapter in Table 1.3. Considering variations across cultures should help us to put our own sexual behaviour in perspective.

The major generalization that emerges from cross-cultural studies (see Figure 1.5) is that all societies regulate sexual behaviour in some way, though the exact regulations vary greatly from one culture to the next (DeLamater, 1987). Apparently, no society has seen fit to leave sexuality totally unregulated, perhaps fearful that social disruption would result. As an example, **incest taboos** are nearly universal: sex is regulated in that intercourse between blood relatives is prohibited (Gregersen, 1996). Most societies also condemn forced sexual relations, such as rape. Both incest and sexual assault are illegal in Canada.

Beyond this generalization, though, regulations vary greatly from one society to the next, and sexual behaviour and attitudes vary correspondingly (see the Sexually Diverse World box). In fact, a recent comparison of data from 59 countries concluded that there are currently large differences in patterns of sexual behaviour from one region of the world to another (Wellings et al., 2006). Let's look at the ways in which various societies treat some key areas of human sexual behaviour.

Figure 1.5   Margaret Mead, an anthropologist, contributed much to the early cross-cultural study of sexuality.

Variations in Sexual Techniques

Kissing is one of the most common sexual techniques in our culture. It is also very common in most other societies (Gregersen, 1996). In a few societies, though, kissing is unknown. For example, when the Thonga of Africa first saw Europeans kissing, they laughed and said, "Look at them; they eat each other's saliva and dirt." There is also some variation in techniques of kissing. For example, among the Kwakiutl of British Columbia and the Trobriand Islanders, kissing consisted of sucking the lips and tongue of the partner, permitting saliva to flow from one mouth to the other.

Cunnilingus (mouth stimulation of the female genitals) is fairly common in our society, and it occurs in a few other societies as well, especially in the South Pacific. A particularly interesting variation is reported on the island of Ponape; the man places a fish in the woman's vulva and then gradually licks it out prior to coitus.

Inflicting pain on a partner is also a part of the sexual

> **Do people in other cultures have sex the same way as people do in Canada?**

Culture: Traditional ideas and values passed down from generation to generation within a group and transmitted to members of the group by symbols (such as language).
Ethnocentrism: The tendency to regard our own ethnic group and culture as superior to others' and to believe that its customs and way of life are the standards by which other cultures should be judged.
Incest taboos: Regulations prohibiting sexual interaction between close blood relatives, such as brother and sister or father and daughter.

A Sexually Diverse World

How Much Can Behaviours Vary? Sexuality in Two Societies

Inis Beag

Inis Beag is a small island off the coast of Ireland. It is probably one of the most naive and sexually repressive societies in the world.

The people of Inis Beag seem to have no knowledge of a number of sexual activities, such as French kissing, mouth stimulation of the breast, or hand stimulation of the partner's penis, much less oral sex or homosexuality. Sex education is virtually nonexistent; parents do not seem to be able to bring themselves to discuss such embarrassing matters with their children, and they simply trust that, after marriage, nature will take its course.

Menstruation and menopause are sources of fear for the island women because they have no idea of their physiological significance. It is commonly believed that menopause can produce insanity; to ward off this condition, some women have retired from life in their mid-40s, and a few have confined themselves to bed until death years later.

The men believe that intercourse is hard on one's health. They will abstain from sex the night before they are to do a job that takes great energy. They do not approach women sexually during menstruation or for months after childbirth; a woman is considered dangerous to the male at these times.

The islanders abhor nudity. Only babies are allowed to bathe while nude. Adults wash only the parts of their bodies that extend beyond their clothing—face, neck, lower arms, hands, lower legs, and feet.

Premarital sex is essentially unknown. In marital sex, foreplay is generally limited to kissing and rough fondling of the buttocks. The husband invariably initiates the activity. The male-on-top is the only position used, and both partners keep their underwear on during the activity. The man has an orgasm quickly and falls asleep immediately. Female orgasm either is believed not to exist or is considered deviant.

Mangaia

In distinct contrast to Inis Beag is Mangaia, an island in the South Pacific. For the Mangaians, sex—for pleasure and for procreation—is a principal interest.

The Mangaian boy first hears of masturbation when he is about seven, and he may begin to masturbate at age eight or nine. At around age 13 he undergoes the superincision ritual (in which a slit is made on the top of the penis, along its entire length). This ritual initiates him into manhood; more important, however, the expert who performs the superincision gives him sexual instruction. He shows the boy how to perform oral sex, how to kiss and suck breasts, and how to bring his partner to orgasm several times before he has his own. About two weeks after the operation, the boy has intercourse with an experienced woman, which removes the scab from the superincision. She provides him with practice in various acts and positions and trains him to hold back until he can have simultaneous orgasms with his partner.

After this, the Mangaian boy actively seeks out girls, or they seek him out; soon he has coitus every night. The girl, who has received sexual instruction from an older woman, expects demonstration of the boy's virility as proof of his desire for her. What is valued is the ability of the male to continue vigorously the in-and-out action of coitus over long periods while the female moves her hips "like a washing machine." Nothing is despised more than a "dead" partner who does not move. A good man is expected to continue his actions for 15 to 30 minutes or more.

Between the ages of 13 and 20, the average girl will have three or four successive boyfriends; the average boy may have 10 or more girlfriends. Mangaian parents encourage their daughters to have sexual experiences with several men. They want them to find marriage partners who are congenial.

At around age 18, the Mangaians typically have sex most nights of the week, with about three orgasms per night. By about age 48, they have sex two or three times per week, with one orgasm each time.

All women in Mangaia apparently learn to have orgasms. Bringing his partner to orgasm is one of the man's chief sources of sexual pleasure.

Sources: Gregor (1985), Marshall (1971), Messenger (1993).

technique in some societies; most commonly men and women mutually inflict pain on each other. The Apinaye woman of the Brazilian highlands may bite off bits of her partner's eyebrows, noisily spitting them aside. Ponapean men usually tug at the woman's eyebrows, occasionally yanking out tufts of hair. People of various societies bite their partners to the point of drawing blood and leaving scars (Frayser, 1985).

The frequency of intercourse for married couples varies considerably from one culture to the next. The lowest frequency seems to be among the Irish natives of Inis Beag, discussed in the Sexually Diverse World box, who engage in intercourse perhaps only once or twice a month; however, the anthropologists who studied them were unable to determine exactly how often couples did have sex because so much secrecy surrounds the act. At the opposite extreme, the Mangaians, also described in the Sexually Diverse World box, have intercourse several times a night, at least among the young. The Santals of southern Asia engage in sexual intercourse as often as five times per day every day early in marriage (Gregersen, 1996). Surveys of Canadian sexuality in the 1990s indicated that our frequency of intercourse was then about in the middle compared with other societies (e.g., "Doing It," 1999).

Very few societies *encourage* people to engage in sexual intercourse at particular times (Frayser, 1985). Instead, most groups have restrictions that *forbid* intercourse at certain times or in certain situations. For example, almost every society has a postpartum sex taboo—that is, a prohibition on sexual intercourse for a time after a woman has given birth, with the taboo lasting from a few days to more than a year (Gregersen, 1996).

Masturbation

Attitudes toward **masturbation**, or sexual self stimulation of the genitals, vary widely across cultures. Some societies tolerate and some encourage masturbation during childhood and adolescence, whereas others condemn the practice at any age. Almost all human societies express some disapproval of adult masturbation, ranging from mild ridicule to severe punishment (Gregersen, 1996). Yet at least some adults in all societies appear to practise it.

Female masturbation certainly occurs in other societies. The African Azande woman uses a phallus made of a wooden root; however, if her husband catches her masturbating, he may beat her severely. The following is a description of the Lesu of the South Pacific, one of the few societies that express no disapproval of adult female masturbation:

A woman will masturbate if she is sexually excited and there is no man to satisfy her. A couple may be having intercourse in the same house, or near enough for her to see them, and she may thus become aroused. She then sits down and bends her right leg so that her heel presses against her genitalia. Even young girls of about six years may do this quite casually as they sit on the ground. The women and men talk about it freely, and there is no shame attached to it. It is a customary position for women to take, and they learn it in childhood. They never use their hands for manipulation. (Powdermaker, 1933, pp. 276–277)

Premarital and Extramarital Sex

Societies differ considerably in their rules regarding premarital sex[3] (Frayser, 1985). At one extreme are the Marquesans of eastern Polynesia. Both boys and girls in that culture have participated in a wide range of sexual experiences before puberty. Their first experience with intercourse occurs with a heterosexual partner who is 30 to 40 years old. Mothers are proud if their daughters have many lovers. Only later does marriage occur. In contrast are the Egyptians of Siwa. In this culture a girl's clitoris is removed at age seven or eight to decrease her potential for sexual excitement and intercourse. Premarital intercourse is believed to bring shame on the family. Marriage usually occurs around the age of 12 or 13, shortening the premarital period and any temptations it might contain.

These two cultures are fairly typical of their regions. According to one study, 90 percent of Pacific Island societies permit premarital sex, as do 88 percent of African and 82 percent of Eurasian societies; however, 73 percent of Mediterranean societies prohibit premarital sex (Frayser, 1985).

Extramarital sex is more complex and conflicted for most cultures. Extramarital sex ranks second only to incest as the most strictly prohibited type of sexual contact. One study found that it was forbidden for one or both partners in 74 percent of the cultures surveyed (Frayser, 1985). Even when extramarital sex is

Masturbation: Self-stimulation of the genitals to produce sexual arousal.

---

[3] Although marriage as an institution is found in most, if not all, cultures, some people never marry or marry late in life. Some people choose not to marry; others are in same-sex relationships and cannot marry legally, as many countries do not permit same-sex marriages. For these individuals the terms *premarital sex* and *extramarital sex* do not have much meaning. For example, is a 50-year-old who has never been married engaging in premarital sex? Is a person who is having sex outside a common-law relationship engaging in extramarital sex? Nonetheless, the pervasiveness of marriage as an institution (for example, 90 to 95 percent of Canadians marry) makes it meaningful to discuss cultural rules regarding premarital and extramarital sex.

permitted, it is subjected to regulations; the most common pattern of restriction is to allow extramarital sex for husbands but not wives.

Sex with Same-Sex Partners

A wide range of attitudes toward same-sex sexual expression exists in various cultures (Murray, 2000). At one extreme are societies that strongly disapprove of same-sex sexual behaviour for people of any age. In contrast, some societies tolerate the behaviour in children but disapprove of it in adults. Still other societies actively encourage all their male members to engage in some same-sex sexual behaviour, usually in conjunction with puberty rites (Herdt, 1984). A few societies have a formalized role for the adult gay man that gives him status and dignity.

Even across European nations, attitudes about homosexuality vary considerably (Lottes & Alkula, 2011). For example, people in Denmark, the Netherlands, and Sweden have the most positive attitudes. Positive attitudes are also found in a large group of countries that includes Austria, Belgium, France, Germany, Great Britain, Greece, Italy, and Spain. Attitudes are more negative in Belarus, Bulgaria, Estonia, and Russia, and the cluster of countries with the most negative attitudes includes Croatia, Lithuania, Poland, Portugal, Romania, and Ukraine.

Although wide variation exists in attitudes toward homosexuality and in same-sex sexual activity, two general rules do seem to emerge (Ford & Beach, 1951; Murray, 2000; Whitam, 1983): (1) no matter what the society's views are, same-sex behaviour always occurs in at least some individuals—that is, same-sex sexuality is found universally; and (2) same-sex sexual activity is never the predominant form of sexual behaviour for adults in any of the societies studied.

The first point, that same-sex sexual behaviour is found universally in all cultures, is so well established that there was quite a stir in 2010 when a team of anthropologists reported that a group of people, the Aka foragers of the Central African Republic (Hewlett & Hewlett, 2010), were not aware of such practices and had no term for them. In fact, it was difficult for the anthropologists to convey what they meant. We may need to amend the earlier statement to say that same-sex sexual behaviour is nearly universal across societies.

In Canada and other Western nations, most people hold an unquestioned assumption that people have a sexual identity, whether gay, lesbian, bisexual, heterosexual, asexual or pansexual. Yet sexual identity as an unvarying, lifelong characteristic of the self is unknown or rare in some cultures, such as Indonesia (Stevenson, 1995). In those cultures, the self and individualism, so prominent in Canadian culture, are downplayed. Instead, a person is defined in relation to others and behaviour is seen as much more the product of the situation than of lifelong personality traits. In such a culture, having a "gay identity" just doesn't make sense. Sexual orientation is discussed in detail in Chapter 14.

Standards of Attractiveness

In all human societies, physical characteristics are important in determining whom one chooses as a sex partner. What is considered attractive varies considerably, though (see Figure 1.6). For example, the region of the body that is judged for attractiveness varies from one culture to the next. For some peoples, the shape and colour of the eyes are especially significant. For others, the shape of the ears is most important. Some societies go directly to the heart of the matter and judge attractiveness by the appearance of the external genitals. In a few societies, elongated labia majora (the pads of fat on either side of the vaginal opening in women) are considered sexually attractive, and it is common practice for a woman to pull on hers to make them longer. Among the Nawa women of Africa, elongated labia majora are considered a mark of beauty and are quite prominent.

Our society's standards are in the minority in one way: in most cultures, a plump woman is considered more attractive than a thin one. In Canada and other Western nations today, the ideal for women, particularly as portrayed in the media, is unrealistically and unhealthily thin.

One standard does seem to be a general rule: a poor complexion is considered unattractive in the majority of human societies. Research on sexual attraction is discussed in detail in Chapter 12.

L05 Regional and Cultural Variation in Sexuality

The discussion so far may have seemed to imply that there is one uniform standard of sexual behaviour in Canada and that all Canadians behave alike sexually. But the Canadian population is composed of many cultural and ethnic groups. These groups have both differences and similarities in sexual behaviour. Some of these subcultural variations can be classified as social-class differences and some as ethnic differences. Here we discuss variations in sexual behaviour and attitudes between French-speaking and English-speaking Canadians of European descent. We also examine sexual behaviour and attitudes among Aboriginal Canadians and in six of the largest ethnocultural communities in Canada.

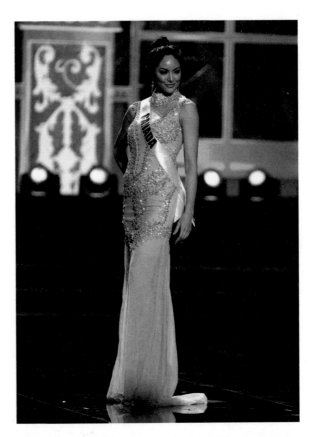

Figure 1.6 Cross-cultural differences, cross-cultural similarities. *(a)* Woman of West Africa. *(b)* Miss Universe Canada 2013, Riza Santos. The custom of female adornment is found in most cultures, although the definition of beauty varies from culture to culture.

Social Class and Sex

Table 1.1 shows data on some social-class variations in sexuality. There was little difference in the percentage of respondents who had engaged in sexual intercourse ever or in the past 12 months based on social class—most respondents in all social classes had done so. However, respondents from the lower social classes were more likely to have first engaged in intercourse when they were 15 years old or younger and to have had one or more sexually transmitted infections. There also are some differences in sexual behaviour across social classes. A study conducted in Montreal by using a francophone sample found that manual workers engaged in both sexual intercourse and oral–genital sex more frequently than respondents with office and professional jobs (Samson et al., 1991, 1993).

Regional Differences in Sexuality

A number of surveys have examined whether regional differences in sexual behaviour and attitudes exist across provinces and territories. These results are based on self-report surveys and typically are conducted in English or French, so they may not be totally accurate. For example, respondents may not remember their behaviour accurately or may give the answer that they think is more socially acceptable (see Chapter 3 for a discussion of possible biases in self-report data). The results of various surveys do not show consistent differences from one province to another, with one exception: francophones in Quebec often are more liberal in many of their attitudes and behaviour than Canadians in other provinces. Just how different are Quebecers from Canadians in other parts of Canada? See Figure 1.7.

Table 1.2 compares Quebecers to Canadians as a whole on a number of attitudes and behaviours related to sexuality. The data for Quebec include not only francophones but also anglophones and allophones (people whose first language is neither English nor French) living in Quebec; these groups differ in many ways from the Québécois. These data show that Quebecers are more liberal in many of their attitudes; for example, parents are more accepting of teenagers engaging in sexual activity. The 2002 *Maclean's* poll (Driedger, 2002) showed that the highest percentage of Canadians who reported having an

Is Quebec a distinct society sexually speaking?

Table 1.1   Social-Class Variations in Sexual Behaviour in Canada

	Low and Low-Middle Income	Middle Income	Upper-Middle and High Incomes
Percentage who have ever had intercourse			
Men	87%	91%	94%
Women	93%	92%	94%
Percentage who had intercourse in the last 12 months			
Men	90%	92%	94%
Women	78%	88%	92%
Percentage who had first sexual intercourse before age 16			
Men	31%	23%	19%
Women	23%	16%	12%
Percentage who had at least one sexually transmitted infection			
Men	4%	1%	1%
Women	3%	2%	2%

Source: This analysis is based on the Statistics Canada National Population Health Survey Public Use Microdata File, 1996–1997. All computations, use, and interpretation of these data are entirely that of the authors. Percentages are based only on members of the sample who responded to the question.

active sex life were in Quebec; in past polls, Newfoundlanders were the most likely to report having an active sex life. In addition, among students studying in the Ottawa-Gatineau area, franco-Quebec students have less sex guilt than do anglo-Canadian students, in part because they have parents who have more permissive sexual attitudes (Gravel et al., 2011).

A higher percentage of Quebecers live in common-law relationships; a smaller percentage live in marital relationships. More adolescents in Quebec than in the

rest of Canada have had sex. However, there are no differences between Quebecers and other Canadians in attitudes toward same-sex marriage or likelihood of fantasizing about a person of the same sex. In terms of sexual health indicators, Quebec women are equally likely to breast feed compared with the national average; the teenage pregnancy rate in Quebec is at the national average; and Quebec has a lower rate of chlamydia, a common STI, than the national average, but so do Ontario and the Atlantic provinces. This result suggests

Figure 1.7   Sexual attitudes in Quebec are more liberal than in the rest of Canada. This advertisement for a Montreal conference on childhood sexuality included a drawing of two children that showed their genitals. Consistent with cultural attitudes, the French-language newspaper in Montreal published the drawing at the left. The children's genitals are not shown in the advertisements run by the English-language newspaper in Toronto (right).

Table 1.2 Comparison of Sexuality in Quebec to Sexuality in Canada Overall

	Quebec	Canada
Parents who agree that teens should be allowed to spend the night together in their home with their sex partner	41%	13%
Parents who agree that it's appropriate for 16-year-olds to have sex outside of marriage	35%	6%
Adolescents who have had sex	62%	54%
In favour of same-sex marriage	63%	64%
Fantasized about having sex with a person of the same sex	5%	7%
Active sex life	76%	62%
Couples living in common-law relationships	32%	17%

Sources: Bibby et al. (2009), Driedger (2002), Ipsos (2013), *Maclean's*/Global Poll (2000), Pew Research (2013), Statistics Canada (2012).

that Quebecers are not distinct from the rest of Canada in their likelihood of engaging in safer sex.

Comparing Canada and the United States

The United States is our closest neighbour. Yet, when it comes to sexual attitudes and behaviour, Canada and the United States are quite different. Some of these differences are depicted in Table 1.3. In general, Canadians are more liberal than Americans are. For example, we are more accepting of premarital sex, abortion, homosexuality, same-sex marriage, and even extramarital sex. Canadian women also have lower rates of adolescent pregnancy and STIs and higher rates of breast-feeding than American women do.

Aboriginal Peoples and Sexuality

Before contact with Europeans, most First Nations populations were considered egalitarian and sexually permissive by European standards (Reeves & Reading, 2013). For example, among First Nations peoples, women were encouraged to take the initiative, and premarital and extramarital sex were acceptable. In many cultures, gay men, lesbians, and Two Spirit people who assumed cross-gender roles were respected and admired. Sex was considered a magical spiritual gift to

Table 1.3 Percentage of Canadians and Americans Who Approve of Various Issues

	Canada	United States
Premarital sex[a]	80%	60%
Legal abortion upon demand[a]	43%	27%
Homosexuality[b]	80%	60%
Same-sex marriage[c]	63%	42%
Extramarital sex[a]	14%	7%

Source: [a]Bibby (2006), [b]Kohut et al. (2013), [c]Ipsos (2013).

humans designed to bring pleasure—a gift that should be used only with respect for others and for ourselves (Newhouse, 1998).

Depictions of Aboriginal peoples in the popular media over the last century have portrayed them as noble savages who are both exotic and erotic (Bird, 1999). Aboriginal men have been shown nearly naked, emphasizing well-developed, masculine bodies. In romance novels of the 1990s, they became cultural icons for vanishing standards of masculinity—handsome and virile yet tender and vulnerable and magnificent lovers for white women (Van Lent, 1996).

Aboriginal women have been less visible in the popular media. When present, they are stereotyped as princesses or squaws (Bird, 1999). The princess is noble, beautiful, and erotic. The Disney animated film *Pocahontas* features such a voluptuous princess. The stereotypical squaw, in contrast, is unattractive, uninteresting, and ignored.

The sexual behaviour and attitudes of most Aboriginal communities have been influenced by the Judeo-Christian tradition, abusive experiences in residential schools, whether they live on or off the reserve, and the poor economic and crowded social conditions in which many live (Reeves & Reading, 2013). For example, Aboriginal women experience a disproportionally high rate of negative sexual health outcomes, including high rates of STIs, unwanted pregnancy, low-birth-weight infants, and sexual violence (Yee et al., 2011). Traditional Aboriginal cultures had strict courtship rules that regulated premarital sex. Today there is great pressure in the youth culture to have sex (Hellerstedt et al., 2006). Unfortunately, there have been few studies of sexual behaviour within Aboriginal communities or of the influence of Aboriginal culture on sexual behaviour. Filling this gap is important because a study of Aboriginal people living on-reserve in Ontario found that cultural variables, such as the traditions of learning through the telling of stories by Elders, had an important influence on sexual behaviour. For example, in many communities AIDS was seen as a gay white man's disease. As a result, safer sex behaviours, such as consistent condom use, are rare (Myers et al., 1994, 1999). However, data from the Canadian Community Health Survey indicate that Aboriginal youth were as likely as non-Aboriginal youth to have used a condom the last time they had intercourse (Rotermann, 2005). Nonetheless, to be effective in addressing the sexual health needs of Aboriginal peoples, it is important to develop culturally safe and sensitive services by using the knowledge of Elders in the community (Hampton et al., 2007; Yee et al., 2011).

Ethnocultural Communities in Canada and Sexuality

Changing patterns of immigration to Canada in recent years have resulted in a Canadian population that is becoming more and more ethnically diverse. According to the 2011 census, 21 percent of Canadians were not born in Canada. There have been few studies of sexual behaviour in Canadian ethnocultural communities (Statistics Canada, 2013). However, a federally funded study, Ethnocultural Communities Facing AIDS, which focused on preventing HIV and AIDS in communities with high levels of recent immigration, examined selected aspects of sexual behaviour and attitudes in six ethnic communities. Participants were from the Chinese, South Asian, Horn of Africa, English-speaking Caribbean, North African Muslim, and Latin American communities.[4] The researchers made sure that the sample was representative of the community in terms of age and how long respondents had lived in Canada. The study used both focus groups (a research procedure in which participants discuss their answers to the research questions in small groups) and questionnaires (Cappon et al., 1996; Manson Singer et al., 1996).

The sexual behaviour of individuals from ethnic minorities is influenced both by the culture of their country of origin and by the process of adapting to Canada's majority culture. The study found that, in many ways, sexual attitudes and behaviour in these Canadian communities resemble attitudes and

---

[4] Communities in Vancouver (Chinese and South Asian), Toronto (English-speaking Caribbean and Horn of Africa), and Montreal (North African Muslim and Latin American) were studied. The Chinese participants came from Hong Kong, Taiwan, and the People's Republic of China. Most of the participants from the South Asian communities were from India and Pakistan. The English-speaking Caribbean participants were from all the English-speaking Caribbean islands and Guyana. Participants from the Horn of Africa came largely from Ethiopia, Eritrea, and Somalia. The North African Muslim participants came mostly from North Africa and the Middle East. The Latin American participants came primarily from Peru, Chile, Guatemala, and El Salvador.

behaviour in the countries of origin. Generally, men and women are seen as having distinct roles, with men expected to be the head of the family and women expected to be the caregivers. Sex is not talked about in the family, even between husbands and wives. Women are expected to be passive and inexperienced, and to fulfill men's sexual needs, whereas men are expected to be sexually active and experienced. Women have little power in sexual relationships to refuse sex or to insist on condom use. In many of these communities, it is expected that men, but not women, will have extramarital affairs or use prostitutes. Homosexuality is often considered abnormal and shameful. Thus, most gay men and lesbians keep their same-sex relationships or feelings secret.

Expectations regarding adolescent dating and sexual behaviour in these ethnocultural communities are different from those in the dominant Canadian culture. In general, virginity at marriage is highly valued in women but is not expected of men. In the South Asian communities, girls may not be allowed to date. On the other hand, young people do not always conform to these expectations and adopt some aspects of the dominant culture after learning about them from friends and the media. This rebellion often creates conflict between youth and their more traditional parents. Parents may see their children's adoption of Canadian norms as threatening their values and way of life (Shirpak et al., 2007). For example, Chinese youth, including girls, are becoming increasingly likely to engage in sexual activity. However, a Vancouver study found that both male and female Asian university students are more conservative and less experienced than are non-Asians in their sexual behaviour. Notably, half as many Asian students (36 percent) as non-Asian students (66 percent) had engaged in sexual intercourse (Meston et al., 1996). However, the attitudes of Asian Canadians become more liberal as they become more acculturated (Brotto et al., 2005, 2007; Meston et al., 1998).

Of course, in many ways the behaviour and attitudes of members of one ethnocultural community are also different from those of other communities. For example, single South Asian men were more likely than single men from Latin America or the English-speaking Caribbean to report having had more than one sexual partner in the previous year. In contrast, married South Asian men were the least likely to report having had more than one partner in the previous year (Maticka-Tyndale et al., 1996).

The Significance of Cross-Cultural Studies

What relevance do cross-cultural data have to an understanding of human sexuality? They are important for two basic reasons. First, they give us a notion of the enormous variation that exists in human sexual behaviour, and they help us put our own standards and behaviour

Figure 1.8 Sexual norms for women are restrictive in Muslim-Canadian families.

in perspective. Second, these studies provide impressive evidence concerning the importance of culture and learning in the shaping of our sexual behaviour; they show us that human sexual behaviour is not completely determined by biology or drives or instincts. For example, a woman of Inis Beag and a woman of Mangaia presumably have vaginas that are similarly constructed and clitorises that are approximately the same size and have the same nerve supply. But the woman of Inis Beag never has an orgasm, and all Mangaian women orgasm.[5] Why? Their cultures are different, and they and their partners learned different things about sex as they were growing up. Culture is a major determinant of human sexual behaviour (see Figure 1.8).

The point of studying sexuality in different groups is to remind ourselves that each group has its own culture, and this culture has a profound influence on the sexual expression of the women and men who grow up in it. We will return with more examples in many of the chapters that follow.

LO6

Cross-Species Perspectives on Sexuality

Humans are just one of many animal species, and all of them display sexual behaviour. To put our own sexual behaviour in evolutionary perspective, it is helpful to explore the similarities and differences between our own sexuality and that of other species. (See Chapter 2

[5] We like to use the word *orgasm* not only as a noun but also as a verb. The reason is that alternative expressions, such as "to achieve orgasm" and "to reach orgasm," reflect the tendency of Canadians to make sex an achievement situation (an idea to be discussed further in Chapter 9). To avoid this, we use "to have an orgasm" or "to orgasm."

for a discussion of evolutionary perspectives). There is one other reason for this particular discussion. Some people classify sexual behaviours as "natural" or "unnatural," depending on whether other species do or do not exhibit those behaviours. Sometimes, though, the data are twisted to suit the purposes of the person making the argument, and so there is a need for a less biased view. Let's see exactly what some other species do!

Masturbation

Humans are definitely not the only species that masturbates. Masturbation is found among many species of mammals, particularly among the primates (monkeys and apes). Male monkeys and apes in zoos can be observed masturbating, often to the horror of the proper folk who have come to see them. At one time it was thought that this behaviour might be the result of the unnatural living conditions of zoos. However, observations of free-living primates indicate that they, too, masturbate. Techniques include hand stimulation of the genitals or rubbing the genitals against an object. In terms of technique, monkeys and nonhuman apes have one advantage over humans: their bodies are so flexible that they can perform mouth–genital sex on themselves. A unique form of male masturbation is found among red deer; during the rutting season they move the tips of their antlers through low-growing vegetation, producing erection and ejaculation (Beach, 1976).

Female masturbation is also found among many species besides our own. The prize for the most inventive technique probably should go to the female porcupine. She holds one end of a stick in her paws and walks around while straddling the stick; as the stick bumps against the ground, it vibrates against her genitals (Ford & Beach, 1951). Human females are apparently not the only ones to enjoy vibrators.

Same-Sex Sexual Behaviour

Same-sex behaviour is found in many species besides our own (Bagemihl, 1999; MacFarlane et al., 2010; Vasey, 2002; Wallen & Parsons, 1997; see Figure 1.9). Indeed, observations of other species indicate that our basic mammalian heritage is bisexual, composed of both heterosexual and homosexual elements (Bagemihl, 1999).

Is same-sex sexual behaviour found in other species?

Males of many species will mount other males, and anal intercourse has been observed in some male primates (Wallen & Parsons, 1997). Among domestic sheep, 9 percent of adult males strongly prefer other males as sex partners (Ellis, 1996; Roselli et al., 2002). In a number of primate species, including bonobos and Japanese macaques, females mount other females and

Figure 1.9   The sexual behaviour of animals. *(a)* Females have various ways of expressing choice. Here a female Barbary macaque presents her sexual swelling to a male. He seems to be interested. *(b)* Same-sex sexuality in animals: two male giraffes "necking." They rub necks and become aroused.

derive sexual rewards from these behaviours (Vasey et al., 2006; Vasey & Duckworth, 2008).

In What Ways Are Humans Unique?

Are humans in any way unique in their sexual behaviour? The general trend is for sexual behaviour to be more hormonally (instinctively) controlled among the lower species, such as fish or rodents, and to be controlled more by the brain (and therefore by learning and social content) in the higher species, like primates (Wallen, 2001). However, environmental influences are much more important in shaping primate—especially human—sexual behaviour than they are in shaping the sexual behaviour of other species.

Nonetheless, research has shown that in addition to instinctual or hard-wired preferences (such as the preference of males for sexually receptive females), learning affects the sexual preferences of a number of different species. For example, Quebec psychologist James Pfaus and his colleagues have shown in laboratory experiments that male rats can be conditioned (see Chapter 2 for an explanation of classical conditioning) to prefer female rats with a particular neutral odour, such as almond or lemon extract, to unscented females by first pairing the neutral odour with ejaculation (Pfaus et al., 2003, 2012). They have found similar results in female rats.

An illustration of this fact is provided by studies of the adult sexual behaviour of animals raised in deprived environments. If mice are reared in isolation, their adult sexual behaviour will nonetheless be normal (Scott, 1964). But if rhesus monkeys are reared in isolation, their adult sexual behaviour is severely disturbed, to the point that they may be incapable of reproducing (Harlow et al., 1963). Thus, environmental experiences are crucial in shaping the sexual behaviour of higher species, particularly humans; for us, sexual behaviour is a lot more than just "doing what comes naturally."

Female sexuality provides a particularly good illustration of the shift in hormonal control from lower to higher species. Throughout most of the animal kingdom, female sexual behaviour is strongly controlled by hormones. In virtually all mammals, females do not engage in sexual behaviour at all except when they are in *heat* (estrus), which is a particular hormonal state. In contrast, human females are capable of engaging in sexual behaviour—and actually do engage in it—during any phase of their hormonal (menstrual) cycle. Thus, the sexual behaviour of human females is not nearly as much under hormonal control as that of females of other species.

Traditionally, it was thought that female orgasm is unique to humans and does not exist in other species. Then some studies found evidence of orgasm in macaques (monkeys), as indicated by the same physiological responses indicative of orgasm in human females—specifically, increased heart rate and uterine contractions (Burton, 1970; Goldfoot et al., 1980; Zumpe & Michael, 1968). Thus, humans can no longer claim to have a corner on the female orgasm market. This fact has interesting implications for understanding the evolution of sexuality. Perhaps the higher species, in which the females are not driven to sexual activity by their hormones, have the pleasure of orgasm as an incentive.

In summary, then, little in human sexuality is completely unique to humans, except for elaborate, complex cultural influences. In other respects, we are on a continuum with other species.

The Nonsexual Uses of Sexual Behaviour

Two male baboons are locked in combat. One begins to emerge as the victor. The other *presents* (the "female" sexual posture, in which the rump is directed toward the other and is elevated somewhat).

Two male monkeys are members of the same troop. Long ago they established which one is dominant and which is subordinate. The dominant one *mounts* (the "male" sexual behaviour) the subordinate one.

These are examples of animals sometimes using sexual behaviour for nonsexual purposes (Small, 1993; Wallen & Zehr, 2004). Commonly, such behaviour signals the end of a fight, as in the first example. The loser indicates his surrender by presenting, and the winner signals victory by mounting. Sexual behaviours can also symbolize an animal's rank in a dominance hierarchy. Dominant animals mount subordinate ones. As another example, male squirrel monkeys sometimes use an exhibitionist display of their erect penis as part of an aggressive display against another male in a phenomenon called *phallic aggression* (Wickler, 1973).

The bonobo, an ape that is perhaps our closest genetic relative, is a particularly interesting example of the use of sexual behaviour for nonsexual purposes (de Waal, 1995). Bonobos live in female-centred, egalitarian groups and use sex for peacemaking in situations that might lead to aggression among other animals, such as situations involving food or jealousy. Since sex is a key part of their social life, bonobos engage in a wide range of sexual behaviours (including oral sex, massage of another's genitals, and intense tongue-kissing) with a wide range of partners, both same sex and other sex. The female is sexually attractive and sexually active during most of her cycle, rather than for just a few days around estrus.

All this is perfectly obvious when we observe it in monkeys. But do humans ever use sexual behaviour for nonsexual purposes? Consider the rapist, who uses sex as an expression of aggression against and power over a woman or a man (Zurbriggen, 2010). Another example is the exhibitionist, who uses a display of his erect penis to shock and frighten women, much as the male squirrel monkey uses such a display to shock and frighten his opponent. Humans also use sex for economic purposes; the best examples are male and female prostitutes.

There are also less extreme examples. Consider the couple who have a fight and then make love to signal an end to the hostilities.[6] Or consider the person who goes to bed with an influential—though unattractive—politician because this gives him or her a vicarious sense of power.

You can probably think of other examples of the nonsexual use of sexual behaviour. Humans, just like members of other species, can use sex for a variety of nonsexual purposes. Indeed, included in the reasons men and women give for why they have sex are wanting to celebrating a special occasion, wanting to increase the emotional connection, doing a favour for someone, wanting to increase their social status, and wanting to feel loved (Meston & Buss, 2007).

 LO7

The Sexual Health Perspective

Sexual health is an important new concept and a social and political movement that is gaining momentum worldwide. Although many discussions of sexual health are actually about sexual diseases, such as HIV infection, **sexual health** is a much broader concept that involves a vision of positive sexual health (Black, Bucio, et al., 2009; Edwards & Coleman, 2004; Parker et al., 2004; Public Health Agency of Canada [PHAC], 2008a). The World Health Organization (WHO, 2006) definition is as follows:

> **Sexual health:** A state of physical, emotional, mental, and social well-being related to sexuality.

> Sexual health is a state of physical, emotional, mental and social well-being in relation to sexuality; it is not merely the absence of disease, dysfunction or infirmity. Sexual health requires a positive and respectful approach to sexuality and sexual relationships, as well as the possibility of having pleasurable and safe sexual experiences, free of coercion, discrimination and violence. For sexual health to be attained and maintained, the sexual rights of all persons must be respected, protected and fulfilled. (p. 5)

Notice that this definition includes not only sexual physical health but also sexual mental health and positive sexual relationships. Therefore, public health efforts to prevent HIV or chlamydia infection, programs to promote women's reproductive rights, efforts to enhance romantic relationships, implementation of sex

---

[6] It has been our observation, particularly for couples in therapy, that this practice may not mean the same thing to men and women. To men it can mean that everything is fine again, but women can be left feeling dissatisfied and not at all convinced that the issues are resolved. Thus, this situation can be a source of miscommunication in heterosexual couples.

education curricula, and activism to end discrimination and violence against sexual and gender minorities all fall under the umbrella of sexual health. Notice also that the definition includes both negative and positive rights. Negative rights are freedoms *from*–for example, freedom from sexual violence. Positive rights are freedoms *to*–for example, the freedom to experience sexual pleasure or the freedom to express sexuality with same-sex partners. The greatest sexual health benefits will be achieved by emphasizing promotion of sexual and reproductive health and prevention of problems (PHAC, 2008a).

With the growth of the sexual health movement, the concept of **sexual rights** has also come to centre stage and, in fact, the term is used in the WHO definition and in the Public Health Agency of Canada guidelines. The idea here is that all human beings have certain basic, inalienable rights regarding sexuality that stem from basic human rights, such as those guaranteed in the *Canadian Charter of Rights and Freedoms*. The question, then, is, What are our basic sexual rights? The principles are new and evolving, but they generally include such elements as a right to reproductive self-determination and freedom from sexual violence, as well as the right to sexual self-expression (providing, of course, that it doesn't interfere with someone else's sexual rights) (Sandfort & Ehrhardt, 2004). According to

Sexual rights: Basic, inalienable rights regarding sexuality, both positive and negative, such as rights to reproductive self-determination and sexual self-expression and freedom from sexual abuse and violence.

the WHO, those rights also include the right to access reproductive health care service, receive sex education, consent or not consent to marriage, and experience a satisfying, safe, and pleasurable sex life (for a complete list of sexual rights see Chapter 20 online at Connect™). Many, particularly Western, cultures have laws to protect individuals' sexual rights and freedoms, although many societies protect some but not all sexual rights. For example, in Canada the *Charter of Rights and Freedoms* protects against discrimination based on sex or sexual orientation. Unfortunately, in many parts of the world people, particularly women, do not have these rights (Maticka-Tyndale & Smylie, 2008). Women may be forced to marry, have no recourse if they experience sexual assault, be expected to tolerate their husband having sex with sex workers even when it puts them at risk for disease, and receive little or no sex education. To ensure that human beings and societies develop healthy sexuality, these sexual rights must be recognized promoted, respected, and defended by all societies through all means. Sexual health is the result of an environment that recognizes, respects, and exercises these sexual rights. In Canada, particular attention needs to be paid to protecting groups whose sexual rights are not well protected–for example, individuals with disabilities and First Nations people (Silverberg & Odette, 2011).

The concepts of sexual health and sexual rights provide yet another broad and thought-provoking perspective on sexuality.

SUMMARY

Sexual activity is activity that produces arousal and increases the chance of orgasm. *Sex* (sexual behaviour and anatomy) is distinct from *gender* (being male or female).

Historically, religion was the main source of information concerning sexuality. Important early sex researchers were Sigmund Freud, Havelock Ellis, Richard von Krafft-Ebing, and Magnus Hirschfeld, all emerging from the Victorian era. By the 1990s, major, well-conducted sex surveys were available. Today, the mass media–whether television, magazines, or the Internet–are a powerful influence on most people's understanding of sexuality. The mass media may have an influence through cultivation, agenda-setting, and social learning.

Studies of various human cultures around the world provide evidence of the enormous variations in human sexual behaviour. Frequency of intercourse may vary from once a week in some cultures to three or four

times a night in others. Attitudes regarding premarital and extramarital sex, masturbation, same-sex sexual behaviour, and gender roles vary considerably across cultures. The great variations provide evidence of the importance of learning in shaping sexual behaviour. Yet all societies regulate sexual behaviour in some way.

Within Canada, sexual behaviour varies with one's social class and ethnic and linguistic group. Canada's ethnocultural communities are characterized by traditional gender roles and restrictions on female sexuality but not on male sexuality. Studies of sexual behaviour in various animal species show that masturbation, mouth–genital stimulation, and same-sex sexual behaviour are by no means limited to humans. In many species, sexual behaviour may be used for a variety of nonsexual purposes, such as expressing dominance.

A new international movement is focusing on sexual health and principles of sexual rights.

QUESTIONS FOR THOUGHT, DISCUSSION, AND DEBATE

1. In the wide spectrum of sexual practices in different cultures, from the conservatism of Inis Beag to the permissiveness of Mangaia, where would you place Canada today? Are we permissive, restrictive, or somewhere in between? Why?

2. Research indicates that masturbation, mouth–genital stimulation, and same-sex sexual activity are present in other species besides humans. What is the significance of that finding?

3. Sally is a newspaper reporter in Captown, the provincial capital. She learns, through a trusted friend, that the highly popular premier, George Smith, has been having a long-term affair with a local female lawyer, despite the fact that each of them is apparently happily married. Should Sally break the news in an article? In terms of communications theories, what effects might she expect her article to have on the public's attitudes about sexuality?

4. How does premarital sexual behaviour in Canada compare with premarital sex in Mangaia and Inis Beag? (See Sexuality in a Diverse World in this chapter.) Which of these three cultures do you think is best for adolescents to grow up in? Why? In which of those three cultures do you think adults are likely to have the most positive feelings about their sexuality? Why?

CHAPTER 2

Are YOU Curious?

1. Could natural selection account for people's tendency to prefer more physically attractive partners?
2. What theory accounts for how the smell of perfume or cologne becomes sexually arousing?
3. Why do most sexual interactions in our society follow the same pattern?

Read this chapter to find out.

Theoretical Perspectives on Sexuality

LEARNING OBJECTIVES

After studying this chapter, you will be able to

LO1 Describe the concepts associated with the evolutionary perspective.

LO2 State the strengths and weaknesses of the various Freudian psychoanalytic concepts.

LO3 Discuss the concepts of learning theory as they relate to the learning of sexual behaviours.

LO4 Show how social exchange theory explains sexual relationships and their satisfaction, stability, and change.

LO5 Demonstrate the relationship between cognition and sexuality and gender.

LO6 Describe the sociological perspective, including the social importance of sexuality and its relationship to the social institutions.

LO7 Show the ways in which laws in the *Criminal Code of Canada* regulate sexual conduct.

LO8 Describe symbolic interaction theory and its relationship to the concept of sexual scripts.

One of the discoveries of psychoanalysis consists of the assertion that impulses, which can only be described as sexual in both the narrower and the wider sense, play a peculiarly large part, never before sufficiently appreciated, in the causation of nervous and mental disorders. Nay, more, that these sexual impulses have contributed invaluably to the highest cultural, artistic, and social achievements of the human mind.*

From an evolutionary perspective, no single decision is more important than the choice of a mate. That single fork in the road determines one's ultimate reproductive fate.†

* Sigmund Freud. (1924). *A general introduction to psychoanalysis.* New York: Permabooks, 1953 (Boni & Liveright edition, 1924), pp. 26–27.
† David Buss. (2000). *The dangerous passion: Why jealousy is as necessary as love and sex.* New York: Free Press, p. 10.

Imagine, for a moment, that you are sitting in a bedroom watching two people making love. Imagine, too, that sitting with you in the room, thinking your same thoughts, are Sigmund Freud (creator of psychoanalytic theory), E. O. Wilson (a leading sociobiologist), Albert Bandura (a prominent social learning theorist), and John Gagnon (a proponent of script theory). The scene you are imagining may evoke arousal and nothing more in you, but your imaginary companions would have a rich set of additional thoughts as they viewed the scene through the lenses of their own theoretical perspectives. Freud might be marvelling at how the biological sex drive, the *libido*, expresses itself so strongly and directly in this couple. Wilson, the sociobiologist, would be thinking how mating behaviour in humans is similar to such behaviour in other species of animals, and how it is clearly the product of evolutionary selection for behaviours that lead to successful reproduction. Bandura might be thinking how sexual arousal and orgasm act as powerful positive reinforcers that will lead the couple to repeat the act frequently, and how they are imitating a technique of neck nibbling that they saw in an X-rated film last week. Finally, Gagnon's thoughts might be about the social scripting of sexuality; this couple begins with kissing, moves on to stroking and fondling, and finishes up with intercourse, following a script written by society.

Some of the major theories in the social sciences have had many—and different—things to say about sexuality, and it is these theories that we consider in this chapter. Theories provide us with answers to the question of why. We often wonder why others do or do not engage in particular sexual behaviours and relationships. We sometimes ask the "why" question about our own sexuality. Creative minds have developed theories to answer such questions. Given the diversity of human sexuality, we need a range of theories to understand it.

L01

Evolutionary Perspectives

Evolutionary perspectives use principles from evolutionary biology to explain why certain patterns of social behaviour and psychological mechanisms have evolved in animals, including humans (Barash, 1982; Buss, 1991). The idea that some behaviours are a result of evolution is called **sociobiology**. Sexual behaviour, of course, is a form of social behaviour, so sociobiologists, often based on observation of other species, argue that certain sexual behaviours evolved because they gave our ancestors an evolutionary advantage. Before we proceed, we should note that in terms of **evolution**, what counts is producing lots of healthy, viable offspring who will carry on our genes. Evolution occurs via **natural selection**, the process by which the individuals who are best adapted to their environment are more likely to survive, reproduce, and pass on their genes to the next generation.

How do humans choose mates? One major criterion is the physical attractiveness of the person (see Chapter 12). The sociobiologist argues that many of the characteristics we evaluate in judging attractiveness—for example, physique and complexion—are indicative of the health and vigour of the individual. These in turn are probably related to the person's reproductive potential; the unhealthy are less likely to produce many vigorous offspring. Natural selection would favour individuals preferring mates who would have maximum reproductive success. Thus, perhaps our

Could natural selection account for people's tendency to prefer more physically attractive partners?

Sociobiology: The application of evolutionary biology to understanding the social behaviour of animals, including humans.

Evolution: A theory that all living things have acquired their present forms through gradual changes in their genetic endowment over successive generations.

Natural selection: A process in nature resulting in greater rates of survival of those plants and animals that are adapted to their environment.

concern with physical attractiveness is a product of evolution and natural selection. (See Barash, 1982, for an extended discussion of this point and the ones that follow.) We choose an attractive, healthy mate who will help us produce many offspring. Can you guess why it is that the sociobiologist thinks most men are attracted to women with large breasts?

If attractiveness is an indicator of health, it should be more important in mate selection in societies where more people are unhealthy. An online survey obtained ratings of the attractiveness of images of male faces from 4800 women ages 21 to 40 from 30 countries. Facial masculinity, manipulated by computer, had more impact on attractiveness ratings in countries with poorer health, as measured by mortality, life expectancy, and communicable disease (DeBruine et al., 2010).

From this viewpoint, hanging out, playing sports, getting engaged, and similar customs are much like the courtship rituals of other species (see Figure 2.1). For example, many falcons and eagles have a flying courtship in which objects are exchanged between the pair in midair. The sociobiologist views this courtship as an opportunity for each member of the prospective couple to assess the other's fitness. For example, any lack of speed or coordination would be apparent during the airborne acrobatics. Perhaps that is exactly what we are doing in our human courtship rituals. The expenditure of money by men on dates indicates their ability to support a family. Dancing permits the assessment of physical prowess, and so on.

Sociobiologists can also explain why the nuclear family structure of a man, a woman, and their offspring is found in every society. Once a man and a woman mate, there are several obstacles to reproductive success, two being infant vulnerability and maternal death. Infant vulnerability is greatly reduced if the mother provides continuing physical care, including breast-feeding. It is further reduced if the father provides resources and security from attack for mother and infant. Two mechanisms that facilitate these conditions are a *pair-bond* between mother and father, and *attachment* between infant and parent (Miller & Fishkin, 1997). Thus, an offspring's chances of survival are greatly increased if the parents bond emotionally (i.e., love each other) and if the parents have a propensity for attachment. Further, an emotional bond might lead to more frequent sexual interaction; the pleasurable consequences of sex in turn will strengthen the bond. Research with small mammals, including mice and voles, demonstrates the advantages of biparental care of offspring and the critical role of bonding (Morell, 1998).

According to this theory, parents are most interested in the survival and reproductive success of their genetic offspring. *Parental investment* refers to the behaviour and resources invested in offspring to achieve this end.

Figure 2.1 *(a)* The courtship rituals of great egrets. *(b)* Dancing is a human dating custom. According to sociobiologists, human customs of dating and becoming engaged are biologically produced and serve the same functions as courtship rituals in other species: they allow potential mates to assess each other's fitness.

Because of the high rates of divorce and remarriage in Canada, many men have both biological children and stepchildren. This situation leads to the prediction that men will tend to invest more in their genetic children than in their stepchildren. Do research results support this prediction? Fathers have been found to invest the most money in the genetic children of their current union and the least money in stepchildren from a past relationship, as would be predicted from parental investment theory. However, they spend an equal amount on their genetic children and the stepchildren of their current relationship, perhaps to cement the pair-bond with their current partner (Anderson et al., 2001).

Research has found that, in men, physiological sexual arousal is specific to stimuli depicting their preferred sexual partner, whereas women show physiological arousal to stimuli depicting both their preferred and nonpreferred sex partners, and even to stimuli of animals (Chivers, 2005; Chivers et al., 2004; Chivers et al., 2007). Some Canadian researchers have argued that natural selection can account for these findings. That is, one explanation is that historically women who automatically responded physiologically with vasocongestion and vaginal lubrication were less likely to be injured during unwilling penile–vaginal intercourse or sexual activity with a chosen partner whom they did not find subjectively attractive (Chivers et al., 2007; Suschinsky et al., 2009). In contrast, lack of lubrication in these situations could lead to vaginal injury or infection, which, in turn, could result in sterility and even death. Thus, natural selection would have favoured women with an automatic or reflexive physiological response to a range of sexual stimuli.

In addition to natural selection, Darwin also proposed a mechanism that is less well known: **sexual selection** (Buss, 2009; Gangestad & Thornhill, 1997). Sexual selection is selection that results from differences in traits affecting access to mates. It consists of two processes: (1) competition among members of one gender (usually males) for mating access to members of the other gender, and (2) preferential choice by members of one gender (usually females) for certain members of the other gender. In other words, in many, though not all, species, males compete among themselves for the right to mate with females; and females, for their part, prefer certain males and mate with them while refusing to mate with other males (Clutton-Brock, 2007).[1] Researchers have tested some of the predictions that come from the theory of sexual selection with humans. For example, the theory predicts that men should compete with each other in ways that involve

displaying material resources that should be attractive to women, and men should engage in these displays more than women do (Buss, 1988). Examples might be giving impressive gifts to potential mates, showing off possessions (e.g., cars, stereos), or displaying personality characteristics that are likely to lead to the acquisition of resources (e.g., ambition). Research shows that men engage in these behaviours significantly more than women do and that both men and women believe these tactics are effective (Buss, 1988).

Evaluation of Sociobiology

Many criticisms of sociobiology have been made. Some critics object to the biological determinism that it implies. Sociobiology also has been criticized for resting on an outmoded version of evolutionary theory that modern biologists consider naive (Gould, 1987). For example, sociobiology has focused mainly on the individual's struggle for survival and efforts to reproduce; modern biologists focus on more complex issues, such as the survival of the group and the species. Further, sociobiologists assume that the central function of sex is reproduction; this may have been true in our evolutionary past, but it probably is not true today.

Recent research does not support some of the evidence that is widely cited in support of the theory. Singh (1993) reported that the winners of the Miss America contest and *Playboy*'s centrefold models have consistently had a waist-to-hip ratio of 0.7, arguing that this reflected a universal standard related to reproductive fitness. A closer look at the data showed that the average is not 0.7 but 0.66. The average for Miss America winners steadily declined from 0.78 in 1921 to 0.64 in 1986, contradicting the claim that a preference for a ratio of 0.7 was hard-wired by evolution thousands of years ago (Freese & Meland, 2002). Research analyzing waist-to-hip ratios across a large number of cultures, Western and non-Western, has found that the 0.7 ratio is most common in societies where women are economically dependent on men, not in all cultures as the theory asserts (Cashdan, 2008).

Evolutionary Psychology

A somewhat different approach is taken by **evolutionary psychology**, which focuses on how natural selection has shaped psychological mechanisms and processes (that is, the mind) rather than on how it has shaped sexual behaviour directly (Buss, 1991). If behaviours evolved in response to selection pressures, it is plausible to argue that cognitive or emotional structures evolved in the same way. Thus, a man who accurately

Sexual selection: Selection that results from differences in traits affecting access to mates.
Evolutionary psychology: The study of psychological mechanisms that have been shaped by natural selection.

---

[1] Sociobiologists use this mechanism to explain gender differences.

judged whether a woman was healthy and fertile would be more successful in reproducing. If his offspring exhibited the same ability to judge accurately, they in turn would have a competitive advantage.

One line of research has concentrated on *sexual strategies* (Buss & Schmitt, 1993). According to this theory, women and men face different adaptive problems in short-term, or casual, mating and in long-term mating and reproduction. These differences lead to different strategies or behaviours designed to solve these problems. In short-term mating, a woman may choose a partner who offers her immediate resources, such as food or money. In long-term mating, a woman may choose a partner who appears able and willing to provide resources for the indefinite future. A man may choose a sexually available woman for a short-term liaison but avoid such women when looking for a long-term mate.

According to the theory, women engage in intrasexual competition for access to men. Women pursuing a long-term strategy should respond negatively to women who make sex easily available to men (a "slut"?) An experimental study found that undergraduate women reacted negatively to a female confederate dressed sexily (cleavage, very short skirt), but not to the same person engaged in the same behaviour dressed in a loose shirt and jeans (Vaillancourt & Aanchai, 2011). On the other hand, women pursuing a short-term strategy want to appear sexy. Women at ovulation choose sexier and more revealing clothing from an online catalogue than they did three or more days before or seven days after ovulation (Durante et al., 2011).

Buss (1994) and others have reported data that support a number of specific predictions based on this theory. However, other research using the same measures with both men and women, and controlling for confounding effects, has found that men and women are very similar in their stated mating preferences. Both prefer long-term mating strategies and few or no short-term partners (Pedersen et al., 2002). Another criticism of evolutionary psychology is that some of the characteristics we observe that are assumed to have some adaptive significance may be simply "design flaws" or side effects of other adaptations (de Waal, 2002).

Like evolutionary psychology, sexual strategies theory is based on assumptions about what the ancestral environment was like. Although we can't study it directly, we can study very traditional societies, such as the Mayan and Asche. Research suggests that male sexual strategies are not consistent but change in response to personal characteristics and environmental contingencies (Waynforth et al., 1998).

Critics also question the data used to support much of this research. Although these theories claim that the processes and behaviours are the result of human evolution, and therefore universal, most of the data testing them comes from WEIRD (Western, educated, industrialized, rich, democratic) societies (Henrich et al., 2010). We don't know whether these results can be applied to persons in other societies. Further, tests of sexual strategies theory rely heavily on data from undergraduate students; note that this criticism applies to research testing other theories as well.

Psychological Theories

Four of the major theories in psychology are relevant to sexuality: psychoanalytic theory, learning theory, social exchange theory, and cognitive theory.

Psychoanalytic Theory

Sigmund Freud's **psychoanalytic theory** has been one of the most influential of all psychological theories. Because Freud saw sex as one of the key forces in human life, his theory gives full treatment to human sexuality.

Freud termed the sex drive or sex energy **libido**, which he saw as one of the two major forces motivating human behaviour (the other being *thanatos*, or the death instinct).

Id, Ego, and Superego

Freud described the human personality as being divided into three major parts: the id, the ego, and the superego. The **id** is the basic part of personality and is present at birth. It is the reservoir of psychic energy (including libido). Basically it operates on the *pleasure principle*—that is, the instinct to seek pleasure and avoid pain to satisfy basic needs.

While the id operates only on the pleasure principle and can thus be pretty irrational, the **ego** operates on the *reality principle* and tries to keep the id in line. The ego functions to make the person have realistic, rational interactions with others.

Finally, the **superego** is the conscience. It contains the values and ideals of society that we learn, and it operates on *idealism*. Thus, its aim is to inhibit the impulses of the id and to persuade the ego to strive for moral goals rather than realistic ones.[2]

---

[2] Fans of the television show *The Simpsons* might have noticed that Homer seems to be ruled primarily by his id and the pleasure principle, Lisa by her superego, and Marge by her ego and the reality principle.

Psychoanalytic theory: A psychological theory originated by Sigmund Freud; it contains a basic assumption that part of human personality is unconscious.

Libido (lih-BEE-doh): In psychoanalytic theory, the term for the sex energy or sex drive.

Id: According to Freud, the part of the personality containing the libido.

Ego: According to Freud, the part of the personality that helps the person have realistic, rational interactions.

Superego: According to Freud, the part of the personality containing the conscience.

To illustrate the operation of these three components of the personality in a sexual situation, consider the case of the CEO of a corporation who is at a meeting of the board of directors; the meeting is also attended by her handsome, buff, hot colleague. She looks at him, and her id says, "He's a real hunk. I want to throw him on the table and make love to him immediately. Let's do it!" The ego intervenes and says, "We can't do it now because the other members of the board are also here. Let's wait until 5 p.m., when they're all gone, and then do it." The superego says, "I shouldn't make love to this hot guy at all because I'm a married woman." What actually happens? It depends on the relative strengths of this woman's id, ego, and superego.

The id, ego, and superego develop sequentially. The id contains the set of instincts present at birth. The ego develops a few years later, as the child learns how to interact realistically with his or her environment and the people in it. The superego develops last, as the child learns moral values.

Erogenous Zones

Freud saw the libido as being focused in various regions of the body known as **erogenous zones**. An erogenous zone is a part of the skin or mucous membrane that is extremely sensitive to stimulation; touching it in certain ways produces feelings of pleasure. The lips and mouth are one such erogenous zone, the genitals a second, and the rectum and anus a third.

Stages of Psychosexual Development

Freud believed that children pass through a series of stages of development. In each of these stages, a different erogenous zone is the focus of pleasure.

According to Freud, the first stage, lasting from birth to about one year of age, is the *oral stage*. The child's chief pleasure is derived from sucking and otherwise stimulating the lips and mouth. Anyone who has observed children of this age knows how they delight in putting anything they can into their mouths. The second stage, which occurs during approximately the second year of life, is the *anal stage*. During this stage, the child's interest is focused on elimination.

The third stage of development, lasting from age three to perhaps age five or six, is the *phallic stage*. Boys' and girls' interest is focused on the genital area—the boy on his phallus (penis) and the girl on her clitoris—and they derive great pleasure from masturbating.[3] Perhaps the most important occurrence in this stage according to Freud is the development of the **Oedipus complex**, which derives its name from the Greek story of Oedipus, who unknowingly killed his father and married his

mother. In the male Oedipus complex, the boy loves his mother and desires her sexually. He hates his father, whom he sees as a rival for the mother's affection. The boy's hostility toward his father grows, but eventually he comes to fear that his father will retaliate by castrating him—cutting off his prized penis. Thus, the boy feels *castration anxiety*. Eventually, the castration anxiety becomes so great that he stops desiring his mother and shifts to identifying with his father, taking on the father's gender role and acquiring the characteristics expected of males by society. Freud considered the Oedipus complex and its resolution to be one of the key factors in human personality development.

The **female Oedipus complex** (sometimes called the *Electra complex*, although not by Freud) is similar to the male Oedipus complex, beginning with the girl's love for her mother and her focus on her clitoris. The little girl realizes, perhaps after observing her father or her brother, that she has no penis. She feels envious and cheated, and she suffers from *penis envy*, wishing that she too had a wonderful wand and the privileges that go along with being male. Thus, she shifts her desire for her mother onto her father, forming the female Oedipus complex. The girl resolves penis envy by identifying with her mother and switching her erogenous zone from her clitoris to her vagina in order to have a baby, a son, as a substitute for a penis. Unlike the boy, the girl is not driven by castration anxiety to resolve her Oedipus complex. Thus the girl's resolution of the Oedipus complex is not as complete as the boy's, and Freud wrote that for the rest of her life, a woman's superego is not as developed as a man's.

Freud said that following the resolution of the Oedipus complex, children pass into a prolonged stage known as *latency*, which lasts until adolescence. During this stage, the sexual impulses are repressed or are in a quiescent state, and so nothing much happens sexually. The postulation of this stage is one of the weaker parts of Freudian theory, because it is clear from the data of modern sex researchers that children do continue to engage in behaviour with sexual components during this period (see Chapter 10).

With puberty, sexual urges reawaken, and the child moves into the *genital stage*. During this stage, sexual urges become more specifically genital, and the oral, anal, and genital urges all fuse together to promote the biological function of reproduction.

According to Freud, people do not always mature from one stage to the next as they should. A person might remain permanently fixated, for example, at the oral stage; symptoms of such a situation would include incessant

---

[3] Masturbation to orgasm is physiologically possible at this age, although males are not capable of ejaculation until they reach puberty (see Chapter 5).

> **Erogenous (eh-RAH-jen-us) zones:** Areas of the body that are particularly sensitive to sexual stimulation.
> **Oedipus (EH-di-pus) complex:** According to Freud, the sexual attraction of a little boy for his mother.
> **Female Oedipus complex:** According to Freud, the sexual attraction of a little girl for her father. Sometimes called the Electra complex.

cigarette smoking or fingernail biting, which gratify oral urges. Most adults have at least traces of earlier stages remaining in their personalities.

Evaluation of Psychoanalytic Theory

From a scientific point of view, one of the major problems with psychoanalytic theory is that most of its concepts cannot be evaluated scientifically to see whether they are accurate. Freud postulated that many of the most important forces in personality are unconscious and thus cannot be studied by using the scientific techniques common to the twentieth century. Recent advances in our ability to image brain activity—for example, with high-powered magnetic resonance imagery—have opened the possibility of testing Freud's ideas (see Figure 2.2). He believed that dreams provide a window into the person's id and that during sleep the activity of the ego and superego are reduced. Research in the developing area of *neuropsychoanalysis* suggests that it is activity in the prefrontal area of the brain that

Figure 2.2 What does a magnetic resonance imaging machine have to do with psychoanalytic theory? The answer is that by studying patterns in brain waves, we can test some of Freud's ideas about the relationship between the id and the ego.

constrains the sometimes bizarre imagery that is generated by the limbic and postcortical regions. During rapid eye movement (REM) sleep, there is a reduction of activity in the former (the ego?) and vivid and bizarre dreams are at times associated with activity in the latter (the id?) (Solms, 1997).

A key concept in psychoanalytic theory is *repression*, a defensive act preventing people from remaining aware of certain information, or motivated forgetting. It has been widely criticized as untestable. However, neural inhibition triggered by social factors could account for repression. Imaging evidence has identified the frontal lobes as the area that mediates the influence of social factors on impulse control, suggesting the neural basis of repression (Boag, 2007).

Another criticism is that Freud derived his data almost exclusively from his work with patients who sought therapy from him. Thus, his theory may provide a view not so much of the human personality as of *disturbances* in the human personality.

Feminists also have been critical of Freudian theory as a male-centred theory that may cause harm to women (Lerman, 1986). They object to Freud's assumption that because they do not have a penis, women are biologically inferior to men. One could just as easily argue that men have a powerful envy of women's reproductive capacity, which is just what psychoanalyst Karen Horney (1973) did when she coined the concept of *womb envy*, although this notion is equally open to criticism. They also criticize the distinction Freud made between *vaginal orgasm* (obtained through heterosexual intercourse with the penis stimulating the vagina) and clitoral orgasm (obtained through *clitoral stimulation*) in women. Research by Masters and Johnson (reviewed in Chapter 9) has shown that there is little or no physiological difference between orgasms resulting from clitoral stimulation and those resulting from heterosexual intercourse. Further, Freud's assertion that vaginal orgasm is more mature is not supported by findings that most adult women orgasm as a result of direct or indirect clitoral stimulation.

Nonetheless, Freud did make some important contributions to our understanding of human behaviour and many of his concepts have become part of everyday language. (Which ones can you think of?) He managed to rise above the sexually repressive Victorian era of which he was a member and teach that the libido is an important part of personality (although he may have overestimated its importance). His recognition that humans pass through stages in their psychological development was a great contribution. Perhaps most important from the perspective of this text, Freud took sex out of the closet, brought it to the attention of the general public, and suggested that we could talk about it and that it was an appropriate topic for scientific research.

Of course, psychoanalytic theory has evolved since Freud did his writing. Most contemporary psycho-analysts feel that Freud overemphasized the biological determinants of behaviour and instincts and that he gave insufficient recognition to the importance of environment and learning. For example, Erikson (1950), an influential theorist in developmental psychology, described how development continues throughout life rather than ending around age five. Most recent psychoanalytic theories, some of which are called object-relations theories, also describe relationships with other people, particularly the child's relationship with his or her primary caretaker (usually his or her mother or father), as crucial to development, although they have not totally abandoned Freud's view that sexuality is important to development. In particular, the type of attachment relationship children have to their mothers and fathers in infancy and childhood may have a profound effect on their romantic relationships in adulthood (see Chapter 12 for more about the attachment theory of love).

 ## Learning Theory

Although psychoanalytic and sociobiological theories are based on the notion that much of human sexual behaviour is biologically controlled, it is also quite apparent that much of it is learned. Some of the best evidence for this point comes from studies of sexual behaviour across different human societies, which were considered in Chapter 1. Here the various principles of modern learning theory will be reviewed, because they can help us understand our own sexuality.

Classical Conditioning

What theory accounts for how the smell of perfume or cologne becomes sexually arousing?

Classical conditioning is a concept usually associated with the work of the Russian scientist Ivan Pavlov (1849–1936). Think of the following situations: You salivate in response to the sight or smell of food, you blink in response to someone poking a finger in your eye, or you experience sexual arousal in response to stroking the inner part of your thigh. In all these cases, an unconditioned stimulus (US; for example, appealing food) automatically, reflexively elicits an unconditioned response (UR; for example, salivation). The process of learning that occurs in classical conditioning takes place when a new stimulus, the conditioned stimulus (CS; for example, the sound of a bell) repeatedly is paired with the original unconditioned stimulus (food). After this happens many times, the conditioned stimulus (ringing bell) can eventually be presented without the unconditioned stimulus (food) and will evoke the original response, now called the conditioned response (CR; salivation).

As an example, suppose that Nadia's first serious boyfriend in high school always wears Erotik cologne when they go out. As they advance in their sexual intimacy, they have many pleasant times in the back seat of the car, where he strokes her thighs and other sexually responsive parts of her body and she feels highly aroused, always with the aroma of Erotik in her nostrils. One day she enters an elevator full of strangers in her office building, and someone is wearing Erotik. Nadia instantly feels sexually aroused, although she is not engaged in any sexual activity. From the point of view of classical conditioning, this makes perfect sense, although Nadia may wonder why she is feeling so aroused in the elevator. The thigh-stroking and sexy touching were the US. Her arousal was the UR. The aroma of the cologne, the CS, was repeatedly paired with the US. Eventually, the aroma by itself evoked arousal, the CR. See Figure 2.3.

Classical conditioning of sexual arousal has been demonstrated in an experiment using male students at Queen's University (Lalumière & Quinsey, 1998). Participants were first shown 20 slides of partially clothed women; a slide rated as 5 on a scale of sexual attractiveness ranging from 1 to 10 was selected as the target slide. Men in the control group saw only the target slide for 11 trials; men in the experimental group were shown the target slide followed by a 40-second segment of a sexually explicit videotape for 11 trials. Each man then rated the 20 original slides again. Arousal was measured by a penile strain gauge, which measures the extent of engorgement or erection of the penis (see Chapter 13). In the control group, men were less aroused by the target slide following the repeated exposure, while in the experimental group, the target slide was associated with an increase in arousal as measured by the strain gauge. Subsequent research has also demonstrated classical conditioning of sexual arousal in women (Hoffmann, Jannsen, & Turner, 2004).

Classical conditioning is useful in explaining a number of phenomena in sexuality. One example is fetishes, discussed in Chapter 15.

Operant Conditioning

Operant conditioning, a concept that is often associated with psychologist B. F. Skinner, refers to the following process. A person performs a particular behaviour (the operant). That behaviour may be followed by either a reward (positive reinforcement) or a punishment. If a reward follows, the person will be likely to repeat the behaviour again in the future; if a punishment follows, the person

> **Classical conditioning:** The learning process in which a previously neutral stimulus (conditioned stimulus) is repeatedly paired with an unconditioned stimulus that reflexively elicits an unconditioned response. Eventually, the conditioned stimulus itself will evoke the response.
>
> **Operant (OP-ur-unt) conditioning:** The process of changing the frequency of a behaviour (the operant) by following it with positive reinforcement (which will make the behaviour more frequent in the future) or punishment (which should make the behaviour less frequent in the future).

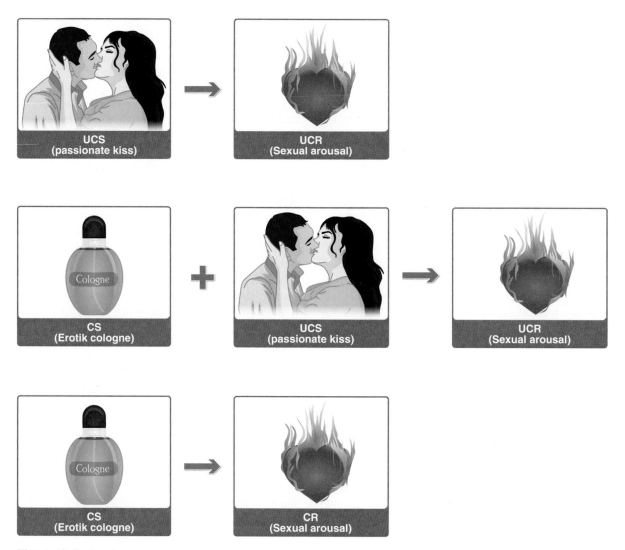

Figure 2.3   In this example of classical conditioning, Erotik cologne (the CS) eventually evokes sexual arousal by itself after it is repeatedly paired with kissing (the UCS).

will be less likely to repeat the behaviour. Thus, if a behaviour is repeatedly rewarded, it may become very frequent, and if it is repeatedly punished, it may become very infrequent or even be eliminated.

Some rewards are considered to be primary reinforcers; that is, there is something intrinsically rewarding about them. Food is one such primary reinforcer; sex is another. Male rats, for example, can be trained to learn a maze if they find a willing sex partner at the end of it. Thus, sexual behaviour plays dual roles in learning theory: it can itself be a positive reinforcer, but it can also be the behaviour that is rewarded or punished.

Simple principles of operant conditioning can help explain some aspects of sex. For example, if a woman repeatedly experiences pain when she has intercourse, she will probably want to have sex infrequently or not at all. In operant conditioning terms, sexual intercourse has repeatedly been associated with a punishment (pain), and so the behaviour becomes less frequent.

Another principle of operant conditioning that is useful in understanding sexual behaviour holds that consequences, whether reinforcement or punishment, are most effective in shaping behaviour when they occur immediately after the behaviour. The longer they are delayed after the behaviour has occurred, the less effective they become. As an example, consider a young man who has had gonorrhea three times yet continues to have unprotected sexual intercourse. The pain associated with gonorrhea is certainly punishing, so why does he persist in having sex without a condom? The delay principle suggests the following explanation. Each time he engages in unprotected intercourse, he finds it highly rewarding; this immediate reward maintains the behaviour; the punishment, gonorrhea, does not occur until several days later and so is not effective in eliminating that behaviour.

A third principle that has emerged in operant conditioning studies is that, compared with rewards, punishments are not very effective in shaping behaviour. Often, as in the case of the child who is punished for taking an illicit cookie, punishments do not eliminate a behaviour but rather teach the person to be sneaky and engage in it without being caught. As an example, some parents, as many commonly did in earlier times in our culture, punish children for masturbating; yet most of those children continue to masturbate, perhaps learning instead to do it under circumstances in which they are not likely to be caught (such as in a bathroom with the door locked).

One important difference between psychoanalytic theory and learning theory should be noted. Psychoanalytic theorists believe that the determinants of human sexual behaviour occur in early childhood, particularly during the Oedipal complex period. Learning theorists, in contrast, believe that sexual behaviour can be learned and changed at any time in one's lifespan—in childhood, in adolescence, in young adulthood, or later. When we try to understand what causes certain sexual behaviours and how to treat people with sex problems, this distinction between the theories has important implications.

Behaviour Therapy

Behaviour therapy involves a set of techniques, based on principles of classical or operant conditioning, that are used to change (or modify) human behaviour. In particular, these methods can be used to modify problematic sexual behaviours—that is, sexual disorders, such as orgasm problems (see Chapter 18) or compulsive sexual behaviour (see Chapter 15). Behaviour therapy methods differ from more traditional methods of psychotherapy, such as psychoanalysis, in that the behavioural therapist considers only the problem behaviour and how to modify it using learning-theory principles; the therapist does not worry about an in-depth analysis of the person's personality to see, for example, what unconscious forces might be motivating the behaviour. Most often treatment programs combine behaviour therapy techniques with cognitive therapy approaches—called cognitive behaviour therapy.

Social Learning

Social learning theory (Bandura, 1977; Bandura & Walters, 1963) is a somewhat more complex form of learning theory. It is based on principles of operant conditioning, but it also recognizes that people learn by observing others, called *observational learning*, whether in person or in the media. This kind of social learning involves two other processes: *imitation* and *identification*. These two processes are useful in explaining the development of gender identity, or our sense of maleness or femaleness. For example, a little girl acquires many characteristics of the female role by identifying

with her mother and imitating her, as when she plays at dressing up after observing her mother getting ready to go to a party. Also, various forms of sexuality may be learned through imitation (see Figure 2.4). In high school, for example, the sexiest girl in the senior class may find that other girls are imitating her behaviours and the way she dresses. Or a boy might see a movie in which the hero's technique seems to "turn women on"; then he tries to use this technique with his own dates. The latter example points to the importance of mass media as a source of images of sexuality that young people imitate and personalities that they identify with. Unfortunately, media images are often inaccurate and unrealistic.

Once a behaviour is learned, the likelihood of its being performed depends on its consequences. The young man who imitates actor Brad Pitt's romantic technique may not succeed in arousing his companion. If the behaviour is not reinforced, he will stop performing it. If it is reinforced, he will repeat it. Successful experiences with an activity over time create a sense of competence or **self-efficacy** at performing the activity (Bandura, 1982). If a woman feels efficacious at using the female condom, she will expend more effort (going to the drugstore to buy one) and will show greater persistence in the face of difficulty (continuing to adjust it until it fits properly) than she did before. The concept of self-efficacy has been widely used in designing health intervention programs, such as those that encourage individuals

> **Behaviour therapy:** A set of techniques based on principles of classical or operant conditioning used to modify human behaviour.
> **Self-efficacy:** A sense of competence at performing an activity.

Figure 2.4 According to social learning theory, children learn about sex and gender in part by imitation. These children may be imitating their parents or a scene they have watched on TV.

A Sexually Diverse World

Ritualized Same-Sex Sexual Activity in a Non-Western Society

Melanesia is an area of the southwest Pacific that includes the islands of New Guinea and Fiji as well as many others. Anthropologists' research on same-sex sexual behaviour in those cultures provides great insight into the ways in which sexual behaviours are the products of the scripts of a culture, as well as of social learning theory. This research is rooted in sociological and anthropological theory. As such, the analysis focuses on the norms of the society and the symbolic meaning that is attached to sexual behaviours.

Among Melanesians, same-sex sexual behaviour has a very different symbolic meaning from the one it has in Western culture. It is viewed as natural, normal, and indeed necessary. The culture actually prescribes the behaviour, in contrast to Western cultures, in which it is forbidden or proscribed. Among Melanesians, age organizes the same-sex sexual behaviour. It is not to occur between two men of the same age. Instead, it occurs between an adolescent and a preadolescent, or between an adult man and a pubertal boy. The older partner is always the inserter for the acts of anal intercourse, the younger partner is the receiver.

Ritualized same-sex sexual behaviour serves several social purposes in these cultures. It is viewed as a means by which a boy at puberty is incorporated into the adult society of men. It is also thought to "finish off" a boy's growth in puberty. In these societies, semen is viewed as a scarce and valuable commodity. Therefore, the same-sex sexual behaviours are viewed as helpful and honourable, a means of passing on strength to younger men and boys. As one anthropologist observed:

> Semen is also necessary for young boys to attain full growth to manhood. . . . They need a boost, as it were. When a boy is eleven or twelve years old, he is engaged for several months in homosexual intercourse with a healthy older man chosen by his father. (This is always an in-law or unrelated person, since the same notions of incestuous relations apply to little boys as to marriageable women.) Men point to the rapid growth of adolescent youths, the appearance of peach fuzz beards, and so on, as the favorable results of this child-rearing practice. (Schieffelin, 1976, p. 124)

In all cases, these men are expected later to marry and father children. These observations defy the commonly held, although not necessarily accurate, view in Western societies that sexual orientation is a permanent characteristic throughout life. This points out the

---

to use condoms to prevent transmission of sexually transmitted infections and HIV (e.g., DeLamater, Wagstaff, & Havens, 2000). These programs provide opportunities for participants to practise the behaviours that are being promoted and be successful.

Social learning can also explain phenomena, such as birth rates (see also the Sexually Diverse World box). Many adults want to have children, that is, they have *fertility intentions*. They also recognize that infant mortality may deprive them of offspring. Most adults are not aware of the infant mortality rate in their country or community. However, they are aware of the fertility outcomes of couples they know and interact with. If women are influenced by the birth and survival experiences of women around them, this would reflect

Social exchange theory: A theory that assumes people will choose actions that maximize rewards and minimize costs.

the impact of social experience and learning on reproduction. Researchers identified the social networks of a group of Nepalese women and assessed the experiences of members of a woman's network on her fertility. As expected, experiences of network members were related to the timing of a woman's births, demonstrating the effects of social learning on birth rates (Sandberg, 2006).

L04 Social Exchange Theory

An important process based on the principle of reinforcement is social exchange. **Social exchange theory** (Cook & Rice, 2003) has emerged out of social learning theory and uses the concept of reinforcement to explain satisfaction, stability, and change in relationships among people. It is also useful in explaining *sexuality* in close contrast between sexual identity and sexual behaviour. The sexual behaviours are ones that we would surely term "homosexual," yet these cultures are so structured that the boys and men who engage in same-sex sexual behaviours do not form a homosexual identity. Indeed, the very concepts of having a "heterosexual identity" or "homosexual identity" are not present in these cultures.

Can social learning theory also explain these patterns of sexual behaviour? It can, according to the analysis of John and Janice Baldwin. First, positive conditioning in the direction of heterosexuality occurs early in life. The boy spends the first seven to ten years of his life with his family. He has a close, warm relationship with his mother. In essence, he has been conditioned to have positive feelings about women.

Second, observational learning occurs. In those same first seven to ten years, the boy observes closely the heterosexual relationship between two adults, his mother and father. This observational learning can be used a decade later when it is time for him to marry and form a heterosexual relationship.

Third, the boy is provided with much cognitive structuring, a notion present in social learning theory and in cognitive psychology. He is instructed that a boy must pass through a series of stages to become a strong, masculine man. These stages include first being the receptive partner to fellatio, then being the inserting partner to fellatio, marrying, defending himself from his wife's first menstruation (girls are usually married before puberty and undergo no homosexual stage of development), and then fathering a child by her. Essentially, he is given all the cognitive structures necessary to convince him that it is perfectly natural, indeed desirable, to engage in sex with men for ten years and then switch to women. Finally, there is some aversive conditioning to the homosexual behaviour that leads it to be not particularly erotic. The boy performs fellatio for the first time after several days of initiation, when he is exhausted. The activities are staged so that the boy feels fearful about it. He must do it in darkness with an older boy who may be an enemy, and he is required to do it with many males in succession. In essence, unpleasantness or punishment is associated with some of the homosexual behaviour.

Ritualized same-sex sexual behaviours are declining as these cultures are colonized by Westerners. It is fortunate that anthropologists were able to make their observations over the last several decades to document these interesting and meaningful practices before they disappear.

Sources: Baldwin & Baldwin (1989), Herdt (1984).

relationships (Byers & Wang, 2004). The theory assumes that we have freedom of choice and often face choices among alternative actions. Every action provides some rewards and entails certain costs. There are many kinds of rewards (money, goods, services, sexual gratification, approval by others) and costs (time, effort, money, embarrassment, emotional distance). The theory states that we try to maximize rewards and minimize costs when we act. Thus, we choose actions that produce a favourable balance of rewards to costs or profits (profits equalling rewards minus costs), and avoid actions that produce poor profits.

As its name indicates, social exchange theory views social relationships primarily as exchanges of goods and services among persons. People participate in relationships only if they find that the relationships provide profitable outcomes. An individual judges the attractiveness of a relationship by comparing the profits it provides against both the profits he or she thinks should be received in the relationship and the profits available in alternative relationships. The level of expected outcomes is called the *comparison level*; the level of outcomes in the best alternative relationship is called the *comparison level for alternatives* (Byers & Wang, 2004). These ideas have been applied to personal relationships. Studies of heterosexual couples in long-term relationships have found that the concepts of rewards and costs can explain whether people stay in a relationship (Rusbult, 1983; Rusbult, Johnson, & Morrow, 1986). Individuals are more likely to stay in when the partner is physically and personally attractive, when the relationship does not entail undue costs (such as high monetary commitments, broken promises, or arguments), and when romantic relationships with attractive others are not available. In other words, they are more likely to stay in a relationship when its rewards are high, its costs are low, rewards and costs compare favourably to expectations, and the comparison level for alternatives is low.

Social exchange theory also predicts the conditions under which people try to change their relationships. A central concept is *equity* or *equality* (Walster, Walster, & Berscheid, 1978; Hatfield, Walster, & Berscheid, 1978). A state of equity exists when participants in a relationship believe that the rewards they receive from it are proportional to the costs they bear. Equality exists when both partners experience the same balance of rewards to costs (profit). If a person feels that the allocation of rewards and costs is inequitable or unequal, then the relationship is unstable. People find inequity unpleasant and may feel cheated or angry. As we will see in Chapter 11, a person experiencing inequity may engage in *extradyadic* sex (i.e., sex with someone other than their partner) as a result.

Social exchange theory has also been used to explain various other aspects of sexuality in close relationships such as partner selection, sexual frequency, and sexual satisfaction (for a review, see Byers & Wang, 2004). For example, one of this book's authors, New Brunswick psychologist Sandra Byers, and her colleagues have shown that, in both dating and long-term relationships, sexual satisfaction is higher the more sexual rewards exceed sexual costs (i.e., profit is high), sexual rewards and costs compare favourably to expectations, and sexual rewards and costs between partners are equal (Byers, Demmons, & Lawrance, 1998; Byers & MacNeil, 2006; Lawrance & Byers, 1995).

Social exchange theories have been criticized for applying the ideas of rewards and costs to romantic relationships. Some people believe that love is not and should not be about what one can get out of a relationship (i.e., its rewards). A related criticism is that social exchange theories downplay other motivations. Because of the emphasis on rewards and costs, such theories cannot explain, for example, selfless behaviours, such as altruism and martyrdom.

 Cognitive Theory

In the 1980s and 1990s, a "cognitive revolution" swept through psychology. In contrast to the older behaviourist tradition (which insisted that psychologists should study only behaviours that could be directly observed), cognitive psychologists believe that it is very important to study people's cognitions—that is, the way people perceive and think.

Schema (SKEE-muh): A general knowledge framework that a person has about a particular topic.

Cognition and Sexuality

Cognitive psychology can readily explain some aspects of human sexuality. A basic assumption is that what we think influences what we feel. If we think happy, positive thoughts, we will tend to feel better than if we think negative ones. Therapists using a cognitive approach believe that psychological distress is often a result of unpleasant thoughts that do not reflect reality and include misconceptions, distortions, exaggerations of problems, and unreasonably negative evaluations of events.

To the cognitive psychologist, how we perceive and evaluate a sexual event makes all the difference in the world (Walen & Roth, 1987). For example, suppose that a man engaged in sexual activity with his partner does not get an erection. Starting from that basic event, his thoughts might take one of two directions. In the first, he thinks that it is quite common for a man in his age group (50s) not to get an erection every time he has sex; this has happened to him a few times before, once every two or three months, and it's nothing to worry about. At any rate, the oral sex was fun, and his partner had an orgasm from that, so all in all it was a nice enough encounter. In the second possibility, he began the sexual activity thinking that he had to have an erection, had to have intercourse, and had to have an orgasm. When he didn't get an erection, he mentally labelled it *impotence* and worried that he would never again have an erection. He thought of the whole episode as a frustrating disaster because he never had an orgasm. Who do you think would be more likely to experience sexual problems the next time he has sex?

As cognitive psychologists point out, our perception, labelling, and evaluation of events are crucial. In one case, the man perceived a slight problem, labelled it a temporary erection problem, and evaluated his sexual experience as pretty good. In the other case, the man perceived a serious problem, labelled it impotence, and evaluated the experience as horrible.

We will see cognitive psychology several times again in this book, as theorists use it to understand the cycle of sexual arousal (see Chapter 9), the causes of some sexual variations, such as fetishes (see Chapter 15), and the causes and treatment of sexual disorders (see Chapter 18). Before we leave cognitive psychology, however, we will look at one cognitive theory, schema theory, that has been used especially to understand issues of sex and gender.

Gender Schema Theory

Psychologist Sandra Bem (1981, 1993) has proposed a schema theory to explain gender-role development and the impact of gender on people's daily lives and thinking. *Schema* is a term taken from cognitive psychology. A **schema** is a general knowledge framework that a person has about a particular topic. A schema organizes and guides perception; it helps us remember, but it sometimes also distorts our memory, especially if the information is inconsistent with our schema. Thus, for example, you might have a hockey game schema, the set of ideas you have about what elements should be present at the game (two teams, spectators, stands, etc.) and what kinds of activities should occur (opening face-off, occasional goal, penalties, power plays, etc.).

It is Bem's contention that all of us possess a *gender schema*—a cognitive structure comprising the set of attributes (behaviours, personality, appearance) that we associate with males and females. Children learn not only about appropriate roles for men and women but also that the distinctions between men and women and between masculine and feminine are extremely important ways to understand reality. Thus our gender schema, according to Bem, predisposes us to process information on the basis of gender. That is, we tend to think of things as gender-related and to want to dichotomize them on the basis of gender. A good example is the case of the infant whose gender isn't clear when we meet him or her. We eagerly seek out the information or feel awkward if we don't, because we seem to need to know the baby's gender to continue to process information about it.

Bem (1981) has done a number of experiments that provide evidence for her theory, and there are confirming experiments by other researchers as well, although the evidence is not always completely consistent (Ruble & Stangor, 1986). In one of the most interesting of these experiments, five- and six-year-old children were shown pictures of males or females performing activities that were either stereotype-consistent activities (such as a girl baking cookies) or stereotype-inconsistent (such as girls boxing) at that time (Martin & Halverson, 1983; see Figure 2.5 for examples). One week later the children were tested for their recall of the pictures. The results indicated that the children distorted information by changing the gender of people in the stereotype-inconsistent pictures, while not making such changes for the stereotype-consistent pictures. That is, children tended to remember a picture of girls boxing as having been a picture of boys boxing. These results are just what would be predicted by gender schema theory. The schema helps us remember schema-consistent (stereotype-consistent) information well, but it distorts our memory of information that is inconsistent with the schema (stereotype-inconsistent).

Our gender schema influences many everyday behaviours, for example, what we look at in magazines. Male and female undergraduate students completed a measure of the masculinity-femininity of their self-concept. They were later allowed to select from three male-typed (*Men's Health, Game Informer, Sports Illustrated*), three female-typed (*Shape, Us Weekly, Glamour*), and three gender-neutral news magazines. Gender schema (masculinity-femininity) influenced what they read in the selected magazine(s) (Knobloch-Westerwick & Hoplamazian, 2012).

One of the interesting implications of gender schema theory is that stereotypes—whether they are about males and females, or heterosexuals and homosexuals,

(a)

(b)

Figure 2.5 Pictures like these were used in the Martin and Halverson research on gender schemas and children's memory. *(a)* A girl engaged in a stereotype-consistent activity. *(b)* Girls engaged in a stereotype-inconsistent activity. In a test of recall a week later, children tended to distort the stereotype-inconsistent pictures to make them stereotype consistent; for example, they remembered that they had seen boys boxing.

or other groups—may be very slow to change. The reason is that our schemas tend to filter out stereotype-inconsistent (that is, schema-inconsistent) information so that we don't even remember it.

Sociological Perspectives

Sociologists are most interested in the ways in which society or culture shapes human sexuality. (For a detailed articulation of the sociological perspective, see DeLamater, 1987; the arguments that follow are taken from that source.)

Sociologists approach the study of sexuality with three basic assumptions:

1. Every society regulates the sexuality of its members. (For a discussion of the reasons why, see Horrocks, 1997.)
2. Basic institutions of society (such as religion and the family) affect the rules governing sexuality in that society.
3. The appropriateness or inappropriateness of a particular sexual behaviour depends on the culture in which it occurs.

Sociologists view societal influences on human sexuality as occurring on several levels, including the macro level, or society as a whole, and the subcultural level, at which a person's social class or ethnic group may have an impact on sexuality. Our discussion in this section emphasizes the macro level of influence.

Social Institutions

According to the sociological perspective, at the macro level our sexuality is influenced by powerful social institutions, including religion, the family, the economy, medicine, and the law. Each major institution supports a sexual ideology, or discourse, about sexual activity. This ideology influences the beliefs and behaviours of those affiliated with the institution.

Religion

Historically, the Judeo-Christian religious tradition has been a powerful shaper of sexual norms in Western culture. A detailed discussion of that religious tradition and its teachings on sexuality is provided in Chapter 20. Suffice it to say here that the Christian religion (but not the Jewish religion) has contained within it a tradition of asceticism, in which abstinence from sexual pleasures—especially by certain persons, such as monks and priests—is seen as virtuous. The tradition, at least until recently, has also been oriented toward

procreation—that is, a belief that sexuality is legitimate only within traditional heterosexual marriage and only with the goal of having children, a *procreational ideology*. This view has created within our culture a set of norms, or standards for behaviour, that say, for example, that sex before marriage, outside of marriage, and with a same-sex partner is wrong. The procreational ideology is one argument that some people use for asserting that marriage is exclusively for a man and a woman, since only a mixed-sex couple can procreate without intervention. Many of these norms are changing, so that today many Canadians do not subscribe to some of these views. Further, many Canadians come from non-Christian traditions, such as Judaism, Islam, Hinduism, Buddhism, or humanism, that have their own views about sexuality. These traditions are also described in Chapter 20 online at Connect™.

The Economy

The nature and structure of the economy is another macro-level influence on sexuality. Before the industrial revolution, most work was done in the family unit in the home or farm. This kind of togetherness permitted rather strict surveillance of family members' sexuality and thus strict norms could be enforced. However, with the industrial revolution, people—most frequently men—spent many hours per day at work away from the home. Thus they were under less surveillance, and scripts such as extramarital affairs and same-sex sexual activity could be acted out more often.

Today we see evidence of the extent to which economic conditions can affect sexuality. For example, the average monthly wage is very low in Russia. As a result, few people can afford to use condoms and the rate of STIs is very high. Economic conditions have also led to a major increase in the number of prostitutes. It is difficult to support a family on the salary earned in most jobs, including professional jobs. In contrast, a Russian sex workers may earn the equivalent of the average monthly salary in just a few hours. As a result, many Russian sex workers are highly educated and choose prostitution for financial reasons. Many Russians see prostitution as a viable way of earning a living (Byers & Slattery, 1997).

In a capitalist economy, such as Canada, goods and services become commodities that can be sold for a price (an exchange). Not surprisingly, this includes sexual images and sexual gratification, giving rise to the sale of sexually explicit materials in stores and on the Internet, and commercial sex work. The increasing globalization of the economy has led to the development of sex tourism, in which affluent men and women travel to other cultures, such as Thailand, to purchase sexual gratification from exotic (e.g., Asian) sex workers (see Chapter 17).

The Family

The family is a third institution influencing sexuality (see Figure 2.6). As we noted earlier, before the industrial revolution the family was an important economic unit, producing the goods necessary for survival. As that function waned after the industrial revolution, there was increased emphasis on the quality of interpersonal relationships in the family. At the same time, love was increasingly seen as an important reason for marriage. Thus, a triple linkage between love, marriage, and sex was formed. Ironically, the linkage eventually became a direct one between love and sex so that, by the 1970s, some people were arguing that sex outside of marriage, if in the context of a loving relationship, was permissible, as was same-sex sexual activity, again if the relationship was a loving one. This is the *relational ideology*.

The family exerts a particularly important force on sexuality through its *socialization* of children. That is, parents socialize their children—teach them appropriate norms for behaviour—in many areas, including sexuality. Others, of course, such as the peer group, also have important socializing influences.

Medicine

The institution of medicine has become a major influence on our sexuality over the last 100 years. Physicians tell us what is healthy and what is unhealthy. In the late

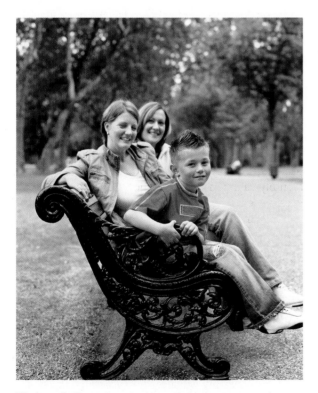

Figure 2.6 Families today are no longer defined by traditional stereotypes. Here, a lesbian couple enjoy the park with their son.

nineteenth century, physicians warned that masturbation could cause various pathologies. Today sex therapists tell us that sexual expression is natural and healthy and sometimes even "prescribe" masturbation as a treatment. Another example is provided by childbirth; until the end of the nineteenth century, most babies were born at home, with an experienced woman (a midwife) providing assistance to the labouring woman. Today the vast majority of births occur in hospitals and birthing facilities, with medical personnel in charge. We tend to have great confidence in medical advice, so the pronouncements of the medical establishment, based on a *therapeutic ideology*, have an enormous impact on sexuality.

The increasing influence of medicine on sexuality has not been taken lying down. The domination of contemporary theory and research by the biomedical model is referred to as the **medicalization of sexuality** (Tiefer, 2004). Medicalization has two components: certain behaviours or conditions are defined in terms of health and illness; and these "problematic behaviours" are then given medical treatment (Polzer & Knabe, 2012). The medicalization of male sexuality is being hastened by the development of drugs to treat erectile dysfunction, and many physicians and pharmaceutical companies are seeking to medicalize female sexual dysfunction by finding a pill that will "cure" them (discussed further in Chapter 18). In contrast, the sexual health perceptive described in Chapter 1 is geared toward enhancing health and preventing illness; it takes a biopsychosocial perspective, acknowledging the interaction of biological, psychological, and social factors on sexual health. There are efforts in the medical community in Canada to encourage health care providers to take a broader perspective, for example, the Female Sexual Health Guidelines developed by the Society of Obstetricians and Gynaecolgists of Canada (Lamont et al., 2012).

 The Law

The legal system is another institution influencing sexuality at the macro level. From a sociological perspective, the law influences people's sexual behaviour in a number of ways. First, laws help to determine norms. Generally, we think that what is legal is right and what is illegal is wrong. In Canada, only the federal government has the right to pass criminal laws, and all sexual offences are contained in the *Criminal Code of Canada* and apply to all Canadians regardless of the province or territory in which they live (Roach, 2000). Provincial and municipal governments have the right to enact regulatory offences, such as zoning bylaws and licensing requirements, to help them govern matters within their jurisdiction, as long as these regulations do not stray into the

Medicalization of sexuality: The process by which certain sexual behaviours or conditions are defined in terms of health and illness, and problematic experiences or practices are given medical treatment.

criminal area. In contrast, in the United States and Australia, states have the right to enact criminal laws, resulting in significant differences in sexual offences from one state to another.

A major change to Canadian criminal law occurred in 1969 when, under Prime Minister Pierre Elliott Trudeau, the House of Commons passed an omnibus bill that introduced sweeping changes to the *Criminal Code of Canada* (see Figure 2.7). This bill removed provisions that had made consensual sexual behaviours between adults done in private illegal, such as use of contraception, oral sex, and anal sex. These changes may have reflected the fact that laws that go against prevailing social or subcultural norms are often ignored, and most Canadians agreed with Trudeau when he said, "The state has no business in the bedrooms of the nation." In contrast, although arrests for criminal sexual conduct are

Figure 2.7 In 1969, under Prime Minister Pierre Elliott Trudeau, Parliament decriminalized consensual sexual behaviour between two adults in private, including providing birth control information and engaging in anal or oral sex.

rare in the United States, in many states oral intercourse, anal intercourse ("sodomy"), sex with someone who is legally married to someone else (adultery), cohabitation, sex between two unmarried persons ("fornication"), and sexual contact between two persons of the same gender are crimes (Posner, 1992). Thus, every day millions of Americans engage in sexual behaviours that are illegal.

Second, laws are the basis for the mechanisms of social control. They may specify punishments for certain acts and thus discourage people from engaging in them. It seems obvious that people ought to be free from sexual assault and coercion and that children should not be exploited, and, indeed, the *Criminal Code of Canada* has a number of laws prohibiting sexual assault of adults and children (see Table 2.1). However, sex laws also have been designed to control other behaviours that are more open to debate. For example, historically one rationale for laws against adultery or desertion of a spouse was that these laws would preserve the family as the principal unit of the social order. A current example is the law prohibiting nudity in a public place. One wonders how many people would prefer to be nude at the beach if they did not fear arrest and the possible embarrassing publicity, such as having their names in the paper as the result of an arrest.

Third, the law reflects the interests of the powerful, dominant groups within a society. In part, the law functions to confirm the superiority of the ideologies of these dominant groups although the arguments in favour of these laws often centre on the protection of society's morals. The concern for public morality results in laws against nonprocreative sex, for reasons outlined in Chapter 20 (available online). Thus, there have been laws against same-sex sexual activity, bestiality, and contraception. In fact, same-sex couples had to challenge the law that restricted marriage to the union of one man and one woman province by province to establish their legal right to marry (see Chapter 14). Consider also the Mormons in Canada and the United States. In the past, their religion approved of polygyny (a man having several wives). Mormons did not become the dominant group in North America. Rather, the Judeo-Christian tradition was the ideology of the dominant group and that tradition takes a dim view of polygyny. Accordingly, polygyny is illegal in both Canada and the United States. However, there is a breakaway sect of the Mormon Church, called the Fundamentalist Church of Jesus Christ of Latter Day Saints, located in Bountiful, British Columbia. This sect of about 1000 people practises polygyny. In 2010 the B.C. government asked the B.C. Supreme Court to rule on whether the federal law banning polygamy violates the *Charter of Rights and Freedoms*. In 2011 the Court ruled that the ban against polygamy is constitutional. Even though the law violates freedom of religion, the harm to women and children

Table 2.1 What Are the Sexual Offences in the *Criminal Code of Canada* in 2010?

Offence	Description	Sentence
Sexual assault	Sexual assault involving minor or no physical injuries to the complainant	10 years
Sexual assault with a weapon or threats	Sexual assault with a weapon, threats, or causing bodily harm, use of restricted or prohibited firearm, or use of any firearm if the offence involves a criminal organization	14 years
Aggravated sexual assault	Sexual assault resulting in wounding, maiming, or disfiguring or endangering the life of the complainant, use of restricted or prohibited firearm, or use of any firearm if the offence involves a criminal organization	Life
Sexual interference	Direct or indirect touching (for a sexual purpose) of a person under the age of 16 using a part of the body or an object	10 years
Invitation to sexual touching	Inviting, counselling, or inciting a person under the age of 16 to touch (for a sexual purpose) the body of any person directly or indirectly with a part of the body or with an object	10 years
Sexual exploitation	Sexual interference or invitation to sexual touching by a person in a position of trust or authority toward a young person age 16 to 18 with whom the young person is in a position of dependency or toward a person with a disability	10 years
Parent or guardian procuring, permitting sexual activity, or corrupting children	A parent or guardian or other person enticing or forcing a person under 18 to engage in an act prohibited under the Code or permitting them to engage in such an act on their premises	5 years
Corrupting children	Engaging in adultery or sexual immorality in the home of a child rendering the home unfit for the child	2 years
Luring a child	Using a computer to facilitate the commission of a sexual offence against a child under 18 years	10 years
Incest	When an individual has sexual intercourse with a person that has a known defined blood relationship with them	14 years
Anal intercourse	Anal intercourse between two people if either is under 18 or if more than two people take part or are present or if engaged in a public place	10 years
Bestiality	Having sex with an animal, compelling someone to have sex with an animal, or having sex with an animal in the presence of a child	10 years
Voyeurism	Surreptitiously observing or making a visual recording of a person in a private place who is nude or engaging in sexual activity. Also anyone who distributes such visual recordings.	5 years
Communicating for the purpose of engaging in prostitution	Communicating with another person in public to buy or sell sexual services	6 months and/or $2000
Bawdy-house offences	Keeping, transporting a person to, or occupying a place used for prostitution or indecent acts	2 years
Procuring	Procuring or enticing or forcing another person to engage in prostitution or living on the income of another person's prostitution activities. Also purchasing the sexual services of someone under 18.	14 years
Corrupting morals	Making, publishing, or distributing any obscene written matter, photograph, videotape, etc.	2 years
Child pornography	Possessing, making, or distributing any material that shows a person under 18 or who is depicted as being under 18 engaging in sexual activity or shows their genitals for a sexual purpose unless the material has artistic merit or an educational, scientific, or medical purpose	5–10 years
Immoral theatrical performance	Taking part in or presenting an immoral, indecent, or obscene performance or entertainment	2 years
Mailing obscene matter	Mailing anything that is obscene, indecent, immoral, or scurrilous	2 years
Indecent acts/exposure	Committing an indecent act in a public place or exposing genitals to a person under the age of 16	6 months and/or $2000
Nudity	Being nude in a public place or in public view on private property	6 months and/or $5000

Source: Adapted by permission of Canada Law Book, a division of Thomson Reuters Canada Limited, from *Martin's Online Criminal Code*, eds. Edward L. Greenspan, The Honourable Justice Marc Rosenberg, and Marie Henein, (A91350-11) http://clb5.canadalawbook.ca/.

from the practice outweighs that concern. Canadian immigrants from some African cultures that practise polygyny cannot do so in Canada because it is illegal. Nonetheless, in keeping with ethnocultural norms, many of these men have multiple relationships although they are married to only one woman, and this is accepted in their community (Maticka-Tyndale et al., 1996).

It can also be argued that another principal source of sex laws is sexism, which is deeply rooted in Western culture. Men have historically held the power and made the laws. One scholar has suggested that the history of the regulation of sexual activity could as well be called the history of the double standard (Parker, 1983). In fact, women were considered "not persons in matters of rights and privileges" under Canadian law before 1929. The Supreme Court of Canada had ruled that the word "persons" in the *British North America Act* of 1867 referred only to men. On October 18, 1929, this decision was overturned by the Judicial Committee of the Privy Council of Britain, the highest court of appeal, which ruled that the word "persons" included both men and women. It is probably not coincidental that the movement for sex-law reform has gone hand in hand with the movement for the equality of women.

The *Canadian Charter of Rights and Freedoms* guarantees freedom of conscience and religion as well as equality. Therefore, criminal law cannot be based on the religious views and practices of one specific religion or be used to enforce morality per se (Roach, 2000). To the extent that today's laws are derived from the Judeo-Christian (or any other) religious tradition, they violate this principle. Increasingly, statutes in the *Criminal Code* that reflected specific moral values have been eliminated or rewritten, in part as the result of Supreme Court of Canada decisions based on *Charter* rights. For example, the Supreme Court found that statutes on abortion and those that did not extend the same benefits to same-sex couples as to mixed-sex couples violated the equality guarantees in the *Charter*. Some experts argue that other laws, such as those pertaining to prostitution and obscenity, stem from a particular moral view or ideology.

In summary, then, the sociological perspective focuses on how society or culture shapes and controls our sexual expression, from institutional levels, such as those of religion and the law, to the interpersonal level of socialization by family and peers.

 ### Symbolic Interaction Theory

An important sociological theory is **symbolic interaction theory** (Charon, 1995; Stryker, 1987). Its premise is that human nature and the social order are products of symbolic communication among people. A person's behaviour is

Symbolic interaction theory: A theory that proposes human nature and the social order are products of communication among people.

constructed through his or her interactions with others. People can communicate successfully with one another only to the extent that they ascribe similar meanings to objects and people. An object's meaning for a person depends not on the properties of the object but on what the person might do with it; an object takes on meaning only in relation to a person's plans. Thus, the theory views people as proactive and goal-seeking. Achieving most goals requires the cooperation of others. This is especially true of many forms of sexual expression. For example, suppose a woman invites a person she is dating to her apartment; what meaning does this invitation have? Does she want to prolong the conversation or engage in intimate sexual activity? The woman and her partner will have to achieve an agreement about the purpose of the visit before joint activity is possible. In terms of the theory, they have to develop a *definition of the situation*. Thus, to fit their actions together and achieve agreement, people interacting with each other must continually reaffirm old meanings or negotiate new ones.

Central to social interaction is the process of *role-taking*, in which an individual imagines how he or she looks from the other person's viewpoint. By viewing the self and potential actions from the perspective of the other person, we are often able to anticipate what behaviour will enable us to achieve our goal. One consequence of role-taking is self-control; we see ourselves from the viewpoint of others and so strive to meet their standards. In the process, we exercise control over our behaviour.

Can a woman go to a strip club and get a lap dance? It depends on whether she can, in interaction with one of the dancers, create a definition of herself as a *patron*. Many strippers are oriented toward male customers and pass over women because they perceive them as unlikely to pay for a dance. A few perceive the situation as different and negotiate with women; the result may be more intimate contact than the typical male lap dance (Wosick-Correa & Joseph, 2008).

This perspective emphasizes the importance of symbolic communication (see Chapter 12). It alerts us to the mutual effort required to arrive at a definition of the situation. Criticisms of this theory include the fact that it emphasizes rational, conscious thought, whereas in the realm of sexuality, emotions are very important in many interactions. Also, this perspective portrays humans as *other-directed individuals*, concerned primarily with meeting other people's standards. A third criticism is that we don't always consciously role-take and communicate in an effort to achieve agreement. Sometimes we rely on past experience and habit. Situations such as these are the province of script theory.

Sexual Scripts

The outcome of these social influences, according to symbolic interaction theories, is that each of us learns the meanings of various behaviours through our interactions with others (Plummer, 1975). We also learn a set of *sexual scripts* (Gagnon, 1990; Gagnon & Simon, 1973). The idea is that sexual behaviour is a result of extensive prior learning that teaches us sexual etiquette and how to interpret specific situations. According to this concept, we have all learned an elaborate script that tells us the who, what, when, where, and why of sexual behaviour. For example, the "who" part of the dominant Canadian script tells us that sex should occur with someone of the other gender, of approximately our own age, of our own race, and so on. Even the sequence of sexual activity is scripted. *Scripts*, then, are plans that people carry around in their heads for what they are doing and what they are going to do (see Figure 2.8); they are also devices for helping people remember what they have done in the past (Gagnon, 1977, p. 6).

How can we study these scripts? How can we find out if there are widely shared beliefs about how we should behave in a specific situation? One way is to ask people to describe what a person should do in such a situation. Researchers asked male and female college students to describe a typical "hook-up" (Holman & Sillars, 2012). The hypothetical script written by many participants included a basic sequence: attending a party, friends present, drinking alcohol, flirting, hanging out/talking, dancing, and a sexual encounter. Reflecting the ambiguity of a hookup, the sexual encounter might include, oral, anal, or vaginal intercourse, just "fooling around" (not intercourse), or "only hugging and kissing." The results also reflect contemporary gender roles; men were more likely to provide a script than were women. The widely shared nature of this script enables relative strangers to interact smoothly.

One study attempted to identify the sequence of sexual behaviours that is scripted for male–female relationships in our culture (Jemail & Geer, 1977; see also Edgar & Fitzpatrick, 1993). People were given 25 sentences, each describing an event in a heterosexual interaction. They were asked to rearrange the sentences in a sequence that was the most likely to occur. There was a high degree of agreement among the participants about what the sequence should be. There was also high agreement between men and women. The standard sequence was kissing, hand stimulation of the breasts, hand stimulation of the genitals, mouth–genital stimulation, intercourse, and orgasm. Does this sound familiar? Interestingly, not only is this the sequence in a sexual encounter, it is also the sequence that occurs as a couple progresses in a relationship. These results suggest that there are culturally defined sequences of behaviours that we all have learned, much as the notion of a script suggests. Scripts also tell us the meaning we should attach to a particular sexual event (Gagnon, 1990). Television programs and films frequently suggest but do not show sexual activity between people. How do we make sense out of these implicit portrayals?

> **Why do most sexual interactions in our society follow the same pattern?**

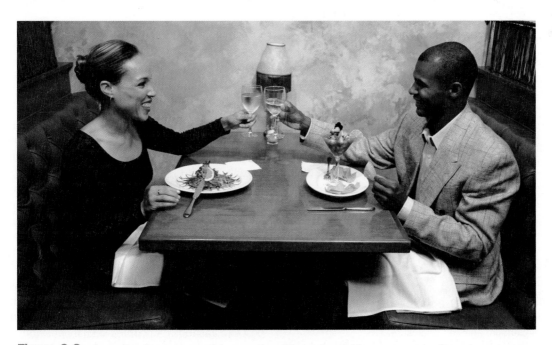

Figure 2.8 According to some people's sexual scripts, a man taking a woman to dinner is one scene of the first act in a heterosexual sexual script that features intercourse as the finale.

A study of how women interpret such scenes in films found that they use scripts. If the film showed a couple engaging in two actions that are part of the accepted script for sexual intercourse (e.g., kissing and undressing each other) and then faded out, viewers inferred that intercourse had occurred (Meischke, 1995).

The Social Importance of Sexuality

Reiss (1986) has proposed a sociological theory of human sexuality (see Figure 2.9). He defines sexuality as "erotic and genital responses produced by the cultural scripts of a society" (p. 37). Because it focuses on societal influences, a sociological theory must be able to account for both cross-cultural variations and cross-cultural universals. One universal is that all societies believe that sexuality is important. Even cultures that are sexually repressive accord great importance to sex as something that is dangerous and needs to be controlled. Why? Many theorists claim it is the link between sexuality and making babies, but Reiss points out some societies do not understand the link between sex and reproduction yet consider sex important. Indeed, in North America today effective contraception has allowed us to separate the two, but we still think sexuality is really important.

Reiss's explanation for the universal importance of sexuality points to two components: (1) sexuality is associated with great physical pleasure, and (2) sexual interactions are associated with personal self-disclosure, not only of our bodies but our thoughts and feelings as well. Humans find great value in the physical pleasure and psychic satisfaction associated with sex. In fact, these are the basic elements of social bonding. Recall

our discussion of the importance of social bonding to the welfare of children.

According to Reiss, sexuality is linked to social structure in three areas: the kinship system, the power structure, and the ideology of the society.

First, because sexuality is the source of reproduction, it is always linked to *kinship*, and all societies seek to maintain stable kinship systems. This explains sexual jealousy. Jealousy sets boundaries on relationships that are considered very important, such as marriage; jealousy in marriage about extramarital sex exists in all societies. Kin define what relationships are and are not acceptable, and enforce the resulting rules and norms. All societies have structured ways of dealing with such jealousy; even in societies that practise polygyny, there are rituals designed to minimize jealousy among the wives. Thus, no society will be able to eliminate sexual jealousy, because it reflects the value that kin groups and individuals attach to a particular relationship.

Second, sexuality is always linked to the *power structure* of a society. Powerful groups in any society generally seek to control the sexuality of the less powerful. Males are more powerful in many societies, and so they typically control female sexuality.

Third, sexuality is closely linked to the *ideologies*—fundamental assumptions about human nature—of a culture. Societies define carefully what sexual practices are normal and abnormal, and which are right and wrong. Some cultures define homosexuality as abnormal, whereas others define it as normal—but the point is that all cultures define it one way or the other.

Theoretical Perspectives Revisited

We started this chapter by showing how differently various theorists might view the same behaviour. Does this mean that only one of these theories is correct? No it doesn't. Rather, there is at least some truth in all of these theories. One theory might apply best in a particular situation. Another theory might play a role at a particular time in a person's life but not at another stage. Yet another theory might be best for developing treatments to help people deal with their sexual problems. Human sexual development and behaviour are complex, and there is no one theory that explains everything. As a result, we will refer to each of these theories at different places in this textbook—that is, where they provide the best explanations for people's sexual behaviour.

Figure 2.9 According to Reiss's sociological theory, sex is important to us because it is associated with great physical pleasure and self-disclosure.

SUMMARY

Theories provide explanations for sexual phenomena. Sociobiologists view human sexual behaviours as the product of natural selection in evolution, and thus view these behavioural patterns as being genetically controlled. Contemporary evolutionary theorists view behaviour as the result of an interaction between evolved mechanisms and environmental influence.

Among the psychological theories, Freud's psychoanalytic theory views the sex energy, or libido, as a major influence on personality and behaviour. Freud introduced the concepts of erogenous zones and psychosexual stages of development. Learning theory emphasizes how sexual behaviour is learned and modified through reinforcements and punishments according to principles of operant conditioning. Behaviour therapy techniques—therapies based on learning theory—are used in treating sexual variations and sexual disorders.

Social learning theory adds the concepts of imitation, identification, and self-efficacy to learning theory. Social exchange theory highlights the role of rewards and costs in relationships. Cognitive psychologists focus on people's thoughts and perceptions—whether positive or negative—and how these influence sexuality.

Sociologists study the ways in which society influences our sexual expression. At the macro level of analysis, sociologists investigate the ways in which institutions such as religion, the economy, the family, medicine, and the law influence sexuality. Symbolic interaction theory draws attention to processes of communication and interaction. Sexual scripts provide us with guidelines for behaviour in many situations. Reiss's sociological theory argues that all societies regard sexuality as important because it is associated with great physical pleasure and self-disclosure.

QUESTIONS FOR THOUGHT, DISCUSSION, AND DEBATE

1. Compare and contrast how a sociobiologist, a psychoanalyst, and a sociologist would explain why people engage in premarital intercourse.

2. You are visiting your married sister and her family for the holidays. Her six-year-old asks you a question: "Why do mommies stay home with kids?" Drawing on the knowledge you gained from Chapter 2, how would you answer this question? Which ideas about parental investment, social learning, or social norms and scripts would you use to explain why, in most cultures, women perform the child-rearing activities?

3. From a sociologist's point of view, how have social institutions controlled female sexuality?

4. Could script theory explain the pattern of same-sex and mixed-sex sexual behaviour of Melanesian males described in the Sexually Diverse World box? Explain your answer.

5. Find out more about a recent decision by the Supreme Court of Canada with respect to a sex law. Do you agree or disagree with the decision? To what extent does the decision reflect current Canadian social norms?

connect LEARNSMART SMARTBOOK™

For more information on the resources available from McGraw-Hill Ryerson, go to **www.mheducation.ca/he/solutions**.

Are YOU Curious?

1. How would you conduct an effective sex survey?
2. What types of sex research are taking place in Canada?
3. Is it possible to study sexuality scientifically with methods other than questionnaires?

Read this chapter to find out.

CHAPTER

3

Sex Research

LEARNING OBJECTIVES

After studying this chapter, you will be able to

LO1 Compare and evaluate the different methods that are used in sex research.

LO2 Evaluate the basic ethical principles employed by sex researchers.

LO3 Explain the basic statistical concepts necessary for understanding sex research results.

LO4 Summarize the methods and limitations of the major research projects described in this chapter.

LO5 Illustrate how media analysis is done and its importance.

LO6 Differentiate between qualitative research and quantitative research.

LO7 Compare the concepts of independent variables and dependent variables and how they relate to drawing causal inferences.

W hat is research, but a blind date with knowledge.

—William Henry

Over the last several decades, sex research has made great advances, and the names Kinsey and Masters and Johnson have become household words. This chapter is about sex research. You might be thinking, why do we need sex research? What are its goals? Don't we already know everything we need to know about human sexuality? Isn't common sense sufficient?

The reality is there are still many things we do not know about human sexuality. People often have opinions and views about these issues and believe that their opinions are based on fact. Yet too often they are based on misinformation and sometimes even on stereotypes or prejudice. Research is important because it creates accurate knowledge. Research puts beliefs, opinions, and theories to the systematic test.

Sex research has a number of goals. First, it can be geared toward creating basic knowledge and understanding. For example, we might want to know what percentage of 15-year-olds have engaged in sexual activity, how often long-term couples have sex, or how effective the male condom is in preventing sexually transmitted infections.

Second, research can be directed toward enhancing our understanding and can influence sexual behaviour. For example, we might want to identify risk factors for individuals who might commit a sexual offence so that we can prevent child sexual abuse; we might want to determine factors that affect sexual satisfaction in long-term relationships to help couples maintain satisfying sexual relationships; or we might want to find out whether prepared childbirth techniques are effective in reducing anxiety and discomfort during labour and delivery. How can we provide effective prevention or intervention programs without this kind of knowledge on which to base these programs?

Third, research can be geared toward public policy. For example, sexual health education is often a very controversial topic. An important question is whether individuals opposed to comprehensive sexual health education represent a majority of parents or a vocal minority of parents. Research can answer this question, thus allowing governments and school boards to take the wishes of the majority of parents into account when designing their sexual health education curriculum. Similarly, research can inform laws and regulations on a variety of issues, including access to emergency contraception, new reproductive technologies, pornography, and sex work.

How exactly do sex researchers do it? How valid are their conclusions? The answer is that sex research takes on many forms. However, basically the techniques vary in terms of the following: (1) how sex is measured, whether from people's self-reports, through observation of behaviour, or by using biological measures; (2) whether large numbers of people are studied in surveys or a smaller number of people are studied in laboratory studies and qualitative research; (3) whether the studies are conducted in the laboratory or in the field; and (4) whether sexual behaviour is studied as it occurs naturally or some attempt is made to manipulate it experimentally. Examples of studies that use all these techniques are considered and evaluated later in this chapter.

It is important to understand the techniques of sex research and their strengths and limitations. This knowledge will help you evaluate the studies that are cited as evidence for various conclusions in later chapters and will also help you decide how willing you are to accept these conclusions. Perhaps more important, this knowledge will help you evaluate future sex research. Much sex research has been conducted already, but much more will be done. The information in this chapter should help you understand and evaluate sex research that appears 10 or 20 years from now. Moreover, the media often report poor-quality research as enthusiastically as high-quality research. You should be equipped to tell the difference.

Measuring Sex

The first thing that researchers have to decide is how to measure the particular aspect of sexuality that they want to study. Multiple methods are available, including self-reports, behavioural measures, implicit measures, and biological measures, each of which is discussed in the sections that follow.

Self-Reports

The most common method for measuring sexuality is self-reports, in which the participants are asked questions about their sexual behaviour, such as the following:

- At what age did you begin masturbating?
- Did you use a condom the last time you had sex?

Self-reports are also used to measure attitudes about sexuality:

Regarding gay marriage, I (circle the number that applies)

Strongly disapprove	Moderately disapprove	Neither approve nor disapprove	Moderately approve	Strongly approve
1	2	3	4	5

Self-reports can be collected in a number of ways: with paper questionnaires, in interviews, and online. The strengths and weaknesses of self-reports are discussed in the section Issues in Sex Research later in the chapter.

Behavioural Measures

Several alternatives are available for behavioural measures of sexuality. One is **direct observation**, in which the scientist directly observes the behaviour and records it. As one example, sex researcher Charles Moser observed S/M (sadomasochistic) interactions in semipublic settings, attending more than 200 S/M parties (Moser, 1998). Masters and Johnson (1966), in research discussed later in this chapter, collected direct observations of sexual behaviour in laboratory studies of sexual intercourse and masturbation. As described in First Person, a number of Canadian researchers conduct similar psychophysiological research.

Psychologists have devised other clever behavioural measures. One of these is **eye-tracking**, in which participants, in the laboratory, wear an eye-tracking device that measures their point of gaze over time, as they are shown pictures on a computer. For example, in one study researchers tracked the eye movements of adult men as they were shown photos of a front-posed naked woman, with multiple photos created through Photoshop to show different sized breasts and different waist-to-hip ratios (e.g., small waist relative to hips) (Dixson et al., 2011). With this method, the researchers could answer such questions as, Where do men look first? It turns out that the first thing men look at is the breasts or the waist, not the genitals. Relatedly, Canadian psychologists measured the amount of time individuals spent viewing pictures of naked and clothed men and women as a behavioural measure of bisexual sexual interest (Ebsworth & Lalumière, 2012). They found that bisexuals did not look longer at pictures of one sex, but heterosexual and homosexual men and women did.

For those studying illegal sexual behaviours, such as sexual assault or child pornography, one possible behavioural measure to use is police reports. The problem with this sort of measure, though, is that it detects only cases that are reported to or identified by the police. In the case of sexual assault, for example, we know that only a small proportion of cases are reported, and the great majority go unreported.

Implicit Measures

Most researchers who measure attitudes about sexuality use self-reports. However, newer measures are available. For example, a method used to measure implicit stereotypes and underlying associations between constructs is the Implicit Association Test (IAT), which measures the relative strength of association an individual makes between different pairs of concepts (Nosek et al., 2002). The key to measuring these associations is reaction time, measured on a computer in milliseconds. We react quickly to two concepts that we associate strongly, and we react more slowly to two concepts that we do not associate strongly. One of the great features of this measure is that people can't fake their reaction times. For example, they cannot hide their socially unacceptable stereotyped ideas.

In one New Brunswick experiment, the researchers developed an IAT to compare young adults men's and women's attitudes toward sex and romance (Thompson & O'Sullivan, 2012). Their IAT comprised five phases: three practice phases and two test phases. The three practice phases were designed to introduce participants to the stimuli by having them sort the stimuli into their appropriate categories. So, for example, participants had to distinguish between sexual images (e.g., sexual intercourse, oral sex) and romantic images (e.g., a couple walking on a beach holding hands) in one practice phase by using the left key for sexual images and the right key for romantic images (or vice versa; see Figure 3.1). In another practice phase, they had to distinguish between pleasant words (e.g., good, beautiful) and unpleasant words (e.g., bad, gross). The test then had participants pair the images and attributes. For example, in the first test phase, participants were required to press the left key if they saw either a sexual image or a pleasant word and the right key if they saw either a romantic image or an unpleasant word (or vice versa). In the second test phase, the attributes (words) were reversed: participants had to press the left key if they saw either a sexual image or an unpleasant word

Direct observation: A behavioural measure in which the scientist directly observes the behaviour being studied.
Eye-tracking: A behavioural measure in which a device measures the participant's point of gaze over time.

Figure 3.1 The Implicit Association Test measures the relative strength of the association that an individual makes between different pairs of concepts. For example, researchers might compare the strength of the association between the concepts of pleasant and unpleasant images depicting romance compared with images depicting sex.

and the left key for either a romantic image or a pleasant word. The researchers measured how quickly and accurately these different pairings were sorted. The results allowed the researchers to determine whether men and women had a stronger association between sex and pleasant or between romance and pleasant. Based on gender stereotypes, the authors predicted that women would be quicker and more accurate when romantic images and pleasant words occurred together than when sexual images and pleasant words occurred together; they expected the reverse for men. However, they found that both men and women more strongly associated romantic images, not sexual images, with the pleasant category, suggesting that both implicitly preferred romance over sex.

If you want to try an IAT yourself, you can do it online at www.implicit.harvard.edu.

Biological Measures

Masters and Johnson (1966) pioneered the biological measurement of sexual response (see Milestones in Sex Research). Today, many biological measures are available.

Genital measures of sexual response assess arousal by using devices that measure erection in men and vaginal changes in women (Chivers et al., 2010). In men, penile plethysmography is used, in which a flexible loop is placed around the penis that measures changes in volume. In females, a vaginal photoplethysmograph inserted into the vagina is used to optically measure blood flow to the vagina. (See Figure 13.6 to find out what these devices look like.) Quebec researchers have shown that *thermography*–that is, assessing temperature change–is also useful for measuring sexual arousal (Kukkonen et al., 2007, 2010). The advantage of thermography is that it does not require any genital manipulation of contact–a camera pointed at the genitals detects changes in temperature with arousal.

MRI (magnetic resonance imaging) and fMRI (functional magnetic resonance imaging) are being used increasingly in sex research. MRI looks at *anatomy*, such as the size of shape of specific brain regions or the genitals, by using magnets to send and receive signals that give information, while participants lie in the centre of the magnet (scanner). For example, an MRI scan that shows the internal structure of the clitoris is shown in Chapter 4. One strength of an MRI is that it provides good contrast between different soft tissues of the body. Another strength is that it is

Milestones in Sex Research

Masters and Johnson: How Did They Study Sexual Response in the Laboratory?

Willliam Masters began his research on the physiology of sexual response in 1954. No one had ever studied human sexual behaviour in the laboratory before, so he had to develop all the necessary research techniques from scratch. He began by interviewing 188 female prostitutes, as well as 27 male prostitutes working for a gay clientele. They gave him important preliminary data in which they "described many methods for elevating and controlling sexual tensions and demonstrated innumerable variations in stimulative techniques," some of which were useful in the later program of therapy for sexual disorders.

Meanwhile, Masters began setting up his laboratory and equipping it with the necessary instruments: an electrocardiograph to measure changes in heart rate over the sexual cycle, an electromyograph to measure muscular contractions in the body during sexual response, and a pH meter to measure the acidity of the vagina during the various stages of sexual response.

Sampling

Masters made a major breakthrough when he decided that it should be possible to recruit participants from the general population and have them engage in sexual behaviour in the laboratory, where their behaviour and physiological responses could be carefully observed and measured. This approach had never been used before, as even the daring Kinsey had settled for people's verbal reports of their behaviour.

Masters let it be known in the medical school and university community that he needed volunteers for laboratory studies of human sexual response. Some people volunteered because of their belief in the importance of the research. Some, of course, came out of curiosity or because they were exhibitionists; they were weeded out in the initial interviews. Participants were paid for their

hours in the laboratory, as is typical in medical research, so many medical students and graduate students participated because it was a way to earn money.

Initially, all prospective participants were given detailed interviews by Masters and his colleague, Virginia Johnson (see Figure 3.2). People who had histories of emotional problems or who seemed uncomfortable with the topic of sex either failed to come back after this interview or were eliminated even if they were willing to proceed. Participants were also assured that the anonymity and confidentiality of their participation would be protected carefully. In all, 382 women and 312 men participated in the laboratory studies reported in *Human Sexual Response* (Masters & Johnson, 1966). The men ranged in age from 21 to 89, while the women ranged from 18 to 78.

Certainly, the group of people Masters and Johnson studied were not a random sample of the population of the United States. In fact, one might imagine that people

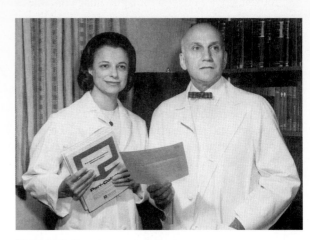

Figure 3.2   Masters and Johnson pioneered the biological measurement of sexual response.

noninvasive—that is, in the old days, to get at brain structure, anatomists had to dissect the brain of a dead person. Today, researchers can look inside the brain of a living person, without disturbing it! An fMRI looks

at brain *activity* by measuring relative levels of blood flow. In this way, scientists can measure the difference in activity in different regions of the brain when the person is looking at, for example, a sexual picture who would agree to participate in such research would be rather unusual. The data indicate that they were more educated than the general population, and the sample was mostly white, with only a few persons from ethnic minority groups participating. Paying the participants probably helped broaden the sample since it attracted some people who simply needed the money. The sample omitted two notable types of people: those who were not sexually experienced or did not respond to sexual stimulation and those who were unwilling to have their sexual behaviour studied in the laboratory. Therefore, the results Masters and Johnson obtained might not generalize to such people.

In defence of their sampling techniques, even if Masters and Johnson had identified an initial probability sample, they would still almost surely would have had a very high refusal rate, higher than in survey research, and the probability sample would have been ruined. At present, this seems to be an unsolvable problem in this type of research.

Data Collection Techniques

After they were accepted for the project, participants proceeded to the laboratory phase of the study. First, they had a "practice session," in which they engaged in sexual activity in the laboratory in complete privacy, with no data being recorded and no researchers present. The purpose of this was to allow the participants to become comfortable with engaging in sexual behaviour in a laboratory setting.

The physical responses of the participants were then recorded during sexual intercourse, masturbation, and "artificial coition." Masters and Johnson made an important technical advance with the development of the artificial coition technique. In it, a female participant stimulates herself with an artificial penis constructed of clear plastic; it is powered by an electric motor, and the woman can adjust the depth and frequency of the thrust. There is a light and a recording apparatus inside the artificial penis, so the changes occurring inside the vagina can be photographed.

Measures such as these avoid the problems of distortion that are possible with self-reports. They also answer much different questions. That is, it would be impossible from such measures to tell whether the person had engaged in same-sex sexual activity or how frequently he or she masturbated. Instead, they ascertain how the body responds to sexual stimulation, with a kind of accuracy and detail that would be impossible to obtain through self-reports.

One final potential problem also deserves mention. It has to do with the problems of laboratory studies: Do people respond the same sexually in the laboratory as they do in the privacy of their own homes?

Ethical Considerations

Masters and Johnson were attentive to ethical principles. They were careful to use informed consent. Potential participants were given detailed explanations of the kinds of things they would be required to do in the research and were given ample opportunity at all stages to withdraw from the research if they so desired. Furthermore, Masters and Johnson eliminated people who appeared too anxious or distressed during the preliminary interviews.

It is also possible that participating in the research itself might have been harmful in some way to some people. Masters and Johnson were particularly concerned with the long-term effects of participating in the research. Accordingly, they made follow-up contacts with the participants at five-year intervals. In no case did a participant report developing a sexual disorder. In fact, many of the couples reported specific ways in which participating in the research enriched their marriages. Thus, the available data seem to indicate that such research does not harm the participants and may in some ways benefit them, not to mention the benefit to society from gaining information in such an important area.

versus a boring picture. An example of fMRI research is given in Chapter 9 in Milestones in Sex Research: What Happens in the Brain During Sex? Some regions of the brain are very active, with large changes in blood flow, when the person looks at a sexual stimulus, and other regions have less blood flow or no change in blood flow. Because fMRI does not measure neural activity directly but rather measures blood flow, fMRI is an indirect measure of neural activity. In addition, fMRI data has a lot of "noise," and complex statistical analyses are required to get at the important patterns. Two limitations that affect fMRI use in sex research are that (1) participants must lie very still to get good images, and (2) fMRI depends on contrasting the difference between two stimuli (for example, blood flow while looking at sexual stimuli versus other stimuli). Therefore, the results depend very much on the choice of each set of stimuli.

Other biological measures include measures of pupil dilation. Devices are available that detect and record the amount of dilation. Our pupils dilate when we look at something that is especially interesting or arousing or that puts a big load on our brain. Pupil dilation is sometimes used with sex offenders, for example, to determine if they are especially interested in children (Flak et al., 2007). If we asked a sex offender about his interest in children by using a self-report measure, he might very well lie about his illegal and taboo behaviour. Experts hope that pupil dilation measures will get around this problem, although they are not perfect.

LO1

Issues in Sex Research

Population: A group of people a researcher wants to study and make inferences about.

Sample: A part of a population.

Probability sampling: A method of sampling in research in which each member of the population has a known probability of being included in the sample.

Random sampling: An excellent method of sampling in research in which each member of the population has an equal chance of being included in the sample.

Stratified random sampling: A method of sampling in which the population is divided into groups and then random sampling occurs in each group.

Problem of refusal or nonresponse: The problem that some people will refuse to participate in a sex survey, thus making it difficult to have a random sample.

Volunteer bias: A bias in the results of sex surveys that arises when some people refuse to participate so that those who are in the sample are volunteers who may in some ways differ from those who refused to participate.

Sampling

An important step in conducting sex research is identifying the appropriate **population** of people to be studied. Does the population in question consist of all adult human beings, all adults in Canada, all adolescents in Saskatchewan, all people guilty of sex crimes, or all married couples who engage in swinging? Generally, of course, the scientist is unable to get data for all the people in the population, and so a **sample** is taken.

At this point, things begin to get sticky. If the sample is a representative sample of the population in question and if it is a reasonably large sample, then results obtained from it can safely be generalized to the population that was originally identified. One way of obtaining a representative sample is by using **probability sampling**. The simplest form of probability sampling is **random**

sampling. That is, if a researcher has really randomly selected 1 out of every 50 adolescents in Canada, then the results obtained from that sample are probably true of all adolescents in Canada. Another technique that is sometimes used to get such a sample is **stratified random sampling**.[1] But if the sample consists only of adolescents with certain characteristics—for example, only those whose parents agree to let them participate in sex research—then the results obtained from that sample may not be true of all adolescents. Sampling has been a serious challenge in sex research.

Typically, sampling proceeds in three phases: the population is identified, a method for obtaining a sample is adopted, and the people in the sample are contacted and asked to participate. What is perhaps the thorniest problem occurs in the last phase: getting the people identified for the sample to participate. If any of the people refuse to participate, then the great probability sample is ruined. This is called the **problem of refusal or nonresponse**. As a result, the researcher is essentially studying volunteers; that is, people who agree to be in the research. The outcomes of the research may therefore contain distortions, called **volunteer bias**. The problem of refusal in sex research is difficult, since there is no ethical way of forcing people to participate when they do not want to.

The problem of volunteer bias would not be so great if those who refused to participate were identical in their sexual behaviour to those who participated. But it is likely that those who refuse to participate differ in

---

[1] A detailed discussion of stratified random sampling is beyond the scope of this book. For a good description of this method as applied to sex research, see Cochran et al. (1953). In brief, with a random sample, each individual in the population has an equal probability of being chosen. With a stratified random sample, the researchers can set a higher probability of inclusion for certain groups, a technique called oversampling. For example, if we had funds to interview 1000 people in Canada, a random sample would yield about 30 Aboriginal individuals and 30 Chinese Canadian individuals because each group constitutes about 3 percent of the Canadian population. We might not feel confident reaching conclusions about Aboriginal individuals or Chinese Canadians based on only 30 people, so we could decide to use stratified random sampling and give each of these groups a higher probability of inclusion compared with whites. If we tripled the probability of including these ethnocultural minority groups, the resulting sample of 1000 would include 90 Aboriginal individuals, 90 Chinese Canadians, 82 individuals from other visible ethnocultural minority groups (e.g., South Asian, Black), and 738 Canadians from non-visible-minority groups. Although these minority samples are still small, we would feel more confident about making conclusions about each group. We could do even more oversampling of Aboriginal individuals or of other ethnocultural groups that constitute even smaller percentages of the Canadian population to increase our confidence in our conclusions.

Table 3.1 The Percentage of People Reporting Having Sex at Least Once a Week: Comparing a Convenience Sample with a Probability Sample

	Men		Women	
Age	Convenience Sample (Janus Report)	Probability Sample (General Social Survey)	Convenience Sample (Janus Report)	Probability Sample (General Social Survey)
18–26	72%	57%	68%	58%
27–38	83	69	78	61
39–50	83	56	68	49
51–64	81	43	65	25
Over 65	69	17	74	6

Source: Review of the *Janus Report on Sexual Behavior* by Samuel S. Janus & Cynthia L. Janus in *Contemporary Sociology,* Vol. 23, no. 2 (March 1994), p. 222, table 1. Reprinted by permission of the American Sociological Association and Andrew M. Greeley.

some ways from those who agree to, and that means the sample is biased. Evidence suggests that volunteers who participate in sex research hold more permissive attitudes about sexuality and are more sexually experienced than those who don't; for example, they masturbate more frequently and have had more sexual partners (Bogaert, 1996; Boynton, 2003; Dunne et al., 1997). In addition, women are less likely to volunteer for some but not all types of sex research than men are (Boynton, 2003; Gaither et al., 2003; Senn & Desmarais, 2001) so that female samples are even more highly selected than male samples. In sum, volunteer bias is potentially a serious problem when we try to reach conclusions based on sex research.

Table 3.1 shows how different the results of sex surveys can be, depending on how carefully the sampling is done (Greeley, 1994). The table shows results from two American surveys. The Janus report (Janus & Janus, 1993) used sampling methods so haphazard that the researchers ended up with what some call a **convenience sample**. It included volunteers who came to sex therapists' offices and friends recruited by the original volunteers. In contrast, the General Social Survey conducted in 1993 by the University of Chicago obtained a probability sample. Notice that a considerably higher level of sexual activity is reported by the convenience sample in the Janus report, compared with the probability sample. This difference is especially pronounced among older adults. Convenience samples simply do not give us a very good picture of what is going on in the general population.

Accuracy of Measurement

Earlier we described various methods for measuring sexuality. How accurate are those measures? We focus mainly on self-reports because they are used so frequently in sex research.

Purposeful Distortion

If you were an interviewer in a sex research project and a 90-year-old man said that he and his wife made love twice a day, would you believe him, or would you suspect that he might be exaggerating slightly? If a 35-year-old woman told you that she had never masturbated, would you believe her, or would you suspect that she had masturbated but was unwilling to admit it?

How would you conduct an effective sex survey?

Respondents in sex research may, for one reason or another, engage in **purposeful distortion**, intentionally giving self-reports that are distortions of reality. These distortions may be in either of two directions. People may exaggerate their sexual activity (a tendency toward *enlargement*), or they may minimize their sexual activity or hide the fact that they have done certain things (*concealment*). Participants will often distort responses in the direction that they believe will be seen as more acceptable by the researcher, called **social desirability**. For example, an individual in a long-term relationship who believes that he or she engages in sexual activity with his or her partner much less often and masturbates much more often than other people do may exaggerate his or her sexual frequency but minimize his or her masturbation frequency. Participants are often not aware that social desirability is affecting their answers.

Distortion is a basic problem when using self-reports (McCallum & Peterson, 2012). To minimize distortion, participants must be strongly reminded of the fact that because the study will be used for scientific purposes, their reports must be as accurate as possible. They must also be assured that their responses will be completely anonymous. If they are not anonymous, people will be likely

Convenience sample: A sample chosen in a haphazard manner relative to the population of interest. Not a random or probability sample.
Purposeful distortion: Purposely giving false information in a survey.
Social desirability: The tendency to distort answers to a survey in the direction perceived to be more acceptable.

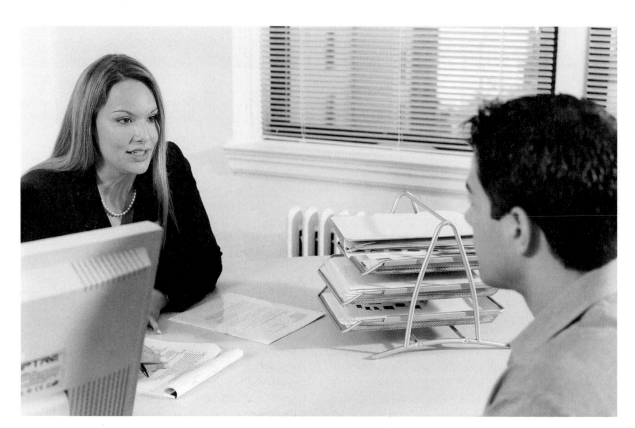

Figure 3.3 The reliability of self-reports of sexual behaviour: If you were interviewing this man in a sex survey and he said that he had never masturbated, would you believe him, or would you think that he was concealing a taboo behaviour?

to hide behaviours that they do not want other people to know about or that embarrass them, such as an extra-marital affair or a history of sex with animals. Research-ers sometimes include additional scales or items that detect whether people are purposefully distorting their answers—for example, by giving only socially desir-able responses. The phrasing of questions may also affect how likely people are to give honest answers (Figure 3.3). For example, people are more likely to hon-estly answer questions that first normalize the behaviour (e.g., Many people engage in oral sex. How many oral sex partners have you had?). They are also more likely to report behaviour when the question is asked in a neutral way (e.g., How often have you engaged in oral sex in the previous six months? rather than Have you engaged in oral sex in the previous six months?).

But even if all respondents were very truthful and tried to give as accurate information as possible, three factors might still cause their self-reports to be inaccurate: memory, difficulties with estimates, and interpreting the question in a different way than the researcher intended.

Memory

Some of the questions asked in sex surveys require respondents to recall what their sexual behaviour was like many years before. For example, some of the data we have on sexual behaviour in childhood come from the Kinsey study in which adults were asked about their childhood sexual behaviour. This might involve asking a 50-year-old man to remember at what age he began masturbating and how frequently he masturbated when he was 16 years old. It might be difficult to remember such facts accurately. The alternative is to ask people about their current sexual behaviour, but getting data like these from children raises serious ethical and prac-tical problems. However, people may also have diffi-culty accurately remembering recent behaviour, such as the number of times they had sex in the past month. One solution to this is the *daily diary* method in which people report their behaviour every day for the previous 24 hours and so are more likely to remember it accu-rately (Gilmore et al., 2010; Vannier & O'Sullivan, 2008). For example, Canadian psychologists used daily diaries completed online to study changes in women's fanta-sies across the menstrual cycle (Dawson et al., 2012).

Difficulties with Estimates

One of the questions sex researchers have asked is, How long, on average, do you spend in precoital foreplay? If you were asked this question, how accurate a response do you think you could give? It is rather difficult to estimate time to begin with, and it is even more difficult to do so when engaged in an absorbing activity. For example, New Brunswick researchers found that, on average, men estimated the duration of foreplay as 13.4 minutes, which was significantly longer than the 11.3 minutes estimated by their female partners, suggesting that the men or the women or both were not accurate in the estimates of the duration of foreplay (Miller & Byers, 2004). The men and women both estimated the duration of intercourse at between seven and eight minutes, however. The point is that in some sex surveys, people are asked to give estimates of things that they probably cannot estimate very accurately. This may be another source of inaccuracy in self-report data.

Interpreting the Question

One of the questions that sex researchers often ask is, How many sexual partners have you had? This question assumes that participants all give the same meaning to the term *sexual partner* as the research intended. Yet research in New Brunswick has shown that university students do not agree in their definitions of sexual terms including the terms *having sex, sexual partner*, and *abstinence* (Randall & Byers, 2003; Byers et al., 2009). For example, about two-thirds of students would call a person they engaged in oral sex with a sexual partner, but one-third would not. Thus, estimates participants provide about the number of sexual partners will be affected not only by the accuracy of their memory but also by how they define sexual partner.

Evidence on the Reliability of Self-Reports

Scientists have developed several methods for assessing how reliable or accurate people's self-reports are (Catania et al., 1995). One is the method of **test–retest reliability**. The respondent is asked a series of questions and then is asked the same set of questions after some time has passed, for example, a week or a month. The correlation between answers at the two times (test and retest) measures the reliability of responses; correlations are discussed later in this chapter.

In one study, urban African-American and Latina girls between the ages of 12 and 14 were interviewed about their sexual experiences and then were interviewed again three weeks later (Hearn et al., 2003). The test–retest reliability was .84 for the age at which they had their first crush and .95 for the age at which they first touched a penis, which indicates excellent reliability (a value of 1.0 indicates perfect reliability). Other research generally indicates that respondents give their best estimates about short, recent time intervals (Catania et al., 1990).

Another method for assessing reliability involves obtaining independent reports from two different people who share sexual activity, such as both members of a couple. One study found that on a simple item, such as whether a couple had engaged in intercourse in the last month, there was 93 percent agreement. Agreement on the number of times they had had intercourse in the last month, something that requires more difficult estimation, was .80, which is lower but still good (Hyde et al., 1996). Similarly, researchers in Quebec asked partners to indicate the behaviours that had occurred during lovemaking. The partners agreed 87 percent of the time on average, which is a high level of agreement (Ochs & Binik, 1999).

A recent innovation is the **computer-assisted self-interview method (CASI)**, which can be combined with an audio component so that the respondent not only reads but also hears the questions. This method offers the privacy of the written questionnaire while accommodating poor readers. The computer can be programmed to follow varying sequences of questions depending on respondents' answers, just as a human interviewer does. In a survey of 15-year-old boys, 16 percent reported in a personal interview that they had engaged in vaginal intercourse, but 25 percent said they had done so when CASI was used (Mosher et al., 2005). Although these findings suggest that CASI produces more honest responses, it is also possible that the some boys exaggerated their sexual history on the computer. (For similar results with adults see Lau et al., 2003.)

Web-Based Surveys

The possibility of administering questionnaires over the Internet has opened a whole new era in sex research. Compared with other methods for administering surveys, Web-based surveys have many advantages but also some disadvantages (Bowen, 2005; Gosling et al., 2004; Kraut et al., 2004; Ochs et al., 2002).

Web-based sex surveys can recruit much larger samples than can traditional interview or questionnaire studies. For example, one Web survey of men who have sex with men yielded 1052 completed surveys in less than two months (Matthews et al., 2012). In addition, Web surveys can potentially produce broader samples than traditional survey methods can. For example, researchers in New Brunswick conducted an online survey on the sexual well-being of individuals with autism spectrum disorders living in the community (Byers, Nichols, & Voyer, 2013; Byers Nichols, Voyer, & Reilly, 2012). By using a Web-based survey, they were able to recruit participants from across Canada, as well as from the United States, Australia/New Zealand, the United Kingdom, and Europe. These new methods open up exciting possibilities for cross-cultural research.

Test–retest reliability: A method for testing whether self-reports are reliable or accurate; participants are interviewed (or given a questionnaire) and then interviewed a second time some time later to determine whether their answers are the same both times.

Computer-assisted self-interview method (CASI): A method of data collection in which the respondent fills out questionnaires on a computer. Headphones and a soundtrack reading the questions can be added for young children or poor readers.

Web-based surveys have particular advantages for studying special populations defined by their sexual behaviour, particularly if the behaviour is taboo. For example, traditional studies of gays and lesbians have used methods such as recruiting the sample through gay activist organizations and gay bars. These methods have been criticized because they omit from the sample individuals who are in the closet and those who do not actively participate in organizations or go to bars. Closeted gays have equal access to Web-based surveys and can answer them in a highly anonymous way, respecting their own decision to remain closeted. Therefore, Web methods can access this population that had previously been studied very little and can yield a much wider sample of gays and lesbians. Web methods can also locate stigmatized sexual minorities, such as those involved in sadomasochism, bondage, and discipline, by recruiting participants through virtual communities and websites specialized for that particular sexual group.

Web-based surveys have the ability to eliminate extraneous influences on responding (discussed in the next section). For example, the gender or ethnicity of the interviewer may influence an individual's responses, but these factors are eliminated in a Web-administered questionnaire. In addition, Web-based surveys can be used in diary studies in which participants record their behaviour at fixed intervals (for example every day or even several times a day) to avoid problems of faulty memory. An innovative way of doing this is with hand-held computers (Vannier & O'Sullivan, 2008).

Web-based surveys, then, have substantial strengths on the issue of sampling. Do all these substantial advantages come with any disadvantages? They still rely on self-reports, which as we saw earlier can be inaccurate to some degree. Some bias is introduced because not everyone has Internet access. Access grows every day, but Internet users still, on average, have incomes above the national average. Internet samples are nonetheless considerably more diverse than the university-student samples used in much research. The researcher lacks control of the environment in which the respondent completes the survey—something that can be controlled in personal interviews but cannot in mailed-out questionnaires. One can imagine, for example, a group of students living in residence filling out a Web sex survey together and having fun faking the answers. Individuals might complete the survey more than once or might actually try to sabotage or skew the results to show a particular outcome. Internal checks can be built into the sequence of questions that can detect faked patterns of answers, and methods have been devised to detect repeat responders. Nonetheless, these issues continue to be a concern.

On balance, Web-based surveys offer substantial advantages over traditional survey methods. Researchers will have to continue to monitor and control potential problems, such as repeat responders.

Accuracy of Behavioural Observations

As we noted earlier, one of the major ways of classifying techniques of sex research is by whether the scientist relied on people's self-reports of their behaviour or observed the sexual behaviour directly.

The problems of self-reports have just been discussed: self-reports may be inaccurate, although the evidence indicates that they are generally accurate. Direct observations have a major advantage over self-reports in that they are accurate. No purposeful distortion or inaccurate memory can intervene. On the other hand, direct observations have their own set of problems. They are expensive and time-consuming, with the result that generally only a rather small sample is studied. Furthermore, obtaining a representative sample of the population is even more difficult than in survey research. Although some people are reticent about completing a questionnaire concerning their sexual behaviour, even more would be unwilling to come to a laboratory where their sexual behaviour would be observed by a scientist or where they would be hooked up to recording instruments while they engaged in sex. Thus, results obtained from the unusual group of volunteers who would be willing to do this might not be generalizable to the rest of the population. One study showed that volunteers for a laboratory study of sexual arousal reported lower levels of sex guilt and were more sexually experienced than nonvolunteers (Plaud et al., 1999). Moreover, only 27 percent of men and 7 percent of women volunteered, showing how selective the sample was.

Extraneous Factors

Various extraneous factors, such as the gender, race, or age of the interviewer, may influence the outcome of sex research. Questionnaires do not get around these problems, since such simple factors as the wording of a question may affect the results. In one study, respondents were given either standard or supportive wording of some items (Catania et al., 1995). For the question about extramarital sex, the standard wording was as follows:

> At any time while you were married during the past 10 years, did you have sex with someone other than your (husband/wife)?

The supportive wording was as follows:

> Many people feel that being sexually faithful to a spouse is important, and some do not. However, even those who think being faithful is important have found themselves in situations where they ended up having sex with someone other than their (husband/wife). At any time while you were married during the past 10 years, did you have sex with someone other than your (husband/wife)?

PEARLS BEFORE SWINE   BY STEPHAN PASTIS

Figure 3.4 Sex research can be more difficult than other kinds of behavioural research.

Source: PEARLS BEFORE SWINE © Stephen Pastis/Dist. By UNIVERSAL UCLICK. Reprinted with permission.

The supportive wording significantly increased reports of extramarital sex from 12 percent with the standard wording to 16 percent with the supportive wording if the interviewer was of the same gender as the respondent; the wording made no difference when the interviewer and respondent were of different genders. Sex researchers must be careful to control these extraneous factors so that they influence the results as little as possible (Figure 3.4).

L02 Ethical Issues

Ethical problems are always a possibility in doing research. Ethical problems are particularly difficult in sex research, because people are more likely to feel that their privacy has been invaded when you ask them about sex than when you ask them to name their favourite political candidate or memorize a list of words. All research conducted at Canadian universities must conform to the *Tri-Council Policy Statement: Ethical Conduct for Research Involving Humans*, developed by the three federal granting agencies, which sets standards for conducting ethical research involving human participants. The cardinal ethical principle is respect for human dignity: researchers must keep this in mind when they are establishing the goals and the procedures of their research. The principle of respect for human dignity leads to several other ethical principles, including respect for free and informed consent and protection from harm.

Free and Informed Consent

According to the principle of **free and informed consent**, participants have a right to be told, before they participate, what the purpose of the research is and what they will be asked to do. They can choose not to participate or not to continue. An investigator may not coerce people to be in a study, and it is the scientist's responsibility to see to it that all participants understand exactly what they are agreeing to do. In the case of children who may be too young to give truly informed consent, the parents usually give consent.

The principle of informed consent was adopted by scientific organizations in the 1970s. It was violated in some of the earlier sex studies, as will be discussed later in this chapter.

Protection from Harm

Investigators should minimize the amount of physical and psychological stress to people in their research. Thus, for example, if an investigator must shock participants during a study, there should be a good reason for doing this. Questioning people about their sexual behaviour may be psychologically stressful to them and might conceivably harm them in some way, so sex researchers must be careful to minimize the stress involved in their procedure. The principle of respect for privacy and confidentiality of response, for example, by making sure that responses are anonymous, is important to ensure that participants will not suffer afterward for their participation in research.

Justice

The **justice principle** in research ethics holds that the risks of

Free and informed consent: An ethical principle in research, in which people have a right to be informed, before participating, of what they will be asked to do in the research.
Justice principle: An ethical principle in research that holds that the risks of participation should be distributed fairly across groups in society, as should the benefits.

participating in research and benefits of the results of the research should be distributed fairly across groups in society. For example, early testing of the birth control pill was done on poor women in Puerto Rico, not on wealthy women in Vancouver. The risks were not distributed fairly, and a particular group bore a disproportionate burden. As a second example, research on the potential benefits of taking Aspirin for preventing heart attacks was conducted with an all-male sample. Whether this effect works for women as well remains unknown. Thus, the benefits of the research did not extend fairly to everyone. Researchers have an obligation to make sure that they conduct their research in a way that benefits as wide a range of persons as possible.

Balancing Harms and Benefits

Considering the possible risks involved in sex research, is it ethical to do such research? Officials in universities and government agencies sponsoring sex research must answer this question for every proposed sex research study. In doing so, they must do a **harms–benefits analysis**. That is, the stress to research participants should be minimized as much as possible, but some stresses will remain; they are the harms. This is particularly true in sex research because most people consider sexuality very private, and they may find it embarrassing or distressing to disclose their sexual experiences, behaviour, and attitudes. The question then becomes, Will the benefits that result from the research be greater than the harm? That is, will the participants benefit in some way from being in the study, and will science and society in general benefit from the knowledge resulting from the study? Do these benefits outweigh the potential harms? If they do, the research is justifiable; otherwise, it is not.

As an example, Masters and Johnson considered these issues carefully and concluded that their research participants benefited from being in their research; they collected data from former participants that confirm this belief. Thus, a harms–benefits analysis would suggest that their research was ethical, even though their participants might have been temporarily stressed by it. In another study, 15- to 25-year olds completed a questionnaire about sex; later they rated how distressing and how positive the experience had been for them (Kuyper et al., 2012). Participants reported little distress and predominantly positive feelings. Overall, 89 percent agreed that surveys like this should be carried out. The one group that reported distress was people who had experienced sexual coercion in the past.

Harms–benefits analysis: An approach to analyzing the ethics of a research study, based on weighing the harms of the research (such as stress to subjects) against the benefits of the research (gaining knowledge about human sexuality).
Mean: The average of respondents' scores calculated by adding the scores and dividing by the number of people.
Median: The middle score.
Mode: The most frequent score.

In all research, the potential harms to the participants should be weighed against the benefits that accrue to society from being informed about this aspect of sexual behaviour. The "Tuskegee Study of Untreated Syphilis in the Negro Male" is an example of a study in which this was not done. Between 1932 and 1972, the U.S. government followed 399 poor, uneducated African American men living in a rural area of Alabama to learn about the course of untreated syphilis. Participants did not give informed consent, did not get the treatment they were promised, and were offered incentives that would have been coercive for people who were so poor (e.g., hot meals, burial insurance, treatment for minor ailments) to continue in the experiment. When penicillin became available as an effective treatment for syphilis, participants were denied access to it and were warned not to take it (Walker, 2009). Although we learned a great deal about syphilis from the experiment, clearly the harm to participants far outweighed the benefits. In 1997, President Bill Clinton issued a formal apology for the wrongs done to these men by the American government.

Some Statistical Concepts

Before you can understand reports of sex research, you need to understand some basic statistical concepts.

Average

Suppose we get data from a sample of common-law couples on how many times per week they have sexual intercourse. How can we summarize the data? One way to do this is to compute some average value; this will tell us how often, on average, these people have intercourse. In sex research, the number that is usually calculated is either the mean or the median, although the mode is sometimes used; all of these give us an indication of approximately where the average value for that group of people is. The **mean** or average is calculated by adding up all the scores and dividing by the number of people. The **median** is the score that splits the sample in half, with half the respondents scoring below that number and half scoring above it. The **mode** is the score with the greatest number of responses. People whose thoughts, feelings, and behaviour are close to the average for their group might be said to be typical of that group.

Variability

In addition to having an indication of the average for the sample of respondents, it is also important to know how much variability there is from one respondent to the next in the numbers reported. That is, it is one thing

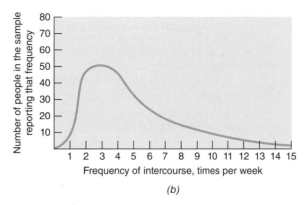

(a)   *(b)*

Figure 3.5 Two hypothetical graphs of the frequency of intercourse for common-law couples in a sample. In both, the average frequency is about three times per week, but in *(a)* there is little variability (almost everyone has a frequency between two and four times per week), whereas in *(b)* there is great variability (the frequency ranges from 0 to 15 or more times per week). The graph for most sexual behaviour looks like *(b)*, with great variability.

to say that the average common-law couple in a sample had intercourse three times per week, with a range in the sample from two to four times per week, and it is quite another thing to say that the average was three times per week, with a range from zero to 15 times per week. In both cases the mean is the same, but in the first there is little variability, and in the second there is a great deal of variability. These two alternatives are shown graphically in Figure 3.5. Great variability exists in virtually all sexual behaviour.

Average Versus Normal

It is interesting and informative to report the average frequency of a particular sexual behaviour, but this also introduces the danger that people will confuse *average* with *normal*. That is, there is a tendency, when reading a statistic like "the average person has intercourse twice per week" to think of our own sexual behaviour, compare it with that average, and then conclude that we are abnormal if we differ much from the average. If you read that statistic and your frequency of intercourse is only once a week, you may begin to worry that you are undersexed or that you are not getting as much as you should. If you are having intercourse seven times per week, you might begin worrying that you are oversexed. Such conclusions are a mistake, first, because they can make you miserable and, second, because so much variability exists in sexual behaviour that any behaviour (or frequency or length of time) within a wide range is perfectly normal. Don't confuse average with normal.

Incidence Versus Frequency

In sex statistics, the terms *incidence* and *frequency* are often used. **Incidence** refers to the percentage of people who have engaged in a certain behaviour. **Frequency** refers to how often people do something. Thus, we

might say that the incidence of masturbation among males is 92 percent (meaning that 92 percent of all males masturbate at least once in their lives), whereas the average frequency of masturbation among males between the ages of 16 and 20 is about once per week.

A closely related concept is that of *cumulative incidence*. If we consider a sexual behaviour according to the age at which each person in the sample first engaged in it, the cumulative incidence refers to the percentage of people who have engaged in that behaviour before a certain age. Thus, the cumulative incidence of masturbation in males might be 10 percent by age 11; 25 percent by age 12; 80 percent by age 15; and 95 percent by age 20. Graphs of cumulative incidence always begin in the lower left-hand corner and move toward the upper right-hand corner. An example of a cumulative-incidence curve is shown in Figure 3.6.

Correlation

The term *correlation* is used by laypeople in contexts such as the following: "There seems to be a correlation here between how warm the days are and how fast the corn is growing." But what do statisticians mean by the term *correlation*? A **correlation** is a number that measures the relationship between two variables. A correlation can be positive or negative. A positive correlation occurs when a positive relationship exists between the two variables; that is, people who have high scores on one variable tend to have high scores on the other variable, and low scores go with low scores. A negative correlation occurs when an opposite relationship exists between the two variables; that is, people with high scores on one variable tend to have low scores on the other

Incidence: The percentage of people giving a particular response.
Frequency: How often a person does something.
Correlation: A number that measures the relationship between two variables.

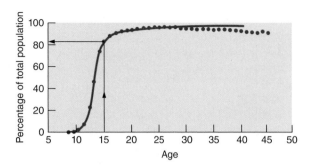

Figure 3.6 A cumulative-incidence curve for masturbation in males. From the graph, you can read off the percentage of males who report having masturbated by a given age. For example, about 82 percent have masturbated to orgasm by age 15.

variable. We might want to know, for example, whether there is a correlation between the number of years a couple has been together and the frequency with which they have sexual intercourse. In this case we might expect that there would be a negative correlation, and that is just what researchers have found. That is, the *greater* the number of years together, the *lower* the frequency of intercourse.

Correlations range between +1.0 and −1.0. A correlation of +1.0 indicates a perfect positive relationship between two variables, meaning that the person in the sample who scores highest on one variable also has the highest score on the other variable, the person with the second highest score on the first variable also has the second highest score on the other variable, and so on. A correlation of 0 indicates no relationship between the two variables. Knowing a person's score on one variable tells us nothing about whether the person will have a high or a low score on the other variable. Positive correlations between 0 and +1.0—for example, +.62—say that the relationship is positive but not a perfect relationship.

As discussed earlier in this chapter, we use correlations to assess test–retest reliability. Suppose we administer a questionnaire to a sample of adults. One of the questions asks, "How many times did you masturbate to orgasm during the month of September?" We ask this question of the sample on October 1 and again on October 8. If each person in the sample gives us exactly the same answer on October 1 and on October 8, the correlation between the two variables (the number given on October 1 and the number given on October 8) would be +1.0 and the test–retest reliability would be a perfect +1.0. Test–retest reliabilities for questions about sex typically range between +.60 and +.90, indicating that people's answers on the two occasions are not identical but are very similar.

The Major Sex Surveys

In the major sex surveys, the data were collected from a large sample of people by means of questionnaires or interviews. Unfortunately, no large-scale, comprehensive sex surveys have been done in Canada with the exception of a few questions contained in the National Population Health Survey and other general surveys. However, such surveys have been conducted in a number of other countries including the United States, the United Kingdom, Australia, and France. The best known of these studies is the U.S. survey done by Alfred Kinsey, so we will consider it first. His data were collected in the late 1930s and 1940s in the United States, and thus the results are now largely of historical interest. However, Kinsey documented his methods with extraordinary care, so his research is a good example to study for both the good and the bad points of surveys.

The Kinsey Report
The Sample
Kinsey (see Milestones in Sex Research) and his colleagues interviewed 5300 men and 5940 women between 1938 and 1949 in the United States.

Initially, Kinsey was not much concerned with sampling issues. His goal was simply to collect sex histories from as wide a variety of people as possible. In the 1953 volume on women, Kinsey said that he and his colleagues had deliberately chosen not to use probability sampling methods because of the problems of nonresponse. This is a legitimate point. But as a result, we have almost no information on how adequate the sample was; the sampling was haphazard but not random. Generally, the following kinds of people were overrepresented in the sample: university students, young people, well-educated people, Protestants, people living in cities, and people living in Indiana and the Northeast United States. Underrepresented groups included manual labourers, less-well-educated people, older people, Roman Catholics, Jews, members of racial minority groups, and people living in rural areas.

The Interviews
Although scientists generally regard Kinsey's sampling methods with some dismay, his face-to-face interviewing techniques are highly regarded. More than 50 percent of the interviews were done by Kinsey himself and the rest by his associates, whom he trained carefully. The interviewers made every attempt to establish rapport with the people they spoke to, and they treated all reports matter-of-factly. They were also skilful at phrasing questions in language that was easily understood.

Questions were worded so as to encourage people to report anything they had done. For example, rather than asking, "Have you ever masturbated?" the interviewers asked, "At what age did you begin masturbating?" They also developed a number of methods for cross-checking a person's report so that false information would be detected. Wardell Pomeroy recounted an example:

> Kinsey illustrated this point with the case of an older Negro male who at first was wary and evasive in his answers. From the fact that he listed a number of minor jobs when asked about his occupation and seemed reluctant to go into any of them [Kinsey] deduced that he might have been active in the underworld, so he began to follow up by asking the man whether he had ever been married. He denied it, at which Kinsey resorted to the vernacular and inquired if he had ever "lived common law." The man admitted he had, and that it had first happened when he was 14.
>
> "How old was the woman?" [Kinsey] asked.
>
> "Thirty-five," he admitted, smiling.
>
> Kinsey showed no surprise. "She was a hustler, wasn't she?" he said flatly.
>
> At this the subject's eyes opened wide. Then he smiled in a friendly way for the first time, and said, "Well, sir, since you appear to know something about these things, I'll tell you straight."
>
> After that, [Kinsey] got an extraordinary record of this man's history as a pimp.... (Pomeroy, 1972, pp. 115–116)

Put simply, the interviewing techniques were probably very successful in minimizing purposeful distortion.

Kinsey took strict precautions to ensure that responses were anonymous and that they remained anonymous. The data were stored on IBM cards but used a code that had been memorized by only a few people directly involved in the project and was never written down. The research team had even made contingency plans for destroying the data in the event that the police tried to demand access to the records for prosecuting people.

How Accurate Were the Kinsey Statistics?

How accurate were the statistics presented by Kinsey? The American Statistical Association appointed a blue-ribbon panel to evaluate the Kinsey reports (Cochran et al., 1953; for other evaluations, see Terman, 1948; Wallin, 1949). While the panel members generally felt that the interview techniques had been excellent, they were dismayed by Kinsey's failure to use probability sampling and concluded, somewhat pessimistically:

> In the absence of a probability-sample benchmark, the present results must be regarded as subject to systematic errors of unknown magnitude due to selective sampling (via volunteering and the like). (Cochran et al., 1953, p. 711)

However, they also felt that this was a nearly insoluble problem for sex research; even if a probability sample were used, refusals would still create serious problems.

The statisticians who evaluated Kinsey's methods felt that one aspect of his findings might have been particularly subject to error: the generally high levels of sexual activity and particularly the high incidence of same-sex sexual activity These conclusions might, they felt, have been seriously influenced by sampling problems, particularly Kinsey's tendency to seek out persons with unusual sexual practices.

It is impossible to say how accurate the Kinsey statistics are; some may be very accurate and some may contain serious errors. Probably the single most doubtful figure is the high incidence of homosexuality.

Sexual Behaviour in the United States Today

U.S. researchers identified a need to conduct a large-scale, national survey of sexuality using probability sampling methods to determine what Americans' patterns of sexual behaviour are today. Such a study appeared in 1994. The research team was headed by Edward Laumann, a distinguished sociologist at the University of Chicago, and was conducted by the National Opinion Research Center, one of the best-respected survey organizations in the United States. The survey was called the National Health and Social Life Survey (NHSLS) (Laumann et al., 1994; Michael et al., 1994).

The research method involved a probability sampling of households in the United States. This sampling excluded less than 3 percent of Americans but did exclude people living in institutions (e.g., prisons, university dormitories) and the homeless. People were eligible if they were adults between the ages of 18 and 59.

The researchers obtained an impressive 79 percent response rate. Apparently, the great majority of people are willing to respond to a carefully conducted sex survey. The response rate is particularly impressive in view of the fact that today even surveys of more neutral topics, such as political opinions, generally have a response rate of only about 75 percent.

The data were obtained in face-to-face interviews supplemented by brief written questionnaires, which were handed to the respondents for particularly sensitive topics (such as masturbation) and sealed in a "privacy envelope" when they had been completed. The researchers chose the face-to-face interview because they felt that it would yield a higher response rate than a written questionnaire alone, and it allowed the researchers to ask more complex, detailed sequences of questions than would have been possible with just a written questionnaire or a telephone interview.

Milestones in Sex Research

What Is the Legacy of Alfred C. Kinsey?

Alfred C. Kinsey was born in 1894 in New Jersey, the first child of uneducated parents. In high school he did not date, and a classmate recalled that he was "the shyest guy around girls you could think of."

His father was determined that Kinsey become a mechanical engineer. From 1912 to 1914 he tried studying mechanical engineering at Stevens Institute, but he showed little talent for it. At one point he was close to failing physics, but a compromise was reached with the professor, who agreed to pass him if he would not attempt any advanced work in the field! In 1914 Kinsey made his break and enrolled at Bowdoin College to pursue his real love: biology. Because this went against his father's wishes, Kinsey was left on his own financially.

In 1916 he began graduate work at Harvard. There he developed an interest in insects, specializing in gall wasps. While still a graduate student, he wrote a definitive book on the edible plants of eastern North America.

In 1920 he went to Bloomington, Indiana, to take a job as assistant professor of zoology at Indiana University. That fall he met Clara McMillen, whom he married six months later. They soon had four children.

With his intense curiosity and driving ambition, Kinsey quickly gained academic success. He published a high school biology text in 1926, which received enthusiastic reviews. By 1936 he had published two major books on gall wasps; they established his reputation as a leading authority in the field.

Kinsey came to the study of human sexual behaviour as a biologist. His shift to the study of sex began in 1938, when Indiana University began a "marriage" course; Kinsey chaired the faculty committee teaching it. When confronted with teaching the course, he became aware of the appalling lack of information on human sexual behaviour. Thus, his research resulted in part from his realization of the need of people, especially young people, for sex information. In 1939 he made his first field trip to collect sex histories in Chicago. His lifetime goal was to collect 100,000 sex histories.

His work culminated in the publication of the Kinsey reports in 1948 (*Sexual Behavior in the Human Male*) and 1953 (*Sexual Behavior in the Human Female*). While the scientific community generally received them as a landmark contribution, they also provoked hate mail.

In 1947 Kinsey founded the Institute for Sex Research (known popularly as the Kinsey Institute) at Indiana University. It was financed by a grant from the Rockefeller Foundation and, later, by book royalties. But

The NHSLS is one of the best sex surveys of the general population of the United States available today, and its findings will be referred to in many chapters in this book. The researchers made outstanding efforts to use the best sampling methods and interview techniques.

Nonetheless, the study has some limitations. It sampled only people between 18 and 59, giving us no information about the sexuality of older adults. The sample did not include enough people from some minority groups to compute reliable statistics for them (see Figure 3.8). No doubt some respondents engaged in concealment and perhaps also in enlargement, because self-reports were used. The skill of the interviewers and their ability to build rapport are crucial in overcoming such problems.

The most recent major national U.S. sex survey is the National Survey of Sexual Health and Behavior (NSSHB), with data collected in 2009 from people between the ages of 14 and 94 (Herbenick et al., 2010a; Reece et al., 2010a). A probability sample was identified based on a combination of random-digit dialling of telephone numbers and sampling of residential addresses from the U.S. Postal Service's list of deliverable addresses. For the adolescent part of the sample, parents were contacted first to provide consent and 62 percent agreed, and 62 percent of the eligible adolescents participated, for a sample of 820 adolescents. In addition, 9600 potential adult participants were contacted and 53 percent provided data. The overall sample size, then, combining adults and adolescents, was 5865. Participants completed the in the 1950s United States Senator Joseph McCarthy, the communist baiter, was in power. He made a particularly vicious attack on the Institute and its research, claiming that its effect was to weaken American morality and thus make the nation more susceptible to a communist takeover. Under his pressure, the Rockefeller Foundation terminated its support.

Kinsey's health began to fail, partly as a result of the heavy workload he set for himself and partly because he saw financial support for the research collapsing. He died in 1956 at the age of 62 of heart failure while honouring a lecture engagement when his doctor had ordered him to convalesce.

By 1957, McCarthy had been discredited and the grant funds returned. The Kinsey Institute was then headed by Paul Gebhard (see Figure 3.7), an anthropologist who had been a member of the staff for many years. The Institute continues to do research today; it also houses a large library on sex and an archival collection that includes countless works of sexual art.

In a highly publicized, tell-all biography of Kinsey, James Jones (1997) argued that, although Kinsey's public self was a heterosexual married man, he was homosexual (more accurately, bisexual) and practised masochism. According to Jones, this discredits Kinsey's research. Jones's logic is poor, though, because we can evaluate the quality of the research methods independent of our views about Kinsey's personal

Figure 3.7 Alfred C. Kinsey (second from right, holding the folder), with colleagues Martin, Gebhard, and Pomeroy.

sex life. Moreover, Kinsey's sexual experimenting may have contributed to the innovativeness of his research.

Sources: Bancroft (2004), Christensen (1971), Gathorne-Hardy (2000), Gebhard (1976), and Jones (1997).

survey on the Internet, and those without computers were provided them for completing the questionnaire. Results from the survey will be presented in many chapters that follow.

How good was the NSSHB? The methods for identifying the initial probability sample—random-digit dialling of phone numbers and sampling of residential addresses—were excellent. The response rate was 50 percent, which is considerably lower than what the NHSLS obtained, but it is probably getting more difficult to recruit participants because Americans are increasingly oversaturated with solicitations from fundraising organizations, telemarketers, and so on. Statistically, with a 50 percent response rate, we cannot be sure that the results generalize to the whole population, but

volunteer bias is always a problem with sex research. And, generally, administering sex questionnaires online is a good idea because respondents feel more anonymous and therefore presumably answer more truthfully.

Sexual Behaviour in Britain and Australia

Stimulated by a need for far better information about sexual behaviour to deal with the AIDS crisis, a team of researchers led by Anne Johnson (Johnson et al., 1992, 2001) conducted a major sex survey in Great Britain. It yielded data for 18,876 men and women ages 16 to 59. The study is called the National Survey of Sexual Attitudes and Lifestyles (NATSAL). The data indicate

Figure 3.8 Research conducted among members of racial and ethnic minority groups must be culturally sensitive. Ideally, for example, interviewers should be of the same cultural background as research participants.

that, for the entire sample, 14 percent of the men and 7 percent of the women had had multiple sex partners in the past 12 months, figures quite similar to those in the NHSLS. However, when one looks just at 16- to 24-year olds, 27 percent of the men and 16 percent of the women had had two or more partners in the past 12 months—a considerably greater percentage.

Another team of researchers conducted a major sex survey in Australia (Rissel et al., 2003a; Rissel et al., 2003b; Smith et al., 2003) called the Australian Study of Health and Relationships (ASHR). Using computer-assisted telephone interviews, the researchers recruited a sample of 19,307 men and women ages 16 to 59. Their response rate was 73 percent, which is comparable to the NHSLS. Their findings indicate that the age of first intercourse has declined over the last several decades, consistent with trends in North America (Rissel et al., 2003b). In the youngest cohort, respondents ages 16 to 19, 27 percent of the men and 25 percent of the women reported that they had engaged in intercourse before age 16. Finally, 38 percent of the men and 27 percent of the women reported that they used no contraception the first time they had intercourse, a pattern that is also similar to North America and is of great concern.

Sexual Behaviour in Canada

Because no large-scale comprehensive Canadian sex surveys have been done, we often use the American surveys to draw conclusions about the situation in Canada. However, Canadians differ from Americans in ways that are likely to affect sexual behaviour, such as family patterns, laws, attitudes, and health (Barrett et al., 1997). Thus, it is impossible to be certain of the extent to which these data reflect the sexual behaviour of Canadians. This makes it difficult to

What types of sex research are taking place in Canada?

develop a clear picture of the sexual behaviour of adult Canadians. In contrast, as just described, the United States, Britain, and Australia have all conducted this kind of large-scale survey in recent years. Many of the statistics in the British surveys (and some surveys done in France) match quite closely those from the United States. Thus, it is likely that a Canadian survey would also have similar, but not identical, findings.

Many sex researchers, however, are active in Canada (see First Person). These researchers have conducted surveys of selected groups, such as university students, teenagers, First Nations peoples, sex trade workers, people living with chronic illnesses, and gay and bisexual men, some of which are described in this chapter.

The Canada Youth, Sexual Health, and HIV/AIDS Study

Researchers from four Canadian universities—Queen's, Acadia, Laval, and the University of Alberta—conducted a study on youth sexuality and sexual health called the Canada Youth, Sexual Health, and HIV/AIDS Study, or CYSHHAS for short (Boyce et al., 2003). It examined a number of factors thought to influence adolescent sexual knowledge, attitudes, and behaviour. Many of these questions were also used in the Canada Youth and AIDS Study conducted in 1987 by Alan King and his colleagues (King et al., 1988), allowing comparisons between the two studies. Because the CYSHHAS focused on sexual health, it is not a comprehensive survey of adolescent sexual behaviour and attitudes.

The researchers collected data in all 10 provinces as well as in Yukon and the Northwest Territories. They surveyed 11,074 youth in Grades 7, 9, and 11. However, to be acceptable to school administrations, the Grade 7 version included only one question about sexual experiences. The study was conducted in both French and English. The researchers used excellent sampling methods. They designed their sampling procedure so that the data would be representative of Canada as a whole and so they would have enough participants to present the findings separately for each province. However, some selected schools refused to participate. This resulted in a sample that was not equally representative of the whole country and was too small to analyze by province or territory. There also were some problems related to potential volunteer bias. For example, 18 percent of students either failed to return their signed permission slip or had parents who refused to give them permission to participate, and 5 percent of the students refused to participate. The students who did participate may differ in some important ways from those who did not.

The researchers found that many youth had begun engaging in sexual intercourse by age 14. For example, 23 percent of boys and 19 percent of girls in Grade 9 and 40 percent of boys and 46 percent of girls in Grade 11 reported having engaged in sexual intercourse at least once. These percentages are similar to, and if anything somewhat lower than, those obtained in the Canada Youth and AIDS Study in 1987, indicating that the percentage of students engaging in sexual intercourse does not appear to be increasing. However, the students who are engaging in sexual intercourse reported doing so more frequently than did students in 1987. Although 78 percent of the boys and 68 percent of the girls said that they had used a condom at last intercourse, between 5 and 10 percent had not used any form of birth control. Further, students who participated in 2002 were less accurate in their sexual knowledge than were the students who participated in 1987. Although this study assessed both anglophone and francophone youth, the researchers did not assess ethnicity. Thus, we do not know how cultural background affects the sexual attitudes and behaviours of Canadian youth.

Magazine Surveys

Many large-scale sex surveys have been conducted through magazines. Often the survey is printed in one issue of the magazine and readers are asked to respond. The result can be a huge sample—perhaps 20,000 people—which sounds impressive. But are these magazine surveys really all they claim to be?

Sampling is just plain out of control with magazine surveys. The survey is distributed just to readers of the magazine, and different magazines have different clienteles. No one magazine reaches a representative sample of Canadians. If the survey appeared in *Chatelaine*, it would go to certain kinds of women; if it were in *Canadian Living*, it would go to others. It would be risky to assume that women who read *Chatelaine* have the same sexual patterns as those who read *Canadian Living*. To make matters worse, the response rate is unknown. We can't know how many people saw the survey and did not fill it out compared with the number who did. We do not, therefore, even have a random sample of readers of that magazine.

As an example, let's consider a survey that was reported in the August 2009 issue of *Cosmopolitan*. The headline on the cover announces "Guys Rate 125 Sex Moves." The description of the methods in the article says that *Cosmo* "paired up with AskMen.com and got thousands of guys between the ages of 18 and 35 to confess what they want in bed." A subtitle clarifies that "thousands" actually means 6000 horny guys. That sample is twice the size of the NHSLS but, in sex surveys as in some other aspects of sexuality, bigger is not always better. What we can't tell from the article is who these 6000 horny guys are. Are they representative of all North American men between the ages of 18 and

35? That's highly unlikely, because only men who go to AskMen.com saw the survey. How can we know the response rate? Among the respondents, how many were married? Single? What about their ethnic backgrounds? Of course, these details are not the sort of thing that *Cosmo* probably thinks will entertain its readers. Nonetheless, they could have printed the information in a small box at the end of the article. More important, these details are crucial in evaluating whether one can take their claims seriously.

One question asked about the absolute sexiest sight she can treat you to. Of the men who were polled, the most frequent choice (34 percent of those polled) was "touching herself in front of me." From this, can we conclude that 34 percent of men are most turned on by the sight of their partner touching herself? That conclusion would require a leap of logic that is too big for safety. *Cosmo* wasn't even close to having a random sample in this survey.

For all these reasons, it would not be legitimate to infer that these statistics characterize North American men in general. We could continue with more examples of magazine surveys, but the general conclusion should be clear by now. Although they may appear impressive because of their large number of respondents, magazine sex surveys actually are poor in quality because the sample generally is seriously biased.

Studies of Special Populations

In addition to the large-scale surveys of Americans and of Canadian youth discussed earlier, many studies of special populations have been done. The Ontario First Nations AIDS and Healthy Lifestyle Survey is one such example (of course, there are many others).

The Ontario First Nations AIDS and Healthy Lifestyle Survey was conducted by Ted Myers and his colleagues (1994) at the Division of Community Health at the University of Toronto in collaboration with the First Nations Steering Committee. The goal of the study was to assess knowledge, attitudes, and behaviours related to HIV infection among First Nations peoples in Ontario. All decisions were made by consensus between the academic researchers and the Steering Committee to take the unique concerns of communities into account. The researchers used random selection to obtain a representative sample. They selected equal numbers of men and women, as well as equal numbers within each of four age groups (Myers et al., 1994).

The data were collected by using face-to-face interviews and an answer booklet for highly personal questions. All interviewers were hired from participating

Where Can I Go in Canada to Become a Sex Researcher?

C anada has many active sex researchers, and their numbers are growing. Most are in academic departments within specific disciplines, such as psychology, sociology, family studies, or medicine. Most supervise students. The only Department of Sexology located in Canada operates in French at l'Université du Québec à Montréal. However, York University has a program in sexuality studies. Although it is impossible to name all Canadian sex researchers, here are some of the most active researchers (from east to west) who also supervise student research.

At Acadia University in Nova Scotia, psychologist Lisa Price studies sexual coercion and risky sexual behaviour among adolescents. At Dalhousie University, psychologist Natalie Rosen studies the influence of relationship factors on sexual pain disorders. At St. Francis Xavier University, psychologist Angela Weaver studies body image, alternative sexualities, and sexuality in film. At the University of New Brunswick, psychologist Sandra Byers is particularly well known for her research on sexual interactions in close relationships, including sexual satisfaction, sexual dysfunction, and sexual coercion; Lucia O'Sullivan is an expert in adolescent sexual health; and Scott Ronis conducts research on childhood sexual experiences.

In Quebec, psychologist Francine Lavoie of Laval University studies high school students' sexually coercive experiences. In the Département de sexologie, l'Université du Québec à Montréal, Joseph Levy and Joanne Otis have been active in assessing the sexual behaviour of Quebecers. In the same department,

Martine Hébert investigates child sexual abuse, Marie-Aude Boislard studies adolescent sexuality, and Line Chamberland studies sexual minorities. In the Département de psychologie at UQAM, Danielle Julien studies sexual and gender minorities (see www.sexologie.uqam.ca/personnel/ for a complete list of faculty at UQAM). At l'Université de Montréal, psychologist Sophie Bergeron studies women's sexual pain disorders, and psychologist Katherine Péloquin studies couples' sexual relationships. At McGill University, psychologist Yitzchak Binik studies sexual pain in women. At Concordia University, sociologist Frances Shaver is a leading researcher on sex work, and James Pfaus studies the neurochemical and molecular events underlying sexual behaviour.

A number of Ontario universities have active sex research programs. At Queen's University, psychologist Caroline Pukall does research related to sexual pain and its effects on sexual and marital functioning, and psychologist Meredith Chivers studies sexual psychophysiology. At the University of Ottawa, psychologist Elke Reissing investigates sexual pain disorders and sexual adjustment following treatment for cancer, Martin Lalumière does research on sexual aggression, and Peggy Kleinplatz does research on optimal sexuality. At the Centre for Addiction and Mental Health, Clarke Division, in Toronto, psychologist Ken Zucker is well known for his work on gender identity disorders in children and adults, and psychologist James Cantor for his work on pedophilia. At the University of Toronto, Michael Seto studies sexual offenders, and Ted Myers

communities, spoke the appropriate First Nations language, and participated in two days of training. For questions about sexual behaviour, respondents were given a choice of using technical terms or slang terms. Most communities took steps to promote the study.

The researchers found that many participants had engaged in high-risk sexual behaviours. For example, 40 percent of the men and 18 percent of the women reported two or more sexual partners in the past year. Sixty percent of respondents did not consistently

use a condom when engaging in vaginal or anal intercourse.

The methodology used in this study demonstrates several issues that need to be kept in mind in doing research with different cultural groups (Ford & Norris, 1991). First, respondents should be interviewed by an interviewer of the same gender and ethnic background as they are. This practice is important for building rapport and establishing trust during the interview, both of which are critical in obtaining honest answers.

does research related to HIV. At York University, Nick Mulé and Maurice Kwong-Lai Poon conduct research on sexual orientation, and Bobby Noble conducts research on transgender issues. At Ryerson University, Maria Gurevich studies constructions of gender, sexuality, and identity.

Psychologist Anthony Bogaert at Brock University is well known for his work on the origins of sexual orientation and on asexuality. Psychologist Terry Humphreys at Trent University does research related to human sexuality and social psychology. At the University of Waterloo, psychologist B. J. Rye studies HIV/AIDS and attitudes toward sexual minorities, and Christine Purdon examines the role of anxiety in sexual functioning. At the University of Guelph, Robin Milhausen does research related to sexual arousal and sexual health, Tuuli Kukkonen studies biological and social factors affecting sexual health, and Serge Demarais investigates sexual coercion. Psychologist William Fisher at the University of Western Ontario has an international reputation for his work on the prevention of teen pregnancy, STIs, and HIV infection (see Milestones in Sex Research to learn more about him). At the University of Windsor, sociologist Eleanor Maticka-Tyndale is well known for her qualitative and multimethod research on risk behaviour related to pregnancy and STI/HIV infection, sociologist Barry Adam does research on HIV and same-sex relationships, and psychologist Charlene Senn studies sexual violence.

At the University of Saskatchewan, psychologist Melanie Morrison studies prejudice and discrimination toward sexual minorities, and psychologist Todd Morrison studies gay and lesbian psychology. At the University of Alberta, Kris Wells conducts research on sexual and gender minority youth. Paul Vasey at the University of Lethbridge studies sexuality and gender from a bio-cognitive perspective.

At the University of British Columbia, psychologist Lori Brotto studies women with sexual dysfunction and cross-cultural issues in women's sexual health, psychologist Judith Daniluk is well known for her research on infertility, psychologist Boris Gorzalka conducts psychophysiological sex research, and nursing professor Elizabeth Saewyc studies stigma and adolescent sexual health. Cari Miller, a professor of health sciences at Simon Fraser University, studies adolescent sexual and reproductive health nationally and internationally. Sociologist Aaron Devor at the University of Victoria has made important contributions with his work on conceptualization of gender dysphoria.

Canadian sex researchers publish their findings in both national and international journals. One Canadian journal is committed to the dissemination of sex research: the quarterly *Canadian Journal of Human Sexuality*. Many researchers belong to the Canadian Sex Research Forum, the only national association for sex researchers, as well as to international sexological organizations. The Canadian Sex Research Forum also welcomes students who are interested in sex research (for more information visit www.canadiansexresearchforum .com). Finally, the Guelph Sexuality Conference is held each year at the University of Guelph featuring Canadian and international speakers who provide research-based education and training to practitioners working in sexual health.

Language is another important issue in constructing interviews. Many people, including those from the majority Canadian culture, do not know scientific terms for sexual concepts. Interviewers therefore have to be ready with a supply of slang terms so that they can switch to these if a respondent does not understand a question. This problem becomes more complex when interviewing people whose first language is not English. In keeping with these recommendations, Myers and his colleagues used interviewers from the communities involved in the study, allowed interviewers to translate the question into the appropriate First Nations language as they conducted the interview, if required, and trained them in both technical and slang terms.

This research also demonstrates another important principle—representatives of the target communities participated in the design and management of the study. This has two advantages. First, it allows the communities to have input into the research design and methodology to ensure that the research takes the unique

Milestones in Sex Research

Confessions of a Scientist: The Career of Dr. William Fisher

As listed in the First Person box, many excellent sex researchers work in Canada. Here we share the story of how one of the Canadian leaders in the field, Dr. William Fisher (see Figure 3.9), became a sex researcher. Dr. Fisher is a professor in the Department of Psychology and the Department of Obstetrics and Gynaecology at the University of Western Ontario. He received his PhD in social psychology from Purdue University in 1978. He is world-renowned for the information–motivation–behavioural skills model, his conceptualization of the factors that drive sexual and reproductive health behaviour, and for his work on HIV/AIDS prevention and on the effects of pornography on men's and women's behaviour. Dr. Fisher's work is described throughout this book (see Chapters 7, 10, and 17). He has received a National Health Scientist Award from Health Canada and the Hellmuth Award for Achievement in Science from the University of Western Ontario, and he is a Fellow of the Society for the Scientific Study of Sexuality. Here he reflects, with humour, on how he came to be a sexuality researcher.

Coming out of the chaos, commitment, and politics of the Vietnam and Civil Rights era in the 1960s, I resolved, naively, to try to understand and improve the human condition, a delusional state from which I have yet to recover. Accordingly, I applied for admission to a graduate school that featured stellar researchers in the areas of human attraction and human aggression—which seemed to me at the time to be the issues we need to understand if we are to have any chance to survive as a species. Astoundingly, Donn Byrne, one of the world's premier scientists in the area of love and attraction, accepted me for graduate study. He had just shifted his research focus from interpersonal attraction to sexual behaviour—a natural progression, in retrospect, and we were off to the races.

As a graduate student I conducted research on the effects of pornography (what else?), and two things caught my eye immediately. First, I found that men and women who viewed pornography and who were most revolted by it showed large increases in their sexual activity levels in the days following exposure. (As an aside, the study was published in both the *Journal of Personality and Social Psychology* and in *Screw* magazine. Fortunately, the publication in *Screw* magazine did not turn out to be a career ender—no prospective employer ever admitted to having seen it). Second, I found that men and women who responded to pornography with the most pronounced negative emotions also, and puzzlingly, had the most children. At first it was difficult to understand why—and indeed how—this happened. Then we realized that erotophobic persons—that is, people who are emotionally negative to sex—have a

concerns of each community into account. Second, members of minority groups are more likely to agree to participate in research if they know that representatives of their communities were involved in designing the study.

In conclusion, doing sex research with people from diverse ethnocultural communities in Canada requires more than just administering the same old surveys to samples of people from these groups. It requires revisions to methodology that are culturally sensitive to issues such as the ethnicity of the interviewer, the language used in the interview, and the special sensitivity of some groups regarding some topics.

L05

Media Content Analysis

So far, we have focused on methods used to analyze people's sexuality and have touched on the profound impact of the mass media on Canadians' sexuality. To be able to understand this impact, we need to be able to analyze the media. As an example, let's suppose that your friend Rachel says that it is deeply disturbing that women are shown in nothing but traditional roles on prime-time TV and that this situation hasn't improved a bit over the years. Your other friend Monique disagrees, really tough time doing just about everything you need to do to not have children. That is, they find it hard to learn about contraception, talk with a partner about it, acquire it from a physician or a pharmacy, and use it consistently.

That was my start, and since graduate school, building on this observation, I have worked toward development of a theory of the basic psychological factors that drive human sexual behaviour. My research has been aimed at improving people's sexual and reproductive health by applying this theory in areas as diverse as adolescent pregnancy prevention, HIV prevention, and reproductive health care seeking. I have been fortunate to do this work in settings as varied and challenging as inner-city high schools in the United States, South African AIDS treatment centres, and Israeli–Palestinian HIV containment programs. I've been at this work for years. I've published more than 150 papers in this area, and I feel like I've barely begun.

Why I Do What I Do

I do what I do because I believe that the development and application of psychological theory in the area of sexual and reproductive health is important for the human condition. I do what I do because I enjoy creating conceptual models that can with power and precision be used to predict and promote human sexual and reproductive health outcomes. I do what I do because my work has had the unintended but often enjoyable effect of inflaming both the political right (see my work

Figure 3.9 Dr. William Fisher is a well-known psychologist and sex researcher.

on contraceptive behaviour and how to promote it) and the political left (see my work on pornography and failure to find that it has negative effects), so I know I must be doing something right.

Proudest Achievements

Catching the occasional fish. Not really. My proudest achievements involve my resolute insistence on following my data, regardless of their political correctness or incorrectness, and insisting on maintaining fundamental human values and principles, regardless of my data.

saying that there may still be some traditional images of women, but there are many examples of women in nontraditional roles, such as doctors, and the media's portrayals of women have changed a lot over the years. How can you decide who is right? Arguing won't settle the debate. However, you could use a technique called **content analysis** to analyze how the media portray women today and how they have portrayed women in the past (Krippendorff, 2004).

Content analysis refers to a set of procedures used to make valid inferences about text (see Figure 3.10). The "text" might be romance novels, advice columns

in *Chatelaine* magazine, lyrics from rap music, or scripts from movies or prime-time television programs. As it turns out, many of the same methodological issues discussed earlier also come into play with content analysis. Here, we have used a recently published study by Canadian researchers on descriptions in popular magazines of how to achieve "great sex" (Ménard & Kleinplatz, 2008).

Sampling is one such issue. The first thing the researchers conducting this study needed to do was define the population. Were

Content analysis: A set of procedures used to make valid inferences about text.

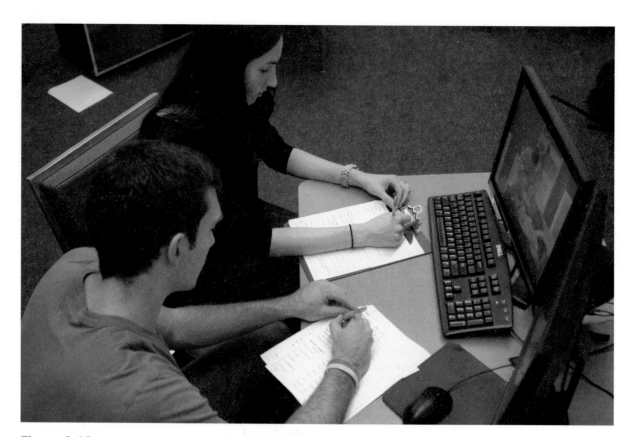

Figure 3.10 Precise methods have been developed for analyzing the content of the media.

they interested in all magazines or particular types of magazines? Next, they needed to define the time period of interest: magazines published in the current year, the past five years, the past ten years, and so on. Finally, they needed to decide whether to analyze all magazines that met these criteria or a sample of these magazines, and whether to analyze the entire magazine or selected parts of the magazine. The researchers decided to include the issues from 2005 of an equal number of male and female magazines targeted at single readers between the ages of 18 and 35 and that regularly include sexual content.

The next step is to create a coding protocol. First, the researchers needed to define the recording unit—was it the magazine, the article, or specific statements? The authors chose to use explicit tips on how to have great sex within an article or blurb—that is, specific statements. Next, perhaps more importantly, they needed to define coding categories. Creating the coding scheme involves defining the basic content categories, the presence or absence of which will be recorded; the coding categories used depend on the research questions. In this instance, the researchers

> **Is it possible to study sexuality scientifically with methods other than questionnaires?**

Intercoder or interrater reliability: In content analysis, the correlation or percentage of agreement between two coders independently rating the same texts.

developed their coding categories by doing a qualitative analysis in which they read and reread the articles and blurbs. This resulted in five major categories: technical/mechanical/physical factors, variety, relationship factors including sexual communication and emotional connection, personal and psychological factors, and presex preparation.

Researchers doing content analysis must demonstrate that their data are reliable and objective and not biased. Usually, a measure called **intercoder or interrater reliability** is used. Two or more trained individuals independently code all or some of the text in the sample. This is done to ensure that the coding is accurate and the coder is not either overreporting (e.g., recording statements as a sexual technique when they did not actually include a technical suggestion) or underreporting (e.g., failing to record statements that include a technique). To give a measure of the interrater reliability, the researcher computes a correlation or percentage agreement between the two coders' results. In this study, the percent agreement for assigning specific tips to one of the five categories was 73 percent. This result is sufficiently high to consider the coding to be reliable but not as high as it could be, since if the coders agreed exactly the percent agreement would be 100 percent.

Content analysis is a powerful scientific technique that allows us to know how the media portray sexuality. For example, in this study, researchers found 443 tips in the magazines. Overall, most advice was related to technical/mechanical/physical factors, such as sexual technique and duration of sex. In fact, between 25 and 40 percent of the tips in the magazine were in this category. Another strong focus was on sexual variety, including use of different props, engaging in "kinky" activities, and watching sexually explicit movies. These tips accounted for between 16 and 41 percent of the tips across the different magazines. Interestingly, what these magazines identified as great sex was quite different from the components identified by people who report having experienced "great sex" (Kleinplatz, Ménard, Paquet, et al., 2009). You can find the results of the interviews with these individuals in Chapter 11.

A related topic to content analysis is *critical discourse analysis*, which analyzes written texts for their underlying meaning. One such study examined how HIV/AIDS was portrayed in the 20 highest-circulating Canadian magazines in 1991, 1996, and 2001 (Clarke, 2006). The results showed that these stories were still characterized by heterosexism and homonegativity, although more subtly than in the past (see Chapter 14 for a discussion of heterosexism and homonegativity).

Qualitative Methods

Most of the research methods discussed so far are **quantitative methods**; that is, people's responses are quantified or given numerical values. For example, respondents rate their attitudes about gay marriage on a scale from (1) strongly disapprove to (7) strongly approve; or participants report their number of sexual partners in the past year.

An alternative to quantitative methods is **qualitative research**, in which the results are conveyed not in numbers but in words—what is sometimes called *thick description* (Berg, 2007; Denzin & Lincoln, 2005). Qualitative research actually encompasses a collection of methods that may involve the researcher's participation in a setting, direct observation, or in-depth and open-ended interviews. In qualitative research, the researchers try to make sense of experiences in terms of the meanings that people give to them (Denzin & Lincoln, 1994). It seeks to understand people in their natural environment, not in a lab or an experiment, and it seeks a complete picture of the participants and their context, not focusing just on one or two variables. Thus, qualitative researchers emphasize the participant's point of view and represent this point of view by providing quotations from participants rather than by giving statistics.

An example of qualitative research is a study conducted by Eleanor Maticka-Tyndale and her colleagues of exotic dancers working at strip clubs in Southern Ontario (Lewis & Maticka-Tyndale, 1998; Maticka-Tyndale et al., 1999). Their goal was to determine whether the dancers' activities, both inside and outside the club, put them at risk for STIs, including HIV infection. They interviewed 30 female exotic dancers who had been dancing from 1 to 22 years.

It is difficult to recruit a representative sample of sex workers because of the stigma attached to the work and because sex workers are often distrustful of researchers (Benoit et al., 2005). Therefore, the researchers used a procedure called *nonprobability purposive sampling* to maximize the diversity in the small sample. They wanted to make sure that the conclusions drawn from the research would reflect all the situations in which dancers find themselves. Participants were identified by key informants, by research assistants who had worked as dancers themselves, and by dancers who participated in the study, a technique called **snowball sampling** (Salganik & Heckathorn, 2004). Thus, as with all qualitative research, this was not a random or representative sample, and we cannot draw conclusions about frequencies and prevalence. Nonetheless, it provides an in-depth understanding of the world of exotic dancers. Participants responded to an informal set of open-ended questions that allowed them to freely express themselves. The interviews were analyzed to identify themes that emerged from the sex workers' responses.

The researchers found that women begin dancing primarily for the money, with the view that it will be temporary. There were two different types of dancers. Goal-oriented dancers continue to treat dancing as a temporary job and usually do not use alcohol or drugs or engage in sexual activity as part of the job. College and university students are one group of goal-oriented dancers. Dancing is attractive to them because it pays well and can fit into their class schedule. However, some women shift from viewing dancing as a temporary job to viewing it as a career. These career dancers are usually part of the strip club culture, are often heavy drinkers, and may be involved in drug use. They may have sex with customers as part of the dancing or on dates with the men they meet while dancing at the clubs.

Qualitative research generally differs from quantitative research in several ways. Qualitative

Quantitative methods: Research in which people's responses are quantified or given numerical values.
Qualitative research: Research, usually involving interviews, in which the researchers try to make sense of the meanings that people give to their experiences.
Snowball sampling: A method for acquiring a sample of people where current participants suggest names of future participants to be recruited.

researchers typically do not use random or probability samples, and they typically have small samples, perhaps only 20 people. Compared with quantitative research, qualitative research is more likely to be exploratory and to focus on generating hypotheses rather than testing hypotheses. Qualitative methods and quantitative methods can therefore be used together.

A qualitative research method used by anthropologists and sociologists is the **participant-observer technique**. In this type of research, the scientist tries to become a part of the community to be studied, and she or he makes observations from inside the community. In the study of sexual behaviour, the researcher thus may be able to get direct observations of sexual behaviour combined with interview data.

Examples of this type of research are studies of sexual behaviour in other cultures, such as those done in Mangaia and Inis Beag, which were discussed in Chapter 1. One other example is Charles Moser's study of S/M (sadomasochistic) parties.

Sex researcher Charles Moser observed S/M interactions in semipublic settings in the United States, attending more than 200 S/M parties (Moser, 1998). Parties are typically highly scripted. The person who gives the party may advertise it widely (e.g., on the Internet) or may issue personal invitations to only a very select list. The parties may have a particular theme, such as female dominant/male submissive only or women only. The party might be held at a person's home or in a rented space.

Each party has a particular set of rules, which vary from one party to another, and guests may be required to sign a written agreement to follow the rules. Issues covered in these rules include who may talk to whom (can a submissive be spoken to?), who may play with whom, who may have sex with whom, prohibited S/M or sexual behaviours, what constitutes safer sex, not blocking equipment by sitting on it, and so on. Drunkenness is never acceptable; some parties allow wine or beer, but others ban all alcohol.

Some individuals plan to have a first "date" at a party. Parties clearly have the function of ensuring safety for participants, since others are always present if an interaction goes too far. Potential partners negotiate what kind of interaction they desire—for example, pain versus humiliation.

Perhaps most interesting is the fact that coitus and genitally focused activity designed to produce orgasm are very rare at these parties. The participants describe the S/M experience as highly sexual, but orgasm typically is not the goal.

Moser did not report that he obtained informed consent from the people he observed. However, their behaviour was public, leading to a relaxation of human subjects regulations. In his report, he was careful not to divulge any identifying information about individuals.

Experiments

All the studies discussed so far have had one thing in common: they were all studies of people's sexual behaviour as it occurs naturally, conducted by means of either self-reports or direct observations. Such reports are **correlational studies**; that is, at best the data they obtain can tell us that certain factors are related. They cannot tell us, however, what causes various aspects of sexual behaviour.

For instance, suppose we conduct a survey and find that women who masturbated to orgasm before marriage are more likely to have a high consistency of orgasm in marriage than women who did not. From this it would be tempting to conclude that practice in masturbating causes women to have more orgasms in heterosexual sex. Unfortunately, this is not a legitimate conclusion to draw from the data, since many other factors might also explain the results. For example, it could be that some women have a higher sex drive than others, which causes them to masturbate and also to have orgasms in heterosexual sex. Therefore, the most we can conclude is that masturbation experience is related to (or correlated with) orgasm consistency in marital sex.

An alternative method that does allow researchers to determine the causes of various aspects of behaviour is the **experiment**. According to its technical definition, in an experiment one factor must be manipulated while all other factors are held constant. Thus, any differences among the groups of people who received different treatments on that one factor can be said to be caused by that factor. For obvious reasons, most experimental research is conducted in the laboratory.

As an example of an experiment, let us consider a study that investigated whether being interviewed face-to-face causes children to underreport their sexual experiences (Romer et al., 1997). The participants were approximately 400 low-income children between the ages of 9 and 15. Some were assigned to a face-to-face interview with an experienced adult interviewer of their own gender. Others were assigned to be interviewed by

Participant-observer technique: A research method in which the scientist becomes part of the community to be studied and makes observations from inside the community.
Correlational studies: Studies in which the researcher does not manipulate variables but rather studies naturally occurring relationships (correlations) among variables.
Experiment: A type of research study in which one variable (the independent variable) is manipulated by the experimenter while all other factors are held constant; the researcher can then study the effects of the independent variable on some measured variable (the dependent variable); the researcher is permitted to make causal inferences about the effects of the independent variable on the dependent variable.

Figure 3.11 An innovation in surveys of children is the use of "talking computers" to ask questions, with the child entering answers by using the mouse or the keyboard.

a "talking computer," which had the same questions programmed into it. The questions appeared on the screen and, simultaneously, came through headphones for those who were not good readers (Figure 3.11). Presumably in the talking computer condition, the child feels more of a sense of privacy and anonymity and therefore responds more truthfully.

Among 13-year-old boys interviewed by the talking computer, 76 percent said they had "had sex," compared with only 50 percent of the boys in the face-to-face interview. Forty-eight percent of 13-year-old girls interviewed by computer said they had had sex, compared with 25 percent of those interviewed by a human. The children clearly reported more sexual activity to the computer than to a human interviewer.

In the language of experimental design, the *independent variable* (manipulated variable) was the type of interview (computer or human interviewer). The *dependent variable* (the measured variable) was whether the children reported that they had had sex (there were a number of other dependent variables as well, but a discussion of them would take us too far afield).

The results indicated that children interviewed by humans reported significantly less sexual activity than those interviewed by computer. Because the research design was experimental, we can make causal inferences. We can say confidently that the type of interview had an effect on children's answers. We might also say that a face-to-face interview causes children to under-report their activity. That statement is a bit shakier than the previous one, because it assumes that the answers given to the talking computer were true. It is possible that children overreported or exaggerated in responding to the computer and that their answers to the human interviewer were accurate.

Experimental sex research permits us to make much more powerful statements about the causes of various kinds of sexual phenomena. That is, it allows us to make **causal inferences**—inferring that the independent variable actually influences the dependent variable. As for disadvantages, much of the experimental sex research, including the study described here, still relies on self-reports. Experimental sex research is time-consuming and costly, and it can generally be done only on small samples of participants. Sometimes in their efforts to control all variables except the independent variable, researchers control too much. Finally, experiments cannot address some of the most interesting, but most complex, questions in the field of sexual behaviour, such as what factors cause people to develop a heterosexual, homosexual, or bisexual orientation.

Causal inference: Concluding that one factor actually causes or influences an outcome.

SUMMARY

Researchers measure various aspects of human sexuality by using (1) self-reports, (2) behavioural measures (e.g., direct observation, eye-tracking), (3) implicit measures (e.g., the IAT), and (4) biological measures (e.g., plethysmography, fMRI, pupil dilation). In Web-based research, sex researchers collect data online, which is especially useful in tapping hidden populations.

Three crucial methodological issues in sex research are the following:

1. *Sampling.* Random samples or probability samples are best but are difficult to obtain because some people refuse to participate.

2. *The accuracy of measurement.* Much sex research relies on people's reports of their own sexual behaviour. Research shows that these self-reports are generally accurate, but they can also be distorted in several ways, such as purposeful distortion, faulty memory, and difficulty estimating.

3. *Ethical issues.* Sex researchers, like all researchers, are bound by the rules of informed consent, protection from harm, and justice.

Statistical concepts that are important for understanding reports of sex research include average, mean, median, mode, variability, incidence, frequency, and correlation.

No major national sex surveys have been conducted in Canada. However, there are three large scale U.S. surveys of sexual behaviour: Kinsey's interview study, the NHSLS, and the NSSHB, which was based on probability sampling. Similar surveys have been conducted in the United Kingdom and Australia. The CYSHHAS assessed adolescent sexuality across Canada. Canadian studies of special populations include a survey of First Nations peoples headed by Myers.

Media content analysis involves a set of scientific procedures used to make valid inferences about some aspects of the media, such as sexuality in prime-time television programs or the content of advice columns.

Qualitative methods yield results that are conveyed not in numbers but in words and aim at an in-depth description of people in their natural environment from their own perspective. Participant-observer studies are one kind of qualitative method. The scientist becomes a part of the community to be studied and makes observations from inside the community.

Experiments are a type of research in which one variable (the independent variable) is manipulated so that the researcher can study the effects on the dependent variable.

QUESTIONS FOR THOUGHT, DISCUSSION, AND DEBATE

1. Find a recent sex survey in a magazine. Evaluate the quality of the study by using concepts you have learned in this chapter.

2. Of the research techniques in this chapter—surveys, direct observations, media content analysis, participant-observer studies, experiments—which do you think is best for learning about human sexuality? Why?

3. You want to conduct a survey, using face-to-face interviews, to determine whether there are differences in the sexual behaviour and attitudes of Asian Canadian and white Canadian teenagers ages 15 to 19. In what ways would you tailor the research methods to make them culturally sensitive?

4. Imagine that you have been hired by your college or university to produce a report on the patterns of sexual behaviour of the students there, with the goal of helping the administration plan better in such areas as health services and counselling. You are given a generous budget for data collection. How would you go about collecting the data you would need to produce a truly excellent report?

connect **LEARNSMART** **SMARTBOOK**

For more information on the resources available from McGraw-Hill Ryerson, go to **www.mheducation.ca/he/solutions**.

Are **YOU** Curious?

1. Do women ejaculate?
2. Are there any medical advantages to circumcising baby boys?
3. Do any cancers of the sex organs affect young men?

Read this chapter and find out.

CHAPTER 4

Sexual Anatomy

LEARNING OBJECTIVES

After studying this chapter, you will be able to

LO1 Describe the relationship between genital self-image and genital cosmetic surgery.

LO2 Describe the major structures of the female external and internal genitalia and their functions.

LO3 Describe the forms of female genital cutting and their health consequences.

LO4 Illustrate the structure and function of the breast.

LO5 Describe the major structures of the male external and internal genitalia and their functions.

LO6 Restate the history and evaluate the practice of male circumcision.

LO7 Differentiate between the different types of, detection of, and treatments for the reproductive cancers.

Men and women, all in all, behave just like our basic sexual elements. If you watch single men on a weekend night they really act very much like sperm—all disorganized, bumping into their friends, swimming in the wrong direction.

"I was first."

"Let me through."

"You're on my tail."

"That's my spot."

We're like the three billion stooges.

But the egg is very cool: "Well, who's it going to be? I can divide. I can wait a month. I'm not swimming anywhere."*

* Jerry Seinfeld. (1993). *SeinLanguage*. New York: Bantam Books, p. 17.

Today we have moved away from the elitist view that only a select group of people—physicians—should understand the functioning of the body and toward the view that everyone needs more information about his or her own body. This change is consistent with the sexual health perspective described in Chapter 1. The purpose of this chapter is to provide basic information about the structure and functions of the parts of the body that are involved in sexuality and reproduction. In this way, you will be in a better position to identify the myths and misinformation about breast and genital size and shape that are so prevalent in the media and can lead people to have a poor genital self-image. Some readers may anticipate that this will be a boring exercise. Everyone, after all, knows what a penis is and what a vagina is. But even today, we find some bright college and university students who think a woman's urine passes out through her vagina. And how many of you know what the epididymis and the seminiferous tubules are? Even if you know, keep reading. You may find out a few interesting things that you were not aware of.

LO1

Genital Self-Image

You may have heard of body image (how we feel about our bodies), but have you thought about how people feel about their genitals? **Genital self-image** can be defined as our attitudes and feelings about our genitals. Research has shown that although on average the genital self-image of most people is positive, some people see their own genitals quite negatively (Berman et al., 2003; Morrison et al., 2006). People's feelings about their genitals may be affected by whether they perceive that their genitals fit with general cultural

Genital self-image: Our attitudes and feelings toward our genitals.

norms (too big, too small), their sexual experiences (e.g., child sexual abuse), and medical conditions (such as genital surgery). For example, an Alberta study found that men who viewed pornography on the Internet had more negative feelings about their genitals (Morrison et al., 2006). This may be because they came to see their penises as "too small" after viewing the very large penises of men on the Internet. Having a negative genital self-image may negatively affect men's and women's sexual well-being. Researchers have found that women with a more negative genital self-image are more self-conscious during sexual activity and report lower sexual self-esteem and sexual satisfaction, as well as more sexual problems (Herbenick & Reece, 2010; Schick et al., 2010). Similarly, men who are dissatisfied with the size of their penis are less likely to undress in front of their partner and more likely to hide their penis during sexual activity (Lever et al., 2006).

Perhaps as a result, some people with poor genital body image are choosing to undergo genital cosmetic surgery. For example, vulval surgery is the fastest-growing trend in cosmetic surgery (Laliberté, 2006). Women choose to have this surgery because they believe that it will make their vulva more beautiful and erotic. So-called *vaginal enhancement surgery* includes vaginoplasty (tightening of the vagina), hoodectomy (removing the clitoral hood), labia minora reduction, labia majora remodelling, and pubis tuck (removing excess skin above the pubic area to elevate the pubis). Most popular among the patients of one Toronto plastic surgeon and costing thousands of dollars is the "Toronto Trim," which involves reduction of the labia and clitoral hood (Laliberté, 2006). Note that even though surgeons sometimes talk about creating "designer vaginas," this is a misnomer since the surgery is to the vulva (external genitals) not to the vagina (an internal organ). Similarly, some Canadian men are undergoing penis enlargement surgery because they believe (often incorrectly) that their partners would be more satisfied if they had a larger penis. Such surgery results in cosmetic penis enlargement, not actual penis enlargement.

Why is genital cosmetic surgery so controversial? First, men and women are opting for genital surgery because they feel that they are defective in some way. Yet there is wide variation in genital appearance. Most individuals undergoing surgery feel insecure about their genital appearance even though they have genitals that are perfectly normal. They feel that their genitals do not match the "cultural ideal" (Tiefer, 2008). Second, marketing of genital surgery (and there has been a great deal of marketing) promises better sex and fails to mention the potential risks and complications, such as infection, altered sensation, pain, adhesions, and scarring (American Congress of Obstetricians and Gynecologists [ACOG], 2007). Yet there is no evidence that this kind of surgery results in sexual enhancement or that these procedures are safe (ACOG, 2007; Tiefer, 2008).

Although not specifically related to poor genital self-image, some people seek to enhance the appearance of their genitals and sexual pleasure by getting a genital piercing. People seeking genital piercing should make themselves aware of the possible complications. If they choose to go ahead, they should ensure that the piercing is done by a trained professional under sterile conditions to avoid infections.

Female Sexual Organs

The female sexual organs can be classified into two categories: the *external organs* and the *internal organs*.

External Organs
The external genitals of the female consist of the clitoris, the mons pubis, the inner lips, the outer lips, and the vaginal opening (see Figure 4.1). Collectively, they are known as the **vulva** (*crotch*; other terms, such as *cunt* and *pussy* may refer either to the vulva or to the vagina, and some ethnic groups use *cock* for the vulva—slang, alas, is not as precise as scientific language).[1] Vulva is a wonderful term but, unfortunately, it tends to be underused—the term, that is. The appearance of the vulva varies greatly from one woman to another (see Figure 4.2).

The Clitoris
The **clitoris** is a sensitive organ that is exceptionally important in female sexual response (Figure 4.3).

---

[1] For a discussion of slang terms for female and male genitals, see Braun and Kitzinger (2001).

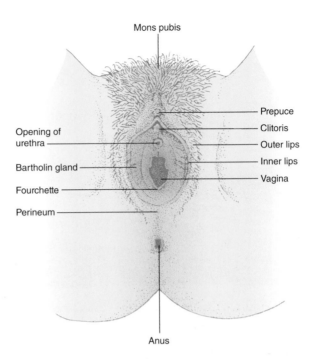

Figure 4.1   The vulva: The external genitals of the female.

It consists of the *tip*, a knob of tissue situated externally in front of the vaginal opening; the *urethral opening*, a shaft consisting of two corpora cavernosa (spongy bodies similar to those in the male's penis) that extends perhaps 2.5 centimetres (1 inch) into the body; and two crura, longer spongy bodies that lie deep in the body and run from the tip of the clitoris to either side of the vagina, under the major lips (Clemente, 1987). Some refer to the entire structure as having a wishbone shape. Close to the crura are the vestibular bulbs, which will be discussed in the section on internal organs.

As discussed in Chapter 5, female sexual organs and male sexual organs develop from similar tissue before birth; thus we can speak of the organs of one gender as being homologous (in the sense of developing from the same source) to the organs of the other gender. The female's clitoris is homologous to the male's penis; that is, both develop from the same embryonic tissue. The clitoris and the penis are similar in several ways. They both have corpora cavernosa, they vary in size from one person to the next, and they are erectile because their internal structures contains corpora cavernosa that fill with blood. The corpora cavernosa and the mechanism of erection will be considered in more detail in the discussion of the male sexual organs. The clitoris has a rich supply of nerve endings, making it very sensitive

Vulva (VULL-vuh): The collective term for the external genitals of the female.
Clitoris (KLIT-or-is): A highly sensitive sexual organ in the female; the glans is found in front of the vaginal entrance and the rest of the clitoris extends deeper into the body.

Figure 4.2   The shape of the vulva varies widely from one woman to the next.

to stroking. Most women find it to be more sensitive to erotic stimulation than any other part of the body.

The clitoris is unique in that it is the only part of the sexual anatomy with no known reproductive function. All the other sexual organs serve sexual and reproductive functions. For example, not only is the vagina used for sexual intercourse, but it also receives the sperm and serves as the passageway through which the baby travels during childbirth. The penis not only produces sexual arousal and pleasure but also is responsible for ejaculation and impregnation. The clitoris clearly has an important function in producing sexual arousal. Unlike the other sexual organs, however, it appears to have no direct function in reproduction. (See A Sexually Diverse World for a discussion on clitoridectomy and other ritualized genital cutting of young girls.)

The Mons

Other parts of the vulva are the mons pubis, the inner lips, and the outer lips. The **mons pubis** (also called the *mons* or the *mons veneris*, for "mountain of Venus") is the rounded, fatty pad of tissue, covered with pubic hair, at the front of the body. It lies on top of the pubic bones.

The Labia

The **outer lips** (or *labia majora*, for "major lips") are rounded pads of fatty tissue lying along both sides of the vaginal opening; they are covered with pubic hair. The **inner lips** (or *labia minora*, for "minor lips") are two hairless folds of skin lying between the outer lips and running right along the edge of the vaginal opening.

Sometimes they are folded over, concealing the vaginal opening until they are spread apart. The inner lips extend forward and come together in front, forming the clitoral hood. The inner and outer lips are well supplied with nerve endings and thus are also important in sexual stimulation and arousal.

Speaking of pubic hair, people are giving it a lot of attention these days. Some women trim theirs and others remove some or all of it, using methods ranging from shaving to waxing. In one study, 60 percent of Australian undergraduate women reported that they removed some of their pubic hair, and 48 percent said they removed most or all of it (Tiggemann & Hodgson, 2008). The women gave a number of reasons for removing pubic hair, including feeling cleaner, feeling attractive, feeling sexy, and making the sexual experience better. Some experts attribute increases in pubic hair removal to increased access to pornography on the Internet (Ramsey et al., 2009). Female porn stars invariably have some form of pubic hair removal, and they therefore show women what they should look like, in addition to teaching men what to expect from women. Many women remove their pubic hair because they believe that this is expected of them by their male partners. Men, too, both gay and straight, are increasingly likely to remove pubic hair (Martins et al., 2008).

A pair of small glands, the **Bartholin glands**, lie just inside the inner lips (refer back to Figure 4.1). Their function is unknown, and they are of interest only because they sometimes become infected.[2]

Mons pubis (PYOO-bis): The fatty pad of tissue under the pubic hair.
Outer lips: Rounded pads of fatty tissue lying on either side of the vaginal entrance.
Inner lips: Thin folds of skin lying on either side of the vaginal entrance.
Bartholin glands: Two tiny glands located on either side of the vaginal entrance.

[2] And there is a limerick about them: There was a young man from Calcutta / Who was heard in his beard to mutter, / "If her Bartholin glands / Don't respond to my hands, / I'm afraid I shall have to use butter." Actually, there is a biological fallacy in the limerick. Can you spot it? If not, see Chapter 9.

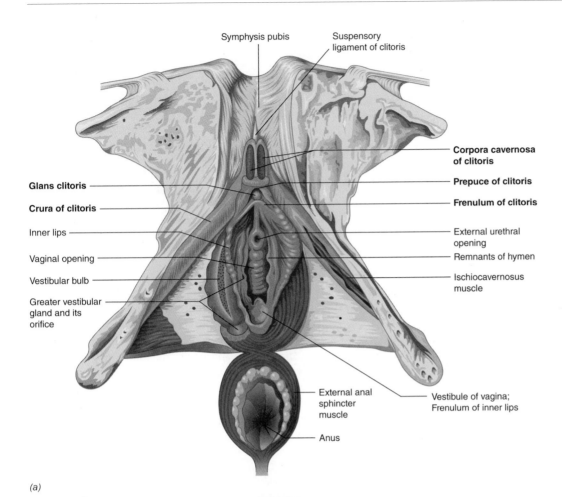

Symphysis pubis

Suspensory
ligament of clitoris

**Corpora cavernosa
of clitoris**

Prepuce of clitoris

Glans clitoris

Frenulum of clitoris

Crura of clitoris

External urethral
opening

Inner lips

Remnants of hymen

Vaginal opening

Ischiocavernosus
muscle

Vestibular bulb

Greater vestibular
gland and its
orifice

External anal
sphincter
muscle

Vestibule of vagina;
Frenulum of inner lips

Anus

(a)

(b)

Figure 4.3 *(a)* The structure of the clitoris and *(b)* an MRI scan of the same region.

A few more landmarks should be noted (see Figure 4.1). The place where the inner lips come together behind the vaginal opening is called the *fourchette*. The area of skin between the vaginal opening and the anus is called the **perineum**. The vaginal opening itself is sometimes called the **introitus**. Notice also that the urinary opening lies about midway between the clitoris and the vaginal opening. Thus urine does not pass out through the clitoris (as might be expected from analogy with the male) or through the vagina, but instead through a separate pathway, the *urethra*, with a separate opening.

The Vulvar Vestibule

The area enclosed by the inner lips is called the **vestibule** ("entranceway"). It contains the openings to the vagina and the urethra. This area is highly sensitive to pleasurable stimulation because it is well supplied with nerve endings. However, some women develop vulvar vestibulitis, in which the vestibule gets extremely sensitive and red such that any touch of the area around the vaginal opening elicits moderate to severe pain. For women with vulvar vestibulitis, pain can result from genital touching during sexual activity and vaginal penetration, but also from biking, exercise, tight clothing, and tampon insertion. Sexual pain disorders are discussed in Chapter 18.

Perineum (pair-ih-NEE-um): The skin between the vaginal entrance and the anus.
Introitus: The vaginal entrance.
Vestibule: Area of the vulva enclosed by the inner lips.

Self-Knowledge

One important difference between the male sex organs and the female sex organs—and a difference that has some important psychological consequences—is that the female's external genitals are much less visible than the male's. A male can view his external genitals directly either by looking down at them or by looking into a mirror while naked. Either of these two strategies for the female, however, will result at best in a view of the mons. The clitoris, the inner and outer lips, and the vaginal opening remain hidden. Indeed, many women have never taken a direct look at their own vulva. This obstacle can be overcome by the simple method of using a mirror. The genitals can be viewed either by putting a mirror on the floor and sitting in front of it or by standing up and putting one foot on the edge of a chair, bed, or something similar and holding the mirror up near the genitals (see Figure 4.4). We recommend that all women use a mirror to identify on their own bodies all the parts shown in Figure 4.1.

The Hymen

The **hymen** (*cherry, maidenhead*) is a thin membrane, which, if present, partially covers the vaginal opening. The hymen may be one of a number of different types (see Figure 4.5), although it generally has some openings in it; otherwise the menstrual flow would not be able to pass.[3] For many women the hymen is broken or stretched at the time of first intercourse as the penis moves into the vagina. This may cause bleeding and possibly some pain. Typically, though, it is an untraumatic occurrence and goes unnoticed in the excitement of the moment. For a woman who is very concerned about her hymen and what will happen to it at first coitus, there are two

Hymen (HYE-men): A thin membrane that may partially cover the vaginal entrance.

Figure 4.4   Body education: The mirror exercise lets women see their own genitals.

possible approaches. A physician can cut the hymen neatly so that it will not tear at the time of first intercourse, or the woman herself can stretch it by repeatedly inserting a finger into the vagina and pressing on it.

The hymen, and its destruction at first intercourse, has captured the interest of people in many cultures. In Europe during the Middle Ages, the lord might claim the right to "deflower" a peasant bride on her wedding night before passing her on to her husband (the practice is called *droit du seigneur* in French for "right of the lord," and *jus primae noctis* in Latin for "law of the first night"). The hymen has been taken as evidence of virginity. Thus bleeding on the wedding night was proof that the bride had been delivered intact to the groom; the parading of the bloody bed sheets on the wedding

---

[3] The rare condition in which the hymen is a tough tissue with no opening is called imperforate hymen and can be corrected with fairly simple surgery.

Annular hymen   Septate hymen   Cribriform hymen   Imperforate hymen

Figure 4.5   There are several types of hymens.

A Sexually Diverse World

What Is Female Genital Cutting?

A worldwide sexual health controversy rages over female genital cutting (FGC, also known as female genital mutilation, or FGM). FGC is practised in many African nations as well as in several countries in the Middle East and among Muslim populations in Indonesia and Malaysia. According to the World Health Organization (WHO), 140 million girls and women worldwide have been subjected to these procedures, 92 million of them in Africa (WHO, 2012). Typically FGC is performed on girls between infancy and age 15. Often it is performed by a native woman without anaesthetic and under unsanitary conditions.

FGC is practised in several forms, depending on the customs of the particular culture. The simplest is clitoridectomy, the partial or total removal of the clitoris, and sometimes just the prepuce. The WHO classifies this as Type 1. Excision (Type 2) involves the partial or total removal of the clitoris and the inner lips. The most extreme form is infibulation (Type 3), in which the clitoris and all of the inner lips are removed, part of the outer lips are removed, and the raw edges of the outer lips are stitched together to cover the urethral opening and the vaginal entrance, with only a small opening left for the passage of urine and menstrual fluid. Type 4 refers to all other female genital procedures for nonmedical purposes, including nicking or piercing the prepuce, which is favoured by some as preserving the tradition but injuring the body the least. The term *female circumcision* is also used, although its definition is less clear; generally it means the Type 1 procedure.

All these procedures pose health risks and infibulation creates especially severe problems. Hemorrhaging may occur, leading to shock and even to bleeding to death. Because of unsanitary conditions present during the procedure, tetanus and other infections are risks. The same instrument may be used on multiple girls, so HIV and hepatitis B can be transmitted. A common problem is that the pain of the wound is so severe and the stitching so tight that the girl avoids urinating or cannot urinate properly, leading to urinary tract infections. A tightly infibulated woman can only urinate drop by drop, and her menstrual period may take 10 days and be extremely painful. Women who have undergone FGC

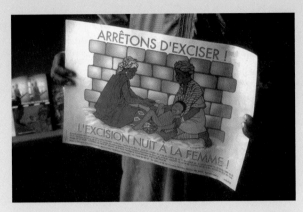

Figure 4.6 Twenty-five African nations practise some form of ritualized genital cutting of young girls as an initiation into womanhood. Clitoridectomy is also practised in Muslim countries outside Africa and was practised in the United States during the Victorian era. Today there is a grassroots movement in Africa to end the practice. The sign says, "let's stop excision!"

are at higher risk of infections such as herpes and bacterial vaginosis.

The sexual and reproductive health consequences are no less severe. Infibulation is an effective method for ensuring virginity until marriage, but on the wedding night the man must force an opening through stitching and scar tissue. It is painful and may take days; a midwife may be called to cut open the tissue. Orgasm would be only a remote possibility for a woman whose clitoris has been removed. Infibulated women have a substantial risk of complications during childbirth and of newborn deaths (WHO, 2012).

FGC has declined in some nations, such as Egypt, with a prevalence of 50 percent in schoolgirls, but a higher rate in rural areas (Tag-Eldin et al., 2008). Villages across Senegal have pledged to end the custom (Dugger, 2011). Nonetheless, it persists in many places. If the procedures are so harmful, why do people continue them? Why do girls submit to them, and even ask for them, and why do their parents permit or even encourage it? The answer lies in the complex and powerful interplay of culture and gender. Infibulation indicates not only virginity but also a woman's loyalty to her culture and its traditions, a particularly sensitive issue for people long dominated by European colonizers. A woman who is not infibulated is not marriageable in these cultures, in which marriage is the only acceptable way of life for an adult woman. When those are the rules of the game, it is less surprising that girls submit or even want to be circumcised and that their parents require them to do it. Some communities may also hold certain beliefs that make these procedures seem necessary. Some Muslims mistakenly believe that it is required by their faith, although it is not mentioned in the Quran. Research also shows that the more empowered women are, the less they favour FGC (Afifi, 2009).

FGC raises a number of dilemmas for North Americans. As a multicultural country, we generally encourage the approach of cultural relativism, an openness to and appreciation of the customs of other cultures. If we apply standards of cultural relativism, we should say, "Great, if that's what those people want." But should cultural relativism have limits? Can one oppose certain practices that pose well-documented, serious health risks, even though they are popular in the culture? Medical personnel in North America face difficult dilemmas. Immigrant women whose daughters are born in North America may request that a physician perform an excision, knowing that the procedure will be far safer if done by a physician in a hospital. However, the World Health Organization and the organizations that regulate the practice of medicine in Canada have condemned the practice of FGC. Both the parents who arrange FGC and the person who performs it may be charged with sexual assault under Canadian law. Recent immigrants to Canada from countries that practise FGC may feel torn between loyalty to their native culture and the realities of Canadian law in deciding about FGC for their daughters. In addition, many immigrant women from these areas who were subjected to FGC before arriving in Canada may have physicians who are not knowledgeable about the practice. Although physicians may cut open an infibulated woman to permit childbirth, they are not allowed to reconstruct the infibulation following childbirth, regardless of the wishes of the woman.

On a more hopeful note, a grassroots movement of women that is dedicated to eliminating these practices has sprung up in a number of African nations, including Kenya, Gambia, Senegal, Sudan, Somalia, and Nigeria (see Figure 4.6). And some surgeons in Western nations are developing reconstructive surgeries to restore anatomy and function to women who experienced FGC; scar tissue is removed and the clitoris is uncovered. These procedures seem to be effective in reducing pain and restoring pleasure (Foldès et al., 2012).

Several points help to put matters into perspective. First, only about 15 percent of cultures that practise FGC do the severe form, infibulation. The remaining cultures practise the milder forms ranging from a slit in the prepuce to clitoridectomy. Second, far more cultures practise male genital modifications than female genital modifications. An example is Canada where about a third of infant boys are circumcised, but FGC is extremely rare.

Third, as discussed in this chapter, a growing trend in Canada advocates genital cosmetic surgeries, such as removal of the inner or outer lips, because people believe that the vulva is more beautiful and erotic that way (Miklos & Moore, 2008). More broadly, genital plastic surgery has become widely available and is raising controversies in the medical community (Liao & Creighton, 2010). Although this is not as extreme as FGC, the message about female genitals is similar: women need to undergo a surgical procedure to make the appearance of their vulva more acceptable. How should a surgeon respond to requests for genital cosmetic surgery? Would education and psychotherapy achieve a better result? And, why are these genital plastic surgeries legal in Western nations where FGC is prohibited (Johnsdotter & Essén, 2010)?

Sources: Afifi (2009), Almroth et al. (2001), Chalmers & Hashi (2000), Gruenbaum (2000), Laliberté (2006), Leonard (2000), Morrison et al. (2006), Shell-Duncan (2008), Tag-Eldin et al. (2008), Yoder et al. (2004).

night, a custom of the Kurds of the Middle East, is one ritual based on this belief.

Such practices rest on the assumption that a woman without a hymen is not a virgin. However, we now know that this is not true. Some girls are simply born without a hymen, and others may tear it in active sports, such as horseback riding. Unfortunately, this means that in cultures that prize female virginity, some women have been humiliated unjustly for their lack of a hymen. Some women who do not have a hymen (because they engaged in sexual intercourse or for some other

reason) are choosing to have plastic surgery to have their hymen "restored," called *hymenoplasty*. After this procedure the woman will then have minor bleeding with her next intercourse, "proving" that she is a virgin.

Internal Organs

The internal sex organs of the female consist of the vagina, the vestibular bulbs, the Skene's glands, the uterus, a pair of ovaries, and a pair of fallopian tubes (see Figure 4.7).

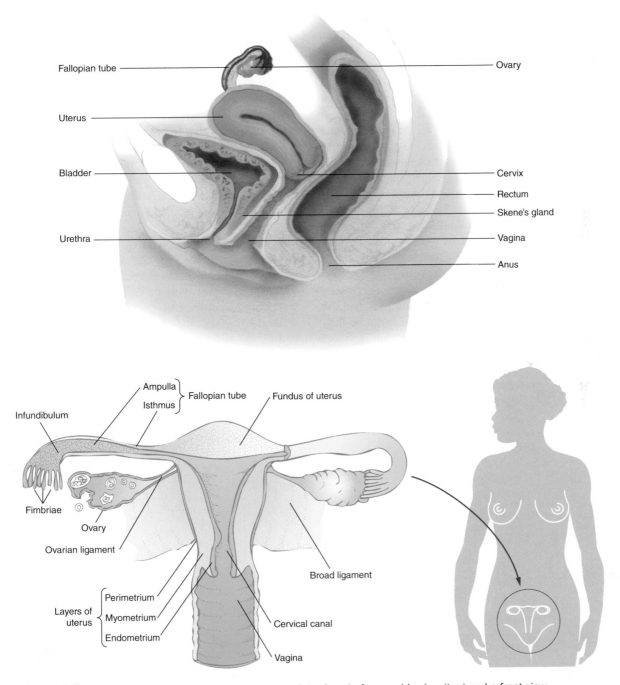

Figure 4.7 Internal sexual and reproductive organs of the female from a side view (top) and a front view.

The Vagina

The **vagina** is the tube-shaped organ into which the penis is inserted during coitus; it also receives the ejaculate. Because it is the passageway through which a baby travels during birth, it is sometimes also called the *birth canal*. In the resting or unaroused state, the vagina is about 8 to 10 centimetres (3 to 4 inches) long and tilts slightly backward from the bottom to the top. At the bottom it ends in the vaginal opening, or *introitus*. At the top it connects with the *cervix* (the lower part of the uterus). The vagina is a very flexible organ that works somewhat like a balloon. In the resting state, its walls lie against each other like the sides of an uninflated balloon; during arousal it expands like an inflated balloon, allowing space to accommodate the penis.

> **Do women ejaculate?**

The walls of the vagina have three layers. The inner layer, the vaginal *mucosa*, is a mucous membrane similar to the inner lining of the mouth. The middle layer is muscular, and the outer layer forms a covering. The walls of the vagina are extremely elastic and are capable of expanding to the extent necessary during intercourse and childbirth, although with age they become thinner and less flexible.

The nerve supply of the vagina is mostly in the lower one-third, near the introitus. That part is sensitive to erotic stimulation. The inner two-thirds of the vagina contains almost no nerve endings and is therefore relatively insensitive except to feelings of deep pressure. Some women have a spot on the front wall of the vagina that is more sensitive than the rest of the vagina, but even it is not nearly so sensitive as the inner lips, outer lips, or clitoris (Schultz et al., 1989). This spot is referred to by some as the G-spot (see Chapter 9).

Vagina (vuh-JINE-uh): The tube-shaped organ in the female into which the penis is inserted during coitus and through which a baby passes during birth.
Pubococcygeus muscle (pyoo-bo-cox-ih-GEE-us): A muscle around the vaginal entrance.
Vestibular bulbs: Erectile tissue running under the inner lips and Skene's gland.
Skene's gland: The female prostate. Also called the paraurethral gland.

The number of slang terms for the vagina (e.g., *beaver, cunt*) and the frequency of their usage testify to its power of fascination across the ages. One concern has been with size: whether some vaginas are too small or too large. As noted earlier, though, the vagina is highly elastic and expandable. Thus, at least in principle, any penis can fit into any vagina. The penis is, after all, not nearly so large as a baby's head, which manages to fit through the vagina. The part of the vagina that is most responsible for a man's sensation, that is "tight," "too tight," or "too loose," is the introitus. One of the things that can stretch the introitus is childbirth; indeed, there is a considerable difference in the appearance of the vulva of a woman who has never had a baby (*nulliparous*) and the vulva of a woman who has (*parous*) (see Figure 4.8).

Surrounding the vagina, the urethra, and the anus is a set of muscles called the *pelvic floor muscles*. One of these muscles, the **pubococcygeus muscle**, is particularly important. It may be stretched during childbirth, or it may simply be weak. However, it can be strengthened through exercises in which the woman contracts the muscle 10 times in a row six times a day, and this is recommended by sex therapists as well as by many popular sex manuals. Details of how to do these exercises are provided in Chapter 18.

The Vestibular Bulbs

The **vestibular bulbs** (or bulbs of the clitoris) are two organs about the size and shape of a pea pod (refer to back Figure 4.3). They lie on either side of the vaginal wall, near the entrance, under the inner lips (O'Connell & DeLancey, 2005). They are erectile tissue and lie close to the crura of the clitoris.

The Skene's Gland, or Female Prostate

The **Skene's gland**, or *female prostate* (also called the *paraurethral gland*), lies between the wall of the urethra

Virginal

In the woman who has had intercourse

In the woman who has delivered a baby vaginally

Figure 4.8 Appearance of the vulva of a woman who is a virgin (see Figure 4.5 for other appearances); a woman who has had intercourse but has not had a baby (nulliparous); and a woman who has (parous) and has delivered it vaginally.

and the wall of the vagina (Zaviačič, Albin, et al., 2000). Its ducts empty into the urethra, but it can be felt on the front wall of the vagina. Although controversial in the past, the evidence indicates that, in some women, it secretes fluid that is biochemically similar to male prostate fluid. Many women find it to be a region of special erotic sensitivity on the wall of the vagina. The size of the female prostate varies considerably from one woman to the next, as does the amount of its secretions. Some women experience no secretion, whereas others have an actual ejaculation when they orgasm. This is the organ dubbed the G-spot, which is responsible for female ejaculation, discussed in Chapter 9.

The Uterus

The **uterus** (womb) is about the size and shape of an upside-down pear. It is usually tilted forward and is held in place by ligaments. The narrow lower third, called the *cervix*, opens into the vagina. The top is the *fundus*, the main part the *body*. The entrance to the uterus through the cervix is very narrow, about the diameter of a drinking straw, and is called the *os* (or cervical canal). The major function of the uterus is to hold and nourish a developing fetus.

The uterus, like the vagina, consists of three layers. The inner layer, or *endometrium*, is richly supplied with glands and blood vessels. Its state varies according to the age of the woman and the phase of the menstrual cycle. It is the endometrium that is sloughed off at menstruation and creates the menstrual discharge. The middle layer, the *myometrium*, is muscular. The muscles are very strong, creating the powerful contractions of labour and orgasm, and also highly elastic, capable of stretching to accommodate a nine-month-old fetus. The outer layer—the *perimetrium*—forms the external cover of the uterus.

The Fallopian Tubes

Extending out from the sides of the upper end of the uterus are the **fallopian tubes**, also called the *oviducts* ("egg ducts") (refer back to Figure 4.7). The fallopian tubes are extremely narrow (0.2 to 0.5 mm) and are lined with hairlike projections called *cilia*. The fallopian tubes are the pathway by which the egg travels toward the uterus and the sperm reach the egg; it is the fallopian tubes that are cut when a woman has her "tubes tied" (called a *tubal ligation*) (see Chapter 7). Fertilization of the egg typically occurs in the infundibulum, the section of the tube closest to the ovary; the fertilized egg then travels the rest of the way through the tube to the uterus. The infundibulum curves around toward the ovary; at its end are numerous fingerlike projections called *fimbriae*, which extend toward the ovary.

The Ovaries

The **ovaries** are two organs about the size and shape of unshelled almonds; they lie on either side of the uterus.

The ovaries have two important functions; they produce *eggs* (*ova*), and they manufacture the sex hormones *estrogen* and *progesterone*.

Each ovary contains numerous follicles. A follicle is a capsule that surrounds an egg (not to be confused with hair follicles, which are quite different). A female is born with an estimated 1 million immature eggs (Federman, 2006). Beginning at puberty, one or several of the follicles mature during each menstrual cycle. When the egg has matured, the follicle bursts open and releases the egg. The ovaries do not actually connect directly to the fallopian tubes. Rather, the egg is released into the body cavity and reaches the tube by moving toward the fimbriae. If the egg does not reach the tube, it may be fertilized outside the tube, resulting in an abdominal pregnancy (see the discussion of ectopic pregnancy in Chapter 6). Cases have been recorded of women who, although they were missing one ovary and the opposite fallopian tube, nonetheless became pregnant. Apparently, in such cases the egg migrates to the tube on the opposite side.

LO4 The Breasts

Although they are secondary sex characteristics and not actually sex organs, the breasts deserve discussion here because of their erotic and reproductive significance. The breast consists of about 15 or 20 clusters of mammary glands, each with a separate opening to the nipple, and fatty and fibrous tissue that surrounds the clusters of glands (see Figure 4.9). The nipple, into which the milk ducts open, is

> **Uterus (YOO-tur-us):** The organ in the female in which the fetus develops.
> **Fallopian (fuh-LOW-pee-un) tubes:** The tubes extending from the uterus to the ovaries; also called the oviducts.
> **Ovaries:** Two organs in the female that produce eggs and sex hormones.

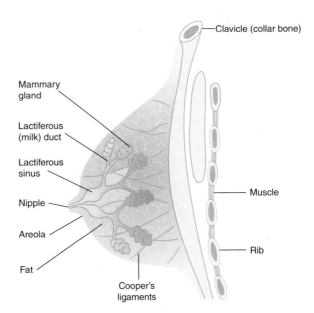

Figure 4.9 The internal structure of the breast.

at the tip of the breast. It is richly supplied with nerve endings and therefore very important in erotic stimulation for many women. The nipple consists of smooth muscle fibres; when they contract, the nipple becomes erect. The darker area surrounding the nipple is called the *areola*. There is wide variation among women in the size and shape of the breasts (see Figure 4.10). One thing is fairly consistent, though: many women are not satisfied with the size of their breasts. Many women think they are either too small, too large, or too droopy (Frederick et al., 2008). It is good to remember that there are the same number of nerve endings in small breasts as in large breasts. It follows that small breasts are

Figure 4.10   Breasts come in many sizes and shapes.

actually more erotically sensitive per square centimetre than are large ones.

Breasts may take on enormous psychological meaning; they can be a symbol of femininity or a means of attracting men. Ours is a very breast-oriented culture. Many Canadian men develop a powerful interest in, and attraction to, women's breasts. The social definition of beauty is a compelling force; many women strive to meet the ideal and a few overadapt (Sansone & Sansone, 2007). As a result, breast augmentation surgery has increased steadily, while other women undergo breast reduction surgery, in both cases to meet a socially defined standard of beauty. Breast reduction is also done for medical reasons—for example, to reduce back pain.

The Major Structures and Functions of the Male External and Internal Genitalia

Externally, the most noticeable parts of the male sexual anatomy are the penis and the scrotum, or scrotal sac, which contains the testes (see Figure 4.11).

External Organs

The Penis

The **penis** (*phallus, prick, cock, johnson,* and many other slang terms too numerous to list) serves important functions in sexual pleasure, reproduction, and elimination of body wastes by urination. It is a tubular organ with an end or tip called the glans. The opening at the end of the glans is the *meatus,* or *urethral opening,* through which urine and semen pass. The main part of the penis is called the *shaft.* The raised ridge at the edge of the glans is called the *corona* ("crown"), or *coronal ridge.* While the entire penis is sensitive to sexual stimulation, the corona and the rest of the glans are the most sexually excitable regions of the male anatomy.

Internally, the penis contains three long cylinders of spongy tissue running parallel to the *urethra,* which is the pathway through which semen and urine pass. The two spongy bodies lying on top are called the **corpora cavernosa**, and the single one lying on the bottom of the penis is called the **corpus spongiosum** (the urethra runs through the middle of it). During erection, the corpus spongiosum can be seen as a raised column on the lower side of the penis. As the names suggest, these bodies are tissues filled with many spaces and cavities, much like a sponge. They are richly supplied with blood vessels and nerves. In the flaccid (unaroused, not erect) state, they contain little blood. *Erection,* or *tumescence,* occurs when

Vas deferens

Pubic bone

Prostate gland

Corpus spongiosum

Corpus cavernosum

Urethra

Corona

Glans

Meatus (urethral opening)

Scrotum

Bladder

Seminal vesicle

Rectum

Cowper's glands

Vas deferens

Epididymis

Testis

Figure 4.11 The male sexual and reproductive organs from a side view.

they become filled with blood (engorged) and expand, making the penis stiff.[4]

Erection is purely a vascular phenomenon; that is, it results entirely from blood flow. It is commonly believed that the penis of the human male contains a bone. This is not true, although in some other species—for example, dogs—the penis does contain a bone, which aids in intromission (insertion of the penis into the vagina). In human males, however, there is none.

The skin of the penis usually is hairless and is arranged in loose folds, permitting expansion during erection. The **foreskin**, or *prepuce*, is an additional layer of skin that forms a sheathlike covering over the glans; it may be present or absent in the adult male, depending on whether he has been circumcised (see Figure 4.12). Under the foreskin are small glands (Tyson's glands) that produce a substance called *smegma*, which is cheesy in texture. The foreskin is easily retractable,[5] and its retraction is extremely important for proper hygiene. If it is not pulled back and the glans washed thoroughly, the smegma may accumulate, producing an unpleasant smell.

 Circumcision

Circumcision refers to the surgical cutting away or removal of the foreskin. Circumcision is practised in many parts of the world. According to a report by the World Health Organization (2007), globally 30 percent of males over the age of 15 are circumcised. However, the rates vary considerably from country to country. For example almost all men are circumcised in the countries in the Middle East, Central Asia, and Muslim Asian countries, as well as in some African countries. In contrast, circumcision rates are very low (less than 20 percent) in Central and South America, Europe, and many parts of Asia. In Canada, when parents choose to circumcise their sons, it is usually done within a few days after birth.

Circumcision may be done for cultural and religious reasons. Circumcision has been a part of Jewish religious practice for thousands of years. It symbolizes the covenant between God and the Jewish people and is done on the eighth day after birth, according to scriptural teaching (Genesis 17:9–27). Circumcision is also common in Muslim cultures. In some cultures circumcision is done at puberty as an initiation ritual, or *rite de passage*. The ability of the young boy to stand the pain may be seen as a proof of manhood.

In the 1980s, an anti-circumcision movement began gaining momentum in North America. Its proponents argue that circumcision does not have any health benefits and does entail some health risk and psychological trauma. According to this view, circumcision is nothing more than cruel mutilation. (For a statement of this anti-circumcision position, see Wallerstein, 1980.)

Are there any medical advantages to circumcising baby boys?

Penis: The male external sexual organ, which functions both in sexual activity and in urination.
Corpora cavernosa: Spongy bodies running the length of the top of the penis.
Corpus spongiosum: A spongy body running the length of the underside of the penis.
Foreskin: A layer of skin covering the glans or tip of the penis in an uncircumcised male; also called the prepuce.
Circumcision: Surgical removal of the foreskin of the penis.

[4] Normally, after stopping psychological and physical stimulation or orgasms, the man loses his erection (see Chapter 9). Priapism is a painful and potentially harmful medical condition in which the erect penis does not return to its flaccid state within about four hours despite stopping stimulation.

[5] In a rare condition, the foreskin is so tight that it cannot be pulled back; this condition is called *phimosis* and requires correction by circumcision.

(a) *(b)*

Figure 4.12 *(a)* A circumcised penis and *(b)* an uncircumcised penis, showing the foreskin.

In 1996, the Canadian Paediatric Society reviewed the literature and reached the conclusion that there are no valid medical indications for circumcision of newborn boys. Reflecting current advice from Canadian physicians, the controversy about circumcision, and the fact that circumcision is not usually covered by provincial health insurance plans, the rate of infant circumcision in Canada has been decreasing. Currently, 32 percent of infant boys are circumcised, although the rate varies considerably across provinces and territories (Public Health Agency of Canada [PHAC], 2009a).

New evidence has accumulated, however, about the potential medical benefits and advantages to circumcision, as well as the potential risks. As a result, the Canadian Paediatric Society is currently reviewing its recommendation against routine circumcision. The evidence indicates, for example, that uncircumcised male babies are 11 times more likely to get urinary tract infections than are circumcised babies, although the risk of urinary tract infections is still low (Wiswell et al., 1987). There is also growing evidence that uncircumcised men have a higher risk of infection with HIV, the virus that causes AIDS (Quinn et al., 2000; Szabo, 2000). It is thought that the inner surface of the foreskin is particularly susceptible to HIV and other viruses. In a study of different geographic and ethnic groups in Africa, some of which practise circumcision and some of which do not, it was found that HIV infection rates were very low among groups that practise circumcision

Supercision (superincision): A form of male genital cutting in which a slit is made the length of the foreskin on top.

Subincision: A form of male genital cutting in which a slit is made on the lower side of the penis along its entire length.

and high among those that do not (Moses et al., 1990). In a five-nation study including Spain, Colombia, Brazil, Thailand, and the Philippines, circumcised men showed lower rates of HPV infection (Catellsagué et al., 2002). HPV is the virus that causes genital warts and predisposes women to cervical cancer. In this same study, the monogamous female partners of the circumcised men had lower rates of cervical cancer. Circumcision also reduces the risk of prostate cancer (Wright et al., 2012). In Kenya and Uganda, adult men who wanted to be circumcised were randomly assigned to either be circumcised immediately or in two years (Bailey et al., 2007; Roehr, 2007). The circumcised men had half the rate of HIV infection compared with the men waiting to be circumcised. Therefore, the trial was halted early over ethical concerns about withholding circumcision from those who wanted it.

Other arguments have focused on whether the circumcised or the uncircumcised man receives more pleasure from sexual intercourse. Researchers in Quebec found no differences in how sensitive the penis of circumcised and uncircumcised men were to touch (Payne et al., 2007).

Other forms of male genital cutting are done throughout the world. In fact, male genital cutting is done in more cultures than is female genital cutting (Gregersen, 1996). A common form across most of Polynesia is **supercision** (also known as *superincision*), which involves making a slit on the length of the foreskin on the top, with the foreskin otherwise remaining intact (Gregersen, 1996). With **subincision**, which is common in some tribes in central Australia, a slit is made on the lower side of the penis along its entire length and to the depth of the urethra. Urine is then excreted at the base rather than at the tip of the penis.

The penis has been the focus of quite a lot of attention throughout history. Not surprisingly, the male genitals were often seen as symbols of fertility and thus were worshipped for their powers of procreativity. In ancient Greece, phallic worship centred on Priapus, the son of Aphrodite (the goddess of love) and Dionysus (the god of fertility and wine). Priapus is usually represented as a grinning man with a huge penis.

In contemporary Canadian society, phallic concern often focuses on the size of the penis. Internet users are bombarded with email spam that promises products to increase penis size. It is commonly believed that a man with a large penis is a better lover and can satisfy a woman more than can a man with a small penis. Masters and Johnson (1966), however, found that this is not true. While the length of the penis varies considerably from one man to the next–the average penis is generally somewhere between 6 centimetres (2 inches) and 10 centimetres (4 inches) in length when flaccid (not erect) (Shamloul, 2005)–there is a tendency for the small penis to grow more in erection than one that starts out large. As a result, there is little correlation between the length of the penis when flaccid and its length when erect. As the saying has it, "Erection is the great equalizer." The average erect penis is 15 centimetres (6 inches) long. Further, as noted earlier, the vagina has relatively few nerve endings and is relatively insensitive. Hence, penetration to the far reaches of the vagina by a very long penis is not essential and may not even be noticeable. Many other factors are more important than penis size in giving a woman pleasure (see Chapters 9 and 18).

Phallic concern has also included an interest in the variations in the shape of the penis when flaccid and when erect, as reflected in this limerick:

> There was a young man of Kent
> Whose kirp in the middle was bent.
> To save himself trouble
> He put it in double,
> And instead of coming, he went.

The Scrotum

The other major external genital structure in the male is the **scrotum**; this is a loose pouch of skin, lightly covered with hair, which contains the **testes** (*balls* or *nuts* in slang).[6] The testes themselves are considered part of the internal genitals.

---

[6] This brings to mind another limerick: There once was a pirate named Gates / Who thought he could rhumba on skates. / He slipped on his cutlass / And now he is nutless / And practically useless on dates.

Internal Organs

The testes are the *gonads*, or reproductive glands, of the male, which are analogous to the female's ovaries. Like the ovaries, they serve two major functions: to manufacture germ cells (*sperm*) and to manufacture sex hormones, in particular *testosterone*. Both testes are about the same size, although the left one usually hangs lower than the right one.

In the internal structure of the testes, two parts are important: the *seminiferous tubules* and the *interstitial cells* (see Figure 4.13). The **seminiferous tubules** carry out the important function of manufacturing and storing sperm, a process called *spermatogenesis*. They are a long series of threadlike tubes curled and packed densely into the testes. The testes have about 1000 of these tubules, which, if they were stretched out end to end, would be several hundred metres in length.

The **interstitial cells** carry out the second important function of the testes, the production of testosterone. These cells are found in the connective tissue lying between the seminiferous tubules. The cells lie close to the blood vessels in the testes and pour the hormones they manufacture directly into the blood vessels. Thus, the testes are endocrine (hormone-secreting) glands.

One of the clever tricks that the scrotum and testes can perform, as any male will testify, is to move up close to the body or down away from it. These changes are brought about mainly by changes in temperature (although emotional factors may also produce them). If a man plunges into a cold lake, the scrotum will shrivel and move

Scrotum (SKROH-tum): The pouch of skin that contains the testes in the male.

Testes: The pair of glands in the scrotum that manufacture sperm and sex hormones.

Seminiferous (sem-ih-NIFF-ur-us) tubules: Tubes in the testes that manufacture sperm.

Interstitial (int-er-STIH-shul) cells: Cells in the testes that manufacture testosterone.

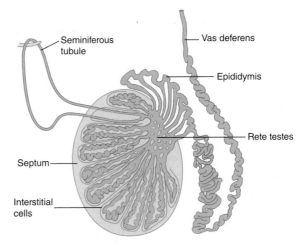

Figure 4.13 Schematic cross-section of the internal structure of a testis.

close to the body.[7] If the man is working in an extremely hot place, the scrotum will hang down and away from the body. This mechanism is important because the testes should remain at a fairly constant temperature, slightly lower than normal body temperature. This constancy of temperature is necessary to protect the sperm, which may be injured by extremes of temperature. Thus, if the air is cold, the testes move closer to the body to maintain warmth, but if the air is too hot, they move away from the body to keep cool. The mechanics of this movement are made possible by the *cremasteric reflex*, named for the cremaster muscle connecting the scrotum to the body wall. Reflex contraction of this muscle pulls the testes up.

Many people believe that taking hot baths, wearing tight athletic supporters, or having a high fever can cause infertility. Indeed, in some countries, men take long, hot baths as a method of contraception. Such a practice has some basis in biological fact, because sperm can be damaged by heat (Paul et al., 2008). However, as a method of contraception, this practice has not been particularly effective. On the other hand, men with problems of infertility can sometimes increase the chance of conception by getting out of their tight jockstraps and jockey shorts.

Following initial cell division in the seminiferous tubules, the male germ cells go through several stages of maturation. At the earliest stage, the cell is called a *spermatogonium*. Then it becomes a *spermatocyte* (first primary and then secondary) and then a *spermatid*. Finally, when fully mature, it is a *spermatozoan*, or **sperm**. *Spermatogenesis*, the manufacture of sperm, occurs continuously in adult men. An average ejaculate contains about 200 million sperm (Bang et al., 2005).

A mature sperm is very tiny—about 60 micrometres, or 60/10,000 millimetre (0.0024 inch), long. A normal human sperm carries 23 chromosomes in the head. These 23 are half the normal number in the other cells of the human body. When the sperm unites with the egg, which also carries 23 chromosomes, the full complement of 46 for the offspring is produced. (See Chapter 6 for a discussion of the sperm's role in conception.)

Sperm: The mature male reproductive cell, capable of fertilizing an egg.

Epididymis (ep-ih-DIH-dih-mus): A highly coiled tube located on the edge of a testis, where sperm mature.

Vas deferens: The tube through which sperm pass on their way from the testes and epididymis, out of the scrotum, and to the urethra.

Seminal vesicles: Saclike structures that lie above the prostate, which produce about 60 percent of the seminal fluid.

Prostate: The gland in the male, located below the bladder, that secretes some of the fluid in semen.

Cowper's glands: Glands that secrete a clear alkaline fluid into the male's urethra.

After the sperm are manufactured in the seminiferous tubules, they proceed into the *rete testes*, a converging network of tubes on the surface of the testis toward the top. The sperm then pass out of the testis and into a single tube, the *epididymis*. The **epididymis** is a long tube (about 6 metres, or 20 feet, in length) coiled into a small crescent-shaped region on the top and side of a testis. The sperm are stored in the epididymis, in which they mature, possibly for as long as six weeks.

On ejaculation, the sperm pass from the epididymis into the **vas deferens** (it is the vas that is cut in a vasectomy—see Chapter 7). The vas passes up and out of the scrotum and then follows a peculiar circular path as it loops over the pubic bone, crosses beside the urinary bladder, and then turns downward toward the prostate. As the tube passes through the prostate, it narrows and at this point is called the *ejaculatory duct*. The ejaculatory duct opens into the *urethra*, which has the dual function of conveying sperm and transporting urine; sperm are ejaculated out through the penis via the urethra.

Sperm have little motility of their own while in the epididymis and vas. That is, they are not capable of movement on their own until they mix with the secretions of the prostate (Breton et al., 1996). Up to this point, they are conveyed by the cilia and by contractions of the epididymis and vas.

The **seminal vesicles** are two saclike structures that lie above the prostate, behind the bladder, and in front of the rectum. They produce about 60 percent of the *seminal fluid*, or *ejaculate*. The remaining 40 percent is produced by the prostate (Ndovi et al., 2007). They empty their fluid into the ejaculatory duct to combine with the sperm.

The **prostate** lies below the bladder and is about the size and shape of a chestnut. It is composed of both muscle and glandular tissue. The prostate secretes a milky alkaline fluid that is part of the ejaculate. The alkalinity of the secretion provides a favourable environment for the sperm and helps prevent their destruction by the acidity of the vagina. The prostate is fairly small at birth, enlarges at puberty, and typically shrinks in old age. It may become enlarged enough so that it interferes with urination, in which case surgery or drug therapy is required. Its size can be determined by rectal examination.

Cowper's glands, or the *bulbourethral glands*, are located just below the prostate and empty into the urethra. During sexual arousal these glands secrete a small amount of a clear, alkaline fluid, which appears as droplets at the tip of the penis before ejaculation occurs. It is thought that the function of this secretion is to neutralize the acidic urethra, allowing safe passage of the sperm. Generally, it is not produced in sufficient quantity to serve as a lubricant in intercourse. The fluid often contains some stray sperm. Thus, it is possible (though not likely) for a woman to become pregnant

---

[7] Fans of the television show *Seinfeld* may recall an episode depicting George's dismay at conclusions a woman drew about his penis size after she saw his penis while he was changing after a cold swim.

from the sperm in this fluid even though the man has not ejaculated.

Cancers of the Sex Organs

Breast Cancer

Cancer of the breast is the most frequently diagnosed cancer (excluding non-melanoma skin cancer) in Canadian women. About one in nine Canadian women is expected to develop breast cancer in her lifetime (Figure 4.14). Every year, about 22,700 women are diagnosed with and 5100 women die of breast cancer in this country (Canadian Cancer Society, 2012). The risk is higher for the woman whose mother, sister, or grandmother has had breast cancer. Although it is much more common in women, men can also develop breast cancer.

Causes

Approximately 5 to 10 percent of the cases of breast cancer in women are due to genetic factors (American

Cancer Society, 2012). Other risk factors include long-term use of menopausal hormone replacement therapy (MHT) and obesity (American Cancer Society, 2012). The evidence indicates that abortion does not increase the risk.

Great breakthroughs have occurred in research into the genetics of breast cancer. First, researchers in Canada and in Britain identified 10 new cancer subtypes based on their genetic characteristics. Second, scientists identified two breast cancer genes, BRCA1 (for BReast CAncer 1) on chromosome 17 and BRCA2 on chromosome 13 (Ezzell, 1994; Miki et al., 1994; Shattuck-Eidens et al., 1995). Mutations of these genes create a high risk of breast cancer. BRCA1 and BRCA2 mutations also increase susceptibility to ovarian cancer. In one study of women having a mutation in BRCA1 or BRCA2, 82 percent eventually developed breast cancer and 54 percent developed ovarian cancer (King et al., 2003). Further, among men carrying mutations of these genes, 16 percent develop prostate cancer. Genetic screening tests are available that detect BRCA mutations in women who have a family history of breast cancer. If a BRCA mutation is found, the woman can be monitored closely or choose to

Figure 4.14 Symbols used to create awareness of breast cancer and prostate cancer. The pink ribbon is linked to breast cancer awareness while Movember is linked to men's health issues.

have preventive surgery; if it is not found, she can feel relieved (see Figure 4.15).

Diagnosis

The Canadian Cancer Society recommends that women examine their own breasts visually and physically. Women need to learn about how their breasts feel normally so that they can detect any changes and report them to their doctor. Although self-exams are no substitute for exams by clinicians and mammograms, many women discover their own cancer through changes in the look and feel of their breasts. Detailed information on one way to do a breast self-exam is provided online at Connect™. However, there isn't a right or wrong way to check your breasts as long as you become familiar with the whole area of breast tissue.

There are three kinds of breast lumps: *cysts* (fluid-filled sacs, also called *fibrocystic* or *cystic mastitis*), *fibroadenomas*, and *malignant tumours*. About 80 percent of breast lumps are cysts or fibroadenomas and are benign—that is, not dangerous. Therefore, if a lump is found in your breast, the chances are fairly good that it is not malignant; of course, you cannot be sure of this until a doctor has performed a biopsy.

The main technique for early detection of breast cancer is the mammography. Basically, *mammography* involves taking an X-ray of the breast. This technique is highly accurate, although some errors are still made. The major advantage, though, is that it is capable of detecting tumours that are so small that they cannot yet be felt; thus, it can detect cancer in very early stages, making recovery more likely. Nonetheless, mammography involves some exposure to radiation, which itself may increase the risk of cancer. The question is, Which is more dangerous—having mammography or not detecting breast cancer until a later stage? Experts agree that the benefits outweigh the risk for women over 50. The Canadian Cancer Society recommends that women over 50 have a screening mammogram every two years. However, scientists disagree about the effectiveness of mammography screening for women who are between 40 and 49. Recently, MRI scans have been developed to detect breast tumours. They are generally recommended only for high-risk women.

Once a lump is discovered, one of several diagnostic procedures may be carried out. One is *needle aspiration*, in which a fine needle is inserted into the breast; if the lump is a cyst, the fluid in the cyst will be drained out. If the lump disappears after this procedure, then it was a cyst; the cyst is gone, and there is no need for further concern. If the lump remains, it must be either a fibroadenoma or a malignant tumour.

Lumpectomy: A surgical treatment for breast cancer in which only the lump and a small bit of surrounding tissue are removed.

Radical mastectomy (mast-ECT-uh-mee): A surgical treatment for breast cancer in which the entire breast, as well as underlying muscles and lymph nodes, is removed.

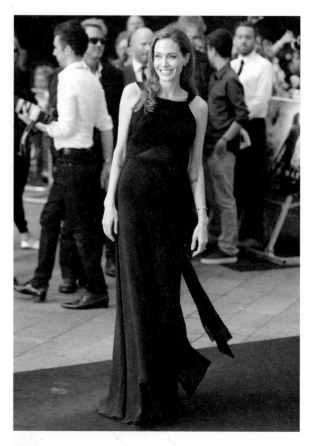

Figure 4.15 Angelina Jolie revealed that she chose to undergo a double mastectomy after tests revealed she has the two breast cancer genes.

Most physicians feel that the only definitive way to differentiate between a fibroadenoma and a malignant tumour is to do a *biopsy*. A small slit is made in the breast, and the lump is removed. A pathologist then examines it to determine whether it is cancerous. If it is simply a fibroadenoma, it has been removed and there is no further need for concern.

Treatment

Several forms of surgery may be performed when a breast lump is found to be malignant. If the lump is small and has not spread, the surgery may involve only a **lumpectomy**, in which the lump and a small bit of surrounding tissues are removed. The breast is thus preserved. In most cases of early breast cancer, when the cancer has not spread beyond the breast (e.g., to the lymph nodes), a lumpectomy followed by radiation therapy is highly effective (Canadian Cancer Society, 2013b). In simple mastectomy, the breast and possibly a few lymph nodes are removed. In a modified radical mastectomy the breast and the underarm lymph nodes are removed; this procedure is used when there is evidence that the cancer has spread to the lymph nodes. If the cancer has spread more, the surgery is a **radical mastectomy**, in which the entire breast, the underlying pectoral muscle, and the underarm lymph nodes are removed.

Following surgery, radiation therapy or chemotherapy or both are used. These may be followed by drug therapy, such as tamoxifen. Researchers in New Brunswick have shown that most women who take tamoxifen experience menopausal symptoms, sometimes very severe, including sexual side effects, such as decreased sexual desire and pain during intercourse related to vaginal dryness (Archibald et al., 2006).

Treatments generally are highly effective and breast cancer deaths have been decreasing. Overall, the survival rate is more than 88 percent five years after treatment (Canadian Cancer Society, 2012). If the cancer is localized, the survival rate is more than 98 percent five years after treatment.

Psychological Aspects

A lot more is at stake with breast cancer and mastectomy than technical details about diagnosis and surgery. The psychological impact of breast cancer and mastectomy and other treatments can be enormous. There seem to be three sources of the trauma: (1) finding out that one has cancer (of any kind), (2) having the surgery and possible amputation of the breast, and (3) experiencing severe menopausal symptoms.

The typical emotional response of breast cancer patients is depression, often associated with anxiety (Compas & Lueken, 2002; Montazeri, 2008). These responses are so common that they can be considered normal. The woman who has a mastectomy must make a number of physical and psychological adaptations, including different positions for sleeping and lovemaking and, for many women, a change to less revealing clothing. Relationship tensions and sexual problems may increase. Reconstruction surgery is available, though (see Figure 4.16), and scientists are exploring the possibility of using stem cells so that breast tissue can be regrown in the body (Findlay et al., 2011).

Figure 4.16 Appearance of a breast reconstructed after mastectomy.

Long-term studies, however, indicate that most women gradually adapt to the stresses they have experienced. One study found that breast cancer survivors did not differ from controls on measures of depression (Cordova et al., 2001). Many women manage to find meaning in the cancer experience, and some show post-traumatic growth, such as finding new meaning in relationships and appreciating life more.

Cancer of the Cervix, Endometrium, and Ovaries

Cancers of the cervix, endometrium, and ovaries are also common cancers, accounting for about 12 percent of all new cancers in women. About 9250 Canadian women are diagnosed with and 3040 die of these cancers every year (Canadian Cancer Society, 2012). Other cancers of the female sexual-reproductive organs include cancer of the vulva, vagina, and fallopian tubes; these are all relatively rare.

Approximately 95 percent of cases of cervical cancer are caused by the human papillomavirus, HPV (see Chapter 8 for a discussion of HPV and the vaccine to prevent it) (Janicek & Averette, 2001). Early initiation of heterosexual intercourse during the teenage years is a known risk factor for cervical cancer, as is intercourse with multiple partners. Both early intercourse and multiple partners, of course, increase the risk of HPV infection. Research shows that tumour-suppressor genes are active in normal cells, preventing them from becoming cancerous. HPV interferes with the activity of those tumour-suppressor genes (Janicek & Averette, 2001).

It is encouraging to note that the death rate from cervical cancer has decreased 78 percent since the mid-1960s, and more than 2 percent since 1994, mainly as a result of the Pap test (invented by G. N. Papanicolaou) and more regular checkups (American Cancer Society, 2009). The Pap test is performed during a pelvic examination (described in Figure 4.17). This highly accurate test can detect cancer long before the person has any symptoms. Therefore, current Canadian recommendations are that all women between ages of 21 and 70 should have routine screening every three years; women with risk factors should be screened more frequently. Unfortunately, women from ethnocultural communities in Canada, such as the Indo-Canadian community and the Chinese Canadian community, are less likely than those of European decent to have a Pap test (Brotto, Chou, et al., 2008; Chang et al., 2010; Woo et al., 2009).

There is considerable variation in the incidence of cervical and endometrial cancers across Canada. For example, the incidence of cervical cancer in some Aboriginal groups is 10 times the provincial average, probably because many Aboriginal women do not have

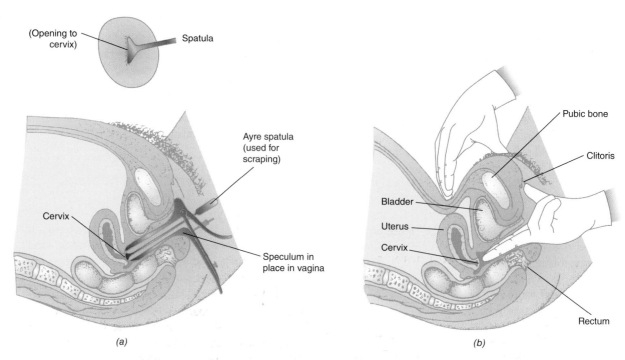

(a)   *(b)*

Figure 4.17   The two primary procedures used during a pelvic exam: *(a)* The speculum, a plastic or metal instrument, is inserted into the vagina to hold the vaginal walls apart to permit examination. The Ayre spatula is used to get a sample of cells from the cervix for the Pap test for cervical cancer. *(b)* The bimanual pelvic exam in which the health care provider slides the index and middle fingers of one hand into the vagina and then, with the other hand, presses down from the outside on the abdominal wall to feel the uterus, tubes, and ovaries.

access to good health care and regular pelvic exams (Health Canada, 1998a). As with most cancers, the likelihood of a woman having a reproductive tract cancer increases with age, although cervical cancer is relatively common among women in their 20s. A vaccine is now available that prevents the most common HPV infections that cause cervical cancer (see Chapter 8). It is approved for use in Canada for females between the ages of 9 and 26, and all girls and women in this group should receive the vaccine, ideally at age 11 or 12. Because of this, it is offered free to girls in Grades 7 and 8 in all Canadian provinces and Yukon. Health Canada also approved the vaccine for boys between the ages of 9 and 26 in 2010, but as yet no provinces are offering free vaccines to boys.

Endometrial and ovarian cancers have multiple symptoms, making diagnosis difficult. Endometrial cancer may be suspected when a woman has vaginal bleeding during times in the menstrual cycle other than her period or after menopause. Ovarian cancer symptoms—abdominal bloating and cramping, vomiting, and diarrhea—can be (and usually are) indicative of less serious conditions like a stomach virus or irritable bowel syndrome. Imaging techniques, such as pelvic sonogram and MRI, and minimally invasive surgical techniques, such as hysteroscopy, can help diagnose these cancers.

Recent research in Quebec had demonstrated that the deadliest subtype of ovarian cancer originates in the fallopian tubes not in the ovaries (Gilbert et al., 2012).

Treatment for cervical cancer varies according to how advanced it is when diagnosed. If it is detected very early, it is quite curable with methods such as cryotherapy, a nonsurgical technique that uses extreme cold to destroy just the abnormal cells. Another common treatment is cone biopsy, in which a segment of the cervix is surgically removed, leaving the cervix largely intact. For women with advanced cervical cancer that has spread beyond a small, localized spot, **hysterectomy** (surgical removal of the uterus) is the usual treatment, although radiation therapy may be an alternative.

For women with endometrial cancer, hysterectomy is the standard treatment. Ovarian cancer is treated by oophorectomy (surgical removal of the ovaries), often accompanied by hysterectomy. These surgeries are typically followed by radiation treatments or chemotherapy.

It is important to note some facts about hysterectomy. Although it carries risks similar to those of any major surgery, hysterectomy does not leave a woman "masculinized," with a beard and deep voice. Beard growth is influenced by testosterone, not estrogen or progesterone. And it is the ovaries that manufacture estrogen and progesterone. They are not removed in a hysterectomy, except in rare cases when the cancer has spread to

Hysterectomy (his-tuh-REK-tuh-mee): Surgical removal of the uterus.

them. Women who have their ovaries removed before age 50 can take hormone replacement therapy (HRT) to avoid the effects of premature menopause but should discontinue treatment at least by the time of expected natural menopause. Another fallacy about hysterectomy is that it prevents a woman from enjoying—or even having—sex. However, about half the women who undergo a hysterectomy for cervical or endometrial cancer report significant sexual problems (Brotto, Heiman, et al., 2008).

Cancer of the Prostate

Cancer of the prostate is the most common form of cancer in Canadian men; one in seven men will develop prostate cancer in his lifetime. Annually, about 26,500 men are diagnosed with and 4000 die from prostate cancer in Canada (Canadian Cancer Society, 2012). Most cases are not lethal, however, and survival rates are high because it generally affects older men (25 percent of men over 90 have prostate cancer), and because the tumours are small and spread (metastasize) very slowly. On the other hand, a percentage of prostate tumours (about 5 percent), particularly in younger men, do spread and are lethal. A prostate cancer gene (HPC1, for hereditary prostate cancer) has been discovered, but it accounts for only about 3 percent of all cases (Pennisi, 1996; Smith et al., 1996). Men of African ancestry are 60 percent more likely to develop prostate cancer than are Caucasian men. They are also likely to be diagnosed at a younger age with more advanced tumours (Canadian Cancer Society, 2013a). Men of Asian ancestry have the lowest rates.

Early symptoms of prostate cancer are frequent urination (especially at night), difficulty in urination, and difficulty emptying the bladder. These are also symptoms of benign prostate enlargement, which itself may require treatment by surgery or drugs but is not cancer. These symptoms result from the pressure of the prostate tumour on the urethra. In the early stages, there may be frequent erections and an increase in sex drive; however, as the disease progresses, there are often problems with sexual functioning.

Preliminary diagnosis of prostate cancer is by a rectal examination, which is simple and causes no more than minimal discomfort. The physician (wearing a lubricated glove) inserts one finger into the rectum and palpates (feels) the prostate. All men over 50 should have a rectal exam at least once a year; men with a family history of the disease should start having exams at 40. If the rectal exam provides evidence of a tumour, further laboratory tests can be conducted as confirmation. The rectal exam has its disadvantages, though. Some men dislike the discomfort it causes, and it is not 100 percent accurate. A blood test for PSA (prostate-specific antigen) is also available and should be done as well.

Treatment often involves surgical removal of some or all of the prostate, and some type of hormone therapy, radiation therapy, or anti-cancer drugs. Because prostate cancer is often a slow-growing cancer, it may be left untreated, particularly if the man is a senior. Surgery often results in erection problems (Perez et al., 2002). Androgen-deprivation therapy is typically used for advanced prostate cancer. It results in a number of physical changes, including loss of erection, lower libido, shrinking of the penis, loss of body hair, hot flashes, and breast growth because of the loss of testosterone (Aucoin & Wassersug, 2006; Elliott et al., 2010). It is important that patients and their partners are provided with education programs that help them maintain their sexual relationship despite these changes (Walker et al., 2013). First Person in this chapter gives one man's experience with androgen-deprivation therapy. Just as research has found that a greater number of sexual partners increases women's risk of cervical cancer, new research indicates that men with a greater number of female partners have an increased risk of prostate cancer (Rosenblatt et al., 2001).

Cancer of the penis is another cancer of the male sexual-reproductive system, but it is rare compared with prostate cancer. It seems to be more common among

Figure 4.18   The technique used in the testicular self-exam.

First Person

Prostate Cancer, Gonadal Hormones, and My Brain

R arely do we have eureka moments in our lives that give us grand insights into how the world works. But most of us have experiences that direct or redirect our interests for years to come. In my case, being treated for prostate cancer propelled me as a scientist, who had spent most of his life studying tadpoles, into studying how androgens and estrogens affect human sex drive, mood, and gender identity.

Assumptions and presumptions are rampant about how hormones affect our thoughts and feelings. Clearly, how a person responds to changes in sex hormone levels is influenced by what they believe beforehand about these compounds. Thus, for example, many male-to-female transsexuals, who desire a more feminine body form, take estrogen as part of the transitioning process. They typically become elated when they develop breasts after starting on estrogen. In addition, many prostate cancer patients take drugs to slow the growth of prostate cancer cells, some of which can have estrogenic effects. These men may become distraught, and rarely become thrilled, at any breast growth they experience. Members of both groups may credit the hormones with directly influencing their mood. But were these mood changes truly a direct effect of the hormones on emotional centres in the brain? Or, were they actually a result of the individual's response to desired versus dreaded side effects?

Being diagnosed with and treated for prostate cancer gave me a chance to explore these questions first hand. Although my sample size of one is hardly definitive science, I have strived to be as open-minded and objective as possible about how these hormones affected my mood and sex drive.

My chance to personally explore how gonadal hormones influence thought processes began when I was diagnosed with prostate cancer in my early 50s. To control my cancer, I started on androgen deprivation therapy with drugs that drove both my testosterone (T) and estradiol (E) into the castrate range—that is, in the range of men who have no functional testicles. (Note: Although estradiol is the main gonadal hormone for females, males have some too, derived from our testosterone.) Technically I became a *eunuch*, the correct term for a castrated individual. It is rare these days for a prostate cancer patient, a transsexual, or for that matter anyone in the western world to self-identify as a eunuch. The label "eunuch" is now derogatory and meant to indicate an exceedingly ineffective individual.

However eunuchs, as a distinct class of citizens, have existed in various societies for thousands of years. Indeed, they have been the most recognized third gender category throughout human history (Wassersug et al., 2012). As part of accepting my situation, I published a personal "coming out as eunuch" essay in the *New York Times* (www.nytimes .com/2007/03/27/health/27case.html) built upon the realization that historically eunuchs were not globally impotent as presumed in contemporary society. To the contrary, for most of the last 3000 years they were diplomats, generals, and senior government officials in all major dynastic regimes of Asia (Aucoin & Wassersug, 2006). I found it therapeutic to know that my hormonal

uncircumcised men than among circumcised men, suggesting that the accumulation of smegma under the foreskin may be related to its cause. Treatment may consist of surgery or radiation therapy.

Cancer of the Testes

Cancer of the testes is not a particularly common form of cancer. Every year in Canada, 940 men are diagnosed with this form of cancer, and about 45 men die from it (Canadian Cancer Society, 2012). However, cancer of the testes tends to be a disease of cancer in young men.

The mortality rate from cancer of the testes in Canada decreased between 1987 and 2004 because, although there have been more cases of testicular cancer, treatments have improved. The survival rate is 95 percent five years after treatment.

The cause of testicular cancer is not known for certain. An undescended testis has a much greater risk of developing cancer. The first sign is usually a painless lump in the testes, or a slight enlargement or change in consistency of the testes. There may be pain in the lower abdomen or groin. Unfortunately, many men do status didn't necessarily park me in the class of the totally incompetent.

As a eunuch, my mood and sex drive dropped. This was not surprising because castrating drugs, like the one I (along with about 600,000 other prostate cancer patients in North America) was taking depress men's libido. In fact, they do that so well that they are offered to individuals with extreme paraphilic disorders who want to be free of their sexual thoughts. And that is not something that patients on those drugs are particularly comfortable talking about (Wassersug, 2010).

I also quickly learned how strongly T influenced how I viewed women. Free of T (and E), I felt that I owed many of the women I had dated earlier in my life an apology for objectifying them so much. Since puberty, I had been particularly attentive to breasts and waist-to-hip ratios of women . . . and, embarrassingly I admit, not much else.

With my brain deprived of both T and E, I also felt like I was in something of a fog. Therefore, after a few years I decided to shift to taking just high dose E as an alternative strategy for androgen deprivation. Both T and E bind to receptors in the brain and, at high concentrations, either hormone can shut down the signal from the brain to the gonads to make these hormones. To my surprise I found that on supplemental E not only did my mood improve and the mental fog lift, but some of my sex drive returned. In fact, I felt so similar with high E as I did with high T that I wasn't sure the androgen deprivation therapy with pure E was controlling my cancer. But blood tests confirmed that my T was indeed at castrate levels and that my cancer's growth was still arrested.

This was my eureka moment. I began to study estrogen's effects in castrated males. A graduate student and I experimented with giving supplemental E to castrated male rats. We were able to show that the E indeed helped to elevate the rats' sexual interest above the castrate level (and we can be confident that the rats had no expectations about how these hormones affected their behaviour). Shortly after we published our rodent results (Wibowo & Wassersug, 2013), a research team at Harvard, working with volunteers on reversible chemical castrating drugs, confirmed that not only T but also E can positively influence men's libido. I happily stayed on the supplemental E for more than a decade and along the way entertained myself with the thought that I was either a very lucky prostate cancer patient or an indifferent male-to-female transsexual, who dressed in (male) drag and declined to shave.

So what have I really learned from my own experience? Both T and E can contribute to libido. My sense is that the male brain (well, my male brain) fueled with either T or E functions quite similarly. The odd-man out (literally and figuratively) is the neutered (i.e., the eunuchoid) brain deprived of both gonadal hormones. Although I await more experimental data with a larger sample size, as I see it emasculation and feminization are not the same. Adding high dose E to the male brain produces a far less drastic effect than removing both the T and E that the male brain normally experiences.

Source: Richard J. Wassersug. (2014). Prostate cancer, gonadal hormones, and my brain. *Journal of Sex & Marital Therapy, 40*(5), 355–357. doi:10.1080/0092623X.2014.921477

not discover the tumour, or if they do, they do not see a physician soon after, and in most cases the cancer has spread to other organs by the time a physician is consulted. When a lump is reported to a physician early, the five-year survival rate is 96 percent (Biggs & Schwartz, 2007). Therefore, the Canadian Cancer Society recommends that men do regular testicular self-examinations every month starting at puberty (see Figure 4.18). The exam should be done during or right after a bath or shower because the scrotal skin is more relaxed and the contents can be felt more easily. Instructions on how to do a testicular exam are provided online at Connect™. However, if the lump is not discovered or the man waits to see a physician and the cancer has progressed to Stage III, the survival rate is between 70 and 75 percent (Biggs & Schwartz, 2007). Unfortunately, men from some ethnocultural communities, such as Chinese Canadians, are less likely to do testicular self-examinations (Woo et al., 2010).

Do any cancers of the sex organs affect young men?

Not every lump in the testes is cancerous. Some lumps are *varicoceles*, that is, varicose veins. Diagnosis is made by a physician's examination of the testes and by ultrasound. Final diagnosis involves surgical removal of the entire testis. This is also the first step in treatment. Fortunately, the other testicle remains so that hormone production and sexual functioning can continue unimpaired. An artificial, gel-filled testicle can be implanted to restore a normal appearance.

SUMMARY

The external sexual organs of the female are the clitoris, the mons, the inner lips, the outer lips, and the vaginal opening. Collectively these are referred to as the vulva. The clitoris is highly sensitive and is very important in female sexual response. Clitoridectomy and infibulation are rituals that involve cutting of the clitoris and inner and outer lips and are practised widely in some African nations and elsewhere. The hymen has taken on great symbolic significance as a sign of virginity, although its absence is not a reliable indicator that a woman is not a virgin. The important internal structures are the vagina; the uterus, which houses the developing fetus; the ovaries, which produce eggs and manufacture sex hormones; and the fallopian tubes, which convey the egg to the uterus. The breasts also function in sexual arousal.

The external sexual organs of the male are the penis and the scrotum. The penis contains the corpora cavernosa and the corpus spongiosum which, when filled with blood, produce an erection. Circumcision, or surgical removal of the foreskin of the penis, is a debated practice in Canada but has some health advantages. The scrotum contains the testes, which are responsible for the manufacture of sperm (in the seminiferous tubules) and sex hormones (in the interstitial cells). Sperm pass out of the testes during ejaculation via the vas deferens, the ejaculatory duct, and the urethra. The seminal vesicles and prostate manufacture most of the fluid that mixes with the sperm to form semen.

Breast cancer is the most common form of cancer in women. Women should do a monthly self-exam, but it is no substitute for exams by a clinician and regular mammograms beginning at age 50. The Pap test is used to detect cervical cancer. Prostate cancer is the most common form of cancer in men, but it generally affects older men. Cancer of the testes, although rare, is the most common cancer in men between the ages of 29 and 35. Men should do a monthly testicular self-exam.

QUESTIONS FOR THOUGHT, DISCUSSION, AND DEBATE

1. Form two groups of students to debate the following: Resolved: Circumcision should not be performed routinely. You can draw on many resources to provide evidence for your debate, including interviews with doctors and nurses, library materials (books and journal articles on the effects of circumcision), and interviews with parents of infants.

2. Clitoridectomy and infibulation are practised widely today, particularly in East Africa. Scientific evidence indicates that these practices can cause serious negative health consequences for women and girls. Some argue that people throughout the world should work to eradicate this practice, perhaps with the help of an institution, such as the World Health Organization. Others argue that these practices are deeply rooted in the cultures of these countries, and that outsiders have no right to judge it, much less try to stop it. What do you think? Why?

3. Do people you know have poor genital self-image? Why do you think so many people are interested in cosmetic genital surgery—women in vaginal enhancement surgery, men in penis enlargement surgery?

connect | **LEARNSMART** | **SMARTBOOK**

For more information on the resources available from McGraw-Hill Ryerson, go to **www.mheducation.ca/he/solutions**.

Are **YOU** Curious?

1. Can chemicals in our environment affect sexual development?
2. What is an *intersex* condition?
3. What determines the age at which a girl first menstruates?

Read this chapter to find out.

CHAPTER

5

Sex Hormones, Sexual Differentiation, and Menstruation

LEARNING OBJECTIVES

After studying this chapter, you will be able to

LO1 Identify the sources and function of each of the sex hormones and how they are regulated.

LO2 Describe the changes that occur across the four phases of the menstrual cycle.

LO3 State the causes of symptoms of the most common menstrual problems.

LO4 Summarize the process of prenatal sexual differentiation.

LO5 Classify the homologous and analogous sex organs in males and females.

LO6 Distinguish the eight variables of gender and their relationship to normal and abnormal gender development.

LO7 Describe the process of puberty in boys and girls.

LO8 Summarize the research surrounding fluctuations in mood, performance, and sexuality across the menstrual cycle and their possible causes.

This way
I have AIS, I guess,
Because there is a god,
And he or she or both,
Peered deep into my heart
To see
That all that I can be
Is best expressed
In female form.
The alternative for me
Would be XY, and I
Would be virilized;
So all that's soft and tender
Would instead surrender

To a strand of DNA.
In the lie of X and Y
I came to challenge the
Immutability
Of "he" and the certainty
Of "she." Blended and infused,
A ruse of gender
That upends
A different fate.
Non-functioning receptors
Have rescued me
Not a failed mess
But a smashing success of
Nature!*

* Sherri Groveman, an intersex individual with androgen insensitivity syndrome (AIS). In *Hermaphrodites with Attitude,* 1995, p. 2. (Contact www.isna.org/library/hwa.) Reprinted by permission of the author.

One of the marvels of human biology is that the complex and different male and female anatomies—males with a penis and scrotum; females with a vagina, uterus, and breasts—arise from a single cell, the fertilized egg, which varies only in whether it carries two X chromosomes (XX) or one X and one Y (XY). Many of the structural differences between males and females arise before birth, during the **prenatal period**, in a complex and delicate process called *prenatal sexual differentiation.*

Yet as the poem on this page suggests, gender is not always a simple matter. Sex and gender and their development are complex and vulnerable to disturbances. Further variety in the human condition results.

In this chapter we examine the process of sexual differentiation both prenatally and during puberty. We also consider the biological and psychological aspects of the menstrual cycle. Let's start, however, with a basic biological system, the endocrine or hormonal system, paying particular attention to the sex hormones. They play a major role in the differentiation process.

Prenatal (pree-NAY-tul) period: The time from conception to birth.
Hormones: Chemical substances secreted by the endocrine glands into the bloodstream.
Testosterone: A hormone secreted by the testes in the male (and also present at lower levels in the female).
Androgens: The group of "male" sex hormones, one of which is testosterone.
Estrogens (ESS-troh-jens): The group of "female" sex hormones.
Progesterone (pro-JES-tur-ohn): A "female" sex hormone secreted by the ovaries.
Pituitary (pih-TOO-ih-tair-ee) gland: A small endocrine gland located on the lower side of the brain below the hypothalamus; the pituitary is important in regulating levels of sex hormones.
Hypothalamus (hy-poh-THAL-ah-mus): A small region of the brain that is important in regulating many body functions, including the functioning of the sex hormones.

Sex Hormones

Hormones are powerful chemical substances manufactured by the *endocrine glands* and secreted directly into the bloodstream. Because they go into the blood, their effects are felt fairly rapidly and at places in the body quite distant from where they were manufactured. The most important sex hormones are **testosterone** (one of a group of hormones called **androgens**) and **estrogens** and **progesterone**. The thyroid, the adrenals, and the pituitary are examples of endocrine glands. We are interested here in the gonads, or sex glands: the testes in the male and the ovaries in the female. The **pituitary gland** and a closely related region of the brain, the **hypothalamus**, are also important to our discussion because the hypothalamus regulates the pituitary, which regulates the other glands, in particular the testes and ovaries. Because of its role, the pituitary has been called the "master gland" of the endocrine system. The pituitary is a small gland, about the size of a pea, which projects down from the lower side of the brain. It is divided into three lobes: the anterior, the intermediary, and the posterior lobe. The anterior lobe is the one that interacts with the gonads. The hypothalamus is a region at the base of the brain just above the pituitary (see Figure 5.1). It plays a part in regulating many vital behaviours, such as eating,

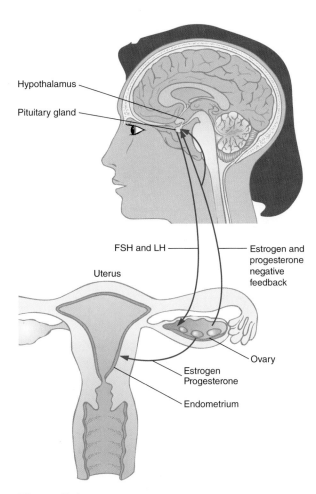

Hypothalamus

Pituitary gland

FSH and LH

Uterus

Estrogen and
progesterone
negative
feedback

Estrogen
Progesterone

Ovary

Endometrium

Figure 5.1 The hypothalamus–pituitary–gonad feed-back loop in women, which regulates production of the sex hormones.

drinking, and sexual behaviour,[1] and is important in regulating the pituitary.

These three structures, then–the hypothalamus, pituitary, and gonads (testes or ovaries)–function together. They influence such important sexual functions as the menstrual cycle, pregnancy, the changes of puberty, and sexual behaviour.

Sex Hormone Systems in Males

The pituitary and the testes both produce hormones. The important hormone produced by the testes is *testosterone*. Testosterone, a "male" or masculinizing sex hormone, has important functions in stimulating and

maintaining the secondary sex characteristics (such as beard growth), maintaining the genitals and their sperm-producing capability, and stimulating the growth of bone and muscle.

The pituitary produces several hormones, two of which are important in this discussion: **follicle-stimulating hormone (FSH)** and **luteinizing hormone (LH)**. These hormones affect the functioning of the testes. FSH controls sperm production, and LH controls testosterone production.

Testosterone levels in males are relatively constant. The hypothalamus, pituitary, and testes operate in a negative feedback loop that maintains these constant levels (see Figure 5.2a). The levels of LH are regulated by a substance called **gonadotropin-releasing hormone (GnRH)**, which is secreted by the hypothalamus (FSH levels are similarly regulated by GnRH). The system comes full circle because the hypothalamus monitors the levels of testosterone present, and in this way testosterone influences the output of GnRH. This feedback loop is sometimes called the **HPG axis**, for hypothalamus–pituitary–gonad axis.

This negative feedback loop operates much like a thermostat-furnace system. If a room is cold, certain changes occur in the thermostat, and it signals the furnace to turn on. The action of the furnace warms the air in the room. Eventually, the air becomes so warm that another change is produced in the thermostat, and it sends a signal to the furnace to turn off. The temperature in the room then gradually falls until it triggers another change in the thermostat, which then turns on the furnace, and the cycle is repeated. This cycle is a *negative* feedback loop because increases in temperature turn *off* the furnace, and *decreases* in temperature turn *on* the furnace.

The hypothalamus, pituitary, and testes work together in a similar negative feedback loop, ensuring that testosterone is maintained at a fairly constant level, just as the temperature of a room is kept fairly constant. The pituitary's production of LH stimulates the testes to produce testosterone. But when testosterone levels get high, the hypothalamus reduces its production of GnRH; the pituitary's production of LH is then reduced, and the production of testosterone by the testes consequently decreases. When testosterone levels fall, the hypothalamus again increases the production of GnRH and the process starts again.

Follicle-stimulating hormone (FSH): A hormone secreted by the pituitary; it stimulates follicle development in females and sperm production in males.

Luteinizing hormone (LH): A hormone secreted by the pituitary; it regulates estrogen secretion and ovum development in the female and testosterone production in the male.

Gonadotropin-releasing hormone (GnRH): A hormone secreted by the hypothalamus that regulates the pituitary's secretion of gonad-stimulating hormones.

HPG axis: Hypothalamus–pituitary–gonad axis, the negative feedback loop that regulates sex hormone production.

---

[1] One psychologist summarized the functions of the hypothalamus as being the four Fs: fighting, feeding, fleeing, and, ahem, sexual behaviour.

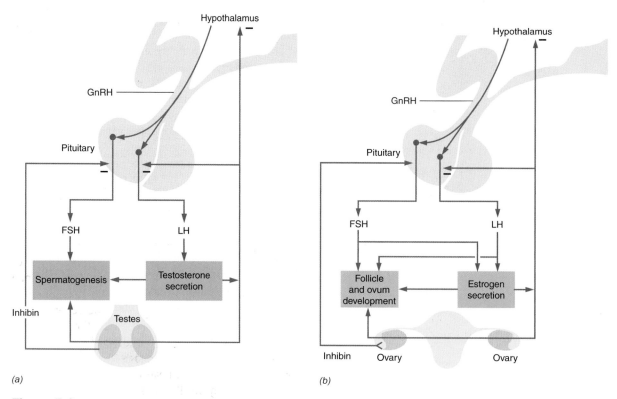

Figure 5.2 Schematic diagram of hormonal control of sex hormones. Note how similar they are in men and women: *(a)* Testosterone secretion and sperm production by the testes. The negative signs indicate that testosterone inhibits LH production, both in the pituitary and in the hypothalamus. *(b)* Estrogen secretion and ovum production by the ovaries (during the follicular phase of the menstrual cycle).

Inhibin is another hormone produced in the testes (by cells called the Sertoli cells). It acts to regulate FSH levels in a negative feedback loop just as testosterone does with LH (Lue et al., 2009). Interest in inhibin has been intense because it shows great promise, at least theoretically, as a male contraceptive. That is, because inhibin suppresses FSH production, sperm production in turn is inhibited.

Cycles in Men

The traditional assumption of both laypeople and scientists has been that monthly biological and psychological cycles are the exclusive property of women and that men experience no monthly cycles. These assumptions are made, at least in part, because men have no obvious signs like menstruation to call attention to the fact that some kind of periodic change is occurring. One study, in fact, found no differences between men and women in day-to-day mood changes—men were no more or less changeable than

women (McFarlane et al., 1988; see also McFarlane & Williams, 1994). However, one study found that men's testosterone levels displayed weekly fluctuations, peaking on weekends (Hirschenhauser et al., 2002). Men who had a female partner and wanted to have a child with her displayed a 28-day cycle of testosterone levels, leading the researchers to hypothesize that the men's hormone cycles might have synchronized with their partner's. Strikingly, men's testosterone levels also vary with sexual activity. In this same study, men who had sex with an unfamiliar partner showed a 100 percent increase in their testosterone levels the following morning!

Sex Hormone Systems in Females

The ovaries produce two important hormones: estrogen[2] and progesterone. Estrogen brings about many of the changes of puberty (stimulating the growth

Inhibin: A substance secreted by the testes and ovaries that regulates FSH levels.

[2] We really should say *estrogens,* because they are a group of hormones. Estradiol is one of the estrogens. To keep things simple, we will just use the term *estrogen.*

of the uterus and vagina, enlarging the pelvis, and stimulating breast growth). Estrogen is also responsible for maintaining the mucous membranes of the vagina and stopping the growth of bone and muscle, which accounts for why women generally are smaller than men.

In women the levels of estrogen and progesterone fluctuate according to the phases of the menstrual cycle and during various other stages, such as pregnancy and menopause. The two pituitary hormones, FSH and LH, regulate the levels of estrogen and progesterone. In this way, the levels of estrogen and progesterone are controlled by a negative feedback loop of the hypothalamus, pituitary, and ovaries, that is similar to the negative feedback loop in the male (look back to Figure 5.2b). For example, as shown in Figure 5.2b, increases in the level of GnRH increase the level of LH, and the increases in LH eventually produce increases in the output of estrogen. Finally, the increases in the level of estrogen inhibit (decrease) the production of GnRH and LH.

Inhibin is produced by the ovaries, just as it is by the testes. It inhibits FSH production and participates in the feedback loop that controls the menstrual cycle.

The pituitary produces two other hormones: *prolactin* and *oxytocin*. Prolactin stimulates production of milk by the mammary glands after a woman has given birth to a child. Oxytocin stimulates ejection of that milk from the nipple. Oxytocin also stimulates contractions of the uterus during childbirth. In addition, oxytocin has gained a popular reputation as the "snuggle chemical" because it seems to promote affectionate bonding, for example, with one's newborn baby (Feldman et al., 2007). Oxytocin is produced in both males and females. In fact, in cotton-top tamarins, a species of monogamous monkeys, males and females have similar oxytocin levels, and oxytocin secretion is stimulated by touching, grooming, and sex (Snowdon et al., 2010).

The female sex hormone system functions much like the male sex hormone system (and their endocrine systems can be affected in similar ways; see Milestones in Sex Research). The ovaries and testes produce many of the same hormones but in different amounts. The functioning of the female sex hormone system and the menstrual cycle will now be described in more detail.

Biology of the Menstrual Cycle

Women's sexual and reproductive lives have a rhythm of changes. One notable sign that marks the changes is menstruation. The events surrounding it are not only biological but also psychological. The biological aspects are discussed here; the psychological aspects are discussed later in this chapter.

Humans are nearly unique among species in having a menstrual cycle. Only a few other species of apes and monkeys also have menstrual cycles. All other species of mammals (e.g., horses and dogs) have *estrous* cycles. What are the differences between estrous cycles and menstrual cycles? First, in animals that have estrous cycles, there is no menstruation; there is either no bleeding or only a slight spotting of blood (as in dogs), which is not real menstruation. Second, the timing of ovulation in relation to bleeding is different in the two cycles. For estrous animals, ovulation occurs while the animal is in "heat," or *estrus*, which is also the time of slight spotting. In the menstrual cycle, however, ovulation occurs about midway between the periods of menstruation. A third difference is that female animals with estrous cycles engage in sexual behaviour only when they are in heat—that is, during the estrus phase of the cycle. Females with menstrual cycles are capable of engaging in and enjoying sexual behaviour throughout the cycle.

L02 The Phases of the Menstrual Cycle

The menstrual cycle has four phases, each characterized by a set of hormonal, ovarian, and uterine changes. Because menstruation is the easiest phase to identify, it is tempting to call it the first phase, but biologically it is actually the last phase. (Note, however, that in numbering the days of the menstrual cycle, the first day of menstruation is counted as day 1 because it is the most identifiable day of the cycle.)

The first phase of the menstrual cycle is called the **follicular phase** (or sometimes the *proliferative phase*). At the beginning of this phase, the pituitary secretes relatively high levels of FSH. As the name of this hormone implies, its function is to stimulate follicles in the ovaries. At the beginning of the follicular phase, it signals one follicle (occasionally more than one) in the ovaries to bring an egg to the final stage of maturity. At the same time, the follicle secretes estrogen.

The second phase of the cycle is **ovulation**, which is the phase during which the follicle ruptures open, releasing the mature egg (see

Follicular (fuh-LIK-you-lur) phase: The first phase of the menstrual cycle, beginning just after menstruation, during which an egg matures in preparation for ovulation.
Ovulation: Release of an egg from the ovaries; the second phase of the menstrual cycle.

Milestones in Sex Research

Is Environmental Pollution Affecting the Endocrine System?

Male Florida panthers have low sperm counts and the same levels of estradiol as females. Frogs are born hermaphroditic, with mixed male and female organs. Along the Oldman River in Alberta, 90 percent of the longnose dace (a small fish) are female. Male turtle doves display reduced courtship and nesting behaviours. A preschool girl begins growing pubic hair. These cases and dozens of others have appeared in the news in the last decade. Are they unrelated bizarre occurrences, or is there a common link?

Scientists believe that underlying all these troubling cases is the phenomenon of **endocrine disrupters**, which are chemicals found in the environment that affect the endocrine system, as well as the biological functioning and behaviour of animals, including humans. Evidence of the effects of endocrine disrupters (also called endocrine disrupting chemicals or EDCs) comes from both studies of animals in the wild and carefully controlled laboratory experiments.

What chemicals are the culprits? Some are pesticides, such as atrazine and DDT, used by farmers and others to kill unwanted insects and weeds. Bisphenol A (BPA) is another endocrine disrupter. It is used in making plastics such as baby bottles. PCBs, which were banned from production in Canada in 1977, were used in making products such as paints, plastics, and printing ink. Some have a half-life of more than 1000 years and so they are still abundant in the environment despite being banned.

How do these chemicals exert their effects on sexual biology and behaviour? All of them affect the endocrine system and, specifically, the sex hormone system. Many have multiple effects. Atrazine, for example, affects both estrogen and testosterone and inhibits their binding to estrogen receptors and androgen receptors. It also depresses the LH surge that causes ovulation. The insecticide DDT affects estrogen, progesterone, and testosterone by mimicking estrogen and binding to estrogen receptors, as well as by altering the metabolism of both progesterone and testosterone. PCBs are both anti-estrogens and anti-androgens. These chemicals are in the food we eat and the water and milk that we drink.

Why should we care about a few hermaphroditic frogs or preschoolers with pubic hair? Scientists see these cases as examples of the proverbial canary in the mine shaft. In other words, they

are small signs that something terribly dangerous is happening. A carefully controlled study showed that pregnant women with high exposure to phthalates (found in plastics and hairspray) are more likely to give birth to baby boys with hypospadias, a condition in which the urethral opening is not at the tip of the penis but somewhere else along it (see Figure 5.3). Studies in both the United States and Denmark show that breast development in girls is occurring one year earlier than it did a few decades ago (Aksglaede et al., 2009). And on a Chippewa reservation in a part of Ontario that is heavily populated with chemical manufacturing plants, only 35 percent of the babies born today are boys. According to an official statement by the Endocrine Society, "The evidence for adverse reproductive outcomes (infertility, cancers, malformations) from endocrine disrupting chemicals is strong" (Diamanti-Kandarakis & Gore, 2009).

Figure 5.3 An example of hypospadia, in which the urethral opening is not at the tip of the penis.

Sources: Aksglaede et al. (2009), Diamanti-Kandarakis & Gore (2009), Hayes et al. (2002), Iwaniuk et al. (2006), Kloas et al. (2009), Ormond et al. (2008), Propper (2005), Sanghavi (2006), Toppari & Juul (2010), Zala & Penn (2004).

Can chemicals in our environment affect sexual development?

Endocrine disrupters: Chemicals found in the environment that affect the endocrine system and the biological functioning and behaviour of animals, including humans.

Figure 5.4). By this time, estrogen has risen to a high level, which inhibits FSH production, and so FSH has fallen back to a low level. The high levels of estrogen also stimulate the hypothalamus to produce GnRH, which causes the pituitary to begin production of LH.[3] A surge of LH triggers ovulation.

The third phase of the cycle is called the **luteal phase** (also called the *secretory phase*). After releasing an egg, the follicle, under stimulation of LH, turns into a glandular mass of cells called the **corpus luteum**[4] (hence the names *luteal phase* and *luteinizing hormone*). The corpus luteum manufactures progesterone, so progesterone levels rise during the luteal phase. But high levels of progesterone also inhibit the pituitary's secretion of LH, and as LH levels decline, the corpus luteum degenerates. With this degeneration comes a sharp decline in estrogen and progesterone levels at the end of the luteal phase. The falling levels of estrogen stimulate the pituitary to begin production of FSH, and the whole cycle begins again.

The fourth and final phase of the cycle is **menstruation**. Physiologically, menstruation is a shedding of the inner lining of the uterus (the endometrium), which then passes out through the cervix and the vagina. During this phase, estrogen and progesterone levels are low and FSH levels are rising. Menstruation is triggered by the sharp decline in estrogen and progesterone levels at the end of the luteal phase.

What has been happening in the uterus while the ovaries and endocrine system were going through the four phases that we just described? During the first, or follicular, phase, the high levels of estrogen stimulate the endometrium of the uterus to grow, thicken, and form glands that will eventually secrete substances to nourish the embryo. In other words, the endometrium proliferates (giving us the alternative name for this first phase, the *proliferative phase*). During the luteal phase, the progesterone secreted by the corpus luteum stimulates the glands of the endometrium to start secreting the nourishing substances (hence the name *secretory phase*). If the egg is fertilized and the timing goes properly, about six days after ovulation the fertilized egg arrives in a uterus that is well prepared to cradle and nourish it.

The corpus luteum continues to produce estrogen and progesterone for about 10 to 12 days. If pregnancy has not occurred, its hormone output declines sharply at the end of this period. The uterine lining thus cannot be maintained, and it is shed, resulting in menstruation. Immediately afterward, a new lining starts forming in the next proliferative phase.

The menstrual fluid itself is a combination of blood (from the endometrium), degenerated cells, and mucus from the cervix and vagina. Normally the discharge for an entire period is only about 60 millilitres (2 ounces or 4 tablespoons). Common practice is to use sanitary pads, which are worn externally, or tampons, which are worn inside the vagina, to absorb the fluid. However, some women use a menstrual cup (brand names The Keeper, The DivaCup, or The Moon Cup) instead of sanitary pads or tampons (see Figure 5.5).

Luteal (LOO-tee-uhl) phase: The third phase of the menstrual cycle, following ovulation.

Corpus luteum: The mass of cells of the follicle remaining after ovulation; it secretes progesterone.

Menstruation: The fourth phase of the menstrual cycle, during which the endometrium of the uterus is sloughed off in the menstrual discharge.

Figure 5.4 Ovulation, showing the egg bursting forth from the wall of the ovary.

---

[3] This statement may seem to contradict the earlier statement that high estrogen levels cause a decline in LH. Both of these effects occur, but at different times in the menstrual cycle (Molitch, 1995). There are two centres in the hypothalamus, one produces a negative feedback loop between estrogen and LH, the other produces a positive feedback loop between the two.

[4] *Corpus luteum* is Latin for "yellow body." The corpus luteum is so named because the mass of cells is yellowish in appearance.

Figure 5.5 The Keeper menstrual cup, a reusable, environmentally friendly alternative to sanitary pad or tampons.

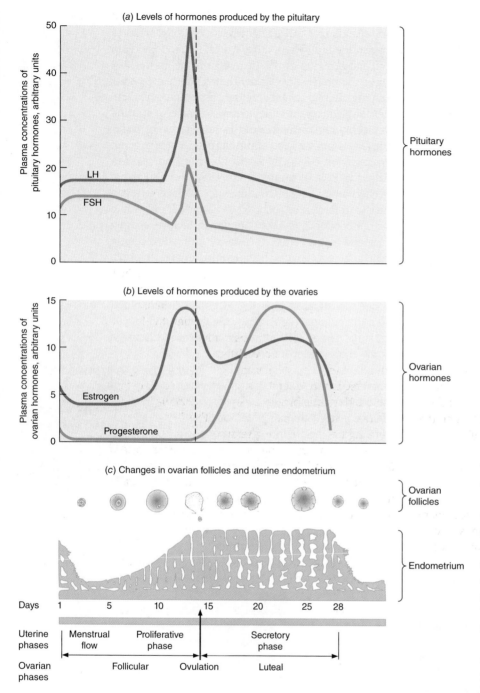

(a) Levels of hormones produced by the pituitary

(b) Levels of hormones produced by the ovaries

(c) Changes in ovarian follicles and uterine endometrium

Figure 5.6   The biological events of the menstrual cycle.

Length and Timing of the Cycle

How long is a normal menstrual cycle? Generally anywhere from 20 to 36 days is considered within the normal range (Figure 5.6). The average is about 28 days, but somehow this number has taken on more significance than it deserves. There is enormous variation from one woman to the next in the average length of the cycle, and for a given woman there can be considerable variation in length from one cycle to the next. Some recent Canadian research suggests that women with greater variability in the length of their cycle have higher levels of androgens (Van Anders & Watson, 2006).

What is the timing of the four phases of the cycle? In a perfectly regular 28-day cycle, menstruation begins on day 1 and continues until about day 4 or 5. The follicular phase extends from about day 5 to about day 13. Ovulation occurs on day 14, and the luteal phase extends from day 15 to the end of the cycle, day 28.

But what if the cycle is not a perfect 28-day one? In cycles that are shorter or longer than 28 days, the principle is that the length of the *luteal* phase is relatively constant. In other words, the time from ovulation to menstruation is always 14 days, give or take only a day or two. Thus, for example, if a woman has a 44-day cycle, she ovulates on about day 30. If she has a 22-day cycle, she ovulates on about day 8.

Some women report that they can actually feel themselves ovulate, a phenomenon called *Mittelschmerz* (*middle pain*). The sensation described is a cramping on one or both sides of the lower abdomen, lasting for about a day.

It is also true that ovulation does not occur in every menstrual cycle. That is, menstruation may take place without ovulation. When this happens the woman is said to have an *anovulatory cycle*. Such cycles occur once or twice a year in women in their 20s and 30s and are fairly common among girls during puberty and among women during menopause.

Other Cyclic Changes

Two other physiological processes that fluctuate with the menstrual cycle deserve mention: the cervical mucus cycle and the basal body temperature cycle.

The cervical mucus cycle involves glands in the cervix that secrete mucus throughout the menstrual cycle. One function of the mucus is to protect the entrance to

This is a small reusable device made of flexible rubber or soft medical-grade silicone that has been approved for sale by Health Canada. It has a pull-tab to facilitate removal and can be washed in soapy water. Because it is reusable, it is more economical and environmentally friendly. Other environmentally friendly options include reusable menstrual pads made of cotton and sea sponge.

the cervix, helping to keep bacteria out. These glands respond to the changing levels of estrogen during the cycle. As estrogen increases at the start of a new cycle, the mucus is alkaline, thick, and viscous. When LH production begins, just before ovulation, the cervical mucus changes markedly. It becomes even more alkaline, thin, and watery. These changes make the environment for sperm passage most hospitable just at ovulation. After ovulation, the mucus returns to its former viscous, less alkaline state. If a sample of mucus is taken just before ovulation and is allowed to dry, the dried mucus takes on a fern-shaped pattern. After ovulation, during the luteal phase, the fernlike patterning will not occur. Thus the *fern test* is one method for detecting ovulation.

A woman's *basal body temperature*, taken with a thermometer before getting up in the morning, also fluctuates with the phases of the menstrual cycle. The temperature is low during the follicular phase and takes a dip on the day of ovulation. Then, on the day after ovulation it rises noticeably, generally by 0.3°C or more, and continues at the higher level for the rest of the cycle. Progesterone raises body temperature, so the higher temperature during the luteal phase is due to the increased production of progesterone during that time (Baker et al., 2002). This change in basal body temperature is important when a couple are using the fertility awareness method of birth control (Chapter 7) and when a woman is trying to determine the time of ovulation so that she may become pregnant (Chapter 6).

L03 Menstrual Problems

The most common menstrual problem is painful menstruation, known as **dysmenorrhea**. Almost every woman experiences at least some menstrual discomfort at various times in her life, but the frequency and severity of the discomfort vary considerably from one woman to the next. Cramping pains in the pelvic region are the most common discomfort; other symptoms may include headaches, backaches, nausea, and a feeling of pressure and bloating in the pelvis.

Dysmenorrhea is caused by **prostaglandins**, hormone-like substances produced by many tissues of the body, including the lining of the uterus (Deligeor-Oglov, 2000). Prostaglandins can cause smooth muscle to contract and can affect the size of blood vessels. Women with severe menstrual pain have unusually high levels of prostaglandins. The high levels cause intense uterine contractions, which in turn choke off some of the uterus's supply of oxygen-carrying blood. Prostaglandins may also cause greater sensitivity in nerve endings. The combination of the uterine contractions, lack of oxygen, and heightened nerve sensitivity produces menstrual cramps.

The best treatment for menstrual cramps is nonsteroidal anti-inflammatory drugs (NSAIDS), such as ibuprofen (Advil) or Naproxen (Aleve) (Hatcher et al., 2007). These drugs are anti-prostaglandins, so they interrupt the basic cause of cramps. Interestingly, Aspirin is also an anti-prostaglandin. Some women find complementary/alternative therapies, such as fish oil, herbs, or acupressure, to be useful; however, research has not yet clearly demonstrated their effectiveness (Stevinson & Ernst, 2001).

A somewhat more provocative remedy suggested by, among others, Masters and Johnson is masturbation. This makes good physiological sense because part of the discomfort of menstruation—the pressure and bloating—results from pelvic edema (a congestion of fluids in the pelvic region). During sexual arousal and orgasm, pelvic congestion increases and after orgasm, the congestion dissipates (see Chapter 9). Thus orgasm, whether produced by masturbation or some other means, should help to relieve the pelvic edema that causes menstrual discomfort. And it's a lot more fun than taking medicine!

A menstrual problem that may be mistaken for dysmenorrhea is **endometriosis**. The endometrium, or lining of the uterus, grows during each menstrual cycle and is sloughed off in menstruation. Endometriosis occurs when the endometrial tissue grows in a place other than the uterus—for example, the ovaries, fallopian tubes, rectum, bladder, vagina, vulva, cervix, or lymph glands. The symptoms vary depending on the location of the growth. Very painful periods that last an unusually long time, pain during sexual activity, and infertility are the most common symptoms. Endometriosis is fairly serious and should be treated by a physician. If left untreated it can lead to sterility. Hormones are generally used in treatment, but if the problem is severe, surgery may be required. Laser surgery is a treatment option.

Another menstrual problem is **amenorrhea**, or the absence of menstruation. It is called *primary amenorrhea* if the girl has not yet menstruated by about age 18. It is called *secondary amenorrhea* if she has had at least one period. Some of the causes of amenorrhea include pregnancy, congenital defects of the reproductive system, hormonal imbalance, cysts or tumours, disease, stress, and emotional factors related to puberty. Amenorrhea can also result from programs of strenuous exercise and from anorexia nervosa.

L04 Prenatal Sexual Differentiation

Sex Chromosomes

At the time of conception the future human being consists of only a single cell, the fertilized egg. What is the difference between the fertilized egg that

---

Dysmenorrhea (dis-men-oh-REE-uh): Painful menstruation.

Prostaglandins: Chemicals secreted by the uterus that cause the uterine muscles to contract; they are a likely cause of painful menstruation.

Endometriosis: A condition in which the endometrium grows abnormally outside the uterus; the symptom is unusually painful periods with excessive bleeding.

Amenorrhea: The absence of menstruation.

will become a female and the fertilized egg that will become a male? The only difference is the sex chromosomes carried in that fertilized egg. If there are two X chromosomes, the result will typically be a female; if there is one X and one Y, the result will typically be a male. While incredibly tiny, the sex chromosomes carry a wealth of information that they transmit to various organs throughout the body, giving them instructions on how to differentiate in the course of development. Because the Y chromosome is smaller (see Figure 5.7), it has fewer genes and carries less information than the X. The Y chromosome has about 80 genes compared with 1090 on the X (Federman, 2006).[5]

Occasionally, individuals receive at conception a sex chromosome combination other than XX or XY. Such atypical sex chromosome complements may lead to a variety of clinical syndromes, such as *Klinefelter's syndrome*. In this syndrome, a genetic male has an extra X chromosome (XXY). As a result, the testes are abnormal, no sperm are produced, and testosterone levels are low (Winter & Couch, 1995).

During development, the single cell divides repeatedly, becoming a two-celled organism, then a four-celled organism, then an eight-celled organism, and so on. By 28 days after conception, the embryo is about 1 centimetre (less than half an inch) long, but the male and female embryos are still identical, save for the sex chromosomes. In other words, the embryo is still in the undifferentiated state. However, by the seventh week after conception, some basic structures have been formed that will eventually become either a male or a female reproductive system. At this point, the embryo has a pair of gonads (each gonad has two parts, an outer cortex and an inner medulla), two sets of ducts (the Müllerian ducts and the Wolffian ducts), and rudimentary external genitals (the genital tubercle, the urethral folds, and the genital swelling) (see Figure 5.8, top).

Sex-determining region, Y chromosome (SRY): A gene on the Y chromosome that causes testes to differentiate prenatally.

Müllerian ducts: Ducts found in both male and female fetuses; in males they degenerate and in females they develop into the fallopian tubes, the uterus, and the upper part of the vagina.

Figure 5.7 Although incredibly tiny, the sex chromosomes carry a wealth of information that they transmit to various organs throughout the body. The Y chromosome (on the right) is smaller, has fewer genes, and carries less information than the X chromosome (on the left).

Gonads

In the seventh week after conception, the sex chromosomes direct the gonads to begin differentiation. In the male, the undifferentiated gonad develops into a testis at about seven weeks. In the female, the process occurs somewhat later, with the ovaries developing at around 10 or 11 weeks.

An important gene that directs the differentiation of the gonads, located on the Y chromosome, is called **sex-determining region, Y chromosome (SRY)** (Skaletsky et al., 2003). If SRY is present, it causes the manufacture of a substance called testis-determining factor (TDF), that makes the gonads differentiate into testes, and male development occurs. If TDF is not present, female development occurs, making female development the default option. The X chromosome carries a number of genes that control normal functioning of the ovaries (Winter & Couch, 1995). Surprisingly, a number of genes on the X chromosome affect cells in the testes that manufacture sperm (Wang et al., 2001).

Prenatal Hormones and the Genitals

Once the ovaries and testes have differentiated, they begin to produce different sex hormones, which then direct the differentiation of the rest of the internal and external genital system (see Figure 5.8).

In the female, the Wolffian ducts degenerate, and the **Müllerian ducts** turn into the fallopian tubes, the uterus, and the upper part of the vagina. The tubercle becomes the clitoris, the folds become the inner lips, and the swelling develops into the outer lips.

The testes secrete Müllerian inhibiting substance (MIS; Vilain, 2000). MIS causes the Müllerian ducts to

---

[5] Although all mammals have X and Y chromosomes as humans do, sex is determined in different exotic ways in different species. For example, in some reptiles, such as alligators and turtles, sex is determined by the temperature at a critical period in development: cooler nests all develop into males; warmer nests hatch as females. Some snails start out male then become female. Earthworms are hermaphrodites (have both male and female sex organs).

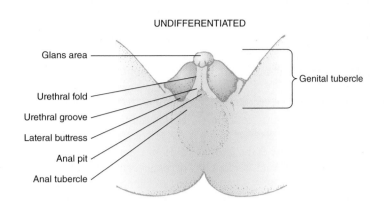

UNDIFFERENTIATED

Glans area

Urethral fold

Urethral groove

Lateral buttress

Anal pit

Anal tubercle

Genital tubercle

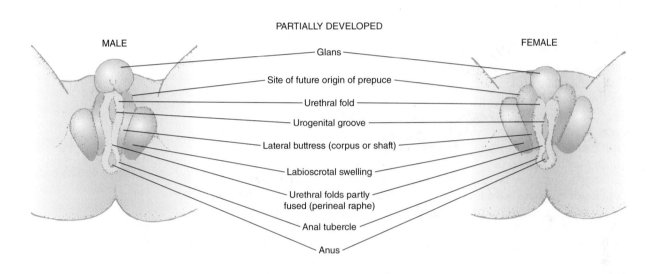

PARTIALLY DEVELOPED

MALE

FEMALE

Glans

Site of future origin of prepuce

Urethral fold

Urogenital groove

Lateral buttress (corpus or shaft)

Labioscrotal swelling

Urethral folds partly fused (perineal raphe)

Anal tubercle

Anus

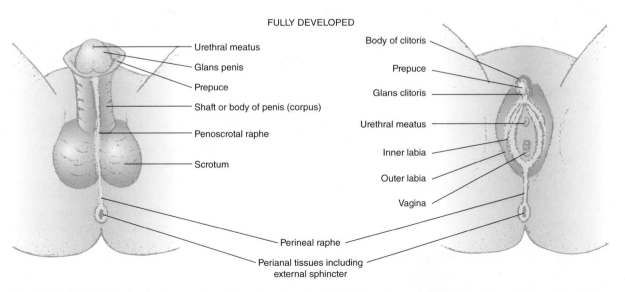

FULLY DEVELOPED

Urethral meatus

Glans penis

Prepuce

Shaft or body of penis (corpus)

Penoscrotal raphe

Scrotum

Body of clitoris

Prepuce

Glans clitoris

Urethral meatus

Inner labia

Outer labia

Vagina

Perineal raphe

Perianal tissues including external sphincter

Figure 5.8 Development of the male and female external genitals from the undifferentiated stage. This occurs during prenatal development. Note homologous organs in the female and male.

degenerate, while the **Wolffian ducts,** supported by testosterone, turn into the epididymis, the vas deferens, and the ejaculatory duct. The tubercle becomes the glans penis, the folds form the shaft of the penis, and the swelling develops into the scrotum.

At least six different genes are involved in prenatal sexual differentiation. A mutation in any one of them can cause an error in development (Vilain, 2000).

By 12 weeks after conception, the gender of the fetus is clear from the appearance of the external genitals (refer again to Figure 5.8).

Descent of the Testes and Ovaries

As these developmental changes are taking place, the ovaries and testes are changing in shape and position. At first, the ovaries and testes lie near the top of the abdominal cavity. By the 10th week, they have grown and have moved down to the level of the upper edge of the pelvis. The ovaries remain there until after birth and later shift to their adult position in the pelvis.

The testes must make a much longer journey, down into the scrotum via a passageway called the *inguinal canal*. Normally, this movement occurs around the seventh month after conception. The inguinal canal closes off after the testes have descended.

Two problems may occur in this process. First, one or both testes may have failed to descend into the scrotum by the time of birth, a condition known as *undescended testes*, or **cryptorchidism**. This condition occurs in about 3 percent of all males. Most frequently, only one testis is undescended and the other is in the normal position. In most of these cases, the testes do descend by the first birthday. If the testes do not descend spontaneously, however, the condition is usually corrected by surgery soon after the first birthday. The optimum time for doing this is before age five. Otherwise, if both testes fail to descend, the man will be sterile because, as discussed in Chapter 4, the high temperature of the testes inside the body inhibits the production of sperm. Undescended testes are also more likely to develop cancer (Canadian Cancer Society, 2013c).

The second possible problem occurs when the inguinal canal does not close off completely. It may then reopen later in life, creating a passageway through which loops of the intestine can enter the scrotum. This condition, called *inguinal hernia*, can be remedied by simple surgery.

Wolffian ducts: Ducts found in both male and female fetuses; in females they degenerate and in males they develop into the epididymis, the vas deferens, and the ejaculatory duct.
Cryptorchidism: Undescended testes; the condition in which the testes do not descend to the scrotum as they should during prenatal development.

Brain Differentiation

During the prenatal period, when sex hormones are having a big impact on genital anatomy, they are also acting on the brain (Arnold, 2003). The results of many experiments with animals indicate that, in certain regions, there are differences between male and female brains. The primary sex-differentiated structure is the hypothalamus, particularly a region of it called the *preoptic area* (Fitch & Bimonte, 2002). The hypothalamus is gender-differentiated in humans as well (Cahill, 2005; Swaab et al., 1995).

One of the most important effects of this early sexual differentiation is determination of the estrogen sensitivity of certain cells in the hypothalamus. Estrogen passes into these cells and binds to specific molecules in the nucleus, called *estrogen receptors* (Choi et al., 2001; McEwen, 2001). If testosterone is present during fetal development, these specialized cells in the hypothalamus become insensitive to estrogen. If estrogen is present, these cells become highly sensitive to levels of estrogen in the bloodstream. This sensitivity is crucial to the hypothalamic–pituitary–gonad feedback loop discussed earlier. Male hypothalamic cells are relatively insensitive to estrogen levels, whereas female hypothalamic cells are highly sensitive to them. Male hypothalamic cells have more androgen receptors (Donahue et al., 2000).

New magnetic resonance imaging (MRI) studies are giving us a view into the brains of alive, awake humans, in contrast to earlier techniques that dissected the brains of dead people and animals (see Chapter 3). The trade-off, at least for now, is that the MRI measures are relatively crude, simple assessments of the volume or size of certain regions. One of these studies found a larger volume of the hypothalamus and amygdala—both brain regions with high densities of estrogen and androgen receptors—in men compared with women (Goldstein et al., 2001). Regions of the brain that have few estrogen and androgen receptors did not show these gender differences in size.

The brains of men and women are actually quite similar in most regions, but a few brain structures show gender differentiation (Eliot, 2009; Joel, 2011). These structures include the hypothalamus, which we have already discussed, and the amygdala, which is important in emotion (Cahill, 2005; Ngun et al., 2011). Modern neuroscientists, however, reject the notion that these represent "hard-wired" differences present from birth (Eliot, 2009). Instead, neuroscientists emphasize the *plasticity* of the brain, which is constantly changing in response to experiences that the person has. For example, an eight-year-old boy has a father who practises tossing footballs with him every day, whereas the father of the eight-year-old girl next door doesn't toss footballs with her. Within weeks, the neural circuits in the boy's brain involved in catching and throwing will have strengthened, whereas the same circuits in the girl's brain will not have. Their brains will now be different in that region, but as a result of their different experiences, not hard-wiring present from birth.

Table 5.1   Homologous and Analogous Organs of the Male and Female Reproductive Systems

	Homologous Organs		Analogous Organs	
Embryonic Source	**In the Adult Male**	**In the Adult Female**	**In the Adult Male**	**In the Adult Female**
Gonad (medulla plus cortex)	Testes (from medulla)	Ovaries (from cortex)	Testes (from medulla)	Ovaries (from cortex)
Genital tubercle	Glans penis	Clitoris	Glans penis	Clitoris
Genital swelling	Scrotum			
Müllerian duct		Outer lips Fallopian tubes, uterus, part of vagina		
Wolffian duct	Epididymis, vas deferens, seminal vesicles			
Urethral primordia	Prostate, Cowper's glands	Skene's glands, Bartholin glands	Prostate, Cowper's glands	Skene's glands, Bartholin glands

 ## Homologous Organs

Our discussion of sexual differentiation highlights the fact that although adult men and women appear to have very different reproductive anatomies, their reproductive organs have similar origins. When an organ in the male and an organ in the female both develop from the same embryonic tissue, the organs are said to be **homologous**. When the two organs have similar functions, they are said to be **analogous**. Table 5.1 summarizes the major homologies and analogies of the male and female reproductive systems. For example, ovaries and testes are homologous (they develop from an undifferentiated gonad) and analogous (they produce gametes and sex hormones).

A Typical Prenatal Gender Differentiation

Gender is not a simple matter, as you may have noted from the preceding discussion. Most people, however, assume that it is. That is, people typically assume that if a person is female, she will have feminine traits; will think of herself as a woman; will be sexually attracted to men; will have a clitoris, vagina, uterus, and ovaries; and will have sex chromosomes XX. They also assume that all males have masculine traits; think of themselves as male; are sexually attracted to women; have a penis, testes, and scrotum; and have sex chromosomes XY.

A great deal of research over the last several decades challenges these assumptions and provides much information about sexuality and gender and their development. Before we discuss the results of this research, however, some background information is helpful.

We can distinguish among the following eight variables of gender (Money, 1987).[6] Note that the first six are biological and the last two are not.

1. *Chromosomal gender.* XX in females; XY in males
2. *Gonadal gender.* Ovaries in females; testes in males
3a. *Prenatal hormonal gender.* Testosterone and MIS in males but not females before birth
3b. *Prenatal and neonatal brain differentiation.* Testosterone present for masculinization, absent for feminization
4. *Internal organs.* Fallopian tubes, uterus, and upper vagina in females; prostate, vas, and seminal vesicles in males
5. *External genital appearance.* Clitoris, inner and outer lips, and vaginal opening in females; penis and scrotum in males
6. *Pubertal hormonal gender.* At puberty, estrogen and progesterone in females; testosterone in males
7. *Assigned gender.* The announcement at birth, "It's a girl" or "It's a boy," based on the appearance of the external genitals; the gender the parents and the rest of society believe the child to be; the gender in which the child is reared
8. *Gender identity.* The person's private, internal sense of maleness or femaleness

What is an *intersex* condition?

These variables might be subdivided into biological variables (the first six) and psychological variables (the last two). (Gender roles, or the way people of one gender are expected to behave, are discussed in Chapter 13.)

In most cases, of course, all the variables are in agreement in an individual. However, as a result of any one of a number of factors during the course of prenatal sexual development, the gender indicated by one or more of these variables may disagree with the gender indicated by others. When the contradictions are among several of the biological

Homologous (huh-MOLL-uh-gus) organs: Organs in the male and female that develop from the same embryonic tissue.

Analogous (an-AL-uh-gus) organs: Organs in the male and female that have similar functions.

---

[6] The distinction between the terms *gender* and *sex*, discussed in Chapter 1, is being maintained here.

variables (1 through 6), the person is said to have an **intersex** condition also called a **disorder of sexual development (DSD)** (Berenbaum, 2006; Hughes et al., 2006; Reis, 2007).[7] Biologically, the gender of such a person is ambiguous. The reproductive structures may be partly male and partly female, or they may be incompletely male or female. Approximately 2 percent of births have an intersex condition (Blackless et al., 2000). The controversy over whether and how to treat intersex individuals is described in A Sexually Diverse World. Individuals whose assigned gender does not match their gender identity are discussed in Chapter 13.

A number of syndromes can cause an intersex condition. Two of the most common are congenital adrenal hyperplasia and the androgen insensitivity syndrome. In **congenital adrenal hyperplasia (CAH)** a genetic female develops ovaries normally as a fetus; later in the course of prenatal development, however, the adrenal gland begins to function abnormally (as a result of a recessive genetic condition unconnected with the sex chromosomes), and produces an excess amount of androgens. Prenatal sexual differentiation then does not follow the typical female course. As a result, the external genitals are partly or completely male in appearance. The labia are partly or totally fused (so there is no vaginal opening), and the clitoris is enlarged to the size of a small penis or even a full-sized one. Hence, at birth these genetic females are sometimes identified as males. Long-term follow-ups indicate that girls with CAH have a female gender identity, tend toward male-stereotyped toy and game preference, and generally function well as girls and women (Meyer-Bahlburg et al., 2004; Meyer-Bahlburg et al., 2006).

In **androgen insensitivity syndrome (AIS)** (Wisniewski et al., 2000) a genetic male fetus produces normal levels of testosterone; however, as a result of a genetic condition, the body tissues are insensitive to the testosterone, and prenatal development is feminized, although this can occur with different levels of severity. Thus, the individual is born with the external appearance of a female: a small vagina (but no internal reproductive organs) and undescended testes. The individual whose poem appears at the beginning of this chapter has AIS.

Intersex: A condition in which an individual has a mixture of male and female reproductive structures, so that it is not clear at birth whether the individual is a male or a female. Formerly called a *pseudohermaphrodite.*

Disorders of sexual development (DSD): A newer term for intersex conditions.

Congenital adrenal hyperplasia (CAH): A condition in which a genetic female produces abnormal levels of testosterone prenatally and therefore has male-appearing genitals at birth.

Androgen-insensitivity syndrome (AIS): A genetic condition in which the body is unresponsive to androgens so that a genetic male may be born with a female-appearing body.

---

[7] The term *hermaphrodite* is taken from Hermaphroditos, the name of the mythological son of Hermes and Aphrodite. The latter was the Greek goddess of love. A true hermaphrodite has both ovarian and testicular tissues.

Intersex persons provide good evidence of the great complexity of sex and gender and their development. Many variables are involved in gender and sex, and there are many steps in gender differentiation, even before birth. Because the process is complex, it is vulnerable to variations, creating conditions such as intersex. Indeed, the research serves to question our basic notions of what it means to be male or female. In CAH, is the genetic female who is born with male external genitals a male or a female? What makes a person male or female? Chromosomal gender? External genital appearance? Gender identity?

A related phenomenon was first studied in a small community in the Dominican Republic (Imperato-McGinley et al., 1974). Because of a genetic-endocrine problem, a large number of genetic males were born there who, at birth, appeared to be females. The syndrome is called *5-alpha reductase deficiency syndrome.* They had a vaginal pouch instead of a scrotum and a clitoris-sized penis. The uneducated parents, according to the researchers, were unaware that there were any problems, and these genetic males were treated as typical females. At puberty, a spontaneous biological change caused a penis to develop. Significantly, the psychological identity of most of these individuals also changed. Despite their rearing as females, their gender identity switched to male, and they developed heterosexual interests. In their culture, these people are called *Guevodoces* ("penis at 12").

Anthropologist Gilbert Herdt (1990) is critical of the research and interpretations about the Guevodoces. The major criticism is that the Western researchers assumed that this culture is a two-gender society, as in Canada, and that people have to fall into one of only two categories, either male or female. Anthropologists, however, have documented the existence of three-gender societies—that is, societies in which there are three, not two, gender categories—and the society in which the Guevodoces grow up is a three-gender society. The third gender is the Guevodoces. Their gender identity is not male or female, but Guevodoce. The 5-alpha reductase deficiency syndrome has also been found among the Sambia of New Guinea, who also have a three-gender culture. Again we see the profound effect of culture on our most basic ideas about sex and gender.

LO7

Sexual Differentiation During Puberty

Puberty is not a point in time, but rather a process during which further sexual differentiation occurs. It is the stage in life during which the body changes from that

Table 5.2 Summary of the Changes of Puberty and Their Sequence

Girls			Boys		
Characteristic	**Average Age of First Appearance (Years)**	**Major Hormonal Influence**	**Characteristic**	**Average Age of First Appearance (Years)**	**Major Hormonal Influence**
Growth of breasts	9–10	Pituitary growth hormone, estrogens, progesterone, thyroxine	Growth of testes, scrotal sac	9–10	Pituitary growth hormone, testosterone
Growth of pubic hair	9–10	Adrenal androgens	Growth of pubic hair	11–12	Testosterone
Body growth	9.5–14.5	Pituitary growth hormone, adrenal androgens, estrogens	Body growth	10.5–16	Pituitary growth hormone, testosterone
Menarche	12–12.5	GnRH, FSH, LH, estrogens, progesterone	Growth of penis	11–14.5	Testosterone
			Change in voice (growth of larynx)	About the same time as penis growth	Testosterone
Underarm hair	About two years after pubic hair	Adrenal androgens	Facial and underarm hair	About two years after pubic hair	Testosterone
Oil- and sweat-producing glands (acne occurs when glands are clogged)	About the same time as underarm hair	Adrenal androgens	Oil- and sweat-producing glands, acne	About the same time as underarm hair	Testosterone

of a child into that of an adult, with secondary sexual characteristics and the ability to reproduce sexually. **Puberty** can be scientifically defined as the time during which there is sudden enlargement and maturation of the gonads, other genitalia, and secondary sex characteristics (such as breasts or a beard), leading to reproductive capacity (Tanner, 1967). It is the second important period—the other being the prenatal period—during which sexual differentiation takes place. Perhaps the most memorable single event in the process is the first ejaculation for boys and the first menstruation for girls. Note that first menstruation is not necessarily a sign of reproductive capability since girls typically do not produce mature eggs until a year or two after the first menstruation.

The physiological process that underlies puberty in both genders is a marked increase in level of sex hormones. Thus the hypothalamus, pituitary, and gonads control the changes.

Adolescence is a socially defined period of development that bears some relationship to puberty. Adolescence represents a psychological transition from the behaviour and attitudes of a child to the behaviour, attitudes, and responsibilities of an adult. In Canada it corresponds roughly to the years from age 10 to age 20. Modern Canadian culture has an unusually long

period of adolescence (Steinberg, 2011). A century ago, adolescence was much shorter; the lengthening of the educational process has served to prolong adolescence. In some cultures, in fact, adolescence does not exist. Instead, the child shifts to being an adult directly, with only a *rite de passage* in between.

Before describing the changes that take place during puberty, we should note two points. First, the timing of the pubertal process differs considerably for boys and girls. Girls begin the change at around 8 to 12 years of age, while boys do so about two years later. Girls reach their full height by about age 16, while boys continue growing until about age 18 or later. Second, there are large individual differences in the age at which puberty begins (Bogaert, 2005). Experiences may also affect the timing of puberty. For example, girls who have been sexually abused tend to experience earlier puberty than do girls who have not been abused (Turner et al., 1999). There is no one normal time to begin menstruating or growing a beard. Thus, we give age ranges in describing the timing of the process.

Changes in Boys

A summary of the physical changes of puberty in boys and girls is provided in Table 5.2. The physical

Puberty: The time during which there is sudden enlargement and maturation of the gonads, other genitalia, and secondary sex characteristics, so that the individual becomes capable of reproduction.

Can Gender Be Assigned? The Story of David Reimer

In Winnipeg in 1965, Janet Reimer gave birth to twin boys, Bruce and Brian. Six months later, the boys developed problems urinating, and their doctor suggested that they be circumcised. However, the doctor did not use the standard procedure for circumcision and botched the surgery, burning off Bruce's entire penis. The Reimers were told that Bruce would have to live without a penis. Some months later, Janet Reimer saw a television program describing the pioneering work of Dr. John Money of Johns Hopkins University in Baltimore. Money believed that gender is determined by how a child is raised, not by his or her biology, providing that assignment is done in infancy and the necessary surgeries and hormone treatments occur.

The Reimers consulted with Money and made the decision to raise Bruce as female even though they had been raising him as a boy up to that time. At the age of 21 months, Bruce's testicles were removed. The Reimers renamed their son Brenda, and following the counsel of Dr. Money resolved not to tell their child the truth. However, despite taking hormones and receiving numerous surgeries, Brenda never really fit in as a girl. She preferred stereotypically male play (e.g., climbing trees) over playing with dolls, and she was frequently made fun of by other children for her masculine mannerisms. Brenda even complained of feeling like a boy. When she reached puberty and was scheduled to have a final surgery to construct a vagina, Brenda refused, despite Money's urging, indicating she would prefer to die. A psychiatrist suggested to Mr. and Mrs. Reimer that they tell Brenda the truth, who later commented about this revelation, "Suddenly it all made sense why I felt the way I did."

Within months of learning the truth about his sex, Bruce/Brenda cut his hair, began wearing masculine clothing, and changed his name to David (see Figure 5.9). He underwent a series of surgeries to give him a more male body, including a mastectomy to remove the breasts he had grown as a result of taking estrogen. Although David was much happier with his gender, he struggled with depression, in part because he thought he would not find a partner who would love him for who he was. However, as a young adult, David met and married Jane and became the father to her three children. David continued to battle depression, which worsened in his late 30s following the death of his twin brother. He also experienced marital and work-related difficulties, and failed financial investments. On May 4, 2004, at the age of 38, David committed suicide.

Babies who are born with genitals that are not clearly male or female (intersex individuals) typically are treated like David was, using a protocol that became standard in the 1960s. The treatment, which is based on Money's work, generally involves surgically altering the infant's genitals to make them clearly male or female. In Canada, such procedures are covered under medicare. However, Accord Alliance, which promotes integrated care for those with disorders of sexual development and their families and the Organisation Internationale des Intersexués (OII, founded in Quebec) have argued that intersexuality represents genital variability—as opposed to genital abnormality (for information about Accord Alliance, the OII, and other sexuality organizations, including websites, see the Directory of Resources online at Connect™). The medical standard is that an infant's organ that is 0.9 centimetres or less should be considered a clitoris and 2.5 centimetres or more should be considered a penis, and an infant's gender is assigned accordingly. Activists argue that these cutoffs are arbitrary. What is wrong with a clitoris that is 1.7 centimetres long, for example? Ontario psychologist Morgan Holmes believes that the surgeries are conducted because doctors and parents are uncomfortable with the idea of a child not having genitals that fit a narrow definition of what genitals should look like. Is it ethical to conduct such surgeries and gender assignments with infants who cannot give informed consent and who may later prefer another gender than that chosen for them by their parents and doctors? Should

Figure 5.9 David Reimer underwent gender reassignment after a botched surgery when he was six months old.

parents be encouraged to lie to their child, as David Reimer's parents were?

Sex researcher Milton Diamond conducted long-term follow-up studies on several individuals who were treated using Money's standard protocol, including David Reimer. Diamond found that, contrary to Money's published paper describing these individuals as well adjusted, many of them had significant adjustment problems that they traced directly to the medical "management" of their condition. Diamond's research sparked a debate over proper treatment of disorders of sexual development. Diamond proposed an alternative protocol for dealing with infants with these disorders in which he urges physicians (1) to make their most informed judgment about the child's eventual gender identity and counsel the parents to rear the child in that gender; (2) not to perform surgeries that might later need to be reversed; and (3) to provide honest counselling and education to the parents and child as he or she grows up so that the child can eventually make an informed decision regarding treatment.

More systematic follow-up studies on individuals with disorders of sexual development have followed. Many individuals who underwent surgery as infants were dissatisfied with their genitals and reported poor sexual functioning (Creighton et al., 2001; Minto et al., 2003; Wisniewski et al., 2001). The results of these studies also seem to support Money's idea that gender is partly determined by environment. Recognizing these new developments, the American Academy of Pediatrics (2000; Lee et al., 2006) issued guidelines for pediatricians on how to care for newborns with genitals that are not clearly male or female. They include what tests to run to determine the cause of the ambiguous genitals, when the baby should be referred to a centre specializing in disorders of sexual development, and what factors should be used to decide the sex of rearing. These factors include fertility potential (e.g., a girl with congenital adrenal hyperplasia is potentially fertile and should be raised as a girl) and capacity for normal sexual functioning. Only with long-term studies will we learn whether these new treatments will yield better results for individuals with disorders of sexual development.

In keeping with the latest thinking about delaying surgical treatment of individual with disorders of sexual development, Germany became the first European country to legally recognize a third gender. Parents of babies with intersex conditions can choose to register their babies as having an undermined or unspecified gender on their birth certificate rather than being forced to identify them as male or female. Australia allows passport holder to indicate X instead of F or M.

Sources: American Academy of Pediatrics (2000), Colapinto (2004); Creighton & Minto (2001), Creighton et al. (2001), Diamond (1996, 1999), Diamond & Sigmundson (1997), Holmes (2002), Meyer-Bahlburg (2004), Money & Ehrhardt (1972), Wisniewski et al. (2000).

causes of puberty in boys parallel those in girls. They are initiated by increased production of FSH and LH by the pituitary. At the beginning of puberty, the increase in LH stimulates the testes to produce testosterone, which is responsible for most of the changes of puberty in boys.

The first noticeable pubertal change in boys is the growth of the testes and scrotal sac, which begins at an average age of 9 to 10 as a result of testosterone stimulation. The growth of pubic hair begins at about the same time. About a year later the penis begins to enlarge, first thickening and then lengthening. This change also results from testosterone stimulation. As the testes enlarge, their production of testosterone increases even more, leading to rapid growth of the penis, testes, and pubic hair at ages 13 and 14.

The growth of facial and axillary hair begins about two years after the beginning of pubic hair growth. The growth of facial hair begins with the appearance of fuzz on the upper lip; adult beards do not appear until two or three years later. Indeed, by age 17, 50 percent of North American males have not yet shaved. These changes also result from testosterone stimulation, which continues to produce growth of facial and chest hair beyond 20 years of age.

Erections increase in frequency and sometimes occur at inopportune times. The organs that produce the fluid of semen, particularly the prostate, enlarge considerably at about the same time the other organs are growing. By age 13 or 14 the boy is capable of ejaculation.[8] By about age 15, the ejaculate contains mature sperm, and the male is now fertile. The pituitary hormone FSH is responsible for initiating and maintaining the production of mature sperm.

Beginning about a year after the first ejaculation, many boys begin having nocturnal emissions, or *wet dreams*. For the boy who has never masturbated, a wet dream may be his first ejaculation.

At about the same time penis growth occurs, the *larynx* (voice box) also begins to grow in response to testosterone. As the larynx enlarges, the boy's voice drops, or "changes." Typically, the transition occurs at around age 13 or 14.

A great spurt of body growth begins in boys at around 11 to 16 years of age (Figure 5.10). Height increases

---

[8] Note that orgasm and ejaculation are two separate processes, even though they generally occur together, at least in males after puberty (see Chapter 9). But orgasm may occur without ejaculation, and ejaculation may occur without orgasm.

Figure 5.10 There is great variability in the onset of puberty and its growth spurt. Each pair of children are the same age.

rapidly. Body contours also change. While the changes in girls involve mainly the increase in fatty tissue in the breasts and hips, the changes in boys involve mainly an increase in muscle mass. Eventually testosterone brings the growth process to an end, although it permits the growth period to continue longer than it does in girls.

Puberty brings changes and also problems. One problem is *acne*, a distressing skin condition that is stimulated by androgens and affects boys more frequently than girls. It is caused by a clogging of the sebaceous (oil-producing) glands, resulting in pustules, blackheads, and redness on the face and possibly the chest and back.

Gynecomastia (breast enlargement) may occur temporarily in boys, creating considerable embarrassment. About 80 percent of boys in puberty experience this growth, which is probably caused by small amounts of female sex hormones being produced by the testes. Obesity may also be a temporary problem, although it is more frequent in girls than boys.

In various cultures around the world, puberty rites are performed to signify the adolescent's passage to adulthood (see Figure 5.11). Many Aboriginal cultures celebrate this life transition for boys and girls. In Canada the other remaining vestiges of such ceremonies are the Jewish bar mitzvah for boys and bat mitzvah for girls. In a sense, it is unfortunate that we do not give more formal recognition to puberty. Puberty rites probably serve an important psychological function in that they are a formal, public announcement of the fact that the boy or girl is passing through an important period of change. In the absence of such rituals, the young person may think that his or her body is doing strange things. This may be particularly problematic for boys, who lack an obvious sign of puberty like the first menstruation (the first ejaculation is probably the closest analogy) to help them identify the stage they are in.

Changes in Girls

The first sign of puberty in girls is the beginning of breast development, on average around 9 to 10 years of age (Sun et al., 2002). The ducts in the nipple area swell, and there is growth of fatty and connective tissue, causing the small, conical buds to increase in size. These changes are produced by increases in the levels of the sex hormones. The average age at which girls

(a)

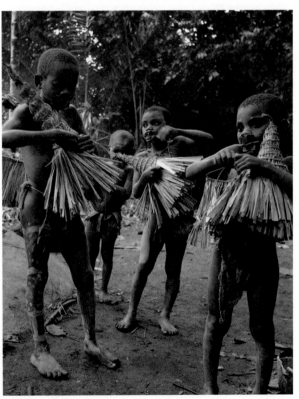

(b)

Figure 5.11 Most cultures celebrate puberty, but cultures vary widely in the nature of the celebration. *(a)* Canadian Jewish youth celebrate a bar mitzvah (for boys) or bat mitzvah (for girls). *(b)* Boys wear ceremonial skirts for their circumcision ceremonies in Democratic Republic of Congo. During their gruelling initiation into manhood, boys about 9 to 12 years old are circumcised and then marched into the forest, where they spend several months hunting and fishing. Each morning the boys are whipped by their elders to instill toughness.

start puberty—that is begin to develop breast tissue—has dropped significantly in recent years, although the average age at which girls begin to menstruate has not changed (Euling et al., 2008). Exposure to endocrine disrupting chemicals may be one cause of this decline; increased obesity may be another factor (Mouritsen et al., 2010). Girls who reach puberty significantly earlier than their peers may be at risk to experience some negative psychosocial consequences including depression, unhealthy behaviours, and school problems (Posner, 2006). On the other hand, reaching puberty significantly later than one's peers may also have negative psychosocial consequences for girls (and boys).

> **What determines the age at which a girl first menstruates?**

As the growth of fatty and supporting tissue increases in the breasts, a similar increase takes place at the hips and buttocks, leading to the rounded contours that distinguish adult female bodies from adult male bodies. Individual females have unique patterns of fat deposits, so there are also considerable individual differences in the resulting female shapes.

Another visible sign of puberty is the growth of pubic hair, which occurs shortly after breast development begins. About two years later, axillary (underarm) hair appears.

Menarche (MEN-ar-key): First menstruation.
Leptin: A protein that is related to the onset of puberty.

Body growth increases sharply during puberty, during the approximate age range of 9.5 to 14.5 years. The growth spurt for girls occurs about two years before the growth spurt for boys (see Figure 5.12). This is consistent with girls' general pattern of maturing earlier than boys.

Estrogen eventually applies the brakes to the growth spurt in girls. The presence of estrogen also causes the growth period to end sooner in girls, thus accounting for the lesser average height of adult women as compared with adult men.

On average, girls in Canada experience **menarche** (first menstruation) when they are 12.7 years old (Al-Sahab, Ardern, et al., 2010). This age is somewhat higher than in the United States but somewhat lower than in other developed countries, such as Australia, Russia, and Norway. However, 15 percent of girls experience menarche when they are less than 11.5 years old; most (67 percent) when they are between 11.5 and 13.9 years old; and 17 percent when they are older than 13.9 years old. Although the average age of menarche has decreased in the past 150 years, likely because of improved nutrition, it has remained constant over the past 50 years (Posner, 2006). Girls are not capable of becoming pregnant until ovulation begins. Typically, girls do not ovulate regularly for one to two years after first ovulation (Metcalf et al., 1983). The first menstruation is not only an important biological event but also a significant psychological one. Various cultures have ceremonies recognizing its importance. In some families, it is a piece of news that spreads quickly to the relatives. Girls themselves display a wide range of reactions to the event, ranging from negative ones, such as fear, shame, or disgust, to positive ones, such as pride and a sense of maturity and womanliness.

Some of the most negative reactions occur when the girl has not been prepared for the menarche, which is still the case surprisingly often. Parents who are concerned about preparing their daughters for the first menstruation should remember that there is a wide range in the age at which it occurs. It is not unusual for a girl to start menstruating in Grade 5, and instances of menarche during Grade 4, while rare, do occur.

What determines the age at which a girl first menstruates? One explanation is the *percent body fat hypothesis* (Frisch & McArthur, 1974; Hopwood et al., 1990; Lassek & Gaulin, 2007). During puberty, deposits of body fat increase in females. According to the percent body fat hypothesis, the percentage of body weight that is fat must rise to a certain level for menstruation to occur for the first time and for it to be maintained. Thus, very thin adolescent girls would tend to be late in the timing of first menstruation. **Leptin**, a hormone, is related to the onset of puberty in girls and in boys (Israel et al., 2012; Terasawa et al., 2012). In pre-pubertal girls and boys, leptin levels rise as body fat increases. Leptin simulates the growth of skeletal bone and the release of LH.

The percent body fat hypothesis also helps to make sense of two related phenomena: the cessation of

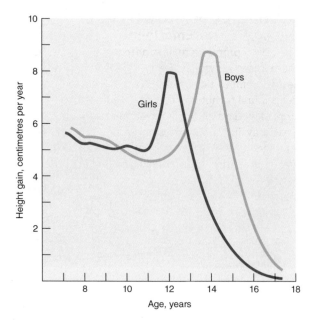

Figure 5.12   The adolescent spurt of growth for boys and girls. Note that girls experience their growth spurt earlier than boys do.

menstruation in women with anorexia nervosa and the cessation of menstruation in female distance runners. *Anorexia nervosa* is a condition in which the person—most commonly an adolescent girl—engages in compulsive, extreme dieting and exercise, perhaps to the point of starving herself to death. As anorexia progresses, the percentage of body fat declines and menstruation ceases. It is also fairly common for women who are runners, and all women who exercise seriously to the point where their body fat is substantially reduced, to cease menstruating. It seems that when the percentage of body fat falls below a critical value, the biological mechanisms that control the menstrual cycle shut down menstruation.[9]

Before leaving the topic of running, we should note that there is some evidence that serious exercise also affects the male reproductive system. One study of male distance runners found that their testosterone levels were only about 68 percent as high, on the average, as a control group's testosterone levels, and many other studies have found similar effects (Hackney, 2008; Wheeler et al., 1984). There are some reports of male long-distance runners complaining of a loss of sex drive, but it is unclear whether this results from reduced testosterone levels or from the perpetual feelings of fatigue from their intensive training (Wheeler et al., 1984).

Other body changes in girls during puberty include a development of the blood supply to the clitoris, a thickening of the walls of the vagina, and a rapid growth of the uterus, which doubles in size between age 10 and age 18. The pelvic bone structure grows and widens, contributing to the rounded shape of the female and creating a passageway large enough for an infant to move through during birth.

The dramatic changes that occur during puberty are produced, basically, by the endocrine system and its upsurge in sex hormone production during puberty. The process begins with the hypothalamus releasing pulses of GnRH, which triggers an increase in secretion of FSH by the pituitary gland. FSH in turn stimulates the ovaries to produce estrogen. Estrogen is responsible for many of the changes that occur; it stimulates breast growth and the growth of the uterus and vagina.

Also involved in puberty are the paired **adrenal glands**, which are located just above the kidneys. In the female, the adrenal glands are the major producer of androgens, which exist at low levels in females. Adrenal androgens stimulate the growth of pubic and axillary hair and are related to the female sex drive. **Adrenarche**—the time of increasing secretion of adrenal androgens—generally begins slightly before age eight (Grumbach & Styne, 1998).

[9] On the other hand, moderate exercise has been associated with reduced menstrual problems, such as cramps (Hightower, 1997).

Changes in Behaviour

Puberty brings not only changes in the body but changes in behaviour as well (Forbes & Dahl, 2010). Puberty has both organizing effects and activating effects. Pubertal development results in changes in the brain and genitals (organizing effects) and also activates certain behaviours. The research evidence indicates that puberty increases sensation-seeking behaviours—that is, wanting high-intensity, exciting experiences—and sex is one sensation that might be sought. Puberty also reorients social behaviour so that adolescents are motivated to seek social experiences with their peers and with potential romantic partners.

LO8 Psychological Aspects of the Menstrual Cycle

"Why do I get so emotional?" screams the ad for Midol in *Seventeen* magazine. It is part of the folk wisdom of our culture that women experience fluctuations in mood over the phases of the menstrual cycle. In particular, women are supposed to be especially cranky and depressed just before and during their periods. In France, if a woman commits a crime during her premenstrual phase, she may use the fact in her defence, claiming "temporary impairment of sanity."

What is the scientific evidence concerning the occurrence of such fluctuations in mood, and, if they do occur, what causes them?

Fluctuations in Mood: Do Women Become Extra Emotional?

The term **premenstrual syndrome (PMS)** refers to those cases in which the woman has a particularly severe combination of physical, psychological, and behavioural symptoms that occur premenstrually and stop a few days after menstruation starts. These symptoms may include depression, irritability, breast pain, and water retention (Stanton et al., 2002). In the last several decades, much research has been done on moods during the premenstrual period and on whether moods fluctuate during the cycle (Taylor, 2006).

Research based on women's daily self-reports throughout the cycle generally finds positive moods around the time of ovulation (that is, mid-cycle), and various symptoms, such as anxiety, irritability, depression, fatigue, and headaches, premenstrually. However, the fluctuations are not large

Adrenal (uh-DREE-nul) glands: Endocrine glands located just above the kidneys; in the female they are the major producers of androgens.

Adrenarche (AD-ren-ar-key): A time of increased secretion of adrenal androgens, usually just before age eight.

Premenstrual syndrome (PMS): A combination of severe physical and psychological symptoms, such as depression and irritability, occurring just before menstruation.

on average. In one study, the average depression score of women was 6.8 around ovulation and 9.3 premenstrually, compared with a mean of 16.0 for depressed psychiatric patients (Golub, 1992).

The evidence supporting mood fluctuations and PMS has been challenged. Of the numerous criticisms that have been made (Chrisler et al., 2006; Stanton et al., 2002), three deserve special mention here. First, much of the evidence depends on subjective retrospective reports of mood and symptoms, which are probably not very reliable. Second, we can question how the direction of the difference is interpreted. The typical interpretation is that women show a psychological "deficit" premenstrually, as compared with the "normal" state at ovulation and during the rest of the cycle. However, the opposite interpretation might also be made: that women are "normal" premenstrually and experience unusual well-being psychologically at mid-cycle. What defines *normal* or *average* mood, then? Men's moods?

Support for a reinterpretation might come from the statistics on violent crimes committed by women. While it may be true that women are somewhat more likely to commit crimes during the eight premenstrual and menstrual days, even during this time they are far less likely to commit crimes than men are. Further, most studies comparing cycles in the moods of women and men have not found differences (Stanton et al., 2002).

Third, PMS is a stereotype in our culture. The stereotype includes beliefs that premenstrual women have sharp mood swings and crying spells and are bloated from water retention. Women in fact report far fewer symptoms for themselves than they think the average woman experiences (Chrisler et al., 2006). PMS may therefore largely be a stereotype that does not match most women's actual experience.

Taking into account the criticisms and available evidence, it seems reasonable to conclude the following:

1. Women do, on average, experience some fluctuations in mood over the phases of the menstrual cycle.
2. Present evidence does not clearly indicate how the direction of the shifts should be interpreted—whether women's moods are unusually low premenstrually or unusually high around the time of ovulation.
3. A great deal of variation occurs from one woman to the next in the size of these shifts and the way they are expressed. Some women experience no shifts or shifts so slight that they are not noticeable, whereas others may experience large shifts. It would be interesting to know how many do show mood fluctuations and how many do not.

Premenstrual dysphoric disorder (PMDD): A diagnostic category in the *DSM-V*, characterized by symptoms such as sadness, anxiety, and irritability in the week before menstruation.

Unfortunately, the studies that have tried to provide this information themselves show substantial variation; the percentage reporting symptoms ranges between 25 percent and 80 percent in various studies (Stanton et al., 2002). It is important to make a distinction between women who have full-blown PMS and women who experience no fluctuation or only moderate fluctuations in mood over the cycle.

The American Psychiatric Association has formalized severe PMS with the diagnosis **premenstrual dysphoric disorder**, or PMDD, in the *Diagnostic and Statistical Manual of Mental Disorders* (5th ed.), or *DSM-V* (American Psychiatric Association, 2013a). Symptoms must occur during the week before the beginning of menstruation and must improve a few days after menstruation starts. The woman must have at least five symptoms, such as marked mood swings, sadness or hopelessness, tension or anxiety, irritability or anger, difficulty concentrating, decreased interest in usual activities, and marked changes in appetite. These symptoms have to have occurred most months for the past year, be as severe as those of other mental disorders, and result in impairment. Thus, only 3 to 5 percent of women would meet the criteria for PMDD (American Psychiatric Association, 2010). This diagnostic category is very controversial, however (Caplan, 1995). Some argue that it represents nothing but a medicalizing and pathologizing of women's experience (Offman & Kleinplatz, 2004; Poulin & Gouliquer, 2003). Others point out that there is no scientific basis for PMDD and that some studies fail to confirm it (Gallant et al., 1992). Still others argue that the PMDD diagnosis is useful for the minority of women who experience such extreme symptoms that their quality of life is affected (Di Giulio & Reissing, 2006).

Fluctuations in Performance

So far, our discussion has concentrated on fluctuations in psychological characteristics, such as depression, anxiety, and irritability. However, in some situations performance is of more practical importance than mood. For example, is a female mechanic's work less accurate premenstrually and menstrually? Is a female athlete's coordination or speed impaired during the premenstrual–menstrual period?

Research on performance—such as intellectual or athletic performance—generally shows no fluctuations over the cycle (Burrows & Bird, 2005). Research has found no fluctuations in academic performance, problem solving, memory, or creative thinking (Epting & Overman, 1988; Stanton et al., 2002).

In one study, 31 percent of female athletes said they believed that they experienced a decline in performance during the premenstrual or menstrual phases; yet when their actual performance was measured, they showed no deficits in strength (weight lifters) or swimming speed (swimming team members) (Quadagno et al., 1991). Thus, there is no reliable evidence indicating that the kinds of performance required in a work situation or an athletic competition fluctuate over the menstrual cycle.

Fluctuations in Sex Drive

Another psychological characteristic that has been investigated for fluctuations over the cycle is women's sex drive or arousability. Studies have yielded contradictory results. Some have found a peak frequency of intercourse around ovulation, which would be biologically functional—that is, increase the chances of conception occurring. But others have found peaks just before and just after menstruation (Zillmann et al., 1994).

Of course, one should be cautious about using frequency of intercourse as a measure of a woman's sex drive. Intercourse requires some agreement between partners and thus reflects not only a woman's desires but her partner's as well. One study assessed both heterosexual women's activity with a partner and self-rated sexual desire (Bullivant et al., 2004). The results indicated that sexual activity initiated by the woman—but not by the man—peaked during the three days before and three days after ovulation. Sexual desire showed the same pattern.

In a sophisticated study conducted by Alberta researchers, women kept daily electronic diaries on a website, reporting their sexual fantasies each day (Dawson et al., 2012). They also completed self-administered urine tests for LH to determine the day of ovulation. The fantasies were then content analyzed, using methods like those described in Chapter 3. The results indicated that both the frequency and the arousability of sexual fantasies was highest at ovulation. The number of males in the fantasies even increased at the time of ovulation. These results seem to indicate that maximum sexual arousability does occur at the time of peak fertility. Interestingly, testosterone levels also peak at ovulation (Van Goozen et al., 1997).

If there is a link between phase of the menstrual cycle and sexual interest, it most likely reflects an association between testosterone levels and sexuality with a peak in sexual interest around the time of ovulation. But with humans, psychological and social factors—such as some couples' dislike of intercourse when the woman is menstruating—play a strong role as well (Allen & Goldberg, 2009).

What Causes the Fluctuations in Mood: Why Do Some Women Get Emotional?

For women who do experience fluctuations in mood during the menstrual cycle, the question arises about what causes these fluctuations. This raises the nature–nurture, or biology–environment, controversy. That is, some researchers argue that mood fluctuations are caused primarily by biological factors—in particular, fluctuations in levels of hormones. Others argue that environmental factors, such as menstrual taboos and cultural expectations, are the primary cause.

On the biology side, changes in mood appear to be related to changes in hormone levels during the cycle (Ross & Steiner, 2003). The fact that depression is more frequent in women premenstrually, at menopause, and postpartum (after having a baby) suggests that there is at least some relationship between sex hormones and depression. The exact hormone–mood relationship is not known, but low or declining levels of estrogen or progesterone or both are the likeliest culprits. Neither is it known exactly what the mechanism is by which hormones influence mood (Golub, 1992). Research does indicate that the estrogen–progesterone system interacts with the production of the neurotransmitters norepinephrine, serotonin, and dopamine, and neurotransmitter levels are linked to mood disorders such as depression (Halbreich & Kahn, 2001; Steiner et al., 2003).

Critics of the hormone point of view note that causality is being inferred from correlational data. In other words, the data show a correlation between cycle phase (hormonal levels) and mood, but they do not show that hormone levels cause the mood shift.

Those arguing the other side—that the fluctuations are due to cultural forces—note the widespread cultural expectations and taboos surrounding menstruation (Stanton et al., 2002; Stubbs, 2008). In some nonindustrialized cultures, women who are menstruating are isolated from the community and may have to stay in a menstrual hut at the edge of town during their period. Often the menstrual blood itself is thought to have supernatural, dangerous powers, and the woman's isolation is considered necessary for the safety of the community. Among the Lele of the Congo, for example:

> A menstruating woman was a danger to the whole community if she entered the forest. Not only was her menstruation certain to wreck any enterprise in the forest that she might undertake, but it was thought to produce unfavorable conditions for men. Hunting would be difficult for a long time after, and rituals based on forest plants would have no efficacy. Women found these rules extremely irksome, especially as they were regularly short-handed and late in their planting, weeding, harvesting, and fishing. (Douglas, 1970, p. 179)

Such practices do not occur only among non-Western people. Note that there is a history of similar practices in our own culture as well. For example, the following passage is from the book of Leviticus in the Bible:

When a woman has a discharge of blood which is her regular discharge from her body, she shall be in her impurity for seven days, and whoever touches her shall be unclean until the evening. . . . And whoever touches her bed shall wash his clothes, and bathe himself in water, and be unclean until the evening; whether it is the bed or anything upon which she sits, when he touches it he shall be unclean until the evening. (Leviticus 15:19–23)

Among the most common menstrual taboos are those prohibiting sexual intercourse with a menstruating woman. For example, the continuation of the passage from Leviticus just quoted is this:

And if any man lies with her, and her impurity is on him, he shall be unclean seven days; and every bed on which he lies shall be unclean. (Leviticus 15:24)

Couples who violated the taboo could be stoned. Orthodox Jews still abstain from sex during the woman's period and for seven days afterward. At the end of this time the woman goes to the *mikvah* (ritual bath) to be cleansed, and only after this cleansing may she resume sexual relations (Guterman, 2008).

Advocates of the cultural explanation argue, then, that women become anxious and depressed around the time of menstruation because of the many cultural forces, such as menstrual taboos, that create negative attitudes toward menstruation. For example, in an Ontario study, one-third of the university women sampled, all of whom were in a romantic relationship, had never engaged in sexual activity during menstruation (Rempel & Baumgartner, 2003).

It's important to realize that, in some cultures, separation of women during menstruation is a form of celebration. For example, in many Canadian First Nations communities, women were honoured for their role as life givers; Moon Time (menstruation; Figure 5.13) was seen as a gift from the Creator (McKenna et al., 2010) and is symbolic of Grandmother Moon, which becomes full once a month just as women do. Women are seen as having powerful energy and being at their greatest strength during the Moon Time. Traditionally, they gathered in the Moon Lodge during their Moon Time. At the Moon Lodge they were taught about various aspects of women's lives, including about birth and menopause, by the Grandmothers (female elders). According to Elder Betty:

When women are in that Moon Lodge you learn how the concept of Grandmother Moon is so vital. . . . We need Grandmother Moon just as much as we need the sun. Grandmother Moon is so powerful that the water will rise up and follow her. The women had all that knowledge and it was passed from the Grandmother to mother and to daughter to granddaughter, aunty to niece. But very rarely did it ever go out to the males because the males lead a different life. It's also important to know that your energy at the Moon Time is powerful. We think of ourselves as a connection to that Mother Earth, that we

Figure 5.13   In some cultures, separation of women during menstruation is a form of celebration. For example, in many Canadian First Nations communities, women were honoured for their role as life givers and gathered in the Moon Lodge during their Moon Time. At the Moon Lodge they were taught about various aspects of women's lives, including about birth and menopause, by the Grandmothers (female Elders).

are a product of Mother Earth, we come from her, we go back to her. (McKenna et al., 2010, p. 232)

Colonialism changed this experience in many Aboriginal cultures. Some Aboriginal women are trying to reclaim this traditional view of Moon Time.

Women's expectations may play a role in their response to menstruation (Stanton et al., 2002). Our culture is filled with teachings that women are supposed to behave strangely just before and during their periods—for example, drug company ads that ask "Why am I so emotional?" (see Figure 5.14). According to this line of reasoning, women are taught that they should be depressed around the time of menstruation, and because they expect to become depressed, they do become depressed. Researchers in British Columbia have proposed an additional role for expectations (McFarlane et al., 1988). Women (and men) experience variability in their moods. Because of cultural stereotypes about PMS, women attribute their negative mood to hormones when they occur premenstrually. However, they attribute their negative moods at other times in their cycle to other causes (e.g., work or family).

Surely such forces do exist in our culture. But is there any evidence that they really have an effect on

Figure 5.14 Does advertising for menstrual drugs contribute to negative stereotypes about women and PMS?

women's moods and behaviour? Psychologist Diane Ruble (1977; see also Klebanov & Jemmott, 1992) did a clever experiment to determine whether women's culturally induced expectations influence their reporting of premenstrual symptoms. University students were tested on the sixth or seventh day before the onset of their next menstrual period. They were told that they would participate in a study on a new technique for predicting the expected date of menstruation by using an electroencephalograph (EEG). After the EEG had

been run (it actually wasn't), the woman was informed of when her next period was to occur, depending on which of three experimental groups she had randomly been assigned to: (1) she was told she was "premenstrual" and her period was due in one or two days; (2) she was told she was "intermenstrual" or "mid-cycle" and her period was not expected for at least a week to 10 days; or (3) she was given no information at all about the predicted date of menstruation (control group). The women then completed a self-report menstrual distress questionnaire. The results indicated that women who had been led to believe they were in the premenstrual phase reported significantly more water retention, pain, and changes in eating habits than did women who had been led to believe they were around mid-cycle. (In fact, women in these groups did not differ significantly in when their periods actually arrived.) There were no significant differences between the groups in ratings of negative moods, however. This study indicates that, probably because of learned beliefs, women overstate the changes in body states that occur over the menstrual cycle. When they think they are in the premenstrual phase, they report more problems than when they think they are at mid-cycle.

This nature–nurture argument will not be easily resolved, particularly because there is evidence for both points of view. Perhaps the best solution is to say that both biology and culture contribute to women's mood fluctuations during the menstrual cycle. In other words, some women probably do experience mood shifts caused by hormonal and possibly other physical factors and, for many others, slight biological influences are magnified by psychological and cultural influences (Hampson & Moffatt, 2004). A woman's premenstrual hormonal state may act as a sort of trigger.

SUMMARY

The major sex hormones are testosterone, which is produced in males by the testes, and estrogen and progesterone, which are produced in females by the ovaries, although both men and women have both testosterone and estrogen. Levels of the sex hormones are regulated by two hormones secreted by the pituitary: FSH (follicle-stimulating hormone) and LH (luteinizing hormone), which in turn are regulated by GnRH (gonadotropin releasing hormone) secreted by the hypothalamus. The gonads, pituitary, and hypothalamus regulate one another's output through a negative feedback loop.

Biologically, the menstrual cycle is divided into four phases: the follicular phase, ovulation, the luteal phase, and menstruation. Corresponding to these phases, there

are changes in the levels of pituitary hormones (FSH and LH) and in the levels of ovarian hormones (estrogen and progesterone), as well as changes in the ovaries and the uterus. A fairly common menstrual problem is dysmenorrhea (painful menstruation).

At conception males and females differ only in the sex chromosomes (XX in females and XY in males). As the male fetus grows, the SRY gene on the Y chromosome directs the gonads to differentiate into the testes. In the absence of the SRY gene, ovaries develop. The ovaries and testes then secrete different hormones in females and males, respectively, and these hormones stimulate further differentiation of the internal and external reproductive structures of males and females. A male organ and a female organ that derive from the same embryonic tissue are said to be homologous to each other.

Intersex conditions (disorders of sex development) are generally the result of various syndromes (such as CAH) and accidents that occur during the course of pre-natal sexual differentiation. Currently, there is a debate over the best medical treatment of these individuals.

Puberty is characterized by a great increase in the production of sex hormones. Pubertal changes in both males and females include body growth, the develop-ment of pubic and axillary hair, and increased output from the oil-producing glands. Changes in the male include growth of the penis and testes, the beginning of ejaculation, and a deepening of the voice. Changes in

the female include breast development and the begin-ning of menstruation.

Research indicates that some, although not all, women experience changes in mood over the phases of the menstrual cycle. For those who experience such changes, their mood is generally positive around the middle of the cycle (around ovulation), whereas depres-sion and irritability are more likely just before and dur-ing menstruation. These negative moods and physical discomforts are termed premenstrual syndrome (PMS). However, research indicates that there are no fluctua-tions in performance over the cycle. Evidence does sug-gest that fluctuations in mood are related to changes in hormone levels as well as to cultural factors.

QUESTIONS FOR THOUGHT, DISCUSSION, AND DEBATE

1. The society in the Dominican Republic in which the Guevodoces are born is a three-gender society, unlike the two-gender society of the dominant Canadian culture. What would Canada be like if it were a three-gender society? Who would be classi-fied in the third gender? Would their lives be better or worse as a result? Could we have a four-gender society? Who would be classified in the fourth gen-der? (For further information, see Herdt, 1990.)

2. Are women's fluctuations in mood over the men-strual cycle caused more by biological factors or by environmental and cultural factors?

3. Teresa has just given birth to her first baby. The doctor approaches her with a worried expression and says that her baby's genitals are unusual and some decisions will have to be made. The phal-lus is too big for a clitoris but too small for a penis. What should Teresa do? What other information should she obtain from the doctor before making a decision?

4. Your 10-year-old daughter tells you that she has heard about PMS and wonders whether she will get it when she begins her periods. What would you tell her?

connect **LEARNSMART** **SMARTBOOK**

For more information on the resources available from McGraw-Hill Ryerson, go to **www.mheducation.ca/he/solutions**.

Are **YOU** Curious?

1. How does sexual activity change during pregnancy?
2. What substances, if taken during pregnancy, threaten the fetus?
3. What training do midwives receive?

Read this chapter to find out.

CHAPTER

6

Conception, Pregnancy, and Childbirth

LEARNING OBJECTIVES

After studying this chapter, you will be able to

LO1 Illustrate the independent voyages of the sperm and the ovum up to and including the moment of conception.

LO2 Describe the changes that occur in the fetus, the mother, and the father during each of the three trimesters of pregnancy.

LO3 Demonstrate the importance of good nutrition and the effects of different teratogenic drugs on fetal development.

LO4 Distinguish the three stages of labour and differentiate vaginal birth procedures from Caesarean section procedures.

LO5 Compare various childbirth options.

LO6 Discuss the physical, sexual, and psychological changes that occur for the mother and father during the postpartum period, including breastfeeding.

LO7 Identify the types of problems and pathologies that can occur during conception and pregnancy.

LO8 Discuss the causes of, effects of, and treatments for infertility.

remember feeling very sexy. We were trying all these different positions. Now that we were having a baby, I felt a lot looser. I used to feel uptight about sex for its own sake, but when I was pregnant I felt a lot freer.

I thought it would never end. I was enormous. I couldn't bend over and wash my feet. And it was incredibly hot.*

*Boston Women's Health Book Collective. (1998). *Our bodies, ourselves for the new century,* New York: Simon and Schuster, pp. 443, 446.

Chapter 5 described the remarkable biological process by which a single fertilized egg develops into a male or a female human being. This chapter is about some equally remarkable processes involved in creating human beings: conception, pregnancy, and childbirth.

Several things people can do to improve the odds of having a healthy mother and baby are listed in First Person.

LO1

Conception

Sperm Meets Egg: The Incredible Journey

In a 28-day menstrual cycle, the woman ovulates on about day 14 (see Chapter 5). The egg is released from the ovary into the body cavity. Typically, it is then picked up by the fimbriae (long fingerlike structures at the end of the fallopian tube—see Figure 6.1) and enters the fallopian tube. It then begins a leisurely trip down the tube toward the uterus, reaching it in about five days if it has been fertilized. Otherwise, it disintegrates in about 48 hours. The egg, unlike the sperm, has no means of moving itself and is propelled by the cilia (hairlike structures) lining the fallopian tube. The egg has begun its part of the journey toward conception.

The woman's cervix secretes mucus that flushes the passageways to prepare for the arrival of the sperm. Meanwhile, the woman has sexual intercourse, and the man has an orgasm and ejaculates inside the woman's vagina. Alternatively, the woman uses assisted insemination to place semen in the vagina.[1] Either way, the sperm are deposited in the vagina, there to begin their journey toward the egg. But they have made an incredible trip even before reaching the vagina. Initially, they were manufactured in the seminiferous tubules of the testes (see Chapter 4). They were then collected and stored in the epididymis. During ejaculation they moved up and over the top of the bladder in the vas deferens; then they travelled down through the ejaculatory duct, mixed with seminal fluid, and went out through the urethra.

The sperm is one of the tiniest cells in the human body. It is composed of a *head*, a *midpiece*, and a *tail* (see Figure 6.2). The head is about 5 micrometres long, and the total length, from the tip of the head to the tip of the tail, is about 60 micrometres (about 0.06 millimetres, or 2/1000 inch). The DNA, which is the sperm's most important contribution when it unites with the egg, is contained in the nucleus, which is in the head of the sperm. Sperm also contain RNA carrying the instructions for early embryonic development, and a large number of proteins (Ainsworth, 2005). The *acrosome*, a chemical reservoir, is also in the head of the sperm. The midpiece contains *mitochondria*, tiny structures in which chemical reactions occur that provide energy. This energy is used when the sperm lashes its tail back and forth. The lashing action (called *flagellation*) propels the sperm forward.

A typical ejaculate has a volume of about 3 millilitres, or about a teaspoonful, and contains about 200 million sperm. Although this might seem to be a wasteful amount of sperm if only one is needed for fertilization, the great majority of the sperm never even get close to the egg. Some of the ejaculate, including half of the sperm, will flow out of the vagina as a result of gravity. Other sperm may be killed by the acidity of the vagina, to which they are very sensitive. Others are deformed. Of those that make it safely into the uterus, half swim up the wrong fallopian tube (the one typically containing no egg).

But here we are, several hours later, with a hearty band of sperm swimming up the fallopian tube toward the egg, against the currents that are bringing the egg down. Sperm are capable of swimming 1 to 3 centimetres (about 1 inch) per hour, although it has been documented that sperm may arrive at the egg within an hour and a half after ejaculation, which is much sooner than would be expected, given their swimming rate. By

---

[1] Increasing numbers of Canadian women are becoming pregnant using assisted reproductive technologies. These are described later in this chapter.

First Person

Planning a Pregnancy?

R esearch has identified a number of things that can cause harm to mother or fetus during pregnancy. Some of these are preventable. Here is a preconception checklist for women.

1. Folic acid can prevent birth defects. Take a multivitamin containing 400 micrograms of folic acid every day.
2. Get your vaccinations up-to-date. Get catch-up vaccines for rubella and varicella at least one month before trying to get pregnant. Tdap, which protects infants against whooping cough, and flu vaccines can be taken in early pregnancy.
3. Women with a family history of sickle cell anemia, thalassemia, Tay-Sachs disease, and cystic fibrosis should consider genetic screening.
4. Healthy moms are more likely to have healthy babies; aim for a healthy weight before you get pregnant. Obese pregnant women are at greater risk for preeclampsia, stillbirth, preterm delivery, and Caesarean sections (C-sections).
5. Women with diabetes need to maintain tight control of blood sugar.
6. No drinking and no smoking; stop before you get pregnant. (Your partner should stop, too).

Source: Fryhofer (2012).

---

the time a sperm reaches the egg, it has swum approximately 3000 times its own length. This feat would be comparable to a swim of more than four kilometres (about 2.5 miles) for a human being.

Contrary to the popular belief that conception occurs in the uterus, typically it occurs in the outer third (the part near the ovary) of the fallopian tube. Of the original 200 million sperm, only about 2000 reach the tube containing the egg. As they approach, a chemical secreted by the egg attracts the sperm to the egg. Chemical receptors on the surface of the sperm respond to the attractant, and the sperm swim toward the egg (Spehr et al., 2003). The egg is surrounded by a thin, gelatinous layer called the *zona pellucida*. Sperm swarm around the egg and secrete an enzyme called **hyaluronidase** (produced by the acrosome located in the head of the sperm–refer to Figure 6.2); this enzyme dissolves the zona pellucida, permitting one sperm to penetrate the egg.[2] Conception has occurred (Figure 6.3).

The fertilized egg, called the **zygote**, continues to travel down the fallopian tube. About 36 hours after conception, it begins the process of cell division, by which the original one cell becomes a mass of two cells, then four cells, then eight cells, and so on. About five to seven days after conception, the mass of cells implants itself in the lining of the uterus, there to be nourished and grow. For the first two weeks of gestation, the *conceptus* (product of conception) is called a zygote, between weeks two and eight it is called an **embryo**, and from then until birth it is called a **fetus**.

Improving the Chances of Conception: Making a Baby

Some couples choose not to have children. However, for couples wanting to conceive, the following are points to keep in mind.

The trick, of course, is to time intercourse so that it occurs around the time of ovulation. To do this, it is necessary to determine when the woman ovulates. For the vast majority of women, the time of ovulation can best be determined by keeping a *basal body temperature chart*. To do this, the woman takes her temperature every morning immediately on waking (that means before getting up and moving around or drinking a cup of coffee). She

Hyaluronidase: An enzyme secreted by the sperm that allows one sperm to penetrate the egg.
Zygote: The developing organism from the time of the union of the sperm and the egg to about the second week of gestation.
Embryo: The developing organism between the second and eighth weeks of gestation.
Fetus: The developing organism from the eighth week of gestation through delivery.

---

[2] Thus, while only one sperm is necessary to accomplish fertilization, it appears that it is important that a lot of other sperm are present to secrete a chemical that facilitates penetration of the egg. Therefore, maintaining a high sperm count seems to be important for conception.

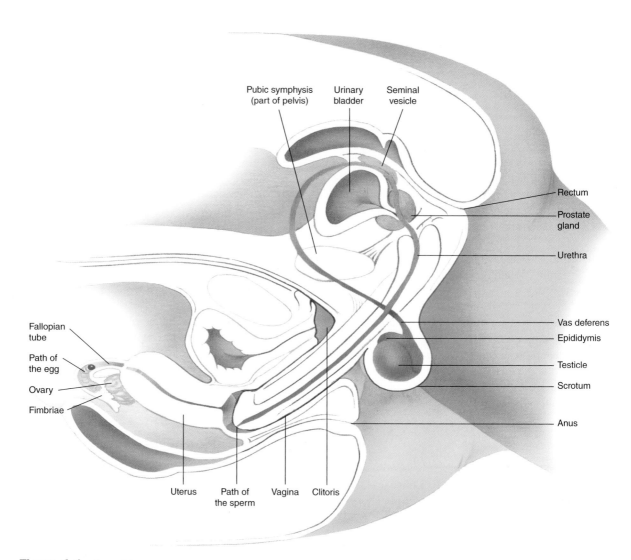

Figure 6.1 Sexual intercourse in the man-on-top position, showing the pathway of sperm and egg from manufacture in the testes and ovary to conception, which typically occurs in the fallopian tube.

then keeps a graph of her temperature. The most reliable indicator of ovulation is the rise in temperature the day after it occurs. From this, the woman can determine the day of ovulation, and that determination should be consistent with menstruation occurring about 14 days later. Other methods for determining when a woman is ovulating are the cervical mucus and sympto-thermal methods, as well as home tests for the detection of ovulation, described in Chapter 7.

Sperm live inside the woman's body for up to five days (Wilcox et al., 1995). The egg is capable of being fertilized for about the first 12 to 24 hours after ovulation. Allowing the sperm some swimming time, this means that intercourse should be timed right at ovulation or one or two days before.

Assuming you have some idea of the time of ovulation, how frequent should intercourse be? While more may be merrier, more is not necessarily more effective.

The reason for this is that it is important for the man's sperm count to be maintained. It takes a while to manufacture 200 million sperm—at least 24 hours. And, as mentioned earlier, maintaining a high sperm count appears to be important in accomplishing the task of fertilizing the egg. For purposes of conceiving, then, it is probably best to have intercourse about every 24 to 48 hours, or about two to three times during the week in which the woman is to ovulate (Mayo Clinic, 2012a).

It is also important to take some steps to ensure that once deposited in the vagina, the sperm get a decent chance to survive and to find their way into the fallopian tubes. Position during and after intercourse is important. For purposes of conceiving, the best position for intercourse is with the woman on her back (man-on-top, or *missionary*, position—see Chapter 9). If the woman is on top, much of the ejaculate may run out of the vagina

Acrosome

Head

Nucleus containing chromosomes

Midpiece containing mitochondria to provide energy for swimming

Tail

Figure 6.2 The structure of a mature human sperm.

Figure 6.3 The egg is fertilized by one sperm as many sperm cluster about.

because of the pull of gravity. After intercourse, she should remain on her back, possibly with her legs pulled up and a pillow under her hips, preferably for about a half hour to an hour. This allows the semen to remain in a pool in the vagina, which gives the sperm a good chance to swim up into the uterus. Because sperm are very sensitive to the pH (acidity-alkalinity) of the vagina, this factor also requires some consideration. Acidity kills sperm. Douching with commercial preparations or with acidic solutions (such as vinegar) should be avoided. Finally, lubricants and suppositories should not be used; they may kill sperm or block their entrance into the uterus (Mayo Clinic, 2012b). On the other hand, lubricants may be necessary to make sex comfortable.

 LO2

Development of the Conceptus

For the nine months (38 weeks, actually) of pregnancy, two organisms—the conceptus and the pregnant woman—coexist. In the past the relationship between the two has been viewed as harmonious. In recent years, a new perspective has been gaining support— pregnancy as a silent struggle (Haig, 1996). Both fetus and mother need a variety of nutrients and may be competing for them. Nature should favour the development of characteristics of each that would give it the edge in

such competitions, enabling it to win (e.g., struggles over calcium). Research with mice suggests that the placenta plays a role in regulating the flow of nutrients to protect the fetus (Broad & Keverne, 2011). Such a struggle can explain aspects of pregnancy that are inconsistent with the view of harmonious coexistence, such as gestational diabetes and pre-eclampsia. Both of these conditions carry serious risk to both the mother and the infant if not treated. Gestational diabetes is the same as other forms of diabetes in that the woman has high blood sugar because the body is not able to make and use all the insulin it needs, but it appears during pregnancy. Pre-eclampsia is a condition that occurs during the third trimester and involves a sharp rise in blood pressure, the presence of protein in the urine, and swelling of the hands, feet, and face.

During pregnancy, the two organisms undergo parallel, dramatic changes. The changes that occur in the developing conceptus will be discussed in this section; later in the chapter we will discuss the changes that take place in the pregnant woman.

Pregnancy lasts for approximately nine months (38 weeks) and is typically divided into three equal periods of three months, called *trimesters*, Thus, the first trimester is months one to three, the second trimester is months four to six, and the third (or last) trimester is months seven to nine.

The Embryo and Its Support Systems

We left the conceptus, which began as a single fertilized egg cell, dividing into many cells as it passed down the fallopian tube, finally arriving in the uterus and implanting itself in the uterine wall. Tendrils from the zygote begin to penetrate the blood vessels in the wall of the uterus.

During the embryonic period of development (the first eight weeks), most of the major organ systems are formed in processes that occur with amazing speed. The inner part of the ball of cells implanted in the uterus now differentiates into two layers, the endoderm and the ectoderm. Later, a third layer, the mesoderm, forms between them. The various organs of the body differentiate themselves out of these layers. The *ectoderm* will form the entire nervous system and the skin. The *endoderm* differentiates into the digestive system—from the pharynx, to the stomach and intestines, to the rectum—and the respiratory system. The muscles, skeleton, connective tissues, and reproductive and circulatory systems derive from the *mesoderm*, Development generally proceeds in a cephalocaudal order. That is, the head develops first, and the lower body last. For this reason, the head of an embryo is enormous compared with the rest of the body.

Meanwhile, another group of cells has differentiated into the *trophoblast*, which has important functions in maintaining the embryo and which will eventually become the placenta. The **placenta** develops out of the mass of tissues that surrounds the conceptus early in development and nurtures its growth by producing tendrils that penetrate the blood vessels in the wall of the uterus. As these tendrils become larger and more complex, they form a separate structure. The placenta has a number of important functions, perhaps the most important of which is that it serves as a site for the exchange of substances between the woman's blood and the fetus's blood. It is important to note that the woman's circulatory system and the fetus's circulatory system are completely separate. That is, with only rare exceptions, the woman's blood never circulates inside the fetus, nor does the fetus's blood circulate in the woman's blood vessels. Instead, the fetus's blood passes out of its body through the umbilical cord to the placenta (the spot where the umbilical cord attaches to the fetus becomes the navel or belly button after birth). There it circulates in the numerous *villi* (tiny fingerlike projections in the placenta). The woman's blood circulates around the outside of these villi. Thus, a membrane barrier exists between the two blood systems. Some substances are capable of passing through this barrier, whereas others are not. Oxygen and nutrients can pass through the barrier, and thus the woman's blood supplies oxygen and nutrients to the fetus, providing substitutes for breathing and eating. Carbon dioxide and waste products similarly pass back from the fetal blood to the woman's blood. Some viruses and other disease-causing organisms can pass through the barrier, including those for rubella and syphilis. But other organisms cannot pass

through the barrier; thus the woman may have a terrible cold, but the fetus will remain completely healthy. Various drugs can also cross the placental barrier, and the woman should therefore be careful about drugs taken during pregnancy (we will discuss substances to avoid during pregnancy later in this chapter).

Another major function of the placenta is that it secretes hormones. The placenta produces large quantities of estrogen and progesterone. Many of the physical symptoms of pregnancy may be caused by these elevated levels of hormones. Another hormone manufactured by the placenta is **human chorionic gonadotropin (hCG)**. This is the hormone that is detected in pregnancy tests.

The **umbilical cord** is formed during the fifth week of embryonic development. The fully developed cord is about 55 centimetres (20 inches) long. Normally, it contains three blood vessels: two arteries and one vein. Some people believe that the fetus's umbilical cord attaches to the woman's navel; actually, the umbilical cord attaches to the placenta, thereby providing for the interchanges of substances just described.

Two membranes surround the fetus, the *chorion* and the *amnion*, the amnion being the innermost. The amnion is filled with a watery liquid called **amniotic fluid**, in which the fetus floats and can readily move. It is the amniotic fluid that is sampled when an amniocentesis (discussed shortly) is performed. The amniotic fluid maintains the fetus at a constant temperature and, most important, cushions the fetus against possible injury. Thus, even if the woman falls down, the fetus will probably remain undisturbed. Indeed, the amniotic fluid might be considered the original waterbed.

Fetal Development

Table 6.1 lists the major milestones of fetal development. It is obvious that the development of the fetus during the first trimester is more remarkable than its development during the second and third trimesters. That's because during the first trimester the small mass of cells implanted in the uterus develops into a fetus with most of the major organ systems present and with recognizable human features (see Figure 6.4).

At the end of the 12th week (end of the first trimester), the fetus is unmistakably human and looks like a small infant. It is about 10 centimetres (4 inches) long and weighs about 19 grams (0.75 ounce). From this point on, development consists mainly of the enlargement and differentiation of structures that are already present. By the 18th week, the woman has been able to feel movement for two to four weeks.

During the seventh month the fetus turns in the uterus to assume a head-down position. If this

---

Placenta (plah-SEN-tuh): An organ formed on the wall of the uterus through which the fetus receives oxygen and nutrients and gets rid of waste products.
Human chorionic gonadotropin (hCG): A hormone secreted by the placenta; it is the hormone detected in pregnancy tests.
Umbilical cord: The tube that connects the fetus to the placenta.
Amniotic fluid: The watery fluid surrounding a developing fetus in the uterus.

Figure 6.4 *(a)* This embryo has divided into four cells and would still be travelling down the fallopian tube. *(b)* The embryo after four weeks of development. The major organs are forming; the bright red, blood-filled heart is just below the lower jaw. *(c)* At nine weeks the human fetus is recognizable as a primate. Limbs have formed and ears are clearly visible. *(d)* By about three months the fetus is approximately 10 centimetres long and weighs about 19 grams. Muscles have formed, which move the limbs and body.

turning does not occur by the time of delivery, there will be a *breech presentation*, Women can try assuming various positions to aid the turning (Boston Women's Health Book Collective, 2005). Physicians and midwives can also perform certain procedures to turn the fetus.

The fetus's growth during the last two months is rapid. Canadian babies born at a gestational age of 36 weeks (about eight months) weigh an average of 2804 grams (6 pounds, 3 ounces) (Kramer et al., 2001). The average full-term baby (after 38 weeks of pregnancy) weighs 3562 grams (7 pounds, 14 ounces) and is 50 centimetres (20 inches) long. Research in British Columbia found that infants of European descent weighed significantly more than infants of Chinese or South Asian descent (Janssen et al., 2007).

Table 6.1   Milestones of Fetal Development

First Trimester	
Weeks 3 and 4	Development of the head
	Nervous system begins to form
	Backbone is constructed
Week 5	Formation of the umbilical cord
Weeks 4 to 8	External body parts develop—eyes, ears, arms, hands, fingers, legs, feet, and toes
	Liver, lungs, pancreas, kidneys, and intestines form, and begin limited functioning
Second Trimester	
Week 14	Fetal movement or quickening
Week 18	Fetal heartbeat detected by examiner
Week 24	Fetus is sensitive to light and sound in utero
Third Trimester	
Week 28	Fat deposits form—gains chubby baby appearance
Weeks 29 to birth	Rapid growth

 L02

Pregnancy

The Stages of Pregnancy

The First Trimester (the First 12 Weeks)

Symptoms of pregnancy. For most women, the first symptom of pregnancy is a missed menstrual period. Of course, there may be a wide variety of reactions to this event. For the woman who has not planned the pregnancy or who feels that she already has enough children, the reaction may be depression, anger, and fear. For the woman who has been trying to conceive, the reaction may be joy and eager anticipation.

There are many other reasons besides pregnancy for a woman to have a late period or miss a period. Illness or emotional stress may delay a period, and women occasionally skip a period for no apparent reason.

It is also true that a woman may continue to experience some cyclic bleeding or spotting during pregnancy. This is not particularly a danger sign, except that in some cases it is a symptom of a miscarriage so the woman should consult her physician.

If the woman has been keeping a basal body temperature chart, it can provide a very early sign that she is pregnant. If her temperature rises abruptly at about the time ovulation would normally occur and then stays up for more than two weeks—say, about three weeks—the chances are fairly good that she is pregnant. The increased temperature results from the high level of progesterone manufactured by the corpus luteum and, later, the placenta.

Other early symptoms of pregnancy are tenderness of the breasts—a tingling sensation and special sensitivity of the nipples—and nausea and vomiting (called *morning sickness*, although these symptoms may actually happen any time during the day). More frequent urination, feelings of fatigue, and a need for more sleep are other early signs of pregnancy. Not all pregnant women experience all of these symptoms.

Pregnancy tests. It is important that early, accurate pregnancy tests be available and that women make use of them. This is true for several reasons. A woman needs to know that she is pregnant as early as possible so that she can see a physician or midwife, begin getting good prenatal care, and get the nutrition she requires during pregnancy (see the section on nutrition later in the chapter). If she does not want to carry the baby to term, she needs to know as soon as possible, because abortions are much safer and simpler when performed in the first trimester than in the second.

A pregnancy test may be done in a physician's office, at a Planned Parenthood or sexual health centre, or at a medical laboratory. The most common pregnancy test is an immunologic test based on detecting the presence of hCG (human chorionic gonadotropin, secreted by the placenta) in the woman's urine. It can be done in a matter of minutes and is very accurate. It involves mixing a drop of urine with certain chemicals, either on a slide or in a tube.

The laboratory tests for pregnancy are 98 to 99 percent accurate. A laboratory test may produce a false negative (i.e., tell the woman she is not pregnant when she really is) if it is done too early or if errors are made in processing. Also, some women simply do not show positive signs in the tests or do not do so until the second or third test. The modern urine tests are 98 percent accurate seven days after implantation (just when a period is missed).

A different type of test, called the *beta-hCG radioim-munoassay*, assesses the presence of beta-hCG in a blood sample. It can detect hCG at very low levels, so it can reliably detect pregnancy seven days after fertilization. It is much more expensive than the urine tests and is available only in laboratories associated with hospitals or large clinics.

Home (over-the-counter) pregnancy tests are widely available in drug stores and on the Internet. They are sold under such names as Clearblue and First Response; all are urine tests designed to measure the presence of hCG. They cost from $16 to $36, depending on the number of tests in the package. There are also hCG test strips sold under a variety of names. The charm lies in their convenience and the privacy of getting the results. Manufacturers claim their tests will accurately detect a pregnancy on the first day of the missed period. Laboratory tests of 18 brands found that only 1 of the 18 detected low levels of hCG and only 8 detected high levels of hCG (Cole et al., 2004). Thus 10 of the 18 would produce a false negative result. This compares to an error rate of 1 or 2 percent for laboratory tests. A comparison of six OTC tests found that two of them were accurate at 99 percent, but the accuracy of the other four ranged from 54 to 67 percent (Cole, 2011). A high rate of false negatives is very serious because it leads a pregnant woman to think she is not pregnant; as a result she might take substances or medicines that would harm the fetus, and she would not seek prenatal care. Rare but dangerous conditions, such as an ectopic pregnancy (discussed below), could go undetected. The accuracy of a test depends on its *sensitivity*, the level of hCG in the urine required to obtain a positive result. Available tests vary from 10 mLU/mL to 100 mLU/mL; the lower the number, the higher the sensitivity (Phillips, 2012; the hCG hormone is measured in milli-international units per millilitre or mLU/mL). Complicating matters is the fact that levels of hCG in early pregnancy vary from one woman to the next. Accuracy also depends on following directions *exactly*. Overall, relying on such tests is not a good idea.

The signs of pregnancy may be classified as *presumptive signs*, *probable signs*, and *positive signs*. Amenorrhea, breast tenderness, nausea, and so on, are presumptive signs. The pregnancy tests discussed previously all provide probable signs. Three signs are interpreted as positive signs, that is, as definite indications of pregnancy: (1) beating of the fetal heart, (2) active fetal movement, and (3) detection of a fetal skeleton by ultrasound. These signs cannot be detected until the fourth month, with the exception of ultrasound, which can be used in the first trimester.

Once the pregnancy has been confirmed, the woman generally is very interested in determining her expected delivery date (called EDC for a rather antiquated expression, "expected date of confinement"). The EDC is calculated by using *Nägele's rule*, The rule says to take the date of the first day of the last menstrual period, subtract three months, add seven days, and finally add one year. Thus, if the first day of the last menstrual period was September 10, 2014, the expected delivery date would be June 17, 2015: subtracting three months from September 10 gives June 10, adding seven days yields June 17, and adding one year gives June 17, 2015. These days, most women have at least one ultrasound during the pregnancy. Since ultrasounds are more accurate than Nägele's rule (although they also have a margin of error), these results are often used to revise the due date. Of course, the due date is rarely the delivery date—many factors influence the date on which the baby is actually born.

Physical changes. The basic physical change that takes place in the woman's body during the first trimester is a large increase in the levels of hormones, especially estrogen and progesterone, that are produced by the placenta. Many of the other physical symptoms of the first trimester arise from these endocrine changes.

The breasts swell and tingle. This results from the development of the mammary glands, which is stimulated by hormones. The nipples and the area around them (areola) may darken and broaden.

Women often a need to urinate more frequently. This is related to changes in the pituitary hormones that affect the adrenals, which in turn change the water balance in the body so that more water is retained. The growing uterus also contributes by pressing against the bladder.

Some women experience morning sickness—feelings of nausea, perhaps to the point of vomiting and revulsion toward food or its odour. The nausea and vomiting may occur on waking or at other times during the day. Their exact cause is not known. One theory is that nausea and vomiting cause pregnant women to expel and subsequently avoid foods containing toxic chemicals (Flaxman & Sherman, 2000). Supporting evidence includes a lower rate of miscarriage among women who experience morning sickness. While these symptoms are quite common, about 25 percent of pregnant women experience no vomiting at all.

Vaginal discharges may also increase at this time, partly because the increased hormone levels change the pH of the vagina and partly because the vaginal secretions are changing in their chemical composition and quantity.

The feelings of fatigue and sleepiness are probably related to the high levels of progesterone, which is known to have a sedative effect.

Psychological changes. Our culture is full of stereotypes about the psychological characteristics of pregnant women. According to one view, pregnancy is supposed to be a time of happiness and calm. Radiant contentment, the "pregnant glow," is said to emanate from the woman's face, making this a good time for her to be photographed. According to another view, pregnancy is a time of emotional ups and downs. The pregnant woman swings from very happy to depressed and crying, and back again. She is irrational, sending her partner out in a blizzard for kosher dill pickles.

Research indicates that the situation is more complex than these stereotypes suggest. A woman's emotional state during pregnancy, often assessed with measures of depression, varies according to several factors. First, her attitude toward the pregnancy makes a difference; women who desire the pregnancy are less anxious than women who do not (Kalil et al., 1993). Women who want to be pregnant are more likely to get prenatal care and less likely to smoke (Cheng et al., 2009). A second factor is social class. Several studies have found that low income is associated with depression during pregnancy. For example, a study involving interviews with 192 poor, inner-city pregnant women found that they were twice as likely as their middle-income counterparts to be depressed (Hobfoll et al., 1995). The depression may be due to the economic situation these women face, or there may be more unwanted pregnancies among low-income women. A third influence is the availability of social support. Women with a supportive partner are less likely to be depressed, perhaps because the partner serves as a buffer against stressful events (Chapman et al., 1997).

Research also shows that a woman's emotional state during pregnancy may have an effect on the developing fetus. In one study, women who experienced multiple stressful events during pregnancy had babies who showed small cognitive deficits at 18 months (Bergman et al., 2007). This result may occur because the stress hormone cortisol crosses the placenta (Talge et al., 2007). In a study of Danish women, high stress at 30 weeks was associated with increased risk of **stillbirth**—delivery of a dead fetus (Wisborg et al., 2008). A longitudinal study of 2900 women found that the experience of stressful events—divorce, residential move—during pregnancy was associated with ADHD behaviours in both boys and girls at age two, and independently with autistic traits in boys at age two (Ronald et al., 2011)

Depression is not uncommon during this time. Women who led very active lives before becoming pregnant may find fatigue and lack of energy especially distressing. Depression during the first trimester is more likely among women experiencing other stressful life events, such as moving, changes in their jobs, changes in relationships, or illnesses (Kalil et al., 1993). In this trimester, women's anxieties often centre on concerns about miscarriage.

The Second Trimester (Weeks 13 to 26)

Physical changes. During the fourth month, the woman becomes aware of the fetus's movements ("quickening"). Many women find this a very exciting experience.

The woman is made even more aware of the pregnancy by her rapidly expanding belly. There are a variety of reactions to this. Some women feel that it is a magnificent symbol of womanhood, and they rush out to buy maternity clothes and wear them before they are even necessary. Other women feel awkward and resentful of their expanding abdomen.

Most of the physical symptoms of the first trimester, such as morning sickness, disappear, and discomforts are at a minimum. Physical problems at this time include constipation and nosebleeds (caused by increased blood volume). **Edema**—water retention and swelling—may be a problem in the face, hands, wrists, ankles, and feet; it results from increased water retention throughout the body.

By about mid-pregnancy, the breasts, under hormonal stimulation, have essentially completed their development in preparation for nursing. Beginning about the nineteenth week, thin amber or yellow fluid called **colostrum** may come out of the nipple, although there is no milk yet.

Psychological changes. Although the first trimester can be relatively tempestuous, particularly with morning sickness, the second trimester is usually a period of relative calm and well-being. The discomforts of the first trimester are past, the tensions associated with labour and delivery not yet present. Fear of miscarriage diminishes as the woman feels fetal movement (Leifer, 1980).

Depression is less likely during the second trimester if the pregnant woman has a cohabiting partner or spouse (Hobfoll et al., 1995). Furthermore, women who report more effective partner support report less anxiety in the second trimester (Rini et al., 2006). Interestingly, women who have had a previous pregnancy are more distressed during this time than women who have not (Wilkinson, 1995). This emotion may reflect the impact of the demands associated with the care of other children when a woman is pregnant. Research also indicates that feelings of nurturance, or maternal responsiveness to the infant, increase steadily from the prepregnant to the postpartum period (Fleming et al., 1997). This increase does not appear to be related to changes in hormone levels during pregnancy.

Stillbirth: Delivery of a dead fetus, especially after the 28th week of gestation.

Edema (eh-DEE-muh): Excessive fluid retention and swelling.

Colostrum: A watery substance that is secreted from the breasts at the end of pregnancy and during the first few days after delivery.

The Third Trimester (Weeks 27 to 38)

Physical changes. The uterus is very large and hard by the third trimester. The woman is increasingly aware of her size and of the fetus (Figure 6.5), which is becoming more and more active. In fact, some women are kept awake at night by its somersaults and hiccups.

The extreme size of the uterus puts pressure on a number of other organs, causing some discomfort. There is pressure on the lungs, which may cause shortness of breath. The stomach is also being squeezed, and indigestion is common. The navel is pushed out. The heart is being strained because of the large increase in blood volume. At this stage most women feel low in energy.

Health Canada recommends a woman should gain between 6.5 and 18 kilograms (15 and 40 pounds) depending on the woman's weight before the pregnancy. Women who are underweight (body mass index [BMI] of less than 18.5) should gain at the high end, 12.5 to 18 kilograms; women who are obese (BMI 30 or more) should gain less, 5 to 10 kilograms. The average Canadian full-term infant at birth weighs 3562 grams (7 pounds, 14 ounces); the rest of the weight gain is accounted for by the placenta (about 450 grams, or 1 pound), the amniotic fluid (about 900 grams, or 2 pounds), enlargement of the uterus (about 900 grams, or 2 pounds), enlargement of the breasts (about 750 grams, or 1.5 pounds), and the additional fat and water retained by the woman (3.5 kilograms, or 8 pounds, or more). Physicians recommend limited weight gain (but not too limited) because the incidence of complications, such as high blood pressure and strain on the heart, is much higher in women who gain an excessive amount of weight. Also, excessive weight gained during pregnancy can be very hard to lose afterward.

The woman's balance is somewhat disturbed because of the large amount of weight that has been added to the front part of her body. She may compensate for this by adopting the characteristic "waddling" walk of the pregnant woman, which can result in back pain.

The uterus tightens occasionally in painless contractions called **Braxton-Hicks contractions**. These contractions are not part of labour. It is thought that they help to strengthen the uterine muscles, preparing them for labour.

In a first pregnancy, around two to four weeks before delivery the head drops into the pelvis. This movement is called *lightening*, *dropping*, or *engagement*. Engagement usually occurs during labour in women who have had babies before.

Some women are concerned about the appropriate amount of activity they should engage in during pregnancy—whether some things constitute "overdoing it." Current thinking holds that for a healthy pregnant woman, moderate activity is not dangerous and is

Figure 6.5 A generation ago, women tried to hide their pregnancies by wearing loose tops. Women now proudly show their pregnant bellies.

actually psychologically and physically beneficial. Modern methods of childbirth encourage sensible exercise for the pregnant woman so that she will be in shape for labour (see the section on childbirth options later in this chapter). The matter, of course, is highly individual.

Psychological changes. The patterns noted earlier continue into the third trimester. Psychological well-being is greater among women who have social support (often from their partner), have higher incomes or are middle class, and experience fewer concurrent stressful life events. A Quebec study found that women who reported more anxiety, daily hassles, and stress during pregnancy were more likely to experience pregnancy complications (Da Costa et al., 1998).

What happens to the relationship of the pregnant woman with her partner? A comparison of women pregnant for the first time with women who had experienced previous pregnancies found that first-time mothers reported a significant increase in dissatisfaction with their husbands from the second to the third trimester (Wilkinson, 1995).

Braxton-Hicks contractions: Contractions of the uterus during pregnancy that are not part of actual labour.

The Father's Experience in Pregnancy

To date, most research has focused on the male partner of the pregnant woman, and there is little research on the experiences of the female partner of pregnant women. One particular issue for lesbian couples is heterosexist assumptions and attitudes from health care providers (Dahl et al., 2013; Larsson & Dykes, 2009; McManus et al., 2006). Because of the lack of research on female partners, only male partners' experiences is discussed below.

Physical changes. Some men experience pregnancy symptoms, including indigestion, gastritis, nausea, change in appetite, and headaches (Kiselica & Scheckel, 1995), referred to as a *couvade syndrome,* These symptoms may be caused by hormonal changes in the male. A longitudinal study of 34 couples collected blood samples from both the men and the women before and after the birth of the infant (Storey et al., 2000). Men and women displayed stage-specific hormone differences, including high levels of prolactin prenatally and low levels of testosterone postnatally. Men with more pregnancy symptoms had higher levels of prolactin prenatally.

In some cultures, this phenomenon takes a more dramatic form, known as *couvade ritual,* In this ritual, the husband retires to bed while his wife is in labour. He suffers all the pains of delivery, moaning and groaning as she does. Couvade is still practised in parts of Asia, South America, and Oceania (Gregersen, 1996).

Psychological changes. In Canada in the twenty-first century, many men expect to be actively involved in fathering (Figure 6.6). Men report engaging in many activities in preparation for becoming fathers, including attending parenting classes, planning father–child activities, observing and talking to other fathers, and daydreaming about the baby. Most of these activities, of course, parallel those done by expectant mothers. Fathers or other partners play an important role in preparing for a baby. The birth or arrival of a first child may require finding a larger home or making physical changes to the present one. There will be visits to medical personnel, tests to be taken, and arrangements to be made. Partners who participate in these activities provide support for the pregnant woman and become more involved themselves. Many couples take some form of classes in preparation for childbirth. The classes often specifically address the partner's role in late pregnancy and during labour and delivery. These joint activities contribute to the bond between the partners, which in turn provides a better foundation for the arrival of the new member of the family.

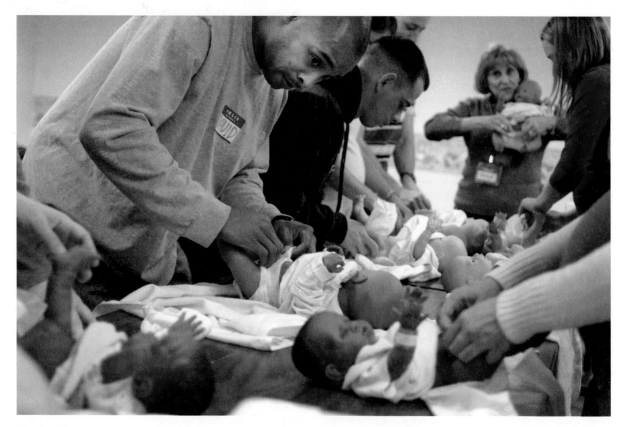

Figure 6.6   Dad learns to change his daughter's diaper at a course for new fathers, which helps new or prospective fathers adjust to their new role.

Recall our discussion in Chapter 2 of the reproductive advantages of a father–infant bond. The likelihood of such a bond depends partly on the father's responsiveness to the infant. In the study of hormonal changes during pregnancy just described, men viewed videotapes with auditory and visual cues from newborns before the blood sample was drawn. Men who showed higher levels of responsiveness had higher levels of prolactin prenatally and lower levels of testosterone postnatally (Storey et al., 2000). Lower levels of testosterone may facilitate paternal behaviour.

Diversity in the Contexts of Pregnancy

Women have babies in many family contexts these days besides the traditional one of being married to the baby's father. These include living in a common-law relationship; not living with the baby's father but seeing him regularly; being a single mother-to-be who has no contact with the baby's father; being a mother-to-be who is pregnant as a result of assisted insemination or other reproductive technologies; and being a woman in a stable relationship with another woman, who is pregnant as a result of assisted insemination or other technologies. Therefore, we use the term *partner* in the following sections.

Sex During Pregnancy

Couples can and do continue to pleasure each other sexually in many ways throughout the pregnancy. However, many heterosexual couples are concerned about whether it is safe or advisable for a pregnant woman to have sexual intercourse, particularly during the later stages of pregnancy. Medical opinion is that—given a normal, healthy pregnancy—intercourse can continue safely (Jones et al., 2011). There is no evidence that intercourse or orgasm is associated with preterm labour (Sayle et al., 2001). In fact, a study involving interviews with pregnant women at 28 weeks gestation and again following delivery found that recent intercourse and orgasm was associated with reduced risk of preterm birth (Sayle et al., 2001; Schaffir, 2006). The only exception is a case where the risk of a miscarriage or preterm labour is already high. Whether and how frequently to engage in sexual activity is a matter for a couple to decide, perhaps in consultation with a physician or midwife.

Most pregnant women with male partners continue to have intercourse throughout the pregnancy (Reamy & White, 1987). The most common pattern is a decline in the frequency of intercourse during the first trimester, variation in the second trimester, and an even greater decline in the third trimester (Fox et al., 2008). Some women report increased arousal during the second trimester. In some cases, the decline in frequency in the third trimester is affected by the partner's perceptions. While some partners find the pregnant woman extremely sexy, others are not attracted to women in the later stages of pregnancy. Little is known about the sexual frequency of pregnant women with female partners.

During the later stages of pregnancy, the woman's shape makes intercourse increasingly awkward, particularly using the man-on-top position. The side-to-side position (see Chapter 9) is probably the most suitable one for intercourse during the late stages of pregnancy. Couples should also remember that they have many ways of experiencing sexual pleasure and orgasm besides having intercourse; hand–genital stimulation or oral–genital sex may be good alternatives.[3] The best guide in this matter is the woman's feelings and comfort.

LO3 Nutrition During Pregnancy

During pregnancy, another living being is growing inside the woman, and she needs lots of energy, protein, vitamins, and minerals at this time. Therefore, diet during pregnancy is extremely important. If the woman's diet is good, she has a much better chance of remaining healthy during pregnancy and of bearing a healthy baby; if her diet is inadequate, she stands more of a chance of developing one of a number of diseases during pregnancy herself and of bearing a child whose weight is low at birth. This difference is a result of the silent struggle for nutrients between mother and fetus discussed earlier. Babies with low birth weights do not have as good a chance of survival as babies with normal birth weights.

How does sexual activity change during pregnancy?

On the other hand, overweight and obese women are at increased risk of negative outcomes for both themselves and the fetus. Risks to the mother include hypertension, gestational diabetes, and Caesarean delivery (Practice Committee of the American Society for Reproductive Medicine, 2008). Risks to the fetus include congenital abnormalities, such as spina bifida, cleft palate, and hydrocephaly (Stothard et al., 2009).

It is particularly important that a pregnant woman get enough protein, folic acid, calcium, magnesium, and vitamin A (Luke, 1994). Protein is important for building new tissues. Folic acid is important for growth; symptoms of folic acid deficiency are anemia and fatigue. A pregnant woman needs much more iron than usual because the fetus draws off iron for itself from the blood that circulates to the placenta. Muscle cramps, nerve pains, uterine ligament pains, sleeplessness, and irritability may all be symptoms of a calcium deficiency.

---

[3] There is, however, some risk associated with cunnilingus for the pregnant woman, as discussed in Chapter 9.

Severe calcium deficiency during pregnancy is associated with increased blood pressure, which may lead to a serious condition called eclampsia, discussed later in this chapter (Repke, 1994). Deficiencies of calcium and magnesium are associated with premature birth. Sometimes even an excellent diet does not provide enough iron, calcium, or folic acid, in which case the pregnant woman should take supplements.

Daily consumption of artificially sweetened soft drinks is linked to increased likelihood of preterm birth (Halldorsson et al., 2010). Women who drank four per day were more likely to have a preterm birth than were women who drank one per day. There was no effect of drinking sugar-sweetened soft drinks.

L03 Substances That May Result in Birth Defects

Substances Taken During Pregnancy

We are such a pill-popping culture that we seldom stop to think about whether we should take a certain drug. The pregnant woman, however, needs to know that when she takes a drug, it not only circulates through her body, but also may circulate through the fetus. Because the fetus develops so rapidly during pregnancy, drugs may produce severe consequences, including serious malformations. Drugs that produce such defects are called **teratogens**.[4] Of course, not all drugs can cross the placental barrier, but many can.

What substances, if taken during pregnancy, threaten the fetus?

Pregnant women should be cautious in using a number of drugs and other substances. A substantial amount of research has documented the risk to a child of maternal alcohol drinking during pregnancy. Alcohol consumed by the woman passes through the membrane barrier in the placenta and circulates through the fetus, so it can have pervasive effects on fetal growth and development (Barr et al., 1990; Jacobson et al., 1993, 1994; Streissguth et al., 1999). The Public Health Agency of Canada ([PHAC], 2012b) has identified maternal drinking as one of the leading causes of preventable birth defects and developmental delays in children; according to the National Longitudinal Survey of Children and Youth, 15 percent of pregnant Canadian women drink some alcohol.

Fetal alcohol spectrum disorder is an umbrella term covering all outcomes associated with any amount of alcohol exposure (Poole, 2008; Sokol et al., 2003). The effects of prenatal alcohol

Teratogens (ter-AH-te-jens): Substances that produce defects in a fetus.
Fetal alcohol spectrum disorder: All outcomes associated with any amount of alcohol exposure during pregnancy.
Fetal alcohol syndrome: Serious growth deficiency and malformations in the child of a mother who abuses alcohol during pregnancy.

[4] Teratogen is from the Greek words *teras,* meaning "monster," and *gen,* meaning "cause."

consumption are dose-dependent; that is, the more alcohol the mother drinks, the larger the number and severity of effects on the child (Figure 6.7). The most serious effects are a pattern of malformations termed **fetal alcohol syndrome**, which is characterized by both prenatal and postnatal growth deficiencies; a small brain; small eye openings; joint, limb, and heart malformations; and cognitive impairment (for a review, see Mattson & Riley, 1998). It affects 1 percent of Canadians (PHAC, 2005). Research indicates that "risk drinking" (seven or more drinks per week or five or more drinks on one occasion) poses a serious health threat to the fetus. In a Danish study of 89,201 pregnant women, women who reported three or more binge drinking episodes (five or more drinks on one occasion) were more likely to experience stillbirth (Strandberg-Larsen, 2008). A study of 655,979 births in the United States found that women who drank during pregnancy were 40 percent more likely to experience a stillbirth.

However, according to the Public Health Agency of Canada (2012b), there is no safe amount of alcohol during pregnancy. Perhaps understandably, there are many reports of well-intentioned bartenders, waitstaff, and patrons approaching pregnant women consuming alcohol and asking them not to drink.

Tobacco use during pregnancy retards fetal growth and increases the risk of infant illness, disability, and death. Maternal smoking is associated with prematurity; low birth weight; cardiovascular anomalies; conditions involving arteries, veins, or the heart; and asthma (Jaakkola & Gissler, 2004; Kai & Pourier, 2001; Woods & Raju, 2001). Results from the Maternity Experience Survey indicate that 11 percent of Canadian women smoke during pregnancy (Al-Sahab, Saqib, et al., 2010). Other substances that may produce low birth weight, birth complications, or defects in the fetus include steroids, some antihistamines, long-term use of antibiotics, excessive amounts of vitamin A, D, B6, and K, caffeine, antidepressant medication, lithium, cocaine, and marijuana. These effects are summarized in Table 6.2.

As with alcohol, the best rule for the pregnant woman considering using a prescription or over-the-counter drug, herbal product, or other substance is to consult her physician. Up-to-date information on the effects of various legal substances is available from the Motherisk Information Line at the Hospital for Sick Children by telephone at 1-877-439-2744 or on the Internet at www.motherisk.org.

Dads and Drugs

Most research has focused on the effects of drugs taken by the pregnant woman. However, new theorizing suggests that drugs taken by men before conception may also cause birth defects, probably because the drugs damage the sperm and their genetic contents (Narod et al., 1988).

(a)   *(b)*

Figure 6.7   The effects of prenatal exposure to alcohol and other drugs. *(a)* A child born with fetal alcohol syndrome. *(b)* A preterm baby whose mother used crack cocaine during pregnancy.

Table 6.2 Teratogenic Effect of Frequently Used Substances on Prenatal Development	
Legal Drugs	**Potential Negative Effects**
Nicotine	Prematurity, low birth weight, delayed intellectual and behavioural development, risk of pneumonia, bronchitis, laryngitis, inner ear infections; fathers' smoking may transmit risk of cancer to offspring.
Alcohol	Fetal alcohol syndrome (physical defects, short stature, mental retardation, hyperactivity, stereotypical behaviours, congenital addiction leading to withdrawal syndrome); father's abuse of alcohol may cause genetic damage that leads to birth defects. The combination of parental smoking and drinking may cause miscarriages, prematurity, low birth weight, and sudden infant death syndrome (SIDS).
Illegal Drugs	
Heroin, morphine, methadone, oxycodone	In mother, difficulty conceiving; in infant, prematurity, low birth weight, addiction, withdrawal, death.
Marijuana	In mother, difficulty conceiving; in infant, prematurity, low birth weight, high-pitched crying; no long-term effects.
Cocaine	In mother, difficulty conceiving; in infant, prematurity, low birth weight, neurological deficits, small head circumference; in father may lead to reduced sperm count and decreased fertility.
Lysergic acid diethylamide (LSD)	Chromosomal breakage.
Medications/Treatments	
Steroids	Heart and circulatory problems; masculinization of female fetus.
Diethylstilbestrol (DES)	In mother, miscarriage; in infant, prematurity, low birth weight; female child may develop cancer of the cervix; male child may have reproductive abnormalities and increased risk of testicular cancer.
Reserpine (tranquillizer)	Respiratory problems in infant.
Antibiotics	Defective skeletal growth in infant, hearing loss, jaundice.
Aspirin	Blood disorders in infant.
Some anticonvulsant medications	Cleft lip and palate in infant; failure of blood coagulation.
Lithium	Cardiovascular abnormalities.
SSRI antidepressant medication	Feeding and breathing difficulties at birth; low birth weight.

Source: Adapted from E. Hetherington and R. Parke, *Child Psychology*, Table 4.2. c McGraw-Hill Companies, Inc. (2003).

For example, marijuana use has been linked to a decreased sperm count, more damaged sperm, and reduced fertility (Gorzalka & Hill, 2006). In addition, one study found that not only did a mother's smoking during the first trimester of pregnancy increase her offspring's risk of cancer in childhood, but a father's smoking during the pregnancy in the absence of the mother's smoking also increased this risk (John et al., 1991).

Viral Illness During Pregnancy

Certain viruses may cross the placental barrier from the woman to the fetus and cause considerable harm, particularly if the illness occurs during the first trimester of pregnancy. The best known example is rubella. If a woman gets rubella during the first month of pregnancy, there is a 50 percent chance that the infant will be born deaf or have cognitive deficits, cataracts, or congenital heart defects. The risk then declines, so that by the third month of pregnancy the chance of abnormalities is only about 10 percent. Although most women have an immunity to rubella because they either had it when they were children or were immunized, a woman who suspects that she is not immune can receive a vaccination that will give her immunity; she should do this well before she becomes pregnant.

Herpes simplex is also *teratogenic*, that is, capable of producing defects in the fetus. Usually, the infant contracts the disease by direct contact with the sore; delivery by Caesarean section can prevent this. Women with herpes genitalis also have a high risk of spontaneously aborting.

A woman who is infected with HIV, the virus that causes AIDS, can pass the virus on to her child during pregnancy, delivery, or after birth through her breast milk. In Canada, pregnant women are given the option of being tested for HIV, but testing is not required. It is important that pregnant women know if they are HIV positive. Without treatment, 28 percent of their babies will become infected; however, if the infected mother takes AZT, an antiretrovirus drug, the likelihood of such perinatal transmission is reduced by two-thirds to 8 percent (Canadian Paediatric Society, 2013).

Detecting Birth Defects

As has been noted, a number of factors, such as substances taken during pregnancy and illness during pregnancy, may cause defects in the fetus. Other causes include genetic defects (e.g., phenylketonuria, PKU, which causes cognitive impairment) and chromosomal defects (e.g., Down syndrome, which causes cognitive impairment as well as other problems).

Amniocentesis (am-nee-oh-sen-TEE-sus): A test to determine whether a fetus has birth defects; done by inserting a fine tube into the woman's abdomen to obtain a sample of amniotic fluid.

Chorionic villus sampling (CVS): A technique for prenatal diagnosis of birth defects; involves taking a sample of cells from the chorionic villus and analyzing them.

Genetic defects are more likely to occur as the age of the mother or the father increases (Society of Obstetricians and Gynaecologists of Canada [SOGC], 2012). As noted earlier, obesity in the mother is associated with congenital abnormalities (Stothard et al., 2009).

About 4 to 5 percent of all babies in Canada are born with a birth defect or anomaly. About one-fourth of miscarried fetuses are malformed. The cause of more than half of these defects is unknown (O'Shea, 1995). However, amniocentesis, chorionic villus sampling, and genetic counselling are options to detect genetic defects, provided that abortion is ethically acceptable to the parents.

Amniocentesis involves inserting a fine tube through the pregnant woman's abdomen and removing some amniotic fluid, including cells sloughed off by the fetus, for analysis. The technique is capable of providing an early diagnosis of most chromosomal abnormalities, some genetically produced biochemical disorders, and sex-linked diseases carried by females but affecting males (hemophilia and muscular dystrophy), although it cannot detect all defects. If a defect is discovered, the woman may then decide to terminate the pregnancy with an abortion.

Amniocentesis should be performed between the 13th and 16th weeks of pregnancy. If a defect is discovered and an abortion is to be performed, it should be done as early as possible (see Chapter 7). Because amniocentesis itself involves some risk, it is generally thought (although the matter is controversial) that it should be performed only on women who have a high risk of bearing a child with a birth defect. A woman is in this category if (1) she has already had one child with a genetic defect; (2) she believes that she is a carrier of a genetic defect, which can usually be established through genetic counselling; and (3) she is over 35, in which case she has a greatly increased chance of bearing a child with a chromosomal abnormality.

Chorionic villus sampling (CVS) is an alternative to amniocentesis for prenatal diagnosis of genetic defects (Doran, 1990; Kolker, 1989). A major problem with amniocentesis is that it cannot be done until the second trimester of pregnancy; if genetic defects are discovered, there may have to be a late abortion. Chorionic villus sampling, in contrast, can be done in the first trimester of pregnancy, usually around 9 to 11 weeks postconception. Chorionic villus sampling can be performed in one of two ways: transcervically, in which a catheter is inserted into the uterus through the cervix, as shown in Figure 6.8; and transabdominally, in which a needle (guided by ultrasound) is inserted through the abdomen. In either case a sample of cells is taken from the chorionic villi (the chorion is the outermost membrane surrounding the fetus, the amnion, and the amniotic fluid), and these cells are analyzed for evidence of

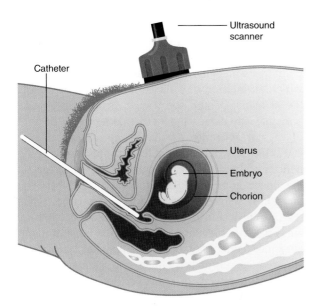

Labels on figure: Ultrasound scanner, Catheter, Uterus, Embryo, Chorion

Figure 6.8 Chorionic villus sampling (CVS) and amniocentesis are both available for prenatal diagnosis of genetic defects. CVS (shown here) is able to detect chromosomal abnormalities and sex-linked diseases.

genetic defects. Studies indicate that CVS is as accurate as amniocentesis. Like amniocentesis, it carries with it a slight risk of fetal loss (caused, for example, by miscarriage). For both amniocentesis and CVS, the fetal loss rate is between 1 and 1.5 percent, but can be as low as 0.02 percent in experienced hands (SOGC, 2007a).

Serious ethical questions are raised when amniocentesis and CVS are used to determine gender and are followed by an abortion if the fetus is not the desired sex.

Birth

The Beginning of Labour

The signs that labour is about to begin vary from one woman to the next. There may be a discharge of a small amount of bloody mucus (the "bloody show"). This is the mucus plug that was in the cervical opening during pregnancy, its purpose being to prevent germs from passing from the vagina up into the uterus. In about 10 percent of women the membranes containing the amniotic fluid rupture (the bag of waters bursts), and there is a gush of warm fluid down the woman's legs. Labour usually begins within 24 hours after this occurs. More commonly, the amniotic sac does not rupture until the end of the first stage of labour. The Braxton-Hicks contractions may increase before labour and actually may be mistaken for labour. Typically, they are distinct from the contractions of labour in that they are very irregular.

The biological mechanism that initiates and maintains labour is not completely understood. The progesterone-withdrawal theory is the leading hypothesis (Schwartz, 1997). Progesterone is known to inhibit uterine contractions. It has been proposed that some mechanism, such as increased production of antiprogesterone, reduces the inhibiting effect of progesterone and labour begins.

The Stages of Labour

Labour is typically divided into three stages, although the length of the stages may vary considerably from one woman to the next. The whole process of childbirth is sometimes referred to as *parturition*.

First-Stage Labour

First-stage labour begins with the regular contractions of the muscles of the uterus. These contractions are responsible for producing two changes in the cervix, both of which must occur before the baby can be delivered. These changes are called **effacement** (thinning out) and **dilation** (opening up). The cervix must dilate until it has an opening 10 centimetres (4 inches) in diameter before the baby can be born.

First-stage labour itself is divided into three stages: early, late, and transition. In *early first stage labour*, contractions are spaced far apart, with perhaps 15 to 20 minutes between them. A contraction typically lasts 45 seconds to a minute. This stage of labour is fairly easy, and the woman is quite comfortable between contractions. Meanwhile, the cervix is effacing and dilating.

Late first-stage labour is marked by the dilation of the cervix from 5 to 8 centimetres (2 to 3 inches). It is generally shorter than the early stage, and the contractions are more frequent and more intense.

The final dilation of the cervix from 8 to 10 centimetres (3 to 4 inches) occurs during the **transition** phase, which is both short and difficult. The contractions are very strong, and it is during this stage that women report the most pain and exhaustion.

The first stage of labour can last anywhere from 2 to 24 hours. It averages about 12 to 15 hours for a first pregnancy and about 8 hours for later pregnancies. (In most respects, first labours are the hardest; later ones are easier.) Women having a physician-assisted birth are usually told to go to the hospital when the contractions are four to five minutes apart. Women having a hospital birth are put in the labour room or birthing room for the rest of first-stage labour. Midwives tell their clients to page

Effacement: A thinning out of the cervix during labour.
Dilation: An opening up of the cervix during labour; also called dilatation.
First-stage labour: The beginning of labour, during which there are regular contractions of the uterus; the stage lasts until the cervix is dilated 8 centimetres.
Transition: The most difficult part of labour at the end of the first stage, during which the cervix dilates from 8 to 10 centimetres.

them when their contractions are five minutes apart, last one minute, and have been that way for an hour. When the woman calls, the midwife does an individual assessment and makes a recommendation about assessing her at home, meeting her at the hospital, or waiting through what sounds like early labour and paging the midwife again when the contractions get stronger.

Second-Stage Labour: Delivery

Second-stage labour (see Figure 6.9) begins when the cervix is fully dilated and the baby's head (or whichever part comes first, if the baby is in some other position; see Figure 6.10) begins to move into the vagina, or birth canal. It lasts from a few minutes to a few hours and is generally much shorter than the first stage. If you have never seen a birth, a number of videos are available on the Internet showing women's birth experiences and choices (e.g., www.givingbirthnaturally.com).

Second-stage labour: The stage during which the baby moves out through the vagina and is delivered.
Episiotomy (ih-pees-ee-ah-tuh-mee): An incision made in the skin just behind the vagina, allowing the baby to be delivered more easily.

During this stage, many women feel an urge to push or bear down, and if done properly, this may be of great assistance in pushing the baby out. With each contraction the baby is pushed farther along.

When the baby's head has traversed the entire length of the vagina, the top of it becomes visible at the vaginal entrance; this is called *crowning,* It is at this point that some physicians perform an **episiotomy**, in which an incision or a slit is made in the perineum, the skin just behind the vagina; in Canada episiotomy rates are decreasing so that currently 17 percent of vaginal deliveries involve an episiotomy (PHAC, 2012b). Most women do not feel the episiotomy being performed because the pressure of the baby against the pelvic floor provides a natural anaesthetic. The incision is stitched closed after the baby is born. The reason physicians give for performing an episiotomy are that it will prevent impaired sexual functioning in later life, reduce the severity of perineal lacerations, and reduce postdelivery pain and medication use. However, a review of relevant research conducted between 1950 and 2004 found no evidence that any of these benefits result from episiotomies (Hartmann et al., 2005). Critics claim that it is unnecessary and is done merely for the doctor's convenience, while causing the woman discomfort later as it is healing. Midwives reduce the likelihood of vaginal tears during childbirth by massaging the vaginal area and applying ointments during delivery (Maticka-Tyndale & Bicher,

(a) (b)

Figure 6.9 Second-stage labour. *(a)* Baby's head crowning and then *(b)* moving out.

(a) (b) (c)

Figure 6.10 Possible positions of the fetus during birth. *(a)* A breech presentation (4 percent of births). *(b)* A transverse presentation (fewer than 1 percent). *(c)* A normal, head-first or cephalic presentation (96 percent of births).

1996). Perineal support, including massage or warm compresses, reduces the risk of third- and fourth-degree lacerations by half (Aasheim et al., 2011). Research in Quebec has shown that perineal massage performed by the woman or her partner during the last few weeks of pregnancy also significantly reduces the risk of tears in the perineum, but only for women who have not had a previous vaginal birth (Eason et al., 2000; Labrecque et al., 1999).

The baby is finally eased completely out of the mother's body. At this point, the baby is still connected to the mother by the umbilical cord, which runs from the baby's navel to the placenta, and the placenta is still inside the mother's uterus. As the baby takes its first breath of air, the functioning of its body changes dramatically. Blood begins to flow to the lungs, there to take on oxygen, and a flap closes between the two atria (chambers) in the heart. This process generally takes a few minutes, during which time the baby changes from a somewhat bluish colour to a healthy, pink hue. At this point, the baby no longer needs the umbilical cord, which is clamped and cut off about 7 centimetres (3 inches) from the body. The stub gradually dries up and falls off.

To avoid the possibility of transmitting gonorrhea or other eye infections from the mother to the baby, drops of silver nitrate or a similar drug are placed in the baby's eyes (see Chapter 8).

Third-Stage Labour

During **third-stage labour**, the placenta detaches from the walls of the uterus, and the afterbirth (placenta and fetal membranes) is expelled. This stage may take from a few minutes to an hour. Several contractions may accompany the expulsion of the placenta. The episiotomy or any tears are sewn up.

Caesarean Section (C-section)

Caesarean section is a surgical procedure for delivery; it is used when normal vaginal birth is impossible or undesirable. Caesarean section may be required for a number of different reasons: if the baby is too large or if the mother's pelvis is too small to allow the baby to move into the vagina; if the labour has been very long and hard and the cervix is not dilating or if the mother is nearing the point of total exhaustion; if the umbilical cord *prolapses* (moves into a position such that it is coming out through the cervix ahead of the baby); if there is a D (Rh) incompatibility; or if there is excessive bleeding or the mother's or the infant's condition suddenly becomes lifethreatening. Another condition requiring a C-section is *placenta previa*, in which the placenta is attached to the wall of the uterus close to or covering the cervix.

In a Caesarean section, an incision is first made through the abdomen and then through the wall of the uterus. The physician lifts out the baby and then sews up the uterine wall and the abdominal wall. It is not true that once a woman has had one delivery by Caesarean she must have all subsequent deliveries by the same method. Vaginal births after Caesareans (VBAC) are possible (Miller et al., 1996). Up to 60 percent of women with a prior Caesarean attempt a subsequent vaginal birth (Lydon-Rochelle et al., 2001). Of these, 63 percent are successful and the success rate increases with each prior VBAC (Mercer et al., 2008). In 2004–2005, 26 percent of Canadian births were by Caesarean section (PHAC, 2009a). The lowest rate of Caesarean delivery was in Nunavut; the highest were in Nova Scotia, Prince Edward Island, and British Columbia. The rate of Caesarean delivery in Canada is considerably higher than in most Western European countries.

There is concern about the high and increasing Canadian Caesarean rates. Reasons that have been proposed to explain the rates include the following: (1) more older women giving birth, and they may have more difficult labours necessitating Caesareans; (2) fetal monitors are used increasingly and can give the physician early warning if the fetus is in distress, necessitating a Caesarean to save the fetus; and (3) more women are requesting (and are having) a Caesarean without clear medical reasons for it. In fact, an analysis of 540,174 primary C-sections and 371,683 repeat Caesarean births in the United States in 2001 classified 11 percent of the former and 55 percent of the latter as potentially unnecessary (Kabir et al., 2005).

There is considerable controversy about these elective C-sections—that is, Caesarean on-demand. On the one hand, some people argue that benefits of elective Caesarean delivery are that not having vaginal deliveries reduces women's risk of urinary incontinence, protects them from fear and pain, and protects the fetus from birth-related injuries (Minkoff & Chervenak, 2003). Thus, they feel that women should be given the choice of having a Caesarean if they want one. On the other hand, opponents argue that having a Caesarean increases health risks to both the mother and the fetus and should be performed only for specific problem situations (Canadian Association of Midwives, 2004). Caesarean deliveries are associated with higher rates of obstetrical trauma (Hines & Jiang, 2012) and of complications requiring hospitalization of mother or infant (Stranges et al., 2011) than vaginal deliveries. Thus, they argue that women should not be given the choice of a Caesarean delivery, and Caesarean surgery should only be performed when medically necessary. Education of both pregnant women and of

Third-stage labour: The stage during which the afterbirth is expelled.
Caesarean section (C-section): A method of delivering a baby surgically, by an incision in the abdomen.

medical staff can reduce rates of unnecessary Caesarean sections (Hollander, 1996).

 ### Childbirth Options

Pregnant women and their partners can choose from a variety of childbirth options. They can take childbirth classes to prepare mentally and physically for labour and delivery. Several options are available regarding the use of anaesthesia during childbirth. Finally, depending on the province or territory, women can often choose to give birth at home, in a birthing centre, or in a hospital labour room.

Prepared Childbirth

There are several methods of prepared childbirth. Most are based on the assumption that fear causes tension and tension causes pain. Thus, programs attempt to eliminate the pain of childbirth by providing education (to eliminate the woman's fears of the unknown) and teaching relaxation techniques (to eliminate tension).

One of the most widely used methods of *prepared childbirth* was developed by French obstetrician Fernand Lamaze. Classes teaching the Lamaze method or variations of it are now offered in most areas of the world. The **Lamaze method** involves two basic techniques, *relaxation* and *controlled breathing* (see Figure 6.11). The woman learns to relax all the muscles in her body. Knowing how to do this has a number of advantages, including conservation of energy during an event that requires considerable endurance and, more important, avoidance of the tension that increases the perception of pain. The woman also learns a series of controlled breathing exercises, which she will use to help her during each contraction.

Some other techniques are taught as well. One, called *effleurage*, consists of a light, circular stroking of the abdomen with the fingertips. Exercises can strengthen specific muscles, such as the leg muscles, which undergo considerable strain during labour and delivery. Finally, because of the assumption that fear and the pain it causes are best eliminated through education, women learn a great deal about the processes involved in pregnancy and childbirth.

One other important component of several methods is the requirement that the woman be accompanied during the training and during child birth itself by her partner or some other person, who serves as coach. The coach plays an integral role in the woman's learning of the techniques and her use of them during labour. The coach is present during labour and delivery. The coach times contractions, checks on the mother's

Lamaze method: A method of "prepared" childbirth involving relaxation and controlled breathing.
Doula: An individual who provides physical and emotional support during childbirth.

Figure 6.11   Practice in relaxation and breathing techniques are important parts of prepared childbirth.

state of relaxation and gives her feedback, suggests breathing patterns, helps elevate her back as she pushes the baby out, and generally provides encouragement and moral support. Aside from the obvious benefits to the mother, this represents real progress in that it allows the partner to play an active role in the birth of the child and to experience more fully one of the most basic and moving of all human experiences. The presence of a companion of the woman's choice during labour and delivery has a positive influence on women's satisfaction with the birth process and does not interfere with other events (Bruggemann et al., 2007).

Some couples also have a **doula** (a Greek word meaning "woman's servant") present during childbirth. The doula does not perform clinical or medical tasks; her role (almost all doulas are female) is to provide physical, emotional, and informational support to the woman and her partner during labour and birth.

One common misunderstanding about prepared childbirth is the belief that the use of anaesthetics is prohibited. In fact, the goal is to teach each woman the techniques she needs to control her reactions to labour so that she will not need an anaesthetic; however, it affirms her right to have an anaesthetic if she wants one.

The topic of anaesthetics in childbirth, which has become quite controversial in recent years, is discussed in the next section.

A number of studies indicate that childbirth training, such as the Lamaze method, has several desirable results. These include reduction in the length of labour, decreased incidence of birth complications, a decrease in the use of anaesthetics, a more positive attitude after birth, increased self-esteem, and a heightened sense of being in control (e.g., Felton & Segelman, 1978; Zax et al., 1975). Lamaze training is associated with increased tolerance for pain and reduced anxiety both before birth and four weeks after birth (Markman & Kadushin, 1986; McClure & Brewer, 1980; Worthington et al., 1983).

Prepared childbirth has undoubtedly improved the childbirth experiences of thousands of women and men. On the other hand, some advocates are so idealistic that they may create unrealistic expectations about delivery, especially for women having their first baby (**primiparas**). The use of prepared childbirth reduces pain in childbirth but does not eliminate it completely. Primiparas often experience a discrepancy between their positive expectations for delivery and the actual outcomes (Booth & Meltzoff, 1984). Thus, while these methods produce excellent outcomes and help women control pain, childbirth still involves some pain, as well as unexpected complications in some cases.

The Use of Anaesthetics in Childbirth

Throughout most of human history, childbirth has taken place without anaesthetics and in the woman's home or other familiar surroundings. The pattern in North America began to change about 250 years ago when male physicians rather than midwives began to assist during birth. Today almost all births occur in hospitals (Maticka-Tyndale & Bicher, 1996). A major change came around the middle of the nineteenth century, with the development of anaesthetics for use in surgery. When their use in childbirth was suggested, there was initial opposition from physicians and clergy (who argued that women's pain in childbirth was prescribed in the Bible, quoting Genesis 3:16: "In sorrow thou shalt bring forth children"). Opposition to the use of anaesthetics virtually ceased, however, when Queen Victoria gave birth under chloroform anaesthesia in 1853. Since then, the use of anaesthetics has become routine (too routine, according to some) and effective. Before discussing the arguments for and against the use of anaesthetics, let us briefly review some of the common techniques of anaesthesia used in childbirth.

Tranquillizers (such as Valium) or narcotics may be administered when labour becomes fairly intense. They relax the woman and take the edge off the pain. Barbiturates (such as Seconal) are administered to put the woman to sleep. Scopolamine may sometimes be used for its amnesic effects; it makes the woman forget what has happened, and thus she has no memory afterward of any pain during childbirth. Regional and local anaesthetics, which numb only the specific region of the body that is painful, are used most commonly. An example is the pudendal block (named for the pudendum, or vulva), in which an injection numbs only the external genitals. Other examples are spinal anaesthesia (a "spinal"), in which an injection near the spinal cord numbs the entire birth area, from the waist down, and the caudal block and epidural anaesthesia, which are both administered by injections in the back and produce regional numbing from the belly to the thighs (for more information, see Coustan, 1995). Overall, 57 percent of Canadian women with a vaginal delivery received an epidural. However, the rates vary considerably across jurisdictions. For example, in 2010–2011, 70 percent of vaginal births in Quebec and 62 percent of births in Ontario involved an epidural. However, only 38 percent of births in Manitoba and 33 percent in BC included one (Canadian Institute for Health Information [CIHI], 2012).

The routine use of anaesthetics has been questioned by some. Proponents of the use of anaesthetics argue that with modern technology, women no longer need to experience pain during childbirth and that they shouldn't suffer unnecessarily. Opponents argue that anaesthetics have a number of well-documented dangerous effects on both mother and infant. Anaesthetics in the mother's bloodstream pass through the placenta to the infant. Thus, while they have the desired effect of depressing the mother's central nervous system, they also depress the infant's nervous system. Anaesthetics prevent the mother from using her body as effectively as she might to help push the baby out. If administered early in labour, anaesthetics may inhibit uterine contractions, slow cervical dilation, and prolong labour. They also numb a woman to one of the most fundamental experiences of her life. However, research shows that the negative effects of epidural anaesthesia, such as the increased likelihood of the use of instruments during delivery and longer second-stage labour, can be reduced by using low dosages and techniques that allow the woman to move around (Comet, 2001).

Perhaps the best resolution of this controversy is to say that a pregnant woman should participate in prepared childbirth classes and should use those techniques during labour. If, when she is in labour, she discovers that she cannot control the pain and wants an anaesthetic, she should be able to request it and to do so without guilt; the anaesthetic should then be administered with great caution.

Primipara: A woman having her first baby.

Home Birth Versus Hospital Birth

We noted in Chapter 2 the process of *medicalization*, in which various life conditions and events are defined in medical terms, as requiring medical treatment. Childbirth is a process that was medicalized in Canada, resulting in the shift of almost all births from homes to hospitals. Further, various interventions, including induction of labour, use of anesthesia and C-sections, have become more common in the past 50 years (Laughon et al., 2012). Bucking this trend are advocates of home birth who argue that the atmosphere in a hospital—with its forbidding machines, regulations, and general lack of homeyness—is stressful to the woman and detracts from what should be a joyous, natural human experience (see Figure 6.12). Furthermore, hospitals are meant to deal with illness, and the delivery of a baby should not be viewed as an illness; hospital births may encourage the use of procedures, such as forceps deliveries and episiotomies, that can themselves be dangerous.

Either a physician or a midwife (in provinces and territories in which midwifery is a legal profession) may assist in a home birth. Birth at home is likely to be more relaxed and less stressful; friends and other children are often present. A study comparing the outcomes of planned home births with a licensed midwife to

Figure 6.12 A home birth.

planned hospital births for low-risk women in Ontario (where midwives are well established and integrated into the health care system) found that negative outcomes were low for both groups and that the two groups did not differ in maternal or fetal outcomes (Hutton et al., 2009). Nonetheless, nearly all births in Canada (98 percent) occur in a hospital or clinic (PHAC, 2009a).

On the other side of the argument, hospital practices in labour and delivery have changed radically, particularly with the increased popularity of prepared childbirth; thus, hospitals are not the forbidding, alien environments they once were. Most hospitals, for example, allow partners and loved ones to be present for the entire labour and delivery, and many allow the partner to be present in the operating room during Caesarean deliveries. Many hospitals have created birthing rooms, containing comfortable beds and armchairs, that permit labour and delivery to occur in a relaxed atmosphere and in the position the woman chooses, while being only a minute away from emergency equipment if it is required. Further, women can still have a midwife and choose to give birth in a hospital.

For any home birth, careful screening is essential. Only women with normal pregnancies and anticipated normal deliveries should attempt a home birth. A qualified physician or midwife must be part of the planning. Finally, there must be access to a hospital in case an emergency arises.

Use of Midwives

Although most babies worldwide are delivered by midwives, in Canada in 2006 only 6 percent of women received prenatal care from a midwife (PHAC, 2009a). However, the status of midwives in Canada is in transition in that it is being recognized as an independent professional in more and more provinces. In 2013 midwifery was a legal and regulated profession in British Columbia, Alberta, Saskatchewan, Manitoba, Ontario, Quebec, Nova Scotia, the Northwest Territories, and Nunavut. Midwives practise independently in these provinces and territories. Further, midwives are publicly funded in all of these provinces and territories so that women can choose to be followed by a physician or by a midwife. In addition, New Brunswick has passed legislation but has not licensed any midwives. According to the Canadian Midwifery Regulators Consortium (2007), registered midwives typically have an undergraduate degree in midwifery; some also have a nursing degree. Six Canadian universities offer this program. To be registered, a midwife must show that she (there is only one male midwife in Canada) is able to deliver competent care as a primary caregiver to women who are considered low risk. Many women are not familiar with midwifery. Nonetheless, more and more women are requesting to have their pregnancy and birth in the

One Woman's Experience Giving Birth Under the Care of a Midwife

I was 27 when I had my first child. I was living in British Columbia and her birth was, of course, a memorable experience. In a few words I would describe it as relaxed, personal, secure, and simple.

I was under the care of a team of two midwives throughout my pregnancy; I had many opportunities to get to know them. My partner attended many appointments as we were able to schedule some in the evening. He preferred one of the two midwives and I preferred the other; we each found something different in the two women that particularly appealed to us. Both my sister and my mom were encouraged to attend appointments with me. They were amazed when they got to hear my daughter's heartbeat very early on.

When my labour began, I'd been aware of having Braxton-Hicks contractions for some time, and even though it was my first childbirth experience, I could tell the difference. Although I was still in early labour, I called my midwife, then went for a walk, and took a bath. By this time I was still having regular contractions and they were still quite far apart. I called my midwife, Sylvia, again. She said she'd come check on me, and if I were further along than she thought, she would stay. Sylvia was the midwife I had felt a stronger connection with. As it turned out, it was not her turn to take calls. However, they were so busy with other births that neither of them had had much rest in 48 hours.

Nonetheless, she stayed. We ate, we watched *Friends* on TV, and my family came by to visit with me in my home while I laboured. Apparently I was coping very well, not sounding like a woman close to active labour. At 8 p.m., I was about 5 cm dilated. I was disappointed because this hadn't changed in a while. I had tremendous back labour, and so when contractions occurred I leaned over all of the couch cushions, while family members took turns applying counter-pressure on my tailbone. In between contractions we chatted and relaxed in anticipation. Within an hour or so, my midwife suggested that we could break my waters if I wanted to because that it might speed things up. My intention was to have a hospital birth, so it was my choice as to whether I wanted to break the water at home or head in to the hospital and do it there. I thought, "Now, why would I want to make all that mess at home when someone else could clean it up?"

By the time we arrived at the hospital 15 minutes later, things were already beginning to progress. As we walked past admitting, Sylvia told the staff, "She's further along than she looks, her husband will look after the paperwork," and upstairs we went. My sister helped me into the shower where I soon found that I couldn't stand up but also couldn't sit because there was too much pressure. Into the hospital bed I went, where I found myself doing squats from a reclined position. Sylvia and two nurses in the delivery room were amazing, talking me through everything, informing me of what would happen next, bringing me back down as I lost a bit of control in transition. "Lost a bit of control" is a polite way of saying that I totally lacked focus, and felt like I just couldn't manage. When I began screaming, the nurse directed me to turn inward. I remembered my yoga chanting and that helped me regain focus and, although I did a lot of moaning, I no longer felt a need to scream.

My husband was by my side holding my hand, and supporting me physically when I needed to pull up and squat with the contractions. Around 10:45 p.m. my sister was watching as my daughter's head crowned (less than an hour after being admitted), with absolute awe she looked at my husband and said, "you have to SEE this!" He took a quick peak, but dared not leave my side. I felt my daughter's hair with my fingers and her head was delivered without incident. Then she rushed out so fast that the she almost flew right past my midwife's arms, tearing me with her shoulder! With great interest Sylvia informed me that my daughter's umbilical cord was longer than she'd ever seen before. She and my husband measured it later to be approximately four feet long!

Within moments my daughter, Breanna, was wiped and swaddled and handed to me. I remember that feeling. It was like she opened a part of my heart I never even knew was there. The love I felt for her had been there all along, long before she was conceived, just waiting to be released. Within moments of her birth, my mother was in the delivery room to meet her first grand-daughter.

Source: Written by Trish McCourt.

care of a midwife—so much so that the demand for midwives far exceeds the supply. (See one woman's experience with a midwife in First Person).

Why do women choose to have their baby delivered by a midwife rather than a physician? First, midwives provide care from early pregnancy to six weeks after the baby is born, therefore providing continuity of care. Thus, the midwife and the family get to know each other well. Second, prenatal visits are typically 45 minutes long (longer than the typical medical visit). As part of these visits, the midwife presents information so that the woman and her family can make informed decisions about the care they receive and their birth experience. Third, midwives offer women a choice of birth place, either a home or hospital or birthing centre birth, depending on the jurisdiction. Finally, the midwife stays with the woman throughout her labour and birth and manages all aspects of her care. Typically, two midwives are present at the birth—the primary midwife and a second midwife who takes care of the baby after it is born. Midwives are trained to know when to refer to a medical specialist when complications arise that are outside their scope of practice, although they stay involved in a supportive way even if they make a referral. Midwives support birth as a normal physiological process and are trained to manage various emergencies.

What training do midwives receive?

Research suggests that women who have their baby delivered by a midwife are the most satisfied with the birth experience. A survey of Canadian women giving birth during a three-month period found that 71 percent of women who had a midwife as their primary caregiver during the birth rated their experience as "very positive," while only 53 percent of women whose primary caregiver was a physician or nurse rated it as "very positive" (Statistics Canada, 2008a).

LO6

After the Baby Is Born: The Postpartum Period

Physical Changes

With the birth of the baby, the woman's body undergoes a drastic physiological change. During pregnancy the placenta produces high levels of both estrogen and progesterone. When the placenta is expelled, the levels of these hormones drop sharply, and thus the postpartum period is characterized by low levels of both estrogen and progesterone. The levels of these hormones gradually return to normal over a few weeks to a few months. Other endocrine changes include an increase in hormones associated with breastfeeding (breastfeeding is discussed later in this chapter).

In addition, the body undergoes considerable stress during labour and delivery, and the woman may feel exhausted. Discomfort from an episiotomy or laceration is common in the first postpartum weeks.

Psychological Changes

On average, Canadian women remain in the hospital for two or three days after parturition; the average length of stay following a Caesarean delivery is three to four days (PHAC, 2012a). For the first two days, women often feel elated; the long pregnancy is over, they have been successful competitors in a demanding athletic event and are pleased with their efforts, and the baby is finally there, to be cuddled and loved.

Following childbirth, many women experience some degree of depression. The depressed mood and other experiences range from mild to severe; the medical literature identifies three types. In the mildest, *postpartum blues* (or "baby blues"), women experience mood swings, with periods of feeling depressed, feeling irritable, and crying, alternating with positive moods. The symptoms usually begin a few days after delivery, are most intense one week postpartum, and lessen or disappear by two weeks postpartum. Between 50 and 80 percent of women experience these mild baby blues (Kennedy & Suttenfield, 2001). **Postpartum depression** is more severe, characterized by depressed mood, insomnia, tearfulness, feelings of inadequacy, and fatigue. It usually begins two to three weeks postpartum but may occur anytime after delivery. Between 8 and 15 percent of women will experience it, with symptoms lasting six to eight weeks (Morris-Rush & Bernstein, 2002; O'Hara & Swain, 1996). The most severe disturbance is *postpartum psychosis*, with early symptoms including restlessness, irritability, and sleep disturbance; later ones include disorganized behaviour, mood swings, delusions, and hallucinations. Its onset can be dramatic, within 72 hours of delivery or four to six weeks postpartum. It is very rare, affecting only 1 or 2 women out of 1000 (Kennedy & Suttenfield, 2001).

It appears that many factors contribute to postpartum depression. Being in a hospital in and of itself is stressful. Once the woman returns home, another set of stresses await her. She has probably not yet returned to her normal level of energy, yet she must perform the tiring task of caring for a newborn infant. For the first several weeks or months she may not get enough sleep, rising several times during the night to tend to a baby that is crying because it is hungry or sick, and she may become exhausted. Clearly, she needs help and support from her partner and friends at this time. Some stresses vary depending on whether this is a first child

Postpartum depression: Mild to moderate depression in women following the birth of a baby.

or a later child. The first child is stressful because of the woman's inexperience; while she is in the hospital she may become anxious, wondering whether she will be capable of caring for the infant when she returns home. In some cases, the mother may become depressed because she did not really want the baby. Risk factors for more severe depression include personal or family history of psychiatric disorder, unwanted pregnancy, serious complications following birth, and lack of social support (Morris-Rush & Bernstein, 2002). Women experiencing multiple births have higher depression symptoms nine months postpartum compared with mothers of singletons (Choi et al., 2009).

Physical stresses are also present during the postpartum period; hormone levels have declined sharply, and the body has been under stress. Thus, it appears that postpartum depression is caused by a combination of psychological, physical, and social factors.

Postpartum depression and psychosis should be treated; for most women, depression improves in response to antidepressant drugs, individual psychotherapy, partner and peer support, and nurse home visits (Gjerdingen, 2003; Mehta & Sheth, 2006). A review of the research using randomized controlled trials to assess psychological interventions reported that the most promising is intensive professional postpartum support (Dennis, 2005).

Fathers, too, sometimes experience depression after the birth of a baby. A study in Great Britain assessed depression in both mothers and fathers eight weeks after delivery. Ten percent of the mothers and 4 percent of the fathers attained high scores. Parents with a history of depression, younger parents (ages 15 to 24), and those living in depressed neighbourhoods are at greater risk of depression (Davé et al., 2010). Paternal depression at eight weeks was associated with having a child with more adverse emotional and behavioural outcomes at 3.5 years of age, over and above the mother's level of depression (Ramchandani et al., 2005).

Attachment to the Baby

While much of the traditional psychological research has focused on the baby's developing attachment to the mother, more recent interest has been about the development of the mother's attachment (bond) to the infant (see Chapter 10). Research shows clearly that this process begins even before the baby is born. Two studies of women expecting their first child found that feelings of nurturance grew during pregnancy, and increased further at birth (Fleming et al., 1997). In this sense, pregnancy is in part a psychological preparation for motherhood.

In the 1970s, pediatricians Marshall Klaus and John Kennell (1976) popularized the idea that there is a kind of "critical period" or "sensitive period" in the minutes and hours immediately after birth, during which the mother and infant should "bond" to each other. Scientists later concluded that there is little or no evidence for the sensitive-period-for-bonding hypothesis (e.g., Goldberg, 1983; Lamb & Hwang, 1982; Myers, 1984). That outcome is fortunate. Otherwise, mothers who give birth by Caesarean section (and may therefore be asleep under a general anaesthetic for an hour or more after the birth) and adoptive parents would have inadequate bonds with their children. We know that, in both cases, strong bonds of love form between parents and children despite the lack of immediate contact following birth. Nonetheless, 73 percent of Canadian hospitals have a policy to facilitate parent-infant bonding by ensuring that the baby stays with the parents immediately after the birth, most for an unlimited amount of time (PHAC, 2012a).

Sex During Postpartum

The birth of a child has a substantial effect on a couple's sexual relationship. Following the birth, the mother is at some risk of infection or hemorrhage (Cunningham et al., 1993), so the couple should wait at least two weeks before resuming penetrative sex. Of course, there is no problem engaging in noncoital intimacy if both partners desire it. When coitus is resumed, it may be uncomfortable or even painful for the woman. If she had an episiotomy or lacerations, she may experience vaginal discomfort; if she had a Caesarean birth, she may experience abdominal discomfort. Fatigue of both the woman and her partner also may influence when they resume sexual activity.

A longitudinal study of the adjustment of heterosexual couples to the birth of a child collected data from 570 women (and 550 partners) four times: during the second trimester of pregnancy, and at one, four, and twelve months postpartum (Hyde et al., 1996). Data on the sexual relationship are displayed in Table 6.3. In the month following birth, only 17 percent had resumed intercourse. By the fourth month, 9 out of 10 couples had—the same percentage as reported intercourse during the second trimester. Reports of cunnilingus showed a similar pattern, while reports of fellatio did not indicate a marked decline. Note that although sexual behaviour was much less frequent in the month following birth, satisfaction with the sexual relationship remained high. A major influence on when the couple resumed intercourse was whether the mother was breastfeeding. At both one month and four months after birth, breastfeeding women reported significantly less sexual activity and lower sexual satisfaction. One reason is that lactation suppresses estrogen production, which in turn results in decreased vaginal lubrication;

Table 6.3	Sexual Behaviours Within the Previous Month, Reported by Mothers During Pregnancy and the Year Postpartum			
		Postpartum		
Behaviour	**Pregnancy 2nd Trimester**	**1 Month**	**4 Months**	**12 Months**
Intercourse	89%	17%	89%	92%
Mean frequency of intercourse/month	4.97	0.42	5.27	5.1
Fellatio	43%	34%	48%	47%
Cunnilingus	30%	8%	44%	49%
Satisfaction with sexual relationship*	3.76	3.31	3.36	3.53

*Satisfaction with the relationship was rated on a scale from 1 (very dissatisfied) to 5 (very satisfied).

Source: Hyde et al. (1996), pp. 143–151.

this can make intercourse uncomfortable. This problem can be resolved by the use of vaginal lubricants. Androgen production is also reduced, which may result in reduced sexual desire (LaMarre et al., 2003).

A study of Swedish couples in the six months and four years postpartum found that, at both times, the average frequency of sex was one to two times per month, and that sexual contentment did not vary over time. Being too tired for sex was reported as a problem by 42 to 56 percent of the couples (Ahlborg et al., 2008).

 L06

Breastfeeding

Biological Mechanisms

Two hormones, both secreted by the pituitary, are involved in lactation (milk production). One, *prolactin*, stimulates the breasts to produce milk. Prolactin is produced fairly constantly for whatever length of time the woman breastfeeds. The other hormone, *oxytocin*, stimulates the breasts to eject milk. Oxytocin is produced reflexively by the pituitary in response to the infant's sucking of the breast. Thus sucking stimulates nerve cells in the nipple; this nerve signal is transmitted to the brain, which then relays the message to the pituitary, which sends out the messenger oxytocin, which stimulates the breasts to eject milk. Interestingly, research with animals indicates that oxytocin stimulates maternal behaviour (Jenkins & Nussey, 1991).

Milk is not produced for a few days after delivery. At first, the breast secretes colostrum, discussed earlier, which is high in protein and gives the baby temporary immunity to infectious diseases. Two or three days after delivery, true lactation begins; this may be accompanied by discomfort for a day or so because the breasts are swollen and congested.

It is also important to note that, much as in pregnancy, substances ingested by the mother may be transmitted through the milk to the infant. The nursing mother thus needs to be cautious about using alcohol and other substances.

Physical and Mental Health

The Canadian Paediatric Society, Dietitians of Canada, and the Public Health Agency of Canada recommend that babies be fed breast milk exclusively for the first six months, and continue breastfeeding after introduction of solid foods up to two years of age and older. This is because breast milk is the ideal food for a baby (Figure 6.13). It provides the baby with the right mixture of nutrients, it contains antibodies that protect the infant from some diseases, and may help prevent asthma and allergies. It is free from bacteria, and is always the right temperature. Breastfeeding is associated with a reduced risk of obesity at ages five and six (Von Kries et al., 1999). Researchers in Ontario showed that breast milk also helps boost the baby's own immune system (Filipp et al., 2001). Thus, there is little question that normally it is superior to cow's milk and commercial formulas. Nonetheless, the vast majority of babies who are not breastfed grow up healthy.

The percentage of Canadian infants who are breastfed, at least initially, rose from 38 percent in 1963 to 88 percent in 2009 (Statistics Canada, 2011a). However, there are large regional differences in breastfeeding rates, ranging from a low of 61 percent in Newfoundland and Labrador to a high of 97 percent or above in British Columbia and Yukon. Further, about 21 percent of mothers who initiate breastfeeding stop by one month. Only 14 percent of babies are fed only breast milk for their first six months as recommended. Immigrant mothers are more likely to breastfeed than are non-immigrants (Health Canada, 1996a). However, individuals from Canada's ethnocultural communities often believe

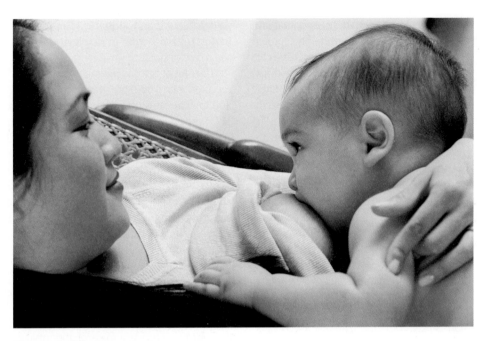

Figure 6.13 Breastfeeding.

that North American women prefer bottle-feeding over breastfeeding. Thus, they are less likely to breastfeed as they become more acculturated (Agnew, 1997). This pattern is also seen in many developing countries, in which urban women are less likely to breastfeed than are rural women, even if they cannot afford to use commercial formula. In terms of the main reasons they give for why they did not attempt to breastfeed, many women give medical reasons; almost as many say that breastfeeding is "unappealing" or "disgusting" or that bottle feeding is easier (Statistics Canada, 2011a).

A systematic review of programs designed to promote breastfeeding concluded that educational sessions that review benefits, lactation, common problems and solutions, and provide skills training as well as in-person or telephone support programs improve initiation rates and the maintenance of breastfeeding at six months (Guise et al., 2003). Programs that involve only giving out materials at the time the new mother leaves the hospital may actually reduce the likelihood that she will breastfeed. Direct encouragement by a health care professional is associated with a much greater likelihood of breastfeeding. The attitudes of the partner are also important. A longitudinal study of 317 first-time mothers and their male partners in Ontario found that male partners' beliefs about breastfeeding affected the women's breastfeeding decisions (Rempel & Rempel, 2004). Women can also use a breast pump to express their milk so that the partner can give the baby a bottle. In this way, the partner can share in the experience of feeding the baby, the mother can get needed sleep if the partner takes over the night-time feeding, or the mother

can go out for a few hours without fear that the baby will get hungry.

From the mother's point of view, breastfeeding has several advantages. These include a quicker shrinking of the uterus to its normal size, reduced postpartum bleeding, and more rapid loss of the weight gained during pregnancy. Breastfeeding reduces the likelihood of pregnancy by inhibiting ovulation. Full breastfeeding, short intervals between feedings, night feedings, and the absence of supplemental feedings are all associated with greater delay in ovulation (Hatcher et al., 2011). However, breastfeeding is not an effective means of birth control—it delays but does not prevent ovulation. Thus, a woman can become pregnant again before she has a period; recall from Chapter 5 that ovulation precedes menstruation. Research indicates that breastfeeding reduces negative moods and perceived stress (Mezzacappa & Katkin, 2002). Breastfeeding is associated with reduced risk of breast cancer; the relative risk decreases by 4 percent for every 12 months of breastfeeding (Collaborative Group on Hormonal Factors in Breast Cancer, 2002).

Some women report sexual arousal during breastfeeding, and a few report having orgasms. Unfortunately, this sometimes produces anxiety in the mother, leading her to discontinue breastfeeding. However, there is nothing wrong with this arousal, which appears to stem from activation of hormonal mechanisms. Clearly, from an adaptive point of view, if breastfeeding is important to the infant's survival, it would be wise for nature to design the process so that it is rewarding to the mother.

The La Leche League is devoted to encouraging women to breastfeed their babies and has helped spread information on breastfeeding. The organization tends to be highly enthusiastic in its advocacy of breastfeeding. Some women are physically unable to breastfeed. Others may experience difficulties with breastfeeding, such as pain during breastfeeding or feeling that the baby is nursing poorly, and need support and information to be able to overcome these difficulties. Others may feel psychologically uncomfortable with the idea, perhaps because of the prevalence of negative messages in our culture about breastfeeding, particularly in public, as well as the labelling of breasts as sexual organs. Also, breastfeeding can be inconvenient for the woman who works outside the home, although working women can express their breast milk or supplement morning and evening feeding with formula while they are at work.

Pregnancy-Related Problems

Ectopic Pregnancy

An **ectopic pregnancy** (misplaced pregnancy) occurs when the fertilized egg implants somewhere other than the uterus. Most commonly, ectopic pregnancies occur when the egg implants in the fallopian tube (tubal pregnancy). In rare cases, implantation may also occur in the abdominal cavity, the ovary, or the cervix.

A tubal pregnancy may occur if, for one reason or another, the egg is prevented from moving down the tube to the uterus, as when the tubes are obstructed—for example, as a result of scarring from a chlamydia infection. Early in a tubal pregnancy, the fertilized egg implants in the tube and begins development, forming a placenta and producing the normal hormones of pregnancy. The woman may experience the early symptoms of pregnancy, such as nausea and amenorrhea, and think she is pregnant; or she may experience some bleeding that she mistakes for a period and think that she is not pregnant. It is therefore quite difficult to diagnose a tubal pregnancy early.

A tubal pregnancy may end in one of two ways. The embryo may spontaneously abort and be released into the abdominal cavity, or the embryo and placenta may continue to expand, stretching the tube until it ruptures. Symptoms of a rupture include sharp abdominal pain or cramping, dull abdominal pain, possibly pain in the shoulder, and vaginal bleeding. Meanwhile, hemorrhaging is occurring, and the woman may go into shock and, possibly, die; thus, it is extremely important for a woman displaying these symptoms to see a doctor quickly.

The rate of ectopic pregnancy in Canada was 12 cases reported per 1000 pregnancies in 2004–2005 (PHAC, 2008b). The rates vary across Canada, from a low of 6 per 1000 reported pregnancies in Prince Edward Island to 32 per 1000 pregnancies in the Northwest Territories. It is thought that high rates are due to (1) increased rates of sexually transmitted infections (STIs), particularly chlamydia, which can lead to blocking of the fallopian tubes; and (2) increased use of contraceptives, such as the IUD and progestin-only methods, that prevent implantation in the uterus but do not necessarily prevent conception. Women with a history of STIs and heavy smoking (more than 20 cigarettes per day) are more likely to have an ectopic pregnancy (Bouyer et al., 2003).

Molar Pregnancy

A *molar pregnancy* is a mass of abnormal tissue (*hydatidiform mole*) inside the uterus. It is thought to be caused either by fertilization of an ovum with no genetic information or when two sperm fertilize the same egg. The woman usually thinks she is pregnant because she experiences all the same pregnancy symptoms during the first trimester as do women with a normal pregnancy, including a missed menstrual period, breast tenderness, and nausea. She may also experience a vaginal discharge, vaginal bleeding, and other symptoms that are unique to a molar pregnancy. A molar pregnancy can be diagnosed with a blood test assessing hCG levels or with an ultrasound. Women who are over age 35, who have a history of molar pregnancy or miscarriage, and who are low in vitamin A are at increased risk for a molar pregnancy.

Pseudocyesis

In **pseudocyesis**, or *false pregnancy*, the woman believes that she is pregnant and shows the signs and symptoms of pregnancy without really being pregnant. She may stop menstruating and may have morning sickness. She may begin gaining weight, and her abdomen may bulge. The condition may persist for several months before it goes away, either spontaneously or as a result of psychotherapy. In rare cases it persists until the woman goes into labour and delivers nothing but air and fluid.

Pregnancy-Induced Hypertension

Pregnancy may cause a woman's blood pressure to rise to an abnormal level. *Pregnancy-induced hypertension* includes three increasingly serious conditions: (1) hypertension, (2) pre-eclampsia, and (3) eclampsia. Hypertension refers to elevated blood pressure alone. **Pre-eclampsia** refers to elevated blood pressure

Ectopic pregnancy: A pregnancy in which the fertilized egg implants somewhere other than the uterus.
Pseudocyesis: False pregnancy, in which the woman displays the signs of pregnancy but is not actually pregnant.
Pre-eclampsia: A serious disease of pregnancy, marked by high blood pressure, severe edema, and proteinuria.

accompanied by generalized edema (fluid retention and swelling) and proteinuria (protein in the urine). The combination of hypertension and proteinuria is associated with an increased risk of fetal death. In severe pre-eclampsia, the earlier symptoms persist and the woman may also experience vision problems, abdominal pain, and severe headaches. In *eclampsia*, the woman has convulsions, may go into a coma, and may die (Cunningham et al., 1993).

Pre-eclampsia may reflect the silent struggle between mother and fetus for resources. It is hypothesized that the fetus, perhaps because of insufficient nutrition, releases a protein that increases the mother's blood pressure, and therefore the flow of nutrients to the placenta. Indeed, research finds elevated levels of the protein sFlt1 associated with pre-eclampsia (Widmer et al., 2007).

Pre-eclampsia usually does not appear until after the 20th week of pregnancy. It is more likely to occur in women who have not completed a pregnancy before. It is especially common among teenagers. The risk of pre-eclampsia rises steadily as pregnancy body mass index increases. For overweight women, a reduction in prepregnancy weight may reduce the risk (Bodner et al., 2004). The possibility of pre-eclampsia emphasizes the need for proper medical care before and during pregnancy. Hypertension and pre-eclampsia can be managed well during their early stages. Most maternal deaths occur among women who do not receive prenatal medical care.

D (Rh) Incompatibility

D antigen (formerly called the Rh factor) is a substance in the blood; if it is present, the person is said to be D positive (D+); if it is absent, the person is said to be D negative (D−). The D antigen is genetically transmitted, with D+ being dominant over D−.

The presence or absence of the D antigen does not constitute a health problem except when a D− person receives a blood transfusion or when a D− woman is pregnant with a D+ fetus (which can happen only if the father is D+). A blood test is done routinely early in pregnancy to determine whether a woman is D−. Fortunately, about 85 percent of whites, 93 percent of blacks, and 99 percent of Aboriginals are D+; thus, the problems associated with being D− are not very common (Beaulieu, 1994).

If some D+ blood gets into D− blood, the D− blood forms antibodies as a reaction against the D antigen in the invading blood. During parturition considerable mixing can occur between the mother and fetus, and the blood of a D+ baby causes the formation of antibodies in a D− woman's blood. During the next pregnancy, some of the woman's blood enters the fetus and the antibodies attack the fetus's red blood cells. The baby may be stillborn, severely anemic, or developmentally delayed. Thus, there is little risk for a D− woman with the first pregnancy because antibodies have not yet formed; however, later pregnancies can be extremely dangerous.

Fortunately, techniques for dealing with this situation have been developed. An injection of a substance called *D immunoglobulin* prevents the woman's blood from producing antibodies. D− women should receive D immunoglobulin at 28 to 29 weeks gestation, within 72 hours after delivery of a D+ infant, and after induced abortion or amniocentesis (Beaulieu, 1994). If necessary, the fetus or newborn infant may get a transfusion.

Miscarriage (Spontaneous Abortion)

Miscarriage, or *spontaneous abortion*, occurs when a pregnancy terminates through natural causes, before the conceptus is viable (capable of surviving on its own). It is not to be confused with *therapeutic abortion*, in which a pregnancy is terminated by mechanical or medicinal means (what is commonly called *abortion—* see Chapter 7), or with *prematurity*, in which the pregnancy terminates early, but after the infant is viable.

It is estimated that 20 percent of all pregnancies end in spontaneous abortion (Frishman, 1995). This is probably an underestimate, since very early spontaneous abortions may not be detected. The woman may not know that she is pregnant and may mistake the products of the miscarriage for a menstrual period. Thus, the true incidence may be closer to 40 percent (Cunningham et al., 1993). Most spontaneous abortions (80 percent) occur during the first trimester of pregnancy. Women who experience a miscarriage in the first 24 weeks of their first pregnancy are at greater risk of obstetrical complications—pre-eclamsia, preterm birth, assisted delivery—in their next pregnancy (Bhattacharya et al., 2008).

Most spontaneous abortions occur because the conceptus is defective. Studies of spontaneously aborted fetuses indicate that 61 percent showed abnormalities that were incompatible with life; for example, many had chromosomal abnormalities (Ljunger et al., 2005). Thus, contrary to popular belief, psychological and physical traumas are not common causes of miscarriage. In fact, spontaneous abortions seem to be functional in that they naturally eliminate many defective fetuses. However, research indicates that maternal obesity, BMI greater than 30, is associated with spontaneous abortion, and with infant death in the year following the birth (Tennant et al., 2011).

Preterm Birth

A major complication during the third trimester of pregnancy is premature labour and delivery of

Miscarriage: The termination of a pregnancy before the fetus is viable, as a result of natural causes (not medical intervention).

the fetus. When delivery occurs before 37 weeks' gestation, it is considered *preterm*, In 2004, 8 percent of the births in Canada were preterm (PHAC, 2008b).

Preterm birth is a cause for concern because the premature infant is much less likely to survive than the full-term infant. It is estimated that 60 to 80 percent of the deaths of newborn babies in Canada are due to preterm birth (PHAC, 2008b). Preterm infants are particularly susceptible to respiratory infections and must receive expert care. Advances in medical techniques have considerably improved survival rates for preterm infants. About 99 percent of infants weighing 2500 grams at birth survive, as do 64 percent of those weighing 1000 grams (Cunningham et al., 1993). However, prematurity may cause damage to an infant who survives. Disability occurs in 60 percent of survivors born at 26 weeks and 30 percent of those born at 31 weeks (Swamy et al., 2008). In children born at 22 to 32 weeks of gestation, cognitive and motor impairment at 5 years of age increase with younger gestational age. Many of these children require specialized care (Larroque et al., 2008).

Maternal factors such as poor health, poor nutrition, obesity, heavy smoking, cocaine use, and syphilis are associated with prematurity. Pregnancy-induced hypertension can also lead to preterm birth. Young teenage mothers, whose bodies are not yet ready to bear children, are also very susceptible to premature labour and delivery. The more risks a pregnant women is exposed to, the greater the risk of preterm birth (Ahluwalia et al., 2001).

Infertility

Infertility refers to a woman's inability to conceive and give birth to a living child or a man's inability to impregnate a woman. About 12 percent of Canadian couples trying to get pregnant are unable to do so (Bushnik et al., 2012). When fertile couples are purposely attempting to conceive a child, about 20 percent succeed within the first menstrual cycle, and about 50 percent succeed within the first six cycles (Hatcher et al., 2007). A couple is considered infertile if they have not conceived after one year of frequent, unprotected intercourse, or after six months if the woman is over 35 (Barrett, 2006). The term *sterile* refers to an individual who has an absolute factor preventing conception.

Causes of Infertility

In about 40 percent of infertile couples, male factors are responsible, and female factors are responsible in an additional 40 percent.

Infertility: A woman's inability to conceive and give birth to a living child or a man's inability to impregnate a woman.

In the remaining 20 percent, either both have problems or the cause is unknown (for a detailed discussion, see Liebmann-Smith, 1987).

Causes in the Female

The most common cause of infertility in women is pelvic inflammatory disease (PID) caused by a sexually transmitted infection, especially gonorrhea or chlamydia. Problems with ovulation may cause 18 to 30 percent of cases. Ovulation disorders are associated with poor diet, high body mass index, and low activity levels (Chavarro et al., 2007; Practice Committee, 2008). Other causes include failure to ovulate, blockage of the fallopian tubes, and "hostile mucus," meaning cervical mucus that blocks the passage of sperm. Less common causes include poor nutrition; eating disorders; exposure to toxic chemicals, such as lead or pesticides; smoking; and use of alcohol, narcotics, or barbiturates. Age may also be a factor; fertility declines in women after 32 years of age, the decline being especially sharp after age 37 (SOGC, 2012). Women who are older than 35 also have an increased likelihood of miscarriage, spontaneous abortion, stillbirth, and pregnancy complications.

Causes in the Male

The most common causes of infertility in men are low sperm count (defined as less than 20 million sperm per millilitre of ejaculate), poor sperm motility (which means that they are not good swimmers), and poor sperm quality. This may be caused by infections in the reproductive system caused by sexually transmitted infections or varicoceles (varicose veins in the testes). Cigarette smoking has been linked to reduced motility, decreased sperm concentration, and mid levels of DNA damage in sperm (Pasqualotto et al., 2008). Less common causes include exposure to toxic agents, such as lead; alcohol and marijuana use; and use of some prescription drugs (Hatcher et al., 2007). Obesity in men is associated with abnormalities in sperm (Practice Committee, 2008). Recent research has shown that exposure to environmental estrogens causes sperm to mature too fast, reducing their fertilizing capacity (Adoya-Osiguwa et al., 2003). Exposure to environmental estrogens comes through contact with substances such as beer and pesticides. Couples concerned about low sperm count may decide to abstain from vaginal intercourse in the hope of increasing the count, but research indicates that this does not work. In men with low sperm counts, the sperm become less motile and begin to show signs of becoming stale after only 24 hours of abstinence (Levitas, 2003).

Research also reports that the quality of semen declines with age. As men age, the volume of the semen as well as the number and motility of the sperm decline (SOGC, 2012).

Also, the rate of sperm with various genomic abnormalities increases with age. Finally, women whose partners are over 40 are more likely to experience a spontaneous abortion (Kleinhaus et al., 2006).

Combined Factors

In some situations, a combination of factors in both the man and the woman causes the infertility. One such factor is an immunologic response. The woman may have an allergic reaction to the man's sperm, causing her to produce antibodies that destroy or damage the sperm. Or her immune system may react to the fetus or placenta. According to one controversial theory, an immune reaction may create the high blood pressure that is associated with pre-eclampsia (Fox, 2002). Immune reactions occur in response to novel cells entering the body; if the body has been exposed to the cells frequently in the past, the reaction is less likely. Frequent prior exposure of a woman to a specific man's semen would reduce the likelihood of rejecting his sperm. So frequent vaginal intercourse without a condom (Robertson & Sharkey, 2001) or oral sex in which the woman swallows the ejaculate (Koelman et al., 2000) before the attempt to get pregnant may increase the chances of a successful pregnancy.

Sperm have a chemical sensor that causes them to swim toward the egg, attracted by a chemical on the surface of the egg (Spehr et al., 2003). Researchers have already identified one chemical that disrupts this process by shutting down the receptor. This chemical, or chemicals, that influence the surface of the egg can cause infertility. Finally, a couple may also simply lack knowledge; for instance, they may not know how to time intercourse correctly so that conception may take place.

Psychological Aspects of Infertility

At some point, most adults in Canadian society attempt to have a child, and infertility may put significant stresses on a couple (Daniluk, 2001a). Because in our society the male role is defined partly by the ability to father children, the man may feel that his masculinity or virility is in question. Similarly, the female role is defined largely by the ability to bear children and be a mother, so infertility may affect a woman's sense of self-worth, adequacy, and femininity (Daniluk, 1999). Historically, in most cultures fertility has been encouraged—and, indeed, demanded; hence, pressures on infertile couples may be high, particularly in traditional cultures, leading to more psychological stress. The psychological stress is greatest for the partner identified as the source of the infertility and for couples whose infertility remains unexplained (Daniluk, 2001a). Research indicates that, among couples entering fertility treatment programs, women perceive themselves as experiencing greater emotional and social stress than do men (Stanton et al., 2002). A study of 545 couples undergoing assisted reproduction found that 31 percent of the women and 10 percent of the men had a psychiatric disorder. Depression was found in 11 percent of the women and 5 percent of the men. Couples whose first attempt at treatment is unsuccessful show elevated levels of anxiety and depression (Schmidt, 2006). Couples whose first attempt is successful report improved emotional well-being (Holter et al., 2006). Only 20 percent of those with a diagnosis had received treatment for it (Volgsten et al., 2008).

Infertility does not significantly reduce relationship satisfaction, but it can lower sexual satisfaction, pleasure, and spontaneity as couples shift from "making love" to "making babies" (Daniluk, 1999, 2001a). As emphasis on population control increases in our society, and being childfree[5] becomes an acceptable and more recognized option, the stress on infertile couples may lessen.

Treatment for infertility also can be long and stressful. British Columbia psychologist Judith Daniluk (2001a) interviewed 65 infertile couples who had received medical intervention for infertility for an average of five years. Couples described their experience with fertility treatments as an emotional rollercoaster. At first they were optimistic that the medical profession, time, and effort could fix the problem. As the process continued, they (particularly the women) experienced a sense of failure every time menstruation occurred and they had to accept that the treatment had, once again, not worked. Couples whose attempts to conceive were unsuccessful after years of medical intervention described being faced with the difficulty of deciding when "enough is enough"—that is, to stop medical interventions, and accept their infertility. They also described the stress in deciding whether to pursue other options to parenthood, a decision that caused conflict between some partners. However, they also described gains that had resulted from treatment, including strengthening their relationship and personal growth. Further, when asked whether they would make the decision to undergo fertility treatments if they had to do it again, all but one couple said yes.

Treatment of Infertility

Some physicians and clinics specialize in the evaluation and treatment of infertility. An infertility evaluation should include an assessment of the couple's knowledge of sexual behaviour and conception, and lifestyle

---

[5] Semantics can make a big difference here. Many couples who choose not to have children prefer to call themselves *childfree* rather than *childless*.

factors such as regular drug use. Infertility caused by such factors can be easily treated.

If the infertility problem stems from the woman's failure to ovulate, the treatment may involve the so-called fertility drugs. The drug of first choice is clomiphene (Clomid). It stimulates the pituitary to produce LH and FSH, thus inducing ovulation. The treatment produces a pregnancy in about half the women who are given it. Multiple births occur about 8 percent of the time with Clomid, compared with 1.2 percent with natural pregnancies. If treatment with Clomid is not successful, a second possibility is injections with *human menopausal gonadotropin* (HMG, a combination of LH and FSH), which may help trigger ovulation.

If the infertility is caused by blocked fallopian tubes, delicate microsurgery can sometimes be effective in removing the blockage. Laparoscopy procedures are less invasive and less likely to cause side effects than abdominal entry (Coughlan, 2008). Endometriosis and endometrial adhesions can also be successfully treated surgically.

If the infertility is caused by varicoceles in the testes, the condition can usually be treated successfully by a surgical procedure known as varicocelectomy.

Finally, a number of new reproductive technologies, such as in vitro fertilization, are now available for those with fertility problems, as discussed in the next section.

A Canadian study is helpful in putting issues of the treatment of infertility into perspective. Among infertile couples seeking treatment, 65 percent subsequently achieved a pregnancy with *no treatment* (Rousseau et al., 1983). For some couples conception just takes a bit longer. However, for those who meet the medical definition of infertility (unable to conceive after 12 months of unprotected intercourse), only about half will conceive a child with treatment (Daniluk, 2001b). Thus, the risks associated with treatments need to be weighed against the possibility that a pregnancy can be achieved without treatment.

Assisted Reproductive Technologies

Reproductive technologies developed in the last four decades mean that there are many ways to conceive and birth babies besides sexual intercourse and pregnancy. These are collectively referred to as assisted reproductive technologies (ART). These options can be used by infertile couples, single individuals, and same-sex couples. The equality provisions in the *Canadian Charter of Rights and Freedoms* guarantee that access to new reproductive technologies cannot discriminate on the basis of family status, marital status, sexual orientation, and so on (Law Reform Commission of Canada, 1992). Canada has 26 fertility clinics that provide assistance with reproduction by using a range of technologies (Gunby et al., 2011).

Assisted Insemination

Assisted insemination (also called *artificial insemination*) involves artificially placing semen in the vagina, uterus, or fallopian tubes to produce a pregnancy; thus, it is a means of accomplishing reproduction without having sexual intercourse. Assisted insemination in animals was first done in 1776. In 1949, when British scientists successfully froze sperm without any apparent damage to them, a new era of reproductive technology began.

There are two kinds of assisted insemination: assisted insemination by the male partner or husband (AIH) and donor insemination (AID). AIH can be used when the man has a low sperm count. Several samples of his semen are collected and pooled to make one sample with a higher count. This sample is then usually placed in the woman's vagina at the time of ovulation. To increase the number of sperm that reach the fallopian tubes, the sperm can also be washed, concentrated, and injected into the woman's uterus. This is called **intrauterine insemination** or IUI.[6] AID is used when the male partner is sterile or when the woman does not have a male partner. A donor provides semen to impregnate the woman. The success rate is about 60 percent after six months for women under the age of 35; it decreases for women who are older. The cost of each donor semen specimen sample is between $400 and $760; there are also other expenses associated with AID that can raise the cost substantially.

Of course, it is not always necessary to do AID in a fertility centre or medical facility; some people choose home insemination. The donor ejaculates into a clean glass jar and keeps the sperm at body temperature. Within one to two hours, the woman injects the sperm into her vagina while lying on her back using a non-latex syringe without a needle. Women who attempt home insemination with fresh sperm run the risk of contracting an STI just as they would if they had unprotected sex, so they should make sure that the donor has not had unprotected sex since being tested. A study of lesbians in Victoria planning to become parents found

---

[6] After taking a human sexuality course in which this textbook was used, a student contacted one of the authors to say that her mother had taken part in a pilot study involving IUI. She was born in 1981 and was one of the first babies, if not the first, born in Canada through IUI.

Assisted insemination: A procedure in which sperm are placed into the vagina by means other than sexual intercourse.

Intrauterine insemination: A procedure in which sperm are washed, concentrated, and injected into a women's uterus.

that 44 percent were planning to use self-insemination at home (McNair et al., 2002).

Surrogacy is also called preconception arrangement or contract motherhood, and occurs when a woman agrees to conceive and carry a baby for someone else (Norris, 2006). Traditionally, surrogate mothers have been used by heterosexual couples in which the woman has a problem with fertility. In this case, the male partner provides the sperm and the surrogate mother becomes pregnant through assisted insemination. However, increasing numbers of gay male couples are using surrogate mothers to become parents through assisted insemination using the sperm of one of the fathers (Figure 6.14).

Sperm Banks

Because it is possible to freeze sperm, it is also possible to store it, which is just what some people are doing: using frozen human *sperm banks*. The sperm banks open up many reproductive choices. For example, suppose that a couple decide, after having had two children, that they want a permanent method of contraception. The husband then has a vasectomy. A few years later the couple decides that they very much want to have another baby, or the couple has divorced and the man wants to have a baby with a new partner. If the man has stored semen in a sperm bank, they can.

Young men can use sperm banks to store sperm before they undergo radiation therapy for cancer. They can later father children without fearing that they will transmit damaged chromosomes (as a result of the radiation) to their offspring.

Since the mid-1990s sperm banks have gone online, making their services available to millions of people around the world (Springen & Noonan, 2003). Canada has three sperm banks that are compliant with Health Canada's screening requirements; they all import sperm from other countries. However, there are many more sperm banks in the United States. Many of these sperm banks have websites that allow prospective parents to browse through a good deal of information about each potential donor, enabling them to select not only on the basis of height, weight, and eye and hair colour but also education and family medical history. As recipients demand more information about prospective donors, it has become harder to maintain the donor's anonymity. Some donors of eggs or sperm advertise directly on the Internet; although the costs may be lower than the costs associated with clinic services, as is often true on the Internet, there is no guarantee that the donor has given accurate information. It is estimated that some 70 percent of the money spent on sperm-bank services in the United States in 2002 (US$65 million) was for purchases via the Internet.

Figure 6.14 "I already know about the birds and the bees, Mom; I want to know about artificial insemination, in vitro fertilization and surrogate mothering!"
Source: Renault/Sacramento Bee, CA/Rothco. Reprinted by permission.

Embryo Transfer

With **embryo transfer**, a fertilized, developing egg (embryo) is transferred from the uterus of one woman to the uterus of another woman. Dr. John Buster of UCLA perfected the technique for use with humans, and the first two births resulting from the procedure were announced in 1984 (Brotman, 1984).

This technique may enable a woman who can conceive but who always miscarries early in the pregnancy to transfer her embryo to another woman who serves as the *surrogate mother*; that is, the person who provides the uterus in which the fetus grows (and whom the media, somewhat callously, have called a "rent-a-womb"). The embryo transfer procedure also essentially can serve as the opposite of assisted insemination. That is, if a woman produces no viable eggs, her male partner's sperm can be used to artificially inseminate another woman (who donates her egg), and the fertilized egg is then transferred from the donor to the mother.

In Vitro Fertilization

It is possible for scientists to make sperm and egg unite in a dish outside the human body. The scientific term for this procedure is **in vitro fertilization**, or IVF (*in vitro* is Latin for "in glass").

Embryo transfer: Procedure in which an embryo is transferred from the uterus of one woman into the uterus of another.

In vitro fertilization (IVF): A procedure in which an egg is fertilized by sperm in a laboratory dish.

The fertilized egg or embryo can then be implanted in the uterus of a woman and carried to term. This technique can be of great benefit to couples who are infertile because the woman's fallopian tubes are blocked. It can also be used for cases of unexplained infertility, ovulation disorders, endometriosis, or severe male infertility. A process called *intracytoplasmic sperm injection* (ICSI) can be used if the man has no sperm or no healthy sperm in his ejaculate. This involves collecting sperm from the epididymis or testes, injecting a single healthy sperm into the ovum, and then using the fertilized egg for IVF (Pinheiro et al., 1999).

A milestone was reached with the birth of Louise Brown, the first test-tube (IVF) baby, in England on July 25, 1978. Obstetrician Patrick Steptoe and physiologist Robert Edwards had fertilized the mother's egg with her husband's sperm in a laboratory dish and implanted the embryo in the mother's uterus. The pregnancy went smoothly, and Louise was born healthy and normal. The first IVF children conceived in Canada were born in Vancouver in 1983. IVF is now performed in a number of countries, with 26 clinics in Canada (Figure 6.15). Edwards was awarded the 2010 Nobel Prize in Physiology and Medicine for developing the technique (Abbott, 2010).

On average across Canadian clinics, 29 percent of all procedures are successful—that is, they resulted in a live birth—and 30 percent of these were multiple births, mostly twins (Gunby et al., 2011). The success rate is higher when the woman is under 40 years old. It is also higher when two embryos are transferred than only one embryo is transferred. The procedure is expensive, between $4400 and $8000 per attempt, not including the cost of medication, which can run from $2000 to $8000. The cost is even higher for ICSI. Quebec is the only province that covers the full cost of IVF; Ontario and the armed forces cover IVF in some cases.

There is also evidence that babies born as a result of IVF are more likely to be low birth weight and have congenital abnormalities (Cohen et al., 2009). A study in Finland found a 30 percent greater risk of abnormalities with in IVF babies (Klemetti et al., 2006). In another study, mothers were interviewed by telephone six weeks to two years after giving birth. Among singleton births, babies conceived by ART were two to four times as likely to have heart defects, cleft lip, and esophageal and anorectal defects (Reefhuis et al., 2009). Using Australian data, researchers assessed the occurrence of nine specific birth defects for five years following 308,974 births. The rate of defects was 8.3 for babies conceived via ART versus 5.8 for unassisted conceptions (Davies, et al., 2012). However, analyses suggested that defects in children conceived via IVF were due to parental factors rather than the procedure. The risk of defects for babies conceived via ICSI remained

(a)

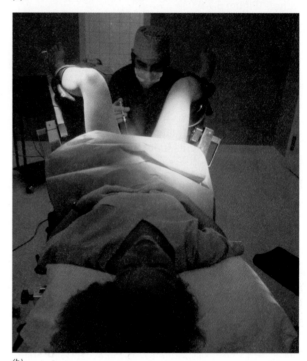

(b)

Figure 6.15 New reproductive technologies. *(a)* With in vitro fertilization, conception is more likely if the egg is scratched, allowing the sperm to enter more easily. *(b)* Vicken Sahakian, MD, medical director of a fertility centre, collects eggs from Deborah, 38. She and her husband, Eric, came in for in vitro fertilization. Out of 13 eggs produced by her, five became fertilized and were reintroduced into Deborah.

after controls for parental characteristics. It is not clear whether the increased risk is due to the procedure or to related factors—for example, mothers are typically older (Kovacs, 2002a). These adverse outcomes are more common in babies born after procedures using donor eggs (Wright et al., 2005).

It is also possible to freeze eggs that have been fertilized in vitro (unfertilized eggs do not freeze well), resulting in frozen embryos. This procedure creates the possibility of donated embryos; the birth of a baby resulting from this procedure was first announced in 1984 in Australia. Research finds that babies born after procedures using thawed embryos were less likely to be low birth weight but more likely to be preterm (Wright et al., 2005). The legal and moral status of the frozen embryo is a difficult question, and some worry about "embryo wastage."

GIFT and ZIFT

GIFT (for gamete intra-fallopian transfer) is an improvement, in some cases, over IVF. Sperm and eggs (gametes) are collected and then inserted together into the fallopian tube, where natural fertilization can take place, followed by natural implantation. Less than 1 percent of the procedures performed in 2002 were of this type (Wright et al., 2005). Because the number is so small, success rates are not reported.

Yet another improvement is ZIFT (zygote intra-fallopian transfer) in which an egg is fertilized with sperm in a laboratory dish, and the developing fertilized egg (zygote) is placed into the fallopian tube, again allowing natural implantation. Again, less than 1 percent of the procedures performed in 2002 involved this technique (Wright et al., 2005).

Assisted reproduction is more likely to be successful if the woman is younger (under 34) and if fresh embryos rather than frozen ones are used. Success rates do not vary by the cause of the infertility. However, success rates vary across racial and ethnic groups (Fujimoto et al., 2008).

Assisted reproduction is likely to result in multiple births—up to 50 percent of infants born through assisted reproduction technology (Wright et al., 2005). These deliveries are associated with greater health risks for mother and infants. The multiple births result from the common practice of transferring several embryos at one time. Medical and public health authorities are increasingly concerned about the problem (see Figure 6.16).

Several Canadian reproductive groups have reviewed the literature and made recommendations regarding the number of embryos to be transferred in IVF. In general, the number depends on the age of the mother, varying from one in women under 35 and in excellent health to no more than four embryos in women over 39 (Joint SOGC-CFAS Guidelines, 2008).

Reproductive Cloning

Cloning is the reproduction of an individual from a single cell taken from a "donor" or "parent." The technique, called intracellular nuclear transfer, involves replacing the nucleus of an ovum with the nucleus from a donor, thus producing an embryo that is genetically identical to the donor. Normally, of course, a child has only

Figure 6.16 The birth of octuplets to Nadya Denise Doud-Suleman, known as Octomom, brought attention to the consequences of implanting multiple fertilized eggs during IVF. Many specialists agree that no more than two should be implanted.

half of its genes in common with the mother; the other half come from the father. Therefore, children are never genetically identical to either parent. But in cloning, no sperm is necessary and the result is an individual who is genetically identical to the donor.

In 1997, researchers announced the birth of Dolly, a sheep cloned from a single cell of an adult ewe. In 2000, six cloned piglets were born, significant because pigs are physiologically close to humans (Prather, 2000). Cloning has great potential—for example, as a source of organs that could be transplanted to replace failing ones, stem cells, or as an alternative in cases of infertility. But it has great risks as well; fewer than 3 percent of cloning efforts succeed, and those that do sometimes suffer from grave, unpredictable genetic defects (Kolata, 2001). In 2004, the federal government passed legislation, the *Assisted Human Reproduction Act*, prohibiting human cloning.

Gender Selection

There is much interest in techniques that will allow couples to choose whether to have a boy or a girl. Such a technology would be useful to parents who have six girls and really want a boy, or for people who would like to have two children, one of each sex. Problems might arise, though. Some scientists fear that the result of being able to choose gender would be a great imbalance in our population, with many more males

GIFT: Gamete intrafallopian transfer, a procedure in which sperm and eggs are collected and then inserted together into the fallopian tube.

than females, because many couples prefer their first child to be a boy. This is already happening in some Asian countries, such as China and India, in which there is a particularly strong preference for sons. For example, a Canadian-led study in India examined the ratio of male to female births for women who already have a daughter compared with women who already have a son. They concluded that, even though gender selection is illegal in India, about half a million female fetuses are aborted each year in India by couples trying for a boy (Jha et al., 2006). An Ontario study demonstrated that gender selection may be happening in Canada as well—women born in India who already had one child or more children were significantly more likely than were women born in Canada to have a boy (Ray et al., 2012).

There is a good deal of conventional wisdom about various home methods of increasing the likelihood that a fetus will be male or female. One technique is timing intercourse in relation to ovulation, based on the belief that sperm carrying a Y chromosome swim faster; thus, intercourse at the time of ovulation should increase the chances of a male, whereas intercourse at a time before and remote from ovulation should favour the slow but hardy sperm carrying an X chromosome, resulting in a female. Several studies have tried to test these ideas, relying on indirect measures of time of ovulation (cervical mucus changes, basal body temperature). They suggest that a female is more likely when intercourse coincides with ovulation. Thus, conventional wisdom is wrong. Studies have also investigated the effect of douching; conventional wisdom has it that douching with vinegar will change the vaginal pH, increasing the chances of a boy. Neither of these (or other) "natural" methods will reliably affect the offspring's gender (Kovacs, 2002b).

As usual, entrepreneurs are taking advantage of people's desire to pick the baby's sex and selling kits that promise results. Some of these kits capitalize on the natural methods, providing the purchaser with thermometers, douching solutions, and other paraphernalia. At least one company is selling kits via the Internet. Again, there is no evidence that these kits will produce the expected results. *Caveat emptor* (buyer beware)!

Several scientific laboratory procedures can be used to separate sperm containing male and female chromosomes. Older techniques involved separation based on swimming speed or immunologic characteristics; these work with 70 to 80 percent accuracy. The latest sorting technique, the Micro-Sort method, uses the fluorescence-activated sorter, which can select sperm with an X chromosome with 90 percent accuracy; this technique greatly reduces sperm count and requires ART. Little data exists on the long-term outcomes of using this procedure (Kovacs, 2002b).

The most reliable method of gender selection is *preimplantation genetic diagnosis* (PGD). This technique involves removing eggs from the woman and fertilizing them via IVF. After three days, a cell is taken from each embryo and its chromosomal makeup is determined. An embryo of the preferred type would then be implanted via ART. This method is very invasive to the woman's body and very expensive. The likelihood that the implanted egg would result in the live birth of a healthy infant is the same as for other ART pregnancies. PGD is banned in Canada and in the United Kingdom.

Prenatal Genetic Diagnosis

Prenatal genetic diagnosis, determining a fetus's genotype at a specific locus, has been done on a small scale for decades. In the past amniocentesis and CVS, discussed earlier, have been the primary procedures. Both are invasive, carry a slight risk of harm, and allow only limited analysis of the cells retrieved. As a result, less than 2 percent of pregnant women undergo these tests, primarily to detect a marker for Down syndrome. In the near future, NIPD, non-invasive, prenatal diagnosis, may become a reality, allowing a sample of maternal blood to be tested for hundreds of fetal traits.

During pregnancy, some fetal cells pass through the placenta into the mother's blood stream (Greely, 2011), including cells containing fetal DNA. If samples of fetal DNA can be isolated in the mother's blood, cheap and sensitive genetic sequencing techniques can be used to analyze the fetal genome. This type of analysis is currently used to determine the D (Rh) type of the fetus (see earlier discussion). Two scientists have developed techniques to analyze fetal cell–free DNA and have published proof that fetal genotype can be identified for thousands of sites. Thus, tests are now feasible for many single cell diseases, such as cystic fibrosis, sickle cell anemia, and Tay-Sachs disease. The same techniques could be used to identify fetal sex, and sexual orientation, not to mention hair and eye colour and IQ.

Two factors will determine how quickly NIPD becomes readily available—its accuracy as an indicator of the specific disease or trait, and its cost. When and if it becomes available, it will be very controversial, raising serious religious, social and political issues. One fundamental issue will be whether it should be used to determine which fetuses should be aborted.

The Legal and Ethical Challenges of New Reproductive Technologies

The technologies discussed here require expert practitioners and appropriate facilities. Further, these and other procedures raise complex legal and ethical questions (discussed in Chapter 20 online at Connect™).

The federal government passed legislation in 2004 to regulate the new reproductive technologies and to deal with some of these issues. The *Assisted Human Reproduction Act* prohibits identifying the sex of an embryo created for reproductive purposes except for medical reasons, paying a woman to be a surrogate mother, paying a donor for sperm or eggs, and buying or selling human embryos.

However, a number of other legal questions remain. One set of questions is to be found in the matter of kinship and parental rights and responsibilities. When a child is born as a result of these techniques, who exactly are the parents? What legal claim do donors and surrogates have to contact with "their" children after birth?

There are also a host of procedural issues. What will the standards of confidentiality be, especially about the identity of nonparent donors? If something goes wrong during one of these procedures—and they are risky—who is liable? Who will take responsibility for a child with a serious disability born through one of these techniques? What should happen to frozen embryos that are not needed and have been abandoned by clinic patients? Should they be made available to infertile couples or destroyed? Finally, there is the question of who should pay for treatment of infertility. Investigations of the causes of infertility are covered by medicare. In addition, the provinces fund some costly treatments for infertility such as tubal surgery in women and repair of varicocele in men (Leader, 1999). However, DI, IVF, and drugs used to treat infertility are not covered by medicare for most Canadians, which makes most infertility treatments unavailable to the majority of Canadians, who cannot afford them.

SUMMARY

Sperm are manufactured in the testes and ejaculated out through the vas deferens and urethra into the vagina. Then they begin their swim through the cervix and uterus and up a fallopian tube to meet the egg, which has already been released from the ovary. When the sperm and egg unite in the fallopian tube, conception occurs. The single fertilized egg cell then begins dividing as it travels down the tube, and finally it implants in the uterus. Various techniques for improving the chances of conception are available.

The placenta, which is important in transmitting substances between the woman and the fetus, develops early in pregnancy. The most remarkable development of the fetus occurs during the first trimester (first three months), when most of the major organ systems are formed and human features develop.

For the woman, early signs of pregnancy include amenorrhea, tenderness of the breasts, and nausea. The most common pregnancy tests are designed to detect hCG in the urine or blood. Physical changes during the first trimester are mainly the result of the increasing levels of estrogen and progesterone produced by the placenta. Despite cultural myths about the radiant contentment of the pregnant woman, some women do have negative feelings during the first trimester. During the second trimester, the woman generally feels better, both physically and psychologically.

Despite many people's concerns, sexual intercourse is generally quite safe during pregnancy. Nutrition is exceptionally important during pregnancy because the woman's body has to supply the materials to create another human being. Pregnant women also must be very careful about ingesting substances because some can penetrate the placental barrier and enter the fetus, possibly causing damage.

Labour is typically divided into three stages. During the first stage, the cervix undergoes effacement (thinning) and dilation. During the second stage, the baby moves out through the vagina. The placenta is delivered during the third stage. Caesarean section is a surgical method of delivering a baby.

Prepared childbirth has become very popular; it emphasizes the use of relaxation and controlled breathing to control contractions and minimize the woman's discomfort. Anaesthetics may not be necessary, which seems desirable, since they are potentially dangerous.

During the postpartum period, hormone levels are very low. Postpartum depression may arise from a combination of this hormonal state and the many environmental stresses on the woman at this time.

Two hormones are involved in lactation: prolactin and oxytocin. Breastfeeding has a number of psychological as well as health advantages.

Problems of pregnancy include ectopic (misplaced) pregnancy, pseudocyesis (false pregnancy), preeclampsia and eclampsia, illness (such as rubella), a defective conceptus, D (Rh) incompatibility, spontaneous abortion, and preterm birth.

The most common cause of infertility in men and women is infection related to sexually transmitted infections (STIs).

Assisted reproductive technologies include assisted insemination, frozen sperm banks, embryo transfer, in vitro fertilization, and GIFT (gamete intrafallopian transfer), all of which are now a reality. These procedures are expensive and have low success rates. In addition, the practice of transferring multiple embryos often results in multiple births, which are riskier for both mother and infants.

On the horizon is widespread use of NIPD to determine fetal genotype. If the technique is used to determine whether a fetus should be aborted, it will create a host of social and ethical debates.

QUESTIONS FOR THOUGHT, DISCUSSION, AND DEBATE

1. Taking the point of view of a pregnant woman, which would you prefer to have, a home birth or a hospital birth? Why?

2. For readers who are men, what role would you envision for yourself during pregnancy and birth? Do you feel that you are adequately prepared for that role? For readers who are women, what role would you ideally like a partner to take during pregnancy and birth?

3. A close friend confides in you that she is afraid of pregnancy. She has heard that pregnant women experience unpleasant physical (aches and pains, fatigue, illness) and psychological (crying spells, depression) symptoms. She is especially concerned that pregnancy might have a bad effect on her relationship with her partner. What information would you give her about these fears?

connect LEARNSMART SMARTBOOK

For more information on the resources available from McGraw-Hill Ryerson, go to **www.mheducation.ca/he/solutions**.

Are YOU Curious?

1. I'd like to use the birth control pill, but I worry about remembering to take a pill every day. What are my other options?
2. Can a man still ejaculate after a vasectomy?
3. Are there any hormonal contraceptive methods for men?
4. What is the difference between a surgical abortion and a medical abortion?

Read this chapter to find out.

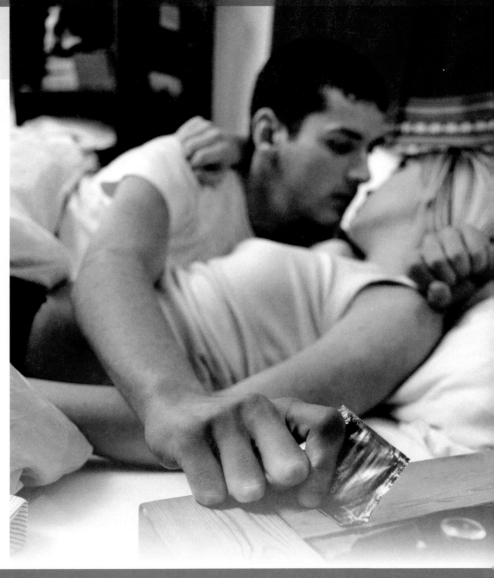

CHAPTER

7

Contraception and Abortion

LEARNING OBJECTIVES

After studying this chapter, you will be able to

LO1   Analyze each contraceptive method.

LO2   Describe the history of birth control and abortion in Canada and the reasons for contraceptive use personally and globally.

LO3   Differentiate between perfect use and typical use failure rates for each contraceptive.

LO4   Summarize the procedure for male and female sterilization and evaluate each.

LO5   Explain the new advances in male and female contraception.

LO6   Identify the psychological processes that influence contraception use.

LO7   Describe the abortion procedures currently available in Canada, and illustrate the unequal accessibility for women across the country.

LO8   Describe the typical psychological outcomes of abortion and compare abortion views from a cross-cultural perspective.

For a short time I worked in an abortion clinic. One day I was counseling a woman who had come in for an abortion. I began to discuss the possible methods of contraception she could use in the future (she had been using rhythm), and I asked her what method she planned to use after the abortion. "Rhythm," she answered. "I used it for eleven months and it worked!"*

* Paula Weideger. (1976). *Menstruation and menopause.* New York: Knopf, p. 42.

The average student of today grew up in the pill era and simply assumes that highly effective methods of contraception are available. It is sometimes difficult to remember that this has not always been true and that previously contraception was a hit-or-miss affair at best. Contraception is less controversial now than it once was: the use of contraceptives was illegal until 1969 when, under Prime Minister Pierre Trudeau, Parliament amended many of the laws pertaining to sexual behaviour (see First Person for a brief history of birth control in Canada).

Before 1969, a person who sold, advertised, or published an advertisement about any "means, instructions, medicine, drug or article intended or represented as a method of preventing conception or causing abortion" could be jailed for up to two years. This statute came under the subheading "Offences Tending to Corrupt Morals" and as such was intended to protect the public and preserve social values (Appleby, 1999). The 1969 amendments to the *Criminal Code of Canada* also allowed abortion under certain restrictive circumstances. The process by which the abortion law was declared unconstitutional by the Supreme Court of Canada in 1988 (abortion is now legal in Canada) is discussed later in this chapter in the section on abortion. These contraception and abortion laws are clear examples of yesterday's values being enshrined in the statute books. They arise from an understanding of reproduction as the only legitimate purpose of sex and the belief in the necessity of vigorous propagation of the species.

Today, people use contraceptives for a variety of reasons. Both babies and mothers are healthier if pregnancies are spaced three to five years apart (Setty-Venugopal & Upadhyay, 2002). Most couples want to limit the size of their family—usually to one or two children. People who are not in a relationship typically want to avoid pregnancy. In some cases a couple know, through genetic counselling, that they have a high risk of bearing a child with a birth defect, and they want prevent pregnancy. And in this era of successful career women, many women feel that it is essential to be able to control when and whether to have children. Of course, a woman's age and relationship status affect her contraceptive use.

For example, Canadian women under 30 who are single are more likely than older women and women who are married or cohabiting to use oral contraceptives or condoms or both (Black, Bucio, et al., 2009).

At the level of society as a whole are other important reasons for encouraging the use of contraceptives. In 2010, 2.8 percent of adolescent girls in Canada got pregnant; some of these were girls under 15 years old (McKay, 2012); adolescent pregnancy is a major social problem. Physicians do not need a parent's or guardian's permission to prescribe contraceptives, providing the teenager is able to understand the risks and benefits of the decision and thus to provide informed consent.

On the global level, overpopulation is a serious problem. In 1900 the world's population was 1.6 billion—and it had taken millions of years to reach that level (Townsend, 2003). By 1950 it had increased to 2.5 billion. In 2012, the world population hit 7 billion, an alarming increase, and experts estimate that it will reach 8.9 billion by 2050. With the resulting destruction of the environment and increased consumption of natural resources, grave concerns arise about the ability of the planet to sustain such a large population, even in the near future. Most experts believe that it is important to limit the size of the world population. For a summary of contraceptive practices among married women around the world, see Table 7.1.

In this chapter we discuss various methods of birth control, how each works, how effective they are, what side effects they have, and their relative advantages and disadvantages. We also discuss abortion and advances in contraceptive technology.

Hormonal Methods

Hormonal methods of contraception are highly effective and come in a number of forms: the pill, the patch, the vaginal ring, implants, and injections.

The Combination Pill

With **combination birth control pills** (sometimes called *oral contraceptives*), such as Alesse and Yasmin,

Combination birth control pills:
Birth control pills that contain a combination of estrogen and progestin (progesterone).

Table 7.1 Contraception Around the World, Reported by Women Ages 15–44
The great variations reflect differences among cultures in such factors as availability of medical service, people's education about contraception, and gender roles.

	Percentage Using Contraceptive Method							
	Voluntary Sterilization						Vaginal Methods** & Fertility	All
Region, Country	Male	Women	Pill	IUD	Male Condom	Injectables*	Awareness	Methods
North America								
Canada	22	11	21	1	15	1	4	88
United States	16	17	17	3	10	42	4	62
Europe								
France	NA	NA	38	21	5	NA	NA	80
Netherlands	9	4	49	3	8	NA	NA	74
Africa (Sub-Saharan)								
Kenya	0	6	9	3	1	12	6	39
Asia								
China	7	33	2	40	4	NA	NA	87
Bangladesh	1	7	23	1	4	7	5	54
India	2	34	2	2	3	0	3	48
Latin America								
Colombia	1	27	12	12	6	4	7	77
Middle East and North Africa								
Egypt	0	1	10	36	1	6	1	56
Morocco	0	3	38	5	1	<1	3	58

NA: Statistics not available

*Includes injections, such as Depo-Provera.

**Includes ring, diaphragm, cervical cap, and spermicides.

Sources: Mosher & Jones (2010), Fisher et al. (2003), U.S. Bureau of the Census, International Data Base (2004), Zlidar et al. (2003).

the woman takes a pill that contains estrogen and progestin (a synthetic progesterone), both at doses higher than natural levels, for 21 days. Then she takes no pill or a placebo for seven days, after which she repeats the cycle.

The traditional 21-on, 7-off pattern is still very common, but variations have been introduced. One is Seasonale, which provides 84 days of combined hormones and 7 days of placebo; this means that the woman has a period only once in three months. Seasonale was approved by Health Canada in 2007. Some women take two packets of pills back-to-back—that is, they start the second packet without taking the seven placebo pills to delay getting their period. Continuous or extended pill use is as effective as the traditional pill and results in fewer menstrual days (Society of Obstetricians and Gynaecologists of Canada [SOGC], 2007b).

The preferred method for a woman starting the pill is quick start. That is, she starts taking the pill the first day

she gets the prescription, regardless of the day of the menstrual cycle.

How It Works

The pill works mainly by preventing ovulation. Recall from Chapter 5 that in a natural menstrual cycle, the low levels of estrogen during and just after the menstrual period trigger the pituitary to produce FSH, which stimulates the process of ovulation. When a woman starts taking the birth control pills, estrogen levels are pushed high. This high level of estrogen inhibits FSH production, and the message to ovulate is never sent out. The high level of progesterone inhibits LH production, further preventing ovulation.

The progestin provides additional backup effects. It keeps the cervical mucus very thick, making it difficult for sperm to get through, and it changes the lining of the uterus in such a way that even if a fertilized egg were to arrive, implantation would be unlikely.

A Brief History of Birth Control in Canada L02

In the early nineteenth century in Canada and in other Western countries, birth control and abortion early in pregnancy were not illegal. However, laws were passed in the nineteenth century to prohibit the use of birth control and the spread of contraceptive information. In the 1892 Canadian *Criminal Code*, a person who sold, advertised, or published an advertisement about any "medicine, drug, or article" intended to prevent conception could be jailed for up to two years. Abortion was also made illegal.

The movement toward legalizing birth control in Canada was started by women's groups in British Columbia that recognized the toll that unwanted pregnancies were having on women's health and well-being. They joined together to form the Canadian Birth Control League. This group was influenced by Margaret Sanger, who had founded the American Birth Control League in 1914, thereby launching the birth control movement in the United States.

A number of other organizations began calling for the legalization of birth control during the 1920s and 1930s, including the Saskatchewan section of the United Farmers of Canada, the Seventh Labour Women's Society and Economic Conference, and the National Council of Jewish Women. A. H. Tyler, a Protestant minister who wrote sex education and birth control publications in the 1930s and 1940s, was responsible for starting the birth control movement in Toronto and founded the Canadian Voluntary Parenthood League in 1931.

The first birth control clinic in Canada was established in Hamilton, Ontario, in 1932 by Mary Hawkins. This clinic, called the Birth Control Society of Hamilton, served hundreds of patients. To allay criticisms by members of the medical profession, a physician was always in attendance. Dr. Elizabeth Bagshaw (see Figure 7.1), one of Hamilton's few female physicians at the time, served the clinic for more than 30 years. The clinic was so successful that the hospital in Hamilton began cooperating with the clinic in 1935. By 1937 there were also birth control clinics in Windsor and Kitchener.

In 1936, Dorothea Palmer, an Ottawa social worker, was charged with distributing birth control information in poor neighbourhoods. She was acquitted in 1937, partly through the efforts of the birth control lobby.

Figure 7.1 Dr. Elizabeth Bagshaw served as a physician for more than 30 years with the clinic run by the Birth Control Society of Hamilton, the first birth control clinic in Canada.

The court recognized that the provision of birth control information was permissible if it were done in the interest of the "public good." However, the sale and distribution of contraceptives was still technically illegal until 1969. In fact, as recently as 1960 a Toronto pharmacist was jailed for selling condoms.

In 1967, Pierre Elliott Trudeau, then the justice minister, introduced the Omnibus Bill, making large-scale changes to the Canadian *Criminal Code*, including in the sections relating to contraception and abortion. In defending the bill, Trudeau made his now-famous statement: "The state has no business in the bedrooms of the nation." The Omnibus Bill was passed in 1969 when Trudeau was prime minister. Among other changes, it made the use of contraceptives legal and allowed abortion under certain restrictive circumstances.

Sources: CARAL (n.d.), Chesler (1992), Planned Parenthood Federation of Canada (n.d.).

When the estrogen and progestin are withdrawn (after day 21 in the traditional pill), the lining of the uterus disintegrates, and withdrawal bleeding or menstruation occurs. The flow is typically reduced because the progestin has inhibited development of the endometrium.

L03 Effectiveness

To understand the effectiveness of the pill, you'll need to understand several technical terms that are used in communicating data on contraceptive effectiveness. If 100 women use a contraceptive method for one year, the number of them who become pregnant during that first year of use is called the **failure rate** or *pregnancy rate*. That is, if 5 women out of 100 become pregnant during a year of using contraceptive A, then A's failure rate is 5 percent. *Effectiveness* is 100 minus the failure rate; thus contraceptive A would be said to be 95 percent effective. We can also talk about two kinds of failure rate: the *failure rate for perfect users* and the *failure rate for typical users*. The perfect-user failure rate refers to studies of the best possible use of the method—for example, when the user has been well taught about the method, uses it with perfect consistency, and so on. The failure rate for typical users is just that—the failure rate when people actually use the method, perhaps imperfectly when they forget to take a pill or do not use a condom every time. The good news is that if you are very responsible about contraception, you can anticipate close to the perfect-user failure rate for yourself.

Combination pills are one of the most effective methods of birth control (see Figure 7.2). The perfect-user failure rate is 0.3 percent (that is, the method is essentially 100 percent effective), and the typical-user failure rate is 3 percent (Hatcher et al., 2011). Failures occur primarily as a result of forgetting to take a pill for two or more days or not taking it at the same time every day. If a woman forgets to take a pill, she should take it as soon as she remembers and take the next one at the regular time; this does not appear to increase the pregnancy

risk appreciably. If she forgets for two days, she should do the same thing—take one as soon as possible and then continue taking one a day. If she forgets for three or more days, she should follow the same instructions, taking one pill as soon as possible and then one pill a day, but in addition she should use condoms or abstain from sex until she has taken hormonal pills for seven days in a row, at which point she will again be well protected (Salem, 2005).

Side Effects

You may have seen reports in the media on the dangerous side effects of birth control pills. Many of these reports are no more than scare stories with little or no evidence behind them. However, the use of the pill does have some well-documented side effects, and women who are using it or who are contemplating using it should be aware of them.

Among the serious side effects associated with use of the pill are slight but significant increases in certain diseases of the circulatory system. One of these is problems of blood clotting (thromboembolic disorders or venous thromboembolism). Women who use the pill have a higher chance than nonusers of developing blood clots (thrombi), particularly women over 35 who smoke. Symptoms of blood clots are severe headaches, severe leg or chest pains, and shortness of breath. For some women, the pill can cause high blood pressure. There is no evidence that the pill is associated with infertility or difficulty conceiving after the woman goes off the pill.

Although the pill actually protects women from endometrial cancer and ovarian cancer (Hatcher et al., 2011), it may aggravate some already existing cancers, such as breast cancer. While these problems are relatively rare, for women who have taken the pill for more than five years, the risk of benign liver tumours increases (Hatcher et al., 2011).

The pill increases the amount of vaginal discharge and the susceptibility to vaginitis (vaginal inflammations, such as *monilia*—see Chapter 8) because it alters the chemical balance of the lining of the vagina. Women on the pill have an increased susceptibility to chlamydia and gonorrhea. Although the matter is controversial, some good evidence indicates that use of the pill—or any hormonal contraceptive—increases the risk of HIV infection (Heffron et al., 2012).

The pill may cause some nausea, although this almost always goes away after the first month or two of use. Some brands of pills can also cause weight gain, by increasing appetite or water retention, but this side effect can often be reversed by switching to another brand.

Failure rate: The pregnancy rate occurring when using a particular contraceptive method; the percentage of women who will be pregnant after a year of use of the method.

Figure 7.2 Birth control pills.

Finally, there may be some psychological effects. About 20 percent of women on the pill report increased irritability and depression, which become worse with the length of time it is used. These side effects are probably related to the progesterone in the pill. Women may also experience changes in sexual desire. Some women report an increase in sexual interest. But others report a decrease in sexual desire, vaginal lubrication, and arousal. Switching brands may be helpful for these effects.

In short, the pill does have some serious potential side effects. However, so do pregnancy and many other medications we take regularly. For example, the risk of blood clots is higher during pregnancy than from the pill (SOGC, 2013a). Thus, it may not be a good choice for high-risk individuals, but for many others it is an extremely effective means of contraception that poses little or no danger.

Advantages and Disadvantages

The pill has a number of advantages. It is close to 100 percent effective if used properly. It does not interfere with intercourse, as do some other methods, such as the cervical cap, the condom, and foam. It is not messy. Some of its side effects are also advantages; it reduces the amount of menstrual flow and thus reduces cramps. Indeed, it is sometimes prescribed for the non-contraceptive purpose of regulating menstruation and eliminating cramps. Iron deficiency anemia is less likely to occur among pill users. The pill can clear up acne and has a protective effect against some rather serious things, including endometriosis and ovarian and endometrial cancer (Hatcher et al., 2011).

The side effects of birth control pills, discussed earlier, are, of course, major disadvantages. Another disadvantage is the cost, which is about $25 a month for as long as they are used, although many women (41 percent) do not pay the full cost (Boroditsky et al., 1996). They also place the entire burden of contraception on the woman. In addition, taking them correctly is a little complicated; the woman must understand that they are to be taken at the same time every day, and she must remember when to take them and when not to take them. This effort is not too taxing for a well-educated woman from a culture that is familiar with various contraceptives. However, currently available information on the use of birth control pills might be inadequate to meet the needs of a woman from a developing country. Appropriate information and direction on how to use the pill is also important for women with intellectual disabilities.

One other criticism of the pill is that for a woman who has intercourse only infrequently (say, once or twice a month or less), it represents contraceptive overkill; that is, the pill makes her infertile every day of the month, and yet she needs it only a few days each month. Women in this situation might consider a method that is used only when needed, such as the cervical cap or condom.

Finally, it is important to recognize that, although it is an excellent contraceptive, the pill provides absolutely no protection against sexually transmitted infections (STIs).

Reversibility

When a woman wants to become pregnant, she simply stops taking pills after the end of one cycle. Some women experience a brief delay (two or three months) in becoming pregnant, but pregnancy rates are about the same as for women who never took the pill.

Drug Interactions

If you are taking birth control pills, you are taking a prescription drug, and it can have interactions with other prescription drugs you take (Hatcher et al., 2011). Some of the interactions are mentioned here, but women on the pill should always consult a pharmacist before taking any new medication, including over-the-counter medication. Some anticonvulsant drugs, for example, decrease the effectiveness of the pill, as do some antiretroviral drugs used to treat HIV infection.

The pill may also increase the metabolism of some drugs, making them more potent (Hatcher et al., 2007). Examples include some anti-anxiety drugs, corticosteroids used for inflammation, and theophylline (a drug used for asthma). Therefore, women using the pill may require lower doses of these drugs.

Some over-the-counter drugs may also interact with the pill. St. John's wort, for example, can decrease the effectiveness of the pill substantially.

Other Kinds of Pills

To this point, the discussion has centred chiefly on the *combination pill,* so named because it contains both estrogen and progestin. This variety of pill is the most widely used, but many kinds of combination pills and several kinds of pills other than combination ones are available.

Combination pills vary from one brand to the next in the dosages of estrogen and progestin. The dose of estrogen is important because higher doses are more likely to induce blood-clotting problems. Most women do well on pills containing no more than 30 to 35 micrograms of estrogen, such as Alesse, Demulen 30, Min-Ovral, and Minestrin (Dickey, 2000). Because of concerns about side effects because of the estrogen in the pill, current pills have considerably lower levels of estrogen than early pills; for example, Ortho 1/35 has one-third the amount of estrogen of the early pill Enovid 10. In January 2005, Yasmin, a new type of contraceptive pill that combines a low dose of estrogen with a synthetic form of progestin (drospirenone), was approved for sale by Health Canada, although in 2011 it also issued a warning that some women taking Yaz or Yasmin have an increased risk of blood clots. High-progestin brands are related to such symptoms as vaginitis and depression. Thus, depending on what side effects the woman wants to avoid, she can choose a brand for its high or low estrogen or progesterone level. (See Hatcher et al., 2011, p. 312, for a list of symptoms related to dosages of estrogen and progestin.)

The **triphasic pill** (e.g., Ortho 7/7/7) contains a steady level of estrogen like the combination pill does, but the levels of progesterone have three phases. The idea is to reduce total hormone exposure, although they do not appear to have an advantage over monophasic pills (Grimes et al., 2006).

Progestin-only pills (Micronor is the only one available in Canada) have also been developed. They are sometimes called *mini-pills*. The pills contain only a low dose of progestin and no estrogen, and were designed to avoid the estrogen-related side effects of the combination pill. The woman takes one beginning on the first day of her period and one every day thereafter; it is important that she takes it at the same time each day. Progestin-only pills work by changing the cervical mucus so that sperm cannot get through, inhibiting implantation, and inhibiting ovulation (although while taking mini-pills about 40 percent of women ovulate consistently).

Progestin-only pills have a typical-user failure rate of 5 percent, which is higher than that of combination pills. Their major side effect is that they produce very irregular menstrual cycles. The mini-pill is probably most useful for women who cannot take combination pills—for example, women over 35 who smoke, or women with a history of high blood pressure or blood-clotting problems.

Progestin-only pills are also useful for women who are breastfeeding and cannot use combination pills because they reduce milk production. Neither kind of pill should be used in the first six weeks after birth when breastfeeding, because trace amounts of the hormones can reach the infant through the breast milk. After that time, though, progestin-only pills are a good choice.

The Patch

The patch (Evra) contains the same hormones as combination birth control pills but is administered transdermally—that is, through the skin. The patch itself is thin, beige, and about the size of a double Band-aid. It consists of an outer protective layer of polyester, an

Figure 7.3 NuvaRing, the vaginal contraceptive ring.

adhesive layer that contains the hormones, and a polyester liner that is removed before applying.

The patch lasts for seven days, so the woman places a new one on once a week for three weeks, and then has a patch-free week. The first time it is used, it takes a couple of days for the hormones to reach effective levels, so a backup method, such as a condom, should be used. One advantage of the patch is that women using it do not have to remember to take a pill every day, only to replace the patch every week. In addition, with the patch the hormones enter the body through the skin, rather than going to the stomach and needing to be digested.

The patch is relatively new (it became available in Canada in 2004), so we do not have extensive data on it yet. Because the hormones are the same as in the pill, the expectation is that the benefits and side effects will be quite similar to those of the pill (Hatcher et al., 2011). It is somewhat less effective in women weighing more than 90 kilograms. There is also concern that a woman gets more estrogen from the patch than she would from the combination pill.

> I'd like to use the birth control pill, but I worry about remembering to take a pill every day. What are my other options?

The Vaginal Ring

It's not the latest in body piercing. Rather, the vaginal ring (NuvaRing; Figure 7.3) is a flexible, transparent ring made of plastic and filled with the same hormones as those in the combination pill, at slightly lower doses. The woman squeezes the two sides of the ring together, and then gently pushes the folded ring into her vagina so that it comes to rest high up in her the vagina. It remains in place for 21 days after which she

Triphasic pill: A birth control pill containing a steady level of estrogen and three phases of progesterone, intended to mimic more closely women's natural hormonal cycles.

removes it and goes ring-free for—you guessed it—7 days. She then inserts a new ring. This method requires even less remembering than the patch does.

The ring, too, was only recently introduced, so the scientific data on it are limited. Because the hormones in it are the same as those in the combination pill, the side effects should be the same. It acts mainly by stopping ovulation. Although it was hoped that its typical-user failure rate would be lower than the pill (because of less need to remember to use it), in fact it is about the same as the pill (Hatcher et al., 2011).

Emergency Contraception

Emergency contraception (EC) is available in pill form for emergencies involving unprotected intercourse that might result in an unwanted pregnancy, such as from forced intercourse or a condom breaking (Public Health Agency of Canada [PHAC], 2007a). In Canada, its brand name is Plan B. Plan B contains levonorgestrel (a progestin), which is also found in some regular birth control pills, although the dose is higher in Plan B (Dunn & Guilbert, 2003). The treatment is most effective if begun within 12 to 24 hours and cannot be delayed longer than 120 hours (five days) after unprotected intercourse. Nausea is a common side effect, but Gravol can be taken to prevent it. EC may also result in irregular vaginal bleeding, fatigue, headache, dizziness, and breast tenderness (PHAC, 2007a).

Emergency contraception may work in any of several ways, depending on when in the cycle it is taken. It may stop ovulation, inhibit the functioning of sperm, prevent fertilization, or inhibit the development of a nourishing endometrium. Its action is to prevent pregnancy, and it will not cause an abortion if the woman is already pregnant (PHAC, 2007a).

Emergency contraception is between 75 and 89 percent effective (Hatcher et al., 2007). Those statistics underestimate the actual effectiveness, though, because they refer to effectiveness during the most fertile part of the cycle. Actual pregnancy rates are between 0.5 and 2 percent (von Hertzen et al., 2002). Emergency contraception is highly effective.

As of May 2008, the emergency contraceptive pill became available over the counter without a written prescription from a physician, with the option, but not a requirement, of speaking with a pharmacist. Opponents of Plan B had argued that making EC widely available in this way would lead women, and especially teenagers, to become irresponsible about contraception. Research in British Columbia, where EC has been available from pharmacists without a prescription since December 2000, found that making it available without a prescription more than doubled its use (Soon et al., 2005). However, this increase was not because women were being irresponsible. The vast majority of these women used EC only once during the period of the study, most often because of birth control failure. Further, research indicates that making Plan B available to teenagers has no effect on whether they have unprotected intercourse or on their number of sexual partners (Harper et al., 2005).

An IUD can also be used for emergency contraception for a woman who wants continuing protection (Cleland et al., 2012). The failure rate is less than 1 percent if inserted within five days of unprotected intercourse.

Implants

Implants are thin rods or tubes containing progestin. They are inserted under the skin in a woman's arm and are effective for three years. Norplant was the first implant available but was removed from the market because of health concerns. One implant is currently available in the United States, Implanon, which uses just a single rod that is four centimetres long and two millimeters wide (Hatcher et al., 2011). It is not approved for use in Canada.

Depo-Provera Injections

Depo-Provera (DMPA) is a progestin administered by injection by any health care provider licensed to provide injections. The injections must be repeated every three months for maximum effectiveness. Depo-Provera was approved for use as a contraceptive in Canada in 1997. A study of women in Saskatchewan using Depo-Provera found that most did so because of its convenience; for example, they did not have to worry about forgetting to take the birth control pill (Hampton et al., 2000).

How It Works

Depo-Provera works like the other progestin-only methods, by inhibiting ovulation, thickening the cervical mucus, and inhibiting the growth of the endometrium. Depo-Provera is highly effective, with a typical-user failure rate of 6 percent, making it a little less effective than the pill.

Advantages and Disadvantages

Depo-Provera has many advantages. It does not interfere with lovemaking. It requires far less reliance on memory than birth control pills do, although the woman must remember to have a new injection every three months. It is available for women who cannot use the combination pill, such as those over 35 who smoke and those with blood pressure problems.

A disadvantage of Depo-Provera is that most users experience amenorrhea (no menstrual periods). Sometimes they have just some spotting. However, this may be an advantage. It can relieve anemia caused by heavy menstrual periods, and Depo-Provera can be used in the treatment of endometriosis.

Side Effects

No lethal side effects of Depo-Provera have been found, although long-term studies have not yet been done. However, in 2005 Health Canada put out a warning that Depo-Provera can result in irreversible bone loss after only two years on the drug and that it should only be used by women who are unable to use other contraceptive methods. To protect against bone loss, women on Depo-Provera should make sure they get enough calcium and vitamin D in their diet or through vitamin supplements.

Reversibility

The method is reversible simply by not getting another injection. Many women are infertile for 6 to 12 months after stopping its use but then are able to become pregnant at normal rates (Hatcher et al., 2007).

 L01

The IUD and IUS

The **intrauterine device (IUD)** is a small piece of plastic; it comes in various shapes. Metal or a hormone may also be part of the device. An IUD is inserted into the uterus by a doctor or nurse practitioner, and it then remains in place until the woman wants to have it removed. One or two plastic strings hang down from the IUD through the cervix, enabling the woman to check to see whether it is in place.

The basic idea for the IUD has been around for some time. In 1909, Burton Richter reported on the use of an IUD made of silkworm gut. In the 1920s German physician Ernst Grafenberg reported data on 2000 insertions of silk or silver wire rings. In spite of its high effectiveness (98.4 percent), his work was poorly received. Not until the 1950s, with the development of plastic and stainless-steel devices, did the method gain much popularity. In the 1970s and 1980s the use of the IUD in North America was sharply reduced by numerous lawsuits against manufacturers by women claiming to have been damaged by the device, specifically by the IUD known as the Dalkon Shield, which was taken off the market (Hubacher, 2002). Some companies stopped producing IUDs, and others declared bankruptcy. Only three IUDs are available in Canada today (Nova-T, Flexi-T, and Liberté). All contain copper (Figure 7.4).

The intrauterine system (IUS) is also available in Canada. It also contains progesterone (Mirena). Thus, it is inserted like an IUD, but it is actually a hormonal method of contraception. Currently, 106 million women worldwide are using an IUD or IUS, 40 million of them in the People's Republic of China, and experts predict a resurgence of enthusiasm for them (Hubacher, 2002).

Figure 7.4 Copper T IUD.

How It Works

The foreign body in the uterus creates an environment that is toxic to both sperm and eggs (Hatcher et al., 2011). In the rare event of fertilization, the IUD prevents implantation. The small amount of copper that is added to the copper T is thought to have an additional contraceptive effect. It seems to alter the functioning of the enzymes involved in implantation. It is also used as an emergency contraceptive within seven days of unprotected intercourse.

The IUS (Mirena) releases progesterone directly into the uterus. One effect is to reduce the endometrium. This results in reduced menstrual flow and reduced risk of anemia, thus overcoming two undesirable side effects of other IUDs. The progestin thickens cervical mucus, disrupts ovulation, and changes the endometrium.

Effectiveness

The IUD is extremely effective; it is in the same category as the pill (and sterilization) in effectiveness. The pregnancy rate for the copper IUD is 0.7 percent for the first year of use; after that, the failure rate is even lower (Hatcher et al., 2011). It is available for use for 3, 5, or 12 years. Mirena is licensed for 5 years. Most failures occur during the first three months of use, either because the IUD/IUS is expelled or for other, unknown reasons. Expulsion is most likely in women who have never been pregnant, in younger women, and in women during menstruation. The expulsion rate is about 2 to 10 percent during the first year (Hatcher et al., 2011).

Side Effects

The most common side effects of the copper T are increased menstrual cramps, irregular bleeding, and increased menstrual flow. These symptoms occur in 10 to 20 percent of women using it and are most likely immediately

Intrauterine device (IUD): A plastic device sometimes containing metal or a hormone that is inserted into the uterus for contraceptive purposes.

after insertion. Mirena, in contrast, reduces menstruation flow and about 20 percent of users stop bleeding altogether. Women who are sensitive to progesterone may experience weight gain, depression, or decreased sexual interest. There is no evidence that the IUD or IUS causes cancer.

Advantages and Disadvantages

Because insertion of the IUD/IUS by a physician is covered by medicare, the initial cost is about $60 for an IUD and $350 for an IUS–the cost of purchasing the device. Thus, the IUD/IUS is a fairly cheap means of contraception over a long time of use, since the cost is incurred only once and the IUD/IUS lasts 5 to 12 years.

The effectiveness of the IUD/IUS is a major advantage. The typical-user failure rate is only 0.8 percent, making it more effective than combination birth control pills and Depo-Provera.

Once inserted, the IUD/IUS is perfectly simple to use. The woman has only to check periodically to see that the strings are in place. Thus it has an advantage over methods like the diaphragm or condom in that it does not interrupt intercourse in any way. It has an advantage over the pill in that the woman does not have to remember to use it. The IUD is a method that can be used safely by women after giving birth and while breastfeeding. Contrary to what some people think, the IUD/IUS does not interfere with the use of a tampon during menstruation; nor does it have any effect on intercourse.

Reversibility

When a woman who is using an IUD/IUS wants to become pregnant, she simply has a physician remove the device. She can become pregnant immediately.

Cervical Caps and the Sponge

The diaphragm was the mainstay of contraception until about 1960. Although diaphragms are still being manufactured, they are no longer available in Canada because most women prefer using a cervical cap or the sponge. However, a single-size SILCS diaphragm has been approved for sale in Europe, which may increase its popularity if it is made available in Canada.

Cervical Caps

FemCap: A method of birth control involving a rubber cap that fits snugly over the cervix.

FemCap is a vaginal barrier device. It is shaped like a sailor's cap (see Figure 7.5), is made of silicone, and has a brim, a dome, a

Figure 7.5 FemCap is a silicone rubber barrier contraceptive shaped like a sailor's hat, with a dome that covers the cervix and a brim that conforms to the vaginal walls.

groove between the dome and the brim, and a removal strap. It comes in three sizes. A woman needs a prescription from a health care provider who will recommend the correct size based on the woman's obstetric history: the smallest size for women who have never been pregnant, the medium size for women who have been pregnant but have not had a vaginal delivery, and the largest size for women who have had a vaginal delivery. It can be inserted several hours before sexual activity and left in place for up to 48 hours. It costs about $90 and can be used for about two years. It should be used with a spermicide or one of the new microbicides.

How It Works

The primary action of FemCap is mechanical; it blocks the entrance to the uterus so that sperm cannot swim up into it. The cream kills any sperm that manage to get past the barrier. Any sperm remaining in the vagina die after about eight hours (this is why it should not be removed until at least six hours after intercourse).

Effectiveness

The typical-user failure rate of the FemCap for women who have never given birth has been estimated to be about 20 percent. Most failures are due to improper use: a woman may not use it every time, it may not fit well, she may not leave it in long enough, or she may not use contraceptive cream or jelly. Even with perfectly proper use, there is still a 9 percent failure rate. To get closer to 100 percent effectiveness, FemCap can be combined with a condom around the time of ovulation or throughout the cycle. For women who have had children, the failure rates can be higher.

Side Effects

FemCap has few side effects. One is the possible irritation of the vagina or the penis; this is caused by the cream or jelly and can be relieved by switching to another brand.

Advantages and Disadvantages

Some women dislike touching their genitals and inserting their fingers into their vagina. Use of the cervical cap is not a good method for them. Cervical caps require some thought and presence of mind on the woman's part. She must remember to put it in ahead of time or have it and a supply of cream or jelly with her when she needs it. She also needs to avoid becoming so carried away with passion that she forgets about it or decides not to use it.

The cost of FemCap is about $90 plus the cost of the contraceptive cream; the office visit is covered by medicare. With proper care, FemCap should last about two years and thus itself is not expensive.

The major advantages of cervical caps are that they have few side effects and, when used properly, are very effective. For this reason, women who are worried about the side effects of the pill or the IUD/IUS should seriously consider a cervical cap as an alternative. They also do not interfere with sensations or sensitivity of either partner, so some people may prefer using a cervical cap to using a condom. There is also evidence of a reduction in the rate of cervical cancer among long-time users of the diaphragm, which may also apply to users of cervical caps. And the cervical cap provides some protection against STIs such as chlamydia because it covers and protects the cervix; it does not protect against most other STIs, however.

Reversibility

If a woman wants to become pregnant, she simply stops using the cervical cap. Its use has no effect on her later chances of conceiving.

The Sponge

The **contraceptive sponge** (see Figure 7.6) is another vaginal barrier method like the FemCap. Made of polyurethane, the sponge is small and shaped like a pillow with a concave dimple on one side. The other side has a woven loop to aid in removal. The sponge contains a spermicide and is inserted much like a cervical cap, with the concave side over the cervix. The sponge is effective for 24 hours, even with multiple acts of intercourse. It should not be left in place for more than 24 hours, though, because of a risk of toxic shock syndrome. It comes in one size and is available over the counter without prescription. The cost is about $15 for four.

Figure 7.6 The contraceptive sponge.

 LO1

Condoms

The Male Condom

The **male condom** (*rubber, prophylactic, jimmy hat, safe*) is a thin sheath that fits over the penis (see Figure 7.7). It comes rolled up in a little packet and must be unrolled onto the penis before use. It may be made of latex (*rubber*), polyurethane, or the intestinal tissue of lambs (*skin*). The polyurethane condom (Avanti, Trojan Supra) is a recent innovation that is helpful to people who are allergic to latex.

The widespread use of the modern condom, both for contraception and for protection against diseases, dates from about 1843, when vulcanized rubber was developed; however, the use of a sheath to cover the penis has been known throughout most of recorded history.[1] Casanova

Contraceptive sponge: A contraceptive method made of polyurethane that contains a spermicide and is placed over the cervix.
Male condom: A contraceptive sheath that is placed over the penis.

---

[1] Condoms have also been the stimulus for humour throughout history, an example being this limerick: There was a young man of Cape Horn / Who wished he had never been born / And he wouldn't have been / If his father had seen / That the end of the rubber was torn.

Figure 7.7   A variety of male condoms.

(1725–1798) was one of the first to popularize the condom for its contraceptive ability, as well as its protective value. Condoms have become increasingly popular because they help protect against STIs, including HIV.

To be effective, the condom must be used properly (see Figure 7.8). It must be unrolled onto the erect penis before the penis ever enters the vagina–*not* just before ejaculation, since long before then some drops containing a few thousand sperm may have been produced. To be effective in preventing STIs, too, it must be put on before penetration. Condoms come in two shapes: those with plain ends and those with a protruding tip that catches the semen. If a plain-ended one is used, about a centimetre or (1/2 inch) of air-free space should be left at the tip to catch the ejaculate. Care should be taken that the condom does not slip during intercourse. After the man has ejaculated, he must hold the rim of the condom against the base of the penis as he withdraws. It is best to withdraw soon after ejaculation, while the man still has an erection, to minimize the chances of leakage. A new condom must be used with each act of intercourse.

Condoms may be either lubricated or unlubricated. Some further lubrication for intercourse may be necessary. A sterile, water-based lubricant such as K-Y Jelly or Sensilube may also be used.

How It Works
The condom catches the semen and thus prevents it from entering the vagina. Spermicide-coated condoms are no longer recommended. They may create allergies to the spermicide for the man or his partner, and the amount of spermicide is probably not sufficient to be very effective. For couples who want to improve on the effectiveness of the condom, it is probably wiser for the woman to use a contraceptive foam or, better yet, a cervical cap.

Effectiveness
Condoms are actually much more effective as a contraceptive than most people think. The perfect-user failure rate is about 2 percent. The typical-user failure rate is about 18 percent, but many failures result from improper or inconsistent use. Health Canada controls the quality of condoms carefully, and thus the chances of a failure caused by a defect in the condom itself are small. Combined with a contraceptive foam or cream or a cervical cap, the condom is close to 100 percent effective.

(a)   (b)

Figure 7.8 Putting on a condom correctly. *(a)* The tip is pinched to keep air out. *(b)* The condom is then rolled down over the erect penis.

Side Effects

The condom has no side effects, except that some users are allergic to latex. For them, non-latex condoms made of polyurethane or other plastics are available.

Advantages and Disadvantages

One disadvantage of the condom is that it must be put on just before intercourse, raising the spontaneity problem again. If the couple can make an enjoyable, erotic ritual of putting it on together, this problem can be minimized.

Some men complain that the condom reduces their sensation and thus lessens their pleasure in intercourse ("It's like taking a shower with a raincoat on"). However, adding a drop or two of lubricant inside the condom will increase the man's sensations. Further, the reduction in sensation may be an advantage for some; for example, it may help the man who ejaculates more quickly than he or his partner wants. Polyurethane condoms are thinner and should provide more sensation. However, today, condoms come in all shapes, sizes, and thinnesses, so if one brand doesn't work well for you, try another.

There are several advantages to condoms. They are the only contraceptive currently available for men except sterilization. They are cheap (around $1.50 to $2.50 for three), they are readily available without a prescription at any drugstore and some convenience stores, and they are fairly easy to use, although the man (or woman) must plan ahead so that one will be available when it is needed.

Finally, a major advantage of condoms is that they provide protection against many STIs (Hatcher et al., 2011). Unlubricated condoms can also easily be made into a *dental dam* to provide protection against STIs during oral–genital activity (see Chapter 8). Over the past several years, some far-right political groups, particularly in the United States, have mounted a campaign to convince the public that condoms are completely ineffective at STI prevention. However, the scientific data say otherwise. Condoms are highly effective protection against STIs that are transmitted mainly through genital secretions (cervical and vaginal secretions as well as semen) because they keep the secretions away from the other person. STIs in this category include chlamydia, gonorrhea, trichomoniasis, hepatitis B, and HIV (Hatcher et al., 2011; McKay, 2007). Condoms can and should be used during anal intercourse for protection against STIs.

Condoms also provide substantial, although not perfect, protection against STIs that are transmitted mainly by skin-to-skin contact, such as herpes, syphilis, and human papillomavirus (McKay, 2007). They won't protect against these diseases, of course, if the area producing the microbe is not covered by the condom—for example, if herpes blisters are on the scrotum. Latex and polyurethane condoms are the effective ones; animal-skin condoms are much less effective because they have larger pores that allow some viruses, such as HIV, to pass through them. For a more complete discussion of the effectiveness of condoms in STI prevention, see Chapter 8.

Reversibility
The method is easily and completely reversible. The man simply stops using condoms if conception is desired.

The Female Condom
The female condom (Reality or FC), became available in 1996. It is made of polyurethane and resembles a clear balloon (see Figure 7.9). There are two rings in it, one at either end. One ring is inserted into the vagina; the other is spread over the vaginal entrance. The inside is prelubricated, but additional lubrication may be applied. The penis must be guided into the female condom so that the penis does not slip in between the condom and the vaginal wall. The condom is removed after intercourse, before the woman stands up. The outer ring is squeezed together and twisted to keep the semen inside. A new female condom must be used with each act of intercourse. A new version, FC2, was approved for use in the Canada in 2009. It makes less noise during intercourse and costs less than Reality.

How It Works
The female condom works by preventing sperm from entering the vagina and by blocking the entrance to the uterus.

Effectiveness
The typical-user failure rate is 21 percent (Hatcher et al., 2011), which is unacceptably high for many women. The perfect-user failure rate is 5 percent.

Side Effects
There are few if any side effects with the female condom. A few women experience vaginal irritation and a few men experience irritation of the penis as a result of using it.

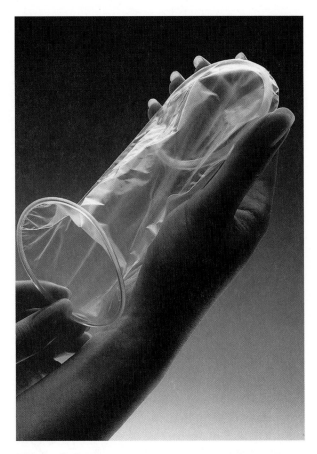

Figure 7.9 The female condom. One ring fits over the cervix, and the other goes outside the body, over the vulva, so that the condom lines the vagina and partly covers the vulva.

Advantages and Disadvantages
The female condom is made of polyurethane, not the latex used in most male condoms. Polyurethane is less susceptible to tearing and does not deteriorate with exposure to oil-based substances in the way that latex does. It does not create the allergic reactions that some people have to latex.

One major advantage is that the female condom is a method that a woman can use herself to reduce her risk of contracting an STI. The polyurethane is impermeable to HIV and to the viruses and bacteria that cause other STIs. Another advantage is that it can be inserted up to eight hours before sexual intercourse.

For disadvantages, the spontaneity problem presents itself again. The female condom, at least the original, is awkward to insert and makes rustling noises while in use, although additional lubricant reduces this problem. It makes the male condom seem sophisticated and unobtrusive by comparison. Also, it is the least effective of the methods discussed so far in this chapter. Another disadvantage is the cost, about $2.50 per condom, which is considerably higher than the cost for male condoms.

Reversibility

The method is easily and completely reversible. The woman simply stops using the condom.

Spermicides

Contraceptive foams, creams, and jellies (e.g., VCF Foam, Contragel Green Gel) are all classified as **spermicides**—that is, sperm killers (Figure 7.10). Most contain non-oxynol-9 (N-9). They come in a tube or a can, along with a plastic applicator. The applicator is filled and inserted into the vagina. The applicator's plunger is then used to push the spermicide out into the vagina near the cervix, so the spermicide is inserted much as a tampon is. It must be left in for six to eight hours after intercourse. One application provides protection for only one act of intercourse.

Spermicides are not to be confused with the various feminine hygiene products (vaginal deodorants) on the market. The latter are not effective as contraceptives.

Figure 7.10 Contraceptive foams, creams, and jellies are all spermicides.

How They Work

Spermicides consist of a spermicidal chemical in an inert base, and they work in two ways: chemical and mechanical. The chemicals in them kill sperm, while the inert base itself mechanically blocks the entrance to the cervix so that sperm cannot swim into it.

Effectiveness

Failure rates for spermicides can be as high as 28 percent. Put simply, they are not very effective. Foams tend to be more effective, and creams and jellies less so. Spermicidal tablets and suppositories are also available, but they are the least effective. Spermicides are highly effective only when used with a cervical cap or condom.

Side Effects

Some people experience an allergic reaction—irritation of the vagina or penis—to spermicides. Because we couldn't find any scientific studies on the incidence of these allergies, we surveyed our sexuality classes. We found that, of the students who had used spermicides, about 2 percent of the men reported an allergic reaction, as did 26 percent of the women.

Advantages and Disadvantages

The major advantage of spermicides is that they are readily available, without a prescription, in any drugstore. Thus, they can be used as a stop-gap method until the woman can see a health care provider and get a more effective contraceptive. Their failure rate is so high, though, that we cannot recommend using them by themselves; always combine them with a second method, such as a condom.

Spermicides provide no protection against bacterial STIs, such as chlamydia and gonorrhea. Neither do they protect against HIV, and there is some evidence that their frequent use increases susceptibility to HIV (Hatcher et al., 2011).

Their major disadvantage is that by themselves, they are not very effective. They also interrupt the spontaneity of sex, although only briefly. Some women dislike the sensation of the spermicide leaking out after intercourse, and some are irritated by the chemicals. Finally, some people find that they taste terrible, so their use interferes with oral sex.

Douching

Some people mistakenly believe that **douching** (flushing the vagina with a liquid) with any one of a variety of solutions is an effective contraceptive technique. A

Spermicide (SPERM-ih-side): A substance that kills sperm.

Douching (DOOSH-ing): Flushing out the inside of the vagina with a liquid.

popular rumour among teenagers is that douching with Coca-Cola after intercourse will prevent pregnancy. Unfortunately, while it is true that acidic solutions will kill sperm, it takes only seconds for some of the sperm to reach the cervical mucus; once there, they are free to continue moving up into the uterus, and no douching solution will reach them. The woman would have to be a champion sprinter to get herself up and douched soon enough. And the douche itself may even push some sperm up into the uterus. Douching, therefore, is just not effective as a contraceptive method.

Withdrawal

Withdrawal (*coitus interruptus, pulling out*) is probably the most ancient form of birth control. (A reference to it is even found in the Bible in Genesis 38:8–9.) Withdrawal is still widely used throughout the world. The man withdraws his penis from his partner's vagina before he has an orgasm and thus ejaculates outside the vagina. To be effective as contraception, the ejaculation must occur completely away from the woman's vulva.

Effectiveness
Withdrawal is not very effective as a method of birth control. The failure rate is around 22 percent. Failures occur for several reasons: the few drops of fluid that come out of the penis during arousal may carry enough sperm for conception to occur; if ejaculation occurs outside the vagina but near or on the vulva, sperm may still get into the vagina and continue up into the uterus; and sometimes the man simply does not withdraw in time.

Side Effects
Withdrawal produces no direct physical side effects. However, over long periods of time, worry about ejaculating before withdrawal may contribute to sexual dysfunctions in the man, such as premature ejaculation, and also sexual dysfunction in the woman (e.g., low arousal) because of anxiety about pregnancy.

Advantages and Disadvantages
The major advantage of withdrawal is that it is the only last-minute method; it can be used when nothing else is available, although if the situation is that desperate, one might consider abstinence or some other form of sexual expression, such as mouth–genital sex as alternatives. Obviously, withdrawal requires no prescription and is completely free.

One major disadvantage is that withdrawal is not very effective. In addition, it requires exceptional motivation on the part of the man, and it may be psychologically stressful to him. He must constantly maintain a kind of self-conscious control (Figure 7.11). The woman may worry about whether he really will withdraw in time, and the situation is certainly less than ideal for her to orgasm.

Fertility Awareness (Rhythm) Methods

Fertility awareness (rhythm) methods, although they are not very effective, are the only form of "natural" birth control. They require abstaining from intercourse during the woman's fertile period (around ovulation). There are several fertility awareness methods, and in each the woman's fertile period is determined in a different way: the calendar method, the basal body temperature method, and the cervical mucus method (Hatcher et al., 2011).

The **calendar method** is based on the assumption that ovulation occurs about 14 days before the onset of menstruation (see Chapter 5). It works best for the woman with the perfectly regular 28-day cycle. She should ovulate on day 14 and almost surely on one of days 13 to 15. Three days are added in front of that period (previously deposited sperm may result in conception), and two days are added after it (to allow for long-lasting eggs); thus, the couple must abstain from sexual intercourse from day 10 to day 17. Therefore, even for the woman with perfectly regular cycles, eight days of abstinence are required in the middle of each cycle. Research shows that sperm can live up to five days inside the female reproductive tract and eggs live less than a day (Hatcher et al., 2011).

Figure 7.11   Male responsibility is a key issue in birth control.

Withdrawal: A method of birth control in which the man withdraws his penis from his partner's vagina before he orgasms.

Fertility awareness (rhythm) methods: Methods of birth control that involve abstaining from intercourse around the time the woman ovulates.

Calendar method: A type of fertility awareness method of birth control in which the woman determines when she ovulates by keeping a calendar record of the length of her menstrual cycles.

The woman who is not perfectly regular must keep a record of her cycles for at least six months and preferably a year. From this she determines the length of her shortest cycle and the length of her longest cycle. The preovulatory safe period is then calculated by subtracting 18 from the number of days in the shortest cycle, and the postovulatory safe period is calculated by subtracting 11 from the number of days in the longest cycle. Thus for a woman who is somewhat irregular–say, with cycles varying from 26 to 33 days in length–a period of abstinence from day 8 to day 22 (a total of 15 days) would be required.

A somewhat more accurate method for determining ovulation is the **basal body temperature (BBT) method**. The principle behind this was discussed in Chapters 5 and 6. The woman takes her temperature every day immediately on waking. During the preovulatory phase her temperature will be at a fairly constant low level. On the day of ovulation it drops (although this does not always occur), and on the day after ovulation it rises sharply, staying at that high level for the rest of the cycle. Intercourse would be safe beginning about three days after ovulation. Some of the psychological stresses involved in using this method have been noted previously. As a form of contraception, the BBT method has a major disadvantage in that it determines safe days only *after* ovulation; theoretically, according to the method, there are no safe days before ovulation. Thus, the BBT method is best used in combination with the calendar method or the cervical mucus method, which determine the preovulatory safe period; the BBT method determines the postovulatory safe period.

Another fertility awareness method, the **cervical mucus method**, is based on variations over the cycle in the mucus produced by the cervix. There are generally a few days just after menstruation during which no mucus is produced, and there is a general sensation of vaginal dryness. This is a relatively safe time. Then there are a number of days of mucus discharge around the middle of the cycle. On the first days, the mucus is white or cloudy and tacky. The amount increases, and the mucus becomes clearer, until there are one or two *peak days,* when the mucus is like raw egg white—clear, slippery, and stringy. There is also a sensation of vaginal lubrication. Ovulation occurs within 24 hours after the last peak day. Abstinence is required from the first day of mucus discharge until four days after the peak days. After that the mucus, if present, is cloudy or white, and intercourse is safe. Combination of the cervical mucus method with BBT is called the **sympto-thermal method**.

Home Ovulation Tests

Recently, home tests for the detection of ovulation have been developed (e.g., Clear Blue). Most such tests have been designed for use by couples wanting to conceive; however, a few are now available for contraception (Hatcher et al., 2011). One kind (PG53, PC 2000, and Maybe Baby) involves mini-microscopes to examine saliva or cervical mucus. Others involve temperature computers that work on the BBT method. Hormone computers (e.g., Persona) assess hormone levels in urine. Costs range between $13 and $169. The effectiveness of these tests is not yet well enough researched for us to recommend them as reliable.

Effectiveness

The effectiveness of the fertility awareness method varies considerably, depending on a number of factors, but basically it is not very effective with typical users (giving rise to its nickname, *Vatican roulette*, and a number of old jokes like, "What do they call people who use the rhythm method?" Answer: "Parents"). Although the typical-user failure rate is around 25 percent for all methods, ideal-user failure rates vary considerably. They are 5 percent for the calendar method, 2 percent for BBT, 2 percent for the sympto-thermal method, and 3 percent for the cervical mucus method (Hatcher et al., 2011). Failure rates are lower when the woman's cycle is very regular and when the couple are highly motivated and have been well instructed in the methods.

Advantages and Disadvantages

The method has no side effects except possible psychological stress, and it is inexpensive. It is easily reversible. It also helps the woman become more aware of her body's functioning. The method requires cooperation from both partners, which may be considered either an advantage or a disadvantage.

Its main disadvantages are its high failure rate and the psychological stress it may cause. Periods of abstinence of at least eight days, and possibly as long as two or three weeks, are necessary, which is an unacceptable requirement for many couples. A certain amount of time, usually several months, is required to collect the data needed to make the method work. Thus, one cannot simply begin using it on the spur of the moment.

Sterilization

Sterilization, or voluntary surgical contraception (VSC), is a surgical procedure whereby an individual is made permanently sterile, that is, unable to reproduce. Some people confuse sterilization

Basal body temperature method: A type of fertility awareness method of birth control in which the woman determines when she ovulates by keeping track of her temperature.
Cervical mucus method: A type of fertility awareness method of birth control in which the woman determines when she ovulates by checking her cervical mucus.
Sympto-thermal method: A type of fertility awareness method of birth control combining the basal body temperature method and the cervical mucus method.
Sterilization: A surgical procedure by which an individual is made sterile, that is, incapable of reproducing.

with castration, though the two are quite different. Sterilization is an emotion-laden topic for a number of reasons. Sterilization means the end of a person's capacity to reproduce, and the ability to impregnate and the ability to bear a child are very important in cultural definitions of manhood and womanhood. We hope that as gender roles become more flexible in our society and as concern about reproduction is replaced by a concern for limiting population size, the word *sterilization* will no longer carry such emotional overtones.

Most physicians are conservative about performing sterilizations; they want to make sure that the patient has made a firm decision on his or her own and will not be back a few months later wanting to have the procedure reversed. The physician has an obligation to follow the principle of "informed consent." This means explaining the procedures involved, telling the patient about the possible risks and advantages, discussing alternative methods, and answering any questions the patient has.

Despite this conservatism, both male sterilization and female sterilization have become increasingly popular as methods of birth control. Sterilization is the most common method of birth control for long-term couples in their fertile years in Canada: 22 percent of men and 17 percent of women. As you would expect, sterilization is more common among couples who are older (Boroditsky et al., 1996).

Can a man still ejaculate after a vasectomy?

Vasectomy (vas-EK-tuh-mee): A surgical procedure for male sterilization involving severing of the vas deferens.

Male Sterilization

The male sterilization operation is called a **vasectomy**, so named for the vas deferens, which is tied or cut. It can be done in a physician's office under local anaesthesia and requires only about 20 minutes to perform. In the traditional procedure, the physician makes a small incision on one side of the upper part of the scrotum. The vas is then separated from the surrounding tissues, tied off, and cut. The procedure is then repeated on the other side, and the incisions are sewn up. For a day or two the man may have to refrain from strenuous activity and be careful not to pull the incision apart.

A newer *no-scalpel vasectomy* procedure has been developed (Hatcher et al., 2011). It involves making just a tiny pierce in the scrotum and has an even lower rate of complications than a standard vasectomy (see Figure 7.12).

Typically, the man can return to having intercourse within a few days. It should not be assumed that he is sterile yet, however. Some stray sperm may still be lurking in his ducts beyond the point of the incision. Men should not rely completely on the vasectomy until three months after it was performed (Hatcher et al., 2011). Until then, an additional method of birth control should be used. Ideally, the man should have a semen analysis after three months to confirm that his ejaculate is sperm-free.

Misunderstandings about the vasectomy abound. A vasectomy creates no physical changes that interfere with erection. Neither does it interfere in any way with sex hormone production; the testes continue to manufacture testosterone and secrete it into the bloodstream. Nor does a vasectomy interfere with the process or sensation of ejaculation. As we noted in Chapter 4, virtually all the fluid of the ejaculate is produced by the seminal vesicles and prostate, and the incision is made long

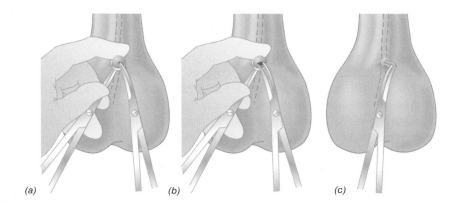

(a)   (b)   (c)

Figure 7.12 The no-scalpel vasectomy. *(a)* The vas (dotted line) is grasped by special ring forceps and the scrotum is pierced by sharp-tipped forceps. *(b)* The forceps stretch the opening slightly. *(c)* The vas is lifted out and then tied off. The other vas is then lifted out through the same small hole and the procedure is repeated.

before that point in the duct system. Thus the ejaculate is completely normal, except that it does not contain any sperm.

How It Works

The vasectomy makes it impossible for sperm to move beyond the cut in the vas. Thus the vasectomy prevents sperm from being in the ejaculate.

Effectiveness

The vasectomy is essentially 100 percent effective; it has a failure rate of 0.1 percent. Failures occur because stray sperm are still present during the first months after surgery, because the physician did not completely sever the vas, or because the ends of the vas have grown back together.

Side Effects

The physical side effects of the vasectomy typically are minimal. In rare cases there is a minor complication from the surgery, such as infection of the vas (Hatcher et al., 2011). Some psychologically based problems may arise. Thus, the man's attitude toward having a vasectomy is extremely important. Only about 5 percent of men regret having had a vasectomy (Hatcher et al., 2011).

Reversibility

Quite a bit of effort has been devoted to developing techniques for reversing vasectomies (the surgical procedure for reversal is termed *vasovasostomy*) and to developing vasectomy techniques that are more reversible. At present, with sophisticated microsurgery techniques, pregnancy rates following reversal are between 38 and 89 percent in various studies (Hatcher et al., 2011). In making a decision about whether to have a vasectomy, though, a man should assume that it is irreversible. After a vasectomy some men begin forming antibodies to their own sperm. Because these antibodies destroy sperm, they might contribute further to the irreversibility of the vasectomy.

Advantages and Disadvantages

The major advantages of the vasectomy are its effectiveness and its minimal health risks. Once performed, it requires no further thought or planning on the man's part. It is a permanent, long-term method of contraception and is free. The operation itself is simple—simpler than the female sterilization procedures—and requires no hospitalization or absence from work. Finally, it is one of the few methods that allow the man to assume contraceptive responsibility.

The permanency of the vasectomy may be either an advantage or a disadvantage. If permanent contraception is desired, the method is certainly much better than something like the birth control pill, which must be used repeatedly. But if the man changes his mind and decides that he wants to have a child (perhaps with a new partner), the permanence is a distinct disadvantage. Some men freeze several samples of their sperm in sperm bank so that assisted insemination can be performed if they do decide to have a child after a vasectomy.

Another disadvantage of the vasectomy is the various psychological problems that might result if the man sees sterilization as a threat to his masculinity or virility. However, studies done around the world show that the majority of vasectomized men say that they have no regrets about having had the sterilization performed, they would recommend it to others, and there has been no change or else an improvement in their happiness and sexual satisfaction in their relationship.

Finally, if a couple use the vasectomy as a permanent method of birth control, the woman is not protected if she has intercourse with someone other than her partner. Similarly, the man is not protected from STIs.

Female Sterilization

Several surgical techniques (sometimes called tubal ligation or "having the tubes tied") are used to sterilize a woman, including minilaparotomy, laparoscopy, and the transcervical approach. These techniques differ in terms of the type of procedure used (see Figure 7.13). They are performed under local or general anaesthesia, and involve blocking the fallopian tubes in some way so that sperm and egg cannot meet.

With **laparoscopy**, a magnifying instrument is inserted in the abdomen. The doctor uses it to identify the fallopian tubes and then blocks them with clips. A variation on this procedure is the *minilaparotomy*, which is used immediately after a woman has given birth. Either procedure takes only about 10 to 20 minutes and does not require that the woman spend the night in the hospital.

Another procedure is the *transcervical approach*, which does not require an incision. Instead, the instruments enter through the cervix and uterus, and a blockage device is placed in each fallopian tube. The devices that are typically used today are called Essure and Adiana. Scar tissue forms around it, blocking the fallopian tube.

The female sterilization procedures do not interfere with the ovaries, and therefore the production of sex hormones continues normally; thus, female sterilization does not bring on premature menopause. Some of the misunderstandings arise from confusion of female sterilization procedures with hysterectomy (surgical removal of the uterus) or oophorectomy (surgical

Laparoscopy: A method of female sterilization.

The fallopian tubes are tied off and cut apart.

Figure 7.13 Tubal ligation using the laparoscopic method.

removal of the ovaries, which does impair hormonal functioning). These latter two operations do produce sterility, but they are generally performed for purposes other than sterilization, such as treatment of cancer.

How It Works

Female sterilization procedures make it impossible for the egg to move down the fallopian tube toward the uterus. They also prevent sperm from reaching the egg.

Effectiveness

These procedures are essentially 100 percent effective. The failure rate of 0.5 percent is due to an occasional rejoining of the ends of the fallopian tubes, and rare cases in which the woman was pregnant before the sterilization procedure was performed.

Side Effects

Occasionally, there are side effects arising from the surgery, such as infections, hemorrhaging, and problems related to the anaesthetic. Generally, only 1 percent of women undergoing the surgery experience complications.

Reversibility

Highly refined microsurgery techniques make it possible to reverse female sterilization in some cases. The success rate varies considerably, depending on the method that was used to perform the sterilization. Pregnancy rates range between 50 and 75 percent, depending on the woman's age and other factors (Gordts et al., 2009). However, in deciding whether to have sterilization

surgery, a woman should assume that it is irreversible. Five years after sterilization, only 7 percent of women regret having had the procedure (Jamieson et al., 2002).

Advantages and Disadvantages

Female sterilization has some of the same advantages as male sterilization in terms of effectiveness, permanence, and cost (it's free) when used for long-term contraception. One disadvantage is that it offers no protection from STIs.

 L05

New Advances in Contraception

According to some, a really good method of contraception is not yet available (see Milestones in Sex Research). The highly effective methods either are permanent (sterilization) or have associated health risks (the pill). Other, safer methods (such as the condom and the cervical cap) have failure rates that cannot be ignored. Most of the methods are for women, not men. With the exception of the condom, none of the methods provide protection from STIs. Because of the limitations of the currently available methods, contraception research continues. Unfortunately, its pace has been slow in the last few years because pharmaceutical companies are leery of lawsuits. There is little incentive for conducting highly innovative research and much incentive for companies to be cautious. Nonetheless, research and innovation continue, even if at a slow pace. Some of the more promising possibilities for the future are discussed here.

Milestone in Sex Research

History of the Development of Sophisticated Methods of Contraception

Late 1700s	Casanova (1725–1798) popularizes and publicizes use of the sheath, or *English riding coat.*
1798	Malthus urges "moral restraint" or abstinence.
1840s	Goodyear vulcanizes rubber. Production of rubber condoms soon follows.
1883	Mensinga invents the diaphragm.
1893	Harrison performs the first vasectomy.
1909	Richter uses the intrauterine silkworm gut.
1910–1920	Sanger pioneers in New York City; the term *birth control* is coined.
1930	Gräfenberg publishes information documenting his 21 years of experience with the ring (silver and copper) and catgut as IUDs.
1930–1931	Knaus and Ogino elucidate "safe and unsafe" periods of the woman's menstrual cycle: the rhythm method.
1932	First birth control clinic in Canada opens in Hamilton, Ontario.
1934	Corner and Beard isolate progesterone.
1937	Makepeace demonstrates that progesterone inhibits ovulation.
1950s	Abortions are used extensively in Japan.
1960s	Many Western nations liberalize abortion laws. Modern IUDs become available. Contraceptive sterilization becomes more acceptable. The laparoscopic tubal ligation technique is developed.
1969	Changes to the *Criminal Code of Canada* legalize contraceptive use and allow abortions under some circumstances.
1970s	Depo-Provera contraceptive injections become available in more than 50 nations (though not in Canada until 1997).
1988	The Supreme Court of Canada rules on abortion.
1996	The female condom becomes available over the counter.
2004	NuvaRing and Ortho Evra patch are approved by Health Canada.
2007	Seasonale is approved by Health Canada.
2008	Plan B emergency contraception is approved for sale over the counter by Health Canada.

Sources: Hatcher et al. (1976), Institute of Medicine (2004).

Male Methods

Several possibilities for new or improved male contraception are being explored (Hatcher et al., 2011; Institute of Medicine, 2004; Wenk & Nieschlag, 2006).

New Condoms

Several new models of condoms are being tested. To deal with the problem of allergies to latex, polyurethane condoms have been developed, as noted earlier. They are thinner than latex, so they should provide more sensation. Another model is one that could be put on before erection.

Male Hormonal Methods

The basic idea underlying the development of male hormonal methods is to suppress the production of LH and FSH by the pituitary so that sperm would not be produced or would not develop properly (Wenk & Nieschlag, 2006). Unfortunately, many of the hormone preparations that have been tried shut down sperm production but also shut down the user's sex drive, making them unacceptable to most men. Current drugs being tested involve a combination of a testosterone and a progestin (such as DMPA, used

Are there any hormonal contraceptive methods for men?

in the Depo-Provera shot for women); the latter would suppress FSH and LH production, leading to the suppression of spermatogenesis (Page et al., 2006). Another group of drugs is the GnRH antagonists. By reducing GnRH activity, they would reduce the production of FSH and LH, which would stop spermatogenesis.

Immunocontraceptives

Scientists have been working on a contraceptive vaccine that would induce the individual's immune system to react in a way that would interrupt one of the steps in the fertility system, for example, one of the stages in the production or maturation of sperm. One option is a vaccine targeting sperm antigens (Naz, 2011). Another is a vaccine for men that would target pituitary FSH, which would block sperm production without stopping the manufacture of testosterone. None of these are in trials yet.

Male Contraceptive Implant

Health Canada has approved a clinical trial for an intra-vas device (IVD) in which two tiny plugs that block sperm are inserted into the vas deferens. Unlike a vasectomy, for which reversal is often not successful, these devices could be removed if the man later decided he wanted to father a child.

Female Methods
Microbicides

Microbicides are substances that kill microbes (bacteria and viruses) and, preferably, sperm. Experts had hoped that current contraceptive foams and gels that contain nonoxynol-9 (N-9) would be effective microbicides, but it turns out that N-9 is ineffective and may actually make women more vulnerable to infection by irritating the vagina. What we need is a microbicide that is highly effective at killing the viruses and bacteria that cause STIs *and* is effective at killing sperm *and* does not irritate the vagina. Several promising microbicides are in clinical trials (Hatcher et al., 2011). One example is Buffer-Gel. These microbicides could be used by themselves or with a cervical cap or condom.

Vaginal Rings

The NuvaRing, discussed earlier, is already available in Canada and contains a combination of estrogen and progestin. A new ring, NES-EE, is being developed and would last 12 months (Ringheim & Gribble, 2009). The NES stands for Nestorone, a progestin.

One company is developing a ring that contains both contraceptive hormones and tenofovir, an antiretroviral that protects against HIV (Hatcher et al., 2011). The idea is to produce multipurpose technologies that work as contraceptives and protect from STIs.

Spray-On Contraception

The Nestorone metered dose transdermal system, a progestin, is now under development in spray form (Upadhyay et al., 2005). It is sprayed on the skin (transdermally) once a day, is quickly absorbed through the skin, and then slowly diffuses into the bloodstream.

Injectables

The contraceptive injection used in Canada today is Depo-Provera, which contains progestin only. Concerns about Depo were discussed earlier in this chapter. Newer injectables are being developed that contain a combination of estrogen and progestin much like the combination pill (Upadhyay et al., 2005).

New IUDs

Several new IUDs are under development. One, Gyne-Fix, is similar to the copper T, but without the T—that is, it is frameless. It simply carries copper tubes on a string and would last for at least five years, but the top of it must be anchored into the endometrium of the uterus. It has been approved in Europe and is available in China.

Implant Inhibition

Selective modulators of progesterone receptors (SPRMS) are anti-progestins that are promising as a postcoital method, or emergency contraception (Rabe, 2007). They have a dual effect, depending on when in the cycle they are used. They prevent the LH surge that triggers ovulation and, if conception occurs, they inhibit implantation. One of these anti-progestins, ella, was approved in the United States in 2010.

Reversible, Nonsurgical Sterilization

This method involves injecting liquid silicone into the fallopian tubes. The silicone hardens and forms a plug. The plugs could later be removed if the woman wanted to become pregnant. It might also be used to plug the vas in men.

Psychological Aspects: Attitudes Toward Contraception

It is a favourite old saying that contraceptives are only as effective as the people who use them. That is, no contraceptive method is effective if it is not used or if it is used improperly. Thus, the user is at least as important as all the technology of contraception.

In 2010, 2.8 percent of teenage girls in Canada or about 31,000 girls (most of them single) became pregnant (McKay, 2012). The rate of teenage pregnancy in Canada has been decreasing in most provinces and territories. However, it increased between 2001 and 2010 in Newfoundland and Labrador, Nova Scotia, New Brunswick, and Yukon. The rate (28.2 per 1000) is considerably higher than in many European countries

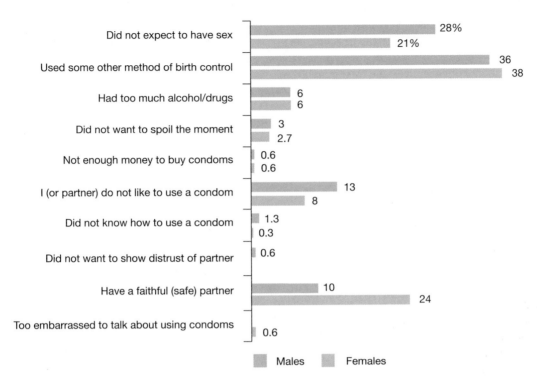

Figure 7.14   Reasons given by Canadian Grade 11 students for not using condoms the last time they had intercourse.

Source: Council of Ministers of Education (2003). Canadian Youth, Sexual Health and HIV/AIDS Study: Factors influencing knowledge, attitude, and behaviours.

(e.g., German, Finland, Switzerland) and much lower than in England and the United States (McKay, 2012). Approximately 53 percent of teenage pregnancies are terminated by abortion, 45 percent result in live births (often to single teenagers), and 2 percent end in miscarriage. Of the teenagers who give birth, most choose to keep the baby.

Most unwanted pregnancies are the result of failure to use contraceptives responsibly. The Canada Youth Sexual Health and HIV/AIDS Study (CYSHHAS) found that between 5 and 10 percent of high school students in Grades 9 and 11 had used no contraceptive method the last time they engaged in sexual intercourse (Boyce et al., 2006). Further, only about three-quarters of Canadian adolescents who engaged in sexual intercourse report always using contraception (Black, Yang, et al., 2009; Fisher et al., 2004). Others do not use contraceptives consistently.[2] Research in five Western countries, including Canada, indicates that in all five countries, adolescents from low-income families are more likely to become pregnant (Darroch et al., 2001).

If we are to understand this issue and take effective steps to address it, we must understand the psychology of contraceptive use and nonuse. Many researchers have been investigating this issue. Why don't adolescents use contraceptives? The CYSHHAS asked Canadian high school students why they had not used condoms the last time they had sexual intercourse (Boyce et al., 2006). As shown in Figure 7.14, one important reason for both Grade 9 and Grade 11 students was that they did not expect to have sex. Another important reason was that they used another method of birth control. Other common reasons were having had too much alcohol or drugs, not wanting to spoil the moment, not having enough money to buy condoms, their or their partner not wanting to use condoms, and feeling that they had a faithful partner. Few students said that they did not know how to use a condom or that they were too embarrassed to talk about condom use. The study did not ask students about some other reasons that adolescents sometimes give for not using contraceptives, such as believing that they could not get pregnant. And some think that pregnancy would not be such a bad thing and might even be a good thing.

What factors affect whether teens are consistent users of contraception? William Fisher, a psychologist at the University of Western Ontario, has developed the information–motivation–behavioural skills (IMB) model

---

[2] Myths teenagers hold about when a woman can and cannot get pregnant may contribute to their inconsistent use of contraception. For example, when she was in high school, the daughter of one of this text's authors (ESB) regularly heard other kids state with certainty that a female cannot get pregnant the first time she has intercourse or if she has intercourse standing up or in water. What have you heard?

to explain such sexual health behaviour as contraceptive use (Fisher & Fisher, 1992, 1998). The first component of this model is *information*. People who lack information about contraceptives and their correct use can scarcely use them effectively. People need the information to be presented in a way that makes it easy for them to put it into practice. That is, people need basic and understandable information about fertility and contraceptives, but they also need specific, practical information about where to acquire contraceptives and how to use them correctly to prevent pregnancy.

The second component of the IMB is *motivation*. People are more motivated to use contraceptives if they have positive attitudes toward the use of contraception, perceive that the use of contraception is socially acceptable, and have the expectation that intercourse could result in pregnancy. Individuals who believe that contraception interferes with lovemaking, think that their friends disapprove of sex or of the use of contraceptives, or believe that there is little chance of pregnancy will be less likely to practise effective contraception. A person's motivation to engage in contraceptive behaviour is also influenced by his or her emotional responses to sexual cues, called *erotophobia-erotophilia* (Byrne, 1983; Fisher et al., 1983). **Erotophobes** tend to have negative emotions related to sex, such as guilt and fear of social disapproval. **Erotophiles** are just the opposite—they feel comfortable with and positive toward sex and sexual stimuli. Most people are somewhere in between.

The third component of the IMB is having the *behavioural skills* to engage in the actions needed to use contraceptives effectively. This includes the skills to acquire contraceptives, discuss contraceptive use with a partner, and refuse to engage in sexual intercourse if contraception is not available. Before individuals will engage in these behaviours, they must accept the fact that they are sexually active and that pregnancy (or STIs) can result from intercourse. They also need to set preventing pregnancy as a personal goal (Fisher & Fisher, 1998). Research shows that many people think the chance is zero, or close to it, that intercourse will result in pregnancy, expressing the expectation that "it can't happen to me." People with that expectation are unlikely to use contraceptives.

Research has shown that erotophobes are less likely to engage in a number of the steps essential for effective contraception (Byrne, 1983; Fisher et al., 1988):

Erotophobes: People with a negative orientation toward sexuality, who feel guilty and fearful about sex.
Erotophiles: People with a positive orientation toward sexuality, who feel comfortable with and positive toward sex.

1. *Obtaining contraceptive information.* Erotophobes have less sex information than erotophiles do, and when exposed to the same sex information, erotophobes learn less than erotophiles do.

2. *Acknowledging that sex may occur.* Erotophobes are less likely to acknowledge that intercourse may occur, which makes contraceptive planning difficult. Gender-role socialization has made it particularly difficult for women to acknowledge such expectations (Hynie & Lydon, 1995).

3. *Obtaining contraceptives.* Erotophobes have more difficulty going to a doctor or a drugstore to obtain contraceptives. In turn, people who are more embarrassed about obtaining contraception are less likely to use it consistently (Herold, 1981).

4. *Communicating with a partner.* Erotophobes have more difficulty talking about sex, and therefore effective communication with their partner about use of contraceptives is unlikely to occur. Each partner may assume that the other will take care of it. An erotophobe may also have more difficulty insisting on contraceptive use with a reluctant partner.

5. *Using contraceptives every time.* Erotophobes may have trouble with actually using the contraceptive. An erotophobic male isn't going to be thrilled about putting on a condom. An erotophobic female won't be thrilled with inserting a cervical cap or thinking about sex every day as she takes her pill.

Although it is generally recognized that fantasy is an important part of sexual expression, fantasy may also play an important role in contraceptive behaviour. Most of us have fantasies about sexual encounters, and we often try to make our real-life sexual encounters turn out like the *scripts* of our fantasies. An important shaper of our fantasies is the mass media. Through movies, television, the Internet, and romance novels, we learn idealized techniques for kissing, holding, lovemaking. But the media's idealized versions of sex almost never include a portrayal of the use of contraceptives (American Academy of Pediatrics, 2010). In the popular TV show *Grey's Anatomy*, Cristina has sex for the first time with a new partner with no contraception in sight and she's a doctor! One content analysis of media (television, magazines, music, and movies) that are popular with adolescents found that on the rare occasion when contraception was presented, it was portrayed as embarrassing or humiliating (Hust et al., 2008).

There were a number of positive examples of discussion of condoms in the original *Degrassi* series (M. Byers, 2005). For example, Caitlin tells Joey that she's ready to have sex with him by slipping a condom into his hand while they are having a romantic dinner in a nice restaurant. More recently, positive examples have come from the television series *Sex and the City*. In one sequence, Miranda has "mercy sex" with her ex-boyfriend Steve, who had just undergone treatment for testicular cancer. They don't use a condom and Miranda gets pregnant. After that, she frequently reminds her friends to use a condom, using herself as an example of the consequences of not using one. These episodes were excellent in showing that negative consequences do occur when contraception is not used, and they provide examples of honest discussions of contraception. If teenagers saw lots of instances of their heroes and heroines behaving responsibly about contraception, it would probably influence their behaviour. But right now that is not what the media usually give them. However, things may be slowly moving in the right direction: 25 percent of television programs that show or strongly imply sexual intercourse also include a reference to safer sex (Kaiser Family Foundation, 2001). For example, in an episode of *Friends,* Monica and Rachel fought over the last condom when both of their boyfriends were staying over.

What are the solutions? Can this research and theorizing on the psychology of contraceptive use be applied to reducing unwanted teenage pregnancy? The most direct solution would be to have better programs of sex education in the schools. In Canada, the nature and extensiveness of school-based sexual health education varies considerably among and within provinces and territories (Barrett et al., 1997). Sex education programs should include a number of components that are typically missing, including legitimizing presex communication about sex and contraception (Milan & Kilmann, 1987); legitimizing the purchase and carrying of contraceptives; discussing how to weigh the costs and benefits of pregnancy, contraception, and abortion; legitimizing noncoital kinds of sexual pleasure, such as masturbation and oral–genital sex; encouraging males to accept equal responsibility for contraception; and enhancing skills through role-playing and other skill-building activities. Some suggestions on how to negotiate safer sex are presented in the Chapter 8, and sexuality education is discussed in more depth in Chapter 19.

So far we have focused only on why many adolescents do not use contraceptives consistently. Before leaving this discussion, it is important to note that it is not just single teenagers who have unwanted pregnancies, and many of the same factors just discussed also apply to older individuals. Further, some single teenage mothers make good parents, whereas some single women in their 20s and 30s do not. For example, a Nova Scotia study found no differences between the children of single teenage mothers and those of older single mothers in either parenting skills or the children's educational achievements (Bissell, 2000; Nova Scotia Department of Community Services, 1991). Research has shown that it is poverty and lack of education, rather than age per se,

that create difficulties for single mothers (Luong, 2008; Maticka-Tyndale, 2001; Singh et al., 2001).

 LO7

Abortion

In the past several decades, **abortion** (the termination of a pregnancy) has been a topic of considerable controversy in North America. Canada currently has no laws related to abortion and so, legally, abortion is treated like any other medical procedure (see First Person for a short history of abortion in Canada). However, some groups would like to see abortion recriminalized. Opposition to abortion comes from a coalition of anti-abortion groups that prefer to call themselves *pro-life* groups. Those seeking to preserve the right of women to legal abortions, who call themselves *pro-choice*, have also organized. Canadians for Choice, for example, has been active in trying ensure reproductive freedom for Canadian women.

What do most Canadians think about abortion? Two national polls conducted in 2012 found that between 49 and 60 percent of Canadians believe abortion should be legal in all circumstances—that is, to any woman who wants one (Gurney, 2012; Kennedy, 2012). The percentage of Canadians favouring legal abortion for any reason was higher among people ages 18 to 34. Most other Canadians take a middle position, believing that abortion should be available under certain circumstances. What are these circumstances? Almost all (92 percent) agreed that a woman should have access to a legal abortion when her health is endangered; 86 percent supported legal abortion if conception is due to rape; 84 percent supported it when the baby is likely to have a serious defect; and 57 percent if the family had a very low income (Bibby, 2006).

In 2011, 92,524 Canadian women obtained a legal abortion (Canadian Institute for Health Information [CIHI], 2011). Nonetheless, all Canadian women do not have equal access to abortion services. Several factors limit Canadian women's access to abortion (Shaw, 2006). One factor is a lack of abortion services in many areas. In general, abortions are more available in urban than in rural areas. Further, as shown in Table 7.2, only 16 percent of hospitals perform abortions, and no abortion services are available on Prince Edward Island. No free-standing abortion clinics exist in Saskatchewan or in any of the territories, although women in these areas do have access to hospital abortions. The process for obtaining an abortion varies across jurisdictions and may make it difficult for some women to receive abortions in a timely fashion. In some provinces, abortions are fully funded by medicare, while

Abortion: The termination of a pregnancy.

A History of Abortion in Canada: Focus on Dr. Henry Morgentaler Ⓛ02

Canada currently has no abortion legislation, and abortion is legal in Canada. However, this has not always been the case. For example, from 1969 to 1988 women could obtain a legal abortion only under certain restricted circumstances. Under this law, many women were not able to get legal abortions. Dr. Henry Morgentaler was instrumental in bringing changes to Canada's abortion laws through a campaign of civil disobedience (Figure 7.15).

Henry Morgentaler was born in Poland in 1923. Both his parents were killed by the Nazis, and he himself was interned in two concentration camps before being liberated by U.S. forces. He immigrated to Canada and graduated with a degree in medicine from l'Université de Montréal in 1953. In 1955 he opened a general medical practice. At first, Dr. Morgentaler refused to perform abortions. However, in 1968, moved by the desperation of some of his poor female patients with unwanted pregnancies, he opened his first abortion clinic in Montreal in violation of Canadian law. He believed that the abortion law was unjust and harmed women. At the time, physicians convicted of performing an abortion could receive a life sentence.

In 1973, Dr. Morgentaler started a campaign of civil disobedience to challenge Canada's abortion laws and provide Canadian women with access to safe legal abortions. At the same time, in his clinics, he developed the vacuum-suction method for performing abortions; this is the procedure that is used for 97 percent of abortions in Canada today. Dr. Morgentaler was charged several times between 1973 and 1986, and was acquitted by juries in Quebec, Ontario, and Manitoba. However, he did spend 10 months in Quebec prisons in 1975–1976, after the Quebec Court of Appeal overturned his jury acquittal and substituted a guilty verdict. (It is no longer legal for an appeal court to substitute a guilty verdict for a jury acquittal, because of this case.)

In 1988, after this series of court cases, the Supreme Court of Canada struck down Canada's abortion law as unconstitutional, calling it the "Morgentaler Decision." This decision effectively decriminalized abortion in Canada and provided most women with easier access to a legal abortion should they want one. In June 2005

Dr. Morgentaler was awarded his first honorary degree by the University of Western Ontario, and he was awarded the Order of Canada in 2008. It's because of the actions of Dr. Morgentaler that abortion is legal in Canada. He continued to fight until his death in 2013 to increase woman's access to abortion through legal action against provincial governments who refuse to fund abortions performed in clinics.

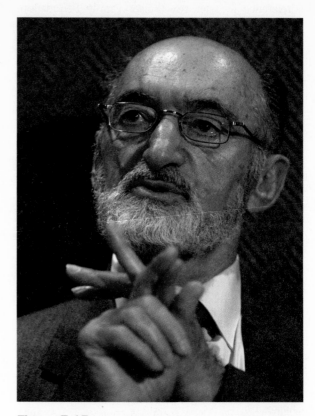

Figure 7.15 Dr. Henry Morgentaler was instrumental in decriminalizing abortion in Canada. Legal challenges against Morgentaler began in 1970 and ended in 1988 when the Supreme Court of Canada found that the section of the *Criminal Code* dealing with abortion was unconstitutional.

Table 7.2   Access to Abortion Across Canada

Province or Territory	Number of Hospitals Providing Abortions	Number of Clinics Providing Abortions	Funding for Abortion
Newfoundland & Labrador	3 of 14 (21%)	1	Full funding for hospitals and clinics
Prince Edward Island	0 of 7 (0%)	0	Can request reimbursement for out-of-province hospital abortions; no funding for clinics
Nova Scotia	4 of 30 (13%)	1	Full funding for hospitals; partial funding for clinics
New Brunswick	1 of 28 (4%)	1	Full funding for hospitals; no funding for clinics
Quebec	31 of 129 (24%)	6 clinics, 12 community health centres	Full funding for hospitals and community health centres; partial funding for clinics
Ontario	33 of 194 (17%)	6	Full funding for hospitals and clinics
Manitoba	2 of 52 (4%)	1	Full funding for hospitals and clinics
Saskatchewan	4 of 68 (6%)	0	Full funding for hospitals
Alberta	6 of 100 (6%)	2	Full funding for hospitals and clinics
British Columbia	26 of 88 (29%)	3	Full funding for hospitals and clinics
Yukon	1 of 2 (50%)	0	Full funding for hospitals and travel grants
Northwest Territories	2 of 3 (67%)	0	Full funding for hospitals and travel grants
Nunavut	1 of 1 (100%)	0	Full funding for hospitals and travel grants

Source: Childbirth by Choice Trust (2003), Shaw (2006).

in other provinces only hospital abortions are covered and women have to pay between $500 and $800 for a clinic abortion. Finally, the activities of anti-abortion groups, such as picketing outside abortion clinics or the homes of physicians who provide abortions, have discouraged some physicians from providing abortion services. They have good reason to be fearful. At least three Canadian physicians have been wounded in their homes by snipers, and the Toronto Morgentaler clinic was destroyed by a firebomb in 1992.

In other countries, policies on abortion vary widely. Abortion is legal and widely practised in Russia and Japan, parts of eastern and central Europe, and South America. The use of abortion in Africa and Asia is limited because of the scarcity of medical facilities, and many women in these countries undergo unsafe abortions. The World Health Organization estimates that there are 19 million unsafe abortions each year and that 68,000 women die as a result (WHO, 2004). Table 7.3 gives rates of abortion in various countries, including Canada. The Canadian abortion rate has remained fairly stable over the past decade (PHAC, 2008b). We discuss methods of abortion and the psychological aspects of abortion here; the ethical aspects will be discussed in Chapter 20, available online at Connect™.

Abortion Procedures

Several methods of abortion are available; which one is used depends on how far the pregnancy has progressed.

Vacuum Aspiration

The **vacuum aspiration** method (also called *vacuum suction* or *vacuum curettage*) can be performed during the first trimester of pregnancy and up to 14 weeks' gestation. It is done on an outpatient basis with a local anaesthetic. The procedure itself takes only about 10 minutes, and the woman stays in the doctor's office, clinic, or hospital for a few hours. It is the most widely used abortion procedure in Canada today, accounting for 97 percent of abortions (Baird & Flinn, 2001).

The woman is prepared as she would be for a pelvic exam, and an instrument is inserted into the vagina; the instrument dilates (stretches open) the opening of the cervix. A tube is then inserted into this opening until one end is in the uterus (see Figure 7.16). The other end is attached to a suction-producing apparatus and the contents of the uterus, including the fetal tissue, are sucked out.

Vacuum aspiration is a simple procedure and entails little risk. There are rare risks of uterine perforation, infection, hemorrhaging, and failure to remove all the fetal material.

Dilation and Evacuation

Dilation and evacuation (D&E) is used mostly for later second-trimester abortions (Hatcher et al., 2011). It is somewhat similar to vacuum aspiration, but it is more

Vacuum aspiration: A method of abortion that is performed during the first trimester and involves suctioning out the contents of the uterus.

Table 7.3   Abortion Rates Around the World

Country	Number of Abortions per Year	Abortion Rate*	% of Pregnancies Ending in Abortion
Bulgaria	24,900	16	21
Canada	94,000	14	14
China	9,173,000	29	NA
Denmark	16,200	15	18
Israel	19,600	13	10
New Zealand	17,900	20	20
Russian Federation	1,208,700	38	NA
Spain	115,800	12	16
United States	1,210,000	20	19

*The abortion rate is the number of abortions per 1,000 women ages 15–44. Statistics are for legal abortions.
Source: Jones & Kooisha (2011), Sedgh et al. (2007).

complicated because the fetus is relatively large by the second trimester.

Induced Labour

During the late part of the second trimester, abortion is usually performed by inducing labour and a miscarriage. The most commonly used version of this method is the saline-induced abortion. A fine tube is inserted through the abdomen into the amniotic sac and saline solution is injected. Within several hours, the solution causes labour to begin. A variation on this technique is the prostaglandin abortion. Prostaglandins (hormone-like substances that cause contractions) are injected and cause labour. Misoprostol can also be used to induce labour for second-trimester abortions (Autry et al., 2002).

Induced labour is used for abortion only if pregnancy has progressed late into the second trimester and accounts for only 1 percent of abortions in Canada (Statistics Canada, 1995). This method is both more hazardous and more costly than the previous methods.

Medical Abortion

Medical abortion involves only the administration of a drug. The two drugs commonly used are mifepristone and methotrexate. Medical abortions account for 3 percent of the abortions in Canada (CIHI, 2010). This compares with 17 percent in the United States, 47 percent in the United Kingdom, and 86 percent in Finland (Heino & Gissler, 2013; Jones & Kooistra, 2011; London Department of Health, 2013).

What is the difference between a surgical abortion and a medical abortion?

Mifepristone

RU-486 (mifepristone): The "abortion pill."

In 1986 French researchers announced the development of a new drug called RU-486 or mifepristone

Figure 7.16   A vacuum aspiration abortion.

(Couzinet et al., 1986; Ulmann et al., 1990). It can induce a very early abortion. It has a powerful anti-progesterone effect, causing the endometrium of the uterus to be sloughed off and thus bringing about an abortion (see Figure 7.17). It is administered as a tablet followed two

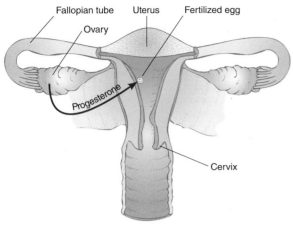

Progesterone, a hormone produced by the ovaries, is necessary for the implantation and development of a fertilized egg.

Taken early in pregnancy, RU-486 blocks the action of progesterone and makes the body react as if it isn't pregnant.

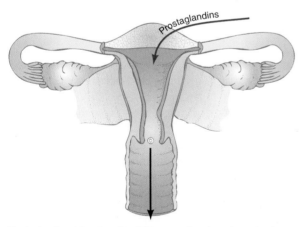

Prostaglandins, taken two days later, cause the uterus to contract and the cervix to soften and dilate. As a result, the embryo is expelled in 97 percent of the cases.

Figure 7.17   How RU-486, or mifepristone, works.

days later by a small dose of prostaglandin (misoprostol), which increases contractions of the uterus, helping to expel the embryo. It can be used during the first seven to nine weeks of pregnancy. Research shows that it is effective in 92 to 96 percent of cases when combined with prostaglandin (Hatcher et al., 2007). It is most effective when the woman has been pregnant less than 49 days. Early research has found little evidence of side effects, although the woman experiences some cramping as the uterine contents are expelled.

In France today, more than half of women who decide to terminate an early pregnancy choose RU-486 rather than conventional abortion methods (Jones & Henshaw, 2002). RU-486 is also widely used in Britain, Sweden, China, and the United States. RU-486 is not available in Canada.

Methotrexate

Another alternative in drug-induced early abortion involves the use of a combination of the drug methotrexate, which is toxic to the embryo, with misoprostol, which causes uterine contractions that expel the dead embryo (Hatcher et al., 2007). Both of these drugs are already widely used for treatment of other diseases and so are available to be used for medical abortions. Like mifepristone, they permit the early induction of abortion in a physician's office rather than an abortion clinic or a hospital. Methotrexate is also used to treat ectopic pregnancy, which is a life-threatening condition.

L08 Psychological Aspects

The discovery of an unwanted pregnancy triggers a complicated set of emotions, as well as a complex decision-making process. Initially, women tend to feel anger and some anxiety. They then embark on the decision-making process studied by psychologist Carol Gilligan (1982). In this process women essentially weigh the need to think of themselves and protect their own welfare against the need to think of the welfare of the fetus. Even focusing only on the welfare of the fetus can lead to conflicting conclusions: Should I complete the pregnancy because the fetus has a right to life? should I have an abortion because the fetus has a right to be born into a stable family with two parents who have completed their education and can provide good financial support? Some women consider whether to give birth to the baby and then give it up for adoption. Many women in Gilligan's study showed considerable psychological growth over the time in which they wrestled with these issues and made their decision. See A Sexually Diverse World for a cross-cultural perspective on abortion.

What is the impact of abortion on women's mental health? Anti-abortion activists claim that women are psychologically traumatized by having an abortion, which they call post-abortion syndrome (Bazelon, 2007). However, other people argue that abortion is a stressful life event that is similar to other types of stressful events that women experience. As such, the impact of this

A Sexually Diverse World

Abortion in Cross-Cultural Perspective

Beliefs about abortion show dramatic variation in different cultures around the world. The following is a sampling from two very different cultures.

Ekiti Yoruba

The Ekiti Yoruba, many of whom have a high school or postsecondary education, live in southwest Nigeria. For them, abortion is not a distinct category from contraception but rather is on a continuum with it (Renne, 1996).

Traditionally in the Ekiti Yoruba culture, the ideal was for a woman to have as many children as possible, spaced at two- to three-year intervals. The spacing of children is made possible by a period of sexual abstinence for two years postpartum. The Ekiti Yoruba believe that sexual intercourse while a woman is still breastfeeding a baby causes illness or death to the child; men whose children have died in infancy have been blamed for breaking the postpartum sex taboo and causing the death. Because of the high value placed on fertility, use of contraceptives and abortion must be kept secret. Even though condoms, foam, and birth control pills are available at a local clinic, few people take advantage of the service because they would not want others to know that they engaged in such practices. Abortion then becomes the chief method of birth control. Estimates are that between 200,000 and 500,000 pregnancies are aborted each year in Nigeria and that about 10,000 women die each year from botched abortions.

If a woman has an unwanted pregnancy, she generally will consult a local divine healer or herbalist first, to "keep the pregnancy from staying." They generally provide pills or substances to insert in the vagina. If the treatment does not work, the woman then goes to a clinic and has a dilation and curettage (D&C; a procedure that is similar to D&E) abortion.

Women who abort generally fall into two categories: single high school or postsecondary students who want to finish their education, and married women who are pregnant because of an affair. Here is one woman's story:

In 1991, when awaiting entrance into university, I became pregnant by one boyfriend whom I later decided not to marry in favor of another. Since I did not want my chosen fiancé to know of the pregnancy, I decided to abort it. I first used 3 Bee-codeine tablets, Andrew's Liver Salt, and Sprite, mixing them together and then drinking them. When this did not work, I went to a clinic in a neighboring town for D&C. The abortion cost N80 and was paid for by my boyfriend. There were no after effects. (Renne, 1996, p. 487)

The ease with which Ekiti Yoruba people rely on abortion is related in part to their understanding of prenatal development. Many believe that the "real child" is not formed until after the fourth month of pregnancy and before that the fetus is lizard-like.

Greece

Birth control for women was legalized in Greece only in 1980, and abortion was legalized in 1986. Yet Greece has had a sharply declining birth rate since World War II, accounted for, in large part, by abortion (Georges, 1996). Among European nations, Greece is unique in its combination of very little use of medical contraception, a low fertility rate, and the highest abortion rate in Europe.

Three powerful institutions—the government, the Greek Orthodox Church, and the medical profession—have exerted a strong pronatalist (in favour of having babies) influence. The Greek Orthodox Church equates abortion with murder and prohibits all methods of birth control except fertility awareness methods and abstinence. The government, for its part, encourages

stressful life event is likely to be affected by the woman's social and cultural context (e.g., what others around her think of abortion), as well as by other factors in the woman's life (e.g., whether she has a history of emotional problems) (Major et al., 2009; Munk-Olsen et al.,

2011). From this perspective, only some women would experience negative psychological consequences from abortion, and those that do would be ones who have poor coping skills or emotional difficulties, or live in a society that stigmatizes abortion (Major et al., 2009).

large families by a variety of measures, including paying a monthly subsidy to families with more than three children, making daycare centres widely available, and keeping female methods of contraception illegal (until 1980). Despite all this, Greek women achieved a low fertility rate, which is regarded by the government as a threat to the Greek "race," Greek Orthodoxy, and the military strength of Greece in relation to hostile neighbours, such as the extremely fertile Turks.

Despite the illegality of abortion in Greece until 1986, abortion was widespread and a very open secret. Abortions were not back-alley affairs but rather were performed by gynecologists in private offices. Physicians, as members of a powerful and prestigious profession, were successful at legal evasion. As a result, Greek women did not have to face the life-threatening risks that occur with illegal abortion in other countries. They had access to safe illegal abortion.

Why is there so much reliance on abortion and so little access to contraception in this modern European nation? As noted earlier, the Greek Orthodox Church opposes all medical contraception, and the Greek government kept contraception illegal until 1980. But even then, contraception did not become widespread. In 1990, only 2 percent of women of reproductive age were using the pill. Some blame this on the medical profession, which is thought to block access to contraception to continue a thriving, more lucrative abortion practice. Greek women, too, resist contraception. They distinguish between *contraception* (such as birth control pills) and *being careful* (withdrawal and condoms). They reject contraception, but being careful—especially the use of withdrawal—is widespread. Fertility awareness methods are not widely used and would not be very successful if they were, since Greek women commonly believe that they are most fertile for the four to seven days just before and after the menstrual period. The mass media have spread scare messages about the pill, and many women believe that it causes cancer.

How do Greek women, the great majority of whom are Orthodox, deal with the contradiction between their church's teaching—that abortion is murder and that a woman who has had an abortion may not receive communion—and their actual practice of having abortions? First, the Greek Orthodox Church is not as absolutist in its application of doctrines regarding abortion as the Roman Catholic Church is. Some attribute this to the fact that Orthodox priests can be married and are therefore more in touch with the realities of family life. In some cases, women do abstain from receiving communion following an abortion but then later make a confession to the priest. Priests typically are forgiving.

In Greece, motherhood is highly esteemed and idealized, yet abortion is not considered contradictory to the high value placed on motherhood. Good motherhood today is thought to require an intense investment of time and energy in the children; by definition, then, the good mother limits family size, and abortion is a means to achieve that goal.

Cross-Cultural Patterns

Several patterns emerge from the study of abortion in these quite distinct cultures and other cultures (e.g., Gursoy, 1996; Johnson et al., 1996; Rigdon, 1996; Rylko-Bauer, 1996). First, no matter how strict the prohibitions against abortion, some women in all cultures choose and manage to obtain abortions. Second, the meaning of abortion is constructed in any particular culture based on factors such as beliefs about prenatal development, when life starts, and how much large families are valued. Third, the legality and morality of abortion in any culture is determined in part by political forces, such as the Greek government's desire to expand the size of the Greek population.

Sources: Georges (1996), Gursoy (1996), Johnson et al. (1996), Renne (1996), Rigdon (1996), and Rylko-Bauer (1996).

What do the scientific data say? The best scientific evidence indicates that most women do not experience severe negative psychological responses to abortion (Major et al., 2009; Schmiege & Russo, 2005). Most women show good adjustment. Typically, they do not feel guilt or sorrow over the decision. Instead, they report feeling relieved, satisfied, and relatively happy, and say that if they had the decision to make over again, they would do the same thing. Nonetheless, some women benefit from talking about their experience, and it is important that post abortion support groups be available (Lewis, 1997). This may be particularly true of women who have had one or more abortions in the past. An Ontario study found that women who were undergoing repeat abortions were significantly more likely to have experienced physical and sexual violence from a male partner and to have a history of child sexual abuse (Fisher et al., 2005).

Research in this area raises many interesting questions. Women generally show good adjustment after having an abortion, but good adjustment compared with what? It is important to compare the psychological responses of women who undergo abortion to women facing an unwanted pregnancy who choose other alternatives. The American Psychological Association reviewed all the research on the relationship between abortion and women's mental health and concluded that women who have a single, legal, first-trimester abortion are not at greater risk for mental health problems than women who deliver an unwanted pregnancy. However, the minority of women who experience significant distress about their decision to have an abortion may experience mental health problems following the abortion (Fergusson et al., 2009). What is the consequence of being denied an abortion on the children born to these women? It is impossible to do this research in Canada now because abortion has been legal since 1988. However, in some other countries access to abortion depends on obtaining official approval. One such country was the former Czechoslovakia. Researchers followed up 220 children born to women denied abortion (the study group) and 220 children born to women who had not requested abortion; the children were studied when they were 9 years old and again when they were 14 to 16 years old, 21 to 23, 30, and 35 (David et al., 2003). By age 14, 43 children from the study group, but only 30 of the controls, had been referred for counselling. Although there were no differences between the groups in tested intelligence, children in the study group did less well in school and were more likely to drop out. Teachers described them as less sociable and more hyperactive compared with the control group. At age 16, the boys (but not the girls) in the study group more frequently rated themselves as feeling neglected or rejected by their mothers and felt that their mothers were less satisfied with them. By their early 20s, the study group reported less job satisfaction, more conflicts with co-workers and supervisors, and fewer and less satisfying friendships. Several other studies have found results similar to the Czech one (David et al., 2003). These results point to the serious long-term consequences for some children whose mothers would have preferred to have an abortion.

Men and Abortion

Only women become pregnant, and only women have abortions, but where do men enter the picture? Do they have a right to contribute to the decision to have an abortion? What are their feelings about abortion?

A large survey of women who had abortions indicated that 82 percent of the male partners knew that they were having an abortion, although the percentage was lower for women in an abusive relationship (Jones et al., 2011). Among the men who knew, 80 percent were supportive of the decision.

A recent Swedish study surveyed 75 men ranging in age from 18 to 50 who were involved in legal abortion (Kero et al., 1999). The majority were in a long-term relationship with the pregnant woman. Among the men, 64 percent indicated that they wanted the woman to have an abortion; 27 percent felt that it was the woman's decision. The main reasons why these men wanted an abortion were related to family planning, such as conflict with life plans (e.g., schooling), feeling unable to offer a child a caring environment, or socioeconomic reasons. The second most common reason was feeling that their relationship with the woman was not stable. What were these men's reactions to the abortion? The most common words the men used to describe their feelings were *anxiety, responsibility, guilt, relief,* and *grief.* That is, more than half the men expressed both positive and negative emotions about the abortion.

Although counselling for women undergoing abortion is a standard procedure, counselling is rarely available for the men who are involved. These findings suggest that some men also need such counselling (see, for example, Coyle & Enright, 1997).

SUMMARY

Table 7.4 provides a comparative summary of the various methods of birth control discussed in this chapter.

Table 7.4   Summary of Information on Methods of Contraception and Abortion

Method	Failure Rate, Perfect Use, %	Failure Rate, Typical Use, %	Death Rate (per 100,000 women)	Yearly Costs, $[*]	Advantages	Disadvantages
Implant	0.05	0.05		NA	Requires less remembering	Not available in Canada
Depo-Provera	0.3	6		140–180	Requires less remembering	
Combination birth control pills	0.3	3	1.6	0–300	Highly effective; not used at time of coitus; improved menstrual cycles	Cost; possible side effects; must take daily; no STI protection
Patch	0.3	8		0–430	Requires less remembering than the pill	
Vaginal ring	0.3	9	—	200–480		
IUD, copper T	0.6	0.8	1.0	30–175[†]	Requires no remembering or motivation	May be expelled
Progesterone T	0.1	0.1				
Condom, male	2	18	1.7	75[*]	Easy to use; protection from STIs	Used at time of coitus; continual expense
Condom, female	5	21	2.0	0–600[*]	Protection from STIs	Awkward
Diaphragm with spermicide	6	16	2.0[§]	250[*]	No side effects; Inexpensive	Aesthetic objections
FemCap with spermicide						
Parous women	26	32	2.0[§]	250	No side effects; inexpensive	—
Nulliparous women	9	20	2.0[§]			
Vaginal foam, cream	18	28	2.0[§]	40[*]	Easy to use; availability	Messy; continual expense
Sponge	9–20	16–32		750[*]		
Withdrawal	4	22	2.0	None	No cost	Requires high motivation
Fertility awareness	3–5	25	2.0	None	No cost	Requires high motivation, prolonged abstinence; not all women can use
Unprotected intercourse	85	85	9	None[¶]		
Legal abortion, first trimester	0	0	0.5	0–800[**]	Available when other methods fail	Expense
Sterilization, male	0.1	0.1	0.3	0–100[***]	Permanent; highly effective	Permanence
Sterilization, female	0.5	0.5	1.5	None	Permanent; highly effective	Permanence

* Based on 150 acts of intercourse.
† Based on a cost of $60–$400 for the IUD/IUS and the assumption that the IUD/IUS will be used for two years.
§ Based on the death rate for pregnancies resulting from the method. Of every 100,000 live births, 12 women die (Cheng et al., 2003).
¶ But having a baby is expensive.
** All hospital abortions are covered by medicare. Only Newfoundland and Labrador, Quebec, Ontario, Manitoba, Alberta, and British Columbia cover abortions done in free-standing clinics.
*** Although vasectomy is covered by medicare, in some provinces there is an additional fee for those done in doctors' offices.
Source: Robert A. Hatcher et al., *Contraceptive technology* (18th ed.), 2007. Adapted by permission of Irvington Publishers.

QUESTIONS FOR THOUGHT, DISCUSSION, AND DEBATE

1. Do you think you are an erotophobe or an erotophile or somewhere in between? In what ways do you think your erotophobia or erotophilia has affected or will affect your use of birth control?

2. Debate the following topic. Resolved: The birth control pill is a safe and effective method of birth control for most women.

3. On your campus, as on all campuses, students probably are inconsistent in their use of birth control or use nothing even though they are engaging in sexual intercourse. Design a program to improve birth control practices on your campus.

4. Knowing that you are taking a human sexuality course and have gained a lot of expertise, Nicole, your best friend, comes to you in a state of crisis. She and her boyfriend had unprotected intercourse last night and she is terrified that she is pregnant. What options would you explain to her, and which one would you recommend?

Are YOU Curious?

1. How can I know whether I have chlamydia?
2. Is there a cure for herpes?
3. Why isn't there a vaccine against HIV?
4. My partner has no symptoms of any STI. Should we still practise safer sex?

Read this chapter to find out.

Can you tell someone has HIV just by looking at them?

Protect yourself. Six in ten Canadians with multiple partners did not use a condom the last time they had sex.

Learn More at **Kisses4CANFAR.com**

Kisses4 **CANFAR**

CHAPTER

8

Sexually Transmitted Infections

LEARNING OBJECTIVES

After studying this chapter, you will be able to

 L01 Describe the transmission, symptoms in males and females, diagnosis, treatment, and prevention strategies for each sexually transmitted infection.

 L02 Give examples of how women, children, and ethnic minorities are being affected by AIDS in Canada and around the world.

 L03 Recognize the psychological considerations surrounding HIV/AIDS.

L04 Illustrate the various ways sexually transmitted infections can be reduced or avoided.

 L05 State the symptoms and treatment for genital infections.

Maria and Louis get home after an evening on the town and enter the house hungry for passion. The two embrace, clinging to each other, longing for each other. Louis slowly undresses Maria, hungry for the silky flesh he feels beneath him. As their passion grows, she begins reaching for him, ripping his clothes off as she explores his body with her tongue. As Louis gets more and more excited, Maria rips a condom package open with her teeth and slowly slides the condom over Louis's erect penis. After an hour of incredible lovemaking, Louis, exhausted with pleasure, turns to Maria and says, "You were right, the BEST sex is SAFER sex with LATEX!"*

* From a student essay.

As noted in Chapter 1, according to the World Health Organization, sexual health is a state of physical, emotional, mental, and social well-being related to sexuality. One aspect of this is the absence of disease, of which sexually transmitted infections (STIs) are an example. Not only do STIs affect an individual's physical sexual health, but the psychological aspects of dealing with an STI also may challenge the emotional, mental, and social aspects of a person's sexual health and well-being. In keeping with the Public Health Agency of Canada, we use the term STI rather than STD (sexually transmitted disease). STD refers only to infections that cause symptoms. STI is more encompassing because it includes infections for which people have symptoms and those for which they have no symptoms—that is, are asymptomatic.

The sexual scene is not the same as it was 30 or 40 years ago. The human papillomavirus (HPV) and HIV/AIDS pose real threats. We need to do many things to combat these dangers. One is that we must rewrite our sexual scripts, as the opening box illustrates. We also need to inform ourselves, and the goal of this chapter is to provide you with the important information you need to make decisions about your sexual activity.[1]

Your health is very important, and a good way to harm it or cause yourself suffering is to have an untreated sexually transmitted infection. Although in 1997 it appeared that there would be a continuing gradual decline in the rates of many STIs, that trend ended and instead there has been an increase in the incidence of newly acquired STIs in Canada (MacDonald & Wong, 2007). Consequently, it is very important to know the symptoms of the various kinds of STIs so that you can seek treatment if you develop one. Also, there are some ways to prevent STIs or at least reduce your chances of getting them, and these are certainly worth knowing about. Finally, after you have read some of the statistics on how many people contract STIs every year and on your chances of getting one, you may want to modify your sexual behaviour somewhat. If you love, love wisely.

One of the most disturbing things about the STI epidemic in Canada is that it disproportionately affects teens and young adults. For example, of 86,489 new cases of chlamydia that occurred in 2009 in Canada, 55,353 (64 percent) were among people between the ages of 15 and 24. For people in this age group, three infections—human papillomavirus, trichomoniasis, and chlamydia—account for the majority of cases, although of these only chlamydia is a reportable infection. Canadian youth with low incomes and from ethnocultural minority groups are at a greater risk of contracting STIs (Wong et al., 2012). Worldwide, of the 60 million people who have been infected with HIV, about half became infected between the ages of 15 and 24 (Kiragu et al., 2001); 42 percent of new infections (excluding neonatal transmission) occurred in this age group (UNAIDS, 2012a). Clearly, prevention efforts, including sexuality education for youth that is not fear-based, must be accorded a higher priority than they have been given in the past.

The STIs are presented in this chapter in the following order. First we look at three—chlamydia, HPV, and herpes—that are frequent among university students. Following that is a discussion of HIV infection and AIDS, which is less common among university students but is one of the world's major public health problems and is generating an enormous amount of research. Next we discuss gonorrhea, syphilis, viral hepatitis, and trichomoniasis. Then comes not an infection but a bug: the pubic louse. After a practical section on preventing STIs, the chapter ends with a section about various other genital infections that, for the most part, are not sexually transmitted.

---

[1] The diagnosis and treatment of sexually transmitted infections is an area of furiously active research. New discoveries are announced almost monthly. Therefore, by the time you read this book, some of the statements in this chapter may have been superseded by newer research.

Some STIs are caused by *bacteria*, some are caused by *viruses*, and a few are caused by other organisms. The distinction between bacterial infections and viral infections is important because bacterial infections can be cured by using antibiotics. Viral infections cannot be cured but they can be treated to reduce symptoms. Chlamydia, gonorrhea, and syphilis are caused by bacteria. Herpes, HIV/AIDS, HPV, and hepatitis B are caused by viruses.

Many statistics throughout this chapter come from the Public Health Agency of Canada (PHAC) website at www.phac-aspc.gc.ca. Data from the PHAC are used so frequently throughout the chapter that we do not provide a citation every time. Information on STIs changes quickly, so to get the most up-to-date information, check the website. Only some STIs, not all, must be reported. Therefore, there are no national data on some of the most common STIs, such as genital herpes and HPV. STI rates vary considerably across provinces and territories. You can look up the rates for the province or territory you live in on the PHAC website.

One final note before we proceed: many photos in this chapter show the symptoms of various STIs, and some students find them distressing. The photos are not meant to scare you but to help you recognize the symptoms of STIs so that you can spot them on a prospective sexual partner and on you. You should consult your physician if you see any change in your genitals, even if it does not look like any of the pictures in this book—most of these photos are of severe cases.

Figure 8.1 Poster developed by the Canadian Federation of Sexual Health for Sexual and Reproductive Health Day. Used with permission of the Canadian Federation for Sexual Health.

 LO1

Chlamydia

Chlamydia trachomatis is a bacterium that is spread by sexual contact and infects the genital organs of both males and females (Figure 8.1). **Chlamydia** has become the most prevalent bacterial STI in Canada. According to the PHAC, there were 57,813 reported cases in women and 29,311 reported cases in men in 2009, a rate of 249 cases per 100,000 people in the population, the most common reported STI in Canada. However, a study that examined the rate of chlamydia in a nationally representative Canadian sample found a much higher rate: 700 cases per 100,000 people (Rotermann et al., 2013). None of these individuals had ever been diagnosed with chlamydia. The rate of chlamydia has been rising steadily since 1997. Adolescent girls have a particularly high rate of infection, more than five times the national rate.

Symptoms

The main symptoms in men are a thin, usually clear discharge and mild discomfort on urination appearing 7 to 21 days after infection (Stamm, 2008). The symptoms are somewhat similar to the symptoms of gonorrhea in men. When a man consults a physician because of a urethral discharge, his chances of having chlamydia are greater than his chances of having gonorrhea. It is important that the correct diagnosis be made since chlamydia does not respond to the drugs used to cure gonorrhea. However, gonorrhea tends to produce more painful urination and a more profuse, puslike discharge. Diagnosis is made from a urine sample in men and from a sample of cells from the vagina (or urine sample) in women. Tests are then used to detect the bacterium. Unfortunately, 75 percent of the cases of chlamydia infection are **asymptomatic** in women. This means that the woman never goes to a clinic for treatment, and she goes undiagnosed and untreated. The consequences of untreated chlamydia in women are discussed in the next section. Even among men, 50 percent of the cases are asymptomatic.

> **How can I know whether I have chlamydia?**

Chlamydia (klah-MIH-dee-uh): An organism causing a sexually transmitted infection; the symptoms in men are a thin, clear discharge and mild pain on urination; women are frequently asymptomatic.
Asymptomatic (ay-simp-toh-MAT-ik): Having no symptoms.

Treatment

Chlamydia is quite curable. It is treated with azithromycin or doxycycline (Workowski & Berman, 2010); it does not respond to penicillin. Poorly treated or undiagnosed cases may lead to a number of complications: urethral damage, epididymitis (infection of the epididymis), Reiter's syndrome,[2] and proctitis in men who have had anal intercourse. Women with untreated or undiagnosed chlamydia may experience serious complications if not treated: **pelvic inflammatory disease (PID)** and possibly infertility caused by scarring of the fallopian tubes. A baby born to an infected mother may develop pneumonia or an eye infection.

Prevention

Scientists doing research on chlamydia have a major goal of developing a vaccine that would prevent infection (Berry et al., 2004). Vaccines have been developed that are effective in mice, but certain technical obstacles prevent their use with humans. An effective vaccine for humans should be available in the next decade.

Until a vaccine is available, one of the most effective tools for prevention (in addition to safer sex) is screening. The problem with chlamydia is that so many infected people are asymptomatic and spread the disease unknowingly. In screening programs, asymptomatic carriers are identified, treated, and cured so that they do not continue to spread the disease. More asymptomatic women are being tested routinely. In fact, the PHAC recommends routine testing by the family doctor of all sexually active women under age 25. However, research in Ontario indicates that only a minority of physicians do any sexual health assessment and that physicians infrequently suggest chlamydia testing (Hardwick et al., 2007). Further, far fewer men than women are screened, even though it is important to screen both men and women if screening is to be effective at reducing the prevalence of chlamydia (McKay, 2006a).

In an innovative program in rural Nova Scotia, self-test screen kits were made available in a private setting to all high-school girls. Girls did not have to first see a nurse for counselling to get a kit (Langille et al., 2008). The girls collected vaginal swabs themselves, and the swabs were subjected to laboratory tests with no names attached. Of the 163 girls who had vaginal intercourse at least once during the study period, only 27 used the self-help kit. Two of the tests were positive, which would have gone undetected if the girls had not been screened. Of the girls who did use the kit, the most common reason for screening was wanting the reassurance of a negative test; few girls said that they were concerned about infection. Even though most students knew that chlamydia is often asymptomatic, the most common reasons for not getting screened was not having any symptoms. Similarly, researchers in Ontario piloted a urine drop-off testing kit for gonorrhea and chlamydia at two bathhouses, studying men who have sex with men (O'Byrne & Dias, 2008). Anonymous self-testing is a promising method for screening individuals who would not see a medical professional for testing, perhaps because of perceived STI-related stigma. On an individual level, the best method of prevention is the consistent use of a condom.

HPV

HPV stands for *human papillomavirus*. There are many more than 40 different types of HPV that are sexually transmitted (Winer & Koutskley, 2008). Some types (6 and 11) cause genital warts and are called low risk because they do not cause cancer; other types cause cervical cancer and are called high risk. Some types have no symptoms at all. In fact, the majority of people infected with HPV are asymptomatic. But a person without symptoms can still transmit the virus.

Infection with HPV is widespread. HPV is not a reportable disease and thus there are no national Canadian data. However, Health Canada estimates that between 20 and 33 percent of women have HPV; between 11 and 25 percent of women have the cancer-causing types of HPV. Two studies tested women having routine Pap tests in Newfoundland and Labrador and Ontario (Ratnam et al., 2000; Sellors et al., 2000). They found that the highest rate of HPV was among women under 25: 16 percent of the young Newfoundland and Labrador women and 24 percent of the young Ontario women had HPV infections. There are no good estimates of the prevalence of HPV in men, although it is likely lower than in women (PHAC, 2012c). The disease is highly infectious, and although condoms reduce the risk of infection, they do not eliminate it. HPV is transmitted through skin-to-skin contact, most often from contact with the penis, scrotum, vagina, vulva, or anus of the infected person.

Genital warts are cauliflower-like warts appearing on the genitals (Figure 8.2), usually around the urethral opening of the penis, the shaft of the penis, or the scrotum in the male, and on the vulva, the walls of the vagina,

---

Pelvic inflammatory disease (PID): An infection and inflammation of the pelvic organs, such as the fallopian tubes and the uterus, in women.
HPV: Human papillomavirus, the organism that causes genital warts.
Genital warts: A sexually transmitted infection causing warts on the genitals and cervical cancer.

---

[2] Reiter's syndrome involves the following symptoms: urethritis, eye inflammations, and arthritis.

or the cervix in the female; warts may also occur on the anus. Typically they appear three to eight months after intercourse with an infected person. A Canadian study showed that experiencing genital warts had a negative impact on quality of life including completing usual activities, experiencing pain and discomfort, experiencing anxiety and depression, creating a poor self-image, and reducing sexual activity (Drolet et al., 2011).

New research shows that oral sex can transmit HPV. Individuals infected this way have an increased rate of oral cancers—that is, cancer of the mouth or throat (D'Souza et al., 2007). HPV causes almost all cases of cervical cancer. HPV 16 and 18 account for 70 percent of the cases of cervical cancer (Dailard, 2006). HPV infection is also associated with cancer of the penis and anus (Health Canada, 2000).

Diagnosis

Diagnosis can sometimes be made simply by inspecting the warts, because their appearance is distinctive. However, some strains of warts are flat and less obvious. Also, the warts may grow inside the vagina and may not be detected there. However, HPV is a silent infection because many individuals with HPV show no obvious signs of infection. Thus, for many women the first indication of HPV is abnormal cells on a Pap test. Men are not routinely tested for HPV.

Treatment

Several treatments for genital warts are available. Chemicals such as podophyllin (Podofilm) or bichloroacetic acid (BCA) can be applied directly to the warts. Typically, these treatments have to be repeated several times, and the warts then fall off. With cryotherapy (often using liquid nitrogen), the warts are frozen off; again, it is typically necessary to apply more than one treatment. Drug such as Podofilox cream can be applied by the patient.

In many cases HPV symptoms go away on their own, but others persist for long periods.

Vaccine

As noted, almost all cases of cervical cancer are linked to HPV infection. Therefore, a vaccine against HPV would prevent most cases of cervical cancer. Two such vaccines are now available in Canada, Gardasil and Cervari, and must be administered in three shots over six months. The idea is to administer it to girls around ages 11 to 12 (or as early as 9 years old), before they have engaged in sexual activity, as well as to women up to the age of 25 who have not had an HPV infection or abnormalities on their Pap tests. Gardasil protects against HPV types 16 and 18 that between them cause 70 percent of cervical cancers and against two other HPV types that cause most cases of genital warts. Cervarix also protects against Types 16 and 18. Randomized controlled trials show the vaccine to be highly (95 percent) effective in stopping infection with these strains of HPV (Winer & Koutsky, 2008). How long the immunity will last is not yet known, but it is at least five years, the length of time since the vaccine was first tested.

The federal government has provided funding to the provinces and territories to establish HPV immunization programs. All Canadian provinces and Yukon now have publically funded school-based programs in place to administer the vaccine to girls in Grades 6, 7, or 8 with parental consent. The vaccine is free. However, it is not without controversy. Some parents argue that it will encourage young girls to engage in sexual activity or that it has not been tested sufficiently to use on young girls. Advocates for administering the vaccine point out the potential health benefits and that vaccines have been around for a long time and have been shown to be safe. They argue that the decision to make Gardasil available is no different from the decision to introduce other new vaccines (e.g., a vaccine

(a)

(b)

Figure 8.2   Genital warts *(a)* on the penis and *(b)* on the vulva.

for chicken pox was recently made available), yet there has been no controversy about those vaccines. An Ontario study demonstrated that parents who were less knowledgeable about the vaccine were less likely to consent to their daughter receiving it (Okoronkwo et al., 2012). We recommend that all girls be given this vaccine against cervical cancer. Health Canada approved the vaccine for boys in 2010 and the National Advisory Committee on Immunization recommended that boys and men between the ages of 9 and 26 be vaccinated, but as yet no provinces or territories are offering free vaccines to boys.

LO1

Genital Herpes

Genital herpes is a disease of the genital organs caused by the herpes simplex virus, **HSV**. Genital herpes is transmitted by sexual intercourse and by oral–genital sex. Two strains of HSV are circulating: HSV-1 and HSV-2. In simpler times, HSV-2 caused genital herpes and HSV-1 caused cold sores around the mouth.

Is there a cure for herpes?

Today, however, there is more crossing over. Genital herpes, then, can be caused by either HSV-1 or HSV-2.

The Canadian Health Measures Survey tested a representative Canadian sample between the ages of 14 and 59 for HSV-2 antibodies between 2009 and 2011. They found that 13.6 percent of the sample were infected (Rotermann et al., 2013), about 2.9 million Canadians. The rate was higher in women (16 percent) than in men (11 percent). The rate increased with age. Only 6 percent of individuals who tested positive for HSV-2 were aware that they had the infection. That is, the great majority of people with HSV are asymptomatic and are not aware that they are

Genital herpes (HER-pees): A sexually transmitted infection, the symptoms of which are small, painful bumps or blisters on the genitals.
HSV: The herpes simplex virus.

infected. These persons transmit the disease to others unknowingly.

Symptoms

The symptoms of genital herpes caused by HSV-2 are small, painful bumps or blisters on the genitals. Typically they appear within two to three weeks of infection. In women, they are usually found on the vaginal lips; in men, they usually occur on the penis (Figure 8.3). They may be found around the anus if the person has had anal intercourse. The blisters burst and can be quite painful. Fever, painful urination, and headaches may occur. The blisters heal on their own in about three weeks in the first episode of infection. The virus continues to live in the body, however. It may remain dormant for the rest of the person's life. But the symptoms may recur unpredictably, so that the person repeatedly undergoes 7- to 14-day periods of sores. HSV-1 infection tends to be less severe.

People with herpes are most infectious when they are having an active outbreak. However, people are infectious even when there is no outbreak or if they have never been symptomatic. Therefore, there is no completely safe period.

Treatment

Unfortunately, no known drug kills the virus; that is, there is no cure. Researchers are pursuing two solutions: drugs that would treat symptoms in someone who is already infected, and vaccinations that would prevent herpes. The drug acyclovir (Zovirax) prevents or reduces the recurring symptoms, although it does not actually cure the disease.

Valacyclovir (Valtrex) and famciclovir (Famvir) are newer drugs that are even more effective at shortening outbreaks and suppressing recurrences (Corey & Wald, 2008). They, as well as acyclovir, also reduce rates of transmission from an infected partner to an

(a)

(b)

Figure 8.3   *(a)* Herpes blisters on the penis. *(b)* Herpes infection of the vulva.

uninfected one. Scientists are actively working to create a method for immunization against herpes (Corey & Wald, 2008).

Long-Term Consequences

Either men or women with recurrent herpes may develop complications, such as meningitis or narrowing of the urethra caused by scarring, leading to difficulties with urination. However, such complications do not affect the majority of those with herpes. There are two more serious long-term consequences. One is that having a herpes infection increases the risk of becoming infected with HIV, probably because the open blisters during an outbreak make it easy for HIV to enter the body. Therefore, people who have herpes should be especially careful to use safer sex practices.

The other serious risk involves the transfer of the virus from mother to infant in childbirth, which in some cases leads to serious illness or death in the baby (Brown et al., 2005). The risk of transmission to the infant is highest in women who have recently been infected and are having their first outbreak. The risk is less with women who have had the disease longer and is low if the woman is not having an outbreak. C-sections are therefore usually performed on women with an outbreak, but vaginal delivery is possible if there is not an outbreak.

Psychological Aspects: Coping with Herpes

The psychological consequences of herpes need to be taken as seriously as the medical consequences (See First Person). The range of psychological responses is enormous. At one end of the spectrum are persons with asymptomatic herpes, who are not aware that they have the disease and are happily sexually active—and at the same time possibly unknowingly spreading the disease to others. At the other end of the spectrum are persons who experience frequent, severe, painful recurrences. These difficulties are aggravated by the fact that outbreaks are often unpredictable, and current scientific evidence indicates that people are at least somewhat infectious even when they are not having an active outbreak. The impact of having herpes is also exacerbated by the fact that many people with herpes feel stigmatized because of their disease and believe that they should abstain from sex to avoid infecting others (Nack, 2008; Ross, 2008). Infections on the genitals are more likely to be stigmatized than a similar infection elsewhere on the body, such as a cold sore (which is also caused by the herpes virus) precisely because they are sexually transmitted. On the other hand, many people with herpes are able to cope.

Psychologists are exploring therapies for herpes patients. One highly effective treatment program consists of a combination of information on herpes, relaxation training, instruction in stress management, and instruction in an imagery technique in which the patient imagines that the genitals are free of lesions and that he or she is highly resistant to the virus (Longo et al., 1988).

 LO1

HIV Infection and AIDS

In 1981 a physician in Los Angeles reported a mysterious and frightening new disease identified in several gay men. The first AIDS case in Canada was reported in February 1982. Within two years, the number of cases had escalated sharply. The disease was named **AIDS**, an acronym for acquired immune deficiency syndrome.

A major breakthrough came in 1984 with the identification of the virus causing AIDS. The virus is called **HIV**, for human immunodeficiency virus. Another strain of the virus, HIV-2, has been identified; it is found almost exclusively in Africa. HIV-1 accounts for almost all infections in North America.

As the name implies, HIV destroys the body's natural system of immunity to diseases. Once HIV has damaged an individual's immune system, opportunistic diseases may take over. They can kill.

 LO2 An Epidemic?

As of the end of 2011, 53,320 Canadians had received a positive test result and were living with HIV. However, these statistics represent only the tip of the iceberg, for they do not count persons who are infected with HIV but have never been tested for it or people who had died of AIDS. The PHAC estimates that almost 18,000 people are infected with HIV and don't know it. Experts estimate that 33 million persons worldwide are infected with HIV, although the majority of them show no symptoms yet and are unaware that they are infected (Duerr et al., 2008).

In 2011 alone, worldwide about 2.5 million people became newly infected with HIV and 1.7 million people died from AIDS (UNAIDS, 2012b, 2012c). The hardest-hit part of the world is sub-Saharan Africa, accounting for 72 percent of all new HIV infections. According to UNAIDS, an agency of the United Nations, 1.8 million people in sub-Saharan Africa became newly infected with HIV in 2011 alone. This brought the total number of adults

AIDS (acquired immune deficiency syndrome): A sexually transmitted disease that destroys the body's natural immunity to infection so that the person is susceptible to and may die from another disease, such as pneumonia or cancer.

HIV: Human immunodeficiency virus, the virus that causes AIDS.

First Person

Coping with Herpes

I t's cliché to say, but I think at some point we all think it: "I just didn't think it could happen to me." I am an intelligent, responsible young adult living in Atlantic Canada while I complete my undergraduate degree. And I have herpes.

I had been seeing my partner exclusively for some time. We were honest and open with each other and cared very much for one another. So after some discussion, we decided to stop using condoms during sex. We both had had a number of previous partners and had both engaged in unprotected sex before. However, we also had both been tested, neither of us had symptoms, and we trusted each other.

One morning, after a particularly wonderful night together, I woke up with a small sore on my genitals. I looked at it carefully. It looked somewhat like an ingrown hair, which I had had before, but it was also somehow different. I was worried because I instantly realized it could be something sexually transmitted. I found myself thinking of my partner. I needed to tell her. I also found my thoughts drifting to her sexual history. Did I get this from her or had I given this to her? What was I going to say? How would she react? I was more scared than I thought possible about the situation.

I waited until we were alone. There wasn't really an easy way to say what I had to say. So I turned to her

and just spit it out: "I have a sore." She looked a little shocked. She turned and said to me that she had one too. She had also been waiting to say something in private. We spent the next hour talking about it; what it looked like, what we knew about herpes and HPV, and what we were going to do. It seemed odd that both of us had one sore, and had gotten it at the same time. But the coincidence both relieved and worried us. We took turns that day calming each other down. I was worried but more than that, I was annoyed and I knew she was too. How could two careful people let this happen to them? We knew that if it was going to be an STI there was nothing we could do to change it. We also knew that we wouldn't know anything for sure until we saw a doctor. I called and made an appointment with my doctor right away.

As time went by, I started to get more signs that something was wrong. I had a burning sensation when I urinated which seemed to subside if I drank a lot of water. My urethral opening sometimes burned, and I felt sore in my groin area. The doctor sent me for all kinds of tests; urine tests, blood tests, and swabbed the sore. She told me that if the tests came back negative, I'd be sent to a different clinic for more tests.

The first round of tests came back negative. By the time my partner got in for tests, her sore had healed, and

and children living with HIV/AIDS in this region to 23.5 million. In contrast, approximately 1.4 million people in Eastern Europe and Central Asia, 300,000 people in the Middle East and North Africa, 1.4 million people in Latin America and the Caribbean, 4.8 million people in Asia and the Pacific, and 2.3 million people in Europe and North America were living with HIV/AIDS in 2011. Thus, the terms *global epidemic* and *pandemic* (a widespread epidemic) have been used, with reason. The somewhat encouraging news is that although the number of people with HIV worldwide continues to grow, the number of new infections each year has been decreasing (WHO, 2009). This suggests that HIV prevention efforts are working in at least some countries.

Transmission

When people speak of HIV being transmitted by an exchange of body fluids, the body fluids they are referring to are semen and blood and possibly secretions of the cervix and vagina. HIV is spread in four ways: (1) by sexual intercourse (either penis-in-vagina intercourse or anal intercourse[3]), (2) by contaminated blood (a risk for people who receive a blood transfusion if the blood has not been screened), (3) by contaminated hypodermic

---

[3] There is also a chance that mouth–genital sex can spread AIDS, particularly if there is ejaculation by an infected person into the mouth.

all her other tests came back negative. For over a month, we didn't know what had happened and assumed that the sores were ingrown hairs. The anxiety I felt at the onset slowly subsided. Then one day my doctor called. The swab tests had finally come back and I needed to go in for an appointment. The swab had come back positive for herpes. I couldn't believe it. Yet, I could. How did I get this? I had read a lot online, trying to sort out my symptoms and realized there was a chance I had herpes. Still, how did I get this? Again, I wondered whether I got it from my partner. If not, did I give it to her? And if not, where did I get it? I was angry; angry that the tests had taken so long, angry that they had come back positive, angry that my partner didn't have the same news, but most of all angry at myself for thinking I was okay to not use condoms in the first place. I called my partner as soon as I left the doctor's office and told her what I found out. I told her she needed to get tested. But she didn't have any sores. There was nothing she could do.

A short time later I had another outbreak. It was just like the first one, so I knew what it was. I was frustrated and upset. How could I let this happen to me? I had been cautious in so many ways. I found myself thinking of all kind of things, my future sex life, having these sores pop up whenever they wanted, knowing that I would always have to be extra careful. I was sad and worried about future partners; when and how would I let them know, how will they react, would I even be able to tell them. I spent a lot of time reading information on herpes. I thought that if I knew more I might feel better. My partner and I talked about it a lot. She was sympathetic and supportive, letting me know I had every right to be frustrated. And she apologized for the fact that we were dealing with this.

As I read about herpes, I learned that I could re-infect myself in other areas, and I could infect or re-infect my sexual partner. I had to be very careful when I had an outbreak. But I also had to be careful at other times. I read about learning to feel changes in my body, and how keeping my stress level down and living a healthy, active life could help prevent breakouts. I also read about medications that could treat symptoms, help prevent outbreaks, and help sores heal faster. After some consideration, I decided the cost of the medication was worth getting rid of my current sore and controlling future outbreaks.

For now, I've come to terms with having herpes. I still get frustrated with myself sometimes but I'm not devastated by it. The reality is that almost one in four people in Canada have it. I am cautious when I have signs of sores, making sure to use barriers for any sexual activity, and washing my hands well if they come in contact with the sore. Now, I use medications to help the sore heal and prevent future outbreaks.

Source: As told to Krystelle Shaughnessy.

needles (a risk for those who inject drugs or health care workers who receive accidental sticks), and (4) from an infected woman to her baby during pregnancy or childbirth or through her breast milk.

Supporting these assertions, statistics indicate that Canadians who were diagnosed with HIV/AIDS in 2011 are primarily from the following exposure categories: (1) men who have sex with men (47 percent), (2) people who inject drugs (14 percent), (3) men who have sex with men and use injection drugs (3 percent), and (4) heterosexuals who have had sexual contact with an infected person (37 percent). About 24 percent were under the age of 30, and 30 percent were between 30 and 40, indicating that they were likely exposed to HIV in their early 20s. Worldwide, 70 percent of the cases result from heterosexual transmission.

How great is your risk of becoming infected with HIV? In essence, it depends on what your sexual practices are (leaving aside the issues of injection drug use, which are beyond the scope of this book) (Varghese et al., 2002). *The sexual behaviour most likely to spread HIV is anal intercourse, and the receiving partner is most at risk.* This is true for both men and women, regardless of sexual orientation. Penile–vaginal intercourse without a condom is a high-risk activity for contracting HIV as well. Whether you are gay or straight, statistically *the greater your number of sexual partners, the greater your risk of getting infected with HIV.* You may have heard the saying "six degrees of separation." It turns out that it is true for HIV as well. One study found that most people are just a few degrees of sexual separation from someone who is HIV-infected (Liljeros et al., 2001). The greater your number of partners, the greater your chances of connecting with that HIV-positive person. However, some people have contracted HIV from their first sexual partner. The risk varies considerably depending on whom you have sex with and whether you use a condom or a dental dam. Penile–vaginal or anal intercourse is riskier if it is with a person who is infected with HIV (seropositive), who has engaged in high-risk behaviours (unprotected anal or vaginal sex, injection drug use), who is hemophiliac, or who is from a country where there is a high rate of HIV infection, or if condoms are not used.

Table 8.1 shows the relative risk of becoming infected with HIV, gonorrhea, or herpes from a single act of intercourse with an infected person, using no condom. Table 8.2 summarizes the STI infection risk when condoms are not used, broken down by type of activity. Perhaps the risk is lower than you thought for some of these STIs—researchers in Quebec have shown that a large majority of university students and health care

Table 8.1 Risk of Being Infected with an STI as a Result of One Act of Sexual Intercourse with an Infected Person, Using No Condom

	Percentage Risk of Transmission from	
	Male to Female	**Female to Male**
Gonorrhea	50% to 90%	20%
Genital herpes	0.2%	0.05%
HIV	0.1% to 20%	0.01% to 10%

Source: Stone (1994, pp. 203–212).

Table 8.2 Sexually Transmitted Infection Risk Chart When Condoms Are Not Used

STI	Anal Sex	Vaginal Sex	Giving Oral Sex	Getting Oral Sex	Deep (French) Kissing	Mutual Masturbation (without exchanging body fluids)	Hugging, Dry Kissing, Massage, Self-Masturbation
Chlamydia	SR	HR	SR	NR	NR	NR	NR
Genital warts/HPV	HR	HR	SR (but low)	SR (but low)		SR	NR
Gonorrhea	HR	HR	HR	SR	SR	NR	NR
Hepatitis B	HR	HR	HR	HR	SR	NR	NR
Herpes	HR	HR	HR	HR	SR	SR	NR (except for kissing if you come into contact with infected area)
HIV/AIDS	HR	HR	SR (but low)	TR	TR	NR	NR
Pubic lice	HR	HR	SR	SR	NR	SR	NR (Except for massage)
Syphilis	HR	HR	HR	SR	SR	NR	NR
Vaginitis (yeast infection, bacterial vaginosis, trichomoniasis)	NA	HR	NA	NR	NA	NR	NR

HR = high risk; NR = no risk; SR = some risk; TR = theoretical risk.

Note: Using condoms for anal and vaginal sex and condoms and dental dams for oral sex reduce but do not completely eliminate the risk of contracting an STI. Theoretical risk means that in theory a person could contract a given STI through a particular activity but no one has been reported as contracting the STI through that activity. Theoretical risk activities are considered low risk.

Source: PHAC (2007b).

providers are not aware of the transmissibility of HIV and chlamydia (Knäuper & Kornik, 2004; Rosen et al., 2005). However, even if the chance of contracting an STI from one unprotected sexual encounter is low, the chances add up with each additional unprotected sexual encounter. This is called the **cumulative risk**. Unfortunately, people tend to underestimate their cumulative risk of contracting an STI, particularly if the partner is appealing to them (Knäuper et al., 2005).

A study of heterosexual transmission of HIV among 415 Ugandan couples in which one partner was infected at the beginning and one was not indicated that 22 percent of the uninfected became infected over a two-year period (Quinn et al., 2000). The male-to-female transmission rates and female-to-male rates were about equal. The higher the viral count in the infected person, the greater the rate of transmission. Interestingly, none of the circumcised men became infected. In fact, based on the results of three studies, the World Health Organization concluded that male circumcision reduces the risk of HIV transmission by as much as 60 percent. Importantly, condoms are 80 to 95 percent effective in protecting against HIV transmission during heterosexual intercourse if used consistently (Steiner et al., 2008). This isn't perfect protection, but it's darned good, and far better than no protection.

The Virus

HIV is one of a group of retroviruses. Retroviruses reproduce only in living cells of the host species, in this case humans. They invade a host cell, and each time the host cell divides, copies of the virus are produced along with more host cells, each containing the genetic code of the virus. Current research is aimed at finding drugs that will prevent the virus from infecting new cells. At least two strains of HIV are found in North America, HIV-1 and HIV-2, and there are several subgroups of HIV-1 that differ genetically (Harrington & Swanstrom, 2008).

HIV specifically invades a group of white blood cells (lymphocytes) called CD4 1 T-lymphocytes. We'll just call them T cells. These cells are critical to the body's immune response in fighting off infections. When HIV reproduces, it destroys the infected T cell. Eventually the HIV-positive person's number of T cells is so reduced that infections cannot be fought off.

Scientists have pressed hard to understand the functioning of HIV. They have identified two *coreceptors* for HIV, CCR5 and CXCR4, which allow HIV to enter T cells (Harrington & Swanstrom, 2008). CCR5 seems to be the important coreceptor in the early stages of the disease and CXCR4 in the later stages. This discovery may lead to advances in treatment if drugs can be used that block these coreceptors.

The Disease

The *Canadian Guidelines on Sexually Transmitted Infections* define four stages of HIV infection (PHAC, 2013):

1. *Primary/acute infection.* This stage is from the initial infection to development of antibodies to it over the next two to four weeks. Most (90 percent) people have some symptoms that are often mild and not specific to HIV, such as a fever, headache, or sore throat. These people may be highly infectious.

2. *Chronic asymptomatic infection.* During this stage, the person is infected with the virus and the virus is replicating, but the person shows no symptoms although lymphadenopathy is frequently present. These symptoms, such as swollen lymph glands and night sweats, are not immediately life threatening. These asymptomatic carriers can infect other persons.

3. *Chronic symptomatic HIV infection.* During this stage, the virus has greatly reduced the T4 cell count so that the person's immune system is not able to fight off infections. Many infected persons go on to develop symptoms that are not immediately life threatening: fever, chronic diarrhea, unexplained weight loss, fatigue, chronic yeast infections in the throat or vagina, shingles, or abnormal or cancerous cells in the cervix. Treatment with AZT, DDI, and other drugs may begin at this time. The evidence suggests that these drug treatments (discussed shortly) are more effective if begun early.

4. *AIDS-defining conditions.* The diagnosis of AIDS is applied when the person is affected by life-threatening opportunistic infections (infections that occur only with severely reduced immunity), such as *Pneumocystis carinii* pneumonia (PCP) and Kaposi's sarcoma (KS), a rare form of skin cancer. The diagnosis is also used when other opportunistic infections or cancers of the lymph tissue are present and the person shows a positive test for HIV antibodies. Neurological problems can occur in people with AIDS because the virus can infect the cells of the brain; symptoms may include seizures and mental problems.

Diagnosis

The blood test that detects the presence of antibodies to HIV uses the ELISA (for enzyme-linked immunosorbent assay) technique. It is easy and cheap to perform. It can be used in two important ways:

Cumulative risk: The likelihood of contracting an STI after repeated unprotected exposure.

1. To screen donated blood. All donated blood in Canada is now screened with ELISA, so infections because of transfusions should rarely occur. However, 1200 Canadians were infected with HIV from infected blood between 1978 and 1985, and a tiny risk remains even with ELISA.[4]

2. To help people determine whether they are infected (HIV positive) but are asymptomatic carriers.

The latter use is important because if people suspect that they are infected and find through the blood test that they are, they should either abstain from sexual activity or, at the very least, use a condom consistently, to not spread the disease to others. Only by responsible behaviour of this kind can the epidemic be brought under control.

ELISA is a very sensitive test; that is, it is highly accurate in detecting HIV antibodies (it has a very low rate of false negatives, in statistical language). However, it does produce a substantial number of false positives—the test saying HIV antibodies are present when they really are not. Thus, positive results on ELISA should always be confirmed by a second, more specific test.

The other major test, using the Western blot or immunoblot method, provides such confirmation. It is more expensive and difficult to perform, so it is not practical for mass screening of blood, as ELISA is. However, it is highly accurate (false positives are rare), and thus it is very useful in confirming or disconfirming a positive test from ELISA.

It should be emphasized that both tests detect only the presence of HIV antibodies. They do not predict whether the person will develop symptoms or will progress to the AIDS classification.

One of the drawbacks to the ELISA test is that it involves a long waiting period—more than a week—before test results are known. A rapid test has been approved for use in Canada. The test takes 60 seconds and only detects antibodies to HIV-1. This test is intended as a screening test and, as with the ELISA test, must be confirmed by a more accurate test. The Canadian AIDS Society (2011) has raised concerns that if these tests are done in doctors' offices rather than in sexual health centres, people may not be given enough pretest counselling to be informed enough to give true consent or be given

AZT: A drug used to treat HIV-infected persons; also called ZDV.

sufficient posttest counselling should they receive a positive test result.

There is now a home test kit for HIV available in the United States, but it is not authorized for use in Canada (although they are available on the Internet). It involves a finger prick and then dried blood spots are mailed to a laboratory for anonymous testing. Introduced in 2012, Ora Quick uses a swab from the mouth and gives results in 20 minutes. The Canadian AIDS Society opposes the use of home test kits because some of them are unreliable, individuals using a home test kit would not have access to counselling and support, and individuals should not have to pay for HIV testing.

Treatment

There is not yet any cure for AIDS. However, treatments are available to control the disease. One antiviral drug, **AZT** (azidothymidine, also called zidovudine or ZDV), has been used widely. It has the effect of stopping the virus from multiplying. However, even when it stops replication of the virus, it cannot repair the person's damaged immune system. Unfortunately, AZT has many side effects and cannot be used by some people or can be used only for limited periods. Therefore, there has been a concerted effort to find new drugs that will slow or stop the progression of the disease.

DDI (dideoxyinosine or didanosine) and DDC (dideoxycytidine) are two examples. Like AZT, they slow the progression of the disease by preventing replication of the virus. D4T is yet another, similar drug. Collectively, these drugs are called ART, for antiretroviral therapy.

A major breakthrough came in 1996 with the availability of a new category of drugs, *protease inhibitors* (Kempf et al., 1995). Protease inhibitors attack the viral enzyme protease, which is necessary for HIV to make copies of itself and multiply. Another breakthrough came in 2006 with the introduction of darunavir, a drug that acts on viruses that are resistant to the protease inhibitors (Simon et al., 2006).

Today, patients take a "drug cocktail" of one of the protease inhibitors combined with AZT and one other anti-HIV drug. This combination is called HAART, for highly active antiretroviral therapy. Within a year of the introduction of HAART, thrilling reports emerged that the HIV count had become undetectable in the blood of persons taking the drug cocktail (Cohen, 1997). Some believed that the cure had been found. The number of deaths from AIDS declined in 1996 for the first year since the disease had been identified. Because in Canada most people with HIV/AIDS are now taking the drug cocktail, in 2005 there were only 468 deaths from AIDS, compared with 1764 deaths in 1995 when the cocktail was not available.

---

[4] The risk that ELISA will miss occasional cases of infected blood results from the fact that it detects antibodies to HIV, not HIV itself. It takes six to eight weeks for antibodies to form. Thus, if a person donates blood within a few weeks of becoming infected and before antibodies form, ELISA will not detect the infection. Usually ELISA is positive within three months of infection.

HIV research, unfortunately, is much like a roller-coaster ride, with elated highs followed by plunges to the depths. HIV mutated to drug-resistant forms. And although HIV had become undetectable in the blood of persons treated with the drug cocktail, it was hiding out in T cells and the lymph nodes and in organs, such as the brain, eyes, and testes (Cohen, 1998; Wong et al., 1997). In short, it is not eradicated by the drug cocktail treatment.

Today, HAART is making HIV infection a manageable disease for many persons who are surviving much longer than they would have without this treatment. A person diagnosed with HIV who receives treatment can now expect to live 20 to 30 years. For others, long-term HAART treatment causes serious side effects, such as diabetes-like problems, brittle bones, and heart disease, which means that they have to stop the treatment or switch to another one (Cohen, 2002). Others simply stop responding to the HAART regimen, and there is concern about the emergence of further resistant strains.

On another front, progress is also being made with drugs that prevent the opportunistic infections that strike people living with AIDS. The drug pentamidine, for example, in aerosol form, is a standard treatment to prevent *Pneumocystis carinii* pneumonia.

LO2 Women, Children, Ethnic Minorities, and AIDS

In the early days of the HIV/AIDS epidemic, men accounted for most cases in Canada, but the picture has changed considerably and the number of infected women is rapidly rising (Figure 8.4). Whereas between 1985 and 1995 women accounted for only 11 percent of positive HIV tests, in 2011, 24 percent of individuals who tested positive for HIV were women. Most contracted HIV through heterosexual contact. About a quarter of women diagnosed with HIV are under 30 years old. The urgency of addressing the needs of women with HIV infection is thus increasing.

New cases of women with AIDS and HIV infection are most likely to be the result of heterosexual contact (77 percent); injection drug use is the second-largest cause at 23 percent (PHAC, 2009b). Women need far more recognition in AIDS research, and intervention programs tailored to their needs should be developed. Such programs should include sexual assertiveness training, in which women are empowered to insist that their sex partners use condoms. Women also need to be included in clinical trials of drug treatments.

Some of the saddest cases are children with AIDS, known as pediatric AIDS. Babies born to infected mothers are often, but not always, infected. Although since 1985, 225 babies have been infected with HIV from their mothers, the number is dropping dramatically;

(a)

(b)

Figure 8.4 AIDS is a multicultural disease. *(a)* A North American man with AIDS. *(b)* An African woman with AIDS.

only 14 HIV-infected babies were born in Canada in 2008. One bright spot is the finding that if a woman uses antiretroviral therapy during pregnancy, it can substantially reduce the rate of infection in their babies to less than 2 percent (PHAC, 2010a). AIDS in infants has nearly been eliminated through helping pregnant women know their HIV status and, for those who test positive, the use of antiretroviral therapy, reduction of HIV exposure during delivery, and avoidance of breast-feeding. Therefore, the Canadian Paediatric Society (2013) recommends that all pregnant women be offered confidential HIV testing.

Worldwide, people of colour have borne a disproportionate burden of the cases of AIDS. In Canada in 2011, of reported AIDS cases for which ethnic identity was recorded, 48 percent identified their ethnic background as white, 14 percent as black, 19 percent as Aboriginal, and 8 percent as Asian. Although the annual number of reported AIDS cases has declined among all ethnic groups since 1993, the decline has been lowest among minority groups, resulting in an increase in the proportion of people with AIDS who are black and Aboriginal. For example, the percentage of newly diagnosed cases of HIV infection among blacks went from 5 percent in 1989 to 14 percent in 2011.

The problem is particularly severe among Aboriginal Canadians. In 1989, Aboriginal people constituted only 1 percent of reported AIDS cases, compared with 24 percent in 2008. However, in 2011, 17 percent of new HIV infections in Canada were in Aboriginal people, even though Aboriginal peoples make up less than 3.8 percent of the population. This means that in 2011 the overall infection rate among Aboriginal people was more than 3.5 times the rate in non-Aboriginal people. Aboriginal people also tend to be infected at an earlier age than non-Aboriginals. The percentage of Aboriginal women diagnosed with HIV is more than twice as high as in the non-Aboriginal population.

A lack of prevention programs and poor access to testing are two factors that contribute to the increasing rate of HIV in the Aboriginal population. Some Aboriginal people, particularly in remote communities, also lack basic AIDS information. Mobility between inner cities and rural or reserve communities is an important factor in the introduction and spread of HIV to unexposed populations (Health Canada, 2001).

There is an urgent need to develop education and prevention programs for Aboriginal and other culturally distinct Canadian communities (Poon et al., 2011). These programs must be culturally sensitive, with substantial community involvement in program development and implementation to ensure that the programs are culturally appropriate (Health Canada, 1996b, 1996c; Myers et al., 1999). Researchers in Ontario developed and tested one such program. It was designed for Spanish-speaking gay and bisexual newcomers to Canada because of the steep rise in HIV diagnoses among Latino men who have sex with men (Adam et al., 2011). It addressed both HIV prevention and life skills. The results of the initial evaluation demonstrate that the program has the potential to be effective.

LO3 Psychological Considerations in HIV/AIDS

Psychological issues for those infected with HIV and for people with AIDS are profound. There are some analogies to people who receive a diagnosis of an incurable cancer, for AIDS is—at least at present—incurable. Many patients experience the typical reactions for such situations, including a denial of the reality, followed by anger, depression, or both. However, the analogy to cancer patients is not perfect, for AIDS is a socially stigmatized disease in a way that cancer is not. Thus, the revelation that one has AIDS must often be accompanied by the announcement that one is gay or drug-addicted or engaged in extra-dyadic sex (that is, sex outside the relationship). It may make it more difficult for the person to fill the human need for emotional and physical intimacy. Also, as the person becomes sicker, he or she is unlikely to be able to hold a job, and financial worries become an additional strain.

There is a great need to be sensitive to the psychological needs of people living with HIV/AIDS. Most cities have support groups for people living with HIV/AIDS patients and their families. Social and psychological support from others is essential as people weather this crisis (Pakenham et al., 1994). Research with gay men in Alberta has shown that after sometimes years of struggle with their diagnosis, most come to view their lives more positively (Harris & Alderson, 2006).

Research in Ontario sheds light on the experiences with sexual intimacy of people living with HIV or AIDS (Maticka-Tyndale et al., 2002). The researchers conducted in-depth interviews with 31 men and 4 women who were taking combination antiviral therapies. (See Gurevich et al., 2007, for the impact of an HIV diagnosis on the sexual well-being of Canadian women.) Individuals who were living with a partner described a drop in sexual interest soon after diagnosis. For some participants sexual desire returned over time; for others it did not. According to one woman:

> Toward the very beginning, it [sex] was almost non-existent. We were afraid to. Now we're getting back to our regular sexual relationship—protected sex and it's much better than in the beginning. (Maticka-Tyndale et al., 2002, p. 35)

Some single individuals worried about finding an accepting partner. Others preferred to remain single, often because of concerns about disclosing their HIV-positive status. As one man said:

> I just don't want to bother. . . . You don't realize what it's like to meet someone and find them attractive physically and all and then have to one day look at them and say, "By the way, I'm HIV-positive." (Maticka-Tyndale et al., 2002, p. 37)

Finally, participants discussed the negative impact of both the symptoms of HIV and the side effects of therapies on sexual intimacy. Nonetheless, sexuality continues to be an important part of the lives of many individuals living with HIV. Thus, it is important that HIV-prevention efforts and research are directed at ensuring that HIV-positive individuals do not infect their partners (Fisher et al., 2009).

Cognitive–behavioural therapy combined with stress-management training has been shown to be effective in improving the quality of life and decreasing anxiety and depression in HIV-infected individuals (Cruess et al., 2002; Lechner et al., 2003). The effectiveness of this therapy is important for two reasons. First, it improves the quality of life of affected people. Second, research shows that HIV-positive people who do not have symptoms but are depressed die earlier than similar people who are not depressed (Burack et al., 1993). Psychotherapy is therefore likely to have a positive impact on both mental health and physical health. Therapy also needs to focus on improving sexual satisfaction among persons living with HIV/AIDS, as this is an important aspect of quality of life (Maticka-Tyndale et al., 2002).

In Chapter 16 we discuss the phenomenon of *posttraumatic growth* following sexual assault. Between 60 and 80 percent of people living with HIV infection report positive psychological growth following diagnosis; people who experience posttraumatic growth and are optimistic tend to have higher T-cell counts, helping them to fight disease progression (Milam, 2006).

Recent Progress in HIV/AIDS Research

As this discussion makes clear, much more research on HIV/AIDS is needed. We need better treatments to control this disease, we need a cure for it, and we need a vaccine against it. Those are pretty tall orders, and it is unlikely that any of them will appear in the next few years. However, researchers are pursuing a number of avenues that may bear fruit in the future.

For example, researchers have been working hard to develop a vaccine against HIV, but the job has turned out to be much more difficult than expected (Duerr et al., 2008; Shattock et al., 2011). Researchers in Ontario have developed one vaccine based on genetically modified dead whole virus, and it has been approved for clinical trials. The problem is that HIV has many forms and, to make matters worse, it mutates rapidly and recombines, creating even more forms. In effect, the virus doesn't hold still long enough for a vaccine to take effective aim at it.

Researchers are also working on developing microbicides that will attack HIV and other STIs (Rosenberg et al., 2008). Microbicides are substances, usually in ointment form, that kill microbes, such as HIV. These ointments could be put into the vagina or anus or spread on the penis to battle HIV transmission. Tenofovir gel (tenofovir is an antiretroviral drug) used vaginally by women reduced infection rates by 39 percent (Abdool Karim et al., 2010). That isn't perfect, but it's progress.

In a study that *Science* magazine called the scientific breakthrough of the year for 2011, Cohen and his colleagues (2011) conducted a large-scale clinical trial in several African nations, Brazil, India, Thailand, and the United States. They studied discordant heterosexual couples—that is, one member of the couple was infected with HIV and the other one wasn't. Those in the treatment group started ART (antiretroviral treatment) immediately (even though their T-cell count had fallen only to between 350 and 550), whereas those in the control group did not (their treatment was delayed). Of those partners who became infected during the study period, only one was in the treatment group and all others were in the control group. That is, the ART treatment for the infected person prevented transmission to the sexual partner, with only one exception. Biologically, the result makes sense, because ART reduces the amount of HIV in the infected person's body, but until this trial, no one had an idea that it could be so effective in preventing transmission.

Researchers are also studying various groups of people for clues to breakthroughs in the war against AIDS. One such group is *nonprogressors* (Duerr et al., 2008). Approximately 5 percent of HIV-infected people go for ten years or more without symptoms and with no deterioration of their immune system. Their T-cell count remains higher than 500. Nonprogressors turn out to have less HIV in their bodies, even though they have been infected for over a decade. Why? Nonprogressors also have particularly high levels of defensins, chemicals secreted by white blood cells (Ganz, 2002). Defensins are known to contribute to the killing of microbes, such as HIV. Scientists also have discovered a mutation of a gene and the mutation creates strong resistance to HIV infection (Galvani & Slatkin, 2003; Novembre et al., 2005). They are hoping that this may lead to gene therapy for HIV (Strachan & Read, 2004).

Another major scientific advance is the discovery of killer T cells, also known as CTLs (cytotoxic T lymphocytes) (Moir et al., 2008). Certain lymphocytes (CD8 T cells) battle HIV in the body. They do so by secreting three chemokines. Scientists hope that this discovery may lead to improved treatments for HIV-infected persons and possibly to vaccines that boost the level of chemokines and therefore boost the body's resistance to HIV infection.

Why isn't there a vaccine against HIV?

In the last analysis, prevention is better than cure. Until we have an effective vaccine, our best hope is interventions that aim to change people's behaviour, because it is behaviour (sexual activity, injection drug use) that spreads HIV. The big success story in behavioural prevention is Uganda. In 1991 screening of pregnant women indicated that 21 percent were infected; by 1998 this figure had dropped to 10 percent (Stoneburner & Low-Beer, 2004). In the early 1990s, the Ugandan government launched a bold and forceful program called ABC—for Abstinence, Be faithful, and use Condoms. It blanketed the country with advertising about the program, which urged unmarried persons to abstain from sex, urged married people to be faithful, and urged everyone to use condoms. The whole emphasis was on behaviour change, with no need for the costly drugs that Uganda couldn't afford. It isn't completely clear which of the three components of the program had the most effect, but in any case the program worked, and the epidemic is under control in that country. Scientists have estimated that this intervention had an effect equivalent to a vaccine with 80 percent effectiveness (Stoneburner & Low-Beer, 2004).

 L01

Gonorrhea

Historical records indicate that **gonorrhea** (*the clap, the drip*) is the oldest of the sexual diseases. Its symptoms are described in the Old Testament, in Leviticus 15 (about 3500 years ago). The Greek physician Hippocrates, some 2400 years ago, believed that gonorrhea resulted from "excessive indulgence in the pleasures of Venus," the goddess of love (hence the term "venereal" disease). Albert Neisser identified the bacterium that causes it, the gonococcus *Neisseria gonorrhoeae,* in 1879.

Gonorrhea has always been a particular problem in wartime, when it spreads rapidly among the soldiers and the prostitutes they patronize. In the twentieth century, a gonorrhea epidemic occurred during World War I, and gonorrhea was also a serious problem during World War II. Then, with the discovery of penicillin and its use in curing gonorrhea, the disease became much less prevalent in the 1950s.

There was a resurgence in the incidence of gonorrhea in the 1970s. It is clear that one of the reasons for the resurgence was the shift in contraceptive practices to use of the pill, which (unlike the condom) provides no protection from gonorrhea and actually increases a woman's susceptibility. However, in Canada the reported rate of gonorrhea has declined 93 percent since 1980 through the use of condoms, improved diagnostic services, partner notification, and treatment. In 2009, there were 11,178 reported cases, more than half of which were among 15- to 24-year-olds. This is a rate of 33 per 100,000 people in the population—the rate of chlamydia is almost eight times the rate for gonorrhea.

Gonorrhea (gon-uh-REE-uh): A sexually transmitted infection that usually causes symptoms of a puslike discharge and painful, burning urination in the male but is frequently asymptomatic in the female.

Symptoms

Most cases of gonorrhea result from penis-in-vagina intercourse. In the male, the gonococcus invades the urethra, producing *urethritis* (inflammation of the

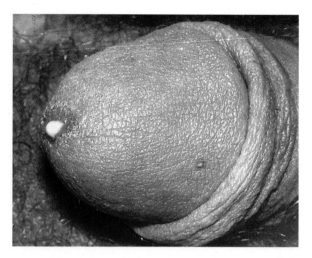

Figure 8.5   Symptoms of gonorrhea in men include a puslike discharge. About 80 percent of women, however, are asymptomatic.

urethra). White blood cells rush to the area and attempt to destroy the bacteria, but the bacteria soon win the battle. In most cases, symptoms appear two to five days after infection, although they may appear as early as the first day or as late as two weeks after infection (Hook & Handsfield, 2008). Initially a thin, clear mucous discharge seeps out of the meatus (the opening at the tip of the penis). Within a day or so it becomes thick and creamy and may be white, yellowish, or yellow-green (see Figure 8.6). This is often referred to as a purulent (puslike) discharge. The area around the meatus may become swollen. About half of infected men experience a painful burning sensation when urinating.

Because the early symptoms of gonorrhea in men are obvious and often painful, most men seek treatment immediately and are cured. If the disease is not treated, however, the urethritis spreads up the urethra, causing inflammations in the prostate (prostatitis), seminal vesicles (seminal vesiculitis), urinary bladder (cystitis), and epididymis (epididymitis). Pain on urination becomes worse and is felt in the whole penis. Then these early symptoms may disappear as the disease spreads to the other organs. If the epididymitis is left untreated, it may spread to the testicles and the resulting scar tissue may cause sterility.

Asymptomatic gonorrhea (gonorrhea with no symptoms) does occur in men, but its incidence is low. In contrast, about 50 to 80 percent of women infected with gonorrhea are asymptomatic during the early stages of the disease. Many women are unaware of their infection unless they are told by a male partner. Therefore, it is extremely important for any man who is infected to inform all his contacts.

The gonorrheal infection in the woman invades the cervix. Pus is discharged, but the amount may be so slight that it is not noticed. When present, it is yellow-green and irritating to the vulva, but it is generally not heavy (it is not to be confused with normal cervical mucus, which is clear or white and nonirritating, or with discharges resulting from the various kinds of vaginitis—discussed later in this chapter—which are irritating but white). Although the cervix is the primary site of infection, the inflammation may also spread to the urethra, causing burning pain on urination (not to be confused with cystitis). If the infection is not treated, the Bartholin glands may become infected. The infection may also be spread to the anus and rectum.

Because so many women are asymptomatic in the early stages of gonorrhea, many receive no treatment, and thus there is a high risk of serious complications. In about 20 percent of women who go untreated, the gonococcus moves up into the uterus. From there it infects the fallopian tubes (Hook & Handsfield, 2008). The tissues become swollen and inflamed, and thus the condition is also called pelvic inflammatory disease (PID)—although PID can be caused by diseases other than gonorrhea. The major symptom is pelvic pain and, in some cases, irregular or painful menstruation. If PID is not treated, scar tissue may form, blocking the tubes and leaving the woman sterile. Indeed, untreated gonorrhea is one of the most common causes of infertility in women. If the tubes are partially blocked, so that sperm can get up them but eggs cannot move down, ectopic pregnancy can result, because the fertilized egg is trapped in the tube.

There are three other major sites for non-genital gonorrhea infection: the mouth and throat, the anus and rectum, and the eyes. If fellatio is performed on an infected man, the gonococcus may invade the throat. (Cunnilingus is less likely to spread gonorrhea, and mouth-to-mouth kissing rarely does.) Such an infection is often asymptomatic; the typical symptom, if there is one, is a sore throat. Rectal gonorrhea is contracted through anal intercourse and thus affects both women in heterosexual relations and, more commonly, men who have sex with men. Symptoms include some discharge from the rectum and itching, but many cases are asymptomatic. Gonorrhea may also invade the eyes. This occurs only rarely in adults, when they touch the genitals and then transfer the bacteria-containing pus to their eyes by touching them. This eye infection is much more common in newborn infants. The infection is transferred from the mother's cervix to the infant's eyes during birth. For this reason, most provinces require that silver nitrate, or erythromycin or some other antibiotic, be put in every newborn's eyes to prevent any such infection. If left untreated, the eyes become swollen and painful within a few days, and there is a discharge of pus. Blindness was a common result in the pre-antibiotic era.

Diagnosis

A urine test is available for men. If gonorrhea in the throat is suspected, a swab should be taken and tested. People who suspect that they may have rectal gonorrhea should request that a swab be taken from the rectum, since many physicians will not automatically think to do this.

A urine test is also available for women. However, a pelvic examination should also be performed because pain during this exam may indicate PID. Women who suspect throat or rectal infection should request that samples be taken from those sites as well.

Treatment

The traditional treatment for gonorrhea was a large dose of penicillin, or tetracycline for those who were allergic to penicillin. However, strains of the gonococcus that are resistant to penicillin and tetracycline have become so common that newer antibiotics, such as ceftriaxone or ciprofloxacin (Cipro), must now be used. They are highly effective, even against resistant strains.

LO1

Syphilis

There has been considerable debate over the exact origins of **syphilis**. The disease, called the Great Pox, was present in Europe during the fifteen century and became a pandemic by 1500. The bacterium that causes syphilis is called *Treponema pallidum*. It is spiral-shaped and is thus often called a *spirochete*.

In 2009 there were 1683 cases of syphilis reported in Canada. Although the rate of syphilis remains low, there has been an increase in cases in the last few years; for example, there were only 174 reported cases in 2000. The increase is largely due to outbreaks in Vancouver involving sex trade workers, in Yukon and northern Alberta among heterosexuals, and in Calgary, Ottawa, and Montreal among men who have sex with men.

Although syphilis is not nearly as common as chlamydia or gonorrhea, its effects are much more serious if left untreated. In most cases, chlamydia or gonorrhea cause only discomfort and, sometimes, sterility; syphilis, if left untreated, can damage the nervous system and even cause death. There are many cases today of co-infection, in which the person is infected with both syphilis and HIV. Syphilis infection makes a person more vulnerable to HIV and vice versa.

Symptoms

The major early symptom of syphilis is the **chancre**. It is a round,

> **Syphilis (SIFF-ih-lis):** A sexually transmitted infection that causes a chancre to appear in the primary stage.
> **Chancre (SHANK-er):** A painless, ulcerlike lesion with a hard, raised edge that is a symptom of syphilis.

ulcerlike lesion with a hard, raised edge, resembling a crater. One of the distinctive things about the chancre is that although it looks terrible, it is painless. It appears about three weeks (as early as ten days or as late as three months) after intercourse with an infected person. The chancre appears at the point where the bacteria entered the body. Typically, the bacteria enter through the mucous membranes of the genitals. Thus, in men the chancre often appears on the penis or scrotum. In women, the chancre often appears on the cervix, and thus the woman does not notice it and is unaware that she is infected (nature's sexism again). The chancre may also appear on the vaginal walls or, externally, on the vulva (see Figure 8.6).

If oral sex or anal intercourse with an infected person occurs, the bacteria can also invade the mucous membranes of the mouth or rectum. Thus, the chancre may appear on the lips, tongue, or tonsils or around the anus. Finally, the bacteria may enter through a cut in the skin anywhere on the body. Thus, it is possible (though rare) to get syphilis by touching the chancre of an infected person. The chancre would then appear on the hand at the point where the bacteria entered through the break in the skin.

The progress of the disease once the person has been infected is generally divided into four stages: primary-stage syphilis, secondary-stage syphilis, latent syphilis, and late syphilis. The phase just described, in which the chancre forms, is *primary-stage syphilis*. If left untreated, the chancre goes away by itself within one to five weeks after it appears. This marks the end of the primary stage. However, the disease has not gone away just because the chancre has healed; it has only gone underground.

Beginning a few months after the original appearance of the chancre, a generalized body rash develops, marking the beginning of *secondary-stage syphilis*. The rash is variable in its appearance, the most distinctive feature being that it does not itch or hurt. Hair loss may also occur during the secondary stage. Usually, the symptoms are troublesome enough to cause the person to seek medical help. With appropriate treatment at this stage, the disease can still be cured, and there will be no permanent effects. Even without treatment, the secondary-stage symptoms go away in a few weeks, leading people to believe mistakenly that the disease has gone away. Instead, it has entered a more dangerous stage.

After the symptoms of the secondary stage have disappeared, the disease is in the latent stage; *latent syphilis* may last for years. Although there are no symptoms in this stage, *T. pallidum* is busily burrowing into the tissues of the body, especially the blood vessels, central nervous system (brain and spinal cord), and bones. After the first year or so of the latent stage, the disease is no longer infectious, except that a pregnant woman can still pass it on to the fetus.

About half of the people who enter the latent stage remain in it permanently, living out the rest of their lives without further complications. The other half, however, move into the dangerous *late syphilis*. In *cardiovascular late syphilis* the heart and major blood vessels are attacked; this occurs 10 to 40 years after the initial infection. Cardiovascular syphilis can lead to death. In *neurosyphilis* the brain and spinal cord are attacked, leading to insanity and paralysis, which appear 10 to 20 years after infection. Neurosyphilis may be fatal.

(a)

(b)

Figure 8.6 The chancre characteristic of primary-stage syphilis *(a)* on the labia majora and *(b)* on the penis.

If a pregnant woman has syphilis, the fetus may be infected when the bacteria cross the placental barrier, and the child gets **congenital syphilis** (meaning present from birth). The infection may cause early death of the fetus (spontaneous abortion) or severe illness at or shortly after birth. It may also lead to late complications that show up only at 10 or 20 years of age. Women are most infectious to their baby when they have primary- or secondary-stage syphilis, but they may transmit the infection to the fetus in utero as long as eight years after the mother's initial infection. If the disease is diagnosed and treated before the fourth month of pregnancy, the fetus will not develop the disease. For this reason, a syphilis test is done as a routine part of the blood analysis in a pregnancy test. In 2009 there was only one case of congenital syphilis in all of Canada.

Diagnosis

Syphilis is somewhat difficult to diagnose from symptoms because, as noted earlier, its symptoms are like those of many other diseases. The physical exam should include inspection not only of the genitals but also of the entire body surface. Women should have a pelvic exam so that the vagina and the cervix can be checked for chancres. If the patient has had anal intercourse, a rectal exam should also be performed.

If a chancre is present, some of its fluid is taken and placed on a slide for inspection under a dark-field microscope. If the person has syphilis, *T. pallidum* should be present. The most common tests for syphilis are blood tests, all of which are based on antibody reactions. The VDRL (venereal disease research laboratory test) is one of these blood tests. It is fairly accurate, cheap, and easy to perform.

Treatment

The treatment of choice for syphilis is penicillin (Workowski & Berman, 2010). *T. pallidum* is actually rather fragile, so large doses are not necessary in treatment. The recommended dose is two shots of penicillin G, one in each of the buttocks. Latent, later, and congenital syphilis require larger doses. For those allergic to penicillin, the recommended treatment is tetracycline or doxycycline, but these should not be given to pregnant women.

 LO1

Viral Hepatitis

Viral hepatitis is a disease of the liver. One symptom is an enlarged liver that is somewhat tender. The disease can vary greatly in severity from asymptomatic cases to ones in which there is a fever, fatigue, jaundice (yellowish skin), and vomiting, much as one might experience with a serious case of the flu. There are five types of viral hepatitis: hepatitis A, B, C, D, and E. The one that is of most interest in a discussion of STIs is hepatitis B. Hepatitis C and D (or delta) can also be transmitted sexually, but they are rare compared with B.

The virus for **hepatitis B** (HBV) can be transmitted through blood, saliva, semen, vaginal secretions, and other body fluids. The behaviours that spread it include sharing needles by people who inject drugs, sharing toothbrushes and razors, getting tattoos and body piercings, having acupuncture, having vaginal and anal intercourse, and having oral–anal sex. Risk factors for HBV infection are intravenous drug use (12 percent), drug snorting (7 percent), multiple heterosexual partners (10 percent), and being a man who has sex with men (10 percent) (PHAC, 2011). It has many similarities to AIDS, although hepatitis B is about 100 times as contagious.

Hepatitis B is more common than most people think because it receives relatively little publicity compared with AIDS and herpes. In 2008 there were 582 new cases of hepatitis B in Canada. People who have had the disease continue to have a positive blood test for it for the rest of their lives.

Many adults infected with HBV are asymptomatic; their bodies fight off the virus and they are left uninfected, with permanent immunity. Others develop an early, acute (short-term) illness and display a variety of symptoms but recover from the illness. A third group develops chronic (long-term) hepatitis B. They continue to be infectious and may develop serious liver disease involving cirrhosis or cancer. Fortunately, antiviral treatments are now available for those with chronic hepatitis B (PHAC, 2010b). Symptoms of hepatitis B can include jaundice (yellowing of the skin and eyes), fatigue, loss of appetite, nausea, dark urine, pale stools, joint pain, and pain in the stomach area. Symptoms typically appear between two and six months after infection. However, about half of people infected with Hepatitis B do not have any symptoms.

The good news is that there is a vaccine against hepatitis B. The current recommendation is that all children be vaccinated and all provinces have school-based immunization programs. The vaccine is also recommended for individuals who are at risk of contracting an HBV infection. As a result of these vaccination programs, the rate of HBV infection has decreased significantly, particularly among children and youth (PHAC, 2011). We urge you to be vaccinated if you are a person who has had a number of partners. You should be tested if there is even a hint that you have been exposed.

Congenital (kun-JEN-ih-tul) syphilis: A syphilis infection in a newborn baby resulting from transmission from an infected mother.
Hepatitis B: A liver disease that can be transmitted sexually or by needle sharing.

L01

Trichomoniasis

Trichomoniasis (*trich*) is caused by a protozoan, *Trichomonas vaginalis* (Hobbs et al., 2008). The organism can survive for a time on toilet seats and other objects so it is occasionally transmitted nonsexually, but it is transmitted mainly through sexual intercourse.

For women, the symptom is vaginal discharge that irritates the vulva and has an unpleasant smell. In men, there may be irritation of the urethra and a discharge from the penis, but some men are asymptomatic. It is important that accurate diagnosis be made, because the drugs used to cure trichomoniasis are different from those used to treat other STIs that have similar symptoms, and the long-term effects of untreated trichomoniasis can be serious, with untreated trich possibly leading to PID and problems with birth (Swygard et al., 2004). It also increases susceptibility to HIV infection. The treatment of choice is metronidazole (Flagyl) taken orally.

> **My partner has no symptoms of any STI. Should we still practise safer sex?**

L01

Pubic Lice

Pubic lice (*crabs* or *pediculosis pubis*) are tiny lice that attach themselves to the base of pubic hairs and there feed on blood from their human host. They are about the size of a pinhead and, under magnification, resemble a crab (see Figure 8.7). They lay their eggs frequently and live for about 30 days, but they die within 24 hours if they are taken off a human host. Lice are transmitted by sexual contact, but

> **Trichomoniasis (trick-oh-moh-NY-us-is):** A form of vaginitis causing a frothy white or yellow discharge with an unpleasant odour.
>
> **Pubic lice:** Tiny lice that attach themselves to the base of pubic hairs and cause itching; also called crabs.

Figure 8.7   A pubic louse, enlarged. The actual size is about the same as the head of a pin.

they may also be picked up from sheets, towels, sleeping bags, or toilet seats. (Yes, there *are* some things you can catch from toilet seats.)

The major symptom of pubic lice is fierce itching in the region of the pubic hair. Diagnosis is made by finding the lice or the eggs attached to the hairs. Pubic lice are treated with the drugs Nix and Rid, which are available without prescription. Both kill the lice. After treatment, the person should put on clean clothing. Since the lice die within 24 hours, it is not necessary to disinfect clothing that has not been used for longer than 24 hours. However, the eggs can live up to six days, and in difficult cases it may be necessary to boil or dry-clean one's clothing or use a spray, such as R and C.

L04

Preventing STIs

While most of the literature on STIs concentrates on their rapid diagnosis and treatment, prevention would be much better than cure, and there are some ways in which we can avoid getting STIs or at least reduce the chances of doing so. The most obvious, of course, is limiting yourself to a monogamous relationship with an uninfected person or abstaining from sexual activity. However, many people in committed monogamous relationships have engaged in behaviours that put them at risk for STIs in the past. They may not be aware that they are infected and thus can pass on the STI to their partner if they engage in unprotected sex even if both partners are monogamous (Misovich et al., 1997). As described in the First Person earlier in this chapter, just because a partner has no obvious symptoms like herpes blisters or warts, don't assume that the person is uninfected. We have seen in this chapter how many of these infections—for example, chlamydia, herpes, and warts—can be asymptomatic. The only way to really know is for both you and your partner to have a complete battery of tests for STIs when you enter a new relationship, a choice people are increasingly making. Not every STI is tested in the standard battery—for example, herpes and HPV usually are not—but it still will catch most infections.

If you are not sure that your partner is uninfected, there are other techniques available. The latex condom, in addition to being a decent contraceptive, gives good (although not perfect) protection against HIV, HPV, chlamydia, gonorrhea, herpes, syphilis, and other STIs (Baldwin et al., 2004; Steiner & Cates, 2006; Wald et al., 2005; Winer et al., 2006). With the rise of the STI epidemic, the condom is again becoming popular. The key is to eroticize condom use (Ploem & Byers, 1997). The diaphragm (although it isn't available in Canada) also provides some protection for women, as does the female condom.

A dental dam gives protection from the spread of STIs during cunnilingus (oral stimulation of the vulva) or anilingus (oral stimulation of the anus). Some stores sell them or you can make them yourself from an unlubricated condom: First, carefully unroll the condom. Then cut off the tip and the rim. Finally, cut down the length of the tube and open the condom. Voila, you have a rectangular piece of latex that can be used during oral sex.

Some simple health precautions are also helpful. Successful prostitutes, who need to be careful about STIs, take such precautions. Washing the genitals before intercourse helps remove bacteria. This may not sound like a romantic prelude to lovemaking, but you can make a sensuous game out of soaping the man's genitals, possibly as part of taking a shower or bath with your partner. Urinating both before and after intercourse also helps to keep bacteria out of the urethra.

Another important technique is inspecting your partner's genitals. If you see a chancre, a wart, a herpes blister, or a discharge, put on your clothes and leave or, at the very least, immediately start a conversation about STI status (do not fall for the "it's only a pimple" routine). This technique may sound a little crude or embarrassing, but if you are intimate enough with someone to have sex with that person, you ought to be intimate enough to look at her or his genitals. Once again, if you are cool about it, you can make this an erotic part of foreplay. Of course, you should also inspect your own genitals on a regular basis to make sure you're not inadvertently passing on an STI to a partner. Women will need to use a hand-held mirror to do so.

One factor that has interfered with efforts to prevent STIs is the stigma and shame associated with being diagnosed with one of these infections (Wong et al., 2012), something we must combat. **STI-related stigma** refers to people's awareness that others will judge them negatively for having an STI. **STI-related shame** refers to the negative feelings people have about themselves when they receive an STI diagnosis (Fortenberry et al., 2002). For example, a young woman in a Toronto study was clearly aware of the stigma associated with an STI diagnosis:

> It's gross. It's scornful. Once you're in that room and the doctor says, "You have chlamydia," you're not going to sit there, you're going to want to go home and bathe your skin and sit in a pot of hot boiling water. You're going to think about it. It's always there. You don't talk about it but you'll always remember it. (Wong et al., 2012, p. 82)

People with higher STI-related stigma and shame are less likely to be tested or screened for STIs. They are also less likely to have an open discussion of sexual histories with their sexual partners. Research in New Brunswick has shown that people who are more socially and sexually conservative experience greater STI-related stigma

and shame (Foster & Byers, 2008). This research also identifies a means to reduce stigma and shame—individuals who had received better sexual health education in school reported less STI-related stigma and shame.

Finally, each person needs to recognize that it is his or her ethical responsibility to seek out early diagnosis and treatment. Probably the most important responsibility is that of informing prospective partners if you have an STI and of informing past partners as soon as you discover that you have one. For example, because so many women are asymptomatic for chlamydia, it is particularly important for men to take the responsibility of informing their female partners if they find that they have the infection. It is important to take care of your own health, but it is equally important to take care of your partner's health.

 LO5

Other Genital Infections

Vaginitis (vaginal inflammation or irritation) is very common among women and is endemic in university populations. Two kinds of vaginitis as well as prostatitis, will be considered here. None of these infections are STIs, because they are not transmitted by sexual contact; they are, however, common infections of the sex organs.

A few simple steps can help prevent vaginitis. Every time you shower or take a bath, wash the vulva carefully and dry it thoroughly. Do not use feminine hygiene deodorant sprays; they are unnecessary and can irritate the vagina. Wear cotton underpants; nylon and other synthetics retain moisture, and vaginitis-producing organisms thrive on moisture. Avoid wearing pants that are too tight in the crotch; they increase moisture and may irritate the vulva. Wipe the anus from front to back so that bacteria from the anus do not get into the vagina. For the same reason, never go immediately from anal intercourse to vaginal intercourse. Finally, if an attack of vaginitis seems to be coming on, placing some plain yogurt with active cultures into the vagina can help restore the good bacteria.

Candida

Candida (also called *yeast infection* and *moniliasis*) is a form of vaginitis caused by the yeast fungus *Candida*. *Candida* is normally present in the vagina, but if the delicate environmental balance there is disturbed (e.g., if the pH is changed), the growth of Candida can get out of hand. Conditions

STI-related stigma: Awareness that people are judged negatively for contracting an STI.
STI-related shame: The negative feelings people have about themselves as a result of receiving an STI diagnosis.
Vaginitis (vaj-in-ITE-is): An irritation or inflammation of the vagina, usually causing a discharge.
Candida: A form of vaginitis causing a thick, white discharge; also called monilia or yeast infection.

that encourage the growth of Candida include long-term use of birth control pills, menstruation, diabetes or a prediabetic condition, pregnancy, and long-term use of antibiotics, such as tetracycline. It is not a sexually transmitted infection, although intercourse may aggravate it.

The major symptom is a thick, white, curdlike vaginal discharge, found on the vaginal lips and the walls of the vagina. The discharge can cause extreme itching, to the point where the woman is not interested in having intercourse.

Treatment is by the drugs miconzole or elotrimazole, both available over the counter. Flucomazole, a single-dose treatment, is available by prescription. If a woman has Candida while she is pregnant, she can transmit it to her baby during birth. The baby gets the yeast in its digestive system, a condition known as *thrush*. Thrush can also result from oral–genital sex.

Prostatitis (pros-tuh-TY-tis): An infection, inflammation, or swelling of the prostate gland.

Bacterial vaginosis is another vaginal infection that produces a similar discharge. The distinctive feature is that the discharge has a foul odour.

Prostatitis

Prostatitis is an inflammation or swelling of the prostate gland. It used to be thought that it was almost always caused by an infection by the bacterium *E. coli,* but it is now known that it can be caused by several different conditions. It can also be caused by gonorrhea or chlamydia. The typical symptoms are fever; chills; pain above the penis or around the scrotum, anus, or rectum; difficulty starting urination; and a need for frequent urination. Research in Ontario has shown that prostatitis may produce sexual dysfunction (Smith et al., 2007). In some cases, prostatitis may be chronic (long-lasting) and may have no symptoms, or only lower-back pain. Antibiotics are used in treatment.

SUMMARY

Table 8.3 provides a summary of the information about STIs discussed in this chapter.

Table 8.3   Summary of Information About STIs

STI Description & Cause	Primary Symptoms	Primary Complications	Treatment
Chlamydia Caused by the bacterium *Chlamydia trachomatis*	*In men* A thin clear discharge from the penis and mild pain on urination *In women* Most have no symptoms	If untreated: *In men* Urethral damage, epididymitis, Reiter's syndrome, proctitis *In women* Pelvic inflammatory disease and infertility	Cured with antibiotics (azithromycin or doxycycline)
HPV Caused by the *human papillomavirus*	Cauliflower-like warts on the genitals Many people have no symptoms	*In men* Cancer of the penis and anus *In women* Cervical cancer	Podofilox or bichloroacetic acid, cryotherapy, laser therapy for warts Vaccine available No cure available
Genital herpes (HSV) Caused by the virus *herpes simplex*	Small painful bumps or blisters on the genitals Fever, painful urination, headaches	Reoccurrences Increased risk of HIV infection Transmission during childbirth	Acyclovir, valacyclovir, and famciclovir to minimize symptoms No cure available
HIV/AIDS Caused by the *human immunodeficiency virus*	Flu-like symptoms (e.g., fever or sore throat) may occur at the initial infection Most people have no symptoms for years	Destroys the immune system, resulting in vulnerability to opportunistic infections	Combination of drugs (protease inhibitor, azidothymidine, and one other drug) called HAART to slow progression No cure

STI Description & Cause	Primary Symptoms	Primary Complications	Treatment
Gonorrhea Caused by the bacterium *Neisseria gonorrhoeae*	*In men* Inflammation of the urethra, thin clear white or yellow discharge from the penis, burning pain on urination *In women* Most (and some men) have no symptoms Vaginal discharge, pain on urination in some	Infertility if left untreated	Cured with antibiotics (penicillin or tetracycline)
Syphilis Caused by the bacterium *Treponema pallidum*	Painless sore with hard, raised edge (chancre) in primary stage A generalized body rash in secondary stage	If left untreated, progresses through several stages that may lead to brain infection and death Infection of the fetus	Cured with antibiotics (penicillin)
Hepatitis B Caused by the virus *hepatitis B*	Jaundice, fatigue, loss of appetite, nausea Many people are asymptomatic	Liver disease involving cirrhosis or cancer	Antiviral drugs to treat chronic cases; vaccine available No cure
Trichomoniasis Caused by protozoan *Trichomonas vaginalis*	*In men* Irritation of the urethra, discharge from the penis *In women* Abundant white or yellowish vaginal discharge with unpleasant smell	*In men* Increased risk of HIV infection *In women* Pelvic inflammatory disease Problems with birth Increased risk of HIV infection	Cured with antibiotics (Flagyl)
Pubic lice Caused by the genital crab louse, *pediculosis pubis*	Intense itching in region of the pubic hair	None	Special soap (Nix, Rid)

QUESTIONS FOR THOUGHT, DISCUSSION, AND DEBATE

1. Design a program to reduce the number of cases of sexually transmitted infections on your campus.
2. Michael has had a monogamous relationship with Sonya for six months. At her annual pelvic exam, Sonya discovers that she has chlamydia and blows up at Michael for giving it to her. Michael has never been tested for anything. What should Michael and Sonya discuss with each other, what other information do they need, and what should they do?
3. If you were designing an intervention for Aboriginal teenagers to reduce the spread of HIV, how would you make that intervention culturally sensitive? Would the approach be different for women and for men? If you feel that you don't know enough about Aboriginal culture, interview some Aboriginal students or community members to find out more.

Are YOU Curious?

1. What happens, biologically, when a man has an erection? When a woman's vagina lubricates?
2. What hormone is most important to sexual desire in men? In women?
3. What is tantric sex?

Read the chapter to find out.

Sexual Response

LEARNING OBJECTIVES

After studying this chapter, you will be able to

LO1 Explain the two basic physiological processes and physiological changes that occur during each of the three stages of the sexual response cycle for men and for women.

LO2 Compare the similarities and differences between the various models of sexual response.

LO3 Illustrate how the brain and spinal cord reflexes affect

sexual response in men and women.

LO4 Identify how hormones and pheromones influence sexual response in men and women.

LO5 Give examples of the techniques that men and women use during one-person sex.

LO6 Describe the techniques that men and women use during

two-person sex with same-sex and other-sex partners.

LO7 Differentiate between aphrodisiacs and anaphrodiasics.

LO8 Explain the difference between *sex as work* and *exceptional sex*.

Here are some colors of different people's orgasms: champagne, all colors and white and gray afterward, red and blue, green, beige and blue, red, blue and gold. Some people never make it because they are trying for plaid.*

* Eric Berne. (1970). *Sex in human loving.* New York: Simon & Schuster, p. 238.

In this chapter, we focus on the ways the body becomes sexually aroused, responds during arousal and orgasm, and the physiological, hormonal, neurological, and social processes involved in these responses. Satisfying sexual expression is essential to good physical and mental health (WHO, 2006). Understanding the processes involved is essential on the social level to providing quality reproductive and sexual health care, and on a personal level to developing mutually pleasurable lovemaking techniques. This information is also important in understanding sexual variations (Chapter 15) and treating sexual dysfunctions (Chapter 18).

First, we examine how the body responds physiologically during arousal and orgasm. Our basic knowledge of these processes comes from the classic research of Masters and Johnson. One of the virtues of science is that it advances because of its public and cumulative character. In this case, criticisms of Masters and Johnson's work led to the development of alternative, expanded models. More recently, research has identified the hormonal and neuroanatomical aspects of the processes Masters and Johnson described. We also consider research on pheromones and their influence on sexual behaviour in animals and humans. Finally, we discuss sexual techniques.

The Sexual Response Cycle

Sex researchers William Masters and Virginia Johnson provided one of the first models of the physiology of human sexual response. Their research culminated in 1966 with the publication of *Human Sexual Response,* which reported data on 382 women and 312 men observed in more than 10,000 sexual cycles of arousal and orgasm. Recent biological research has confirmed many of their findings while questioning a few and augmenting many. All this research is the basis for the sections that follow.

Sexual response typically progresses in three stages: *excitement, orgasm,* and *resolution.* (Masters and Johnson originally proposed that there are four phases: excitement, plateau, orgasm, and resolution. Most researchers now consider the plateau phase to be the late part of the excitement phase.) The two basic physiological processes that occur during these stages are vasocongestion and myotonia. **Vasocongestion** occurs when a great deal of blood flows into the blood vessels in a region, in this case the genitals, as a result of dilation of those blood vessels. **Myotonia** occurs when muscles contract, not only in the genitals but also throughout the body. Let's now consider in detail what occurs in each of the stages.

Excitement

The **excitement** phase is the beginning of erotic arousal. The basic physiological process that occurs during excitement is vasocongestion, which produces the obvious arousal response in men—erection. Erection results when the corpora cavernosa and the corpus spongiosum fill (becoming engorged) with blood (see Figure 9.1). Erection may be produced by direct physical stimulation of the genitals, by stimulation of other parts of the body, or by erotic thoughts. Vasocongestion occurs rapidly, and in young men erection may occur within a few seconds of stimulation, although it may take place more slowly as a result of a number of factors, including age, intake of alcohol, and fatigue. As the man gets closer to orgasm, a few drops of fluid (for some men quite a few) secreted by the Cowper's gland appear at the tip of the penis. Although they are not ejaculate, they may contain active sperm.

Research in the last decade—stimulated, in part, by the search for Viagra—has given us much more detailed information about the physiological processes involved in erection (Adams et al., 1997; Heaton, 2000). Several arteries supply the corpora cavernosa and spongiosum (look back at Figure 4.11). For an erection to occur, these arteries must dilate (vasodilation), allowing a strong flow of blood into the corpora. At the same time, the veins carrying blood away from

> What happens, biologically, when a man has an erection? When a woman's vagina lubricates?

Vasocongestion (vay-so-con-JES-tyun): An accumulation of blood in the blood vessels of a region of the body, especially the genitals; a swelling or erection results.

Myotonia (my-oh-TONE-ee-ah): Muscle contraction.

Excitement: The first stage of sexual response, during which erection in the male and vaginal lubrication in the female occur.

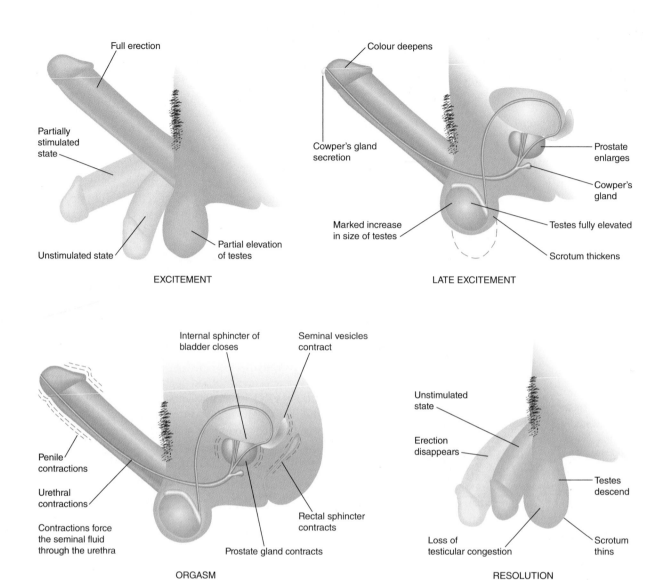

Figure 9.1 Changes during the sexual response cycle in the male.

the penis are compressed, restricting outgoing blood flow. The arteries dilate because the smooth muscle surrounding the arteries relaxes. Multiple neurotransmitters are involved in this process including, especially, nitric oxide (NO). Viagra acts on the NO system.

Of course, erections, nice though they are, would become a pain if they lasted forever, so there is a reverse process—vasoconstriction—that makes an erection go away—for example, following orgasm. The neurotransmitters epinephrine and norepinephrine are involved. These processes occur in the resolution phase, discussed shortly.

An important response of women in the excitement phase is lubrication of the vagina. Although

Orgasmic platform: A tightening of the entrance to the vagina caused by contractions of the bulbospongiosus muscle (which covers the vestibular bulbs) that occur late in the arousal stage of sexual response.

this response might seem much different from the man's, actually they both result from the same physiological process: vasocongestion. During excitement, the capillaries in the walls of the vagina dilate and blood flow through them increases (Levin, 2005). Vaginal lubrication results when fluids seep through the semipermeable membranes of the vaginal walls, producing lubrication as a result of vasocongestion in the tissues surrounding the vagina. This response to arousal is also rapid, though not quite so fast as the man's; lubrication usually begins 10 to 30 seconds after the onset of arousing stimuli. Like the male sexual response, female responding can be affected by factors, such as age, intake of alcohol, and fatigue.

As the woman becomes more aroused and gets closer to orgasm, the **orgasmic platform** forms. This is a tightening of the bulbospongiosus muscle around the entrance to the vagina (Figure 9.2). Thus, the size of the vaginal entrance actually becomes smaller, and there may be a noticeable increase in gripping of the penis.

During the excitement phase the glans of the clitoris (the tip) swells. This results from engorgement of its corpora cavernosa and is similar to erection in men. The clitoris feels larger and harder than usual under excitement. The crura of the clitoris, lying deeper in the body (refer back to Figure 4.3), also swell as a result of vasocongestion. The vestibular bulbs, which lie along the wall of the vagina, are also erectile and swell during the excitement phase. Late in the excitement phase, elevation of the clitoris may occur. The clitoris essentially retracts or draws up into the body.

Vasocongestion in women results from the same underlying physiological processes as in men. That is, relaxation of the smooth muscles surrounding the arteries supplying the glans and crura of the clitoris and the vestibular bulbs occurs, allowing a great deal of blood flow to the region (Berman et al., 2000). As in the male, nitric oxide is a key neurotransmitter involved in the process (Traish et al., 2002). Estrogen helps the vasodilation. In the unaroused state the inner lips are generally folded over, covering the entrance to the vagina, and the outer lips lie close to each other. During excitement the inner lips swell and open up (a vasocongestion response).

Under excitement, the nipples become erect; this results from contractions of the muscle fibres (myotonia) surrounding the nipple. The breasts themselves swell and enlarge somewhat in the late part of the excitement phase (a vasocongestion response). Thus, the nipples may not actually look erect but may appear somewhat flatter against the breast because the breast has swollen. Many males also have nipple erection during the excitement phase.

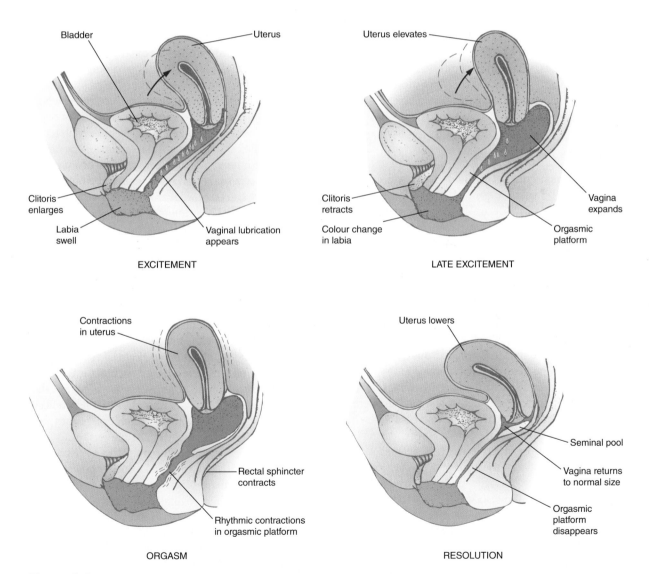

Figure 9.2 Changes during the sexual response cycle in the female.

The vagina shows an important change during excitement. Think of the vagina as being divided into two parts, an upper (or inner) two-thirds and a lower (or outer) one-third. In the unaroused state the walls of the vagina lie against each other, much like the sides of an uninflated balloon. During the excitement phase, the upper two-thirds of the vagina expands dramatically in what is often called a *ballooning response;* that is, it becomes more like an inflated balloon (see Figure 9.2). This helps accommodate penetration. As part of the ballooning, the cervix and uterus also pull up.

During excitement, a *sex flush* may appear on the skin of both men and women, though more commonly of women. The sex flush resembles a measles rash; it often begins on the upper abdomen and spreads over the chest. It may also appear later in the sexual response cycle. Other changes that occur in both men and women include increases in pulse rate and in blood pressure.

In men, the skin of the scrotum thickens. The scrotal sac tenses, and the scrotum is pulled up and closer to the body (Figure 9.1). The spermatic cords shorten, pulling the testes closer to the body. Late in the excitement phase, the process of vasocongestion and myotonia continue to build until there is sufficient tension for orgasm.

Orgasm

In men **orgasm** consists of a series of rhythmic contractions of the pelvic organs at 0.8-second intervals. Actually, male orgasm occurs in two stages. In the preliminary stage, the vas, seminal vesicles, and prostate contract, forcing the ejaculate into a bulb at the base of the urethra (Figure 9.1). Masters and Johnson call the sensation in this stage one of *ejaculatory inevitability* ("cumming"); that is, there is a sensation that ejaculation is just about to happen and cannot be stopped. And, indeed, although men can learn to delay reaching the emission stage of ejaculation, ejaculation cannot be stopped once the man has reached this point. In the second stage, the urethral bulb, muscles at the base of the penis, and the urethra contract rhythmically, forcing the semen through the urethra and out the opening at the tip of the penis. There may also be a difference between ejaculation and the sensation of orgasm (Mah & Binik, 2001). For example, researchers in Quebec have shown that feelings of pleasure and satisfaction from orgasm were more strongly related to psychological and social factors than to physical factors (Mah & Binik, 2005).

In both males and females, there are sharp increases in pulse rate, blood pressure, and breathing rate during orgasm. Muscles contract throughout the body. The face may be contorted in a grimace; the muscles of the arms, legs, thighs, back, and buttocks may contract; and the muscles of the feet and hands may contract in *carpopedal spasms.* Generally, in the passion of the moment, one is not really aware of these occurrences.

The process of orgasm in women is basically similar to that in men. It is a series of rhythmic muscular contractions of the orgasmic platform. The contractions generally occur at about 0.8-second intervals; there may be three or four in a mild orgasm or as many as a dozen in a very intense, prolonged orgasm. The uterus also contracts rhythmically. Other muscles, such as those around the anus, may also contract.

Female orgasm typically leaves no tangible evidence (except for those women who experience emission of fluid), and women often do not reach orgasm as quickly as men do, a point to be discussed in more detail in Chapter 13. As a result, some women, particularly young women, may think they are having an orgasm when they are not; they have never had an orgasm, and they mistake intense arousal for orgasm.

Just what does orgasm in the female feel like? The main feeling is a spreading sensation that begins around the clitoris and then spreads outward through the whole pelvis. There may also be sensations of falling or opening up. The woman may be able to feel the contraction of the muscles around the vaginal entrance. The sensation is more intense than just a warm glow or a pleasant tingling. In one study university men and women gave written descriptions of what an orgasm felt like to them (Vance & Wagner, 1976). Interestingly, a panel of experts (medical students, obstetrician-gynecologists, and clinical psychologists) could not reliably figure out which of the descriptions were written by women and which by men. This suggests that the sensations are quite similar for men and women.

Some of the men in our classes have asked how they can tell whether a woman has really had an orgasm. Their question in itself is interesting. In part it reflects a cultural skepticism about female orgasm. There is usually obvious proof of male orgasm: ejaculation. But there is no consistent proof of female orgasm except that some women do ejaculate. The question also reflects the fact that men know that women sometimes fake orgasm. So do men. A survey of 281 university students reported that 25 percent of the men and 51 percent of the women had faked an orgasm during heterosexual activity (Muehlenhard & Skippee, 2010). Most had pretended during penile–vaginal intercourse. Analyses of their reports of the situation in which they faked suggests faking reflects a shared sexual script (see Chapter 2) in which women should orgasm first, and men are responsible for the orgasms. Faking is a complex issue. It is not a good practice, because it prevents the partner

Orgasm: The second stage of sexual response; an intense sensation that occurs at the peak of sexual arousal and is followed by release of sexual tensions.

from getting valid feedback about sexual technique. On the other hand, we can appreciate that people do it because of the pressures created by the script.

But back to the question: How can a person tell? There really is not any very good way. From a scientific point of view, a good method would be to have the woman hooked up to an instrument that registers pulse rate; there is a sudden sharp increase in the pulse rate at orgasm, and that would be a good indicator. That doesn't seem like a very practical or desirable approach. Probably rather than trying to check up on each other, it would be better for partners to establish good, honest communication and avoid setting up performance goals in sex, points that will be discussed further in later chapters.

Resolution

Following orgasm is the **resolution** phase, during which the body returns physiologically to the unaroused state. Orgasm triggers a massive release of muscular tension and of blood from the engorged blood vessels. Resolution, then, represents a reversal of the processes that build up during the excitement stage.

The first change in women is a reduction in the swelling of the breasts. In the five to ten seconds after the end of the orgasm, the clitoris returns to its normal position, although it takes longer for it to shrink to its normal size. The orgasmic platform relaxes and begins to shrink. The resolution phase generally takes 15 to 30 minutes, but it may take much longer—as much as an hour—in women who have not had an orgasm.

In both males and females, resolution brings a gradual return of pulse rate, blood pressure, and breathing rate to the unaroused levels.

In men, the most obvious occurrence in the resolution phase is *detumescence*, the loss of erection in the penis. This happens in two stages, the first occurring rapidly but leaving the penis still enlarged (this first loss of erection results from an emptying of the corpora cavernosa) and the second occurring more slowly, as a result of the slower emptying of the corpus spongiosum and the glans.

During the resolution phase, men enter a **refractory period**, during which they are refractory to further arousal; that is, they are incapable of being aroused again, having an erection, or having an orgasm. The length of this refractory period varies considerably from one man to the next; in some it may last only a few minutes, and in others it may go on for 24 hours. The refractory period tends to become longer as men grow older. Women usually do not have a refractory period, making it possible for them to experience multiple orgasm, which is discussed in the next section.

Oxytocin is secreted during sexual arousal, and a surge of prolactin occurs at orgasm in both women and men (Exton et al., 1999; Levin, 2003; Krüger et al., 2002). Some researchers think that prolactin is the off switch to sexual arousal and that it creates the refractory period in males, although that does not explain why females do not have a refractory period. Interestingly, in both women and men, much more prolactin is secreted following orgasm from intercourse than orgasm from masturbation (Kruger, 2006).

More on Women's Orgasms

Some people believe that women can have two kinds of orgasm: **clitoral orgasm** and **vaginal orgasm**. The words *clitoral* and *vaginal* refer to the locus of stimulation: an orgasm resulting from clitoral stimulation versus an orgasm resulting from vaginal stimulation. The distinction was originated by Sigmund Freud. Freud believed that in childhood little girls masturbate and thus have orgasms by means of clitoral stimulation, or clitoral orgasms. He thought that as women grow older and mature, that is, after the Oedipal stage, they shift their erogenous zone from their clitoris to their vagina. Consequently, they shift from having orgasms as a result of clitoral stimulation to having them as a result of heterosexual intercourse, that is, by means of vaginal stimulation. Thus he considered vaginal orgasms "mature" and clitoral orgasms "immature" in a developmental sense. Not only were there two types of orgasms, but "mature" has been taken to mean "better," such that many people view one kind of orgasm (orgasms through intercourse alone) as better than the other.

According to the results of Masters and Johnson's research, there is no difference between clitoral and vaginal orgasms. This conclusion is based on two findings. First, their results indicate that all female orgasms are physiologically the same, regardless of the site of stimulation. That is, an orgasm always consists of contractions of the orgasmic platform and the muscles around the vagina whether the stimulation is clitoral or vaginal. Indeed, they found a few women who could orgasm purely through breast stimulation, and that orgasm was the same as the other two. Thus, physiologically there is only one kind of orgasm. (Of course, this does not mean that psychologically there are not different kinds; the experience of orgasm with a partner may be quite different from the experience of orgasm during masturbation.)

Second, clitoral stimulation is almost always involved in producing orgasm, even during vaginal intercourse. The deep

Resolution: The third stage of sexual response, in which the body returns to the unaroused state.
Refractory (ree-FRAK-toh-ree) period: The period following orgasm during which the man cannot be sexually aroused.
Clitoral orgasm: Freud's term for orgasm in the female resulting from stimulation of the clitoris.
Vaginal orgasm: Freud's term for orgasm in the female resulting from stimulation of the vagina in heterosexual intercourse; Freud considered vaginal orgasm to be more mature than clitoral orgasm.

structure of the clitoris (refer again to Figure 4.3) ensures that the crura of the clitoris are stimulated as the penis moves through the vaginal entrance. Thus, even the purely vaginal orgasm results from quite a bit of clitoral stimulation. Clitoral stimulation is usually the trigger to orgasm; the orgasm itself occurs in the vagina and surrounding tissues.

Stimulation of the glans of the clitoris by a thrusting penis in the vagina could contribute to an orgasm. Look again at Figure 4.1. The glans and the vaginal opening are some distance apart, and this distance varies from woman to woman. In 1924 psychoanalyst Marie Bonaparte proposed that a shorter distance would be associated with greater likelihood of experiencing an orgasm during penile–vaginal intercourse. In the interest of standardizing measurement by using two fixed points (instead of the variable "top" of the vaginal opening), she measured the clitoral–urethral meatus distance (CUMD). Wallen and Lloyd (2011) obtained two data sets containing measures of CUMD and measures of orgasm for 78 adult women. Shorter distances were associated with increased likelihood of orgasm. Genital anatomy can make a difference!

Masters and Johnson also discovered that women do not enter into a refractory period, and with continued stimulation they can have **multiple orgasms** within a short time. Actually, women's capacity for multiple orgasms was originally discovered by Kinsey in his interviews with women (Kinsey et al., 1953; see also Terman et al., 1938). The scientific establishment, however, dismissed these reports as another instance of Kinsey's supposed unreliability.

The term *multiple orgasm*, then, refers to a series of orgasms occurring within a short time. They do not differ physiologically from single orgasms. Each is a real orgasm, and they are not minor experiences.

How does multiple orgasm work physiologically? Immediately following an orgasm, both males and females move into the resolution phase. In this phase males typically enter into a refractory period, during which they cannot be aroused again. But women usually do not enter a refractory period, perhaps because after orgasm it takes longer for vasocongestion to return to baseline in women than in men (Mah & Binik, 2001). That is, if stimulation continues most women can immediately be aroused and have another orgasm if they choose to.

Multiple orgasm with a partner is more likely to result from hand–genital or mouth–genital stimulation than from intercourse. Regarding capacity, Masters and Johnson found that through masturbation women might have 5 to 20 orgasms. In some cases, they quit only when physically exhausted. When a vibrator is used, less effort is

Multiple orgasm: A series of orgasms occurring within a short period of time.

"Did the Earth move for you?"

Figure 9.3
Source: Richard Jolley/Cartoon Stock.

required, and some women were capable of having 50 orgasms in a row.

It should be noted that some women who are capable of multiple orgasms are satisfied with one, particularly in intercourse, and do not want to continue. We should be careful not to set multiple orgasm as another of the many goals in sexual performance (Figure 9.3).

Some men are capable of having multiple orgasms (e.g., Hartman & Fithian, 1984; Zilbergeld, 1992). In one study 21 men were interviewed, all of whom had volunteered for research on multiply orgasmic men (Dunn & Trost, 1989). Some of the men reported having been multiply orgasmic since they began having sex, whereas others had developed the pattern later in life, and still others had worked actively to develop the capacity after reading about the possibility. The respondents reported that multiple orgasm did not occur every time they engaged in sexual activity. For these men, detumescence did not always follow an orgasm, allowing for continued stimulation and an additional orgasm. Some reported that some of the orgasms included ejaculation and others in the sequence did not. This study cannot tell us the incidence of multiply orgasmic men in the general population, but it does provide evidence that multiply orgasmic men exist.

L02

Other Models of Sexual Response

Some experts on human sexuality are critical of Masters and Johnson's model. One important criticism is that the Masters and Johnson model ignores the cognitive and subjective aspects of sexual response (Zilbergeld & Evans, 1980). That is, Masters and Johnson focused almost entirely on the physiological aspects of sexual response, ignoring what the person is thinking and feeling emotionally. Desire and passion are not part of the model, and it omits the subjective qualities of arousal and orgasm. An individual's subjective experience may be influenced by the context and the quality of the relationship in which sexual activity occurs as well as by a variety of psychological factors (Mah & Binik, 2001). The omission of the subjective element may be particularly problematic in understanding women's sexual response because women tend to emphasize subjective arousal rather than physical arousal (Working Group for a New View of Women's Sexual Problems, 2001). Women's sense of being aroused is often unrelated to awareness of genital changes (Laan et al., 1994). Research in Quebec has shown that there are two components to orgasm for both men and women: a sensory dimension, made up of the physical sensations, and a cognitive-affective dimension, consisting of pleasure, satisfaction, emotional intimacy, and feelings of ecstasy (Mah & Binik, 2002).

A second important criticism concerns how research participants were selected and how this process may have created a self-fulfilling prophecy for the outcome (Tiefer, 1991). To participate in the research, participants were required to have a history of orgasm both through masturbation and through coitus. Essentially, anyone whose pattern of sexual response did not include orgasm—and therefore did not fit Masters and Johnson's model—was excluded from the research. As such, the model cannot be generalized to the entire population. Masters and Johnson themselves commented that every one of their participants was characterized by high and consistent levels of sexual desire. Yet sexual desire is certainly missing among some members of the general population, or it is present sometimes and absent at others. The research, in short, claims to be objective and universal when it is neither (Tiefer, 1991).

Once these difficulties with the Masters and Johnson research and model of sexual response were recognized, alternative models were proposed. We will examine three of them in the following sections.

Kaplan's Triphasic Model

On the basis of her work on sex therapy (discussed in Chapter 18), Helen Singer Kaplan (1974, 1979) proposed a **triphasic model** of sexual response. Rather than thinking of the sexual response as having successive stages, she conceptualized it as having three relatively independent phases or components: *sexual desire, vasocongestion* of the genitals, and the reflex *muscular contractions* of the orgasm phase. Notice that two of the components (vasocongestion and muscular contractions) are physiological, whereas the other (sexual desire) is psychological. Therefore, Kaplan's model adds

the cognitive component, desire, that was missing in Masters and Johnson's model.

Kaplan's approach has a number of justifications. First, the two physiological components are controlled by different parts of the nervous system. Vasocongestion—producing erection in the male and lubrication in the female—is controlled by the parasympathetic division of the autonomic nervous system. In contrast, ejaculation and orgasm are controlled by the sympathetic division.

Second, the two components involve different anatomical structures: blood vessels for vasocongestion and muscles for the contractions of orgasm.

Third, vasocongestion and orgasm differ in their susceptibility to being disturbed by injury, drugs, or age. For example, the refractory period following orgasm in the male lengthens with age. Accordingly, there is a decrease in the frequency of orgasm with age. In contrast, for many men the capacity for erection is relatively unimpaired with age, although the erection may be slower to make its appearance. An much-older man may have nonorgasmic sex several times a week, with a firm erection, although he may have an orgasm only once a week.

Fourth, the reflex of ejaculation in the male can be brought under voluntary control by most men, but the erection reflex generally cannot.

Finally, the impairment of the vasocongestion response or the orgasm response produce different disturbances (sexual disorders). Erection problems in men are caused by an impairment of the vasocongestion response, whereas rapid ejaculation and delayed ejaculation are disturbances of the orgasm response. Similarly, many women show a strong arousal and vasocongestion response, yet have trouble with the orgasm component of their sexual response.

Kaplan's triphasic model is useful both for understanding the nature of sexual response and for understanding and treating disturbances in it. Her writing on the desire phase is particularly useful in understanding problems of low sexual desire, to be discussed in Chapter 18.

The Intimacy Model

Kaplan's model assumes that desire comes before arousal, motivating the person toward sexual activity and excitement. Vancouver therapist physician Rosemary Basson (2001a) has developed an intimacy-based model of sexual response that does not make this assumption (see Figure 9.4). She argues that some people in long-term relationships, particularly women, may not be motivated to engage in sexual activity by their experience of spontaneous sexual

Triphasic model: Kaplan's model of sexual response, in which there are three components: sexual desire, vasocongestion, and muscular contractions.

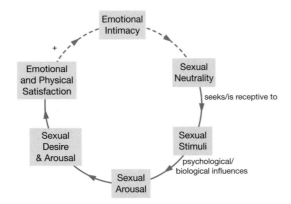

Figure 9.4 Basson's intimacy model of sexual response showing that desire sometimes comes after arousal or excitement.

desire. Rather they are motivated to engage in sexual activity to enhance intimacy, closeness, and commitment with their partner, to enhance their sense of attractiveness, or to share physical sexual pleasure. That is, they begin sexual activity in a sexually neutral state, but are receptive to sexual stimuli that will arouse them. Once sexual activity has begun, the person becomes aroused. This leads them to experience sexual desire and enhanced sexual arousal. Thus, according to Basson, some people may begin sexual activity for intimacy reasons but then continue for sexual as well as intimacy reasons. Basson also acknowledges that, even in long-term relationships, both men and women can and do experience spontaneous sexual desire outside of this intimacy model that may lead to sexual activity with their partner, casual sex, or self-stimulation.

A recent study by Canadian researchers described the Masters and Johnson, Kaplan, and Basson models to women and asked them which fit their experience best (Sand & Fisher, 2007). About equal numbers of women chose each of the three models.

The Dual Control Model

John Bancroft and his colleagues introduced the **dual control model** of sexual response (Bancroft et al., 2009). The model proposes that two basic processes underlie human sexual response: excitation (responding with arousal to sexual stimuli) and inhibition (inhibiting sexual arousal). The Bancroft team argues that almost all sex research has focused on the excitation component, and certainly the Masters and Johnson research falls in that category. They believe that it is equally important to understand the inhibition component. They observe that inhibition of sexual response is adaptive across species; sexual arousal can be a powerful distraction that could

Dual control model: A model that holds that sexual response is controlled both by sexual excitation and by sexual inhibition.

become disadvantageous or even dangerous in certain situations.

According to the dual control model, propensities toward sexual excitation and sexual inhibition vary widely from one person to the next. Most people fall in the moderate range on both and function well. At the extremes, however, problems can occur. People who are very high on the excitation component and low on the inhibition component may engage in high-risk sexual behaviours. People who are very high on inhibition and low on excitation may be more likely to develop sexual disorders, such as erectile dysfunction or low sexual desire.

Bancroft and his colleagues have developed scales to measure individuals' tendencies toward sexual excitation and sexual inhibition (Janssen et al., 2002a, 2002b). These are some examples of *excitation* items:

- When I think of a very attractive person, I easily become sexually aroused.
- When I am taking a shower or a bath, I easily become sexually aroused.
- When a sexually attractive stranger accidentally touches me, I easily become aroused.

These are examples of *inhibition* items (male version/female version):

- I need my penis to be touched to maintain an erection/I need my clitoris to be stimulated to continue feeling aroused.
- Putting on a condom can cause me to lose my erection/Using condoms or other safe-sex products can cause me to lose my arousal.
- If I am masturbating on my own and I realize that someone is likely to come into the room at any moment, I will lose my erection/my sexual arousal.

Data collected with large samples by using these scales support the model's assumption that individuals do vary widely in their tendencies toward excitation and inhibition.

The dual control model also recognizes that, although both excitation and inhibition have biological bases, early learning and culture are critical factors for both men and women because they determine which stimuli the individual will find to be sexually exciting or will set off sexual inhibition (Figure 9.5). For example, media images communicate standards of what women are *supposed* to look like to be considered sexually attractive and desirable, which likely affects what body types men find most attractive. In Canada these models are typically overly thin women with large breasts. Conversely, most men in our culture have learned that

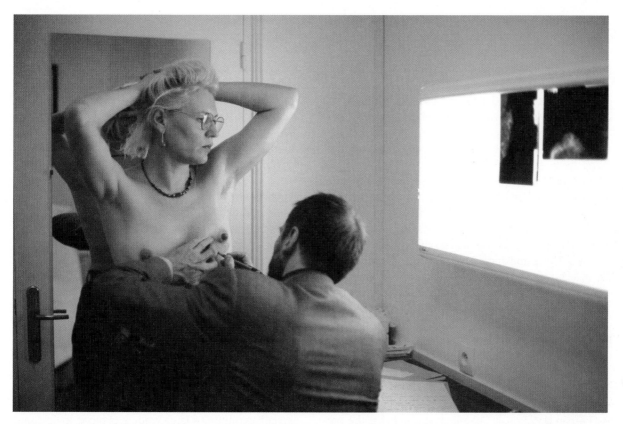

Figure 9.5 Can the dual control model of sexual arousal explain our response to this? Here a man touches a woman's breast, but it is not sexual. Why not? The context, a medical office, leads us not to perceive the woman's breast as a sexual stimulus nor the man's touch as sexual.

children are not appropriate sexual stimuli, so any sexual response to them is inhibited.

Wouldn't evolution have selected purely for sexual excitation? It is the engine that drives reproduction and passing our genes to the next generation. Would inhibition therefore be dysfunctional in an evolutionary sense? Not according to the dual control model. First, sexual activity in some situations could be downright dangerous. Imagine, for example, that the King and Queen are locked in a lusty embrace while the castle is being stormed by enemies, who are eager to kill them both. Sexual inhibition would be very adaptive at that point, so that the King and Queen could engage in nonsexual behaviours that would save their lives. Second, sometimes the environment is not conducive to reproduction and it is better to wait for a better day or a better season. An example is conditions of drought and famine in which women's fertility is usually sharply reduced because any baby that was born would likely die, and the mother might die as well in the attempt to provide food. Inhibiting sexual response and waiting until conditions improve would be the best strategy. Third, excessive sexual behaviour in men, perhaps with ejaculations several times a day, reduces fertility. The body cannot produce sperm quickly enough to have a high sperm count in each of those ejaculations, so the high rate of sexual behaviour would not be adaptive in an evolutionary sense.

Data support many aspects of this model. We will review some of these data in the later section and then return to it in the chapter on sexual disorders, because it is helpful in understanding them.

Emotion and Arousal

A major criticism of Masters and Johnson's model of sexual response was that it was all physiological, ignoring the psychological aspects of sexual responding. The three alternative models that we have reviewed so far—Kaplan's three-component model, the intimacy model, and the excitation–inhibition model—make major strides in filling in some of the psychological missing pieces. Cognitive processes are added with Kaplan's component of sexual desire; motivation and relationship factors are added with the intimacy model; and the excitation–inhibition model emphasizes the importance of culture and early learning in shaping the way the individual processes and evaluates sexual stimuli.

What is still missing, though, is a recognition of the importance of emotion in sexual arousal. No one has proposed a formal model of emotion and arousal, so here we will review one study that provides a preview of what these effects might look like. Researchers recruited 81 mixed-sex and 106 same-sex couples (Ridley et al., 2008). A daily diary method was used in which each participant logged onto a website at the same time each day for 14 days. The questionnaire each day contained questions about emotions and sexual behaviours. Members of the couple were asked to fill it out separately and independently. The results indicated that, over time, positive emotions (e.g., happiness) showed a strong positive association with reports of sexual arousal. That is, when people were happier, they also had more thoughts of sexual arousal. The surprising result was that negative emotions (e.g., anger, anxiety, sadness) were also positively correlated with reports of sexual arousal. When people experienced stronger negative emotions, they also had more thoughts of arousal. The researchers believe that this is because emotions like anxiety and anger involve generalized arousal, which intensifies arousal responses to sexual stimuli. (For other studies investigating the relationship between emotion and sexual expression, see Burleson et al. 2007, and Fortenberry et al., 2005.)

Research in British Columbia suggests that the propensity toward excitement or inhibition as proposed in the dual control model may play a role in the impact of emotion on the sexual response (Winters et al., 2009). However, so far this research has only been done with men. Clearly there is much intriguing research to be done about the role of emotions in sexual responding.

L03

Hormonal and Neural Bases of Sexual Behaviour

Up to this point we have focused on the psychological and genital responses that occur during sexual activity. We have not yet considered the underlying neural and hormonal mechanisms that make this possible; they are the topic of this section.

The Brain, the Spinal Cord, and Sex

The brain and the spinal cord both have important interacting functions in sexual response. First the relatively simple spinal reflexes involved in sexual response will be discussed, then the more complex brain mechanisms will be considered.

Spinal Reflexes

Several important components of sexual behaviour, including erection and ejaculation, are controlled by fairly simple spinal cord reflexes (see the lower part of Figure 9.6). A reflex has three basic components: the *receptors*, which are sensory neurons that detect stimuli and transmit the message to the spinal cord (or brain); the *transmitters*, which are centres in the spinal cord (or brain) that receive the message, interpret it, and send out a message to produce the appropriate response; and the *effectors*, neurons or muscles that respond to the stimulation. The jerking away of the hand when it touches a hot object is a good example of a spinal reflex.

Mechanism of Erection

Erection can be produced by a spinal reflex with a similar mechanism, although it can also be produced by cognitive factors (McKenna, 2000). Tactile stimulation (stroking or rubbing) of the penis (which has lots of receptor neurons) or nearby regions, such as the scrotum or thighs, produces a neural signal that is transmitted to an *erection centre* in the sacral, or lowest, part of the spinal cord (there may also be another erection centre higher in the cord). This centre then sends out a message via the parasympathetic division of the autonomic nervous system to the muscles (the effectors) around the walls of the arteries in the penis. In response to the message, the muscles relax; the arteries then expand, permitting a large volume of blood to flow into them, and erection results. Furthermore, the valves in

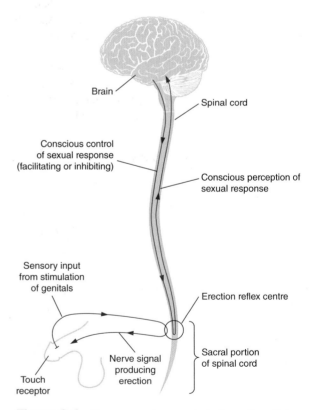

Figure 9.6 Nervous system control of erection. Note both the reflex centre in the spinal cord and brain control.

the veins and the compression of the veins caused by the swelling in the tissue around them reduce the blood flow out of the penis (Adams et al., 1997).

The existence of this reflex is confirmed by the responses of men who have had their spinal cords completely severed, as a result of accidents, at a level above that of the reflex centre. They are capable of having erections and ejaculations produced by rubbing their genitals, although it is clear that no brain effects can be operating, since signals from the brain cannot move past the point at which the spinal cord was severed. (In fact, these men cannot feel anything because neural signals cannot be transmitted up the spinal cord either.) Thus, erection can be produced simply by tactile stimulation of the genitals, which triggers the spinal reflex.

Erection may also be produced by conditions other than tactile stimulation of the genitals; for example, fantasy or other purely psychological factors may produce erection. This points to the importance of the brain in producing erection, a topic that will be discussed in a later section.

Mechanism of Ejaculation

The ejaculation reflex is similar, except that there are two ejaculation centres and they are located higher in the spinal cord, the sympathetic and parasympathetic divisions of the nervous system are involved, and the response is muscular not vasocongestion (Giuliano & Clement, 2005; Rowland & Slob, 1997). In the ejaculation reflex, the penis responds to stimulation by sending a message to the *ejaculation centre,* which is located in the lumbar portion of the spinal cord. A message is then sent out via the nerves in the sympathetic nervous system, and this message triggers muscle contractions in the internal organs that are involved in ejaculation.

Ejaculation can often be controlled voluntarily by controlling the approach to ejaculation (see Chapter 18 for more information). This fact highlights the importance of brain influences on the ejaculation reflex (Truitt & Coolen, 2002).

The three main problems of ejaculation are rapid ejaculation, male orgasmic disorder (delayed ejaculation), and retrograde ejaculation. Rapid ejaculation, which is by far the most common problem, and male orgasmic disorder will be discussed in Chapter 18. **Retrograde ejaculation** occurs when the ejaculate, rather than going out through the tip of the penis, empties into the bladder (Kothari, 1984). A "dry orgasm" results, since no ejaculate is emitted. This problem can be caused by some illnesses, by tranquillizers and drugs used in the treatment of psychoses, and by prostate surgery. The mechanism that causes it is fairly simple (see Figure 9.7). Two sphincters are involved in ejaculation: an internal one, which closes off the entrance to the bladder during a normal ejaculation, and an external one, which opens during a normal ejaculation, allowing the semen to flow out through the penis. In retrograde ejaculation, the actions of these two sphincters are desynchronized; the external one closes, and thus the ejaculate cannot flow out through the penis, and the internal one opens, permitting the ejaculate to go into the bladder. The condition itself is quite harmless, although some men are disturbed by the lack of sensation of emitting semen.

Mechanisms in Women

Unfortunately, there is far less research on similar reflex mechanisms in women. We know that sensory input—such as touch—travels along the dorsal nerve of

> **Retrograde ejaculation:** A condition in which orgasm in the male is not accompanied by an external ejaculation; instead, the ejaculate goes into the urinary bladder.

Bladder muscles relax

Bladder

Sperm duct

Seminal vesicle

Ejaculatory duct

Urethra

Prostate

Compressor muscles contract

Figure 9.7 How a retrograde ejaculation occurs.

the clitoris and continues within the pudendal nerve to a reflex centre in the sacral portion of the spinal cord (Berman et al., 2000). Research with nonhumans—mainly male and female rats—has investigated the urethrogenital reflex, which results in muscle contractions similar to orgasm in humans (Meston et al., 2004). This research suggests that the neural circuits for orgasm in women are very similar to those for orgasm and ejaculation in men. The clitoris has both sympathetic and parasympathetic nerve fibres. The vagina, too, is supplied by both sympathetic and parasympathetic nerves. The limbic system of the brain is crucial to both female and male sexual arousal.

Research indicates that some women emit fluid during orgasm, often referred to as *female ejaculation* (Addiego et al., 1981; Belzer, 1981; Perry & Whipple, 1981). The region responsible is the **Gräfenberg spot or G-spot**, also called the *female prostate* or the *Skene's glands* (Schubach, 2002). It is located on the top side of the vagina (with the woman lying on her back, which is the best position for finding it), about halfway between the pubic bone and the cervix (see Figure 9.8). Its ducts open into the urethra. Stroking it produces an urge to urinate, but if the stroking continues for a few seconds more, it begins to produce sexual pleasure. The original researchers, Perry and Whipple, argued that continued stimulation of it produces a uterine orgasm, characterized by deeper sensations of uterine contractions than the clitorally induced vulvar orgasm investigated in the Masters and Johnson research.

In one survey of women, 40 percent reported having experienced ejaculation at the time of orgasm at least once, and 66 percent reported having an especially sensitive area on the front wall of the vagina (Darling et al., 1990). Biochemical analyses indicate that the female prostate produces *prostate-specific antigen* (PSA), just as the male

Gräfenberg spot (GRAY-fen-berg) or G-spot: A small region on the front wall of the vagina, emptying into the urethra and responsible for female ejaculation. Also called the female prostate or the Skene's glands.
Limbic system: A set of structures in the interior of the brain, including the amygdala, hippocampus, and fornix; believed to be important for sexual behaviour in both animals and humans.

prostate does (Zaviačič, Zajíčková, et al., 2000). In the most recent study, MRI scans identified a female prostate in six of seven women studied (Wimpissinger et al., 2009).

Brain Control of Sexual Response

Sexual responses are controlled by more than simple spinal reflexes. They may be brought under voluntary control, and they may be initiated by purely psychological forces, such as fantasy. Environmental factors, such as having been taught as a child that sex is dirty and sinful, may also affect one's sexual response. All these phenomena point to the critical influence of the brain and its interaction with the spinal reflexes in producing sexual response (see Figure 9.6).

Research using sophisticated imaging techniques is revealing a great deal about brain control of sexual response (see Milestones in Sex Research). The results suggest that distinctive patterns of brain activity are associated with arousal, excitement, orgasm, and the refractory period (Georgiadis & Kringelbach, 2012). The arousal or anticipatory phase (i.e., what happens before tactile stimulation), primarily involves areas in the **limbic system** (Figure 9.9).

Sexual consummation includes a variety of activities capable of producing pleasure or euphoria and creates activity in the dorsal and interhemispheric primary motor cortex (MI). This activity is associated with objective (measured simultaneously by plethysmograph) and subjective (measured by self-report) arousal. The most prominent area of activity related to orgasm is decreased activity in the prefrontal cortex. There is increased activity in the left orbitofrontal cortex, which is associated with subjective ratings of pleasure by the participant. Finally, in studies of men's brains (because they almost always have an orgasm in response to genital stimulation) 3 to 30 minutes after orgasm, activity was observed in the septal area, temporal lobe, and amygdala. The results suggest a *de-arousal neural network*. This network may correspond to the inhibition phase identified in the dual process model.

In Chapter 2, we introduced you to Ms. CEO and Mr. Hunk. At the board of directors meeting, she wanted to throw him on the table and make love to him. In brain control terms, he aroused her *sexual interest network*, which motivated her to have sex. However, being socialized into cultural norms and sexual scripts, her de-arousal neural network was activated and she didn't act on her arousal.

Many of the brain centres for sex are also close to the olfactory centres. This brings up the topic of pheromones and their role in sexual behaviour, which will be discussed later in the chapter.

Neurochemical Influences on Sexual Response

We just described activity in various regions of the brain that are associated with sexual response. This neural

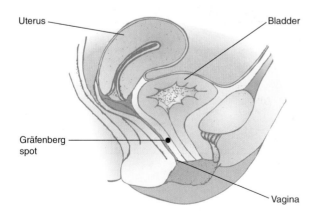

Figure 9.8 The Gräfenberg spot, or G-spot: hypothesized to produce ejaculation in some women.

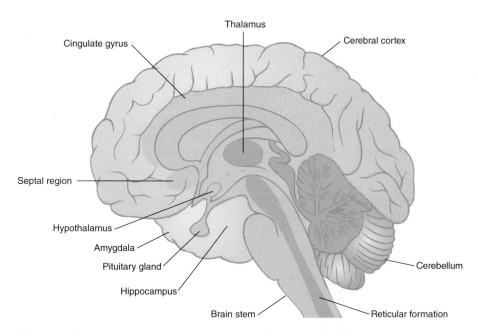

Figure 9.9 The limbic system of the brain, which is important in sexuality.

activity is closely related to neurochemical processes. Distinctive neurochemicals are involved in sexual excitation and sexual inhibition.

During excitation, or the anticipatory and consummatory phases of sexual response, dopamines, melanocortins, oxytocin, and norepinephrine are involved (Pfaus, 2009). Dopamine and melanocortin stimulate attention to sexual stimuli and sexual desire within the limbic system. Noradrenalin and oxytocin stimulate sexual arousal and erection. In part, the activation of these neurochemicals also block the action of inhibitory processes.

Neurochemicals involved in inhibitory processes include opioids, which are released in the cortex, limbic system, hypothalamus, and midbrain in response to sexual pleasure and orgasm or ejaculation. They also include endocannabinoids which induce sedation (and counteract stress!), and serotonin, which induces satiety and the refractory period. (For more detail and diagrams, see Pfaus, 2009.)

The sex hormones androgen, estrogen, and progestin facilitate or prime the brain to respond to sexual incentives by binding to specific hormone receptor complexes, which in turn lead to the synthesis of these neurochemicals.

 Hormones and Sex

The sex hormones are another important physiological force that interacts with the nervous system to influence sexual response.

Organizing Versus Activating Effects

Endocrinologists generally make a distinction between the organizing effects of hormones and their activating effects. As discussed in Chapter 5, hormones present during prenatal development have important influences on genital anatomy, creating male or female genitals. Effects such as these are called the **organizing effects of hormones** because they cause a relatively permanent change in the organization of some structure, whether in the nervous system or in the reproductive system. Typically there are critical periods during which these hormone effects may occur.

It has also been known for some time that if an adult male mouse or rat is castrated (has the testes removed, which removes the source of testosterone), it will cease engaging in sexual behaviour (and will be less aggressive). If that animal is then given injections of testosterone, it will start engaging in sex again. Effects such as these are called the **activating effects of hormones** because they activate (or deactivate) certain behaviours.

The organizing effects of sex hormones on sexual behaviour have been well documented (Keefe, 2002). In a classic experiment, testosterone was administered to pregnant female guinea pigs. The female offspring that had been exposed to testosterone prenatally[1] were, in adulthood, incapable of displaying "female" sexual behaviour (in particular, lordosis, which is a sexual posturing involving arching of the back and raising of the hindquarters so that intromission of the male's

> **Organizing effects of hormones:** Effects of sex hormones early in development, resulting in a permanent change in the brain or reproductive system.
> **Activating effects of hormone:** Effects of sex hormones in adulthood, resulting in the activation of behaviours, especially sexual behaviours and aggressive behaviours.

[1] Note the similarity of these experiments to John Money's observations of human intersex individuals (Chapter 5).

Milestones in Sex Research

What Happens in the Brain During Sex?

Exciting advances in the technology of neuroimaging are giving us inside views of the human brain during various phases of sexual response. Methods such as PET (positron emission tomography) and fMRI (functional magnetic resonance imaging) show which regions of the brain "light up" (have neurons most actively firing) while the individual is solving a math problem or thinking about something sad.

Sex researchers have adopted these techniques, with the goal of learning which regions of the brain are most involved in various aspects of sexuality. One of the challenges they have faced is that the participant cannot move while in an MRI scanner. Researchers have dealt with the problem by showing erotic videos to the person inside the scanner.

In one experiment heterosexual men viewed erotic video clips, relaxing clips, and sports clips in random order (Arnow et al., 2002). Meanwhile, their brains were being scanned in an MRI machine and the erection of the penis was measured. One has to admire these men for being able to become aroused while in an MRI scanner! Pictures from the brain scans are shown in Figure 9.10. When the men were exposed to erotic clips and were sexually aroused, as indicated by erection, intense brain activity was found in the right insula and claustrum, striatum (left caudate nucleus and putamen), cingulate gyrus, and—you guessed it—the hypothalamus. The insula is known to be involved in sensory processing, particularly of touch sensations. The cingulate cortex has been demonstrated in other studies to be involved in attentional

processes and in guiding responsiveness to new environmental stimuli. Doubtless it was activated because of the men's attention to the erotic film.

Another study used fMRI to assess brain activation in both men and women while viewing erotic video segments (Karama et al., 2002). This study found brain activation in roughly the same regions as the study discussed previously. Almost all regions responded similarly in women and men. This study also found evidence of activation of the amygdala during sexual arousal. The amygdala is part of the limbic system, and as noted in this chapter, plays a role in sexual response. The amygdala is known to be involved in emotion, and its activation speaks to the strong emotions—sometimes positive, sometimes negative—that are evoked by sexual stimuli.

Research with women with spinal-cord injury indicates that they experience sexual arousal and orgasm as a result of genital stimulation (Komisaruk & Whipple, 2005). The neural signals do not travel up the spinal cord, which has been damaged, but rather pass up to the brain through the vagus nerves. fMRI scans indicate that the brain regions activated during arousal include the hypothalamus, amygdala, hippocampus, and the rest of the list of structures identified in fMRI research on people without spinal-cord injuries.

These studies are fascinating in themselves as they allow us to view the workings of the brain during sexual responding. As research advances, future studies will help us understand the brain regions and associated neurotransmitters involved in sexual dysfunction, which may

---

penis is possible) (Phoenix et al., 1959). It is thought that this result occurred because the testosterone "organized" the brain tissue (particularly the hypothalamus) in a male fashion. These female offspring were also born with masculinized genitals, and thus their reproductive systems had also been organized in the male direction. But the important point here is that the prenatal doses of testosterone had masculinized their sexual behaviour. Similar results have been obtained in experiments with many other species.

These hormonally masculinized females in adulthood displayed mounting behaviour, a male sexual behaviour.[2] When they were given testosterone in adulthood, they showed about as much mounting

---

[2] The term *male sexual behaviour* is being used here to refer to a sexual behaviour that is displayed by normal males of the species and either is absent in females of that species or is present at a much lower frequency. Normal females do mount, but they do so less frequently than males do. *Female sexual behaviour* is defined similarly.

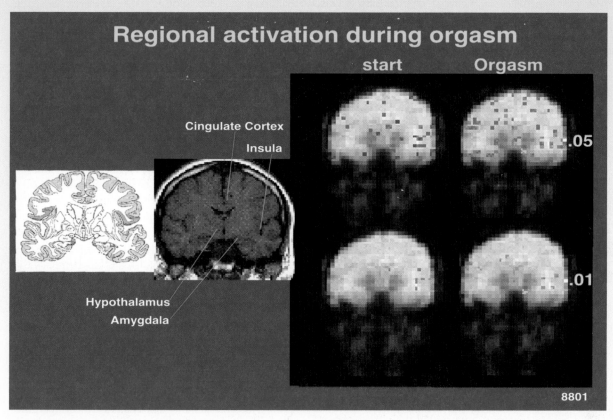

Figure 9.10 fMRI scans of the brain are opening up exciting opportunities to learn how the brain is involved in sexual response.

lead to more effective treatments for these problems. They will also allow us to better understand and treat arousal problems, such as those suffered by pedophiles, who are aroused by completely inappropriate stimuli—children.

Sources: Arnow et al. (2002), Holstege et al. (2003), Karama et al. (2002), Komisaruk & Whipple (2005), Schultz et al. (1999).

behaviour as males did. Thus, the testosterone administered in adulthood *activated* male patterns of sexual behaviour.

The analogous experiment on males would be castration at birth, followed by administration of ovarian hormones in adulthood. When this was done with rats, female sexual behaviour resulted; these males responded to mating attempts by other males essentially in the same way females do (Harris & Levine, 1965). Their brain tissue had been organized in a

"female" direction during an early critical period when testosterone was absent, and the female behaviour patterns were activated in adulthood by administration of ovarian hormones.

It thus seems that males and females initially have capacities for both male and female sexual behaviours; if testosterone is present early in development, the capacity for exhibiting female behaviours is suppressed. Sex hormones in adulthood then activate the behaviour patterns that were differentiated early in development.

How relevant is this research to humans? Generally, the trend is for the behaviour of lower species to be more under hormonal control and for the behaviour of higher species to be more under brain (neural) control. Thus, human sexual behaviour is less under hormonal control than rat sexual behaviour; human sexual behaviour is more controlled by the brain, and thus learning from past experiences and cultural conventions, which are stored in the brain, are more likely to have a profound effect (Wallen, 2001).

Let us now consider in more detail the known activating effects of sex hormones on the sexual behaviour of adult humans.

Testosterone and Sexual Desire

Testosterone has well-documented effects on libido, or sexual desire, in humans (Carani et al., 1990; Carter, 1992; Everitt & Bancroft, 1991). In men deprived of their main source of testosterone by castration or by illness, there is a dramatic decrease in sexual behaviour in some, but not all, cases. Sexual desire is rapidly lost if a man is given an anti-androgen drug. Thus, testosterone seems to have an activating effect in maintaining sexual desire in men. However, in cases of castration, sexual behaviour may decline very slowly and may be present for several years after the source of testosterone is gone; this points to the importance of experience and brain control of sexual behaviour in humans.

It has also been demonstrated that levels of testosterone are correlated with sexual behaviour in boys around the time of puberty (Udry et al., 1985). Boys in Grades 8, 9, and 10 filled out a questionnaire about their sexual behaviour and gave blood samples from which their level of testosterone was measured. Among the boys whose testosterone level was in the highest quartile (25 percent of the sample), 69 percent had engaged in sexual intercourse, whereas only 16 percent of the boys whose testosterone level was in the lowest quartile had. Similarly, of the boys with testosterone levels in the highest quartile, 62 percent had masturbated, compared with 12 percent for the boys in the lowest quartile. These effects were uncorrelated with age, so it wasn't simply a matter of the older boys having more testosterone and more sexual experience. The authors concluded that at puberty testosterone affects sexual motivation directly.

Research indicates that androgens are related to sexual desire in some women also (Hutchinson, 1995; Sherwin, 1991).[3] If all sources of androgens (the adrenals and the ovaries) are removed, women lose sexual desire. Women who have undergone *oophorectomy* (surgical removal of the ovaries, typically

> **What hormone is most important to sexual desire in men? In women?**

Pheromones (FARE-oh-mones): Biochemicals secreted outside the body that are important in communication between animals and that may serve as sex attractants.

because of cancer) report marked decreases in their sexual desire. If they are treated with testosterone, their sexual desire increases (Shifren et al., 1998; Shifren et al., 2000). Androgen levels decline with age in women, and research shows that administration of DHEA (a pretestosterone hormone) to women over age 60 may result in their having increased sexual desire (Baulieu et al., 2000; Spourk, 2002). However, the sexual desire of other women does not appear to be sensitive to levels of testosterone (Bancroft, 2010). Further, in premenopausal women, the level of testosterone is not related to their sexual desire (van Anders et al., 2009).

Pheromones

Scientists and laypeople alike are intrigued by the role that pheromones play in sexual behaviour (Cutler, 1999; McClintock, 2000). Pheromones are somewhat like hormones. Recall that hormones are biochemicals that are manufactured in the body and secreted into the bloodstream to be carried to the organs that they affect. **Pheromones**, in contrast, are biochemicals that are secreted outside the body. Through the sense of smell, they are an important means of communication between animals. Often the pheromones are contained in the animal's urine. The dog that does scent marking is depositing pheromones. Some pheromones appear to be important in sexual communication, and some have even been called *sex attractants*.

Much of the research on pheromones has been done with animals and demonstrates the importance of pheromones in sexual and reproductive functioning (Figure 9.11). For example, pheromones present in female urine have an influence on male sexual behaviour (Snowdon et al., 2006).

The sense of smell (olfaction) is essential for pheromone effects to occur. Removal of the olfactory bulbs, specifically a region called the *vomeronasal organ* (VNO), dramatically reduces the sexual behaviour of males from such species as mice and guinea pigs (Thorne & Amrein, 2003). The VNO, located inside the nose, is a chemoreceptor—that is, it is activated by chemicals, such as pheromones. Neuroscientists even recorded the activity of single neurons in the VNO of male mice and found that certain neurons fire when the animal comes into contact with another male, but different neurons

---

[3] Lest the reader be distressed by the thought that women's considerably lower levels of testosterone might mean that they have lower sex drives, it should be noted that the sensitivity of cells to hormone levels is critical. Women's cells may be more sensitive to testosterone than men's are. Thus for women, a little testosterone may go a long way.

(a)   (b)

Figure 9.11   Pheromones. *(a)* Pheromones are a major means of communication between animals. *(b)* Are there human pheromones that are sex attractants?

fire when he comes into contact with a female (Luo et al., 2003). Activation of the VNO then activates cells in the hypothalamus (Keverne, 1999); as we have seen, the hypothalamus is crucial to sexuality. The VNO is a kind of second olfactory pathway, sometimes called the *accessory olfactory bulb,* that functions in addition to the main sense of smell.

What relevance does all this have for humans? Humans are not, by and large, scent animals. Olfaction is much less important for us than for most other species. We tend to rely mostly on vision and, secondarily, hearing. Does this mean that pheromones have no influence on our sexual behaviour?

New research may provide an answer to this question. Researchers have discovered that there is a long-overlooked cranial nerve, called nerve zero, that sprouts from the base of the brain, connects to parts of the brain controlling reproduction, and releases gonadotropin-releasing hormone (GnRH) into the blood (Fields, 2007). Nerve zero has been found in animals and humans. Nerve zero may sense pheromones even if they do not have an odour and thus may influence behaviour even though we are not conscious of them. More research is needed before the role of nerve zero in human sexual and reproductive behaviour is clear (Fields, 2007).

It is clear that human pheromones exist and may play an important role in sexuality (Wyatt, 2003). Indeed, pheromones may be exactly the "body chemistry" that attracts people to each other. Perfumes with musky scents have become popular and presumably increase

sexual attractiveness, perhaps because they smell like pheromones. The perfume industry has eagerly tried to capitalize on pheromone research, making rather large claims for the effects of their products on attraction (e.g., "makes good girls go bad").

What scientific evidence is there regarding the existence and effects of pheromones in humans? First, although its function is not clear, the VNO—which, as noted, is related to olfaction and sexual behaviour in other species and essentially seems to function as a pheromone sensor—is present in most humans (Brennan & Zufall, 2006; Garcia-Velasco & Mondragon, 1991). This makes one wonder whether plastic surgery to create a straight nose might inadvertently harm the person's sex life.

Second, androstenol, an odorous steroid that is well documented as a pheromone in pigs, has been isolated in the underarm sweat of humans (Gower & Ruparelia, 1993). Short-chain fatty acids that are known to be sex-attractant pheromones to male rhesus monkeys have been isolated in human vaginal secretions (Cowley & Brooksbank, 1991). It is clear, therefore, that humans do secrete pheromones.

In one experiment, a synthesized female pheromone was added to women's perfume in one group; a placebo was added to the perfume in the control group (McCoy & Pitino, 2002; Rako & Friebely, 2004). The women recorded their sexual behaviour over the next three months. Compared with the control group, pheromone-treated women showed a significantly greater frequency of intercourse, dates, sexual fondling, and kissing. They did not differ in frequency of masturbation. The researchers concluded that the pheromone had increased the women's attractiveness to men. In an imaging study, eight heterosexual men were exposed to women's perfume (Huh et al., 2008). Two reported "strong" arousal and three reported "moderate" arousal. All eight experienced brain activity in the insula, the gyrus, and the hypothalamus, areas we noted earlier are involved in arousal.

Classic research by Martha McClintock (1971) documented the existence of a phenomenon known as **menstrual synchrony**: the convergence, over several months, of the dates of onset of menstrual periods among women who are in close contact with each other (McClintock, 1998; Weller et al., 1995). This phenomenon is now thought to be due to pheromones produced by the women.

In perhaps the most dramatic experiment to date in humans, the results indicated that the timing of ovulation could be experimentally manipulated with human pheromones (Stern & McClintock, 1998). Odourless secretions from women's armpits were collected in the late follicular phase—that is, just before ovulation. Recipient women exposed to these secretions showed an accelerated appearance of the LH surge that triggers ovulation. Underarm secretions from the same donors collected later in the menstrual cycle had the opposite effect: they delayed the LH surge of recipients and lengthened the time to menstruation. In another study, men smelled T-shirts worn by (1) women near ovulation, (2) women far from ovulation, or (3) no one. Men exposed to the scent of an ovulating woman subsequently had elevated levels of testosterone (Miller & Maner, 2010).

Other pheromone research has found that preference for human body odours and brain responses to pheromones differ as a function of sexual orientation (Berglund et al., 2006; Martins et al., 2005). In one study, armpit secretions were collected from heterosexual men, heterosexual women, gay men, and lesbians (Martins et al., 2005). Odour evaluators then rated the pleasantness of these odours, not knowing the source of them. Heterosexual men, for example, gave the lowest pleasantness ratings to the pheromones from gay men. Gay men gave low ratings to the pheromones of heterosexual men. The researchers concluded that human *odour prints* may help us identify groups of people who are potential sexual partners.

If these speculations about the effects of pheromones on human sexual behaviour are correct, our hyperclean society may be destroying the scents that attract people to each other.

Menstrual synchrony: The convergence, over several months, of the dates of onset of menstrual periods among women who are in close contact with each other.

Sexual Techniques

In the earlier sections of this chapter, we discussed some of the wonderful things that happen to the body during sexual arousal and orgasm. How do we get to these marvellous states, both for ourselves and our partners?

We live in the era of sex manuals. Books like *Electrify Your Sex Life*, *The Illustrated Guide to Extended Massive Orgasm*, and *The Complete Guide to Sexual Fulfillment*, as well as feature articles and advice columns in many magazines and talk shows, give us advice on how to produce bigger and longer orgasms in ourselves and our partners. The sex manuals may also set up impossible standards of sexual performance that none of us can meet.

On the other hand, we live in a society that has a history of leaving the learning of sexual techniques to nature or to chance, in contrast to some other societies in which adolescents are given explicit instruction in methods for producing sexual pleasure. For human beings, sexual behaviour is a lot more than doing what comes naturally; we all need some means for learning about sexual techniques, and the sex manuals may help to fill that need. People with disabilities may need specific suggestions about how to adapt conventional ideas about sexual techniques to their own unique circumstances (see First Person for a discussion of sexuality and disability).

In the sections that follow, we consider techniques that bring people sexual pleasure. Of course, sexual techniques are not enough to build a satisfying sexual relationship with another person, so we also consider factors that contribute to "great sex" (Kleinplatz & Ménard, 2007). We discuss two of these components, loving attachment and communication, in Chapter 12.

Erogenous Zones

Although the notion of erogenous zones originated in Freud's work, the term is now part of our general vocabulary. It refers to parts of the body that are sexually sensitive; stroking them or otherwise stimulating them produces sexual arousal. The genitals and the breasts are good examples. The lips, neck, and thighs are generally also erogenous zones. But even some rather unlikely regions—such as the back, the ears, the stomach, and the feet—can also be erogenous. One person's erogenous zones can be different from another's. Thus, it is impossible to give a list of sure turn-ons. The best way to find out is to communicate with your partner, verbally and nonverbally (see Chapter 12).

One-Person Sex

It does not necessarily take two to have sex. People can create their own sexual stimulation. Sexual self-stimulation is called **autoeroticism**.[4] Two examples are masturbation and fantasy.

Masturbation

Here the term hand–genital stimulation will be reserved for stimulation of another's genitals and the term **masturbation** for self-stimulation, either with the hand or with some object, such as a pillow or a vibrator. Masturbation is a very common sexual behaviour; almost all men and the majority of women in Canada masturbate to orgasm at least a few times during their lives. In the National Survey of Sexual Health and Behavior, 72 to 84 percent of men (depending on age and other factors) ages 18 to 60 reported that they had masturbated in the preceding year, as did 54 to 65 percent of the women (Herbenick et al., 2010a, 2010b). Fifty-six to 66 percent of the men and 26 to 52 percent of the women had masturbated in the previous month.

Although there are no national data on masturbation, our research has found that most Canadian university students (92 percent of the men and 72 percent of the women in one study) have masturbated at least once. Further, 65 percent of Canadians have positive attitudes toward masturbation. A study of German university students found that the percentage of students who report masturbating was not affected by whether they had a sexual partner; rather masturbation was seen as a sexual activity in its own right (Dekker & Schmidt, 2002).

The techniques used by men and women in masturbation are interesting in part because they provide information to their partners concerning the best techniques to use in lovemaking (Figure 9.12).

Most commonly women masturbate by manipulating the clitoris and the inner lips. They may rub up and down or in a circular motion, sometimes lightly and sometimes applying more pressure to the clitoris. Some prefer to rub at the side of the clitoris, while a few stimulate the glans of the clitoris directly. The inner lips may also be stroked or tugged. One woman described her technique as follows:

> I use the tips of my fingers for actual stimulation, but it's better to start with patting motions or light rubbing motions over the general area. As excitement increases I begin stroking above the clitoris and finally reach a climax with a rapid, jerky circular motion over the clitoral hood. Usually my legs are apart, and occasionally I also stimulate my nipples with the other hand. (Hite, 1976, p. 20)

[4] For those of you who are interested in the roots of words, *autoeroticism* does not refer to sex in the back seat of a car. The prefix *auto* means "self" (as in *autobiography*); hence, self-stimulation is autoeroticism.

(a)

(b)

Figure 9.12 *(a)* Male masturbation using hand stimulation of the penis. *(b)* Female masturbation using clitoral stimulation.

Other techniques used by women in masturbation include breast stimulation, thigh pressure exerted by crossing the legs and pressing them together rhythmically to stimulate the clitoris, and pressing the genitals against some object, such as a pillow, or massaging them with a stream of water while in the shower. A few women are capable of using fantasy alone to produce orgasm; fantasy-induced orgasms are accompanied by the same physiological changes as orgasms produced by masturbation (Whipple et al., 1992).

Almost all men report masturbating by hand stimulation of the penis. For those interested in speed, an orgasm can be reached in only a minute or two. Most men use the technique of circling the hand around the shaft of the penis and using an up-and-down movement to stimulate the shaft and glans. Because the penis produces no natural lubrication of its own, some men like to use a form of lubrication, such as soapsuds while showering. The tightness of the grip, the speed of movement,

Autoeroticism: Sexual self-stimulation; for example, masturbation.
Masturbation: Stimulation of one's own genitals with the hand or with some object, such as a pillow or vibrator.

First Person

Sex Toys and Physical Disability

All sorts of people use sex toys—people of all ages, abilities, genders, and sexual orientations. There is really no limit to who can benefit from the different sensations and types of stimulation that sex toys may provide. Sex toys can be especially enjoyable and helpful to people who have different abilities.

People with disabilities may experience multiple barriers to sexual pleasure. Some of these barriers are intangible. For instance, *ableism,* which is the oppression and stigmatization of people with disabilities, has worked to misconstrue people with disabilities as nonsexual. The historical medical model of disability posited people with disabilities as weak and infantile and in need of being cured or cared for. This ableist, socially constructed identity did not allow people with disabilities dignity, autonomy, or access to their sexual rights. As political awareness around the rights of people with disabilities grew in the 1970s, the social model of disability began to replace the medical model. The social model of disability views disability holistically and differentiates between an *impairment* and a *disability.* An impairment is a bodily difference, such as having a limp; a disability is the way that an impairment is viewed by society as something that makes that person less valuable simply because their body does not conform to a norm. This social model of disability has been beneficial in that it recognizes that people with disabilities are whole people who deserve full access to human rights (WHO, 1980). However, despite this positive change, historically rooted ideas of people with disabilities as being nonsexual still exist. It is important for all of us to re-imagine such limited ideas of who is sexual and who has the right to sexual pleasure.

There are also other more tangible barriers to individuals with physical disabilities experiencing sexual pleasure, and these ones can be easier to counter. These barriers are physical ones, such as different degrees of sensation and mobility, muscle spasticity, erectile difficulties, and an absence of vaginal lubrication. Sex toys can play a revolutionary role in helping to overcome these physical differences. That is, they can allow people to experience all new bodily sensations and stimulations. What are some ways in which the sex toys described later in this chapter can be used to help overcome the physical barriers experienced by people with disabilities?

Limited Sensation

Many people with different disabilities experience limited degrees of sensation at different points of their body. For example, people with spinal cord injuries, MS, or cerebral palsy, or who are taking certain medications may lack sensation in their genitals. Here vibrators can play a crucial role in allowing them to feel sexual stimulation. People who have limited sensation may want to use a very strong vibrator either externally against their genitals (the clitoris or the shaft of the penis, for example) or internally (inside the vagina or anus). There are a plethora of vibrators each designed to stimulate different parts of the body, making this a very versatile type of toy. Vibrators also range widely in shape, size, and control mechanisms. Some may be easier for people with disabilities to use than others, depending on the

and the amount of glans stimulation vary from one man to the next. Most increase the speed of stimulation as they approach orgasm, slowing or stopping the stimulation at orgasm because further stimulation would be uncomfortable (Masters & Johnson, 1966). At the time of ejaculation, men often grip the shaft of the penis tightly. Immediately after orgasm, the glans and corona are hypersensitive, and men generally avoid further stimulation of the penis at that time.

Some men and woman incorporate the use of mass media into their autoerotic activity. Some people masturbate as they view erotic images in magazines, on video or DVD, or on the Internet. For example, a New Brunswick survey found that 86 percent of male and 39 percent of female undergraduates had viewed sexually explicit materials online in the previous month, and most of these individuals had masturbated while doing so (Shaughnessy et al., 2011).

person's strength, the ease of which the vibrator can be operated (small buttons versus a dial, for example), and how heavy it is.

Different Degrees of Mobility

Some people with disabilities experience different degrees of mobility. This may make it difficult to get into certain sexual positions or to be able to touch some parts of their body or their partner's body. Here again vibrators can be helpful. Vibrators that have a long handle may be able to reach these parts of the body without requiring difficult or painful bending.

Sex furniture can also be of use when it comes to getting into and maintaining different sexual positions. Sex furniture is essentially different designs of pillows and slings that, for example, can help lift up a person's bum, spread the legs, or reposition the neck. They can make it more comfortable to lie in different positions. The Intimate Rider is a piece of sex furniture created specifically for people with disabilities. It is intended to facilitate motion so as to allow for penetrative sex. It has two parts: a low-slung rocking chair (which can be easier to transfer into out of a wheelchair) and a cot positioned at the same height. One person sits in the rocking chair allowing them to thrust, while their partner lies on the cot in front of them.

Concerns Related to the Sexual Response

Some people experience erectile difficulties related to their physical disability. Medication such as Viagra, Levitra, or Cialis may be helpful to them (see Chapter 18). Other people choose to use a penis pump and a ring instead. A pump is a device that is placed over the shaft of the penis and then squeezed, drawing blood into the penis. When blood moves into the shaft it creates an erection. When the pump is removed, the blood could simply cycle back out of the penile shaft, causing the erection to end. This is where rings come in. If a silicone or jelly vinyl ring is pulled around the shaft and the testicles so that it presses against the base of the penis, this can stop blood from flowing out of the shaft. When the blood is trapped inside the shaft, an erection can be maintained.

Some women who have a physical disability have decreased vaginal lubrication, making penetrative sex painful. There are a variety of water-based or silicone-based lubricants that they (or their partner) can apply to the genitals to facilitate penetration and keep the vagina from being irritated. Water-based lubricants may be all natural and mimic natural vaginal lubrication well. Silicone-based lubes are not natural and they feel more like oil; however, they may last longer than a water-based lube because they do not absorb into the body.

Because sexual health is an important facet of human well-being, it is important that health care providers and support workers remember to consider the sexual health needs of persons with disabilities. Some important resources have been developed to help caregivers better support those needs. Two examples are the Sexuality and Access Project (http://sexuality-and-access.com/about-us/), an Ontario-based project, and the booklet titled *Supporting Sexual Health and Intimacy in Care Facilities: Guidelines for Supporting Adults Living in Long-Term Care Facilities and Group Homes in British Columbia, Canada.*

Sources: Silverberg & Odette (2011), Vancouver Coastal Health Authority (2009). Written by Kaleigh Trace.

Fantasy

Sexual fantasy refers to any conscious mental imagery or daydream that includes sexual activity or is sexually arousing (Bivona & Critelli, 2009). Almost all men and women report that they have experienced sexual fantasies; often frequently (Kahr, 2008; Leitenberg & Henning, 1995). However, many people are uncomfortable with acknowledging that they deliberately think about sex and enjoy doing so (Renaud & Byers, 2001).

Researchers in New Brunswick studied the sexual thoughts and fantasies of heterosexual university students (Renaud & Byers, 1999). They found that although men think about sex more frequently than women do, for the most part, the content of their sexual fantasies is similar. The most common themes have to do with intimacy and romance. More than 90 percent of students had fantasies

Sexual fantasy: Sexual thoughts or images that alter the person's emotions or physiological state.

about having intercourse with a loved partner, kissing passionately, making love elsewhere than the bedroom (e.g., out of doors), and giving and receiving oral sex. Compared with the women, the men's fantasies more often revolved around themes of anonymous or impersonal sex. The women had romantic fantasies and fantasies about playing a role during sexual activity—such as exposing themselves provocatively or tying their partner up—more often than the men did. In a survey of a national sample of British adults, men were more likely to report fantasies of sex with multiple and anonymous partners, whereas women reported fantasies involving a same-sex or famous male partner (Wilson, 1997). Interestingly, an Ontario study found similar gender differences in sexual dreams (King et al., 2009). These differences are consistent with predictions based on both evolutionary theory and gender-role socialization.

Gay men and lesbians tend to fantasize about sexual partners of the same gender, although at times they may fantasize about someone of the other gender (Price et al., 1985). Conversely, heterosexuals most often fantasize about sexual activities with someone of the other gender, but they also fantasize about someone of the same gender. Sexual fantasies often involve people, places (DisneyWorld), or animals with which the person has no real-world connection (Kahr, 2008).

Where do sexual fantasies come from? The images may come from past experience, dreams, media portrayals, or stories someone told you. The activity may be dreamlike and sensuous, or explicit and vigorous. Like all fantasy, sexual fantasies represent a fusion of mind, body, and emotions. Sexual fantasies may represent earlier or childhood experiences, pleasant or abusive (Maltz & Boss, 1997). They may be experienced as positive and pleasant or as negative and unwanted (Byers, Purdon, et al., 1998; Renaud & Byers, 1999).

Sexual fantasy can serve a variety of functions for the person doing the fantasizing (Maltz & Boss, 1997). These include enhancing self-esteem and attractiveness, increasing sexual arousal (e.g., during masturbation or partnered sex), and facilitating orgasm. In fact, research has shown that people who engage in more frequent sexual fantasies tend to be better adjusted sexually (Renaud & Byers, 2001). A very important role is enabling the person to mentally rehearse future possibilities. Such rehearsal may enable the person to change behaviour, initiate communication with a partner, or change partners. Although many people use fantasy as part of sexual interactions, others may have no sexual contact with another person and rely exclusively on sexual fantasy and masturbation for their erotic pleasure (Kahr, 2008).

Sometimes sexual thoughts or fantasies can be experienced as negative—that is, unacceptable,

Dildo: A rubber or plastic cylinder, often shaped like a penis.

upsetting, and unpleasant. In fact, research in New Brunswick found that 84 percent of university students had these types of thoughts (Byers, Purdon, et al., 1998). The negative images most frequently reported by men were of having sex in a public place, meeting naked people, and engaging in sex with a person having authority over them. Those most frequently reported by women were of having sex in a public place, having sex with a person having authority over them, and being sexually victimized. Students who have more frequent negative sexual thoughts and fantasies are not more poorly adjusted, although some people experience anxiety and guilt because of the thought (Byers, Purdon, et al., 1998; Renaud & Byers, 2001).

Here is the fantasy of one man when he masturbates:

I lie back on the bed completely naked, but without an erection. A lady dressed only in the sexiest lingerie ever climbs onto the bed, but does not undress or touch me yet with her hands. Slowly, she sits almost upon my face and she slips a hand into her panties and starts to masturbate herself and cums into her panties and just lowers herself enough to allow me to have the slightest taste of her juices with my tongue on her panties. She lowers herself further down my body and slowly gives me oral sex, flicking her tongue around my penis. She gives me slow lingering oral and then we continue to have slow passionate sex together. (Kahr, 2008, pp. 115–116)

Here is the fantasy of one woman:

This involves me as a doctor in a really sexy outfit. My partner is my patient strapped to the bed. I strip for him and make him watch since he can't touch me. I tease him with feathers and ribbons. I then mount him and have rough sex with him while he is tied up (Kahr, 2008, pp. 73–74).

Sex Toys

Various sexual devices, such as vibrators, dildos, cock (penis) rings, butt plugs, and lube (lubricant), are used as *sex toys* by some people in masturbation or by couples as they have sex together. Each type of sex toy comes in endless variations. Some people consider use of sex toys to be examples of *spicy sex,* meaning a change from the usual sexual script, which is sometimes called *vanilla sex* (Rye & Meaney, 2007a). Sex toys used to only be available in specialty sex stores or online. However, they have gone main stream and are now available in pharmacies and other mainstream stores. Here we describe a few of the more common sex toys, but there are many other devices that people can use to enhance their sexual pleasure.

Both male and female artificial genitals can be purchased. A **dildo** is a rubber, silicone, or plastic cylinder, often shaped like a penis; it can be inserted into the vagina or the anus. Dildos are used by some women in masturbation, by same-sex couples, and by heterosexual couples (Figure 9.13). Some couples use a dildo with a harness, often called a *strap-on*. Artificial vaginas, and even inflatable replicas of the entire body, male or female, can also be purchased.

A **vibrator** is a handheld device that vibrates and is used for massage or held against the body to provide sexual stimulation. Vibrators come in a variety of shapes and sizes (from small to large). They also vary in the intensity of the vibrations. Vibrators can be electric, with a cord that plugs into an electric socket, or cordless rechargeable or battery-powered models. Some vibrators are shaped like a penis but others are not. Women may use them to masturbate, stimulating the clitoral and mons area, or may insert them into the vagina. Men may use them during masturbation or during sex with a partner (Reece et al., 2009).

Vibrators designed for woman are not recent; they were invented in the 1880s and sold as a medical device (Maines, 1999). Physicians prescribed their use for the treatment of various female "maladies," especially hysteria.[5] Vibrators disappeared from medicinal use after they were used in pornographic films in the 1920s. Today they are back in full force, with women throwing Passion Parties or Slumber Parties, which are Tupperware-style home parties where you and your friends can buy sex toys from the local salesperson (Jefferson, 2005). Vibrators can also be purchased online or at a sex store. Vibrators provide more intense stimulation than can be provided by oral or manual stimulation and so can be particularly helpful to women who have difficulty reaching orgasm or just want to explore the full depth of their sexual potential and response—they are the easiest way for a woman to have an orgasm or multiple orgasms (see Chapter 18 for a discussion of orgasmic dysfunction).

How common is vibrator use? In one study more than half of women in the United States (53 percent) reported that they had used a vibrator for sexual stimulation; about a fifth (20 percent) had used one in the previous month (Herbenick et al., 2009). Similar numbers of women reported using them during masturbation, intercourse, and sexual play with a partner. About half of men in the United States (45 percent) also report that they have used a vibrator, 10 percent in the previous month (Reece et al., 2009). Interestingly, in these studies the women and men who had used a vibrator engaged in more health-promoting behaviour and had better sexual functioning than those who had never used a vibrator.

Lubricant (lube) can make sex better. It can make sex—vaginal, anal, clitoral stimulation—more comfortable,

Figure 9.13 Vibrators and dildos, used for sexual stimulation.

especially for women who experience genital pain (Sutton et al., 2012). It can also increase stimulation. Lube can be water-based, which can be used with condoms and all sex toys. It can also be silicone-based, which lasts longer. Lubes come from thin to thick, unscented or in a variety of scents, and unflavoured or in a variety of flavours. Some are even organic. Sex stores sell many types of lubricants, but then so do most pharmacies these days.

Body oils are also popular for sexual use. In fact, their use has been encouraged by experts in the field; for example, sex therapists recommend them for the touching or sensate focus exercises that they prescribe for their patients in sex therapy (see Chapter 18). Oils have a sensuous quality that heightens erotic feelings. Furthermore, if you are being stroked or massaged for any extended period of time, the oil helps ensure that the part of your body that is being stimulated will not end up feeling like a piece of wood that has been sandpapered. Sex stores sell oils in a variety of exotic scents, but plain baby oil will also do nicely. Be aware that Vaseline and some other lubricants cause condoms to break.

 Two-Person Sex

When many of us think of techniques of two-person sex,[6] the image that flashes across our mind generally reflects several assumptions. One assumption may be that one of the people is a male and the other a female—that is, that the sex is heterosexual. This reflects a belief that heterosexual sex is normative. We also tend to assume that the man is supposed to do certain things

> **Vibrator:** A handheld device that vibrates and is used for massage or held against the body to provide sexual stimulation.

---

[5] Some of you may have read *The Birth House,* a novel by Ami McKay set in Nova Scotia, which features a physician's use of a vibrator with his female patients.

[6] Of course, some people choose to engage in sexual activities with two or more other persons at the same time. This is called a *threesome, group sex,* or *swinging* depending on who is involved. Swinging is discussed in Chapter 11.

during the act and the woman is supposed to do certain other things, reflecting the sexual scripts of our culture. He, for example, is supposed to take the initiative in deciding what techniques are used, while she is to follow his lead. Although there is nothing particularly evil in these assumptions, they do tend to impose limitations on our own sexual expression and to make people think that their own sexual behaviour is not quite right. Therefore, we will attempt to avoid these assumptions in the sections that follow.

Kissing

Kissing (or what we might call, technically, *mouth-to-mouth stimulation*) is an activity that virtually everyone in our culture has engaged in. In simple kissing, the partners keep their mouths closed and touch each other's lips. In deep kissing (*French kissing*), both people part their lips slightly and insert their tongues into each other's mouths (somehow these clinical descriptions do not make it sound like as much fun as it is). There are endless variations on these two basic approaches, such as nibbling at the partner's lips or tongue or sucking at the lips; they depend only on your imagination and personal preference. There are also plenty of other regions of the body to kiss: the nose, the forehead, the eyelids, the earlobes, the neck, the breasts, the genitals, and even the feet, to give a few examples.

Touching

Enjoying touching and being touched is essential to sexual pleasure. Sensual touching is important to feelings of closeness and desire. In addition, caresses or massages, applied to virtually any area of the body, can be exciting. The regions that are exciting vary a great deal from one person to the next and depend on how the person is feeling at the moment; thus it is important to communicate what sort of touching is most pleasurable to you. (For specific exercises on touching and being touched, see Chapter 18.)

As noted earlier, one of the best ways to find out how to use your hands in stimulating the genitals of another person is to find out how that person masturbates (see Figure 9.12). Alex Comfort (1991), in *The New Joy of Sex,* recommends the following techniques:

> If he isn't circumcised, [you] will probably need to avoid rubbing the glans itself, except in pursuit of very special effects. [Your] best grip is just below the groove, with the skin back as far as it will go, and using two hands—one pressing hard near the root, holding the penis steady, or fondling the scrotum, the other making a thumb-and-first-finger ring, or a whole hand grip. [You] should vary this, and, in prolonged masturbation, change hands often. (p. 85)

One of the things that make hand stimulation most effective is for the man's partner to have a playful delight in, and appreciation of, the man's penis. Most men think their penis is pretty important. If the partner cannot honestly appreciate it and enjoy massaging it, hand stimulation might as well not be done. The hands can be used to stimulate the woman's genitals to produce orgasm, as a preliminary method of arousing the woman before intercourse, or simply because it is pleasurable.

Generally it is best, particularly if the woman is not already aroused, to begin with gentle, light stroking of the inside of the thighs and the inner and outer lips, moving to light stroking of the clitoris. As she becomes more aroused, the stimulation of the clitoris can become firmer. The clitoris is very sensitive and this sensitivity can be either exquisite or painful. Some care has to be used in stimulating it; it cannot be manipulated like a piece of Silly Putty. Generally, the clitoris should not—except, perhaps, for some light stroking—be rubbed while it is dry, for the effect can be abrasive. If the woman is already somewhat aroused, lubrication can be provided by touching the fingers to the vaginal entrance and then spreading the lubrication on the clitoris. If she is not aroused or does not produce much vaginal lubrication, saliva or a water-based lube works well too. Moisture makes the stimulation not only more comfortable but also more sensuous. Some women find direct stimulation of the clitoral glans to be painful in some states of arousal. These women generally prefer stimulation on either side of the clitoris instead.

With these caveats in mind, the clitoris can be stimulated with circular or back-and-forth movements of the finger. The inner and outer lips can also be stroked or rubbed. These techniques, if done with skill and patience, can bring the woman to orgasm. Another technique that can be helpful in producing orgasm is for the partner to place the heel of the hand on the mons, exerting pressure on it while moving the middle finger in and out of the vaginal entrance. If it isn't clear by now, the partner needs to have close-trimmed nails that do not have any jagged edges. This is sensitive tissue we are dealing with.

Many couples engage in sexual activities that do not involve penetration or hand stimulation but nonetheless allow one or both partners to receive genital stimulation (the slang term for two people rubbing their bodies, usually fully clothed, together for sexual stimulation is *dry humping*). For example, a woman may lie on top of her partner and rub her clitoris against her partner's genitals (when two women do this, it is sometimes called *tribadism*). Alternatively, a man may move his penis between the thighs of his partner, a technique that has been referred to as *interfemoral intercourse.*

The Other Senses

So far, this chapter has been focused on tactile (touch) sensations in sexual arousal. However, the other senses—vision, smell, and hearing—can also make contributions.

The things you see can contribute to your arousal. Men seem, in general, to be turned on by a variety of visual stimuli, such as an attractive person, or partially dressed or nude bodies. As we discussed earlier, both men and women respond with physiological, neural, and neurochemical arousal to portrayals of partnered sexual activity. Just as erotica may be used during auto-erotic activity, viewing sexual activity on a video or on the Internet may contribute to partnered sexual activities. Some men, and a few women, have mild fetishes (see Chapter 15 for more detail) and like to see their partner wearing certain types of clothing, such as leather or rubber clothing, or schoolgirl dresses. A good rule here, as elsewhere, is to communicate with your partner to find out what he or she would find arousing.

Perhaps the biggest visual turn-on comes simply from looking at your own and your partner's body. According to the National Health and Social Life Survey, watching a partner undress is one of the most appealing sexual activities (Michael et al., 1994, Table 12).

Odours can be turn-ons or turn-offs. The scent of a body that is clean, having been washed with soap and water, is a natural turn-on. It does not need to be covered up with an "intimate deodorant."[7] In a sense, the scent of your skin, armpits, or genitals is your *aroma signature* and can be quite arousing.

Many people respond with arousal to specific musical stimuli, probably reflecting classical conditioning (see Chapter 2). Research in Ontario assessing genital arousal to audio narratives of sexual or neutral interactions with male and female strangers, friends, or a long-term partner found that men responded to stories involving women. Women responded to stories involving both men and women, and more strongly to stories involving friends or partners (Chivers & Timmers, 2012).

A body that has not been washed or a mouth that has not been cleaned or has recently been used for smoking cigarettes can be a real turn-off. Breath that reeks of garlic may turn a desire for closeness into a desire for distance. Ideally, the communication between partners is honest and trusting enough so that if one offends, the other can request that the appropriate clean-up be done.

Fantasy During Two-Person Sex

Fantasies can be done solo or can heighten the experience of sex with another person. Particularly in a long-term, monogamous relationship, sexual monotony can become a problem; fantasies are one way to introduce some variety and excitement without violating an agreement to be faithful to the other person. It is important to view such fantasies in this way, rather than as a sign of disloyalty to, or dissatisfaction with, one's sexual partner.

Fantasies during two-person sex are generally quite similar to the ones people have while masturbating. In one study, 84 percent of males and 82 percent of females reported that they fantasized at least some of the time during intercourse (Cado & Leitenberg, 1990). This kind of fantasizing is quite common. Some sexual partners enjoy sharing their fantasies with each other. Describing a sexual fantasy to your partner can be a turn-on for both of you. Some couples act out all or part of a fantasy and find it very gratifying. One man says:

> I fantasized about being a fourteen-year-old girl. This is a long-lived fantasy of mine. The girl is pretty, with a petite body, probably five-one, five-two, cute ass, maybe light blond or dark brown pussy hair. Small to medium size breasts. Kind of sweet-looking, virginal.... Anyway, Sue got into it, like we were two girlfriends sleeping over and she was a couple years older and she was going to show me some things. I happen to be very sensitive around my nipples, so she'd say, "Oh, you have nice little nipples, you're going to have very pretty breasts." Then she'd massage my crotch like she was massaging a vagina: "Do you like it when I pet you down there?" And she'd show me what to do to pleasure her, how to masturbate her and go down on her. We played around with that for a few months. (Maurer, 1994, p. 231)

Positions of Penile–Vaginal Intercourse

One of the most common heterosexual techniques involves the insertion of the penis into the vagina; this is called **coitus**[8] or *sexual intercourse*. Ancient love manuals and other sources illustrate many positions of intercourse.

Some authorities state that there are only four positions of intercourse. Personally, we prefer to believe that there are an infinite number. Consider how many different angles your arms, legs, and torso may be in, in relation to those of your partner, and all the various ways in which you can intertwine your limbs—that's a lot of positions. We trust that given sufficient creativity and time, you can discover them all for yourself. We would agree, though, that there are a few basic positions. One basic variation depends on whether the couple face each other (face-to-face position) or whether one partner faces the other's back (rear-entry position); if you try the other obvious variation, a back-to-back position, you will quickly find that you cannot accomplish

Coitus: Sexual intercourse; insertion of the penis into the vagina.

---

[7] With the increased popularity of mouth–genital sex, some women worry that the scent of their genitals might be offensive. The advertisements for feminine hygiene deodorant sprays prey on these fears. These sprays should not be used because they may irritate the vagina. Besides, there is nothing offensive about the scent of a vulva that has been washed; many people, in fact, find it arousing.

[8] From the Latin word *coire*, meaning "to go together."

Figure 9.14   The man-on-top position of intercourse.

much that way. The other basic variation depends on whether one partner is on top of the other or whether the couple are side by side. Let us consider four basic positions that illustrate these variations. As cookbooks often do, we'll give you the basic recipes and let you decide on the embellishments.

The face-to-face, *man-on-top position* (*missionary* position—see Figure 9.14) is probably the one used most frequently by heterosexual couples in Canada. In this position the man and woman stimulate each other until he has an erection, she is producing vaginal lubrication,

and preferably both are highly aroused. Then he moves on top of her as she spreads her legs apart, either he or she spreads the vaginal lips apart, and he inserts his penis into her vagina. He supports himself on his knees and hands or elbows and moves his penis in and out of the vagina (pelvic thrusting). Some men worry that their heavy weight will crush the poor woman under them; however, because the weight is spread out over so great an area, most women do not find this to be a problem at all, and many find the sensation of contact to be pleasurable.

The woman can have her legs in a number of positions that create variations. She may have them straight out horizontally, a position that produces a tight rub on the penis but does not permit it to go deeply into the vagina. She may bend her legs and elevate them to varying degrees, or she may hook them over the man's back or over his shoulders. The last approach permits the penis to move deeply into the vagina. The woman can also move her pelvis, either up and down or side to side, to produce further stimulation.

The man-on-top position has some advantages and some disadvantages. It is the best position for ensuring conception, if that is what you want. The couple may feel better able to express their love or to communicate other feelings, since they are facing each other. This position, however, does not work well if the woman is in the advanced stages of pregnancy or if either she or the man is extremely obese. Sex therapists have also found that it is not a very good position if the man wants to control his ejaculation; the woman-on-top position is better for this.

For the *woman-on-top* position (see Figure 9.15), the woman kneels over the man,

Figure 9.15   The woman-on-top position of intercourse.

Figure 9.16 The rear-entry position of intercourse.

with one knee on either side of his hips. Then his hand or her hand guides the erect penis into the vagina as she lowers herself onto it. She then moves her hips to produce the stimulation. Beyond that, there are numerous variations, depending on where she puts her legs. She can remain on her knees, or she can straighten out her legs behind her, putting them outside his legs or between them. Or she can even turn around and face toward his feet.

This position has a number of advantages. It provides a lot of clitoral stimulation, and the woman can control the kind of stimulation she gets; thus many women find it the best position for them to have an orgasm. It is also a good position for the man who wants to delay his ejaculation, and for this reason it is used in sex therapy.

In the *rear-entry* position, the man faces the woman's back. One way to do this is to have the woman kneel with her head down; the man kneels behind her and inserts his penis into her vagina (see Figure 9.16). (This is sometimes called the *doggie position*, because it

is the manner in which dogs and most other animals copulate.) Another possibility is for the woman to lie on her stomach, raising her hips slightly so that the man can insert his penis while kneeling over her. Rear entry can also be accomplished when the couple are in the side-to-side position. A small amount of air may enter the vagina when this position is used, producing interesting noises when it comes out.

In the *side-to-side* position, the man and woman lie beside each other, either face to face or in a rear-entry position (see Figure 9.17). The side-to-side position is good for leisurely or prolonged intercourse or if one or both of the partners are tired. It is also good for the pregnant and the obese.

Aside from the variations in these basic positions that can be produced by switching the position of the legs, there are many other possibilities. For example, the man-on-top position can be varied by having the woman lie on the edge of a bed with her feet on the floor while the man kneels on the floor. Or the woman

Figure 9.17   The side-to-side position of intercourse.

can lie on the edge of a table while the man stands (don't forget to close the curtains first). Both of these positions produce a somewhat tighter vagina and therefore more stimulation for the penis. Or the man can sit on a chair and insert the penis as the woman sits on his lap, using either a face-to-face or a rear-entry approach. Or with both partners standing, the man can lift the woman onto his erect penis as she wraps her legs around his back, or she can put one leg over his shoulder (you have to be pretty flexible to manage this one, however). For even more advanced positions, see A Sexually Diverse World.

Mouth–Genital Stimulation

One of the most striking features of the sexual revolution of the last few decades is the increased popularity of mouth–genital, or oral–genital, techniques (Hunt & Curtis, 2006). There are two kinds of mouth–genital stimulation (*going down on* a partner): cunnilingus and fellatio.[9]

In **cunnilingus**, or *eating* (from the Latin words *cunnus,* meaning "vulva," and *lingere,* meaning "to lick"), the woman's genitals are stimulated by her male or female partner's mouth. Generally, the focus of stimulation is the clitoris. The tongue stimulates it and the surrounding area with quick darting or thrusting movements, or the mouth can suck at the clitoris. A good prelude to cunnilingus can be kissing of the inner thighs or the belly, gradually moving to the clitoris. The mouth can also suck at the inner lips, or the tongue can stimulate the vaginal entrance or be inserted into the

Cunnilingus (cun-ih-LING-us): Mouth stimulation of the female genitals.

vagina. During cunnilingus, some women also enjoy having a finger inserted into the vagina or the anus for added stimulation. The best way to know what she wants is through communication between partners, either verbal or nonverbal.

Many women are enthusiastic about cunnilingus and say that it is the best way, or perhaps the only way, for them to orgasm. Such responses are well within the normal range of female sexuality. As one woman put it:

> A tongue offers gentleness and precision and wetness and is the perfect organ for contact. And, besides, it produces sensational orgasms. (Hite, 1976, p. 234)

In one large, well-sampled study of Australians, respondents reported the specific sexual practices that were used in their most recent heterosexual encounter (Richters et al., 2006). If women had intercourse only, 50 percent had an orgasm, but when they had cunnilingus plus intercourse, 73 percent had an orgasm. In contrast, among men who engaged only in intercourse, 95 percent had an orgasm. It just isn't fair.

Cunnilingus (like fellatio, discussed next) can transmit some sexually transmitted infections, such as gonorrhea. Oral sex can also result in the transmission of HPV and HSV from the genitals of an infected person to the mouth of the partner or vice versa. Some cases of oral cancers involve the HPV-16 strain, which may have been transmitted by oral sex (Herrero et al., 2003). Therefore, you need to be as careful about with whom you engage in mouth–genital sex as about with whom you would engage in intercourse. A small sheet of plastic, called a dental dam, can be placed over the vulva for those wanting to practise safer sex. Unlubricated condoms can also be cut open and used in place of a dental dam.

---

[9] Early marriage manuals in North America called cunnilingus and fellatio the *genital kiss*—definitely a more romantic term (Hunt & Curtis, 2006).

Figure 9.18 Simultaneous heterosexual mouth–genital stimulation in the sixty-nine position.

One other possible problem should be noted as well. Some women enjoy having their partner blow air forcefully into the vagina. While this technique is not dangerous under normal circumstances, when used on a pregnant woman it has been known to cause death (apparently as the result of air getting into the uterine veins), damage to the placenta, and embolism. Thus it should not be used on a pregnant woman.

In **fellatio**[10] (*sucking, a blow job*) the man's penis is stimulated by his partner's mouth. The partner licks the glans of the penis, its shaft, and perhaps the testicles. The penis is gently taken into the mouth. If it is not fully erect, an erection can generally be produced by stronger sucking combined with hand stimulation along the penis. After that, the partner can produce an in-and-out motion by moving the lips down toward the base of the penis and then back up, always being careful not to scrape the penis with the teeth. Or the tongue can be flicked back and forth around the tip of the penis or along the corona.

To bring the man to orgasm, the in-and-out motion is continued, moving the penis deeper and deeper into the mouth and perhaps also using the fingers to encircle the base of the penis and give further stimulation. Sometimes when the penis moves deeply toward the throat, it stimulates a gag reflex, which occurs anytime something comes into contact with that part of the throat. To avoid this, the partner should concentrate on relaxing the throat muscles while firming the lips to provide more stimulation to the penis.

When a couple are engaged in fellatio, the big question in their minds may concern ejaculation. The man may, of course, simply withdraw his penis from his partner's mouth and ejaculate outside it. Or he may ejaculate into it, and his partner may enjoy swallowing the ejaculate. The ejaculate resembles partially cooked egg white in texture; it does not have a very distinctive flavour but often leaves a salty aftertaste. Because some people have mixed feelings about having the semen in their mouths, it is probably a good idea for the couple to discuss ahead of time (or during the activity) what they plan to do, particularly because ejaculation into the mouth is an unsafe practice in the AIDS era (see Chapter 8).

Most men find fellatio to be a highly stimulating experience, which no doubt accounts for the high frequency with which prostitutes are asked to do it. Enjoyment of fellatio is certainly within the common range of male sexuality.

Both partners can perform mouth–genital stimulation simultaneously. This is often called **sixty-nining** because the numerals 69 suggest the position of the two bodies during simultaneous mouth–genital sex. Sixty-nining may be done either side to side or with one person on top of the other, each with the mouth on the other's genitals (Figure 9.18).

Simultaneous mouth–genital sex allows both people to enjoy the pleasure of that stimulation at the same time. It can give a feeling of total body involvement and total involvement between partners. Some couples, however, feel that this technique requires doing too many things at once and is more

---

[10] *Fellatio* is from the Latin word *fellare*, meaning "to suck." Partners should not take the sucking part too literally. The penis, particularly at the tip, is a delicate organ and should not be treated like a straw in an extra-thick milkshake.

Fellatio (fen-LAY-shoh): Mouth stimulation of the male genitals.
Sixty-nining: Simultaneous mouth–genital stimulation; also called *soixante-neuf.*

A Sexually Diverse World

What Is Tantric Sex?

Many people have heard of tantric sex, particularly after Sting boasted that he and his wife, Trudie Styler, were advocates of tantric sex and could make love for up to eight hours at a time. (By the way, he later clarified that this was a major exaggeration.) What exactly is tantric sex? The word *tantric* is thought to come from the Sanskrit *tantra*, which means "writing or a written text." Tantric texts, also known as tantric threads or fundamentals, are ancient texts that offer sexual instructions (Figure 9.19). They come down to us from a number of ancient spiritual traditions including the *Kama Sutra* and the *Ananga Rang* from South Asia, *The Perfumed Garden* from the Middle East, *The Tao of Sex* from the Far East, and other "pillow books."

If tantric texts are simply old sex manuals, why does tantric sex seem to enjoy a kind of sexual mystique or reverence? Tantric texts have typically emerged from a spiritual approach to sex rather than biological, physiological, or empirical traditions. More than simple sexual how-to manuals, tantric texts often claim that adherents can not only have great sex but also, in so doing, can attain a greater spiritual awareness of themselves, their partner, and even the universe as a whole. Sexual "energy" is a recurrent theme in tantric writings. According to these texts, sexual energy can be stored and moved from one part of the body to another through energy channels or lines (sometimes referred as *chakras*), as well as to and from sexual partners. In some tantric traditions transfer between partners is seen as particularly important, because men and women are believed to possess complementary forms of energy. Adherents believe that people can learn the skills needed to gain control

over and manipulate this sexual energy and then use it to intensify orgasm. Summoning and discharging sexual energy through orgasm is then used to attain a higher state of consciousness and becomes a tool to allow contact with universal energies or spirits. It is claimed that long-time practitioners of tantric sex can induce orgasmic responses simply through meditation, eliminating the need for a partner and his or her energies. Unfortunately, there is little scientific evidence to support any of these claims.

Ancient tantric writings assume that sex would occur between a man and a woman; they view the combining of male and female energies as necessary to reach greater enlightenment. More contemporary tantric writers dismiss this idea and claim, for example, that men or women engaging in the sixty-nine position with a same-sex partner can achieve this same type of enlightenment.

Tantric teachings advocate delaying ejaculation and orgasm: a prolonged period of sex without ejaculation or orgasm is believed to allow sexual energy to be built up, manipulated, and transferred to a partner. They suggest specific techniques, often considered mystical or secret, for both men and women to use to delay orgasm and increase their chances of having multiple orgasms. These include focusing on breathing patterns and learning how to coordinate breath, thrusting movements, and other sexual acts; attending to the emotional and sexual needs of the partner to facilitate buildup and transfer of sexual energy; and using all manner of sexual techniques and intercourse positions so that sexual activity remains exciting and playful.

Intercourse positions are frequently given metaphorical or mystical names. Sexual intercourse standing up

complicated than enjoyable. For example, a woman may be distracted from enjoying the marvellous clitoral stimulation she is receiving because she has to concentrate at the same time on using her mouth to stimulate her partner's genitals. If sixty-nine is done with one partner on top, the bottom partner may feel that

he or she has no control over the movement and may be choked.

Anal Intercourse

In **anal intercourse** the man inserts his penis into his female or male partner's rectum. In legal circles, anal intercourse used to be called *sodomy* (although this term

Anal intercourse: Insertion of the penis into the partner's rectum.

is called Congress of the Monkey. The Large Bee posi-tion is a woman-on-top intercourse position where she leans back and, while supporting herself with her hands, twists her hips while the man is inside her. The Tail of the Ostrich intercourse position is achieved when she is on her back and he kneels between her legs. She then puts her legs over his shoulders and he lifts her up until only her head touches the ground. In the process, he enters her. The Wife of Indra, con-sidered to be one of the most advanced positions, is achieved when, while in a sitting position, the woman puts her ankles behind her head. The man then enters her and pinches her nose, forcing her to breathe deeply from her diaphragm.

There are intriguing parallels between the advice given by sex therapists and some of the teachings in ancient tantric texts. For example, sex therapists often encourage people interested in experiencing more powerful orgasms to allow natural muscular tension or myotonia and vasocongestion to build up during sex play before orgasming. Higher levels of myotonia and vasocongestion before orgasm often feel more pleasur-able and satisfying when released. Some of the tantric techniques are quite similar to the behavioural exercises used in contemporary sex therapy (see Chapter 18). For example, Eastern approaches emphasize mindfulness or the ability to focus on sexual stimuli and stay in the present in a nonjudgmental manner (Brotto et al., 2009). Sensate focus exercises used by sex therapists also have this goal. Sex therapists emphasize the importance for sexual satisfaction of relationship satisfaction, sexual communication, adopting a mutually enjoyable sexual script that is not routine and predictable, and not focus-ing on orgasm. Nonetheless, if stripped of its mysticism, colourful language, and secrecy, tantric sexual practices may augment what one would learn from a sex thera-pist (Brotto et al., 2009).

Figure 9.19   Erotic sculptures at the Temple of Kan-dariya Mahadevo, India, built in 1000 CE.

Sources: Written by Guy Grenier, PhD, based on Craze (2003), Lacroix (2003), Tannahill (1980).

may also refer to other sexual practices such as inter-course with animals), and it is sometimes referred to as having sex *Greek style.*

Anal intercourse may be somewhat difficult because the rectum has no natural lubrication and because it is surrounded by fairly tight muscles. The man should therefore begin by moistening the partner's anus, either with saliva or with a sterile surgical lubricant such as K-Y Jelly (*not* Vaseline). He should also lubricate his penis. He then inserts it gently into the rectum and begins controlled pelvic thrusting. It is typically done in the rear-entry position or in the man-on-top position. The more the partner can relax and be in control, the more pleasurable it is; if it is done properly, it need involve no pain. Although some couples are not interested in anal sex, others delight in it. Some women report orgasm during anal intercourse, particularly when it is accompanied by hand stimulation of the clitoris. Men also report orgasms from anal intercourse, primarily because of stimulation of the prostate.

There are some health risks associated with anal intercourse. It can lead to infections with various organisms. Of greatest concern, HIV can be transmitted through anal intercourse. Thus, safer sex consists of either refraining from engaging in anal intercourse, or using a condom if one does (or doing it only in a mutually monogamous relationship with an uninfected partner). Furthermore, for heterosexuals the penis should never be inserted into the vagina after anal intercourse unless the penis has been washed thoroughly. The reason for this is that the rectum contains bacteria that do not belong in the vagina and that can cause a dandy case of vaginitis if they happen to get there. Also, sex toys or other objects inserted in the anus should be thoroughly washed following removal.

Another variation is **anilingus** (*rimming, rim job,* or *tossing the salad* in slang), in which the tongue and mouth stimulate the anus. The anus may also be stimulated by the hand, and some people report that having a finger inserted into the rectum near the time of orgasm provides a heightened sexual sensation. Anilingus carries with it the risk of HIV, hepatitis, or *E. coli* infections.

Sexual Scripts

The sexual scripts of heterosexual, gay, and lesbian couples are quite similar, and same-sex partners and mixed-sex partners mostly engage in the same behaviours (Holmberg & Blair, 2009). That is, for most couples—straight and gay—hugging, kissing, caressing, and snuggling are very important. These behaviours are often precursors to oral–genital sex (fellatio or cunnilingus), mutual masturbation, and (less frequently) anal intercourse. For most mixed-sex couples, lovemaking involves and often culminates in vaginal–penile intercourse. Among gay men, there appears to be a strong enjoyment or strong dislike of anal play, with significant numbers of men in each camp (Lever, 1994). Relative to anal sex, more gay men prefer giving and receiving oral sex (fellatio), masturbation, licking and sucking testicles, and sucking nipples. Female couples commonly engage in rubbing each other's genitals, and oral stimulation (cunnilingus). Further, many lesbians (and other couples) report using a hand-held or strap-on dildo—43 percent of lesbians have used a hand-held dildo and 27 percent have used a strap-on dildo, according to one survey (Lever, 1995).

Anilingus (ay-nih-LING-us): Mouth stimulation of the partner's anus.

Masters and Johnson (1979), in their laboratory studies, made direct observations of the lovemaking techniques of lesbians (Figure 9.20) and gay men (Figure 9.21) and compared them with those of heterosexuals. They found no differences in masturbation techniques. However, in couple interactions there were some substantial differences. The major one was that gay men and lesbians took their time—that is, they seemed not to have any goal orientation. Heterosexual couples, on the other hand, seemed to be performance-oriented—they seemed to strive toward a goal of orgasm for each partner. In the initial approach to stimulating the woman, heterosexuals and lesbians began with holding and kissing, but this lasted only about 30 seconds for the heterosexuals, who quickly moved on to genital stimulation. Lesbians, on the other hand, spent more time in holding and kissing and then went on to a long period of breast stimulation, which sometimes resulted in orgasm in the absence of genital stimulation. Lesbians also appeared to communicate more with each other. In the initial approach to stimulating the man, gay men did extensive stimulation of the nipples, generally producing erection; such a technique was rare among heterosexuals (with only 3 of 100 couples). Gay men were also much more likely to stimulate the frenulum (the area of the penis on the lower side, just below the corona). They also used a *teasing technique* in which the man brings his partner near orgasm, then relaxes the stimulation, then increases the stimulation again, and so on, essentially prolonging the pleasure. Among heterosexuals, the man's most frequent complaint was that his partner did not grasp the shaft of the penis tightly enough. Masters and Johnson argued that heterosexuals can learn from gay men and lesbians; the technique of gay men and lesbians benefits from stimulating another body like their own.

Two-Person Cybersex

The Internet provides not only visual sexual images for people wanting to masturbate but also creates the opportunity for two-person cybersex. People report forming relationships on the Internet that they consider to be sexually intimate, even though they have never actually met the person face to face (Ross, 2005). Researchers in New Brunswick found that 25 percent of male students and 13 percent of female students reported engaging in online sexual activities with a partner in the previous month, although most did so infrequently (Shaughnessy et al., 2011). People engage in cybersex both with strangers and with people they know. Cybersex has also created a new sexual space that is somewhere between fantasy and action. Essentially, one can type sexual acts without actually doing them (Ross, 2005). In Chapter 11, we discuss data from a survey of persons who used the Internet to meet partners, and the

Figure 9.20 Female-to-female sexual expression.

activities that they engaged in. It is also possible to have cybersex using webcams, social networking sites, and avatars in virtual worlds. Indeed, the increasing integration of online communication into everyday life suggests that cybersex is likely to become more frequent and more common. These Internet activities challenge us to think more clearly about our definitions of sexual activity. For example, a woman accuses her partner of having a cybersex affair with another woman and he replies that he was only typing. Who is right?

L07 Aphrodisiacs
Is There a Good Aphrodisiac?

An **aphrodisiac** is a substance—such as a food, a drug, or a perfume—that excites sexual desire. Throughout history people have searched for the surefire aphrodisiac. Before arousing your hopes, we should note that the search has been unsuccessful; there is no known substance that works well as an aphrodisiac.

> **Aphrodisiac (ah-froh-DIZ-ih-ak):** A substance that increases sexual desire.

Figure 9.21 Male-to-male sexual expression.

A number of foods are thought to be aphrodisiacs, perhaps because they resemble the sex organs. These include oysters (which resemble the testes), elk antler velvet, seal penis, powdered rhinoceros horn, bananas, and asparagus (which resemble the penis). In addition, the current interest in nutrition and natural and organic foods and supplements has created a market for natural aphrodisiacs. According to one industry source, the popular herbs purchased for this purpose include yohimbe, cayenne, arginine, avena sativa, and damiana. Some companies sell herbal combinations, edible syrups, and brews that are claimed to increase sexual desire, sexual performance, sexual stamina, or all three. Again, there is no evidence that any of these foods or products affect sexual desire. However, with all these substances, the belief that they will be arousing may enhance sexual functioning. Perhaps this is why people continue to believe that they are aphrodisiacs.

What about various drugs? The effects of alcohol on sexual functioning will be discussed in Chapter 18. Briefly, drinking small quantities of alcohol may, for some people, decrease psychological inhibitions and therefore increase sexual desire. Moderate to large quantities, however, rapidly lead to an inability to function sexually.

Users of marijuana report that it acts as a sexual stimulant (McKay, 2005a). Probably this is due, in part, to the fact that marijuana produces the sensation that time is being stretched out, thus prolonging and intensifying sensations, including sexual sensations. There is no scientific documentation of the aphrodisiac effects of marijuana except for the reports of users. Possible negative effects of marijuana on sexual functioning are discussed in Chapter 18.

Unfortunately, some of the substances that are thought to enhance sexual functioning are quite dangerous. For example, cantharides (Spanish fly) has a reputation as an aphrodisiac, but it is poisonous and an irritant.

Amyl nitrite (*poppers*) is popular among some people. Because it relaxes the sphincter muscle of the anus, it is used by those engaging in anal intercourse (Taberner, 1985). Users report that it produces heightened sensations during orgasms (Everett, 1975). Probably it acts by dilating the blood vessels in the genitals. It may, however, have side effects, including dizziness, headaches, fainting, and, in rare cases, death; thus it can be dangerous (Taberner, 1985).

Butyl nitrite—sold under such trade names as Rush, Locker Room, and Climax—is a chemical relative of amyl nitrite. It is used to heighten sexual pleasure. Although no deaths have been reported from inhaling it, there are reported deaths from swallowing it (UPI, 1981).

In contrast to these street drugs, several prescription drugs have been approved by Health Canada for use in treating male sexual dysfunction. Viagra, Cialis, and Levitra are designed to increase the flow of blood to the penis and maintain the resulting erection. Note that none of these drugs increases desire. (For more information, see Chapter 18.) It is dangerous to combine these drugs with amyl nitrite. There is no evidence that these prescription drugs increase sexual desire or performance in women.

Anaphrodisiacs

Just as people have searched for aphrodisiacs, so they have sought **anaphrodisiacs**—substances or practices that would diminish sexual desire. Cold showers are reputed to have such effects as does potassium nitrate (saltpeter). The latter contains nothing that decreases sexual drive, but it does act as a diuretic; it makes the person want to urinate frequently, which may be distracting enough so that he or she is not much interested in sex.

There has been some medical interest in finding drugs that would decrease sex drive for use in treating aggressive sexual offenders. One such drug is cyproterone acetate, which is an anti-androgen (for more information, see Chapter 16).

Other drugs that may lead to a loss of sexual functioning are discussed in Chapter 18.

(L08) Approaches to Lovemaking

As the old joke goes, sex is like pizza: When it's good, it's very, very good and when it bad, it's still pretty good. Jokes aside, what differentiates *good sex* from *great sex*?

Sex as Work

Western culture has traditionally held the belief that intercourse is the important part of sex. The view that orgasm is the goal toward which both partners must strive is pervasive. This belief system is reflected in the term *foreplay,* which implies that activities like hand stimulation of the genitals, kissing, and mouth–genital sex are only preliminaries that take place before intercourse, the last being "real sex." In reality all these activities and more can result in sexual pleasure (Rye & Meaney, 2007a). In short, our achievement drives now seem to be channelled into our sexual behaviours, and sex has become work—something at which we must work hard and become successful (Perel, 2006). As a result, our discussions of sex tend to focus on the physical aspects while ignoring our feelings about sex. Orgasm is the observable product, and we are concerned with how many orgasms we can produce or have, much as a plant manager is concerned with how many cans of soup are produced on the assembly line each day. Similar beliefs are reflected in the commonly used phrase *achieving orgasm,* as if orgasm were something to be achieved like a promotion on the job.[11] Viagra has only made this situation worse because it encourages people to reduce sexuality to an erection.

Anaphrodisiacs (an-ah-froh-DIZ-ih-ak): Substances that decrease sexual desire.

---

[11] To avoid this whole notion, we never use the phrase "to achieve orgasm" in this book. Instead, we prefer "to have an orgasm" or simply "to orgasm." Why not turn it into a verb so that we will not feel we have to work at achieving it?

The emphasis on simultaneous orgasm expresses how clock-oriented we are. It is important to have things running on schedule and happening at exactly the right time, and so orgasms must be timed perfectly.

As sex therapist Esther Perel (2006) puts it,

> We are indeed a nation that prides itself on efficiency. But here's the catch: eroticism is inefficient. It loves to squander time and resources. . . . We glorify efficiency and fail to recognize that the erotic space is a radiant interlude in which we luxuriate, indifferent to demands of productivity; pleasure is the only goal. (p. 75)

The best approach is to enjoy all the various aspects of lovemaking for themselves, rather than as techniques for achieving something. We need to experience sex as a feast of the senses, rather than as an achievement competition. We need to broaden our view of sexual expression to recognize that a broad continuum of activities may provide sexual pleasure—a dream, a thought, a conversation, cuddling, kissing, sensual message, dancing, oral–genital stimulation, and intercourse (Chalker, 1995; Rye & Meaney, 2007a).

Couples who delight in the process of lovemaking also spend more time pleasing each other. In one New Brunswick study, 21 percent of men and 24 percent of women in long-term relationships complained that they and their partner spent too little time in foreplay before intercourse (MacNeil & Byers, 1997). How much longer do men and women want lovemaking to last? A study of 152 Canadian heterosexual couples in long-term relationships asked the men and women how long foreplay[12] and intercourse typically last in their relationship and how long they would ideally like each to last (Miller & Byers, 2004). The researchers found that on average the women wanted foreplay to last about eight minutes longer and the men wanted it to last about five minutes longer than it typically did. They also wanted intercourse to last longer—on average women wanted about 7 more minutes and men wanted about 11 more minutes of intercourse. In short, we need to think of sex as play, not as work.

---

[12] We used the term *foreplay* in this study because it is easily understood by participants and has been used in other research. We don't use this term in this book, because it implies a rigid sexual script in which intercourse is the main event and other activities are merely warm-ups.

 Exceptional Sex

What are the ingredients for absolutely great sex? Sex researchers in Ontario interviewed a diverse sample of adults and asked them about the difference between very good sex and great sex, as well as about the characteristics of the best sexual experiences they had ever had (Kleinplatz, 2010; Kleinplatz, Ménard, Paquet, et al., 2009). The components of great sex that emerged from these interviews were (for information on great sex in older adults, see Milestones in Sex Research in Chapter 11):

1. Being fully present and focused: attention was focused intensely on the sexual interaction.
2. Sense of connection, merger, being in synch: the person felt a deep connection with the partner, even a sense of merging together for a time.
3. Deep intimacy: this refers to the kind of emotional and erotic intimacy with the partner that is discussed in Chapter 12.
4. Extraordinary communication: this quality goes far beyond the techniques of good communication discussed in Chapter 12 and involves a total sharing between partners, as well as a nonverbal component of touching with exceptional sensitivity to the other.
5. Authenticity, being genuine, uninhibited: the person felt totally uninhibited and unselfconscious.
6. Exploration, interpersonal risk-taking, fun: with a sense of humour and fun—not a dogged determination to perform well—the sexual interaction seemed like an adventure.
7. Letting go and being vulnerable: this refers to surrendering control and letting oneself be swept away by and vulnerable to the other person.
8. Moments of transcendence and awe: during these experiences the person often experiences an altered mental state similar to the one achieved during meditation that were often growth-enhancing.

Interestingly, none of these participants felt that they had a natural talent for being a great lover. Rather, they learned the components of optimal sex over time. We could all learn something from these ideas.

SUMMARY

William Masters and Virginia Johnson conducted an important program of research on the physiology of human sexual response. They found that two basic physiological processes occur during arousal and orgasm: vasocongestion and myotonia. The sexual response cycle occurs in three stages: excitement, orgasm, and resolution. Their research indicates that

there is no physiological distinction between clitoral and vaginal orgasms in women, which refutes an early idea of Freud's. They also provided convincing evidence of the existence of multiple orgasm in women.

Criticisms of Masters and Johnson's model are that (1) they ignored cognitive and affective factors, and

(2) their selection of research participants may have led to a self-fulfilling prophecy in their results.

According to Kaplan's cognitive-physiological model, three components are involved in sexual responses: desire, vasocongestion, and muscle contraction. According to the intimacy model, some people rarely experience spontaneous desire and desire for intimacy motivates them to engage in sexual activity. The dual control model holds that two basic processes—excitation and inhibition—are involved in sexual response, and that our responses to sexual stimuli are shaped by culture and early learning. Emotion is another important psychological aspect of sexual response.

The nervous system and sex hormones are important in sexual response. The nervous system functions in sexual response by a combination of spinal reflexes (best documented for erection and ejaculation) and brain influences (particularly of the limbic system). Hormones are important to sexual behaviour, both in their influences on prenatal development (organizing effects) and in their stimulating influence on adult sexual behaviour (activating effects). Testosterone is crucial for maintaining sexual desire in both men and women. Neurochemical changes during sexual response parallel arousal and inhibition.

Pheromones are biochemicals secreted outside the body that play an important role in sexual communication and attraction. Much of the evidence is based on research with animals, but evidence in humans is accumulating rapidly.

Sexual pleasure is produced by stimulation of various areas of the body called erogenous zones. Sexual self-stimulation, or autoeroticism, includes masturbation and sexual fantasies. Many people have sexual fantasies while masturbating or having sex with a partner. An important technique in two-person sex is hand stimulation of the partner's genitals. Touching other areas of the body and kissing are also important. The other senses—sight, smell, and hearing—can also be used in creating sexual arousal. Although there are infinite varieties in the positions in which one can have penile-vaginal intercourse, there are four basic positions: man on top (the missionary position), woman on top, rear entry, and side to side.

There are two kinds of mouth–genital stimulation: cunnilingus (mouth stimulation of the female genitals) and fellatio (mouth stimulation of the male genitals).

Anal intercourse involves inserting the penis into the rectum.

An aphrodisiac is a substance that arouses sexual desire. There is no known reliable aphrodisiac, and some of the substances that are popularly thought to act as aphrodisiacs can be dangerous.

We have a tendency in our culture to view sex as work and to turn sex into an achievement situation, as witnessed by expressions such as *achieving orgasm*. Such attitudes make sex less pleasurable and may set the stage for sexual failures or sexual disorders. These are quite different from the characteristics individuals identify as part of great sex, which including being fully present in the moment, having a deep sense of connection and feeling of intimacy with your partner, being totally uninhibited and unselfconscious, and extraordinary communication.

QUESTIONS FOR THOUGHT, DISCUSSION, AND DEBATE

1. Your little sister, Katie, is a second-year university student and is in the fourth month of what looks like will be a wonderful long-term relationship. Katie and her boyfriend now seem to have a full sexual relationship. As a benevolent older brother or sister, you want Katie to enjoy much sexual pleasure in this relationship. What information from this chapter would you tell Katie about, if you hoped to ensure her sexual satisfaction and sexual pleasure?

2. What do you think about sexual fantasizing? Is it harmful, or is it a good way to enrich one's sexual expression? Are your ideas consistent with the results of the research discussed in this chapter?

3. You have been in an intimate relationship for two years. You find you are getting bored with your sexual activity. List five things that could make your sexual relationship more satisfying. How would you communicate your desire to do each of these to your partner?

Are **YOU** Curious?

1. What is the sexualization of children and why is it a problem?
2. Do media portrayals of sex really affect my sexual attitudes and behaviours?
3. How many Canadian teens have engaged in sexual intercourse by Grade 11?
4. What should I consider before sexting?

Read this chapter to find out.

CHAPTER

10

Sexuality and the Life Cycle: Childhood and Adolescence

LEARNING OBJECTIVES

After studying this chapter, you will be able to

LO1 List examples of some problems associated with accurate sexuality data collection in infancy, childhood, and adolescence, and the sources of the information we have.

LO2 Describe sexual development in infancy and the preschool years.

LO3 Identify the types of sexual development in childhood.

LO4 Explain the process of the sexualization of children.

LO5 Describe sexual development in adolescence.

LO6 Illustrate the types of sexual development in late adolescence.

LO7 Describe how sexuality aids in development.

My son Jeremy . . . naively decided to wear barrettes to nursery school. Several times that day, another boy insisted that Jeremy must be a girl because "only girls wear barrettes." After repeatedly asserting that "wearing barrettes doesn't matter; being a boy means having a penis and testicles," Jeremy finally pulled down his pants as a way of making his point more convincingly. The boy was not impressed. He simply said, "Everybody has a penis; only girls wear barrettes."*

* Sandra L. Bem, 1989, Genital knowledge and gender consistency in preschool children. *Child Development*, 60, 649–662. Blackwell Publishing Ltd.

Stop for a moment and think of the first sexual experience you ever had (you will find examples of some youths' first sexual experience in First Person). Some of you will think of the first time you had sexual intercourse. New Brunswick researchers have shown that we tend to use the terms *having sex* and *sexual intercourse* synonymously (Byers et al., 2009; Randall & Byers, 2003). For example, Randall and Byers (2003) found that fewer than 15 percent of students thought that genital fondling and fewer than 25 percent thought that oral sex was having sex. Further, research in Alberta has shown that students are more likely to label a behaviour as having sex if it occurs in a mixed-sex relationship than in a same-sex relationship (Trotter & Alderson, 2007). Nonetheless, sex is more than just having heterosexual sexual intercourse. Others of you will think of earlier episodes, like playing doctor with the other kids in the neighbourhood, or your first passionate kiss, or orgasms with a partner through manual or oral stimulation. Unfortunately, some of you will think of abusive sexual experiences in childhood or adolescence. Child sexual abuse and sexual coercion and assault are discussed in Chapter 16.

Now think of the kind of sex life you had, or expect to have, in your early 20s. Finally, imagine yourself at 65 and the kinds of sexual behaviour you will be engaging in then.

Scientists think of human development, including sexual development, as a process that occurs throughout the lifespan. This process is influenced by biological, psychological, social, and cultural factors. This chapter and Chapter 11 are based on the contemporary approach to **lifespan development**, the study of sexuality throughout the course of our lives. The things you were asked to remember and imagine about your own sexual functioning in the paragraph above will give you an idea of the sweep of this approach to development. In Chapter 19 you will find a discussion of sex education across the lifespan as well as tips for parents who want to do a better job of talking to their children about sex.

Lifespan development: Development from birth through old age.

L01
Data Sources

What kinds of scientific data are available on the sexual behaviour of people during childhood and adolescence? Most of the data come from surveys in which adults are questioned about their pasts. Their responses form some of the data to be discussed in this chapter. As noted in Chapter 3, these are self-report data and thus may be subject to reporting biases, such as exaggeration and purposeful concealment. These responses may be even more problematic than some of the other kinds of data from self-report studies, though. For example, a 50- or 60-year-old man is asked to report on his sexual behaviour at age ten. How accurately will he remember things that happened 40 or 50 years ago? Surely there will be some forgetting. Thus, the data on childhood sexual behaviour may be subject to errors that result from faulty memory.

An alternative would be to interview children about their sexual behaviour or perhaps even to observe their sexual behaviour. Few researchers have done either, for obvious reasons. Such a study would arouse opposition from many parents, religious leaders, and politicians, who might argue that it is unnecessary or that it would harm the children who were studied. These reactions reflect in part the widespread beliefs that children are not yet sexual beings and should not be exposed to questions about sex. Such research also raises ethical issues: At what age can a child give truly informed consent to participate in such a study?

In a few studies children have been questioned directly about their sexual behaviour. Kinsey interviewed 432 children, ages 4 to 14, and the results of the study were published after his death by Elias and Gebhard (1969). An innovation is the use of a "talking" computer to interview children (Romer et al., 1997). The computer is programmed to present the questions through headphones, and the child enters his or her answers by using the keyboard. This process preserves confidentiality, even when others are present, because only the child knows the question. In one study, this

What Was Your First Sexual Experience?

T hink about your first sexual experience. What was it like? Where and how did it happen? How old were you? Was it planned? Are you thinking of your first kiss? The first time you had sexual intercourse? The first time you engaged in oral sex? Was it with a boyfriend or girlfriend or someone you just met? Did the two of you talk about it beforehand or did it "just happen"?

We asked youth to tell us about their first sexual experience. As you will see, no two first sexual experiences are alike.

Kirsten from Saskatchewan

My first real sexual experience happened when I was 15. It was the long weekend in May, and a bunch of us from my high school were out drinking at a friend's cabin. There was this guy who was in the same grade as me, and he and I found ourselves walking on a gravel road alone. We sat down to "talk." We chatted awkwardly for a while, and it took him forever to slyly nudge closer to me, and finally we worked up the courage, aided in no small part by all the booze. We fooled around for a while until some friends of his came along and we jumped up (and zipped up) like frightened animals. I quickly scurried off to find the rest of the girls and tell them what had just happened. He and I couldn't look each other in the eye for months.

Trishia from Nova Scotia

My first sexual experience was with my best friend in Grade 6; we were both 12 and 13 years old at the time. She had come for a sleepover and we were sharing my double bed. I do not recall much being said at the time, or how we both started kissing one another. It just happened, nothing ever discussed. As I recall we took turns kissing each other in various areas and moving around on top of one another. We never spoke of what happened that night.

Simon from Alberta

As a 16-year-old, the only thing I wanted to do was to have sex, because I heard it was a great experience. I also heard that it hurt a lot at the first time but you get used to it, and that I had to be very careful. I was also told that it would make me a man. On February 7th, I found my first boyfriend. He was some years older than me, but I didn't care at the time. We dated for one week, and I was so excited that I finally found a boyfriend, and I was so glad that I could finally have sex. So the moment finally happened and it did hurt for the first time. But I felt that I was finally a man.

Emily from New Brunswick

The first time I had sex was a very positive experience. I was 16 and had been with my boyfriend at the time for eight months and it was a great relationship. We were in love. We had discussed the desire to have sex for a few months and were well prepared. I went on birth control three months before we had intercourse. We wanted to make sure we were being safe. The opportunity arose one afternoon in July at my cottage; we brought blankets down to the beach and made love. It was comfortable and I felt like we were ready to go there in our relationship. I have very positive memories about the entire situation. We were together for the following two years.

Jeff from Alberta

I was 16 years old when I had my first sexual experience. I am gay and had not come out to many people at that point. I was attending a cross-Canada high school music festival away from home. I had my eye on one guy in particular but was too shy to do anything except exchange friendly pleasantries with him. On the very last night of the festival, however, everything changed. We had been drinking, and I found the courage to come out to a small group of friends. The guy that I liked overheard our conversation, and he cornered me later in the hallway, telling me he was gay too. I was a little scared. I had never discussed my sexuality with another gay man before. It was freeing, too, to be able to talk so openly. We slept together that night, and how it felt is hard to describe. It felt really good and right to be intimate with another man, but I still felt guilty and nervous at the same time. I was still very young. I threw up afterwards because I was so nervous. It was not the most romantic ending.

Paige from New Brunswick

I had hooked up with some guys but I had never had sex. Then I started dating Paul. The first time we had sex, we hadn't seen each other in like 2 weeks because of exams. We were hanging out at one of our mutual friends' birthday parties. We came back to my house from that. He had slept over before. He would sleep in the basement and I'd go upstairs. This time, I didn't go upstairs and it just kind of sort of happened. I'd been thinking about it for a little bit before then because we'd been together for a little bit and that was our month anniversary. There wasn't a lot of pre-planning involved.

procedure was used to gather data from samples of high-risk youth ages 9 to 15 (Romer et al., 1997). More children reported sexual experience to the computer than in face-to-face interviews.

Many studies of adolescent sexual behaviour and attitudes have also been done. The Canadian Youth, Sexual Health, and HIV/AIDS Study (CYSHHAS; Boyce et al., 2003, 2006) and its predecessor, the Canada Youth and AIDS Study (King et al., 1988), are important national surveys. A series of surveys by sociologist Reginald Bibby (Bibby, 2001; Bibby et al., 2009) also provide some information about adolescent sexuality in Canada. We can have particular confidence in recent, well-sampled studies of adolescent sexuality.

The studies of child and adolescent sexual behaviour have mostly involved surveys that have used either questionnaires or interviews. Virtually no researchers have made systematic, direct observations of children's sexual behaviour (we know of only one) although some have asked parents to report on their children's sexual behaviour (de Graaf & Rademakers, 2011). Once children have learned that sexual behaviour has to be kept private or hidden, though, parents may not be able to report their children's behaviour very accurately.

Similar to conclusions drawn from cross-cultural research (see Chapter 1), the sexual attitudes and behaviour of children and adolescents in Canada are affected by culture. That is, children and youth from Canada's ethnocultural minority groups (for example, from Asia, South America, or Muslim cultures) are influenced by the sexual attitudes, expectations, and parenting practices of their family and community. However, they are also influenced by the dominant Canadian culture and by the behaviour of their peers from the majority culture. This can and does cause conflict between parents and children. However, there has been little research on the sexual development of children and adolescents in Canada from these ethnocultural communities. Thus, some of the data reported here, particularly for older children and adolescents, may not conform closely to the attitudes and experiences of children and youth from some ethnocultural communities in Canada.

LO2

Infancy and the Preschool Years (Birth to 4 Years)

Before 1890, it was thought that sexuality was something that magically appeared at puberty. Sigmund Freud first expressed the notion that children—in fact, infants—have sexual urges and engage in sexual behaviour.

The capacity of the human body to show a sexual response is present from birth. Male infants, for example, get erections. Indeed, boy babies are sometimes born with erections. Ultrasound studies indicate that reflex erections occur in the male fetus for several months before birth (Masters et al., 1982). Vaginal lubrication has been found in baby girls in the 24 hours after birth.

The first intimate relationship most children experience is with their mother, and perhaps their father in families in which fathers participate equally in child rearing. The mother–infant relationship involves a good deal of physical contact and typically engages the infant's tactile, olfactory, visual, and auditory senses (Frayser, 1994). Breastfeeding especially involves close physical contact, but other activities involved in caring for infants, such as diaper changing or bathing, involve intimate contact that can produce sensuous responses in the infant (Martinson, 1994; Figure 10.1).

Attachment

The quality of the relationship with the parents in infancy can be very important to the child's capacity for later sexual and emotional relationships. In psychological terms, an **attachment** (or bond) forms between the infant and the mother, father, or other caregiver. The bond begins in the hours immediately following birth and continues throughout the period of infancy (Coustan & Angelini, 1995). It is facilitated by cuddling and other forms of physical contact. Later, attachments form to other familiar people. These are the individual's earliest experiences with love and emotional attachment. The quality of these attachments—whether they are stable, secure, and satisfying or unstable, insecure, and frustrating—affects the person's capacity for emotional

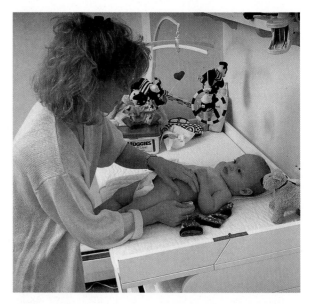

Figure 10.1 Some activities associated with nurturing an infant are potentially sensuous, because they involve pleasant physical contact.

Attachment: A psychological bond that forms between an infant and the mother, father, or other caregiver.

attachments in adulthood. Recent research (discussed in Chapter 12) indicates that adults' styles of romantic attachment are similar to the kinds of attachment they remember having with their parents in childhood.

Self-Stimulation

Infants are often observed fondling their own genitals (Figure 10.2). Generally the progression is that, between 6 and 12 months of age, infants discover their genitals by unintentionally touching them (de Graaf & Rademakers, 2006). They learn to walk, their coordination improves, and by 15 to 19 months, some boys and girls increase genital touching. A survey of Swedish parents of three- to five-year-olds found that 71 percent of boys and 43 percent of girls touched their genitals at home, and 28 percent of boys and 18 percent of girls masturbated with their hand (de Graaf & Rademakers, 2006). The comparable data for U.S. parents of two- to five-year-olds showed that 60 percent of boys and 44 percent of girls touched their genitals at home, and 17 percent of boys and 16 percent of girls masturbated with their hand. These behaviours, then, are quite normal and do not indicate pathology. Orgasms from self-stimulation are possible even at this early age, although before puberty boys are not capable of ejaculation.

Child–Child Encounters

Infants and young children are very self-centred. Even when they seem to be playing with another child, they

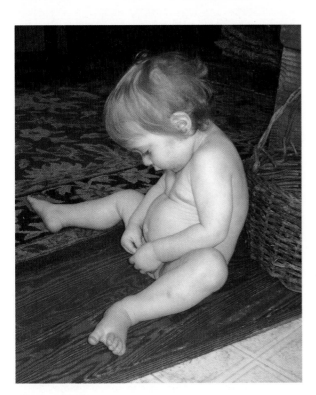

Figure 10.2   Infant self-stimulation.

may simply be playing alongside the other child, actually in a world all their own.

By the age of four or five, though, children have become more social and some heterosexual play occurs. Boys and girls may hug each other or hold hands in imitation of adults. "Playing doctor" can be a popular game at this age. Research indicates that roughly 25 to 50 percent of children engage in this type of play (de Graaf & Rademakers, 2006). It generally involves no more than exhibiting one's own genitals, looking at those of others, and perhaps engaging in a little fondling or touching. One woman recalled,

> It was at the age of 5 that I, along with my three friends who were sisters and lived next door, first viewed the genitals of a boy. They had a male cousin who came to visit and we all ended up behind the furnace playing doctor. No matter what he would say his symptoms were, we were so fascinated with his penis that it was always the center of our examinations. I remember giggling as I punched it and dunking it in some red food-colored water that we were using for medicine. This seemed to give him great enjoyment. One girl put hand lotion and a bandage on his penis and in the process he had an erection. We asked him to do it again, but their [sic] was no such luck. (Martinson, 1994, p. 37)

Some children first learn about heterosexual behaviour by seeing or hearing their parents engaging in sexual intercourse, that is, witnessing the primal scene. Freud believed that this experience could inhibit the child's subsequent psychosexual development. What little data we have, though, suggest that the experience is not damaging. In surveys, about 20 percent of middle-class parents report that their child observed them when the child was four to six years of age typically as a result of accidentally entering the parents' room. Parents report reactions such as curiosity ("Why are you bobbing up and down?"), amusement and giggling, or embarrassment and closing the door (Okami, 1995).

Sexual Knowledge and Interests

In the preschool years, children become interested in sexuality and begin to develop a simple understanding of some aspects of sexuality, although their knowledge is typically vague. For example, preschoolers are often interested in viewing people nude and they may touch their mother's or other women's breasts (de Graaf & Rademakers, 2011; Kenny & Wurtele, 2012). They become interested in different postures for urinating and some girls attempt to urinate while standing, just like boys do. Children at this age are very affectionate and enjoy hugging and kissing their parents. They may even propose marriage to the parent of the other gender.

By about the age of five, children have formed a concept of marriage—or at least of its nongenital aspects. They know that a member of the other gender is the appropriate marriage partner, and they are committed to marrying when they get older. They practise marriage roles as they "play house."

Because, in Canada, children usually learn early that sex is taboo, they may turn to their peers for learning as they play games of "show" or "doctor." One young man recalled,

> One of my favorite pasttimes was playing doctor with my little sister. During this doctor game we would both be nude and I would sit on her as if we were having intercourse. On one occasion, I was touching my sister's genital area and mother discovered us. We were sternly switched and told it was dirty and to never get caught again or we would be whipped twice as bad. So, we made sure we were never caught again. (Starks & Morrison, 1996).

In one study in Germany, the researcher interviewed children between the ages of two and six about their sexual knowledge (Volbert, 2000). When the children were shown a drawing of an unclothed child or adult, all three- and four-year-olds correctly identified whether it was male or female, but when asked to explain why, they generally gave answers based on characteristics such as hair. The five- and six-year-olds provided explanations based on the genitals. By age four 80 percent of the children knew some term for the genitals.

It is important to remember that children's sex play at this age is motivated largely by curiosity and is part of the general learning experiences of childhood.

Knowledge About Gender

By age two and half or three, children know what gender they are (see Chapter 13). This is the first step in developing a gender identity. Awareness of being a boy or a girl motivates them to be like other members of that group (Martin & Ruble, 2004). They know that they are like the parent of the same gender and different from the parent of the other gender and children of the other gender. At ages four to six, ideas about gender are very rigid, as reflected in the opening vignette. As noted above, three- and four-year olds typically do not understand the genital differences between males and females, but they acquire this knowledge by five or six). Some children's gender identity does not match their biological sex (see Chapter 13 for a discussion of transgender children).

Childhood (5 to 11 Years)

Freud used the term *latency* to refer to the period of childhood following the resolution of the Oedipus complex (see Chapter 2). He believed that the sexual urges go "underground" during latency and are not

Adrenarche: In childhood, the maturation of the adrenal glands, resulting in increased secretion of androgens.

expressed. The evidence indicates, however, that Freud was wrong and that children's interest in and expression of sexuality remain lively throughout this period (Figure 10.3). For many children, sexual awakening does not occur until adolescence, but for others it is a very real and poignant part of childhood.

Adrenarche, the maturation of the adrenal glands, occurs around eight to ten years of age (as early as six for some) and leads to increased levels of androgens in both boys and girls (Del Giudice et al., 2009). In short, some sex hormone action occurs in childhood, well before adolescence. Across several studies of adolescents and adults, the average age at which participants recalled first experiencing sexual attraction to another person was at age ten, probably linked to adrenarche and the rise in androgens (McClintock & Herdt, 1996).

Masturbation

During childhood, more and more children gain experience with masturbation. About 40 percent of university students recall masturbating before puberty (Bancroft et al., 2003). Generally boys start masturbating earlier than girls, a trend that is even more pronounced in adolescence. About 40 percent of boys and 20 percent of girls report orgasms from masturbation by age 12 (Larsson & Svedin, 2002).

Boys and girls tend to learn about masturbation in different ways. Typically boys are told about it by their

Figure 10.3 Between the ages of three and seven, children show a marked increase in sexual interest.

male peers, they see their peers doing it, or they read about it; girls most frequently learn about masturbation through accidental self-discovery (Langfeldt, 1981).

Mixed-Sex Behaviour

There is generally little mixed-sex[1] sexual behaviour during childhood, mainly because boys and girls divide themselves into groups rigidly by gender. However, children commonly hear about heterosexual sexual intercourse for the first time during this period. For example, in a sample of adult women, 61 percent recalled having learned about intercourse by age 12 (Wyatt et al., 1988). Children's reactions to this new information are an amusing combination of shock and disbelief—particularly disbelief that their parents would do such a thing. A university woman recalled:

> One of my girlfriends told me about sexual intercourse. It was one of the biggest shocks of my life. She took me aside one day, and I could tell she was in great distress. I thought she was going to tell me about menstruation, so I said that I already knew, and she said, "No, this is *worse!*" Her description went like this: "A guy puts his thing up a girl's hole, and she has a baby." The hole was, to us, the anus, because we did not even know about the vagina and we knew that the urethra was too small. I pictured the act as a single, violent and painful stabbing at the anus by the penis. Somehow, the idea of a baby was forgotten by me. I was horrified and repulsed, and I thought of that awful penis I had seen years ago. At first I insisted that it wasn't true, and my friend said she didn't know for sure, but that's what her cousin told her. But we looked at each other, and we knew it was true. We held each other and cried. We insisted that "my parents would never do that," and "I'll never let anyone do it to me." We were frightened, sickened, and threatened by the idea of some lusty male jabbing at us with his horrid penis. (From a student essay)

There is some boy–girl contact (Figure 10.4). A study of Swedish high-school students asked them to recall consensual childhood sexual experiences with another child (Larsson & Svedin, 2002b). More than 80 percent reported having had at least one experience when they were between 6 to 12 years old, but most of this occurred at ages 11 or 12, the beginning of adolescence Nonetheless, a substantial number (17 to 44 percent, depending on the behaviour) reported kissing and hugging, showing their genitals, or another child touching their genitals, between ages six and ten. Turning to the gender of the partner, 57 percent of the boys reported such experiences with girls, 11 percent with another boy, and 33 percent with

Figure 10.4   Hanging out, group dating, and heterosexual parties emerge during preadolescence and may include making out.

both boys and girls. For girls, the percentages were 31 with a boy, 29 with a girl, and 40 with both. Five percent of male adolescents and 1 percent of female adolescents in Canada report that they had engaged in sexual intercourse by the age of 12 (Maticka-Tyndale, 1997). Compared with their peers who first engage in intercourse during adolescence, Canadian youth who engage in intercourse during preadolescence are more likely to report having a poor relationship with their parents, having experienced pressure to engage in unwanted sex, having used drugs other than marijuana, and believing that they must break the rules to be popular (Boyce et al., 2008).

For some children, sexual activity occurs in a coercive relationship with a family member—whether a sibling, parent, stepparent, or other relative. This topic is discussed in detail in Chapter 16.

Same-Sex Behaviour

It is important to understand same-sex sexual activity as a normal part of the sexual development of children. In childhood, children have a **gender-segregated social organization**. That is, boys play separately from girls, and thus children spend most of their time with members of their own sex. Some of this social separation is actually comical; boys, for example, may be convinced that girls have "cooties" and that they must be very careful to stay away from them.

Given that children are spending time mainly with members of

> **Gender-segregated social organization:** A form of social grouping in which males play and associate with other males, and females play and associate with other females; that is, the genders are separate from each other.

---

[1] We have chosen to use the rather unusual term *mixed-sex* instead of the more common term *opposite sex* because males and females are not opposites. In fact, as discussed in Chapter 13, males and females are more similar than they are different.

their own sex, sexual exploring at this age is likely to be with partners of the same sex. These activities generally involve masturbation, showing the genitals, and fondling others' genitals. Boys, for example, may engage in a *circle jerk*, in which they masturbate as a team. Girls are less likely to engage in such group activities, perhaps because the spectacle of them masturbating is not as impressive or perhaps because they already sense greater cultural restrictions on their sexuality. Nonetheless, girls have their own behaviours, as reported by one team of interviewers:

> Fiona (first grade) said, "Chloe keeps kissing me in school! She kissed me on the back of the neck in line today." Chloe said, "I did, like this," and she crawled over to Fiona and kissed her on the back of her neck. Fiona said, "See!" Fiona was exasperated by these kisses, but she was also amused. Chloe was her best friend. And the kissing clearly entertained the whole group. (Myers & Raymond, 2010, p. 183)

A study of lesbian, gay, and bisexual youth found that the participants reported their first experience of same-sex sexual attraction at age 10 or 11 on average (Rosario et al., 1996). This age is comparable to that of first experiences of heterosexual attraction.

Sex Knowledge and Interests

Children learn very early that male–female pairings are the norm. That is, they learn **heteronormativity**, the belief that heterosexuality is the only pattern that is normal and natural. Intertwined with this view are beliefs that boys and girls are very different from each other, that boys should be attracted to girls, and that girls should be attracted to boys. A study of girls in kindergarten through Grade 5 used group interviews, which seem to be good for understanding children's experiences at these ages (Myers & Raymond, 2010). The girls' responses revealed well-learned heteronormativity. Even though they were initially embarrassed to talk about the topic, the girls revealed crushes on boys and then had excited discussions of their crushes. They used the term *hottie* for celebrity adolescent boys, such as *American Idol* contestants, and were excited about them as well. Yet, despite all this talk, the girls thought that actual behaviours, such as kissing, were inappropriate: "Kissing is gross!"

Heteronormativity: The belief that heterosexuality is the norm.
Sexualization: When a person is valued only for sex appeal or behaviour, is held to a standard that equates physical attractiveness with being sexy, is sexually objectified, or sexuality is inappropriately imposed on a person.

What is the sexualization of children and why is it a problem?

 L04 ## Sexualization of Children

A major concern of some parents, educators, and researchers is the sexualization of girls and boys in Canadian society. **Sexualization,** as defined in an authoritative report from the American Psychological Association (2007), occurs when

- a person's value comes only from his or her sexual appeal or behavior;
- a person is held to a standard that equates physical attractiveness with being sexy;
- a person is sexually objectified;
- sexuality is inappropriately imposed upon a person.

One example is beauty pageants for girls, such as in the television series *Toddlers and Tiaras,* in which girls as young as four are thrust into elaborate dresses and "dolled up" with sexy makeup and pouffy hairdos as they compete in this beauty pageant for children. Another example is sexual harassment by peers, which will be discussed in more detail in Chapter 16. Sexualized products are involved as well, such as Bratz or Barbie dolls, books, and sexy clothing (Figure 10.5).

Boys are exposed to TV shows, video games, and movies that often teach messages that males should have "buff" bodies, they should be physically powerful and always ready to fight, and that sex for men involves aggressive domination of beautiful women for the pleasure of the man (Levin, 2009, p. 79).

Sexualization also results when girls are treated like sexual objects by peers, family, teachers, or other adults. As a result of learning to view themselves as sexual objects, many girls and women engage in self-sexualization, leading them to purchase clothing because it is sexy and undergoing cosmetic surgery at a young age (American Psychological Association, 2007).

Experts are concerned that sexualization may lead to reduced self-esteem and body dissatisfaction because the child does not meet the cultural standard of sexy appearance. Cognitive performance, such as math performance, can be impaired as well because of distracting thoughts resulting from sexualization (Gervais et al., 2011). Educational and career aspirations may be reduced. In adolescence, viewing oneself as a sexual object may lead young people to initiate sexual activity, to engage in unwanted sexual activity and relationships, and to engage in risky sexual behaviour, such as unprotected vaginal intercourse.

The APA report suggested many ways to counteract sexualization. Within the schools, we can provide media literacy programs, a broader range of athletic opportunities, and comprehensive sexuality education. Within the family, parents can watch TV and movies and navigate the Internet with their children, sharing their values about appropriate and inappropriate content. Youth can create alternative media including zines, blogs, and alternative magazines and books. Finally, parents, educators, and boys and girls can engage in

Figure 10.5 The sexualization of children occurs in part through cultural messages in sexy clothing and sexy dolls. The Bratz dolls are a good example.

activism and resistance, such as campaigning against companies that use sexualized images to sell products.

L05

Adolescence (12 to 18 Years)

Researchers today define adolescence as a bit more than the teenage years—that is, beginning at age 11 or 12 and extending through the college and university years, to age 21 or 22 (Steinberg, 2011). Here we use the category of adolescence for ages 12 to 18, through the end of high school. Then we devote a section to sex during the college and university years, often called emerging adulthood.

A tension exists in thinking about adolescent sexuality. On the one hand, sexuality is a normative part of adolescent development, and it plays an important positive role in growth and development (Halpern, 2010; Tolman & McClelland, 2011). Adolescent relationships, including sexual relationships, provide the context in which the individual develops the skills and learns the scripts needed to sustain long-term intimate relationships (O'Sullivan & Meyer-Bahlburg, 2003). The last section of this chapter is devoted to the ways in which sexuality aids in psychological development. On the other hand, not all adolescent sex is good sex. Sometimes the person is too young, or the sex is coerced, or the sex is risky and unprotected. Quite frankly, researchers have focused much more of their energy on the second, negative aspect of adolescent sexuality than they have on the first, positive aspect. They have done so because of the enormous potential for negative consequences for the individual, the family, and the broader society when adolescent sex goes awry. In this chapter, though, we will focus mainly on the normative aspects of sexual development.

A surge of sexual interest occurs around puberty and continues through adolescence. This heightened sexuality may be caused by a number of factors, including bodily changes and an awareness of them, rises in levels of sex hormones, increased cultural emphasis on sex (see Milestones in Sex Research for a discussion of the effects of the media on adolescent sexuality), and rehearsal for adult gender roles. We can see evidence of this heightened sexuality particularly in the data on masturbation. But before examining those data, let's consider some theoretical ideas about how hormones and social forces might interact as influences on adolescent sexuality.

Udry (1988) has proposed a theoretical model that recognizes that both social and biological factors are potent in adolescent sexuality. He studied students in Grades 8, 9, and 10 (13 to 16 years old), measuring their hormone levels (testosterone, estrogen, and progesterone) and a number of sociological factors (e.g., whether they were in a two-parent family, their parents' educational level, the teenager's response to a scale measuring sexually permissive attitudes, and the teenager's attachment to conventional institutions, such as involvement in school sports and church attendance). Overall, 35 percent of the boys and 14 percent of the girls had engaged in sexual intercourse.

For boys, testosterone levels had a strong relationship to sexual activity (including coitus, masturbation, and feeling sexually turned on). Sexually permissive attitudes, a social variable, also were related to sexuality among boys although they had a smaller effect than testosterone did. For girls, there was a relationship between testosterone level and sexual activity although it was not as strong as it was for boys—and it was testosterone that was related to sexuality not estrogen or progesterone. Pubertal development (developing a curvy figure) had an effect, probably by increasing boys' attention. And the effects of testosterone were accentuated among girls in father-absent families. Permissive attitudes and church attendance played a role as well.

Milestones in Sex Research

What Impact Do the Mass Media Have on Adolescent Sexuality?

Do media portrayals of sex really affect my sexual attitudes and behaviours?

A major developmental task of adolescence is learning how to manage physical and emotional intimacy in relationships with others. It is not surprising, therefore, that young people are curious about sex and seek information about it. An increasingly important source of information is the mass media. Although most Canadian students identify school as their main source of information on human sexuality, many also get this information from the media. In one study of youth ages 14 to 17, 54 percent of the participants identified television and 44 percent identified the Internet as a source for information about sex and sexual health (Canadian Association for Adolescent Health, 2006). Further, Canadian youth are influenced by both the Canadian and the U.S. media. *Law & Order: SVU* provides information on sexual assault and the sexual abuse of children. *The Jersey Shore* features plenty of sexual images. In 2000, a *Maclean's*/Global poll found that 47 percent of Canadians felt that there is too much sexually explicit programming on prime-time TV. But how much sexual content actually is there in the mass media? To what extent are children and adolescents exposed to it, and what is the impact of this exposure?

Media are a major part of adolescents' lives. On average, they have more than 11 hours of exposure per day, including TV, music, computers, video games, print media, and movies; TV leads that list at four and a half hours a day (Rideout et al., 2010). More than 99 percent of adolescents live in a home with a TV, 97 percent have a DVD or VCR player, 84 percent have Internet access in the home, and 80 percent have their own iPod/MP3 player. On average, there are 3.8 TVs per home, and 71 percent of youth have a TV in their bedroom.

In analyzing how much sexual content there is in the mass media in the United States, sexual material is defined to include talk about sex, sexually suggestive behaviour, and explicit portrayals of sex. Using the methods of media content analysis (described in Chapter 3), a major project analyzed sexual material on television in 2004–2005 (Kunkel et al., 2005). The sample included more than 1000 programs on the four commercial US networks, public television, four cable networks (including HBO), and one independent broadcaster. The sample included all types of programs broadcast between 6 a.m. and 10 p.m. Sexual material was carefully defined and these definitions were used by trained coders to analyze the content of each program. On prime-time television, 70 percent of the programs included sexual material; 4.6 scenes per hour

included talk about sex, and 2 scenes per hour included sexual behaviour. These numbers represent substantial increases since the 1990s, when a similar project was carried out. Portrayals of risks or responsibilities associated with sex were notably absent; only 4 percent of scenes carried such material.

Cable movie networks have the largest proportion of programs with sexual content (Fisher et al., 2004). The most frequent portrayals are of unmarried heterosexual intercourse, often in a context of alcohol and drug use. There are no safer sex messages here!

How much of this sexual material are adolescents exposed to? In one study, adolescents (in Grades 8 to 10) completed questionnaires about their media "diets" (Schooler et al., 2009). The 25 most frequently viewed TV programs were then content-analyzed for sexual material. The results indicated that, in a typical hour of television viewing, these adolescents were exposed to an average of 17 references to sexual talk or behaviour.

The newer media, especially the Internet, also contain plenty of sexual content. In one study of U.S. adolescents (12–14 years old), 66 percent of boys and 39 percent of girls had seen at least one form of sexually explicit media (Internet sites, X-rated movies, adult magazines) in the past year (Brown & L'Engle, 2009). It would be a mistake, though, to think of adolescents as passive victims of an onslaught of media sex; research indicates that teens actively seek sexual content in their media choices (Bleakley et al., 2011). (Pornography is discussed in more detail in Chapter 17.)

There are some differences between Canadian and U.S. television shows. In particular, some topics can be introduced into Canadian television shows that would not be considered acceptable by the U.S. networks. For 30 years, *Degrassi* (and its predecessors *Degrassi: The Next Generation, Degrassi High,* and *Degrassi Junior High*) has portrayed youth sexuality in diverse ways and used storylines to explore different sexual choices, such as the decision to engage in intercourse, as well as the realistic consequences of sexual behaviour (M. Byers, 2005). The results have often been ground-breaking and a source of discussion and controversy. For example, throughout the *Degrassi* series, some of the female characters became pregnant; some chose to parent, some placed their baby for adoption, and some obtained abortions. Although all these episodes were shown on the Canadian network carrying the show, the American cable station that carried it would not air the abortion episodes. American television explores pregnancy issues in shows such as *The Secret Life of the American*

Teenager, 16 and Pregnant, and spinoff *Teen Mom,* all of which portray teens who are pregnant, parenting, or post-adoption, rarely discussing the option of abortion. Further, on American TV when abortion issues develop, it often turns out to be a false alarm, the character miscarries, or she has the baby. If the character does have an abortion, negative consequences follow—she is punished or experiences extreme guilt (M. Byers, 2005).

Some popular television programs and movies meant for adolescent audiences do explore teen sexuality in a more realistic and sex-positive way and encourage positive behaviour: Teens talk about sex and obtain consent from their partners for sexual activities; abstinence is respected as a choice; condoms are discussed and used; and youth obtain STI/HIV testing, use birth control, and discuss their pregnancy options with partners and health practitioners. Media representations of gay and lesbian adolescent characters have increased, giving gay, lesbian, bisexual, queer, and questioning youth more characters they can identify with. Popular prime-time U.S. television shows *Glee* and *90210,* and Canadian classic *Degrassi,* all present realities faced by these youth. Such portrayals of adolescent queer desire and empathetic views of queer and questioning youth experiences means less isolation for these youth, as well as education for their heterosexual counterparts. *Degrassi* has not only become increasingly representative of lesbian, gay, and bisexual youth, but has also introduced the first recurring transgender character. *Degrassi* portrays the impact of transphobic bullying, coming out transgender, family relationships, and what the discovery of sexual and emotional desire can be like for a transgender youth.

Nonetheless, these examples of positive messages about sex and sexual health in the media are still in the minority, with the majority of portrayals of sex being confusing or negative. What effect do these portrayals have on adolescents? Experts say that these portrayals represent *sexual socialization* by the media (Wright, 2009). Youth may learn scripts that influence their later sexual decision making and behaviour. For example, one team of researchers developed measures of a *heterosexual script* that includes guidelines for men's and women's behaviours (Kim et al., 2007). In this script, masculinity is defined, in part, by sexual conquest and experience, by taking the initiative in relationships and aggressively seeking sex, and by limiting emotional commitment. The script defines femininity as being chaste yet seductive, setting sexual limits, attaining power and status by sexually objectifying oneself, and by seeking commitment. The researchers' analysis of prime-time network TV programs indicated that there were 15.5 portrayals of elements of this heterosexual script per hour.

One college student, recalling his first sexual intercourse, described it in relation to media portrayals.

Interviewer: What were you thinking at the time?

Michael: When I had sex with her? "Let's see if this is really as good as everyone says." And it wasn't. It was pretty bad actually. Just because there was like, no love, no passion, she wasn't like I thought she'd be. You know, you always have these sexual fantasy ideas—the movies, the magazines—you see all this stuff and you're like "Oh yeah! This is the way it is!" And then in real life it's like. . . . It was just not a good experience. (Albanesi, 2010, p. 124)

Many studies demonstrate correlations between the amount of sexual media consumption and adolescents' sexual attitudes and behaviours. For example, university students who view more reality dating programs are more likely to endorse a sexual double standard and to believe that men are sex-driven, that appearance is important in dating, and that dating is a game (Zurbriggen & Morgan, 2006). In another study, university students' use of sexually explicit materials was correlated with number of intercourse partners, but higher use of sexually explicit materials was also associated with less sexual and relationship satisfaction (Morgan, 2011). The media may also influence standards of physical attractiveness and contribute to the dissatisfaction with their bodies that many, especially women, feel. For example, research has shown that viewing as little as 30 minutes of television can change women's perceptions of their bodies, which the authors term the "elastic body image" (Myers & Biocca, 1992). Of course, as we noted in Chapter 3, we should not make causal inferences from correlational data. We cannot conclude, for example, that exposure to the reality dating programs affected students' attitudes. Therefore, researchers have turned to other designs to test the effects of the media on sexuality—in particular, to longitudinal designs and experimental designs.

Several longitudinal studies have assessed adolescents' TV viewing at one time (baseline) and then followed them a year or more later to measure changes in their sexual behaviour (Ashby et al., 2006; Bleakley et al., 2008; Brown et al., 2006; Collins et al., 2004). Youth who view more sexual content at baseline are more likely to progress to more advanced sexual activities and to engage in first intercourse in the following year. Researchers believe that this occurs for two reasons (Brown & Bobkowski, 2011). First, exposure to the media content may increase viewers' sense of self-efficacy for engaging in sexual behaviour—that is, it helps them figure out what to do and feel confident about doing it. Second, the media portrayals may arouse viewers sexually so that they want to engage in sexual behaviour.

Experiments, too, indicate that the media have an impact on sexual attitudes and behaviour. For example, in one study youth exposed to four music videos with

Continued

Continued

stereotypic male and female characters expressed more traditional views of gender and sexual relationships, compared with the control group (Ward et al., 2005).

The evidence is strong that media portrayals have an important impact on adolescents' sexual knowledge, attitudes, and behaviour (Wright, 2011). Adolescents report that the media are an important source of their knowledge. The problem lies in the fact that these portrayals are not realistic. For example, in sharp contrast to the high rates of nonmarital sex portrayed in the media, most sexual activity involves persons who are married or in long-term, committed relationships (see Chapter 11). Many couples in real life, whether married or not, are responsible users of birth control. Many adolescents and adults use condoms to prevent STIs. It is unfortunate that these realities are invisible in media portrayals of sexual behaviour. It is also unfortunate that the media have generally not taken advantage of their opportunity to provide positive sexuality education.

As a final note, most adolescents are not only exposed to sexuality in the mass media but are also increasingly exposed to sexual depictions in pornography, which they easily access over the Internet. Pornography is characterized by unrealistic body types (very thin women with large breasts, men with very large penises), unrealistic sexual expectations (for example, in terms of ejaculatory control), and unequal gender roles (women's roles typically being to satisfy men's needs). There is concern that viewing pornography at a young age can affect adolescents' views of the ideal male or female body or of the expected sexual script (Löfgren-Mårtenson & Månsson, 2010; Štulhofer et al., 2010). On the other hand, for the most part, young people believe that they can differentiate between the fantasy depicted in pornography and real life (Löfgren-Mårtenson & Månsson, 2010). (Pornography is discussed in more detail in Chapter 17.)

Source: With updates and contributions from Erica Doty.

The bottom line in this study is that it shows that testosterone levels have a substantial impact on the sexuality of adolescent boys and girls. Social psychological variables (permissive attitudes, father absence for girls, and church attendance) then interact with the biological effects, in some cases magnifying them and in some cases suppressing them. Similarly, a study with gay and lesbian youth found that increases in hormone levels with puberty resulted in increases in homoerotic sexual feelings and behaviours (Savin-Williams, 1995).

Masturbation

According to the Kinsey data, there is a sharp increase in the incidence of masturbation for boys between the ages of 13 and 15, as illustrated in Figure 10.6. Note that the curve is steepest between the ages of 13 and 15, indicating that most boys begin masturbating to orgasm during that period. By age 15, 82 percent of the boys in

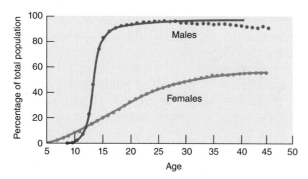

Figure 10.6 Cumulative incidence of males and females who have masturbated to orgasm, according to Kinsey's data. Current data suggest that contemporary youth begin masturbating one or two years earlier.

Kinsey's study had masturbated. Many girls also begin masturbating in adolescence, but note that the curve on the graph is flatter for them, indicating that many girls do not begin masturbating until later. The increase in their masturbation behaviour is much more gradual for girls than for boys and continues past adolescence.

A study at the University of British Columbia asked students whether they had ever masturbated (Meston et al., 1996). Overall, 80 percent of the male students and 48 percent of the female students reported masturbating at least once. Asian students were significantly less likely to report having masturbated than were non-Asian students. Eighty-five percent of non-Asian males compared with 74 percent of Asian males reported that they had masturbated. The difference between non-Asian and Asian females was even greater—59 percent compared with 39 percent. A German study found that 94 percent of male university students and 74 percent of female students reported that they had masturbated in the previous year; interestingly, being in a satisfying sexual relationship did not affect how likely they were to report masturbating (Dekker & Schmidt, 2002). On average, female students reported masturbating about three times a month and male students about eight times a month.

More recent data indicate that children and adolescents begin to masturbate earlier today, and thus the Kinsey data need to be pushed back about a year. However, the general shape of the curves still holds (Bancroft et al., 2003).

Attitudes Toward Masturbation

Attitudes toward masturbation underwent a dramatic change in the twentieth century. As a result, adolescents are now given much different information about masturbation than were earlier adolescents, and this may affect both their behaviour and their feelings. For example, a popular handbook, *What a Boy Should Know*, written in 1913 by two doctors, advised its readers:

> Whenever unnatural emissions are produced...the body becomes "slack." A boy will not feel so vigorous and springy; he will be more easily tired.... He will probably look pale and pasty, and he is lucky if he escapes indigestion and getting his bowels confined, both of which will probably give him spots and pimples on his face....

> The results on the mind are the more severe and more easily recognized.... A boy who practices this habit can never be the best that Nature intended him to be. His wits are not so sharp. His memory is not so good. His power of fixing his attention on whatever he is doing is lessened.... A boy like this is a poor thing to look at....

> The effect of self-abuse on a boy's character always tends to weaken it, and in fact, to make him untrustworthy, unreliable, untruthful, and probably even dishonest. (Schofield & Vaughan-Jackson, 1913, pp. 30–42)

Masturbation, in short, was once believed to cause everything from warts to insanity.[2]

Attitudes toward masturbation are now considerably more positive, and today few people would subscribe to notions like those expressed earlier; most individuals see masturbation as normal (Morrison et al., 2008). Indeed, sex therapists recommend masturbation as a way for people to increase their awareness of their own sexual response and as a step in overcoming a number of sexual problems and concerns. As psychiatrist Thomas Szasz (1973, p. 10) said, the shift in attitudes toward masturbation has been so great that in a generation it has changed from a disease to a form of therapy.

Same-Sex Sexual Behaviour

Grade 9 and 11 students in the CYSHHAS were asked about their sexual attraction. About 5 percent of the girls reported being attracted to girls or to both boys and girls. Among the boys, 2 to 6 percent reported being attracted to boys or to both boys and girls. According to the National Survey of Family Growth, a large, nationally representative U.S. survey, 7 percent of girls and 2 percent of boys between the ages of 15 and 19 report having engaged in oral sex with a same-sex partner (Chandra et al., 2011). It seems that girls are more willing to engage in these behaviours than boys are. Many youth engage in these behaviours as a trial—that is, to learn more about their own sexuality. Others have already formed a gay, lesbian, or bisexual identity. About 10 percent of men and 6 percent of women in university report having had a same-sex partner in high school (Bancroft et al., 2003). Some youth who are aware of their same-sex attraction in adolescence go on to adopt a gay, lesbian, or bisexual identity, usually within five years (D'Augelli, 2002). For example, a survey of students in Grades 7 through 12 in British Columbia found that 8 percent of the male students and 9 percent of the female students self-identified as bisexual, gay, lesbian, or not sure (McCreary Centre Society, 2007). Adolescents are generally accepting of same-sex sexual behaviour (Figure 10.7). Alberta sociologist Reginald Bibby (Bibby et al., 2009) surveyed 5564 teenagers across Canada, ages 15 to 19. He found that only 44 percent approved of sexual relations between two people of the same sex; however an additional 28 percent did not approve of it but nonetheless accepted it.

---

[2] In case you're wondering why boys' advice books were saying such awful things, there is a rather interesting history that produced those pronouncements (Money, 1986). Swiss physician Simon André Tissot (1728–1797) wrote an influential book called *Treatise on the Diseases Produced by Onanism,* taking the term from the biblical story of Onan (Genesis 38:9). In this work he articulated a degeneracy theory, in which loss of semen was believed to weaken a man's body; Tissot had some very inventive physiological explanations for his idea. The famous American physician of the nineteenth century Benjamin Rush was influenced by Tissot and spread degeneracy theory in North America. The theory became popularized by Sylvester Graham (1794–1851), a religious zealot and health reformer, who was a vegetarian and whose passion for health foods gave us the names for Graham flour and Graham crackers. To be healthy, according to Graham, one needed to follow the Graham diet and practise sexual abstinence. Then John Harvey Kellogg (1852–1943) of—you guessed it—cornflakes fame entered the story. He was an ardent follower of Graham and his doctrines of health food and sexual abstinence. While experimenting with healthful foods, he invented cornflakes. His younger brother, Will Keith Kellogg, thought to add sugar and made a fortune. John Harvey Kellogg contributed further to public fears about masturbation by writing (during his honeymoon, no less) *Plain Facts for Old and Young: Embracing the Natural History and Hygiene of Organic Life,* which provided detailed descriptions of the horrible diseases supposedly caused by masturbation. These ideas then found their way into the advice books for boys in the early twentieth century.

Figure 10.7 A crowd gathers on the street saluting gay youth celebrating their coming out.

Many sexual minority adolescents experience prejudice and rejection within their families or their schools (Saewyc, 2011). Calling someone *gay* is a common form of peer harassment in middle schools and high schools. Nonetheless, most sexual minority youth successfully navigate these difficulties and emerge at the end of adolescence with well-being comparable to their heterosexual peers (Saewyc, 2011). Having a Gay-Straight Alliance in the school helps youth deal with these difficulties (see http://mygsa.ca for information on establishing a Gay-Straight Alliance).

Mixed-Sex Sexual Behaviour

In middle and late adolescence, more and more young people engage in sex with a member of the other gender, with more and more frequency. Thus heterosexual behaviour gains prominence and becomes the major sexual outlet. Many adolescents who go on to adopt gay, lesbian, or bisexual identities report having engaged in heterosexual activity during adolescence—74 percent of the females and 57 percent of the males in one study (D'Augelli, 2002). Only a small percentage of these youth engage in only same-sex activity and no other sex activity (Savin-Williams & Cohen, 2007). As noted above, the reverse is also true—many heterosexuals engage in same-sex experimentation during adolescence.

Generally there is a progression beginning with kissing, then breast and genital fondling, moving on to oral sex, and then to penis-in vagina intercourse (Boyce et al., 2006; de Graaf et al., 2009). To use terminology introduced in Chapter 2, these behaviours tend to follow a sexual script. Variations on the normative sequence can occur based on factors such as social class and ethnicity. Initially there were claims that most of the oral sex involved girls "servicing" boys; however, research indicates a general pattern of gender equality in giving and receiving oral sex (Tolman & McClelland, 2011).

The progression in sexual behaviour is evident from data provided in Table 10.1 on the percentage of Canadian adolescents who have engaged in five different sexual behaviours. For example, in Grade 9, almost three

How many Canadian teens have engaged in sexual intercourse by Grade 11?

times as many students had engaged in deep kissing and more than twice as many had engaged in touching below the waist than had engaged in sexual intercourse. Further, more students had engaged in oral sex than had engaged in sexual intercourse. The progression of sexual experience is also evident in the finding that the percentage of students who had engaged in each of the five sexual behaviours was greatest for Grade 11 students, intermediate for Grade 9 students, and lowest for Grade 7 students. As shown in Table 10.1, by Grade 11 almost half of students report that they have engaged in intercourse; about 10 percent had engaged in fellatio or cunnilingus but not in intercourse (Boyce et al., 2006). Many sexually experienced youth have had two or more sexual partners (Fisher & Boroditsky, 2000). For example, almost half of the Grade 9 and 11 students surveyed in the CYSHHAS who had engaged in sexual intercourse had had two or more partners (Boyce et al., 2003). More recent data from the Canadian Community Health Survey in 2009–2010 found that 30 percent of 15- to 17-year-olds and 68 percent of 18- and 19-year-olds reported that they had engaged in intercourse (Roterman, 2012).

It is interesting to compare youth involvement in sexual activity in the CYSHHAS to the results from the Canadian Youth and AIDS Study conducted in 1988 (King et al., 1988). The percentage of students who reported having engaged in deep kissing and sexual touching changed very little over the 14 years between the two studies. However, somewhat fewer students reported having engaged in sexual intercourse in 2003 than in 1988. The earlier survey did not ask about oral sex. Other researchers have also found that the average age of first intercourse in Canada is no longer decreasing and may even be increasing (Maticka-Tyndale, 2008; Rotermann, 2008). For example, research in British Columbia shows that from 1992 to 2003, the percentage of both male and female adolescents who have had intercourse decreased as did the percentage who engaged in intercourse before the age of 14 (Saewyc et al., 2008). However, this differs from one region of Canada to the next (Canadian

Table 10.1 Percentage of Canadian Youth Who Have at Least Once Engaged in Various Sexual Behaviours

	Grade 7		Grade 9		Grade 11	
	Boys	Girls	Boys	Girls	Boys	Girls
Deep (open-mouth) kissing	49%	35%	65%	67%	81%	82%
Touching above the waist	46%	34%	67%	64%	81%	81%
Touching below the waist	33%	23%	57%	54%	75%	74%
Oral sex			32%	28%	53%	52%
Sexual intercourse			3%	19%	40%	46%

Source: Boyce et al. (2006). Sexual health of Canadian youth: Findings from the Canadian Youth, Sexual Health and HIV/AIDS Study. *The Canadian Journal of Human Sexuality, 15,* 59–68.

Federation for Sexual Health, 2007). Teens in Quebec are most likely to report having engaged in sexual intercourse (Rotermann, 2008).

When Canadian high school students were asked the most important reason for engaging in sexual intercourse, 60 percent of female Grade 11 students but only 39 percent of male students gave love as the reason. Curiosity and experimentation was also an important reason given by 21 percent of males but only 14 percent of females (Boyce et al., 2006). In other research adolescents also identify relationship goals, such as increased intimacy, sexual pleasure (let's not forget that one!), and increased social status (Ott et al., 2006).

Adolescents also have a variety of reasons for not engaging in intercourse. In the CYSHHAS, the most common reasons were not feeling ready, not having had the opportunity, and not having met the right person (Boyce et al., 2006).

What do we know about people's first intercourse experiences? An Ontario study found that 60 percent of participants had their first intercourse experience with a serious dating partner, 20 percent with a casual dating partner, 16 percent with a friend or an acquaintance, and 4 percent with someone they just met (Reissing et al., 2011). Women were more likely than men were to be in a serious relationship. The researchers have also analyzed their participants' emotional reactions to first coitus. Almost all the men (91 percent) and three-quarters of the women (73 percent) overall had a positive emotional reaction to their first intercourse experience. Nonetheless, despite our culture's romanticized high expectations that the first intercourse experience will be like fireworks on Canada Day, it turns out to be much less thrilling than that for many people. The Ontario study found that only 6 percent of the women compared with 62 percent of the men experienced orgasm during their first experience (Reissing et al., 2011). In addition, research in Alberta found that only about half the women and men in their study reported being emotionally satisfied after their first intercourse experience, and only 40 percent rated the experience as very good or excellent (Tsui & Nicoladis, 2004).

Many people assume that having penile–vagina intercourse for the first time equals losing one's virginity. However, research in Alberta has shown that students have a broader definition of what constitutes "having sex" than of "virginity loss" (Trotter & Alderson, 2007). Indeed, a qualitative study involving in-depth case studies of 61 men and women found that virginity loss is socially constructed (Carpenter, 2001). Many believed that virginity could not be lost by rape and conversely that behaviours other than penile–vaginal intercourse could constitute loss of virginity. Carpenter identified three distinct interpretations of virginity: as a gift, a stigma, or a process. Each was associated with distinctive individual choices about the transition to

nonvirginity. Adolescents who viewed virginity as a gift were likely to lose it with a lover or "soul mate"; those who viewed it as a stigma often lost it with a stranger or nonlover. A Canadian study found that 54 percent of adolescents who had experienced penile–vaginal intercourse were process-oriented, 38 percent were gift-oriented, and 8 percent were stigma-oriented at first coitus (Humphreys, 2012). Men were more likely to be stigma-oriented than were women (Eriksson & Humphreys, 2013).

Even though there has been a slight decline recently in the percentage of high school students who have engaged in intercourse, adolescents today are engaging in intercourse for the first time at younger ages compared with persons born 40 years ago. Figure 10.8 provides data from studies conducted in the 1960s through the late 1990s in the United States and Canada (Wells & Twenge, 2005). The mean age of first intercourse for boys declined from 18 in the 1960s to 15 in 2000. Among girls, it declined from 18.5 to 15.5 across the same period. Similar declines in age of first intercourse have been reported in Australia (Smith et al., 2003). The majority of Canadians first engage in intercourse between the ages of 16 and 19 (Maticka-Tyndale, 1997).

These trends reflect, in part, the impact of the sexual revolution of the 1960s and 1970s, which encouraged greater openness about sexuality and acceptance of sex between unmarried people, particularly for women. For all age groups included in the National Population Health Survey, immigrants to Canada initiated intercourse at later ages than those born in Canada did. For

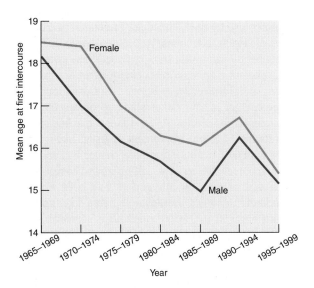

Figure 10.8 Young people are engaging in first intercourse at younger ages than men and women 50 years ago.

Source: Brooke E. Wells & Jean M. Twenge, "Changes in young people's sexual behavior and attitudes, 1943–1999: A cross-temporal meta-analysis," *Review of General Psychology*, 9, 2005, 249–261 (Figure 2). Reprinted by permission of the American Psychological Association and the author.

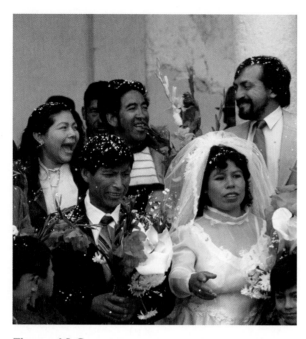

Figure 10.9 In South American nations, the percentage of unmarried young women who engage in premarital intercourse is lower than in North America owing to the strong influence of the Catholic Church.

example, for the age group that was between 20 and 24 at the time of the survey, 41 percent of immigrant men compared with 60 percent of Canadian-born men had engaged in intercourse by age 17. The difference was even larger for women; 18 percent of immigrant women between the ages of 20 and 24 and 58 percent of Canadian-born women in that age group had engaged in intercourse by age 17 (Maticka-Tyndale et al., 2000a). Rates of sexual intercourse also differ substantially for young people who were born in Canada but who come from different ethnocultural backgrounds. For example, a study at the University of British Columbia found that 36 percent of female Asian students compared with 69 percent of female non-Asian students had engaged in intercourse. Similarly, 36 percent of Asian males compared with 63 percent of non-Asian males had engaged in intercourse (Meston et al., 1996). Length of residence in Canada or whether the student had been born in Canada did not affect the Asian students' likelihood of having engaged in sexual intercourse. However, British Columbia psychologist Lori Brotto found in a university sample that coitally experienced Asian women who were more acculturated into mainstream Canadian culture reported more sexual experiences than did less-acculturated Asian women (Brotto et al., 2005).

These ethnocultural differences mirror the substantial variations in patterns of adolescent intercourse in different cultures around the world, as the data in Table 10.2 indicate. Most of the data were collected by the Demographic and Health Surveys Program, which administers the same questions to people in different countries. Note that the timeframes are different from the United States and Canada than for the other countries. Several interesting points emerge from the data. First, the percentage of young women who report intercourse is smaller in Latin and South American countries than in African nations, partly because of the greater influence of the Catholic Church in Latin America (Figure 10.9). Second, there is not much variation across nations in the average age of first intercourse; it is either 16, 17, or 18 in all but one country.

In many countries around the world, the incidence of adolescent intercourse has risen in the last several decades. Around the globe, especially where modernization has been rapid, adolescents are less and less under the influence of family, community, and religion and more and more responsive to peers and the mass media (Liskin et al., 1985).

Too Early Sex

Although sex is a normative part of adolescent development, sometimes sex occurs too early. Experts agree that sex at age 15 or earlier is "early" sex and that it carries a number of risks (Price & Hyde, 2009). Those who engage in intercourse early are more likely not to use a condom and to have sex with more than one partner. The result is increased risk for teen pregnancies and sexually transmitted infections. According to the results of the Canadian Community Health Survey, 8.2 percent of female adolescents and 10.8 percent of male adolescents have engaged in sexual intercourse before the age of 15 (Rotermann, 2012). Another 25 percent had intercourse for the first time at age 15 or 16.

Researchers in Quebec have identified a number of factors that predict engaging in early sex including (1) living in a single-parent family, (2) having more depressive symptoms, (3) displaying more antisocial behaviour, (4) having less self-disclosure to parents and more parent–child conflict, (5) having more other-sex friends and friends who use alcohol and drugs, and (6) having lower academic achievement (Boislard & Poulin, 2011). These same factors also tend to predict a higher number of sexual partners (Lansford et al., 2010). In contrast, Ontario researchers have shown that adolescents' perceptions that their parents would disapprove of them engaging in sexual intercourse are unrelated to their behaviour (Hampton et al., 2005).

One college woman, reflecting back on her decision to have sex at age 14, said this,

> **Interviewer:** And in junior high? What did you think about sex before you had sex?
> **Shari:** I didn't like it much. It was more about feeling grown up and stuff. Plus everyone was doing it. Plus if I did it early maybe it would be better.

Interviewer: Why would it be better?

Shari: Because of all of my friends I would be the first one, so it would be kinda cool. That's what I thought.

Interviewer: So did you decide beforehand ... or was it just something that happened?

Shari: I decided beforehand. (Albanesi, 2010, p. 23)

Adolescent Romantic Relationships

Adolescent sexual activity often occurs within the context of a romantic relationship (Collins et al., 2009; Giordano et al., 2010). Most Canadian teens say that they have had a boyfriend or girlfriend, although some of these are likely short-lived (Price et al., 2000). These relationships are a context in which sexual activity occurs.

Experts believe that these relationships can contribute to psychological development, but they can also have negative outcomes, such as dating violence (Collins et al., 2009). Low-quality relationships are characterized by antagonism, high levels of conflict, and controlling behaviour; they have been linked to lower academic performance and poor emotional health. High-quality relationships are marked by qualities such as supportiveness and emotional intimacy, and relationships such as these can contribute to an adolescent's feelings of self-worth.

Adolescent relationships provide the context in which the individual develops the skills and learns the scripts needed to sustain long-term intimate relationships (O'Sullivan & Meyer-Bahlburg, 2003). Research indicates that the process begins around ages 9 to 12 with a first boyfriend or girlfriend; often there is little direct interaction between the two, but the relationship does provide an opportunity to play an "adult" role. Later comes group dating and perhaps mixed-sex social events at school. These situations provide an opportunity for conversation and for peers to observe and instruct the person in sexual scripts. In mid- to late- adolescence, youth begin to spend time in mixed-sex, unsupervised interaction, which provides an opportunity for more sexual expression.

We can apply symbolic interaction theory, explained in Chapter 2, to understanding adolescents' romantic relationships (Giordano et al., 2010). The meaning of an adolescent romantic relationship to the individuals depends very much on the communication between them. Intimate self-disclosure (see Chapter 12) heightens feelings of emotional intimacy, for example. Power dynamics can be involved as well, as the romantic partner becomes an important influence on behaviour and attitudes.

Most lesbian and gay youth do not date those they are most attracted to out of very real fear of harassment from their peers. Further, gay and lesbian youth in Canada are more likely to be the victims of harassment and violence than are their heterosexual peers (D'Augelli, 2006; McCreary Centre Society, 2007). Many date partners of the other gender to conform to societal expectations (Savin-Williams, 1995).

Table 10.2 A Global Perspective on Female Adolescent Intercourse

Country and Year	Age of Respondents (years)	Percentage Having Had Intercourse (last four weeks)*	Median Age of First Coitus (years)
Africa			
Cameroon, 1998	15–19	33.7	16.3
Kenya, 1998	15–19	19.4	17.3
Nigeria, 1999	15–19	24.6	18.1
Tanzania, 1996	15–19	28.2	17.4
Zambia, 1996	15–19	26.9	16.6
Central America			
Mexico, 1985	15–19	13.0	17.0
Nicaragua, 1998	15–19	21.7	18.1
South America			
Bolivia, 1998	15–19	8.6	19.6
Brazil, 1996	15–19	21.5	18.7
United States, 2005	15–18	34.6**	17.4[†]
Canada, 2000	15–19	52.7***	16.0

* These percentages are of all women, so some of these women are married.

** Had intercourse in the last three months.

*** Had intercourse in the last 12 months.

[†] Mean age of first intercourse.

Source: Data for the United States are from the 2005 Youth Risk Behavior Survey conducted by the Centers for Disease Control and Prevention. The data for other countries are from the Demographic and Health Surveys Program, which collects comparable data from many countries around the world. The results are published in individual volumes for each country by Macro International, Inc., Calverton, MD. The typical reference is *Kenya: Demographic and Health Survey, 1998.* Calverton MD: Macro International, 1999. The data for Canada are from the Canadian Community Health Survey, 2000–2001.

Adolescents also engage in extradyadic sexual activity. New Brunswick researchers found in their sample of 15- to 19-year-olds, 21 percent reported having kissed someone romantically other than their boyfriend or girlfriend while in a romantic relationship (O'Sullivan & Ronis, 2013). Even more adolescents (26 percent) reported kissing someone romantically who they knew was in a relationship with someone else. The same percentage of male and female adolescents reported engaging in these behaviours.

Internet Use, Risk, and Sexting

New technologies have had a major impact on the ways in which adolescents and young adults communicate. One popular technique is the use of social networking sites, such as Facebook. Roughly 90 percent of teens and young adults have a profile on such a site (National Campaign to Prevent Teen and Unplanned Pregnancy, 2009).

One purpose of maintaining an online profile is to keep up with friends; about 85 percent of adolescents use social networking sites for this purpose (Valkenburger & Peter, 2009). This kind of online communication stimulates self-disclosure. This may be because other people are not actually present, thereby reducing concerns about how others will react and leading to self-disclosure of more personal information. Research indicates that self-disclosure enhances relationship quality and high-quality peer relationships improve personal well-being (see Chapter 12). So rather than leading to reduced social integration and connection, these online exchanges can increase it.

Another purpose is to meet people or make new friends. Users often self-disclose via text or pictures in the hope of attracting certain kinds of people. In this context, personal information can put the poster at risk. A content analysis of 500 Web profiles of 18-year-olds considered references to sexual behaviour, substance (alcohol or other drugs) use, and violence to be risky (Moreno et al., 2009). Whether true or not, such references attract others who may want to take advantage of or exploit the poster. Of the profiles that were analyzed, 54 percent contained risk behaviour information; 24 percent referred to risk behaviour related to sex, 41 percent to substance use, and 14 percent to violence. The researchers suggested many youth should be more cautious about what they post on their profiles.

What should I consider before sexting?

Sexting, sending sexually charged messages or images by cellphone or other electronic media, has gained national attention (Figure 10.10). According to a New Brunswick survey of 15- to 19-year-olds, 15 percent reported having sent a nude or semi-nude photograph of themselves over the Internet, and 30 percent reported having received such a photograph (O'Sullivan, 2011). Young men reported receiving photos more than young women, but there were no differences found in their reports of sending photos. Therefore, it is far from true that all adolescents are involved in sexting.

Sexting: Sending sexually charged messages or images by cellphone.

Figure 10.10 Sexting: Think carefully about the potential consequences.

In one innovative study, the BlackBerry Project, 15-year-olds were each given a BlackBerry device with a prepaid plan; their text messages were then stored and content-analyzed (Underwood et al., 2011). Roughly 7 percent of the messages contained sexual themes, again indicating that sending sexual messages is not a normative behaviour for adolescents.

Nonetheless, the consequences can be serious for those who do engage in sexting. The *Criminal Code of Canada* defines nude photos and videos of persons under 18 as child pornography. In 2001, a ruling by the Supreme Court of Canada established what has been called the intimate photo exception. It ruled that if the photo or video was taken by one of the people involved, was consensual, and is kept private, the image is not child pornography even if the person is under 18. However, if the photo is nonconsensual or was distributed without permission or maliciously, child pornography charges can be laid. The federal government is considering whether there should be a new criminal offence specifically addressing the nonconsensual distribution of intimate images; this law would not only apply to minors.

A study of youth Internet victimization found that in 2010, 23 percent of adolescents reported unwanted exposure to pornography and 9 percent of adolescents had received an unwanted sexual solicitation via the Internet (Jones et al., 2012). These rates actually represent a decline from 2000, suggesting that various protective measures for the online environment (for example, Internet education programs, spam filters for email) have been at least partially successful.

Based on concerns about negative consequences for both those who send and those who receive sexual messages or images, five things to think about before pressing Send was developed by the U.S. National Campaign to Prevent Teen Pregnancy (see Table 10.3).

Contraceptive and Condom Use

Research indicates that adolescents are not consistent in using contraceptives and condoms to prevent pregnancy and STIs, although this varies from one ethnic group to another (Boroditsky et al., 1996; Levy et al., 1992). As a consequence about 2.8 percent of all Canadian teenage girls became pregnant in 2010, and adolescents and young adults were disproportionately likely to be diagnosed with an STI. The rates of teen pregnancy and contracting an STI vary considerably across provinces and territories, however (McKay, 2012).

The CYSHHAS found that only 54 percent of Grade 9 students and 41 percent of Grade 11 students used a condom the last time they had sexual intercourse (Boyce et al., 2006). Even fewer adolescents use a condom every time they have intercourse (Calzavara et al., 1998; King

Table 10.3 Five Things to Think About Before Pressing Send

Don't assume anything you send or post is going to remain private.
Your messages and images will get passed around, even if you think they won't: 40 percent of teens and young adults say they have had a sexually suggestive message (originally meant to be private) shown to them and 20 percent say they have shared such a message with someone other than the person for whom it was originally meant.

There is no changing your mind in cyberspace—anything you send or post will never truly go away.
Something that seems fun and flirty and is done on a whim will never really die. Potential employers, college recruiters, teachers, coaches, parents, friends, enemies, strangers, and others may all be able to find your past posts, even after you delete them. And it is nearly impossible to control what other people are posting about you. Think about it: Even if you have second thoughts and delete a racy photo, there is no telling who has already copied that photo and posted it elsewhere.

Don't give in to the pressure to do something that makes you uncomfortable, even in cyberspace.
More than 40 percent of teens and young adults (42 percent total, 47 percent of teens, 38 percent of young adults) say "pressure from guys" is a reason girls and women send and post sexually suggestive messages and images. More than 20 percent of teens and young adults (22 percent total, 24 percent teens, 20 percent young adults) say "pressure from friends" is a reason guys send and post sexually suggestive messages and images.

Consider the recipient's reaction.
Just because a message is meant to be fun doesn't mean the person who gets it will see it that way. Four in ten teen girls who have sent sexually suggestive content did so "as a joke" but many teen boys (29 percent) agree that girls who send such content are "expected to date or hook up in real life." It's easier to be more provocative or outgoing online, but whatever you write, post or send does contribute to the real-life impression you're making.

Nothing is truly anonymous.
Nearly one in five young people who send sexually suggestive messages and images do so to people they only know online (18 percent total, 15 percent teens, 19 percent young adults). It is important to remember that even if someone only knows you by screen name, online profile, phone number, or email address, that they can probably find you if they try hard enough.

Source: National Campaign to Prevent Teen and Unplanned Pregnancy, 2009. Reprinted with permission.

et al., 1988; Langille et al., 1994). Condoms are used most frequently at the beginning of relationships or in casual encounters, and adolescents in mixed-sex relationships are likely to stop using condoms and switch to the birth control pill as they get to know a partner better (Bolton et al., 2010; Fisher & Boroditsky, 2000; McMahon et al., 2004). One factor that may interfere with condom use is

that adolescents feel embarrassed and concerned about being exposed ("Everyone is thinking 'I know what they are doing tonight'") when purchasing condoms (Ronis & LeBouthillier, 2013). This study found that adolescents who were less religious, had more positive attitudes toward birth control, were lower in neuroticism, and who had engaged in more extensive discussions of sexuality with their parents were more comfortable purchasing condoms.

Research by Ontario sociologist Eleanor Maticka-Tyndale (1992) identified two beliefs that account for why young people do not perceive themselves to be at risk to contract an STI. First, teenagers minimize the seriousness of contracting an STI, such as HIV, through their beliefs that medical science will find a cure in time should they need one. Second, they believe that by choosing partners who are like themselves and their peers they can ensure that their partners are not infected. In addition, the sexual script for an affectionate, trusting relationship does not fit with the idea that a partner can be infected and either not know it or not disclose such information, and so it does not include continued condom use (Bolton et al., 2010; Hynie et al., 1998). Teenagers are particularly likely to underestimate their cumulative risk (risk from repeated unprotected sex) of becoming infected with an STI from a partner if they are committed to the partner or if the partner is particularly appealing to them (Knäuper et al., 2005). Finally, teenagers are more likely to use condoms when they have the motivation (e.g., positive attitudes toward condoms and the perception that their peer group supports condom use with romantic partners) and skills (e.g., ideas about how easy or hard it would be to use them; confidence that they can do so) (Fazekas et al., 2001; Fullerton et al., 2013; Ploem & Byers, 1997; Tremblay & Frignon, 2004) to do so. The information–motivation–behavioural skills model described in Chapter 7 (Fisher & Fisher, 1998) provides a framework to design effective interventions to increase condom use among adolescents.

The rate of teenage pregnancy in Canada is less than half that in the United States and United Kingdom but significantly higher than in France, Germany, and some northern European countries (Maticka-Tyndale, 2001; McKay, 2012; Singh & Darroch, 2000). The levels of sexual activity or the ages at which teenagers start engaging in sexual intercourse do not differ across Western countries, so what accounts for the differences in teenage pregnancy rates?

To answer this question, a team of researchers from Sweden, France, Canada, Great Britain, and the United States conducted a large-scale investigation into factors that account for the differences in teenage pregnancy rates in their five countries (Darroch et al., 2001). Of these countries, the lowest rates are in Sweden and France; Canada and Great Britain have intermediate rates; and the United States has the highest rate. The authors concluded that there are five primary factors that contribute to these differences:

1. The rates are higher in countries in which teenagers are less likely to use effective contraception.

2. Teenagers from poor and disadvantaged families are less likely to use contraception.

3. National programs that support the transition to adult economic roles and parenthood provide young people with greater incentives and means to delay childbearing.

4. Countries with lower rates have greater societal acceptance of sexual activity among young people.

5. Teenagers are more likely to use contraceptives if they know where to obtain information and services, can reach a provider easily, are assured of receiving confidential, nonjudgmental services, and can obtain contraceptive supplies at little or no cost.

Canada's scores on these five factors were mixed—we scored high on some and intermediate on others compared with the other four countries. Within Canada there are differences in adolescent pregnancy rates across provinces, territories, and communities (McKay, 2012; McKay & Barrett, 2010).

The teenage pregnancy rate has dropped substantially in the past ten years, especially among younger teenagers, probably because of teens' increasingly consistent use of contraceptives and teens increasingly choosing to delay sexual activity to later ages (McKay, 2012; McKay & Barrett, 2010). So why is teenage pregnancy considered a major social problem in Canada? The reason is that 45 percent of teenagers who get pregnant give birth to a child, and infants born to teenagers are more likely to have health problems. Most of these births are to single mothers from low-income homes, so having a baby as a teenager may limit the mother's economic and education opportunities (Rotermann, 2007b). However, some ethnocultural communities, including northern Aboriginal and First Nations communities, are accepting of teenage girls having babies (SIECCAN, 2004).

A Nova Scotia study that followed pregnant women for up to ten years after they gave birth gives us important information on the effects of teenage pregnancy on the mother and the child (Bissell, 2000; Nova Scotia Department of Community Services, 1991) This study compared 403 unmarried women with 416 married women, dividing these women into teenage mothers (19 years old or younger) and nonteenage mothers (20 or older). The study also included psychological and educational testing with the children. Unmarried mothers of all ages were most dissatisfied with their educational achievement. Women who were still in school before the pregnancy were most likely to return to school after the birth. Fifty-two percent of the single teenage mothers lived in

poverty, but so did 54 percent of the older unmarried women and 29 percent of the teenage married women. The young unmarried mothers made the most economic gains over the ten years, but they never caught up to the older married group. Eighty-seven percent subsequently married. There were few differences in their children's educational achievement. There were also no differences in the ways in which teenage mothers and older mothers dealt with their children's behaviour.

In short, the negative consequences associated with teenage pregnancy are largely a result of the fact that teenage mothers have less education and lower incomes rather than with the age of the mother (Bissell, 2000; Hardwick & Patychuk, 1999; Luong, 2008; Maticka-Tyndale, 2001; Singh et al., 2001). Two critical factors for successful outcomes for adolescent mothers are finishing high school (and preferably going for even more education; Figure 10.11) and postponing other births (Furstenberg, 1987; Luong, 2008). Teenage mothers are more likely to marry in their teens, on average have more children, and have lower incomes than women who were adult mothers (Luong, 2008). Thus, it is important to have social programs to assist adolescent mothers in finishing high school (such as school-based daycare), as well as effective sex education programs and access to contraception. See First

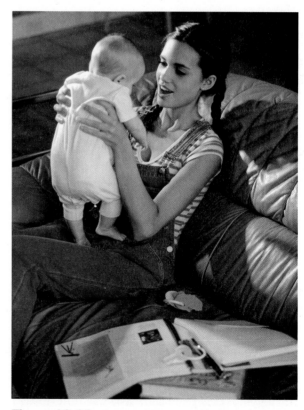

Figure 10.11 An important factor in life success for a pregnant teenager is the existence of special programs that allow her to complete high school.

Person for a success story: one woman's challenging but empowering experience of being a teen mother.

Late Adolescence (19 to 22 Years)

As noted earlier, adolescence researchers now classify traditional-age university and college students (ages 19 to 22) as late adolescents, although some refer to them as emerging adults. Whatever the terminology, the college or university years are now seen by students as a time for sexual experimenting with little or no responsibility (Bogle, 2008). Adult commitments are seen as being a long way away in the future. Almost all the research on the sexual behaviour of people in this age range has been conducted with university students, so we know little about the nonuniversity population.

Masturbation

Typically about 98 percent of the men and 80 percent of the women in our undergraduate human sexuality classes report that they masturbate. These numbers may be a bit higher than one would see in the general university population because students who choose to take a sexuality course tend to be somewhat more sexually liberal than average. Nonetheless, it seems likely that almost all university men and the great majority of university women do masturbate.

Undergraduates report that they have learned that masturbation is somewhat taboo, yet at the same time it is a source of great pleasure (Kaestle & Allen, 2011). Most men resolve this contradiction in favour of pleasure, whereas women are more likely to struggle with the contradiction.

Patterns of Mixed-Sex Behaviour

One study of new students found that, the summer before starting university, 44 percent had already engaged in intercourse (Patrick & Lee, 2010). An additional 11 percent began engaging in intercourse over the next six months, and 48 percent still had not engaged in intercourse six months into their first year. Another study showed that, by ages 20 to 24 (a sample a bit older than those in the first study), 85 percent have engaged in sexual intercourse (Chandra et al., 2011). In a British Columbia study, 64 percent of the non-Asian male students had engaged in fellatio and 59 percent had performed cunnilingus, although the rates were lower for the Asian male students (Meston et al., 1996). Interestingly, in contrast to many media depictions, researchers in New Brunswick have shown that most oral sex encounters occur within a committed relationship that typically also includes intercourse (Vannier & O'Sullivan, 2012). Fellatio was more common than cunnilingus.

Different students show very different patterns of sexual behaviour. One study aimed at characterizing these different patterns in a sample of 20- to 21-year-olds, 69 percent of whom were attending university and the remainder of whom were not (McGuire & Barber, 2010). At that point, 8 percent were married and an additional 8 percent were engaged or cohabiting; 12 percent had children. Eighty-six percent had engaged in sexual intercourse. Those who were engaging in intercourse fell into several distinct clusters. One group was called Active Unprotected—they had a relatively high frequency of sex and were moderately satisfied with their sex lives, but they did not practise safer sex. The Satisfied group were very satisfied with their sex life while placing low importance on having regular sex; they also scored high in risk reduction, both in terms of using contraceptives and limiting their number of partners. Those in the Inactive group had a low frequency of sex and gave low ratings to the importance of a sexual relationship, but their satisfaction was also low. The Pressured group reported more frequently being pressured or coerced into sex, and their satisfaction was low. The stories we hear in the mass media tend to characterize all university students as alike in their sex lives—as happy hooker-uppers. Certainly there is a hookup culture at most universities today, but this study shows how very diverse the patterns of sexuality can be for people of this age.

Casual Sex: Hookups and Friends with Benefits

College and university students commonly engage in casual sex relationships (Figure 10.12). Researchers in

Figure 10.12 Hooking up has become common on postsecondary campuses.

First Person

Becoming a Teen Mother: An Aboriginal Woman's Story

I am a thirty-seven-year-old First Nations mother of four sons and one daughter. I also am a third generation residential school survivor. My *Kohkum* and *Moosum* attended residential school and all of their children did as well, including my mother. This was mandatory for First Nations families, so they had no choice about whether their children would go. Thankfully, when I was child, the Indian Act had changed and I was not forced to attend residential school. However, residential school not only had a direct impact on my parents and grandparents, it also has directly affected my life. I believe the legacy of their experiences attending residential school is why I became a teen mother at the age of 15.

I am the youngest of my four sisters and have a younger brother. Growing up, sexuality was not a topic of conversation at any time in my family—it was NEVER discussed. My siblings and I are trying to stop the cycle by which residential schools continue to affect generation after generation by breaking the silence about sexual health and educating our children and our nieces and nephews about sexual health. We want to make sure that the next generation can make choices about their sexuality, practise safe sex if they choose to have sex, and plan when they would like to become parents.

My older sisters and I experienced our moon time (menstruation) without the traditional supports and information required when experiencing the gift from the Creator of becoming a First Nations woman. Also our grandmothers did not tell us the traditional stories that were passed on in previous generations when a girl becomes a woman. I was not educated about my sexuality and did not know how a woman experiences her moon time or becomes pregnant. I was not taught about sexuality, sexual health, or pregnancy at home, at school or by my peers.

I twice became a teen mother in the mid-1980s, a time when sexuality as a First Nations urban young woman was not discussed. I was very ill and nauseous while visiting my boyfriend on the reserve. While he went to town with his mother, I had a discussion with one of his older brothers. I mentioned that I was not feeling well and he grabbed a book called *The Book of Home Remedies*. After consulting this book, he told me that he believed I was pregnant. I was quite confused and honestly did not understand how this happened. I later visited a doctor who confirmed that I was indeed pregnant. That day my life changed forever. From the moment I knew I was carrying a child, I changed the direction of my life. My child is the reason why I am

---

Ontario asked students about the implicit and explicit rules that guide different types of casual sex relationships (Wentland & Reissing, 2011). They found that they could be differentiated based on five characteristics: frequency of contact, type of contact, personal disclosure, discussion of the relationship, and friendship. Figure 10.13 describes four types of casual sexual relationships as well as committed relationships on each of these dimensions.

Hooking up refers to a sexual encounter that involves people who are strangers or brief acquaintances, without an expectation of forming a committed relationship, that is, a one night stand. The behaviour itself may range from making out to oral sex or intercourse (Bogle, 2008; Heldman & Wade, 2010). In one U.S. study,

Hooking up: A sexual encounter that involves people who are strangers or brief acquaintances, without an expectation of forming a committed relationship; the behaviour itself may range from making out to oral sex or intercourse.

60 percent of white undergraduates reported hooking up in the past year, compared with only 30 to 40 percent for Black students (Owen et al., 2010).

An unfortunate reality is that much hookup sex is bad sex, whether because it is not pleasurable or because it is actually coercive (Heldman & Wade, 2010). In one study of university students, 78 percent of coerced sex occurred while hooking up (Flack et al., 2007). Another factor contributing to the bad sex is that there is an "orgasm gap," with women being much less likely to orgasm in such encounters than men are. Happily, though, women of the same age are much more likely to have orgasms when the sex occurs in the context of a committed relationship (Armstrong et al., 2012). In addition, women often appreciate receiving cunnilingus, but it is not part of the hookup script—although it is part of the script in committed relationships (Backstrom et al., 2012).

where I am today. I realized that I wanted to live for the future and provide for my child's needs in every way—physically, mentally, emotionally, and spiritually.

At the time I became pregnant, I was attending a high school in a small town. I experienced stigma and discrimination and was shunned by many of the educators at my high school because I was pregnant. To make matters worse, I wasn't just a teen mom, I was an urban First Nations pregnant teenager. That title alone carried a tremendous amount of stigma. The way I was treated was very stressful for me. I made the choice that it was important for me to continue my education if I was to provide for the needs of my unborn child. Therefore, I returned to Regina, where I had grown up, to complete high school. When the high school in Regina learned that I was expecting, they called a meeting with the principal, the vice principal and the student support counsellors. They informed me that I would not be able to attend school there any longer and that I would have to transfer to the pregnant mothers program. When I left the meeting I felt disappointed. However, soon my disappointment turned to anger and then to the drive and dedication to not leave the high school. I fought to remain there. I was informed that being a pregnant teen would affect all adolescents in the school and this might become "contagious" among my peers. Thankfully, in the end, I won the right to continue to attend this high school. The teen mom program that the school wanted me to attend did not provide the same level of education as I got in the regular high school.

Becoming a teen mother was a challenge, yet it was an empowering experience. I welcomed my son, Raymond into the world on January 16th, 1986. I was in labour for over 36 hours and started to have numerous complications, so Raymond was delivered by Caesarean section. I brought my son home with the passion to provide for his needs the best that I could. Twenty months later, I became a teen mother again. On May 2nd, 1988, Rowan joined our family, and I was a single teen mom determined to provide for both of my sons as well as to achieve all of my dreams. Having two children assisted me to make the right choices, to complete my high school education, and to work hard to follow my dreams. I am currently completing my PhD in clinical psychology, and I am a professor at the First Nations University of Canada. I am living my dreams to the fullest and would not change anything in my life. My journey has been tremendously hard at times, especially as a single teen mom of two young sons, but it has been so worth it!

Source: Kim McKay-McNabb, MA, who is originally from Sakimay First Nation. Her husband Patrick is from George Gordon First Nation.

Hookups typically occur in the context of parties, whether residence-hall or off-campus (Bersamin et al., 2012). Alcohol use is heavy, again contributing to bad sex and unprotected sex.

Some students are enthusiastic about their experiences with hooking up, but others report emotional distress (Heldman & Wade, 2010; Owen & Fincham, 2011b). Often there is a discrepancy between what students want and what they get in such encounters, and the lack of emotional connection can leave some feeling lonely. One study found that hookups that involved oral, vaginal, or anal sex increased psychological distress for female students but not for male students (Fielder & Carey, 2010).

A double standard exists in hookup culture. Men can gain status by acquiring a large number of partners. On the surface, hooking up is equally acceptable for women and men, but in reality, if a woman has too many partners, she can come to be labelled as a slut (Bogle, 2008).

Another variation on the casual sex theme is **friends with benefits** (FWB), which refers to a situation in which two people who are friends (not romantic partners) occasionally have sex with each other. In one study of university students, 54 percent of the men and 43 percent of the women reported at least one FWB relationship (Owen & Fincham, 2011a). Unlike hookups, FWB relationships involve just that—a relationship, which involves support, companionship, and common activities. Yet the sex occurs without the expectation that the relationship will become romantic. A Nova Scotia study demonstrated that late adolescents who

Friends with benefits: Two people who are friends (not romantic partners) occasionally have sex with each other.

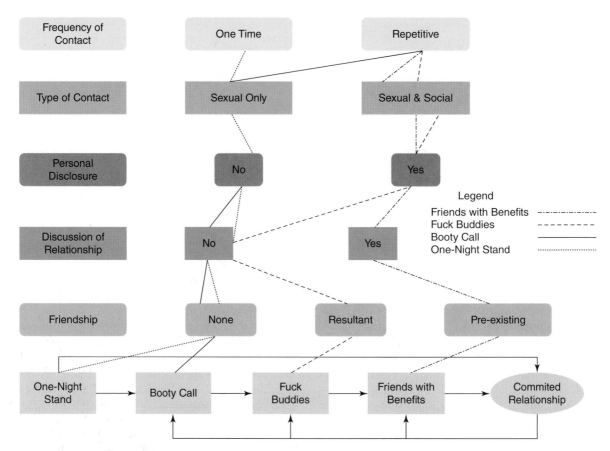

Figure 10.13   Four types of casual sexual relationships can be differentiated based on frequency of contact, type of contact, personal disclosure, discussion of the relationship, and friendship.

Source: Wentland, J.J., & Reissing, E.D., "Taking casual sex not too casually: Arriving at consensus definitions for different types of casual sexual relationships." Canadian Journal of Human Sexuality, 75–91, 2011. Used with permission.

have engaged in FWB relationships agreed on what the unstated rules are about these types of relationships. They also identified some downsides (such as unreciprocated feelings) as well as a range of benefits (Weaver et al., 2011). As one man explained,

> You want to experience sexual things and you'd rather do it with a best friend and have no attachments than figure out later on, like when you're in a relationship and don't want to do things for the first time because it might ruin your relationship . . . we were exploring, I guess. You know, just figuring things out. (Weaver et al., 2011, p. 47)

Yet another variation is the **booty call**, which refers to a communication to a person who is not a relationship partner but is an acquaintance, conveying an urgent request for sexual activity, perhaps including intercourse (Jonason et al., 2009; Jonason et al., 2011). Most often the message is delivered by phone (thus booty *call*), but it also may be delivered by texting or online

Booty call: A communication to a person who is not a relationship partner, conveying an urgent request for sexual activity, perhaps including intercourse.

chatting. In contrast to hooking up, the people are not in the same room with each other, at least not initially. Men are more likely to initiate booty calls, and women are more likely to receive them. Reasons for agreeing to the request include the physical attractiveness of the other person and having time for it. Two people can have a booty-call relationship, in which they engage in booty calls repeatedly over time; therefore, this kind of relationship is different from a one-night stand. Behaviours in a booty-call relationship show some signs of intimacy, such as kissing, but they also are characterized by such behaviours as leaving immediately after sex that keep the relationship from evolving into a long-term romantic relationship.

Same-Sex Sexual Behaviour

Well-sampled research in the U.S. shows that, among 20- to 24-year-olds, 16 percent of women have engaged in same-sex sexual behaviour and 6 percent of men have (Chandra et al., 2011). At these ages, people can show distinct changes in their sexual identity, attractions, and behaviour over time, a point discussed in more detail in Chapter 13.

L07

How Sexuality Aids in Development

Erik Erikson postulated a model of psychosocial development according to which we experience crises at each of eight stages of our lives (Erikson, 1950, 1968). Each crisis may be resolved in one of two directions. Erikson emphasized the idea that social influences are particularly important in determining the outcomes of these crises.

The stages postulated by Erikson are listed in Table 10.4. Notice that the outcomes of several of them may be closely linked to sexuality. For example, in early childhood there is a crisis between autonomy and shame, and later between initiative and guilt. The child who masturbates at age five is showing autonomy and initiative. But if the parents react to this activity by severely punishing the child, their actions may produce shame and guilt. Thus they may be encouraging the child to feel ashamed and consequently to suffer a loss of self-esteem.

In adolescence, the crisis is between identity and role confusion. Gender roles are among the most important; in later adolescence, the person may emerge with a stable, self-confident sense of manhood or womanhood or, alternatively, may feel in conflict about gender roles. A choice of career is important in this developing sense of identity, and gender roles influence career choice. A sexual identity also emerges—for example, heterosexual, gay, lesbian, bisexual, or asexual.

In young adulthood, the crisis is between intimacy and isolation. Sexuality, of course, can function in an important way as people develop their capacity for intimacy. Researchers in Nova Scotia have

Table 10.4 Erikson's Stages of Psychosocial Development

Approximate Stage in the Life Cycle	Crisis
Infancy	Basic trust versus mistrust
Ages 1½ to 3 years	Autonomy versus shame and doubt
Ages 3 to 5½ years	Initiative versus guilt
Ages 6 to 12 years	Industry versus inferiority
Adolescence	Identity versus role confusion
Young adulthood	Intimacy versus isolation
Adulthood	Generativity versus stagnation
Maturity	Ego integrity versus despair

demonstrated that an individual's sexual behaviour can be understood within an attachment framework (Szielasko et al., 2013).

Furman (2002), a developmental psychologist, proposed that the behavioural sequence from adolescence through emerging adulthood parallels a developmental one. Early relationships reflect simple interest. Subsequent ones fulfill primarily affiliative and sexual needs as young people explore their sexual feelings. As the person moves into late adolescence and early adulthood, longer-term relationships fulfill needs for attachment and mutual caring. One important consequence of this process is the development of a sexual identity with regard to both sexual orientation and the sense of one's own sexual attractiveness. The timing of this process varies from one person to another, one influence being culture with some cultures insisting on more parental control over adolescents. Furman points out that many social and cultural arrangements facilitate the emergence of heterosexual relationships and at the same time deter gay and lesbian relationships.

Clearly, sexuality is an integral part of adolescent development.

SUMMARY

Data on sexuality in childhood are often based on surveys of adults, asking them to recall their childhood behaviour. In addition, parents are sometimes asked about their children's sexual behaviour. Much more data are available on adolescents' sexual behavior based on direct information from adolescents.

A capacity for sexual response is present from infancy. Attachment processes are important in infancy and may have an impact on the person's capacity for adult romantic relationships. Parents of two- to

five-year-olds report that about 17 percent of boys and girls masturbate with their hand. Children also engage in some heterosexual play, with games of doctor. Preschoolers are interested in learning about sexuality, although they often have misunderstandings.

Adrenarche causes increased levels of androgens and occurs around eight to ten years of age. More children begin to masturbate in this age range. Children have a gender-segregated social organization, so their sex play tends to occur with same-gender peers. Children also quickly learn heteronormativity. Many experts are concerned about the sexualization of children.

A tension exists between thinking about adolescent sexuality as a normative, growth-promoting part of development and thinking that much adolescent sexuality is risky. According to one theory, the increase in sexual activity in adolescence is influenced by the interaction of biological factors (increasing testosterone levels) and social and psychological factors (for example, sexually permissive attitudes). By age 15, most boys have masturbated, but girls tend to begin masturbating somewhat later than boys and fewer of them do masturbate. The research evidence indicates that the media have an impact on adolescent sexuality. Some girls and boys engage in same-sex sexual behavior in adolescence, and about 43 percent of high school students have engaged in heterosexual intercourse. Heterosexual sex that occurs too early (age 15 or before) is more likely to be risky sex and is a cause for concern. Social networking through sites such as Facebook, is a popular way for adolescents to communicate. Sexting is not as common as media reports suggest, but it can be serious for those involved.

Patterns of mixed-sex sexual behavior for university students can be quite varied. Casual sex, involving hookups and friends with benefits, is one pattern. Other students engage in same-sex sexual behaviour or bisexual behaviour.

Following Erik Erikson's theory, experiences with sexuality can serve important functions in a person's psychological development. They may be important, for example, in the process of developing an identity and in developing a capacity for intimacy.

QUESTIONS FOR THOUGHT, DISCUSSION, AND DEBATE

1. Are adolescents today more liberal, more conservative, or the same in their sexual attitudes and behaviours compared with adolescents 10 or 20 years ago?

2. What challenges do most gay, lesbian, and bisexual youth face in terms of their sexual development that most heterosexual youth do not face? What challenges are similar? How can we change Canadian society to make it easier for gay, lesbian, and bisexual youth?

3. Does permissiveness with affection characterize the standard for sexual intercourse among the 18- to 22-year-olds you know?

4. The mother of a five-year-old child tells you that her son has been masturbating while he watches TV in the family room. She asks you what she should do about his behaviour. What would you tell her?

5. You have been put in charge of designing a program to increase consistent condom use by adolescents. Based on the information provided in this chapter, and on your knowledge of the 18- to 22-year-olds you know, what would you include in the program that you design? How might you need to tailor the program differently for the different ethnocultural groups in Canada?

Are YOU Curious?

1. Do young single adults go to bars to hook up?
2. Do single people have sex more frequently than married people?
3. What happens to sex in long-term relationships over time?
4. How does sex change for older adults?

Read this chapter to find out.

CHAPTER

11

Sexuality and the Life Cycle: Adulthood

LEARNING OBJECTIVES

After studying this chapter, you will be able to

LO1 Describe the continuing sexual development that occurs throughout young adulthood.

LO2 Identify the various never-married groups and describe the single lifestyles.

LO3 Describe the rates of and influences on cohabitation, as well as the sexual lives of people who live together.

LO4 Describe sex in marriage.

LO5 Differentiate the qualities seen in happy versus unhappy couples.

LO6 Define the different kinds of extradyadic sex and their prevalence, acceptance, and causes among Canadians.

LO7 Describe the sexual lives of divorced and widowed men and women.

LO8 Describe the physical, psychological, and behavioural effects of aging on sexuality and how these compare with attitudes toward sexuality and aging.

Grow old along with me!
The best is yet to be.*
Life begins at forty.**

* Robert Browning. (1864). *Rabbi Ben Ezra.*
** Attributed to Sophie Tucker.

This chapter continues to trace the development of sexuality across the lifespan. We will look at various aspects of sexuality in adulthood: sex and the single person, cohabitation, common-law and marital sexuality, nonmonogamous sexuality, sex in a second long-term relationship, and sex among older adults. Each lifestyle is an option, reflecting the diversity of choices available in Canada today. We have incorporated information about both same-sex and mixed-sex couples into this chapter, although we consider lifestyles specific to same-sex partners in more detail in Chapter 14.

The fact that these lifestyles are options today represents a huge social change from 1960, when three-quarters of all adults were married. In a major report, the Pew Research Center (2010) summarizes this change as "the decline of marriage and the rise of new families." Several new relationship and family forms have emerged, as we will see.

LO1

Sex and the Single Person

Sexual Unfolding Development

The process of sexual development discussed in Chapter 10 continues into adulthood. There remains a need to define one's sexual identity and orientation.

Heterosexuality is the norm in our society, and some people slip into it easily. Others sense that they are different. Some sense that their orientation is gay or lesbian and must struggle with society's **heterosexism** and negative messages about these groups. Others sense that they are attracted to both men and women and may experience sexual fluidity (see Chapter 14). These struggles over sexual orientation seem to be more difficult for men than for women because heterosexuality is such an important cornerstone of the male role in many societies, including ours (see Chapter 13).

Another step toward maturity is identifying our sexual likes and dislikes and how they vary across situations. Learning what they like and dislike may occur naturally as individuals experience

Heterosexism: The belief that heterosexuality is the only legitimate, acceptable, and healthy way for people to be; homosexuality is denigrated.

various behaviours over time. Alternatively, some people intentionally seek opportunities to engage in novel behaviours or in sexual intimacy with novel partners. Of course, it is not enough to know our likes and dislikes; we must also learn to communicate them to a partner. Learning to communicate with sexual partners is difficult for many persons, perhaps because there are few role models in our society showing us how to engage in direct, honest communication. Effective sexual communication is described in Chapter 12.

Two more issues are important in achieving sexual maturity: becoming responsible about sex, and developing a capacity for intimacy. Taking responsibility includes being careful about contraception and sexually transmitted infections, and being responsible for yourself and for your partner. Intimacy (see Chapter 12) involves a deep emotional sharing between two people that goes beyond casual sex or manipulative sex.

The media influence our ideas of what constitutes mature sexuality. Most television shows promote a rather stereotyped and heterosexist view of sex and the single person. Recently, there has been an increase in the number of television programs that have sexuality as a major focus, and some of them are tackling topics that never used to be discussed on television. For example, in the early 1990s, the main characters in *Seinfeld* had a competition to see who could go the longest without masturbating. In an episode of *Friends*, Rachel and Monica struggle over who gets the last condom and, by implication, which one of them gets to have sex. *Queer as Folk* and *The L Word* introduced gay men and lesbians as central characters. In fact, *Queer as Folk* was one of the first television shows about the lives of gays and lesbians. It also regularly featured scenes of explicit same-sex sexual activity, often emphasizing the use of condoms. More recently *Orange Is the New Black* has a female character who doesn't define her sexual identity. For example, she says, "I like hot girls, I like hot boys, I like hot people." *Sex and the City* introduced single female characters who were not only comfortable with their sexuality but actively pursued sex for pleasure and talked openly about it. Of course, most single television characters still fit societal stereotypes and, even in the more progressive shows, characters tend to fit the media ideal of young, thin, and attractive. Nonetheless, even though they are isolated examples, these shows expose and challenge the hidden and explicit media messages about sexuality and the single person.

LO2 The Never-Married

The term *never married* refers to adults who have never been legally married. This group includes those who intend to marry someday and those who have decided to remain single, perhaps living in a long-term common-law relationship. People are also waiting longer to get married. In the 2006 census, 93 percent of people ages 20 to 24 and 70 percent of those ages 25 to 29 were never married, compared with 56 percent and 21 percent, respectively, in the 1971 census. About 20 percent of these never-married individuals are in a common-law relationship with someone of the same or other gender. Most (91 percent) expect to have children (Stobert & Kemeny, 2003).

Most adults in Canada (up to 95 percent) do marry. The average age of first marriage in 2003 was 28.5 years for women and 30.6 years for men (Statistics Canada, 2007), so the typical person who marries spends several adult years in the never-married category. Canadians are older at the age of first marriage now than in the past, largely because most live together first and delay getting married. Some of these men and women spend this entire time in one relationship that eventually leads to marriage. According to the National Health and Social Life Survey (NHSLS), among married persons 20 to 29 years old, 46 percent of the men and 65 percent of the women are in this category (Laumann et al., 1994). Other young adults continue the pattern of *serial monogamy*, which (as we saw in Chapter 10) characterizes adolescent intimate relationships; they are involved in two or more sexually intimate relationships before marriage. According to the NHSLS, among married persons 20 to 29, 40 percent of the men and 28 percent of the women had two or more sexual partners before they married.

Many never-married individuals are in a romantic relationship. Some of these individuals are cohabiting. Others choose to live in a different residence than their partner (sometimes called *living apart together* or LAT relationship). This may be because they want to maintain their independence or keep their own residence, or because they are caring for children or aging parents (Levin & Trost, 1999). In addition, increasing numbers of these relationships are long distance. This kind of geographic separation can be stressful and lonely. People in long-distance romantic relationships report greater depression and lower relationship satisfaction (Cameron & Ross, 2007). However, long-distance relationships are not necessarily less stable than other dating relationships (Van Horn et al., 1997). What factors predict whether a long-distance relationship will survive or end? Research has shown that long-distance relationships are less likely to end if people have more trust and faith in their partner's commitment, expect more support from their partner, and are more optimistic about the future of the relationship (Cameron & Ross, 2007). Long-distance relationships are also more stable when partners see the relationship in an idealized rather than in a realistic way. They are more likely to maintain idealized notions about the relationship if they see each other less frequently (Stafford & Merolla, 2007). Interestingly, long-distance relationships often end when partners start living in the same location.

The person who passes age 30 without forming a long-term relationship gradually enters a new world. The social structures that supported meeting new people—such as college or university—are gone, and more people of the same age are married.

The attitudes of singles about their status vary widely. Some young men and women decide to live both single and sexually celibate or **chaste** (abstaining from sexual intercourse). Little research has been done on celibacy, and published studies often do not distinguish voluntary from involuntary celibates. Research using a questionnaire posted on the Internet (Donnelly et al., 2001) identified three types of involuntary celibates. *Virgins* had never had intercourse, had rarely dated, and often had not engaged in any partnered sexual intimacy. Some had not made the developmental transitions discussed earlier; others had chosen not to engage in intercourse before marriage. *Singles* had sexual experience but often reported that it was not satisfying; they were unable to find and maintain long-term relationships. Both their residential and work arrangements made it difficult for persons in either group to meet potential partners. The third type are *partnered* persons in sexless relationships. Typically the relationship had included sex in the past but the frequency gradually declined over time.

Some people plan to remain single but not chaste. They find the single lifestyle exciting and enjoy their freedom. A survey of 3600 Canadian adolescents found that only 88 percent expect to marry (Bibby, 2001). Other men and women are searching for a spouse. According to a recent online survey, about 61 percent of the straight women and 66 percent of the straight men not in a relationship wished they were in one ("Sex Survey," n.d.). The search for a spouse affects some people with increasing desperation as the years go by. According to one researcher, their desperation is fuelled by **singleism**, the stigmatizing and stereotyping of people who are not in a socially

Chaste: Abstaining from sexual intercourse; sexually celibate.
Singleism: The stigmatizing and stereotyping of people who are not in a socially recognized couple relationship.

recognized couple relationship (DePaulo, 2006). She argues that singles can and do live "happily ever after."

How do never-married Canadians over 30 years old who expect to marry differ from those who do not expect to ever marry? The "won't marry" group are more likely to be single parents, have lower incomes, and have less education. They also view love, marriage, and family as less important (Crompton, 2005).

L02 Being Single

At one extreme, there is the *singles scene*. It is institutionalized in such forms as singles apartment complexes and singles bars. Fitness centres, religious groups, and parties provide opportunities for meeting others (Figure 11.1). A recent innovation, intended for the busy urban professional, is *speed dating*. Singles attend a dating event involving 15 to 25 other singles. They are given a sticker with a number on it and then speak to each of the other attendees for a short and fixed time that often depends on the number of attendees, but typically ranges between four and ten minutes. At the end of the evening they indicate their interest in seeing each individual again (yes or no) on a form and wait to see whether there is a match. This process is not without its anxieties. Attendees may find it difficult to remember the characteristics and qualities of the many people they meet, worry about finding something interesting to say in the short time allotted, and feel disappointed and despondent if none of the attendees they were interested in indicated reciprocal interest in them.

Do young single adults go to bars to hook up?

The urban bar provides a visible display of the singles scene (Grazian, 2008). Young men and women, most of them single, engage in *sporting rituals*, game-oriented cultural scripts for nightlife participation. These rituals involve elaborate preparations for all genders: careful attention to grooming, to clothing choice, and to adornment; stiletto heels are required and young women want to be "alluring" and to display (not too much) skin. There is usually drinking in advance at home, both to jump-start the alcohol and to save money. The number and type of companions are also often chosen to reflect the night's purpose; a group of five or six often goes out to have fun, flirt, be seen, dance, and perhaps collect some phone numbers. If the purpose is to find a sexual partner, a pair usually works better. Public behaviour in the bars is intended to display traditional masculinity and femininity. The "pick up" is usually not the purpose according to Grazian; most participants know it is unlikely but when it is the purpose, it has its own elaborate rituals. For example, researchers in Ontario have shown that most women prefer to be approached in a nonsexual manner. Researchers also observed behaviour in dance clubs, pubs, and lounges. They found that use of sexual overt approach behaviours is common in the sexualized atmosphere on the dance floor (Huber & Herold, 2006). The most common overt behaviour was grinding, which was sometimes initiated by men and sometimes initiated by women. For example, the researchers observed the following interaction:

> A female wearing jeans and a white button-down shirt, approached a seemingly unacquainted man to grind from behind. The man smiled and continued dancing with her. A moment later, a second woman, a friend of the first, approached the man to grind pelvis-to-pelvis, forming a "sandwich." After approximately 10 seconds, the group spontaneously dispersed. (Huber & Herold, 2006, p. 139)

Many singles, however, do not go to singles bars. Some are turned off by the idea; some feel that they cannot compete, that they are too old or not attractive enough; and some live in rural areas where they have no access to such places. An alternative way of meeting

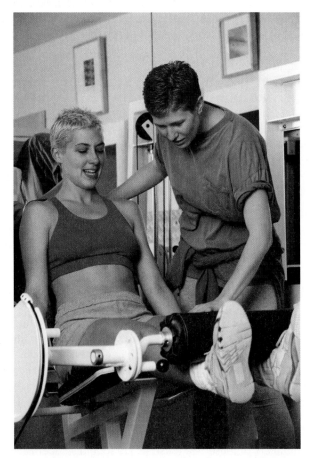

Figure 11.1 Fitness clubs are one current alternative to singles bars for some people who are hoping to meet that special someone.

people is through singles ads, most frequently these days on the Internet as part of online dating. There are hundreds of sites where people can post ads or create a personal Web page. Some are general sites. For example, Toronto-based Lavalife.com has three separate streams for individuals seeking partners of the same or the other sex (labelled "dating," "relationship," and "intimate encounters"), as well as a stream for individuals over 45 years old. Lavalife has more than 1.7 million active members who exchange more than 700,000 messages per day. There also are smaller sites geared toward individuals with specific interests, such as vegetarians, pet lovers, members of a particular religious group, or seniors. Internet dating sites have been important in reducing the isolation experienced by some sexual-minority individuals—that is, gay, lesbian, bisexual, intersex, and transgender individuals.

Online ads typically include information about the type of partner a person is searching for, as well as the person's age, ethnicity, height, and area of residence. They often include a photograph. Those seeking partners can search the ads and home pages on these characteristics. Contacts made online can lead to an off-line relationship or to a continuing online one. The relationship may evolve to include **cybersex**, where partners engage in sexual talk online for the purposes of sexual pleasure. It may or may not involve masturbation. It can also include real-time videos or webcams (Shaughnessy et al., 2011).

A survey of 769 Canadian university students found that 18 percent of the men and 10 percent of the women had used an online dating site in the previous 12 months (Boies, 2002). Researchers in Ontario have shown that, compared with Internet users who are not online daters, Internet daters are more likely to be male, single, divorced, employed, urban, and have higher incomes (Brym & Lenton, 2003). The online daters were not socially isolated, as has sometimes been assumed. They belonged to clubs, socialized with family and friends, and saw themselves as self-confident.

The visibility of online dating, singles bars, singles tours, and other activities geared toward single adults suggests a fun-loving lifestyle with frequent sexual activity. Undoubtedly, some single persons live such a life. As Figure 11.2 indicates, among 18- to 24-year-old Americans, 10 percent of the men and 13 percent of the women who completed the National Survey of Sexual Health and Behavior (NSSHB) online survey reported having vaginal intercourse two or more times per week. Among singles ages 30 to 39, 41 percent of the men but only 4 percent of the women reported vaginal intercourse that often. The reality is different for other singles; among 18- to 24-year-olds, 57 percent of the men and 51 percent of the women did not have vaginal intercourse in the preceding year. Among those 30 to 39, single men were much more likely to experience intercourse than their younger counterparts, but three-fourths of the single women had not had intercourse in the past year. Bibby (2006) has shown that 42 percent of single Canadians engage in sexual intercourse on a weekly basis or more often.

> **Do single people have sex more frequently than married people?**

LO3

Cohabitation

In early adulthood, it is common for couples to experiment with various levels of commitment, such as an exclusive dating relationship or living together. Even when living together, there are different levels of commitment, from "living together apart" to "some days and nights" to "all the time." Living together is an important turning point not only because it represents commitment but also because it is a public declaration of a sexual relationship. It is rare for two people who are going out to live together just because it will save on rent. Cohabiting is an opportunity to explore a more serious commitment, at least to some extent. Forty-two percent of Canadians have lived with a nonmarital partner at some point in their lives; this percentage is even higher for people under 40 years old (Bibby, 2006). Most of these individuals indicate that they want to be married at some point in their lives. Increasingly, middle-aged and older individuals are living common law (Statistics Canada, 2007).

Cohabitation has become an increasingly common alternative to marriage, particularly in Quebec (see Chapter 1 for discussion of Quebec as a distinct society sexually), and most Canadians (93 percent) accept people living together without being married (Bibby, 2006, Le Bourdais & Lapierre-Adamcyk, 2004). According to the 2011 Canadian census, the number of common-law couples had grown four times as fast as the number of married couples since 2006. Under federal law, when two people live together as a couple for 12 continuous months but are not legally married to each other, they are in a **common-law relationship**. People in a common-law relationship are entitled to most but not all of the rights of people who are married. According to the 2011 census, 17 percent of Canadians were living in common-law relationships, up from 6 percent in 1981. The rate of cohabitation is higher among same-sex couples—67 percent of same sex couples were common law. The

Cybersex: Online sexually oriented communication, activities, or exchanges with a partner.
Common-law relationship: Two people who have lived together as a couple for 12 continuous months but are not legally married to each other.

rate is highest in Quebec and in the territories, where 25 to 33 percent of couples are common law. Common-law relationships are most common among people ages 20 to 24. Interestingly, the rate of cohabitation in Canada is twice the rate of cohabitation in the United States (Popenoe, 2009).

Slightly more than half of couples living together eventually marry, although this percentage is lower in Quebec. That is, in most of Canada cohabitation is typically seen as a relationship stage preceding marriage (Le Bourdais & Lapierre-Adamcyk, 2004). Two-thirds of cohabiting couples that marry do so within two years of starting to live together. However, common-law relationships break up more often than marriages do. About 60 percent of people who end common-law relationships do so before the age of 30; most of these couples do not have children (Statistics Canada, 2007). Common-law relationships that end do so, on average, after four years, compared with marriages that end, which do so after an average of 14 years. However, in Quebec, cohabitation is more often seen as replacing marriage rather than as a stage preceding marriage and as an appropriate relationship within which to have and raise children (Le Bourdais & Lapierre-Adamcyk, 2004). According to Le Bourdais and Lapierre-Adamcyk (2004), the higher rate of common-law relationships in place of marriage in Quebec has to do with stronger acceptance of egalitarian roles for men and women in Quebec than elsewhere in Canada. It is also in keeping with the more liberal attitudes toward sexuality held by Quebecers (see Chapter 1 for a discussion of other differences between Quebec and the rest of Canada).

Does living together before marriage make it less likely that the marriage will end in divorce? Contrary to what many people think, marriages that are preceded by cohabitation are more (not less) likely to end in separation than marriages that are not preceded by cohabitation (Clark & Crompton, 2006; Le Bourdais & Lapierre-Adamcyk, 2004; Rhoades et al., 2009). Does this mean that cohabiting causes divorce? If so, it might be because some couples who live together get married even though they would not have gotten married had they not lived together, perhaps because of inertia (Stanley et al., 2006). In keeping with this view, a longitudinal study compared couples who cohabited before they were engaged, couples who cohabited after engagement/before marriage, and couples who did not live together until after marriage (Kline et al., 2004). Couples were assessed twice, following engagement and after ten months of marriage. At both times, couples who lived together before engagement had more negative interactions (e.g., criticizing their partner), lower commitment, and lower relationship quality. Thus, the seeds of divorce were sown in the pre-engagement relationship. A related

study found that men in pre-engagement cohabiting relationships were less committed to the partner than those who were not cohabiting (Rhoades et al., 2006). However, other researchers have found that cohabitation has little effect on divorce rates after taking personal and cultural characteristics of individuals into account (Woods & Emery, 2002). Taken together, these data suggest that living together does not cause divorce, even though the rate of divorce is higher for couples who have lived together before marriage.

The popular image of cohabitation is that it involves young, never-married couples without children. However, almost half of common-law couples have children living in the home (Statistics Canada, 2011b). Canadians whose first marriage has dissolved often choose common-law over remarriage. This accounts for more than one-quarter of common-law relationships in Canada and is especially true of people in their 30s and 40s. People living in common-law relationships of some permanence are entitled to most of the same legal rights as married individuals.

With respect to sexual behaviour, Bibby (1995) found that 60 percent of married persons reported having sexual intercourse once a week or more, whereas 71 percent of cohabiting persons had sexual intercourse with that frequency (see Figure 11.2b). Similarly, an analysis of data from a large, representative sample of adults in the United States found that married persons reported having intercourse 8 to 11 times a month, whereas cohabiters reported a frequency of 11 to 13 times per month (Call et al., 1995). The NHHSB found that partnered men reported more frequent sex than did married men (see Figure 11.2). However, notice the wide variation; some partnered men and women report having sex only a few times per year. It is interesting that, on average, cohabiting couples have sex more often than married couples do. Some cohabitors are concerned about the stability of the relationship (Bumpass et al., 1991); they may have sex more frequently in the hope that it will strengthen the relationship (Blumstein & Schwartz, 1983).

Although 25 to 30 percent of gay men and lesbians live with a same-sex partner, there has been little research on sexuality within committed same-sex relationships (Peplau et al., 2004). Among both gay men and lesbians, there is considerable variability in the frequency with which couples have sex. Generally, the longer couples have been together, the less frequently they have sex. Most individuals in same-sex relationships report being sexually satisfied. Sexual exclusiveness or monogamy tends to be the norm for lesbians whereas many gay men are in relationships that are, by agreement, sexually open (Peplau et al., 2004).

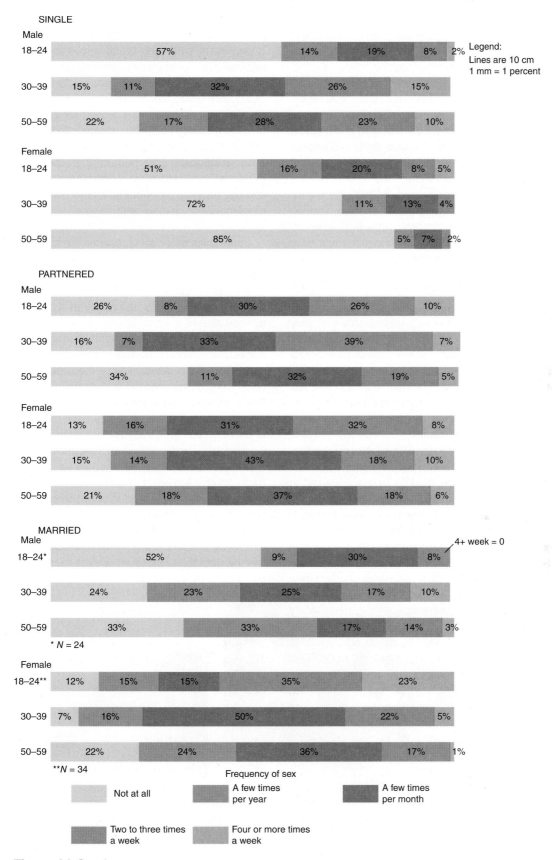

Figure 11.2 Frequency of sexual activity is closely related to marital status. Note that there is substantial variability in frequency within each status as well. Frequency also varies by age, within each status.
Sources: Herbenick et al. (2010b), Reece et al. (2010b).

LO4

Marriage

In 2000 the Supreme Court of Canada ruled that, for the most part, under the equality provision of the *Charter of Rights and Freedoms,* same-sex couples (and heterosexual common-law couples) have the same rights and responsibilities as heterosexual married couples (the situation in Quebec is somewhat different because they operate under civil law not common law). In 2005 the federal government passed legislation that ensured that all Canadians have the right to marry, regardless of sexual orientation. According to the 2011 census, there were 21,015 same-sex married couples in Canada; that is three times as many same-sex married couples as in 2006 (Statistics Canada, 2011b). More than half (53.7 percent) of same-sex married spouses are men. Same-sex weddings in Canada are now sufficiently mainstream that they have even spawned a prime-time reality television show, *My Fabulous Gay Wedding.* However, it will probably be a number of years before we have research on sexuality within same-sex marriages. Therefore, the following sections focus on sex in heterosexual marriages.

Given that common-law couples have many of the same rights and responsibilities as married couples, why do people want to marry? Marriage is a psychological turning point for many people (Figure 11.3). The decision to get married is a real decision these days, in contrast to previous decades when everyone assumed that they would marry and the only question was to whom. Today, most couples have had a full sexual relationship, sometimes for years, before they marry. The three most important reasons Canadians give for

getting married are that it signifies their commitment, is consistent with their moral values and beliefs, and reflects their belief that children should have married parents (Bibby, 2006). Married and engaged lesbian, gay, or bisexual (LGB) individuals also identify demonstrating their commitment as a reason for getting married (Alderson, 2004). Other reasons included the legal protection that marriage provides, the further cementing of the relationship, the political fight for equality and public acknowledgement of same-sex relationships, and the importance of being able to use the language of marriage (e.g., spouse, wife, husband, daughter-in-law) (Alderson, 2004; MacIntosh et al., 2010).

Some psychological pressures seem to intensify with marriage, and these pressures may result in problems where there were none previously. For many people, marriage is a tangible statement that one has left the family of origin (the family in which you grew up) and shifted to creating one's own family (in which many people become the parents rearing children); for some, this separation from parents is difficult. The pressure for sexual performance may become more intense once people are married, as sexual dissatisfactions that were easy to overlook in the early, rose-coloured-glasses phase of the relationship have more and more impact on each individual's sexual satisfaction. Finally, marriage still carries with it an assumption of a lifelong commitment to fidelity or faithfulness, a promise that is hard for some to keep.

In any long-term relationship, there is a need to work out issues of roles. Who will do what? Some of the decisions are as tame as who cooks supper. However, who initiates sex is far more sensitive, and who has the right to say no to sex is even more so.

(a)

(b)

Figure 11.3   Sexual turning points. *(a)* Marriage and the commitment it represents is a major turning point. *(b)* The birth of a baby is a turning point that can have a negative impact on sexual aspects of the relationship, but couples who are aware of this possibility can work to overcome these problems and keep the romance going.

This is the era of two-career couples or at least dual-earner couples. There are issues here of finding time for sex and for just being with each other.

As a relationship progresses, it cannot stay forever as blushingly beautiful as it seemed when it began. The nature of love changes (see Chapter 12), and for some couples there is a gradual disenchantment with sex. Couples need to take steps to avoid boredom in the bedroom. Sexual disorders (see Chapter 18) occur in many long-term relationships, and couples need to find ways to resolve them.

Frequency of Intercourse

According to the 2006 census, 90 percent of Canadians ages 50 to 69 are or have been legally married. However, it is expected that only 73 percent of men and 78 percent of women ages 30 to 39 will marry. About a third of first marriages end in divorce; the rate is somewhat higher for remarriages (Ambert, 2009). Of those who divorce, 70 percent of the men and 58 percent of the women remarry (Ambert, 2009). In our society, marriage is also the context in which sexual expression has the most legitimacy. Therefore, sex in marriage is one of the commonest forms of sexual expression for adults.

Research in the United States shows that the average married heterosexual couple has coitus two to three times per week when they are in their 20s, with the frequency gradually declining as they get older (there are no data on sexual frequency in same-sex marriages). The data on this point from three studies are shown in Table 11.1. Several things can be noted from the table. First, the frequency of marital sex remained about the same from the 1940s to the 2000s. In each survey, people in their 20s reported having intercourse about every three days. Second, the frequency of intercourse declines with age; however, in 2003, among couples in their 50s, the frequency was still once per week. A survey of 19,307 Australians reported similar results

(Rissel et al., 2003a, 2003b). Social characteristics such as race, social status, and religion are generally not related to marital sexual frequency (Christopher & Sprecher, 2000).

Two general explanations have been suggested for the age-related decline in frequency: biological aging and habituation to sex with the partner (Call et al., 1995). With regard to aging, physical factors may be associated with age that affect sexual frequency, such as a decrease in vaginal lubrication in women or increased likelihood of poor health. The habituation explanation states that we lose interest in sex as the partner becomes more and more familiar. Recent data indicate a sharp decline in frequency after the first year and a slow, steady decline thereafter. The decline after the first year may reflect habituation (Call et al., 1995). It is often assumed that this decline in frequency reflects a loss of interest in sex, meaning a decline in quality. However, there is an alternative possibility: learning about your partner's sexual desires, preferences, and habits may result in increased marital sexual quality, if not frequency (Liu, 2003). But analysis of the data on satisfaction with the marital sexual relationship from the NHSLS found a significant decline with length of marriage, controlling for age, consistent with the habituation hypothesis. A third factor is the arrival of children, as discussed later.

> What happens to sex in long-term relationships over time?

It is important to note that there is wide variability in these frequencies. For example, 2 percent of couples in their 20s report not engaging in intercourse at all; 6 percent of married couples had not had sex in the 12 months before the interview (Smith, 2003). Research on a sample of 6029 married couples found that sexual inactivity was associated with unhappiness with the marriage, lack of shared activity, the presence of children, increased age, and poor health (Donnelly, 1993). In contrast, a married couple in Seattle have claimed

Table 11.1 Marital Coitus: Frequency per Week (Male and Female Estimates Combined), 1938–1949, 1970, and 2003

1938–1949 (Kinsey)		1970 (Westoff)		2003 (Smith)	
Age	Median Frequency per Week	Age	Mean Frequency per Week	Age	Mean Frequency per Week
16–25	2.45	20–24	2.5	18–29	2.1
26–35	1.95	25–34	2.1	30–39	1.7
36–45	1.40	35–44	1.6	40–49	1.4
46–55	0.85			50–59	1.0
56–60	0.55			60–69	0.6
				70+	0.3

the world record, having had intercourse more than 900 times in 700 days! Data from the NHSLS and Bibby (1995) also confirm this wide variability, as was shown in Figure 11.2.

Sexual Techniques

The NHSLS (Laumann et al., 1994) asked respondents to estimate the duration of their last sexual interaction. Sixteen percent of their married participants reported that sex lasted 15 minutes or less; 9 percent re-ported that it lasted one hour or more. Participants in the *Maclean's/CTV* poll (1994) reported on the average length of their sexual encounters: 12 percent reported that their sexual encounters lasted 15 minutes or less; 25 percent reported that they lasted more than an hour. A New Brunswick study found that, on average, sexual encounters lasted about 20 minutes (Miller & Byers, 2004).

Mouth–genital techniques are very common in long-term relationships. In the NHSLS data, 74 percent of women reported that their partners had stimulated their genitals orally, and 70 percent of them had stimulated their partner orally. Similarly, a Montreal study found that almost 80 percent of married and cohabiting respondents had stimulated their partner's genitals orally and that on average this occurred once a week (Samson et al., 1993). Younger respondents were most likely to include oral sex in their sexual repertoires. For example, 90 percent of people ages 18 to 34 had stimulated their partner orally, compared with only 40 percent of people in the 55 and older age group. People with higher levels of education and incomes were more likely to report engaging in oral sex, showing that there are some social-class differences.

According to the NHSLS data, 27 percent of the married men and 21 percent of the married women reported having engaged in anal intercourse (Laumann et al., 1994).

Negotiating Sex

Before executing any of these techniques, there is typically a "mating dance" between partners. Sexual scripts are played out in established and in new relationships, as in other aspects of sex (Gagnon, 1977, pp. 208–209). Some scripts involve direct verbal statements. One person may say, "Let's go make love." The partner might reply, "What are we waiting for?" or "Not now. Dinner is almost ready." Some scripts are behavioural. One woman said, "We'd get into bed, and he'd roll over to me and kind of bing me in the back end with his penis, so I'd know, Okay, tonight's the night" (Maurer, 1994, p. 180). For other couples, deciding to make love involves preliminary negotiations, which are phrased in indirect or euphemistic language, in part so that the person's feelings can be salvaged if her or his partner is not

interested. For example, an individual may say, "I think I'll go take a shower" or "I think I'll go take a nap" (that means, "I want to, do you?"). The partner might respond with, "I think I'll take one too" or "The kids will be home any moment" or "I have a report to finish for tomorrow." Conversely, the individual may kiss their partner a bit more passionately than usual after work (that is the offer). The partner may respond with, "I had an exhausting day at work" or "I'll meet you upstairs." Although in these latter examples, the partner never says "yes" or "no," the meaning is clear. To avoid some of the risk of rejection inherent in such negotiations, some couples ritualize sex so they both understand when it will and when it will not occur—Thursday night may be their time or perhaps Sunday afternoon.

Which of these strategies do heterosexual couples use most frequently? A New Brunswick study found that people most frequently use a direct verbal statement to initiate sex (Byers & Heinlein, 1989). The second most frequent strategy is more ambiguous—kissing passionately without saying anything. This study also examined the stereotype that men are more interested in sex than women are. They had people in long-term mixed-sex relationships keep track of sexual initiations by the man and sexual initiations by the woman over a one-week period. On average the men initiated sex almost twice as often as the women did—about twice a week for the men compared with once a week for the women. Interestingly, the men and the women were equally likely to respond positively to the initiation—about three-quarters of the time. Thus, traditional gender roles persist in some areas, with men more often having the initiating role. There was also some evidence of liberation. Women initiated sex regularly (and in some couples were the usual initiator) and usually were interested in engaging in sex when their partner suggested it. Contrary to the male stereotype, the men were not always interested in sex and were equally likely to refuse their partner's initiations. There may be differences in how men and women respond when their partner refuses their initiation. According to traditional stereotypes, a woman's refusal can be attributed to her lesser sexual appetite. However, refusals by men go against traditional views of male sexuality. Therefore, a woman may conclude that the man's refusal means that he is not interested in her. Nonetheless, most of the time couples are satisfied with how they resolve disagreements about whether to have sex (Byers & Heinlein, 1989).

Masturbation

Many adults continue to masturbate even though they are married and have ready access to sexual activity with a partner. For example, the NSSHB found that 41 to 61 percent of married men and 44 to 55 percent of married women ages 18 to 49 reported solo masturbation in the preceding 90 days (Herbenick et al., 2010b; Reece et al., 2010b). This behaviour is perfectly normal, although it sometimes evokes feelings of guilt and may be done secretly. According to the NHSLS, married people were more likely to report that they masturbated than were single people (Michael et al., 1994). Masturbation can serve very legitimate sexual needs in long-term relationships. It feels good whether one is living with a partner or not. It can provide sexual gratification while allowing the partner to remain faithful to a spouse when they are separated or cannot have sex for some reason such as illness.[1] Masturbation can also be a pleasant adjunct to relationship sex. According to a 49-year-old man:

> One of the other things we do a lot is masturbation. We have it developed to a fine art. We rent a porno movie, take a bath, rub each other down with baby oil. My wife and I not only masturbate each other at the same time, but we get pleasure watching each other masturbate individually as well. It's a terrifically exciting thing. (Janus & Janus, 1993, p. 383)

Sexual Satisfaction

Sexual satisfaction is an important aspect of most people's lives (Byers & Rehman, 2013; Rehman et al., 2013). Sexual satisfaction is not just physical pleasure, nor is it simply the absence of dissatisfaction or problems. In fact, couples with sexual difficulties may feel sexually satisfied, and couples with no sexual problems may not feel satisfied at all (MacNeil & Byers, 1997). Rather, sexual satisfaction is the overall feeling we are left with after considering the positive and negative aspects (or sexual rewards and costs) of our sexual relationship. Of course, one person's reward may be another person's cost. For example, having sex every day might be a reward for someone who desires sex frequently. It may be a cost for someone who prefers to have sex less frequently, say twice a week. A New Brunswick study found that for men in long-term relationships, the most frequently identified sexual rewards were feeling comfortable with their partner, feeling good about themselves during and after sex, and having fun during sexual activity. For women the most frequent rewards were being treated well by their partner during sex, feeling comfortable with their partner, and having sex in the context of a long-term relationship (Lawrance & Byers, 1995).

Canadian psychologists Kelli-an Lawrance and Sandra Byers developed the interpersonal exchange model of sexual satisfaction, which identifies four distinct aspects of relationships that influence sexual satisfaction (Lawrance & Byers, 1995). According to this model, we are more sexually satisfied if (1) we perceive ourselves to be getting many sexual rewards and few sexual costs, (2) we perceive that we are getting more rewards and fewer costs than we expect to get, (3) we perceive our own and our partner's rewards and costs to be relatively equal, and (4) we are happy with the non-sexual aspects of the relationship. A longitudinal study of 244 heterosexual New Brunswick adults living with a partner found that these four components measured at Time 1 predicted sexual satisfaction three months later. Studies involving Canadian dating couples and married Chinese individuals living in Beijing and Shanghai found similar results (Byers, Demmons, et al., 1998a; Renaud et al., 1997). As you might expect, we are also more sexually satisfied if our partner also experiences high sexual rewards and low sexual costs (Byers & MacNeil, 2006). Clearly, our assessment of the rewards and costs in our intimate relationships are associated with our feelings of sexual satisfaction. One factor that is important in ensuring that couples experience high sexual rewards and low sexual costs is having good sexual communication skills (Byers & Rehman, 2013; Rehman et al., 2013).

How we get along outside the bedroom and how we perceive the overall relationship also affects our sexual satisfaction (Byers & Rehman, 2013; Rehman et al., 2013). For example, married men and women are significantly more satisfied than are cohabiting or single men and women in a continuing relationship (Waite & Joyner, 2000). This suggests that the stronger emotional commitment and sexual exclusivity associated with marriage result in higher sexual satisfaction. Conversely, sexual satisfaction is an important contributor to marital quality and stability (Yeh et al., 2006). Thus, sex and relational education programs that increase sexual satisfaction for both partners have the potential to lower the divorce rate.

In-depth interviews with 52 people, ages 12 to 69, straight, gay, lesbian, and bisexual, identified four factors that differentiate people who are happy with their sex lives (Maurer, 1994). First, there is a sense of calm about, and acceptance of, their sexuality. Second, happy people delight in giving their partners sexual pleasure. Third, these people *listen* to their partners and are aware of the partner's quirks, moods, likes, and dislikes. Fourth, they *talk*, both in and out of bed, even though it is often difficult. These interviews remind us that good communication is essential to a satisfying relationship (see Chapter 12).

Sexual Patterns

The level of sexual desire experienced by each person influences sexual patterns in marriage. A study of

---

[1] As an old navy saying has it, "If your wife can't be at your right hand, let your right hand be your wife." This saying probably should be updated to refer to both men and women.

24 married couples obtained daily ratings of relationship affect (positive or negative), relationship status (closeness, equality of power), and lust from each partner (Ridley et al., 2006). Researchers identified four patterns in ratings of desire: (1) stable and low, (2) slight fluctuations (1 point on a 1-to-5 scale) and low, (3) moderate fluctuations, and (4) highly fluctuating. On days when positive affect toward the spouse was high, lust was high; when negative affect was high, lust was low. Interestingly, on days when people reported high closeness to their spouse, the link between positive (negative) affect and lust was stronger. Finally, there was a significant positive association between own lust and partner's lust each day.

Sexual patterns can change during the course of a marriage. After ten years of marriage they may be quite different from what they were during the first year. One stereotype is that sex becomes duller as marriage wears on, and certainly that happens in some marriages. In a survey of adults in the United States, 23 percent of the sexually active men and women reported that their sexual relationship was often or always "routine"; 38 percent said it was never or hardly ever routine (Kaiser Family Foundation, 1998). A boring sexual relationship can be spiced up by telling each other what you really want to do and then doing it, by consulting a how-to manual or watching videos about improving your sex life, or by acting out fantasies (see Table 11.2). There are also relationships in which the sex remains very exciting. A 36-year-old engineer said:

> [Though my wife's career] is tremendously important to her, she manages to look attractive, and to dress chicly, and though she is not what many would call a beautiful woman, she is, to me, a handsome woman. In bed, she is the hottest, most exciting woman I have ever known. We have been married seven years. . . . When we get to bed, and she lets herself go, we get wild together. (Janus & Janus, 1993, p. 191)

Having a baby—what researchers call the transition to parenthood—has an impact on the sexual relationship of the couple. According to one 44-year-old mother of three children, "There's the passionate period when you can't get enough of each other, and after a few years it wanes, and after kids it really wanes" (Maurer, 1994, p. 403). Trying to get pregnant and the threat of infertility, which are so much publicized, can be potent forces on people's identity as sexual beings (Daniluk, 2001a). Pregnancy itself can influence a couple's sexual interactions, particularly in the last few months (see Chapter 6). For the first few weeks after the baby is born, intercourse is typically uncomfortable for the woman. While estrogen levels are low—which lasts longer when breastfeeding—the vagina does not lubricate well. Then, too, the parents (including nonbiological parents) feel exhausted with 2 a.m. feedings. The first few months after a baby is born are usually not the peak times in a sexual relationship, and so that, too, must be negotiated between partners. A follow-up study of parents six months and four years after the birth of their first child found that sexual frequency did not change significantly, but it remained low (Ahlborg et al., 2008).

Not all couples have children. For example, data from the 2001 General Social Survey (GSS) indicate that 26 percent of Canadian women ages 30 to 34 do not have children (Stobert & Kemeny, 2003). Some of these women were delaying childbearing while they completed their education and established their careers; 20 percent of women in the 30-to-34 age group do not have children but intend to have a child. The average age of first childbirth was 28 years in 2006, up from 24 years in the 1960s (Statistics Canada, 2007). There is some risk in this strategy; fertility declines with age, so some of these women may be unable to have a child if they want to. Other women have made a decision to remain childfree. According to the GSS, 5 percent of women do

Table 11.2 Frequency of Activities to Enhance Sexual Interactions Reported by Adults[*]

	Very Often	Often	Sometimes	Hardly Ever	Never	Don't Know
Do romantic things like eat by candlelight	8%	18%	35%	30%	6%	3%
Act out fantasies together	4	10	28	39	12	7
Wear sexy lingerie (women[**])	9	10	28	35	12	6
Try different sexual positions	11	19	35	23	4	8
Read books or watch videos about improving your sex life	2	3	14	52	26	3
Go out on special evenings or dates or go away on weekends alone	11	22	37	22	5	3

[*] Number of respondents = 1109
[**] Number of female respondents = 564
Source: Kaiser Family Foundation (1998).

not expect to have children. A third group of women are those who choose to adopt; adopting an infant probably has effects on relationships and sexual activities similar to those of having a baby.

Some people will experience fundamental changes in their sexual experience at least once over the course of the marriage. The change may result from developing a capacity to give as well as receive sexual pleasure and to expand our sexual scripts beyond traditional expectations for men and women. A man may outgrow performance anxiety and enlarge his focus to include his partner. A woman may learn that she can take care of her own sexual needs as well as her partner's. Aging may produce change in sexual experience, a topic we consider later in this chapter. There are changes caused by illness, which can lead to sexual disaster or triumph depending on how the couple copes with it.

Sex and the Two-Career Family

In our busy, achievement-oriented society, do work commitments interfere with a couple's sex life? One couple, both of whom are professionals, commented to us that they actually have to make an appointment with each other to make love.

Research with married couples shows that there is little cause for concern (Figure 11.4). A longitudinal study followed 570 women and 550 of their husbands for one year following the birth of a baby (Hyde et al., 1998). The women were categorized according to the number of hours worked per week: homemakers, employed part time (6 to 31 hours/week), employed full time (32 to 44 hours), and employed high full time (45 or more hours). There were no significant differences among the four groups in frequency of sexual intercourse, sexual satisfaction, or sexual desire. It was not the number of hours of work outside the home, but rather the quality of work that was associated with sexual outcomes. Women and men who had satisfying jobs reported that sex was better compared with people who expressed dissatisfaction with their jobs. For women, fatigue was associated with decreased sexual satisfaction, but that was true for both homemakers and employed women; and homemakers reported the same level of fatigue as employed women.

Research using data from the National Survey of Families and Households analyzed the relationship between hour per week spent in housework, hours per week spent in paid work, and frequency of sexual intercourse (Gager & Yabiku, 2010). Results from 6877 married men and women indicate that the more hours of housework and paid work per week, the more frequently the person reported sexual activity. Clearly, there is not a trade-off between work/career and sexual frequency. Further, the presence of young children did not change the relationship between work and sex.

L05 Maintaining a Long-Term Relationship

Most couples who establish a long-term relationship intend to stay together. However, we know that not all

(a)

(b)

Figure 11.4 Sex and the two-career family. *(a)* Research indicates that sexual relationships do not suffer if the woman works outside the home. *(b)* However, for those working 60 or more hours per week, some experts are concerned because these workaholics literally take their work to bed with them.

couples succeed. In Canada, about 40 percent of marriages end in divorce; this rate is considerably lower than in the United States (Roterman, 2007a). The rate of breakup is even higher for common-law relationships. Further, the end of a relationship is often associated with depression and other psychological distress (Goldfarb et al., 2007; Roterman, 2007a). What differences have researchers found between nondistressed (happy) couples and distressed (unhappy) couples?

1. Nondistressed couples have good listening and communication skills. Suggestions for enhancing communication skills are outlined in Chapter 12.

2. Nondistressed couples have effective problem-solving skills. In contrast, distressed couples may discuss problems, but they rarely resolve them. As a result, the same problems tend to come up repeatedly.

3. Nondistressed couples have many positive interactions and few negative interactions. For example, they have many enjoyable shared leisure-time activities, are affectionate with each other, and feel good about their communication. In fact, Gottman (1994) found that nondistressed couples have five times as much positive interaction as negative interaction.

4. Nondistressed couples tend to have realistic expectations about what relationships should be like. In contrast, distressed couples may believe that disagreements are destructive, that one must be a perfect sexual partner at all times, or that people who are in love feel intensively passionate about their partner at all times. None of these expectations is realistic.

5. Nondistressed couples tend to interpret their partner's behaviour and the causes of that behaviour positively. For example, if the woman is late for dinner, her partner is likely to assume that it was due to something beyond her control, such as heavy traffic. A distressed partner is more likely to see this as an example of her being thoughtless.

6. Nondistressed couples are more likely to share a common view of roles and responsibilities within the relationship. Unhappy couples may disagree on how the relationship should work; for example, they may have different ideas about financial decision making or how involved each should be with taking care of the children.

These research findings have implications for maintaining a satisfying long-term relationship. That is, couples with good communication and problem-solving skills, many positive and few negative interactions, and realistic expectations about their relationship, who do

not engage in blaming, and who share a common view of relationships are likely to have happy and stable relationships. Of course, feelings of love and intimacy are also important to maintaining a long-term relationship (see Chapter 12 for a discussion of love in long-term relationships). These feelings often are what motivate couples to work through the problems that inevitably come up. Feelings of equity in the relationship (discussed later in this chapter) are also important.

Relationship satisfaction is one of the key elements contributing to sexual satisfaction, so many of these factors also contribute to sexual satisfaction and optimal sexual experiences (Kleinplatz et al., 2013; Lawrance & Byers, 1995). Further, dissatisfaction with the relationship and conflict between spouses are associated with susceptibility to extradyadic sexual activity, which is discussed next (Buss & Shackelford, 1997b). For example, one woman used her dissatisfaction with her relationship to explain her serious affair: "I'm definitely not looking for more sex. The affair I'm having is for emotional reasons. Freddie [her husband] is very self-centered. He's not an emotional support. He's distant, and we have nothing in common" (Maurer, 1994, p. 391).

In a study, 355 Canadians in same-sex and mixed-sex relationships were asked about their use of 19 different mate-retention tactics (VanderLaan & Vasey, 2008). There were marked gender differences in the reported actions. Men in mixed-sex relationships reported greater use of resources display (e.g., giving her money). Women in mixed-sex relationships reported more frequent use of monopolizing their partner's time, punishing threats of infidelity, saying derogatory things about competitors, providing sexual inducements, and enhancing their appearance or attractiveness. The tactics used by men in same-sex relationships were similar to those used by men in mixed-sex relationships, with the exception that gay men tended to use resource display more frequently than did heterosexual men. In contrast, women in same-sex relationships tended to use tactics that were more similar to those of heterosexual men than to those of heterosexual women. Thus, men's and heterosexual women's, but not lesbian women's, most frequent mate-retention strategies fall along traditional gender lines. Unfortunately, these strategies do not address the problems typical of distressed couples just listed.

Nonmonogamous Relationships

People in Canada who marry usually make a public vow to be (sexually) faithful to the partner, to be monogamous. In the past, those who found it impossible to keep the vow engaged in *adultery*, sex with someone other than the spouse, and usually tried to hide the activity, sometimes going to great lengths to do so. Similarly, people entering into cohabiting, or even committed ("exclusively dating"), relationships expected themselves and the partners to be sexually faithful. But there has been a decline in marriage and the rise of alternative relationship forms in the recent past. Accompanying this change has been a decline in fidelity, with as many as one-third of people dating, cohabiting, and in marriages reporting one or more instances of having sex with someone other than the partner while in the relationship.

Within committed or marital relationships, several new relationship forms have developed. One is Internet infidelity, which, like adultery, is often kept secret. Two others, swinging and polyamory, however, are done with the knowledge and often participation of the long-term partner. These are quite different, reflecting a process of negotiation involving not only the partners but others as well. We need a new term to incorporate all of these, and *nonmonogamous relationships* seems appropriate. Following the lead of researchers (Frank & DeLamater, 2010), we will distinguish between secret nonmonogamy, sexual activity involving a person in a committed relationship with a third person without the knowledge of the partner, and open nonmonogamy, sexual activity involving a person in a committed relationship with a third (or multiple) person(s) with the consent of the partner. Most of the research in this area has focused on extradyadic sex, and has assumed that it is kept secret from the partner, so adultery and Internet infidelity will be treated as secret. Negotiated nonmonogamy (e.g., every other Friday from 7 p.m. to midnight), swinging, and polyamory will be discussed as open nonmonogamy.

Extradyadic sex refers to sexual activity between a person in a committed relationship–gay, lesbian, or straight–and someone other than that person's partner. When a person who is married engages in extradyadic sex, we call it **extramarital sex** (traditionally called adultery.) Extradyadic sex can occur under several different circumstances (Pittman, 1993). Sometimes it is *accidental*, unintended, and not characteristic of the person; it "just happens." *Romantic infidelity* occurs when the two people fall in love and consider or establish a long-term relationship; this situation can be very destructive to partners, children, and careers. Dissatisfaction with the relationship is especially likely to lead to romantic infidelity. Accidental and romantic infidelities begin without the partner's knowledge, and may remain secret. Finally, there are *philanderers* who repeatedly engage in sexual liaisons outside their committed relationship. Some philanderers use dating websites to meet new sexual partners. Typically, the desire for sexual gratification does not motivate these men and women; they are searching for self-affirmation.

What makes men and women susceptible to extradyadic sexual activity? A study of 107 couples married less than one year asked each partner how likely he or she was to be "unfaithful" in the next year (Buss & Shackelford, 1997b). Each was asked the likelihood that she or he would flirt, kiss passionately, and have a romantic date, a one-night stand, a brief affair, or a serious affair with someone of the opposite sex. Thirty-seven percent of the men and 38 percent of the women predicted they would flirt, while 5 percent of the men and 7 percent of the women said they would kiss. Two percent (of men and of women) predicted a one-night stand, and less than 1 percent (of men and women) thought they would have a serious affair.

People engage in extradyadic sexual behaviour for a number of reasons. Some people believe that extradyadic sexual behaviour is acceptable, and they may have an agreement with their partner about the circumstances under which it can occur. Other people, particularly people in long-term relationships, engage in extradyadic sex because they find it particularly exciting. The excitement may be a result of being with a new partner, being found attractive and desirable, or doing something that the individual knows to be forbidden. Finally, some people may engage in extradyadic sex because there are problems in their relationship.

Our awareness of the possibility of extradyadic sexual activity sometimes leads us to engage in behaviours designed to preserve the relationship, or *mate-retention tactics* (Buss & Shackelford, 1997a). Such tactics may be elicited by our own fear that the partner is losing interest or is dissatisfied, or because we observe some clues to extradyadic sexual activity.

Most of the research on extradyadic sexual behaviour has been on extramarital sex, which we turn to next. However, individuals in dating relationships also engage in extradyadic sexual behaviour, although men are more likely to do so than are women. For example, in one study of university students, 65 percent of the men and 49 percent of the women had experienced extradyadic kissing and fondling; 49 percent of the men and 31 percent of the women had experienced extradyadic sexual intercourse (Wiederman & Hurd, 1999).

How Many People Engage in Extradyadic Sex?

Extramarital sexual activity is not as common as many people believe. According to the NHSLS, in the United States about 25 percent of married men and 15 percent of married women reported having engaged in extradyadic sex at least once (Laumann et al.,

Extradyadic sex: Sexual activity between a person in a serious or exclusive relationship and someone other than that person's steady partner.

Extramarital sex: Sexual activity between a married person and someone other than that person's spouse.

1994). A *Maclean's*/CTV poll conducted in 1995 found a considerably lower percentage of Canadians who reported having had an affair while married—14 percent of men and 7 percent of women. These differences may reflect cultural differences between Canada and the United States. They may also reflect differences in the methodologies used in the two studies that may have affected participants' willingness to report a behaviour that is generally frowned upon (see Chapter 3). According to the National Survey of Family Growth (NSFG), 8 percent of married men and 6 percent of married women ages 15 to 44 report more than one sexual partner in the preceding 12 months (Mosher et al., 2005). The comparable percentages were 5 percent and 3 percent in the Australian survey (Rissel et al., 2003c).

The Kinsey Institute posted an online survey that included questions about infidelity in couples; 918 respondents from Canada and the United States said they were heterosexual and in a committed relationship. Among married respondents, 26 percent of men and 23 percent of women reported "engaging in sexual interactions with someone other than the primary partner" that could harm the relationship. Among the not-married (single and cohabiting), the results were 19 percent of men and 16 percent of women. The questionnaire included the sexual inhibition scale (SIS) and the sexual excitation scale (SES) (see Chapter 9). Men and women who reported cheating had higher scores on sexual excitation and lower scores on sexual inhibition; the women also reported lower happiness in their relationship (Mark et al., 2011).

The incidence of extradyadic sex varies from one group to another and one region to another. As noted in Chapter 1, the rate of extradyadic sexual activity is highest in Quebec.

There is no indication that extramarital sex is casual or frequent. In one Canadian survey, of the respondents who had had extramarital sex, 40 percent had done so with only one partner (Gallup, 1988).

Attitudes Toward Extradyadic Sex

Most people in Canada disapprove of extramarital sex. According to a series of well-sampled surveys conducted by Bibby and his associates (1995), in 1975, 50 percent of Canadian adults felt that it is always wrong to have sex with someone other than the spouse. In 1995, this figure had risen to 60 percent. A 2005 COMPAS poll found that most Canadians feel that extradyadic sexual activity by their partner would probably (27 percent) or definitely (41 percent) mean the end of a relationship.

Attitudes toward extramarital sex are not very good predictors of extramarital sexual behaviour (Thompson, 1983). That is, the person who approves of extramarital

Cyberaffair: A romantic or sexual relationship initiated by online contact and maintained primarily via online communication.

sex is no more likely to engage in extramarital sex than the person who disapproves of it. Several other factors are related to attitudes toward sex outside the primary relationship, including gender, education, and social class—men, people with more education, and people who are upper-middle-class are more tolerant of it (Willetts et al., 2004).

Because our society condemns extramarital sex, the individual who engages in it typically has confused, ambivalent feelings. A young married woman describes her feelings:

> I don't like the illicit part of the affair. Mostly, it's a nuisance, because it's very difficult to find time, and I don't like lying to Freddie and sneaking around. If he wouldn't mind, I'd tell him. I don't think he would go for that. He'd show up with a gun. (Maurer, 1994, p. 393)

Internet Infidelity

The proliferation of websites designed to connect people looking for romantic or sexual partners, along with chat rooms and other forms of digital communication, has created new opportunities for people in committed relationships to engage in sexual activity with people other than their partner (see Milestones in Sex Research). Indeed, there are websites with millions of members (e.g., AshleyMadison.com) specifically for individuals in attached relationships looking to engage in extradyadic sexual activity. A **cyberaffair** is a romantic or sexual relationship initiated by online contact and maintained primarily via online communication (Young et al., 2000). A new twist on cyberaffairs occurs when two people's avatars engage in sexual activity in virtual reality worlds, such as Second Life. After establishing a relationship online, contacts can turn into mutual erotic dialogue, which may be accompanied by masturbation. In some cases, the participants arrange to meet face to face and may then engage in sexual intimacy. Most people think that people are unfaithful if they engage in cybersex with someone other than their partner, even if the two individuals never meet (Randall & Byers, 2003).

An online survey collected data about the seeking of online sex from 15,246 men and women with an average age of 38 years who varied in their marital status and sexual identity. The results provide a statistical snapshot of the phenomena (Albright, 2008). However, given that participants were recruited online for a "Cybersex Survey," the percentages are likely higher than would be found in the general population. As shown in Table 11.3, there were no differences in the percentage of men and women who had accessed a personals site. However, more LGB individuals than straight individuals had done so. Divorced individuals were more likely to go on personal sites than were never married or married individuals. Of those who had accessed an online site, most in all groups went on to post a profile; straight

Table 11.3 Accessing Personal Sites Online

	Accessed Online Personal Ads	Created a Profile (of those who had accessed a site)
Gender		
Men	58%	75%
Women	55	72
Sexual identity		
Straight	54%	71%
Bisexual	78	82
Gay	87	87
Marital status		
Never married	69%	80%
Married	42	61
Divorced	81	83

Source: Based on data from Albright, J. M. (2008). Sex in America Online: An Exploration of Sex, Marital Status, and Sexual Identity in Internet Sex-Seeking and Its Impacts. *Journal of Sex Research,* 45:2, 175–186.

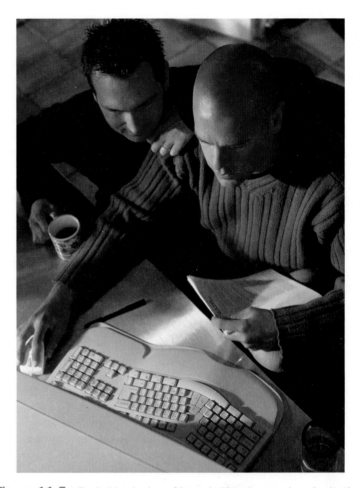

Figure 11.5 Equitable sharing of household tasks—such as budgeting and paying bills—in a marriage. According to equity theory, if a person perceives that the marital relationship is inequitable and feels underbenefited, he or she is more likely to engage in extramarital sex.

individuals and married individuals were least likely to have posted a profile. What about the married individuals—that is, the ones who were engaging in cyberaffairs? Of the married individuals who had accessed a site, 36 percent had sent one email and 27 percent had sent two or more emails; similar percentages had met one or more contacts in person. Married individuals were five times as likely to be seeking a serious relationship than were singles and were also more likely than singles to go on a date as a result of being on a sex-related site. Albright uses equity theory (next section) to suggest that married people who go online seeking sex may be dissatisfied with their relationship, that is, perceive their marriages as inequitable; the Internet provides literally tens of thousands of potential alternative partners.

There has been little empirical study of cyberaffairs. Professionals engaged in relationship and sexual counselling report working with couples whose problems include loss of trust by one person over another's online relationships. Some partners define such a relationship as infidelity even if it did not involve sexual conversation or activity. Note that these can be mixed-sex or same-sex couples, who are married, cohabiting, or committed to each other.

Equity and Extradyadic Sex

Social exchange theories are a type of social-psychological theory that have been used to explain sexuality in close relationships. Unlike most theories that focus on the individual, the social exchange perspective takes the interpersonal context in which most sexual activities occur into account (Byers & Wang,

2004). One such theory, **equity theory**, has been used to predict patterns of extradyadic sex (Hatfield, 1978).

The basic idea in equity theory is that in a relationship, people mentally tabulate their inputs to it and what they get out of it (benefits or rewards); then they calculate whether these are equitable or not.

According to equity theory, if individuals perceive a relationship as inequitable (if they feel they are not getting what they put in), they become distressed. The more inequitable the relationship, the more distressed they feel. To relieve the distress, they attempt to restore equity in the relationship. For example, people who feel they are putting too much into a relationship and not getting enough out of it might let their appearance go, or not work as hard to earn money, or refuse to have sex or contribute to conversations. The idea is that such actions will restore equity (Figure 11.5).

Equity theory: A social exchange theory that states that people mentally calculate the benefits and costs for them in a relationship; their behaviour is then affected by whether they feel there is equity or inequity, and they will act to restore equity if there is inequity.

Milestones in Sex Research

Sex on the Internet

When people think about sex, they generally think about two people engaging in face-to-face bodily contact. The Internet introduces all kinds of other possibilities when it comes to sexual expression. Online sexual activities (OSA) range from using the Internet for sexual information to finding and connecting with prospective dating or sex partners to accessing or producing sexually explicit materials. These activities are often referred to as solitary-arousal OSA because they do not involve a partner. Most people would not see any of these activities as "having sex" (Randall & Byers, 2003).

People also engage in interactive, interpersonal sexual experiences—that is, activities that involve another person—online through text, words, or images. For example, people describe in detail sexual activities or a sexual scene back and forth with another person as if it were happening, create a story based on sexual fantasies where each person adds to the story as it goes, or behave (or watch someone behave) sexually for another person to watch. All these are examples of interpersonal sexual activity online. These interactions can and do occur through a variety of forums and formats including emails, instant messaging, social networking sites, and video chat. These activities are referred to as *partnered-arousal OSA* because they require that at least two people be involved and are generally geared around sexual arousal. Pop culture has also provided us with terms that capture these kinds of sexual interactions, such as *cybering* or *cybersex*. However, people do not agree on exactly which activities constitute cybersex (Shaughnessy et al., 2011). The term *sexting* is generally used to refer to sexual interaction that occurs through text messaging or picture messaging on cellphones or smartphones.

Another venue for cybersex is in virtual worlds. In virtual worlds, people can visually recreate sex by having their avatars engage in sexual activities with other avatars. Second Life is a free 3D virtual world designed for online social interaction, connection, and creation. It essentially focuses on re-creating the "real world" in a virtual forum. In Second Life, online sexual interaction can occur in all the contexts that it occurs in the real world—with virtual romantic partners, virtual friends, virtual hookups, virtual sex work, and so on. However, Second Life is not specifically designed for sexual purposes. Some virtual worlds, such as Red Light Center, are for adults only and are designed specifically for avatars to engage in sexual activities. As technologies continue to advance, the possibilities of sexual interaction increase. For example, recently developers in Japan have been working on a device that would simulate kissing across Internet connections.

Given the range of interpersonal sexual behaviours that can occur online and the fact that new possibilities emerge with each advance in technology, it is important to have a definition of what constitutes cybersex. According to Shaughnessy et al. (2011), cybersex is

> a real-time communication with another person that occurs through a device connected with the Internet (e.g., computer, cellphone, smart phone) in which one or both of you describe or share in other ways sexual activities, sexual behaviours, sexual fantasies, or sexual desires that may lead to feelings of sexual pleasure or physical intimacy. You and/or your partner may or may not be stimulating yourself/himself/herself sexually during this conversation.

How common is cybersex? At the turn of the twenty-first century, between 8 and 13 percent of undergraduate

If these equity processes do occur, they might help to explain patterns of extradyadic sex. That is, engaging in extradyadic sex would be a way of restoring equity in an inequitable relationship. Social psychologist Elaine Hatfield (1978) tested this notion. Her prediction was

that people who felt underbenefited in their marriages (that is, they felt that there was an inequity and that they were not getting as much as they deserved) would be the ones to engage in extradyadic sex. Confirming this notion, people who felt they were underbenefited men and women reported having had an online sex partner, visiting and participating in a sexual chat room, or having cybersex with an online partner (Boies, 2002; Goodson, McCormick, & Evans, 2001). Shaughnessy et al. (2011) found that 23 percent of their student sample reported engaging in cybersex. More recently, Shaughnessy and Byers (2013) found that 75 percent of students and 53 percent of an online community sample reported participating in at least one of these specific cybersex activities. These recent figures suggest that cybersex, or at least some specific types of cybersex, are becoming more common.

Is there something wrong with engaging in cybersex? Media discussions of cybersex usually focus on problematic activities online highlighting stories of cybersex addicts, cybersex infidelity, and illegal forms of cybersex. This suggests that people who engage in cybersex have a problem. Similarly, most early research on cybersex focused on cybersex addiction. However, researchers have consistently found that less than 10 percent of survey respondents report levels of cybersex and OSA experience that can be considered compulsive or addictive (Cooper et al., 2004; Daneback, Cooper, & Månsson, 2005). This means that many more people participate in recreational cybersex. People who engage in recreational cybersex spend only a few hours online per week or less participating in cybersex, and report few, if any negative outcomes. They also report a few positive outcomes of cybersex, suggesting that recreational cybersex has fairly neutral effects on participants (Shaughnessy & Byers, 2013).

Why do people participate in cybersex? Just like with offline sex, people who participate in cybersex do so for a variety of reasons and with partners, acquaintances, or strangers. Having cybersex can be a source of sexual/physical excitement, arousal, pleasure, or release. It can be a way to relieve stress or anxiety, or a distraction from offline life—such as a break from work, housework, or boredom. Some people use cybersex (whether with their offline partner or someone else) as a way to avoid problems in their offline life or relationship. For example, some people engage in cybersex because they do not want the complexities of having an offline relationship, or to avoid the risks associated with offline sex, such as STIs and pregnancy. Others use cybersex to help address problems in their sexual relationship with their partner, for example, by alleviating anxiety or creating a space to communicate about unexpressed sexual desires. Some people use cybersex to feel a sense of emotional connection or intimacy with another person. For partners who are geographically separated for a period, cybersex can be an important part of maintaining sexual intimacy while apart. Finally, for some people the Internet provides a safe space to explore or express aspects of their sexual selves that they are not comfortable exploring or expressing offline. This can be especially important to people who are members of sexual minorities.

The commonality and impact of cybersex has evolved along with technological developments and the increased pervasiveness of the Internet. Just as online social connections have become part of regular life, online sexual interactions have become increasingly mainstream. Thus, it is likely that cybersex will become a regular part of adult sexual experience in the future.

Source: Written by Krystelle Shaughnessy.

began engaging in extradyadic sex earlier in their marriages and had more extradyadic partners than did people who felt equitably treated or overbenefited. (As an aside, equitable marriages were rated as happier than inequitable ones.)

Equity theory includes rewards and costs of all kinds, as indicated by our examples. However, as noted earlier in this chapter, our perceptions of our *sexual* rewards and costs have a particular impact on our satisfaction (Lawrance & Byers, 1995). For example, people who, during sex, are happy with their communication with their partner, the level of affection, the frequency of specific techniques, such as oral sex, and their ease in reaching orgasm are likely to be sexually satisfied. Individuals with a more favourable balance of sexual rewards to sexual costs are also more satisfied with the relationship in general. Greater sexual satisfaction, in turn, is associated with higher frequencies of affection and sexual behaviour, and fewer sexual concerns and problems.

Clearly, both our perceptions of equity and equality in our intimate relationships, as well as our levels of sexual rewards and costs, may affect our satisfaction with those relationships and the likelihood that we will become involved in extramarital (or extradyadic) sexuality.

Evolution and Extradyadic Sex

Extradyadic sex is not unique to Canada. In fact, it occurs in virtually every society. When evolutionary psychologists observe a behaviour that occurs in all societies, they are inclined to explain that behaviour in terms of evolutionary processes. That is, some people engage in extradyadic sex because they carry in their genetic makeup something that motivates them to do so.

Why would some people carry these types of genes? From an evolutionary perspective, the genes that enable their bearers to produce larger numbers of offspring are more likely to survive from one generation to the next than genes that do not. A man who mates with one woman for life may produce a maximum of 6 to 12 offspring, depending on the length of time infants are breastfed, postpartum sex taboos, and so on. If that same man occasionally has sex with a second woman (or a series of other women), he could produce 12 to 24 offspring. We think you get the picture. Historically, men who sought out other women produced more offspring, who in turn produced more offspring carrying the genetic makeup that leads to extradyadic liaisons (Fisher, 1992). One study reported an association between a dopamine receptor gene (DRD4) and reports of extradyadic sexual experiences (Garcia et al., 2010).

What about women? They cannot increase the number of their offspring by increasing the number of their sexual partners. However, there are ways in which having more than one sexual partner might have been biologically adaptive for women. First, sexual liaisons with other men might have enabled a woman to acquire extra goods and services, which enhanced her offspring's chances for survival. Second, having another partner could serve as "insurance"; if her husband died, she would have another man to turn to for food, shelter, and protection. Third, a woman married to a timid, unproductive hunter could "upgrade her genetic line" by mating with another man. Finally, having children with multiple partners increases the genetic diversity of one's offspring, increasing the chances that some of them will survive. Research on this point with animal populations reports mixed results. In some cases, offspring of extra-pair matings are more fit (Gerlach et al., 2012), in others not (Sardell et al., 2012). In the latter study, extra-pair offspring were less likely to hatch!

According to this sociobiological perspective, then, extradyadic sex occurs because some men and women carry in their genetic makeup something that motivates them to be unfaithful. If there are environments in which extradyadic sex is adaptive in contemporary society, people with those genes would have a selective advantage. Yet more and more societies that at one time allowed polygyny have moved to monogamy. Why might this be? Researchers in British Columbia concluded that monogamy has evolutionary advantages at the societal level for two primary reasons (Henrich et al., 2012). It reduces competition between men, resulting in less crime. It also increases paternal investment in each child, resulting in lower rates of child neglect and abuse and improving child outcomes.

Swinging

One form of open nonmonogamy is **swinging**, in which married couples exchange partners with other couples, or engage in sexual activity with a third person, with the knowledge and consent of all involved.[2]

Swingers may find their partners in several ways. Often they advertise, in tabloid newspapers, in "lifestyle" magazines such as *Maritime Connection*, or on specialized bulletin boards and websites on the Internet. The following is an example:

> We are engaged bicouple lookin to meet bim, bif and bicouples for friendship and fun . . . we are into nudism, motorcycling, fishin, volleyball, pool and campin . . . she is 22 5'5" 180# 38-d blond blue . . . he is 24 5'10" 145# blond green 7' and very thick. email: (www. . ./~ gnkfoxx/nefriend.htm)

Swingers may also meet potential partners at swingers' clubs, parties, or resorts. Many of these places advertise in swingers' magazines and newsletters and are listed on specialized websites.

Several organizations and many local groups or couples sponsor parties. The date and general location of the party are publicized in magazines and on the Internet. Interested persons call or email a contact

Swinging: A form of extradyadic sex in which married couples exchange partners with each other.

---

[2] Swinging was originally called "wife-swapping." However, because of the sexist connotations of that term and the fact that women were often as eager to swap husbands as men were to swap wives, the more equitable "mate-swapping" or "swinging" was substituted.

person who screens them. If they pass, they are told the exact location of the party, often a private home or a hotel. A fee per couple may be charged for membership or entry to the party. There are estimated to be more than a dozen swinger clubs across Canada, from Dartmouth, Nova Scotia, to Prince George, British Columbia (McClelland, 1999). In 1998, police raided a members-only swing club in Montreal and charged the owner with running a common bawdy house—that is, a place "for the purpose of prostitution or the practice of acts of indecency" (Figure 11.6). The Supreme Court eventually ruled that swinging is legal in Canada as long as it takes place in private and that "consensual sexual conduct behind code-locked doors can hardly be supposed to jeopardize a society as vigorous and tolerant as Canadian Society." A CROP poll (Gallant, 2003) found that 64 percent of Canadians (76 percent of Quebecers) were accepting of swingers clubs. That is, swinging passes the community standards of tolerance test (see Chapter 17).

A man who frequently hosts parties describes what happens:

> A lot of people have the idea that swinger parties are big orgies, where everybody jumps on everybody else. It isn't that way. People are selective, like they are any-place else. [It starts with the eyes.] So if the interest continues from eye contact to talking, and to desire, there's touching. You just go with it. So you go from talking to touching, and at a swinging party you can go from touching to bed. (Maurer, 1994, p. 120)

Swinging may be closed or open. In *closed swinging*, the couples meet and exchange partners, and each pair goes off separately to a private place to have sex, returning to the meeting place at an agreed time. In *open swinging*, the pairs get together for sex in the same room for at least part of the time. Many swingers start with *soft swinging*, which involves watching another couple engage in sexual activity, and sometimes participating in kissing, fondling, or oral sex, but not intercourse.

What kind of people are swingers? A review of 15 published studies, most of them involving small, convenience samples, concluded that the majority are upper or middle class, above average in education and income, and employed in the professions and in management (Jenks, 1998). Although one might expect them to be politically liberal, in one study only 27 percent described themselves as politically liberal—the rest were moderate or conservative (Jenks, 1985). The evidence indicates that at least two-thirds were raised in a religious home, but as adults they did not attend services and were not affiliated with a denomination. Swingers tend to report high marital satisfaction and that swinging improved their relationship (Bergstrand & Williams, 2000).

Swinging appears to involve a small minority of people. Published estimates range from less than 1 to 2 percent, although none of these is current.

Figure 11.6 A mannequin hangs from the ceiling of this members-only swingers' club in Montreal, which the police shut down in 1998. It later reopened after the Supreme Court ruled that swinging is legal in Canada as long as it takes place in private.

Polyamory

Polyamory (often referred to as *poly*) is "the non-possessive, honest, responsible, and ethical philosophy and practice of loving multiple people simultaneously" (Ve Ard & Veaux, 2003). You will notice that the focus in the definition is on love (*amory*) rather than on sex, although polyamorous relationships typically are also sexual relationships. There are several forms of such relationships, including the *intentional family*, involving three or more persons; the *group relationship*, with committed, loving relationships involving three or more partners; and *group marriage*, involving three or more persons. One specific type of *group relationship* is a triad involving a married couple and an additional man or woman, all of whom share sexual intimacy; the third person and one or both members of the couple may be bisexual. Other arrangements involve two or more men and two or more women. Unlike the extradyadic affair, there is (ideally) full disclosure of the network of relationships to all participants.

Polyamory: The "non-possessive, honest, responsible and ethical philosophy and practice of loving multiple people simultaneously" (Ve Ard & Veaux, 2003); often referred to as poly.

Unlike swinging, the emphasis is on long-term intimate relationships. Unlike polygyny, both men and women can have multiple partners. Thus, individuals in polyamorous relationships would not consider themselves to be uncommitted or unfaithful (Ritchie & Barker, 2006). Such arrangements have even made it to popular television; you may be familiar with the television show *Big Love*, which depicts a man with three wives.

The legality of polygamy was tested in the B.C. Supreme Court. In 2010, based on polygamist marriages in the Fundamentalist Church of Jesus Christ of Latter Day Saints located in Bountiful, British Columbia, the B.C. Government asked the Court to rule on whether the federal law banning polygamy violated the *Charter of Rights and Freedoms*. The court ruled that the ban against polygamy is constitutional. The judges ruled that even though the law violates religious freedom of fundamentalist Mormons, the harm against women and children outweighed that concern.

What do Canadians think about people being able to have more than one marital partner at a time? Only 4 percent approve of it; an additional 16 percent do not approve but are willing to accept it (Bibby, 2004). That is, overall 80 percent of Canadians do not accept being married to more than one person; this figure is slightly lower, although still overwhelmingly negative, for younger Canadians.

Research involving in-depth interviews with 20 men and 20 women provided information about people in polyamorous relationships in one geographic area in the United States (Sheff, 2005). Those interviewed were in their mid-30s to late 50s, usually university educated, and employed in professional occupations; most were white. Their high social status and access to resources may be a prerequisite for participating in the polyamory lifestyle. The interviewees noted that persons outside the polyamorous community, including members of their family of origin (parents, siblings), often react negatively and with hostility toward community members. Their status insulates them against some potential sanctions.

Women involved in polyamory report expanding their familial, gender, and sexual roles. For example, some of these women rejected monogamy in favour of a network of intimate partner relationships. With respect to gender roles, the women adopted a much more assertive style in their relationships with men. In the realm of sexuality, the women often recognized their high sex drive, the emotional and sexual value of intimacy with other women, and their bisexual interests or identities. Moving away from traditional roles was reported to be both liberating and frightening; creating new roles was often difficult.

In multiethnic settings, such as Hong Kong, polyamorous relationships may cross ethnic, racial, and social-class boundaries (Sik Ying Ho, 2006). For example, a 37-year-old woman described concurrent sexual relationships with both men and women, of different races and social classes. Such relationships provide novel experiences that may both be anxiety provoking and expand one's understanding of sexual diversity.

Interestingly, research in British Columbia has shown that compared with people in other types of relationships, men and women in polyamorous relationships have higher testosterone levels (van Anders et al., 2007).

 L07

Postrelationship Sex

From the point of view of developmental psychologists, the sexual relationship in a second union, perhaps following a divorce or the death of one's partner, is especially interesting. In what ways is it the same, and how does it differ, from the sexual relationship in the first long-term relationship? It represents the blending of things that are unique and consistent about the person with things that are unique to the new situation and new partner. As we develop sexually throughout the lifespan, these two strands continue to be intertwined—the developmental continuities (the things that are us and always will be) and the developmental changes (things that differ at various times in our lives, either because we are older or have experienced more, or because our partner or the situation is different).

Almost all Canadians agree that ideally their marriage should last for the rest of their life (Bibby, 2006). Nonetheless, about 40 percent of Canadian marriages will end in divorce, on average when people are in their 40s (Roterman, 2007a). The younger people are when they marry, the more likely they are to divorce (Clark & Crompton, 2006). Most divorced individuals say that they do not intend to remarry—64 percent of the women compared to 58 percent of the men (Beaupré, 2008). However, some of these individuals are living in common-law relationships, indicating that they are interested in being in a long-term relationship, just not in marriage.

People who are divorced or widowed are in a somewhat unusual situation in that they are used to regular sexual expression and suddenly find themselves in a situation in which they no longer have a regular sexual partner. Partly recognizing this dilemma, our society places few restrictions on postrelationship sexual activity. However, among heterosexuals, divorced and widowed Canadians are least likely to be satisfied with their sex life; 51 percent are satisfied, compared with 79 percent of people living with a partner and 75 percent of never-married individuals. An increasing concern is that many of these individuals do not practise safer sex (Idso, 2009), and thus are at risk for sexually transmitted infections (STIs).

Most divorced women, but fewer widowed women, return to an active sex life. An American study found that 77 percent of the widowed had not engaged in intercourse in the last year, compared with 29 percent of the divorced (Smith, 2003). Table 11.4 presents data on the number of sexual partners in the past year by a person's current marital status (Fryar et al., 2007). Among women, more than 26 percent of the widowed, divorced, or separated reported two or more (male) partners; more than one-third of the men in this status report more than two (female) partners. Note that never-married persons are 6 and 9 percent less likely to report this many partners. It is interesting that cohabiting women and men were more than twice as likely as married women and men to report this many partners. We noted earlier that the greater extrarelationship sexual activity of cohabiting individuals is thought to reflect their lower commitment, compared with married persons. Finally, note that in every category men reported a larger number of partners than did women.

The lower incidence of postmarital sex among widows, compared with divorced women, is due in part to the fact that widows are, on the average, older than divorced women; but even when matched for age, widows are still less likely than divorcees to engage in postmarital sex. One likely reason for this is that widows have the continuing social support system of in-laws and friends, and so they are less motivated to seek new friendships.

Divorced women also face complex problems of adjustment. These problems may include reduced income, a lower perceived standard of living, and reduced availability of social support. Some divorced men face similar problems. These problems may increase the motivation to establish a new long-term relationship.

Widowed and divorced women who have postmarital sex often begin a relationship within one year of the end of the marriage. Evidence from an American survey suggests that these are long-term relationships (Stack & Gundlach, 1992). The average frequency of intercourse was twice a month, and divorced men are more sexually active than divorced women are.

Earlier in this chapter, we noted that substantial numbers of men and women cohabit. Like marriages, these relationships break up. What are the similarities and differences between formerly married and formerly cohabiting men and women? To answer this question, Wade and DeLamater (2002) used the NHSLS data to analyze the rate of acquisition of new partners following the dissolution of a relationship. The results indicate that these newly single men and women do not acquire new sexual partners at a high rate, and there were no significant differences between formerly married and formerly cohabiting men and women. Newly single

Table 11.4	Number of Heterosexual Partners in the Past Year, Adults 20–59, United States		
	None	**1**	**2 or more**
Women			
Married	6%	91%	3%
Widowed, divorced, or separated	32	42	26
Never married	47	36	17
Cohabiting	11	81	8
Men			
Married	7%	86%	7%
Widowed, divorced, or separated	25	39	36
Never married	41	30	30
Cohabiting	5	80	15

Source: Fryar et al. (2007, Tables 8 and 10).

persons acquire new partners at a significantly higher rate than single, never-married persons in the year following a breakup. Men with custody of children and men and women with low incomes have higher rates of new-partner acquisition, perhaps reflecting the impact of familial and economic instability associated with the dissolution. The results suggest that the postdissolution experience is similar across various demographic groups; given the high rates of breaking up in Canada and the United States, dissolution may, we suggest, be considered a significant life stage with its own specific characteristics.

Older men and women may find the loss of a long-term partner emotionally traumatic and may find it difficult or impossible to establish a new relationship. They may also encounter resistance or hostility from their families, including their adult children, to any effort to find a new partner.

Sex in Later Life

When Freud suggested that young children, even infants, have sexual thoughts and feelings, his ideas met with considerable resistance. When, 50 years later, researchers began to suggest that senior men and women also have sexual thoughts and feelings, there was similar resistance (Pfeiffer et al., 1968). This section deals with the sexual behaviour of older men and women, the physical changes they undergo, and the attitudes that influence them.

Physical Changes in Women

Biological Changes

The climacteric is a period lasting about 15 or 20 years (from about ages 45 to 60) during which a woman's body makes the transition from being able to reproduce to not being able to reproduce; the climacteric is marked particularly by a decline in the functioning of the ovaries. However, climacteric changes occur in many other body tissues and systems as well. This period is often called **perimenopause**. The woman knows that she is in the early perimenopausal stage when she either has skipped a menstrual period or has periods that are more irregular by more than seven days (Brotto & Luria, 2008). **Menopause** (the *change of life*, the *change*) refers to one specific event in this process: the cessation of menstruation; this occurs, on average, at around age 51 (with a normal menopause occurring anywhere between the ages of 40 and 60).

Biologically, as a woman grows older, the pituitary continues a normal output of FSH (follicle-stimulating hormone) and LH (luteinizing hormone); however, as the ovaries age, they become less able to respond to the pituitary hormones. In addition, the brain—including the hypothalamus-pituitary unit—ages (Lamberts et al., 1997). With the aging of the ovaries, there is an accompanying decline in the output of their two major products: eggs and the sex hormones estrogen and progesterone. More specifically, the ovaries become less capable of responding to FSH by maturing and releasing an egg. The hormonal changes of menopause involve a decline in estrogen and progesterone levels and hormonal imbalance (see Figure 11.7). Androgen levels also decline during perimenopause (Brotto & Luria, 2008).

Physical symptoms of menopause may include hot flashes or hot flushes, night sweats, and vaginal dryness. For some women, a long-range effect of the decline in estrogen levels is *osteoporosis* (porous and brittle bones). The hot flash is probably the best known of the symptoms, particularly in Western cultures. Typically, it is described as a sudden wave of heat from the waist up. The woman may get red and perspire a lot; when the flush goes away, she may feel chilled and sometimes may shiver. The flashes may last from a few seconds to half an hour and occur several or many times a day. They may also occur at night, causing insomnia, and the resulting perspiration can soak the sheets. Research in Ontario also showed that women have poorer working memories after menopause. This appears to be due to decreased levels of estrogen; estrogen levels did not

Perimenopause: The time before menopause and the first year after the last menstrual period.
Menopause: The cessation of menstruation that usually occurs in middle age.

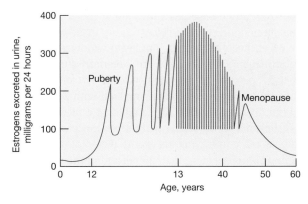

Figure 11.7 Levels of estrogen production in women across the lifespan.

affect passive recall (Duff & Hampson, 2000). However, menopausal symptoms and reactions to them are not universal and vary considerably from one culture to the next (Brotto & Luria, 2008).

Do all Canadian women experience these menopausal symptoms? No. About one-quarter of women do not experience hot flashes; 50 to 75 percent of women do, but the majority report that they are not bothered by them (Avis & McKinlay, 1995; McKinlay et al., 1992). Further, menopausal symptoms are not associated with reports of daily stress, meaning women with more symptoms do not report more stress in their lives as a result (Woods et al., 2009).

Hormone therapy (HT) may be helpful to menopausal women, particularly for relief of physical discomfort, such as hot flashes, and some sexual problems, such as lack of vaginal lubrication. The treatment today may include both estrogen and progesterone. The treatment today is controversial, and its benefits need to be weighed against potential risks. HT does convey some benefits, including protecting women from osteoporosis (which may cause a broken hip, which often leads to death in older women) (Kamel et al., 2001).

A large clinical trial in the United States found that long-term use of HT increased the risk of coronary heart disease, strokes, heart attacks, and breast and ovarian cancer but reduced the risk of colorectal cancer and hip and other fractures from osteoporosis (Enserink, 2002; Rossouw et al., 2007). There was no difference in overall mortality. However, short-term use of HT for one or two years for the management of severe menopausal symptoms is safe for most women according to the Society of Obstetricians and Gynaecologists of Canada (SOGC, 2006). Current recommendations are to use the lowest does of HT for the shortest period that allows successful treatment (Pinkerton et al., 2009). Naturopathic therapy, including black cohosh and red clover, may be effective in treating mild menopausal symptoms (Cramer et al., 2003; SOGC, 2006).

Sexuality and Menopause

During the climacteric, physical changes occur in women's genitals. The decline in estrogen causes the vagina to become less acidic, which leaves it more vulnerable to infections. Estrogen is also responsible for maintaining the mucous membranes of the vaginal walls. As a result of decreased estrogen, the walls of the vagina become thin and inelastic. The vagina and labia majora shrink, and there is a decline in vaginal lubrication during arousal. These changes may make intercourse somewhat more difficult and painful for the woman. Several remedies are available, including use of artificial lubricants or local estrogen therapy (SOGC, 2006). On the other hand, some women report that sex is even better after menopause, when fear of pregnancy no longer inhibits them. Furthermore, women have the same physical capacity for arousal and orgasm at 80 as they did at 30. For example, researchers in British Columbia examined premenopausal and postmenopausal women's physiological and subjective arousal to an erotic film and found no differences between the two groups (Brotto & Gorzalka, 2002).

It also appears that these changes are related in part to sexual activity—or, rather, to the lack of it. A study of healthy women between 60 and 70 years of age with a male partner found consistent differences between the 39 women who were sexually active and the 20 women who were not (Bachmann & Leiblum, 1991). Those who were sexually active reported having intercourse an average of five times per month. They reported having higher levels of sexual desire, greater comfort about expressing their sexual needs, and greater sexual satisfaction. A pelvic exam by a physician who was unaware of which women were sexually active found less genital atrophy in the sexually active women. These are correlational data, so we cannot be sure what is cause and what is effect.

Experts reviewing the research on women's sexuality during and after menopause have reached the following conclusions (Dennerstein et al., 2003; McCoy, 1996, 1997): (1) The majority of women with partners continue to engage in sexual activity and most enjoy it both during and after menopause. (2) There is some decline in sexual functioning, on average, during perimenopause and particularly after the last period. (3) Estrogen is related to the decline in sexual functioning, in part because low estrogen levels cause vaginal dryness. There is some evidence that higher estrogen levels are associated with better sexual functioning. (4) Testosterone is also important; a woman's sexual desire may decline as her levels of ovarian testosterone decline.

One study analyzed the data from an American Association of Retired Persons (AARP) survey of persons ages 45 and older (DeLamater & Moorman, 2007). The AARP survey included questions about various factors that might affect the frequency of sexual behaviour, including physical limitations, such as prior stroke and arthritis; emotional problems, such as depression; and use of various medications. Although some men and women reported these conditions, they were relatively uncommon and were not significantly related to the frequency of oral sexual activity or vaginal intercourse. The factors that were significantly related were high scores on an index of sexual desire (frequent sexual thoughts, desire), positive attitudes toward sex for oneself, and the presence of a partner with no limitations related to sexuality. Men and women who reported that their partner had limitations that interfered with sexual expression were significantly more likely to report masturbating.

Some people believe that having a hysterectomy means the end of a woman's sex life. In fact, sex hormone production is not affected as long as the ovaries are not removed (surgical removal of the ovaries is called **oophorectomy** or ovariectomy). The majority of women report that a hysterectomy has no effect on their sex lives. However, approximately one-third of women who have had hysterectomies report problems with sexual response (Zussman et al., 1981). There are two possible physiological causes for these problems. If the ovaries have been removed, hormonal changes may be responsible; the ovaries produce androgens, and they may play a role in sexual response. Alternatively, hysterectomy may change the sexual response if the cervix serves as a trigger for orgasm or if contractions of the uterus contribute to sexual pleasure.

Androgen therapy may improve sexual functioning and sexual well-being in women who had both ovaries removed and are experiencing androgen insufficiency syndrome (Chu & Lobo, 2004).

Changes in Men

Physical Changes

Although people use the term *male menopause*, in the technical sense men do not experience a menopause; never having menstruated, they can scarcely cease menstruating. However, men do experience a very gradual decline in the manufacture of both testosterone and sperm by the testes, a mild version of the climacteric process in women (see Figure 11.8). Some refer to this time of life as **andropause**, referring to declining levels of androgens (Lamberts et al., 1997). Others prefer the term ADAM for *androgen decline in the aging male* (Morales et al., 2000). Some experts argue that a low testosterone syndrome occurs in some older men and that *testosterone replacement therapy* is beneficial (Bain, 2007, 2010).

Oophorectomy (OH-uh-fuh-REK-tuh-mee): Surgical removal of the ovaries.
Andropause: The time of declining androgen levels in middle-aged men. The male version of menopause. Also called ADAM (androgen decline in the aging male).

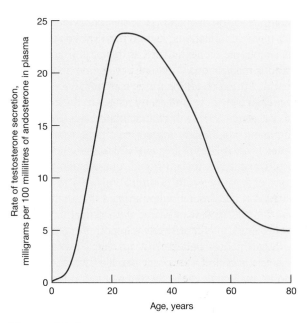

Figure 11.8 Levels of testosterone production in men across the lifespan.

Vascular diseases, such as hardening of the arteries, are increasingly common with age in men, which may cause erection problems because good circulation is essential to erection (Riportella-Muller, 1989). A major change is that erections occur more slowly. It is important for men to know that this is a perfectly natural slowdown so that they will not jump to the conclusion that they are developing an erection problem. It is also important for partners to know about this so that they will use effective techniques of stimulating the man and will not mistake slowness for lack of interest.

The refractory period lengthens with age; thus for an older man, it may be 24 hours after an orgasm before he can get an erection again. (Note that women do not undergo a similar change; most women do not enter into a refractory period and are still capable of multiple orgasms at age 80.) Other signs of sexual excitement—the sex flush and muscle tension—diminish with age.

The volume of the ejaculate gradually decreases, and the force of ejaculation lessens. The testes become somewhat smaller, but even very old men produce viable sperm. Ninety-year-old men have been known to father children.

One advantage is that middle-aged and older men may have better control over orgasm than young men may; thus, they can prolong sexual intercourse and may be better sexual partners.

A study of healthy men, ages 45 to 74, all married, assessed their biological, psychological, and behavioural functioning (Schiavi et al., 1994). Erectile problems, low sexual information,

Prostatectomy (pros-tuh-TEK-tuh-mee): Surgical removal of the prostate.

and low marital adjustment were associated with lower general satisfaction. Accurate information is important because it may result in more realistic expectations for sexual performance.

One of the most common physical problems for middle-aged and older men is noncancerous enlargement of the prostate gland, which is believed to be related to changes in hormone levels. Enlargement of the prostate causes urination problems; there is difficulty in voluntarily initiating urination, as well as frequent nocturnal urination. Surgery to remove the part of the gland pressing against the urethra usually remedies these symptoms. Unfortunately, complications of the surgery include retrograde ejaculation in about 65 percent of men and erection problems in about 10 percent (American Urological Association Practice Guidelines Committee, 2003). New treatments have recently been developed to avoid these problems, including anti-androgen drugs and laser treatments.

Some people believe that prostate surgery or removal of the prostate (**prostatectomy**) means the end of a man's sex life. It is true that the volume of the ejaculate will decrease. Prostatectomy can cause damage to the nerves supplying the penis, creating erectile problems. In other cases, retrograde ejaculation may result. Whether there are such problems depends on which of several available methods of surgery is used. Radiation, used in treating prostate cancer, may result in erectile dysfunction. Unfortunately, many men equate sex with sexual intercourse and stop engaging in all sexual activity if they develop erection difficulties as a result of prostate surgery or radiation (Letts et al., 2010).

In sum, the evidence suggests that there need be no time limit on sexual expression for either men or women. A 73-year-old man reported,

I can't begin to tell you how happy I am. I am married to a wonderful woman who loves me as much as I love her. My children gave me a hard time of it at first, especially because she is a bit younger than me. [My son] was telling me that marrying again and trying to have a lot of sex—imagine that, saying to me trying to have sex—could be dangerous to the marriage. So, I said to him with a straight face, "Do you think she'll survive it?" He was so shocked, he laughed. (Janus & Janus, 1993, p. 8)

Attitudes About Sex and Older Adults

Our society has a negative attitude toward sexual expression among older adults. People are uncomfortable with the idea of two 70-year-old people having sex with each other and even more uncomfortable with the thought of a 70-year-old masturbating. These negative attitudes become particularly obvious in assisted living and care facilities, where staff members may frown on sexual activity among the residents. Somehow, what is

Figure 11.9 Affection, romance, and sex are not just for the young.

virility at 25 becomes lechery at 75. Attitudes toward sexual expression in gay, lesbian, and bisexual individuals may be even more negative, given that they face stigma associated with both their sexual orientation and their age (Figure 11.9). Some are forced to go back in the closet when they move to assisted living facilities.

Cross-cultural research indicates that the sexual behaviour of older adults is related to these cultural expectations (Winn & Newton, 1982). Older adults continue to be sexually active in 70 percent of societies and in precisely those societies where they are expected to be sexually active. Indeed, in 22 percent of societies, women are expected to become more uninhibited about sexuality when they become older.

Why does our society have such negative attitudes toward sex among older adults? In part, these attitudes stem from the fact that ours is a youth-oriented culture. We value youth, and the physical characteristics that are considered sexy are youthful ones, such as a trim, firm body and smooth skin. It is therefore hard to believe that someone with old, wrinkled skin could be sexually active. According to one youthful-looking 59-year-old woman,

> No one looks at me today with any kind of sexual interest. I mean, I don't even get the time of day from any man. I'm an older woman. I want men to be aggressive now. I'm not going to approach a man, because I'm afraid to be rejected. So I've just given up. (Maurer, 1994, p. 475)

A study of heterosexual, mid-life women assessed menopausal status, self-rated attractiveness, sexual desire, and frequency of sexual intercourse (Koch et al., 2005). Regardless of menopausal status, women who

perceived themselves as less attractive than ten years earlier reported a decline in both sexual desire and sexual behaviour. Women who perceived themselves as more attractive reported an increase in sexual desire, frequency of sex, and frequency of orgasm. This study demonstrates a link between feelings of attractiveness and sexual behaviour. Of course, because these data are correlational, it is not known whether changes in feelings of attractiveness caused the decline in sexual desire and behaviour.

Our negative attitudes may be a holdover from the belief that sex was for reproductive purposes only—and those past the age of reproduction should therefore not engage in it (Pfeiffer, 1975). Also, we tend to identify older people with our parents or grandparents and find it hard to think of them as sexual beings. This attitude is encouraged by the fact that many parents take great pains to hide their sexual activity from their children.

These attitudes affect the way older people are treated, and older adults, whether gay or straight, may hold such attitudes themselves (Badeau & Bergeron, 1997). The current generation of older people was raised in a time in which they had little access to accurate sex information and myths about sexuality in older adults were common. Thus, older people today may be particularly affected by their own negative attitudes. For example, a Montreal study found that older men had less tolerant views about sexual expression in older people than did middle-aged men (Libman, 1989). One remedy that has been proposed for these negative attitudes is a "coming out of the closet"; as one 67-year-old commented,

> The common view that the aging and aged are non-sexual, I believe, can only be corrected by a dramatic and courageous process—the *coming out of the closet* of sexually active older women and men, so that people can see for themselves what the later years are really like. (Brecher, 1984, p. 21)

Various specific misunderstandings may influence sexuality. For example, a man might believe that sex will precipitate a heart attack or, if he has already had a heart attack, that it will bring on another one. Although heart rate accelerates during sexual intercourse, the mean heart rate during orgasm is only 117 beats per minute, which is about that attained during many common forms of daily exercise. This rate is about the equivalent of climbing two flights of stairs at a moderate pace. Thus, the demands of sex on the heart are not unreasonable (Jackson, 2009). A study of patients who had had a heart attack questioned them about their activities immediately before the attack and in the year before the attack (Muller et al., 1996). The results indicate that the increase in risk caused by sexual activity is one chance in a million for a healthy individual. Furthermore, the relative risk is no greater in patients with a history of cardiac disease.

Ideas such as this, as well as such factors as illness or hospitalization, may lead to a period of sexual inactivity. However, being sexually inactive is one of the most effective ways of diminishing sexuality. Masters and Johnson emphasized that two factors are critical in maintaining sexual capacity in old age:

1. *Good physical and mental health.* An excellent study confirms this notion (Persson, 1980). A representative sample of 70-year-olds in one town in Sweden was selected, and 85 percent agreed to participate in the detailed interviews. For both men and women, those who continued to have sexual intercourse had better mental health as rated by a psychiatrist and more positive attitudes toward sexual activity among older adults.

2. *Regularity of sexual expression.* As was noted earlier, there is evidence that some physical changes of the sex organs in old age are related to sexual inactivity. As the saying goes, "Use it or lose it." In fact, the results of a longitudinal study suggest that, for men, frequency of orgasm is positively associated with longevity. The study involved men ages 45 to 59. At the beginning of the study, the men completed a standard medical history and a questionnaire that assessed sexual behaviour. Ten years later, the researchers found out who had died, and compared their questionnaire answers with those of the survivors. Men who reported fewer than one orgasm per month at the beginning of the study were more than twice as likely to die as the men who reported two orgasms per month (Smith et al., 1997). Of course, these data are correlational (see Chapter 3), so we cannot conclude that more frequent sexual expression causes men to live longer.

Apparently, some older people have caught on to this fact. As one 80-year-old husband said of his relationship with his 75-year-old wife,

> My wife and I both believe that keeping active sexually delays the aging process . . . if we are troubled with an erection or lubrication, we turn to oral methods or masturbation of each other. We keep our interest alive by a great deal of caressing and fondling of each other's genitals. We feel it is much better to wear out than to rust out. (Brecher, 1984, p. 33)

Reformers urge us to change our attitudes about sex and older adults. Nursing homes particularly need to revise their practices and staff need to become more comfortable discussing sexuality with residents (Figure 11.10). Changes such as knocking before entering a resident's room would help (people masturbate,

Figure 11.10   Romance is important for many nursing-home residents.

you know). Other reforms would include making provisions for partners to stay overnight and allowing couples—married or unmarried—to share a bedroom.

Sexual Behaviour

Although sexual desire and sexual behavior do decline somewhat with age, substantial numbers of older men and women have active sex lives. The National Social Life, Health and Aging Project (NSHAP) interviewed 3000 women and men ages 57 to 85 in 2005–2006 (Tessler Lindau et al, 2007). Among men ages 75 to 80, more than 40 percent had frequent sexual thoughts, 30 percent had masturbated in the preceding year, and 45 percent had had sexual intercourse. Among women ages 75 to 80, the percentages were about 10, 18, and 20, respectively (Das et al., 2012). There does not seem to be any age beyond which all people are sexually inactive.

Some older people do, for various reasons, stop having intercourse after a certain age. For example, a Montreal study found that 27 percent of men and women over 60 reported that sex did not interest them very much, whereas only 5 percent of participants under 60 responded this way (Trudel, 2002). Analyses of the data from NSHAP (men and women ages 57 to 72) and NHSLS (men and women ages 44 to 59) found that, for both men and women, frequency of intercourse declined with age. Among men, declining frequency was also associated with declining happiness in the past year and declining physical health. The relationship between frequency and happiness was stronger among younger men. Among women, declining frequency was associated with happiness and especially with widowhood (Karraker et al., 2011). Subsequent analyses of NSHAP data indicate that, among men and women ages 57 to 85 who are married, overall two-thirds remain sexually active; when sexual activity within a marriage stops, it is primarily because of declining health (Karraker & DeLamater, 2013).

Further, researchers in Ontario found that some older adults reported that sex improved with age, maturity, and experience (Kleinplatz, Ménard, Paradis, et al., 2009). They counter the stereotype that aging leads to loss of sexual well-being by showing that older adults can and do experience "great sex." Indeed, many older adults would like to engage in sexual activity more often than they do (Ginsberg et al., 2005).

One of the most important influences on sexuality in older adults is that there are far more older women than older men. Because of both men's earlier mortality and their preference for younger women, older women are more likely to be living alone and to have less access to sexual partners. Men ages 65 and older are much more likely to live with a spouse or partner than are women in that age group. For example, in the 2011 Canadian census, overall 72 percent of the men but only 44 percent of the women ages 65 and older were living with a spouse or common-law partner. The discrepancy is even larger in older age groups. For example, for those ages 85 and over, 46 percent of the men and only 10 percent of the women were living with a partner. Some innovative solutions have been proposed, such as senior women forming same-sex relationships. Of course, some widowed women remarry. A British Columbia study of remarried older women found that many of them described strong sexual chemistry and a passionate sex life with their second husband that was often better than their early sexual experiences. As one woman who remarried at the age of 72 said,

> There was an incredible chemical reaction with my second husband, for both of us. Quite different from the first marriage which evolves . . . there was an absolute click. Absolutely incredible! I mean, at that age. It was like a couple of teenagers. I can't tell you. Um, oh, we had a lot of fun. (Clarke, 2006, p. 132)

Lesbians do not face the same problem of lack of suitable partners that heterosexual women face because they tend to be attracted to women of their own age (Garnets & Peplau, 2006).

A Montreal study of 144 married men ranging in age from 51 to 80 and 71 of their female spouses provides some data on how age affects sexual expression (Libman, 1989). All participants were in good health and all the men had previously undergone one of two non-life-threatening surgical procedures. The sample

was divided into younger (under 65) and older (age 65 and older) groups. The two groups did not differ in their frequency of sexual activity or in their satisfaction with their sex lives—both groups were generally satisfied. However, the older men and women experienced a desire for sex less often and the older men had more concerns about erectile difficulties (erectile difficulties themselves were infrequent in both male age groups, about 15 percent of the time).

A large representative survey on the sexuality of older adults living in the community was conducted in the United States in 2004 (Tessler Lindau et al., 2007). The researchers interviewed 3005 adults between the ages of 57 and 85. Because older adults who are sick or in care facilities are unlikely to have completed the survey, we must regard this as a survey of older adults who are above average in health and who are doubtless more sexually active than some older adults (see Milestones in Sex Research). In addition, few gay men and lesbians completed the survey, so the data apply only to heterosexual individuals. Indeed, there is little research on the effects of aging on same-sex sexual relationships. Nonetheless, this survey is a very important source of information about sex in later life.

Some statistics from the survey, presented by age group, are included in Table 11.5. Note that women over 60 are much less likely to have a sexual partner available, so the women reported much lower frequencies of partnered activities than the men did. For both men and women, the likelihood of having engaged in sexual activity with a partner declined with age. Of those in the 64-to-74 age group who had engaged in sexual activity, about two-thirds had engaged in intercourse at least weekly and half had engaged in oral sex. Among individuals who had engaged in sexual activity, the frequency of sex was lower among those who were 75 to 85 years of age, and one-third had engaged in oral sex. The frequency of masturbation also decreased with age, and was higher for men than for women. Having a current partner did not affect the likelihood of having masturbated in the previous 12 months.

About half of the respondents reported having at least one bothersome sexual problem. Erectile difficulties, reported by 37 percent of the men, were the most common problem for men. Low desire, reported by 43 percent of the women, was the most common problem reported by women. As shown in Table 11.5, about one-quarter of the men also reported a lack of interest in sex. Most men and women described sexual activity as an important part of their life.

We see, then, that many older people who are healthy engage in a range of sexual activities with a partner and consider sex an important part of their life.

How does sex change for older adults?

Milestones in Sex Research

Older Adults Who Have Optimal Sexual Experiences

There are many stereotypes of sexuality and older adults and most of these are negative. That is, the common view is that extraordinary sex is for the young and that older adults, if they have sex at all, must settle for infrequent boring sex fraught with sexual problems. But is this necessarily the case? Can sex get even better as we get older? As part of a larger investigation into the nature and contributors to optimal sexuality, Kleinplatz, Ménard, Campbell, Paradis, and their colleagues (Kleinplatz, 2010; Kleinplatz, Ménard, Paquet, et al., 2009; Kleinplatz, Ménard, Paradis, et al., 2009) conducted in-depth interviews with individuals over the age of 60 who had been in relationships for 25 years or more about their recent experiences of optimal sexuality. They ranged in age from 60 to 84. What could be learned about optimal sexuality by studying those who have made it last a lifetime? Six lessons emerged:

1. *Great lovers are made—not born.* None of the participants in this study felt that his/her facility for optimal sexuality was a natural talent that had suddenly appeared in youth. Participants identified the beginnings of "great" sex with clear and distinct improvement in their sex lives as they reached emotional maturity in mid-life. As one man put it, "It's like, there's not a goal, and I think before one of the differences was . . . it was like reaching a peak and ejaculating or something and that was the end product and I don't think of it that way, I think of it more as riding a wave and trying to stay on the crest as long as you can. It seems now silly to focus on the end, on an end state, on any end state as if that's what you've got to do. It just seems silly and counterproductive and just inconsequential [laughing] to the experience. But that's been a big change for me." For those who choose to expend the effort, the heights of sexual relations could grow given time, experience and the commitment to making sex extraordinary.

2. *Developing optimal sexuality required jettisoning normative sex scripts.* Ironically, most stated that a prerequisite for developing the capacity to experience great sex was unlearning everything they had learned about sex while growing up. They emphasized the necessity of overcoming conventional sexual scripts and the shame with which they had been raised, letting go of concerns about body image, performance expectations and the idea that sex should be "natural and spontaneous." One woman stated, "For the first few times I just assumed I had to lie there and the guy would do all the work and, and somehow I was supposed to be in ecstasy and I learned that no, I had to be an active participant . . ." To become great lovers, they had to reject old one-size-fits-all norms that had never actually fit at all.

3. *Less willing to settle.* With experience, many found that they were less willing to settle for anything less than what they really wanted. Participants emphasized the importance of sex between equals, which entailed going beyond conventional gender role norms to seek lovers who would be full partners with equal input in sexual relations. As one man stated, "The older I've gotten, the more particular I have been in my choice of partners. . . . And I'm willing to make fewer compromises about what I want sexually as I get older."

4. *"Great sex" takes a lot of time, devotion, and intentionality.* A major lesson from these interviews was that sex of this calibre does not simply "happen" but requires considerable planning, prioritizing, being deliberate, and intentionality. All the participants emphasized devoting a lot of time to sex. One man stated, "We'll play for six hours until maybe eleven at night or twelve at night." Many

described the importance of creating an environment suited to the couple's sexual inclinations. The details of such an environment might vary but the intent was invariant: "The most important thing is that it not interfere with whatever kind of sex you wanted to have that day. So it could be quiet and private and comfortable with no interruptions for about four days or it could be that the participants lose themselves in a room with other people in it or nearby. It depends what you want" (as described by a woman).

5. *Exploration and familiarity both have advantages.* Participants spoke about the opportunity for self-exploration afforded in truly intimate relationships. This was not about trying out new activities or novelty for its own sake so much as a chance for revealing themselves and one another anew and in ever-deeper ways. As one participant described it, "The better we are, the more I am dazzling and dazzled by you." The role of familiarity often is overlooked but together, exploration and familiarity create an atmosphere rich with "anticipated surprise." For these participants, a balance was required between discovery and trust. "It's the thing that makes me feel freest . . . when I feel safe" (as stated by a man). As described by another man, "You've been through so many ups and downs that you know you're going to come out of it OK."

6. *Aging, chronic illness, and disability are not necessarily obstacles to optimal sexuality.* Almost all of the participants believed that sex improved with increasing age, personal growth, and maturity. As one older man put it, "Young people are more performance and . . . they're just too anxious. Older people have more understanding for what it takes. . . . Sex comes with maturity. Sex becomes better and better with time," or as another noted, "We can still revel in sexuality." Many participants saw aging, chronic illness, and disability as assets

towards optimal sexual development. "You can always have sex in a new form" said one older woman. Another older woman who had survived breast cancer spoke of never having enjoyed sexuality or her body and body image more than since her mastectomy, which had freed her to move beyond conventional ideas of sexiness. An older man stated, "Someone who looks on themselves as being somehow broken . . . need not map to any kind of externally defined disability. . . . It never struck me as being a defining issue in terms of sexual engagement, sexual passion. . . . If there were a disability that restricts one's access to sexual fulfillment, I would say it was a disability of the energy or the imagination." Or as another participant reflected, "A lot of barriers to great sex [exist] for able-bodied people as they hold themselves to standards that get in the way of open-mindedness and experimentation."

A variety of implications emerge from these findings: It may be necessary to redefine and reconceptualize how we define "sex" and dispense with the notion that sex is supposed to be "natural and spontaneous." Older people who self-identify as having "great sex" demonstrate that sexual functioning and optimal sexuality are very different phenomena: Being sexually functional is neither *necessary* nor *sufficient* for optimal sexual experiences. Aging may be an asset for optimal sexual development. Among those having extraordinary sex, the capacity was acquired and developed rather deliberately, thus allowing for the prospect that others who might value optimal sexuality could cultivate the ability as they mature, too.

Source: Kleinplatz, P., Ménard, A. D., Paquet, M.-P., et al. (2009). The components of optimal sexuality: A portrait of "great sex." *Canadian Journal of Human Sexuality, 18,* (1–2), 1–13.

Table 11.5 Sexual Activity in a Sample of Persons Ages 57 to 85

Women	57 to 64 (492)	65 to 74 (545)	75 to 85 (513)
Sexual activity with partner in previous 12 months	61.6%	39.5%	16.7%
Have sexual activity at least once a week*	62.6%	65.4%	54.1%
Vaginal–penile intercourse*	86.8%	85.4%	74.4%
Oral sex*	52.7%	46.5%	35.0%
Masturbate in last 12 months	31.6%	21.9%	16.4%
Lack of interest in sexual activity in last 12 months	44.2%	38.4%	49.3%
Men	**(528)**	**(547)**	**(380)**
Sexual activity with partner in previous 12 months	83.7%	67.0%	38.5%
Have sexual activity at least once a week*	67.5%	65.4%	54.2%
Vaginal–penile intercourse*	91.1%	78.5%	83.5%
Oral sex*	62.1%	47.9%	28.3%
Masturbate in last 12 months	63.4%	53.0%	27.9%
Lack of interest in sexual activity in last 12 months	28.2%	28.5%	24.2%

*Of people who had engaged in sexual activity within the preceding 12 months.
Source: Tessler Lindau et al. (2007).

SUMMARY

Sexuality continues to develop throughout the life-span. It may be expressed in being single, cohabitation, common-law relationships, marriage, nonmonogamous relationships, relationships following divorce, or in a variety of contexts as the individual ages.

Young adults grow toward sexual maturity. Many do so in the context of a single relationship that results in marriage. Others are involved in two or more relationships before they begin to live with or marry someone. Never-married people over 30 may find themselves part of the singles scene.

Cohabitation is a stage that up to 40 percent of people experience. Sixty percent of cohabiting couples marry. Some cohabiting couples have children, either together or with previous partners. Men and women who are living together engage in sexual activity more often, on average, than those who are married or dating.

Marriage represents a major turning point as couples face new responsibilities and problems and try to find time for each other. Married mixed-sex couples in their 20s engage in sexual intercourse two or three times per week on average, with the frequency declining to two or three times per month among couples over age 60. Perhaps the most dramatic change in marital sex practices in recent decades is the increased popularity of oral–genital sex. Many married people continue to masturbate. Most people today–both women and men–express general satisfaction with their marital sex life.

Sexual patterns in marriage, however, show great variability. There are no data on the sexual activity of married same-sex couples.

Between 14 and 25 percent of heterosexual married men and between 7 and 15 percent of married women engage in extradyadic sex at some time. Our society disapproves of extramarital sex, and it is generally carried on in secrecy. In a few cases, it is agreed that both partners can have extradyadic sex, as in negotiated non-monogamy, swinging, and polyamory. Equity theory and the sociobiological perspective may be helpful in understanding patterns of extramarital sex.

Virtually all widowed and divorced men return to an active sex life, as do most divorced women and about half of widowed women. A particular set of sexual norms characterizes the divorce subculture.

The climacteric is the period in middle age during which the functioning of the ovaries (both hormone and egg production) declines gradually. One symptom of this process is menopause, the cessation of menstruation. Physical symptoms during this time, such as hot flashes, result from declining levels of estrogen. Men experience a much more gradual decline in the functioning of their gonads, leading to decreasing levels of testosterone and sperm production. Men and women may experience a psychological transition in middle age.

Although sexual activity declines somewhat with age, many people remain sexually active into their

80s and 90s. Problems with sex or the cessation of inter-course may be related to physical factors. In women declining estrogen levels result in a thinner, less elastic vagina and less lubrication; in men there is lowered testosterone production and increased vascular disease, combined with slower erections and longer refractory periods. Psychological factors can also be involved, such as the belief that seniors cannot or should not have sex. Masters and Johnson emphasized that two factors are critical to maintaining sexual capacity in old age: good physical and mental health, and regularity of sexual expression. A recent survey indicates that most older people who are healthy engage in sexual activity with a partner and consider it an important part of their life.

QUESTIONS FOR THOUGHT, DISCUSSION, AND DEBATE

1. What is your response when you see an older couple expressing affection physically with each other, perhaps kissing or holding hands? Why do you think you respond that way?

2. What is your opinion about extradyadic sex? Is it ethical or moral? What are its effects on a relationship—does it destroy or improve it, or perhaps have no effect?

3. If you are currently in a relationship, in what ways is your relationship characteristic of distressed couples? In what ways is it characteristic of non-distressed couples? What changes can you make to improve your relationship satisfaction?

4. You and your partner are talking about establishing a long-term relationship. Your partner says that the main concern is that living together will lead to a decline in how often you have sex. Is that a realistic concern? If so, what could the two of you do to prevent that from occurring?

5. Among the Yoruba of West Africa, younger women may not travel or engage in trade, but older (post-menopausal) women may. Among the Winnebago of North America, old women sit with men; they are considered the same as men. In some cultures, then, women gain in freedom and status after menopause. Does this happen for most women in Canada? Are there variations among ethnic groups in Canada—for example, Aboriginal peoples, blacks, Asians, whites—in the way a postmenopausal woman is viewed and treated? Are there differences between anglophones and francophones? (For more information, see Golub, 1992.)

Are YOU Curious?

1. Do opposites really attract?
2. How do Internet dating sites match people?
3. How important is emotional intimacy in relationships?
4. Why do people get jealous?

Read this chapter to find out.

CHAPTER

12

Attraction, Love, and Communication

LEARNING OBJECTIVES

After studying this chapter, you will be able to

LO1 Describe the factors that influence attraction.

LO2 Describe and evaluate the role of the Internet in dating.

LO3 Explain the nature and the value of emotional intimacy in relationships.

LO4 Describe the four views of love.

LO5 Describe jealousy.

LO6 Describe and evaluate the two-component theory of love.

LO7 Describe how culture influences love and marriage.

LO8 Describe the outcomes and characteristics of effective communication.

The intimacy in sex is never only physical. In a sexual relationship we may discover who we are in ways otherwise unavailable to us, and at the same time we allow our partner to see and know that individual. As we unveil our bodies, we also disclose our persons.*

* Dr. Thomas Moore, "Soul Mates," *Psychology Today*, March–April 1994, downloaded from http://faculty.uccb.ns.ca/pmacintyre/psych365/quotes.htm.

Many people believe that there is (or should be) a close connection between love and sex. The primary sexual standard of today for many is that sex is appropriate if we love the other person. Of course, sex and love do not necessarily go together. Some people have satisfying sexual relationships without emotional involvement; other people are in love with a person with whom they do not have a sexual relationship. Nonetheless, for most people emotional passion and sexual passion are closely linked—without the sexual passion, we might be more likely to think of the person as a friend. People want to express their loving feelings to their romantic partner in a sexual way. Lovemaking, in turn, contributes to their feelings of love. In short, sex is an important part of most romantic relationships. Therefore, it is important in a text on sexuality to spend some time considering the emotion we link so closely to sex: love.

This chapter is organized in terms of the way relationships usually progress—if they progress. We begin by talking about attraction, what brings people together in the first place. Then we consider intimacy, which develops as relationships develop. Next, we look at four different views of what love is. We discuss some of the research on love, including cross-cultural research. Finally, we conclude with one of the requirements for fulfilling, long-term relationships: good communication.

 LO1

Attraction

What causes you to be attracted to another person? Some people are attracted only to men, some only to women, some to both, and some to neither, so gender is an important component of attraction. Sexual orientation, including its causes, is discussed in Chapter 14, so it is not discussed here. However, social psychologists have done extensive research on interpersonal attraction. We consider the major results of this research in this section. Unfortunately, much of the research on attraction has been restricted to studying male–female relationships and has not included same-sex relationships.

The Girl Next Door

Geography and time limit our opportunities to meet people. You may meet that attractive person sitting two rows in front of you in human sexuality class, but you are unlikely to meet the wealthy, brilliant engineering student who sits in your seat two classes later. You are much more likely to meet and be attracted to the boy or girl next door than the one who lives across town.

Among those with whom we work or take the same class, we tend to be more attracted to people we have had contact with several times than we are to people with whom we have had little contact. This tendency has been demonstrated in laboratory studies in which the amount of contact between participants was systematically varied. At the end of the session, people gave higher "liking" ratings to those with whom they had had much contact and lower ratings to those with whom they had had little contact (Saegert et al., 1973). This is the **mere-exposure effect**; repeated exposure to any stimulus, including a person, leads to greater liking for that stimulus (Bornstein, 1989). For this reason, the chance of a boy falling in love with the girl or boy next door is greater than the chance of falling in love with someone he seldom meets.

Birds of a Feather

We tend to like people who are similar to us. We are attracted to people who are approximately the same as we are in age, ethnicity, background, and economic and social status. Similarity on these social characteristics is referred to as **homophily**, the tendency to have contact with people equal in social status. When a person marries someone with whom they share important characteristics (i.e., with whom they are homophilous), it is called *homogamy*. Table 12.1 displays data on homophily from the National Health and Social Life Survey (NHSLS). Note that the greatest homophily is by race/ethnicity, followed by education and age. In Canada, although this percentage has been increasing, only 3.9 percent of couples are in "mixed unions"; mixed unions refer to relationships in

Mere-exposure effect: The tendency to like a person more if we have been exposed to him or her repeatedly.
Homophily: The tendency to have contact with people who share our social characteristics.

Table 12.1 Percentage of American Relationships That Are Homophilous, by Type of Relationship

Type of Homophily	Type of Relationship			
	Marriages*	Cohabitations*	Long-Term Partnerships	Short-Term Partnerships
Racial/ethnic	93%	88%	89%	91%
Age[†]	78	75	76	83
Educational[†]	82	87	83	87
Religious[§]	72	53	56	60

* Percentages of marriages and cohabitational relationships that began in the 10 years before the survey.

† Age homophily is defined as a difference of no more than five years in partners' ages.

‡ Educational homophily is defined as a difference of no more than one educational category. The educational categories used were less than high school, high school graduate, vocational training, four-year college, and graduate degree.

§ Cases in which either partner was reported as "other" or had missing data are omitted.

Source: Edward O. Laumann et al., *The Social Organization of Sexuality: Sexual Practices in the United States*, pp. 82, 98, 177, 305, 458. Copyright © 1994 University of Chicago Press. Reprinted with permission.

which one member of the couple is from a visible minority group and the other is not, or each member is from a different visible minority group (Milan et al., 2010). Couples are least likely to be the same on religion. It is interesting that short-term partnerships are as homophilous as marriages and common-law relationships. These data take a somewhat liberal view of educational homophily. However, educational homophily has been increasing, and currently 54 percent of Canadian couples have the same educational level (Hou & Myles, 2007). How important is homophily to Canadians? Almost one-half (46 percent) prefer a spouse who shares their religious views, and about a third (34 percent) prefer a spouse who shares their ethnic background (Compas Inc., 2005). One of the reasons for homophily by ethnicity is that persons from ethnocultural minorities have tended to live in socially and economically separate communities. In communities where different racial groups have coexisted for generations, such as Nova Scotia, there tend to be more interracial relationships.

Do opposites really attract?

Social psychologist Donn Byrne (1971) has done numerous experiments demonstrating that we are attracted to people whose attitudes and opinions are similar to ours. In these experiments, Byrne typically has people fill out an opinion questionnaire. They are then shown a questionnaire that was supposedly filled out by another person and are asked to rate how much they think they would like that person. In fact, the questionnaire was filled out to show either high or low agreement with the participant's responses. Participants report more liking for a person whose responses are similar to theirs than for one whose responses are quite different. The relationship between similarity and liking may also work in the opposite direction. Research in Manitoba showed that the more satisfied individuals are

with their relationship, the more they assume the other person is similar to them (Morry, 2007).

Folk sayings are sometimes wise and sometimes foolish. The interpersonal-attraction research indicates that the saying "Birds of a feather flock together" contains some truth.

Despite the saying that "opposites attract," dissimilar attitudes tend to cause disliking, not liking (Pilkington & Lydon, 1997). Nonetheless, we may be attracted to people whose interpersonal styles are dissimilar to our own. In one study, dominant people paired with submissive people reported greater satisfaction with their relationship than dominant or submissive people paired with a similar partner (Dryer & Horowitz, 1997).

People vary on a large number of characteristics. Perhaps similarity on some is important to attraction and relationship success, while similarity on others is not. Attitudes are one set of characteristics, personality traits are another, and attachment style is another. The research discussed so far argues that similarity in attitudes is important, but similarity in personality is not.

These predictions were tested in research involving newly married heterosexual couples (Luo & Klohnen, 2005). The average participant was 28 years old, white, fairly well educated, and Christian. The researchers calculated couple similarity scores on numerous measures in the three domains. They compared these real-couple scores with the mean scores of randomly paired couples. As predicted, real couples were significantly more similar on values, religiosity, and political attitudes but no more similar than random couples on personality. The NHSLS found that couples are similar in age, race, and education. Could this homophily account for similarity in attitudes? Researchers tried to predict similarity in attitudes and personality from similarity in background characteristics but could not.

Finally, what is the relationship between similarity and quality of relationship? Among these couples, similarity on attachment styles was associated with indicators of marital satisfaction, but similarity in attitudes was not. Perhaps we need to revise the adage to "Birds of a feather (attitudinal similarity) flock, but may not stick, together."

Physical Attractiveness

A great deal of evidence shows that, given a choice of more than one potential partner, gay, lesbian, and straight individuals prefer the one who is more physically attractive (Bailey et al., 1997; Fisher & Cox, 2009; Hendrick & Hendrick, 1992). Research in Ontario has shown this phenomenon in children as young as three to six years of age; even young children are more attracted to children with attractive faces (Dion, 1973, 1977).

Physical attractiveness is one aspect of sex appeal; in fact, young men and women typically rate physical appearance as most important (Regan, 2004). Other aspects include general body size (measured in various ways) and certain facial features. Much of the research on attractiveness uses data from samples of white persons. One exception is research on the impact of lightness of skin on ratings of attractiveness among African Americans. Skin tone was strongly associated with the attractiveness ratings given female respondents by both male and female interviewers (Hill, 2002). Light skin was rated as more attractive, perhaps reflecting the use of white skin as the standard.

In general, then, we are most attracted to good-looking people. However, among heterosexuals, this effect depends on gender to some extent; physical attractiveness is more important to males evaluating females than it is to females evaluating males (Feingold, 1990). Also, our perception of attractiveness or beauty of another person is influenced by our evaluation of their intelligence, liking, and respect (Kniffin & Wilson, 2004), as well as by our own objective attractiveness (Montoya, 2008). In addition, this phenomenon is somewhat modified by our own feelings of personal worth, as we will discuss later in the chapter. The good news is that although Canadians on average give themselves a 6.7 out of 10 in physical attractiveness, they rate their partner significantly higher, giving their partner a 8.0 out of 10 (Harris/Decima, 2007). Similar results have been found among gay men and lesbians (Swami, 2009). As a final note, a 2001 Compas survey asked 400 Canadians to choose whether their perfect partner would have an ordinary face and an extraordinary body or an extraordinary face and an ordinary body. Twice as many women as men choose the extraordinary face—57 percent to 29 percent (Anderson, 2001).

Figure 12.1 Historically, women's worth has been based on their beauty, whereas men's worth has been based on their success, as exemplified in this photo of Hugh Hefner and his young wife.

The Interpersonal Marketplace

Although this may sound somewhat callous, whom we are attracted to and pair off with depends a lot on how much we think we have to offer and how much we think we can "buy" with it. That is, people seek relationships in which there is equity and both partners receive the same balance of rewards and costs (see Chapter 2 for a discussion of social exchange theory). This tendency for men and women to choose as partners people whose social worth matches their own is called the **matching phenomenon**. Generally, the principle seems to be that women's worth is based on their physical beauty, whereas men's worth is based on their success. There is a tendency, then, for beautiful women to be paired with wealthy, successful men (Figure 12.1).

Data from many studies document this phenomenon in heterosexual relationships. In one study, high school yearbook pictures were rated for attractiveness (Udry & Eckland, 1984). These people were followed up 15 years after graduation, and measures of education, occupational status, and income were obtained. Females rated the most attractive in high school were significantly more likely to have husbands who had high incomes and were highly educated (see also Elder, 1969).

From the Laboratory to Real Life

The phenomena discussed so far—feelings of attraction to people who are similar to us and the choosing of partners whose social worth matches our own—have been demonstrated mainly in psychologists' laboratories. Do these phenomena occur in the real world?

With respect to similarity, much of the research has focused

Matching phenomenon: The tendency for men and women to choose as partners people who match them, that is, who are similar in attitudes, intelligence, and attractiveness.

on actual similarity. It is relatively easy to do this in the laboratory. We reviewed several studies where researchers measured some characteristic and then paired participants based on (dis)similarity of scores. When we move into the everyday world (the field), researchers generally cannot manipulate degree of similarity, so they measure the existing (dis)similarity among couples of various types and correlate it with various outcomes (e.g., attraction). We cannot draw causal conclusions from such data; for that reason, researchers prefer laboratory work to test the theory. Also, as research on the topic expanded, some suggested that what is important is **perceived similarity**, the extent to which the individual believes his or her partner is similar on important characteristics. This research is usually done in field settings.

A meta-analysis assessed the importance of actual and perceived similarity as measured in laboratory and field settings (Montoya et al., 2008). In addition, researchers coded the amount of interaction participants experienced: no interaction, short interaction (e.g., 5 to 10 minutes), and existing relationship. The results indicated that both actual and perceived similarity are associated with interpersonal attraction; the associations were significant and large. Actual similarity was important in studies involving no or short interaction, that is, in the laboratory, but it was not related to attraction in existing relationships. Perceived similarity was associated with attraction in all three settings. In this case, extending the research into everyday life resulted in an important modification of the theory.

With respect to the matching hypothesis, a series of studies combining data from the laboratory and an online dating site (everyday life) found that the nature and importance of matching varies as relationships develop (Taylor et al., 2011). In predicting who individuals would choose from a set of potential partners, researchers found that each individual's rating of self-worth predicted the level of physical and social attractiveness of the choice. In predicting who individuals would communicate with in online dating, matching occurred on popularity rather than physical or social attractiveness. Importantly, as the theory predicts, individuals who rated their self-worth low voluntarily selected less desirable partners. Thus, in a somewhat revised form, the importance of similarity and matching principles apply in everyday life as well as in the psychological laboratory.

Some researchers have investigated the qualities that initially attracted an individual to a person with whom they ultimately formed a romantic relationship. For example, one study asked 120 individuals in same-sex relationships the extent to which a number of qualities

Perceived similarity: The extent to which an individual believes his or her partner is similar on important characteristics.

had initially attracted them to their partner (Felmlee et al., 2010). Qualities related to agreeableness (e.g., kindness, supportiveness, consideration, understanding) were rated as most important. The least important qualities related to status (e.g., potential for a good job, security, success). Physical attractiveness fell between agreeableness and status. Another important finding was there were no gender differences in ratings of any of these qualities.

A handful of published studies have reported that, in everyday life, what women find attractive is influenced by hormonal fluctuations related to the menstrual cycle. The results indicate that near ovulation, women are more likely to show a preference for masculine, dominant men, especially if they are interested in short-term relationships, and to dress in ways that enhance femininity and sex appeal. In general, attempts to replicate these results on other and large samples have been unsuccessful.

L02 Attraction Online

Technology has created a new way to meet potential partners: online (Figure 12.2). Indeed, there are now more than 800 different online dating websites (Marsan, 2008). Some websites, such as Toronto-based Lavalife, have more than a million members. Both Lavalife (www.lavalife.ca) and PlentyOfFish (www.pof.com) claim hundreds of thousands of hits per day. There are also ethnocultural-specific dating sites for individuals looking for a partner who is, for example, Jewish, South Asian, or black.

What accounts for the remarkable growth of this phenomenon? According to a Canadian study (Brym & Lenton, 2001), four social forces are at work. First, a

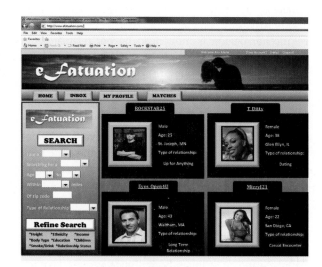

Figure 12.2 Technology has created a new way to meet potential partners: online.

growing proportion of the population is single, so more people are looking. Second, career and time pressures lead people to seek more efficient ways to look. Third, single people are highly mobile, increasing the difficulty of meeting people. Fourth, workplace romance is less acceptable because of concerns about sexual harassment (see Chapter 16).

Online dating has become increasingly common and socially acceptable. There is no longer stigma associated with meeting a partner online, and people feel free to tell their friends and family that they are using online dating (Sritharan et al., 2010; Stephure et al., 2009). Indeed, a recent survey found that, in the United States, 74 percent of the single Internet users looking for a romantic partner had used the Internet to try to meet someone (Madden & Lenhart, 2006). As is the case offline, research in Ontario has shown that physical attractiveness has a strong influence on initial evaluations of potential online partners (Sritharan et al., 2010).

The Internet also provides a mechanism for lesbian, gay, and bisexual individuals to meet people who share their sexual orientation. This is particularly important for youth or individuals in small communities who choose not to be open about their sexual orientation or do not want to risk experiencing rejection from an offline potential partner. Indeed, gay men and lesbians of all ages are more likely than heterosexuals are to meet and form an offline relationship with someone they met online (Lever et al., 2008). In addition, the Internet allows individuals who have specific sexual interests, such as bondage and discipline (see Chapter 15), to meet romantic partners who share their sexual interests rather than risk rejection.

Surveys suggest that the people seeking partners online are educated, affluent, 20- to 40-year-olds who do not have the time or the taste for "singles bars." Telephone interviews in 2005 with a sample of adults found that 11 percent of Internet users had visited an online dating site. Homophily may come into play here if people choose to visit a website specifically for people who share their ethnocultural background.

Advantages and Disadvantages of Online Dating
Users say that one advantage of meeting online is that the technology forces you to focus on the person's interests and values. This focus may facilitate finding a person with whom you have a lot in common; however, individuals who are in relationships that started online report lower relational intimacy than those who are in relationships that started face to face (Scott et al., 2006). Online, you do not have access to body language, facial expressions, posture, and other cues that provide information. As a result, imagination heavily influences impressions, which can create a powerful attraction to the other (Ben-Ze'ev, 2004).

The relative lack of (reliable) information about the person you are chatting or exchanging emails with is the downside of meeting online. She or he may not be all they claim to be or how you imagine the person in your mind. In fact, research suggests that one-quarter of Canadian online daters admit to having misrepresented themselves online (Brym & Lenton, 2001). Kaufmann (2012) analyzed Love Online by studying blog posts of men and women about their experiences. (We have little information about the sample; as computer users, they are probably younger, better educated, and white.) He found that the appeal of online dating was the hundreds of prospects available with a few clicks, giving the user a great sense of control. However, he also found that if you arrange a date, anything can happen: you have doubts about whether to go. The person doesn't show up. Disillusionment occurs at first glance: the person doesn't match the photo, the description, or your fantasy. The person has annoying habits, bad body odour, or poor manners. The person talks incessantly about exes. Indecision about kissing or going to one of your places ruins the date. Mediocre or disastrous sex takes place. You feel like you paid or were paid for sex (this is especially likely after an expensive dinner.) The result according to Kaufmann? Most of those first dates are last dates. Kaufmann argues that this tremendous variety of outcomes, including many that neither party wanted, reflects the lack of scripts for these dates. In part, the lack of scripts reflects the newness of the phenomenon, but in part it reflects the difficulty of devising scripts for diverse types of users with diverse types of motives.

The "Science" of Online Dating
In recent years, online dating sites have enlisted the help of researchers in developing a "scientific" approach to pairing clients (Gottlieb, 2006). The most renowned is eHarmony, thanks to its outgoing founder, Neil Clark Warren. Similar sites include Chemistry.com, whose chief adviser is sociobiologist Helen Fisher, and PerfectMatch.com, whose system was developed by Dr. Pepper Schwartz, a sociologist. Each site uses clients' responses to an online questionnaire to match them.

How do they differ? Each site has its own matching strategy. Following the research on attraction, eHarmony uses a 436-question survey to assess a broad range of attitude, value, and personality domains. Couples are matched based on relative similarity on each domain. Chemistry.com focuses on pairing adults who will experience a "spark" when they meet. Fisher argues that testosterone, dopamine, oxytocin, and vasopressin are the basis of romance (Fisher et al., 2006). Genes associated with these hormones are associated with traits such as calmness, popularity, rationality, and sympathy. Chemistry.com uses a 146-item survey to measure these traits and infers the clients' "chemistry."

PerfectMatch.com uses the Duet system, based on 48 questions assessing eight domains. Schwartz believes that a well-matched couple should be similar on romantic impulsivity, personal energy, outlook, and predictability, and different on flexibility, decision-making style, emotionality, and self-nurturing style. What do you think?

How successful are Internet dating sites at helping people form long-term relationships? First, in one study of Canadian online daters, only two-thirds of people using online dating services met even one person face to face. Of those who did meet someone face to face, 27 percent formed a romantic relationship with a person they met online, but only 3 percent had married someone they met online (Brym & Lenton, 2001). Several researchers assessed online dating from the perspective of relationship science and considered the degree to which online dating algorithms and practices fit with what we know scientifically (Finkel et al., 2012). Online dating sites claim to produce outcomes superior to traditional methods of meeting, dating, and developing a committed relationship; is that likely? Research over the past 40 years has identified three classes of influence on relationship success: personal characteristics, individual change, and external, uncontrollable events (e.g., unemployment, infertility, chronic illness, natural disasters). Online dating sites can measure and provide information only about variables in the first group. Research indicates that variables in that category account for only a small part of the long-term outcome. Bottom line? Claims by these sites to produce superior outcomes are impossible to justify. If a long-term intimate relationship is your goal, online dating is not more likely to get you there.

How do Internet dating sites match people?

Explaining Our Preferences

The research data are quite consistent in showing that we select as potential partners people who are similar to us in social characteristics—age, race, education—and who share our attitudes and beliefs. Moreover, both men and women prefer physically attractive people, although heterosexual women place greater emphasis on a man's social status or earning potential (Sprecher et al., 1994). The obvious question is, Why? Two answers are suggested, one drawing on reinforcement theory and one drawing on sociobiology (see Chapter 2 for discussions of these theories).

Reinforcement Theory: Byrne's Law of Attraction

A rather commonsense idea—and one that psychologists agree with—is that we tend to like people who give us reinforcements or rewards and to dislike people who give us punishments (Figure 12.3). Social psychologist Donn Byrne (1997) has formulated the law of attraction. It says that our attraction to another person is proportionate to the number of reinforcements that person gives us relative to the total number of reinforcements plus punishments the person gives us. Or, simplified even more, we like people who are frequently nice to us and seldom nasty.

According to this explanation, most people prefer to interact with people who are similar to them because interaction with them is rewarding. People who are similar in age, ethnic background, and education are likely to have similar outlooks on life, prefer similar activities, and like the same kinds of people. These shared values and beliefs provide the basis for smooth and rewarding interaction. It will be easy to agree about such things as how important schoolwork is, what TV programs to watch, and what to do on Friday night. Disagreement about such things would cause conflict and hostility, which are definitely not rewards (for most people, anyway). We prefer pretty or handsome partners because we are aware of the high value placed on physical attractiveness in Canadian society; we believe others will have a higher opinion of us if we have a good-looking partner. Finally, we prefer someone with high social status or earning potential because all the material things that people find rewarding cost money.

Figure 12.3   According to Byrne's law of attraction, our liking for a person is influenced by the reinforcements we receive from interacting with them. Shared activities provide the basis for smooth and rewarding interaction.

These findings have some practical implications (Hatfield & Walster, 1978). If you are trying to get a new relationship going well, make sure you give the other person lots of positive reinforcement. Also, make sure that you have some good times together so that you *associate* each other with rewards. Do not spend all your time stripping paint off old furniture or cleaning out the garage. And do not forget to keep the positive reinforcements (or "strokes," if you like that jargon better) going in an old, stable relationship.

A variation of the reinforcement view comes from the implicit egotism perspective (Jones et al., 2004). It states that we are attracted to persons who are similar to us because they activate our positive views of ourselves. For example, archival research found that men and women are more likely to marry people whose names resemble their own.

Sociobiology: Sexual Strategies Theory

Sociobiologists view sexual behaviour within an evolutionary perspective and thus focus on heterosexual relationships. Historically, the function of mating has been reproduction. Men and women who selected mates according to some preferences were more successful than those who chose them based on other preferences. The successful ones produced more offspring, who in turn produced more offspring, carrying their mating preferences to the present.

Men and women face different adaptive problems in their efforts to reproduce (Buss & Schmitt, 1993). Since women bear the offspring, men need to identify reproductively valuable women. Other things being equal, younger women are more likely to be fertile than older women; hence heterosexual men's preference for young women. Also, sociobiologists assert that men want to be certain about the paternity of offspring; hence, they want a woman who will be sexually faithful.

Sociobiologists argue that, other things being equal, a physically attractive person is more likely to be healthy and fertile than someone who is not physically attractive—thus the preference for good-looking partners. If attractiveness is an indicator of health, we would expect it to be more important in societies where chronic diseases are more prevalent. Gangestad and Buss (1993) measured the prevalence of seven pathogens, including those that cause malaria and leprosy, in 29 cultures and also obtained ratings of the importance of 18 attributes of mates. They found that physical attractiveness was considered more important by residents in societies that had a greater prevalence of pathogens. However, one study found that there was no relationship between rated facial attractiveness (based on a photograph) and a clinical assessment of health in a sample of adolescents, suggesting that the assumed link between attractiveness and health is not there. At the same time,

the raters ranked more attractive persons as healthier (Kalick et al., 1998).

Some evolutionary analysts have argued that the critical feature of an attractive face is symmetry, having features on one side of the nose that are mirror images of features on the other side. **Fluctuating asymmetry**, asymmetry of bilateral features that are on average symmetrical in the population, are said to reflect developmental instability (DI), the inability of the developing body to buffer itself against random perturbations (Van Dongen & Gangestad, 2011). Visible asymmetry in the face would reflect DI, which could have caused other anomalies that could impair reproductive success. Thus, attractiveness might be an important indicator of fertility, fetal survival, and normal growth. There have been dozens of studies of the relationship between symmetry and numerous features, including measures of health, fetal outcomes, hormonal functioning, facial attractiveness, and reproduction (number of sexual partners). They indicate that the correlation between symmetry and health and fitness is small (Van Dongen & Gangestad, 2011).

Women must make a much greater personal investment than men to reproduce. They will be pregnant for nine months, and after the birth they must care for the infant and young child for many years. Thus, women want to select as mates men who are reproductively valuable; hence the preference for good-looking mates. They also want mates who are able and willing to invest resources in them and their children. Obviously, men must have resources to invest them, so women prefer men with higher incomes and status. Among young people, women will prefer men with greater earning potential; thus, the preference for men with greater education and higher occupational aspirations. The matter of resources is more important than the problem of identifying a reproductively valuable male, so women rate income and earning potential as more important than good looks.

Note that these arguments assume that women have limited access to resources, forcing their reliance on men. But today, women are increasingly working and controlling their own earnings. These women may place less emphasis on a man's resources in selecting a mate. Analysis of survey data from women ages 18 to 35 (44 percent in a relationship) found that wealthier women prefer older men, and resource control predicted a preference for physical attractiveness over financial prospects (Moore et al., 2006). In effect, wealthier women have more to offer in the relationship marketplace.

These two explanations—reinforcement theory and sociobiology—are not inconsistent. We can think about reinforcement in more general terms. Reproduction is a major goal for most adults in every society. Successful reproduction—that

Fluctuating asymmetry: Asymmetry of bilateral features that are on average symmetrical in the population.

is, having a healthy child who develops normally—is very reinforcing. Following the sexual strategies that we have inherited is likely to lead to such reinforcement. Of course, sexual strategies theory is not a good explanation for same-sex attraction.

Intimacy

What is intimacy? Intimacy is a major component of any close or romantic relationship. Today many people are seeking to increase the intimacy in their relationships. And so, in this section we will explore intimacy in more detail to try to gain a better understanding of it.

Kaufmann (2012) in his analysis of love online suggests that many online daters are searching for a long-term intimate relationship. Intimate relationships are important to us for two reasons. The first is the desire to someday have children and the awareness that raising a child is a lot easier with two people. The other is to obtain the benefits of mutual trust and reciprocal recognition by another person. This benefit is increasingly important in an impersonal and sometimes cruel world that is very stressful for some people. Indeed, stress researchers have long recognized the need for interpersonal support to successfully cope with stress.

> **How important is emotional intimacy in relationships?**

Defining Intimacy

Psychologists have offered a number of definitions of intimacy For example, Perlman & Fehr (1987) propose that the defining features of intimacy include "openness, honesty, mutual self-disclosure; caring, warmth, protecting, helping; being devoted to each other, mutually attentive, mutually committed; surrendering control, dropping defenses; becoming emotional, feeling distressed when separation occurs" (p. 17). Prager (1997) expanded on this definition by making a distinction between intimate interactions and intimate relationships.

Intimate interactions include both intimate experiences and intimate behaviours. **Intimate experiences** are the meaning a person gives to their interactions with another person. Intimate experiences are usually associated with positive emotions. For example, you might perceive meeting your partner's family as an intimate experience because it symbolizes your partner's desire to include you

Intimate experiences: The meaning a person gives to their interactions with another person.
Intimate relationships: Relationships in which intimate interactions occur on a regular and predictable basis. Relationships characterized by affection between partners, mutual trust, and partner cohesiveness.
Intimacy: A quality of relationships characterized by commitment, feelings of closeness and trust, and self-disclosure.
Self-disclosure: Telling personal things about yourself.

in his or her life. Intimate behaviours are more concrete than intimate experiences. Intimate behaviours can be nonverbal, and include behaviours such as eye contact, smiling, physical closeness, or sexual activity. However, the most common type of intimate behaviour is verbal self-disclosure, which includes the sharing of information about one's self with a partner. Self-disclosure is discussed in more detail in the next section.

As you interact with an individual over time, you may develop an intimate relationship. **Intimate relationships** are the result of many intimate interactions with an individual and are typically characterized by love, affection, trust, sharing, and reciprocity. However, intimate interactions can also occur outside the context of an intimate relationship. For example, it is possible to disclose your feelings to a stranger without having an intimate relationship with that person.

Another definition of **intimacy** in romantic relationships is "the level of commitment and positive affective, cognitive, and physical closeness one experiences with a partner in a reciprocal (although not necessarily symmetrical) relationship" (Moss & Schwebel, 1993, p. 33). The emphasis in this definition is on closeness or sharing (intimate behaviour) and on partner responsiveness, which has three dimensions—affective (emotional), cognitive, and physical. Note, too, that whereas intimacy must be reciprocal, it need not be equal. Many people have had the experience of feeling closer to another person than that person seems to feel toward them. Finally, note that although intimacy has a physical dimension, it need not be sexual. Interestingly, although Canadians of European descent and those of Asian descent both conceptualize intimacy in this way, the Asian Canadian daters reported significantly less intimacy in their relationships (Marshall, 2008). This is problematic because, for both groups, lower intimacy was related to a higher likelihood that the relationship would end.

In one study, university students were asked to respond to an open-ended question asking what they thought made a relationship one of intimacy (Roscoe et al., 1987). The qualities that emerged, with great agreement, were sharing, sexual interaction, trust in the partner, and openness. Notice that these qualities are quite similar to the ones listed in the definitions just given.

Intimacy and Self-Disclosure

One of the key characteristics of intimacy appearing in psychologists' and university students' definitions is self-disclosure (Prager, 1997). **Self-disclosure** involves telling your partner personal things about yourself. It may range from telling your partner about something embarrassing that happened to you at work today, to disclosing a very meaningful event that happened between you and your parents 15 years ago, to sharing your innermost thoughts, feelings, and fantasies. Note that self-disclosure does not mean that partners should be saying anything they want to each other without consideration for the other person's feelings. As discussed in the section on communication, even in an open and self-disclosing relationship, it is important that people censor some (not all) thoughts and feelings that would be deliberately hurtful to their partner.

Research consistently shows that self-disclosure leads to reciprocity (Berg & Derlega, 1987; Hendrick & Hendrick, 1992). In other words, if one member of the couple self-discloses, this act seems to prompt the other partner to self-disclose also. Self-disclosure by one member of the couple can essentially get the ball rolling.

Why does this occur? Psychologists have proposed a number of reasons (Hendrick & Hendrick, 1992). First, disclosure by our partner may make us like and trust that person more. Second, as social learning theorists would argue, simple modelling and imitation may occur. That is, one partner's self-disclosing serves as a model for the other partner. Norms of equity may also be involved (see Chapter 11 for a discussion of equity theory). After one partner has self-disclosed, the other person may follow suit to maintain a sense of balance or equity in the relationship.

Self-disclosure relates closely to satisfaction with the overall relationship and, as discussed later in the chapter, with the sexual aspects of the relationship. That is, couples that engage in more self-disclosure are more satisfied with their relationship (MacNeil & Byers, 2005, 2009). Patterns of self-disclosure can actually predict whether a couple stays together or breaks up. Research in which couples are followed for periods ranging from two months to four years shows that the greater the self-disclosure, the greater the likelihood that the relationship will continue, and the less the self-disclosure, the greater the likelihood of breakup (Hendrick et al., 1988; Sprecher, 1987).

Self-disclosure promotes intimacy in a relationship and makes us feel close to the other person. It also is important for the partner to be accepting in response to self-disclosure. If the acceptance is missing, we can feel betrayed or threatened, and we certainly will not feel on more intimate terms with the partner.

A study of naturally occurring interactions examined the relationships between self-disclosure, perceived partner disclosure, and the degree of intimacy experienced (Laurenceau et al., 1998). Young people recorded data about every interaction lasting more than 10 minutes, for 7 or 14 days. Data were analyzed for more than 4000 dyadic (that is, two-person) interactions recorded by 158 participants. Both self-disclosure and partner disclosure were associated with the participant's rating of the intimacy of the interaction. Self-disclosure of

Figure 12.4   Intimacy occurs in a relationship when there is warmth and mutual self-disclosure.

emotion was more closely related to intimacy than was self-disclosure of facts.

Self-disclosure and intimacy, then, mutually build on each other (Figure 12.4). Self-disclosure promotes our feeling that the relationship is intimate, and when we feel that it is, we feel comfortable engaging in further self-disclosure. However, self-disclosure and intimacy do not necessarily increase consistently over time. In some relationships, the pattern may be that an increase in intimacy is followed by a plateau or even a pulling back (Collins & Miller, 1994).

Measuring Intimacy

Psychologists have developed some scales for measuring intimacy that can give us further insights. One such scale is the Personal Assessment of Intimacy in Relationships (PAIR) Inventory (Schaefer & Olson, 1981). It measures emotional intimacy in a relationship by using items such as the following:

1. My partner listens to me when I need someone to talk to.
2. My partner really understands my hurts and joys.

Another scale measuring intimacy in a relationship includes items such as these (Miller & Lefcourt, 1982):

1. How often do you confide very personal information to him or her?
2. How often are you able to understand his or her feelings?
3. How often do you feel close to him or her?
4. How important is your relationship with him or her in your life?

If you are currently in a relationship, answer these questions for yourself and consider what the quality of the intimacy is in your relationship.

Figure 12.5 Communicating about love is often difficult.

Source: PEANUTS reprinted by permission of United Feature Syndicate, Inc.

In summary, an intimate relationship is characterized by commitment, feelings of closeness and understanding, and self-disclosure. We can promote intimacy in our relationships by engaging in self-disclosure and being accepting of the other person's self-disclosure. However, we are unlikely to be willing to self-disclose unless we trust our partner (Figure 12.5).

Theories of Love

At the beginning of this chapter, we noted that there is a connection between love and sex in our society. In everyday life and in theories of love, this connection lies along a continuum (Hendrick & Hendrick, 2004). At one end are *hookups*, short-term sexual relationships on a Saturday night, spring break, or a singles cruise, with little romance (Grello et al., 2006; Lambert et al., 2003; Maticka-Tyndale et al., 2003). In theories of love, this is the "love is really sex" view found, for example, in evolutionary theory. At the other end are romantic love relationships in which sex is nonexistent or incidental, as for example in a nonsexual affair. In theories, this is the view found, for example, in the theory of love as a story. Toward the middle is the "sex is really love" view,

as in the theory of passionate love. In the centre is a relationship that balances the two and theories that recognize both, such as the triangular theory.

In the following sections, we will consider four views of love: the triangular theory, the attachment theory, the love-as-a-story perspective, and the theory of passionate love. We also consider the neuroanatomy and neurochemistry of love.

Triangular Theory of Love

Robert Sternberg (1986) has formulated a triangular theory of the nature of love. According to his theory, love has three fundamental components: intimacy, passion, and commitment. He calls it a triangular theory because he depicts these three components graphically in a love triangle.[1] As shown in Figure 12.6, the top point is intimacy, the left point is passion, and the right point is decision or commitment.

---

[1] This terminology should not be confused with the popular use of the term *love triangle*, which occurs when three people are involved in love, but the love is not reciprocated, and things don't work out quite right. For example, A loves B, B loves C, and C loves A, but A doesn't love C and B doesn't love A. Alas.

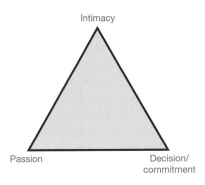

Figure 12.6 The triangle in Sternberg's triangular theory of love.

Three Components of Love

Intimacy is the emotional component of love. It includes our feelings of closeness or bondedness to the other person. The feeling of intimacy usually involves a sense of mutual understanding with the loved one; a sense of sharing one's self; intimate communication with the loved one, involving a sense of having the loved one hear and accept what is shared; and giving and receiving emotional support to and from the loved one. Intimacy, of course, is present in many relationships besides romantic ones. Intimacy here is definitely not a euphemism for sex (as when someone asks, "Have you been intimate with him?"). The kind of emotional closeness involved in intimacy may be found between best friends and between parents and children, just as it is between lovers.

Passion is the motivational component of love. It includes physical attraction and the drive for sexual expression. Physiological arousal is an important part of passion. Passion is the component that differentiates romantic love from other kinds of love, such as the love of best friends or the love between parents and children. Passion is generally the component of love that is faster to arouse, but in a long-term relationship, it is also the component that fades most quickly.

Intimacy and passion are often closely intertwined. In some cases passion comes first, when a couple experiences an initial, powerful physical attraction to each other; emotional intimacy may then follow. In other cases, people know each other only casually, but as emotional intimacy develops, passion follows. Of course, there are also cases where intimacy and passion are completely separate. For example, in cases of casual sex, passion is present but intimacy is not.

Decision or commitment is the third component and is the cognitive component. This component actually has two aspects. The short-term aspect is the decision that one loves the other person. The long-term aspect is the commitment to maintain that relationship. Commitment

is what makes relationships last. Passion comes and goes. All relationships have their better times and their worse times, their ups and their downs. When the words of the traditional marriage ceremony ask whether a person promises to love his or her partner "for better or for worse," the answer "I do" is the promise of commitment.

The Triangular Theory

According to Sternberg, people who have high levels of all three components—intimacy, passion, and commitment—experience consummate love. What term would you use to describe a person who only experiences commitment and intimacy, for example, but not passion? What about someone who has high commitment but low intimacy and passion?

Sternberg's (1986) triangle metaphor allows us to show how the two people in a couple can be well matched or mismatched in the love they feel for each other. Sternberg's research indicates that when there is a good "match" between the two partners' love, both tend to feel satisfied with the relationship. When there is a mismatch in the triangles, they feel dissatisfied with the relationship.

Thinking about practical applications of the theory, if a relationship seems to be in trouble, it may be because there is a mismatch of the triangles. We could analyze the love in the relationship in terms of the three components (intimacy, passion, and commitment) to see where the partners are mismatched. It could be that they are well matched for passion but that one feels and wants more intimacy or commitment than the other person does.

Sternberg also argues that each of the three components of love must be translated into action. The intimacy component is expressed in actions such as communicating personal feelings and information, offering emotional (and perhaps financial) support, and expressing empathy for the other. The passion component is expressed in actions, such as kissing, touching, and making love. The decision or commitment component is demonstrated by actions such as saying "I love you," getting married, and sticking with a relationship through times when it is not particularly convenient.

Evidence for Sternberg's Triangular Theory of Love

What kind of support is there for Sternberg's theory? Sternberg has developed a questionnaire, the Sternberg Triangular Love Scale (STLS), to measure the three components in his theory. Several studies have been done on the characteristics of the scale itself (e.g., Sternberg, 1987, 1997; Whitley, 1993). The scale provides good measures of the components, especially of passion and commitment. Scores for the same relationship are stable for up to two months.

Sternberg makes several predictions about how scores ought to change over time. Acker and Davis (1992) recruited 204 adults, ages 18 to 68; 65 percent were married. The average length of the relationship was 9.5 years. As predicted, commitment scores increased as relationships progressed from dating to marriage. Sternberg expects intimacy behaviours to decrease over time as familiarity with the partner increases; sure enough, behavioural intimacy (sharing inner feelings, trying to understand the partner) decreased as predicted. Similar results were reported in a study of 446 people who were casually dating, exclusively dating, engaged, or married (Lemieux & Hale, 2002). A study of a sample of German adults assessed the relationship between the three components and sexual activity and satisfaction (Grau & Kimpf, 1993). The theory predicts that the amount of passion should be most closely related to sexual activity, but the results indicated that intimacy was most closely related to sexual behaviour and sexual satisfaction.

Qualitative research also provides support for the theory. In-depth interviews with eight heterosexual women focused on what they considered important and positive aspects of romantic love. The women identified intimacy, passion, and commitment (Schafer, 2008).

Attachment Theory of Love

In Chapter 10 we discussed the earliest attachment that humans experience, the attachment between infant and parent. One hypothesis is that the quality of this early attachment—whether secure and pleasant or insecure and unpleasant—profoundly affects us for the rest of our lives, and particularly affects our capacity to form loving attachments to others when we are adults.

The *attachment theory of love* is based on these ideas (Hazaen & Shaver, 1987; Simpson, 1990). According to the most recent formulation proposed by British Columbia psychologist Kim Bartholomew, adults are characterized in their romantic relationships by one of four attachment styles (Bartholomew & Horowitz, 1991). These attachment styles are based on our perceptions of ourselves and on our expectations of how others will respond to us. As shown in Figure 12.7, we either see ourselves in a positive way as worthy of love and support, or we see ourselves in a negative way, as unworthy of love. People with a positive model of self are self-confident; people with a negative model of self are anxious about relationships. Similarly, either we see other people in a positive way as trustworthy and available, or we see them in a negative way as unreliable and rejecting. People with a positive model of others seek others out; people with a negative model of others avoid intimacy.

Secure lovers have a sense of their own lovability and the expectation that other people are generally accepting and responsive. *Preoccupied lovers* have a sense of their own unlovability but a positive evaluation of other people. They try to achieve self-acceptance by gaining the acceptance of people they value. They want desperately to get close to a partner but are so worried that the partner does not love them that they may scare them away. *Fearful lovers* have a negative expectation of both themselves and other people. They expect to be rejected by others and avoid romantic relationships. They are uncomfortable feeling close to, trusting, or depending on another person or having that person feel close to them. Finally, *dismissing lovers* feel themselves to be worthy of love but have negative views of other people. These people may protect themselves against disappointment by avoiding close relationships and maintaining a sense of independence.

Dismissing and fearful lovers are similar in that both avoid intimacy. Preoccupied and fearful lovers are alike in that both depend on acceptance from others to feel good about themselves. Research shows that about 49 percent of adults have a secure attachment style,

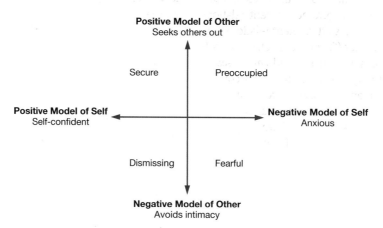

Figure 12.7   Bartholomew's four-category, two-dimensional model of adult attachment (Henderson et al., 2005).

12 percent a preoccupied style, 21 percent a fearful style, and 18 percent a dismissing style (Bartholomew & Horowitz, 1991). The research also shows that separation from parents in childhood—perhaps because of divorce or death—is not related to adult attachment styles (Hazaen & Shaver, 1987). That is, children of divorced parents are no more or less likely to be secure lovers than are children from intact marriages (a finding that is probably fortunate, given the high divorce rate in Canada). What does predict adult attachment style is the person's perception of the *quality* of the relationship with each parent. The quality of friendships in childhood and adolescence also affects adult attachment styles. For example, research using a sample of 191 gay and bisexual men in Vancouver found that both the quality of parental relationships (particularly relationships with fathers) and the quality of peer relationships were associated with adult attachment style (Landott et al., 2004).

A longitudinal study identified one pathway by which attachment in early life relates to adult relationships. Children identified as securely attached at 12 months were rated more socially competent by teachers in elementary school. Social competence predicted more secure friendships at age 16, which, in turn, predicted more positive daily emotional experiences in relationships at ages 20 and 23 (as reported by self and partner) (Simpson et al., 2007).

This research has important implications. First, it helps us understand that adults bring to any particular romantic relationship their own personal history of love and attachment. The forces of that personal history can be strong, and one good and loving partner may not be able to change a dismissing lover into a secure lover. This does not mean that people who have insecure attachment relationships with their parents cannot have a secure attachment relationship with their romantic partner. Research in New Brunswick has shown that although many people form a particular type of attachment relationship with all the important people in their lives, some people with insecure attachment relationships with family have secure attachment relationships with their romantic partner (Caron et al., 2012; Ross & Spinner, 2001). This is sometimes called *earned-secure attachment*. Second, it helps us understand that conflict in some relationships may be caused by a mismatch of attachment styles. A secure lover who wants a close, intimate relationship is likely to feel frustrated and dissatisfied with a dismissing or fearful lover who is uncomfortable with feeling close. Attachment theory suggests that an important form of similarity is similarity in attachment style (Latty-Mann & Davis, 1996). Third, this theory provides some explanation for jealousy (see Milestones in Sex Research), which is most common among preoccupied lovers (although present among the others) because of their early experience of

feeling anxious about their attachment to their parents. Finally, attachment style may help to explain high-risk sexual behaviour. Research in Ontario showed that women who have insecure attachment styles tend to engage in sexual intercourse at a younger age and have more sexual partners than do women with secure attachment styles (Bogaert & Sadava, 2002).

Attachment style affects relationships by affecting the way the partners interact. A study of 128 established couples (average length of relationship 47 months) assessed attachment style, patterns of accommodation, and satisfaction with the relationship (Scharfe & Bartholomew, 1995). Individuals with a secure attachment reported responding constructively to potentially destructive behaviour by the partner, for example, with efforts to discuss and resolve the problem. People who were fearful of attachment to another responded with avoidance or withdrawal. This may affect relationship satisfaction. Research in Nova Scotia has shown that when individuals with an avoidant attachment style enter into new relationships, they expect that their partner will not engage in behaviours that signify commitment (e.g., honesty, spending more time together) and will engage in behaviours that signify the absence of commitment (e.g., infidelity, unequal give and take). This expectation leads them to assume the relationship will end (Birnie et al., 2009). A longitudinal study of university students in Ontario showed that, over a four-month period, participants with a secure attachment style did not change their feelings about the relationship. In contrast, participants with one of the insecure attachment styles reported lower levels of satisfaction and commitment over time (Keelan et al., 1994). Further, research in Ontario and Quebec has shown that when either partner in a couple has an avoidant attachment style, the partners engage in sex less frequently and have lower sexual satisfaction (Brassard et al., 2007; Butzer & Campbell, 2008). Having an insecure attachment style has also been shown to be related to lower sexual satisfaction for the individual and/or their partner (Davis et al., 2006; Péloquin et al., 2013). This happens because insecure attachment interferes with effective sexual communication which, in turn, negatively affects sexual satisfaction (Davis et al., 2006)

Love as a Story

When we think of love, our thoughts often turn to the great love stories: *Romeo and Juliet*, Cinderella and the Prince (Julia Roberts and Richard Gere), King Edward VIII and Wallis Simpson, and *Pygmalion/My Fair Lady*.[2] According to Sternberg (1998), these stories are much more than entertainment. They shape our beliefs about love and relationships, and our beliefs in turn influence our behaviour:

---

[2] Notice that all these stories are about heterosexuals.

Milestones in Sex Research

What Is Jealousy?

J ealousy—the green-eyed monster—is an unpleasant emotion often associated with romantic and sexual relationships. Intense cases of jealousy may result in violence, including partner abuse, assault, and homicide. As a result, it has been the focus of considerable scholarly work. Several perspectives contribute to our understanding of this emotion.

Jealousy is a cognitive, emotional, and behavioural response to a threat to an interpersonal relationship (Guerrero et al., 2004). The cognitive appraisal perspective suggests that jealousy occurs when an individual *interprets* some stimulus as representing a threat to a valued relationship; in reality, there may or may not be a threat to the relationship. A variety of behaviours by the partner may be interpreted as a threat; in one study, individuals in dating relationships said that having their partner just spend time with another person was one of the top three acts of betrayal (Roscoe et al., 1988). Interaction with someone via the Internet, behaviour or remarks by third parties, or coming home late may arouse suspicion and elicit jealousy from a partner.

Two types of jealousy may occur together or separately: emotional and sexual. *Emotional jealousy* occurs when one person believes or knows that the partner is emotionally attached to or in love with another. *Sexual jealousy* occurs when the person believes or knows that the partner wants to engage in or has engaged in sexual intimacy with another. These two can occur together or separately. A study of heterosexual and sexual minority adults found that although both women and men are concerned about both types of infidelity, they are more concerned about the emotional infidelity of a partner (Harris, 2002). Which would concern you more, emotional infidelity or sexual infidelity?

Psychologists Gregory White and Paul Mullen (1989) see jealousy as a constellation including thoughts, emotions, and actions. Two situations, according to their research, activate jealousy. One occurs when there is a threat to our self-esteem. In a good relationship, our romantic partner helps us feel good about ourselves—makes us feel attractive or fun to be with, for example. If a rival appears and our partner shows interest, we may think things like "He finds her more attractive than me" or "She finds him more fun to be with than me." We then feel less attractive or less fun to be with—that is, our self-esteem is threatened. Two experiments report evidence that support the hypothesis that it is threats to the self that cause jealousy (DeSteno et al., 2006).

The second situation that activates jealousy is a threat to the relationship (Figure 12.8). If a rival appears on the scene, we may fear that our partner will separate from us and form a new relationship with the rival. Jealousy is activated because of our negative thoughts and feelings about the loss of a relationship that has been good for us and the loss of all the pleasant things that go along with that relationship, such as companionship and sex.

According to White and Mullen (1989), we go through several stages in the jealousy response, sometimes

Zach and Tammy have been married 28 years. Their friends have been predicting divorce since the day they were married. They fight almost constantly. Tammy threatens to leave Zach; he tells her that nothing would make him happier. They lived happily ever after.

Valerie and Leonard had a perfect marriage. They told each other and all of their friends that they did. Their children say they never fought. Leonard met someone at his office and left Valerie. They are divorced. (Adapted from Sternberg, 1998)

Wait a minute! Aren't those endings reversed? Zach and Tammy should be divorced, and Valerie and Leonard should be living happily ever after. If love is merely the interaction between two people, how they communicate and behave, you are right; the stories have the wrong endings. But there is more to love than interaction; what matters is how each partner *interprets* the interaction. To make sense out of what happens in our relationships, we rely on our love stories.

A **love story** is a story about what love should be like; it has *characters,* a *plot,* and a *theme.* Every love

Love story: A story about what love should be like, including characters, a plot, and a theme.

Figure 12.8 One situation that activates jealousy is a perceived threat to the relationship.

Attempts to cope with jealousy lead to a variety of behaviours. Some of these are constructive, such as effective communication with one's partner. Such communication may lead to an evaluation of the relationship and attempts to change some of the problematic aspects of it. If the problems seem sufficiently serious, a couple may seek help from a mediator or therapist. Other behavioural responses to jealousy are destructive. The threat to one's self-esteem may lead to depression, substance abuse, or suicide. Aggression may be directed at the partner, the third person, or both, and may result in physical or sexual abuse or even murder.

Why do people get jealous?

Research suggests that a person's attachment style may be an important influence on how he or she responds to jealousy (Sharpstein & Kirkpatrick, 1997). Undergraduates were asked how they had reacted in the past to jealousy. Those with a secure attachment style reported that they had expressed their anger to the partner and maintained the relationship. Those with a preoccupied or anxious style reported the most intense anger, but they were most likely to say they did not express that anger. People with a fearful or avoidant style were more likely to direct their anger toward the third person. More recent research suggests that people with a preoccupied attachment style are most likely to be angry and vengeful in response to a relationship breakup (Davis et al., 2003).

Sources: Fisher (1992), Guerrero et al. (2004), Reiss (1986), White & Mullen (1989).

very quickly. The first is cognitive, in which we make an initial appraisal of the situation and find that there is a threat to our self-esteem or to the relationship. Next we experience an emotional reaction that in itself has two phases. The first is a rapid stress response, the "jealous flash." To use the terminology of the two-component theory of love discussed later in this chapter, this stress response is the physiological component of the jealous emotion. The second phase of emotional response occurs as we reappraise the situation and decide how to cope with it. In the reappraisal stage, we may shift from seeing the situation as a threat to seeing it as a challenge, for example. The intense initial emotions quiet down and may be replaced by feelings of moodiness.

story has two central characters who play roles that complement each other. The plot details the kinds of events that occur in the relationship. The theme is central; it provides the meaning of the events that make up the plot and gives direction to the behaviour of the principals.

The story guiding Zach and Tammy's relationship is the *war story*. Each views love as war; a good relationship involves constant fighting. The two central characters are warriors, doing battle, fighting for what they believe. The plot consists of arguments, fights, and threats to leave—in other words, battles. The theme is

that love is war. One may win or lose particular battles, but the war continues. Zach and Tammy's relationship endures because they share this view and because it fits their temperaments. (Can you imagine how long a conflict avoider would last in a relationship with either of them?)

According to this view, *falling in love* occurs when you meet someone with whom you can create a relationship that fits your love story. Further, we are satisfied with relationships in which our partner and we match the characters in our story (Beall & Sternberg, 1995). Valerie and Leonard's marriage looked great on the surface, but it did not fit Leonard's love story. He left when he met his "true love"—that is, a woman who could play the complementary role in his primary love story.

Where do our stories come from? Many of them have their origins in culture, folktales, literature, theatre, films, and television programs. The cultural context interacts with our personal experience and characteristics to create the stories that each of us has (Sternberg, 1996). As we experience relationships, our stories evolve, taking into account unexpected events. Each person has more than one story; the stories often form a hierarchy. One of Leonard's stories was *house and home*, where home was the centre of the relationship, and he (in his role of caretaker) showered attention on the house and kids (not on Valerie). But when he met Sharon, with her aloof air, ambiguous past, and dark glasses, he was hooked—she elicited the *love is a mystery* story, which was more salient to Leonard. He could not explain why he left Valerie and the kids; like most of us he was not consciously aware of his love stories.

You can see from these examples that love stories derive their power from the fact that they can be self-fulfilling. Our love story affects the way we think about and behave in our relationship. That is, we create in our relationships events according to the plot and then interpret those events according to the theme. Our love relationships are literally social constructions. Because our love stories are self-confirming, they can be very difficult to change. As noted, many people are not aware of their love story (Sternberg et al., 2001).

Sternberg and his colleagues have identified 25 common love stories found in North American culture (Sternberg et al., 2001). They have also developed a series of statements that reflect the themes in each story. People who agree with the statements "I think fights actually make a relationship more vital," and "I actually like to fight with my partner" are likely to believe in the *war story*. Sternberg and Hojjat (cited in Sternberg, 1998) studied samples of 43 and 55 couples. They found that couples generally believed in similar stories. The more discrepant the stories of the partners, the less happy the couple was. Some stories were associated with high satisfaction, such as the *garden story*, in which love is a garden that needs ongoing cultivation. Two stories associated with low satisfaction were the *business story* (especially the version in which the roles are employer and employee), and the *horror story*, in which the roles are terrorizer and victim. If you watch *The Simpsons*, what do you think Marge and Homer's love story is?

If love stories are influenced by culture, different stories should be prevalent in different cultures.

Passionate love: A state of intense longing for union with the other person and of intense physiological arousal.

Companionate love: A feeling of deep attachment and commitment to a person with whom one has an intimate relationship.

Researchers recruited dating and married couples in the United States and in China. All participants completed parts of Sternberg's love stories scale. There were several components common to both cultures: objectification-threat (my partner is unpredictable, strange), nurturing-caring (I think about moments we share, nurturing a relationship is important), pornography (I like when we use bizarre sexual techniques; I do what my partner wants sexually even if it is degrading), and pragmatism (there is a recipe for success; I am following the rules). However, there were also components that were unique to each culture. Components unique to Americans were "love as war" and "love as a fairy tale." Unique components for Chinese were "love as current tending" and "the incomprehensibility of a lover" (Jackson et al., 2006).

Passionate and Companionate Love

The three theories considered so far define love as a single phenomenon. A fourth perspective differentiates between two kinds of love: passionate love and companionate love (Berscheid & Hatfield, 1978). **Passionate love** is a state of intense longing for union with the other person and of intense physiological arousal. It has three components: cognitive, emotional, and behavioural (Hatfield & Sprecher, 1986). The cognitive component includes preoccupation with the loved one and idealization of the person or of the relationship. The emotional component includes physiological arousal, sexual attraction, and desire for union. Behavioural elements include taking care of the other and maintaining physical closeness. Passionate love can be overwhelming, obsessive, and all consuming.

Passionate love can also lead to overly optimistic predictions about the likelihood that the relationship will last. Researchers in Ontario asked university students who were in a dating relationship of between one month and one year, their roommates, and their parents to predict how long the students' dating relationships would last (MacDonald & Ross, 1999). The students described their relationship more positively than did the other two groups, because they tended to focus on the strengths and minimize the negative aspects of the relationship. Students predicted that the relationship would last longer than did parents and roommates. Who was right? The results indicated that roommates were the most accurate about whether the couple would still be together one year later; the students were the least accurate.

By contrast, **companionate love** is a feeling of deep attachment and commitment to a person with whom one has an intimate relationship (Hatfield & Rapson, 1993b).

Passionate love is hot; companionate love is warm. Passionate love is often the first stage of a romantic relationship. Two people meet, fall wildly in love, and make a commitment to each other. But as the relationship progresses, a gradual shift to companionate love takes place (Cimbalo et al., 1976; Driscoll et al., 1972). The transformation tends to occur when the relationship is between 6 and 30 months old (Hatfield & Walster, 1978).

Some may find this perspective a rather pessimistic commentary on romantic love because it does not fit the societal love story in which people see stars and hear bells when they fall in love and continue to do so forever after. But it may actually describe a good way for a relationship to develop. Passionate love may be necessary to hold a relationship together in the early stages, while conflicts are being resolved. But past that point, most of us find that what we really need is a friend—someone who shares our interests, who is happy when we succeed, and who empathizes when we fail—and that is just what we get with companionate love. However, even when passionate love has evolved to companionate love, it helps to continue to see our partner and our relationship in somewhat idealized ways. An Ontario study found that couples with these positive relationship "illusions" were more satisfied with their relationship (Murray & Holmes, 1997; Murray et al., 1996). Of course, illusions are not sufficient to maintain a relationship if they are not based on common needs and goals.

Sexual desire and romantic love may often be independent processes (Diamond, 2004). Sexual desire is a motivational state leading to a search for opportunities for sexual activity. It motivates proximity seeking and contact, and it leads to feelings of passion (passionate love). As we have seen, sexual desire responds to reproductive cues, such as physical attractiveness and high status. Romantic love is a motivational state leading to attachment and commitment. It promotes self-disclosure and intimacy, leading to long-term relationships (companionate love).

Research involving observation of romantic couples identified distinctive nonverbal displays of affiliation (smiling, leaning toward partner) and of sexual cues (licking the lips, lip puckering) (Gonzaga, et al., 2006). Displays of affection were associated with subjective reports of feeling love and of happiness. Displays of sexual cues were associated with subjective reports of sexual arousal and desire.

From an evolutionary perspective, successful reproduction requires mating and the establishment of a pair bond to ensure parental care of offspring (see Chapter 2). Fisher and colleagues (2006) propose that there are three internal systems involved in this process: desire to mate, pairing (mating), and parenting. They believe that each system involves reward pathways in the brain and associated hormonal changes. The sex drive motivates a person to seek a partner. Processes of attraction lead to pairing, a focusing of energies on a specific partner. Processes of attachment lead to long-term relationships that facilitate parenting. Research indicates that *priming* (subliminal exposure to) sex-related pictures and words led to outcomes associated with forming and maintaining close relationships (Gillath et al., 2008). These included willingness to self-disclose among women and willingness to sacrifice for one's partner and a preference for positive conflict resolution strategies among men and women.

The Biology of Love

What causes the complex phenomena of passionate and companionate love? Where does the rush of love at first sight come from? Research suggests that it is caused by bodily chemistry and neural activity in the brain (see also Chapter 9). For example, animal studies suggest that dopamine is associated with pair bonding (Curtis & Wang, 2003). Dopamine is also likely important to human experiences of love and is associated with euphoria and craving. A surge of dopamine in the human body can produce increased energy, focused attention, and reduced need for food and sleep; these are common experiences of people in the early stages of love.

The frequent presence of the loved one, produced initially by passionate love, triggers the production of two other chemicals: prolactin and oxytocin. The levels of prolactin rise following orgasm in humans and are also related to pair bonding in voles.

Oxytocin may contribute to long-term relationships. It has been shown to play an important role in pair bonding in some animals (McEwen, 1997). In humans it is stimulated by touch, including sexual touching and orgasm, and produces feelings of pleasure and satisfaction. Research indicates that levels of interpersonal trust correlate positively with oxytocin as well (Zak et al., 2004). In an experiment, researchers administered either oxytocin or a placebo to young men through the nose. Compared with the men who received a placebo, the men who received oxytocin were more likely to take social risks during interactions with another person but not other types of risks (Kosfeld et al., 2005).

The newest research with humans involves the use of magnetic resonance imaging (MRI) to study brain activity related to love. Bartels and Zeki (2004) recruited young men and women who were in love. While their brain activity was being measured, each participant was shown photos of the romantic partner and of a close friend. The picture of the partner activated specific areas of the brain. Which ones? The areas rich in dopamine pathways were enervated, lending weight to the neurochemical findings that suggest dopamine is important in the experience of love. Furthermore, when measures of levels of brain activity in response to the picture of the lover were correlated with scores on the Passionate Love Scale (discussed shortly), the scores were positively correlated.

Visual stimuli associated with the lover stimulate subcortical activity in the ventral tegmental area, caudate nucleus, and putamen (Cacioppo et al., 2012b). As noted above, this area is rich in dopamine pathways. More generally, these are the areas associated with motivation, reward, and euphoria. Activity also occurs in areas associated with complex cognitive processing, including segments of the gyrus and the occipital cortex, such as memory and self-representation. Interestingly, activity in these areas does not vary by length of the love relationship. A study of 21 men and women, married an average of 21 years, found that photos of the spouse triggered activity in these areas but also in areas associated with maternal attachment, such as the thalamus and anterior and posterior cingulate (Acevedo et al., 2011).

Little work has been done with humans to identify neural correlates of companionate love. Animal research suggests that it is associated with oxytocin and vasopressin, and neural activity in the nucleus accumbens and ventral palladium (Cacioppo et al., 2012b).

Is there a difference between passionate love and sexual desire in the brain? (Is love just sex?) Both passionate love and sexual desire activate the same reward-related and higher-order cortical areas in the brain. However, love is associated with reduced activity in the hypothalamus, amygdala, and somatosensory cortex compared with sexual desire. These differences are consistent with the view that sexual desire is a motivation with a specific goal, whereas love is an abstract, behaviourally complex phenomenon not dependent on the physical presence of the object (Cacioppo et al., 2012a). The answer? Love is more than sex (neurally speaking).

Researching Love

You can see that various theorists—Sternberg, Bartholomew, Berscheid, and Hatfield—mean different things when they use the term *love*. One way psychologists and sociologists define terms is by using an **operational definition**. In an operational definition, a concept is defined by the way it is measured. Thus, for example, in the attraction

Operational definition: Defining some concept or term by how it is measured—for example, defining intelligence as those abilities that are measured by IQ tests.

experiment described earlier in the chapter, one of the ways that attraction was operationally defined was how close people stood to each other (Byrne et al., 1970). Operational definitions are very useful because they are precise and because they help clarify exactly what a scientist means by a complex term, such as love.

Measuring Love

We introduced the concept of *passionate love* earlier. Hatfield and Sprecher (1986) developed a paper-and-pencil measure of passionate love. They wrote statements intended to measure the cognitive, emotional, and behavioural components of passionate love. The respondent rated each statement on a scale from 1 (not true at all) to 9 (definitely true of him or her). If you feel that you are in love with someone, think about whether you would agree with each of the following statements, keeping that person in mind.

1. *Cognitive component:*
   Sometimes I feel I can't control my thoughts; they are obsessively on _____.
   For me, _____ is the perfect romantic partner.
2. *Emotional component:*
   I possess a powerful attraction for _____.
   I will love _____ forever.
3. *Behavioural component:*
   I eagerly look for signs indicating _____'s desire for me.
   I feel happy when I am doing things to make _____ happy.

Hatfield and Sprecher (1986) administered their questionnaire along with some other measures to students who were in relationships ranging from casually dating to engaged and living together. The results indicated that scores on the Passionate Love Scale (PLS) were positively correlated with other measures of love and with measures of commitment to and satisfaction with the relationship. These correlations give us evidence that the PLS is valid—in other words, it measures what it is supposed to measure. The findings confirm that the scale measures passion. For example, students who got high scores on the PLS reported a stronger desire to be with, held by, and kissed by the partner, and said that they were sexually excited just thinking about their partner. These findings confirm that the scale is measuring passion. Finally, the passionate love scores increased as the nature of the relationship moved from dating to dating exclusively. Hatfield and Sprecher's research is a good example of how to study an important but complex topic, such as love, scientifically.

L06 Love and Adrenaline

Two-Component Theory of Love

Social psychologists Ellen Berscheid and Elaine Walster (1974) proposed a **two-component theory of love**. According to their theory, passionate love occurs when two conditions exist simultaneously: (1) the person is in a state of intense *physiological arousal,* and (2) the situation is such that the person applies a particular label—*love*—to the sensations being experienced. Their theory is derived from an important theory developed by Stanley Schachter (1964).

Suppose that your heart is pounding, your palms are sweating, and your body is tense. What emotion are you experiencing? Is it love—has reading about passionate love led to obsessive thoughts of another person? Is it fear—are you frantically reading this text because you have an exam tomorrow morning? Is it sexual arousal—are you thinking about physical intimacy later tonight? It could be any of these, or it could be anger or embarrassment. A wide variety of emotions are accompanied by the same physiological states: increased blood pressure, a higher heart rate, increased myotonia (muscular tension), sweating palms. What differentiates these emotions? The key is the way we interpret or label what we are experiencing.

Schachter's (1964) two-component theory of emotion says exactly that; an emotion consists of a physiological arousal state plus the label the person assigns to it (for a critical evaluation of this theory, see Reisenzein, 1983). Berscheid and Walster (1974) have applied this to the emotion of love. They suggest that we feel passionate love when we are aroused and when conditions are such that we identify what we are feeling as love.

Evidence for the Two-Component Theory

Several experiments provide evidence for Berscheid and Walster's two-component theory of love. In one study, male research participants exercised vigorously by running in place; this produced the physiological arousal response of pounding heart and sweaty palms (White et al., 1981). Afterward, they rated their liking for an attractive woman, who actually was a confederate of the experimenters. Men in the running group said they liked the woman significantly more than did men who were in a control condition and had not exercised. This result is consistent with Berscheid and Walster's theory (1974). The effect is called the **misattribution of arousal**; that is, in a situation like this, the men misattribute their arousal—which is actually due to exercise—to their liking for the attractive woman (Figure 12.9). An analysis of 33 experiments found that arousal affects attraction even when the source of the arousal is unambiguous (Foster et al., 1998).

Figure 12.9 The misattribution of arousal. If people are physically aroused (e.g., by jogging), they may misattribute this arousal to love or sexual attraction, provided the situation suggests such an interpretation.

A study conducted in North Vancouver suggests that fear can increase a man's attraction to a woman (Dutton & Aron, 1974). An attractive female interviewer approached male passers-by either on a fear-arousing bridge (you may be familiar with the Capilano Bridge) or on a non-fear-arousing bridge. The fear-arousing bridge was constructed of boards attached to cables and had a tendency to tilt, sway, and wobble; the handrails were low, and there was a 70-metre drop to rocks and shallow rapids below. The control bridge was made of solid cedar; it was firm, and there was only a 3-metre drop to a shallow rivulet below. The interviewer asked subjects to fill out questionnaires that included projective test items. These items were then scored for sexual imagery.

The men in the suspension-bridge group should have been in a state of physiological arousal, whereas those in the control-bridge group should not have been. In fact, there was more sexual imagery in the questionnaires filled out by the men in the suspension-bridge group, and these men made more attempts to contact the attractive interviewer after the experiment than the men on the control bridge. Intuitively, this result might seem to be peculiar: that men who are in a state of fear are more attracted to a woman than men who are relaxed. But in terms of the Berscheid and Walster two-component theory, it makes perfect sense. The fearful men were physiologically aroused, while the men in the control group were

Two-component theory of love: Berscheid and Walster's theory that two conditions must exist simultaneously for passionate love to occur: physiological arousal and attaching a cognitive label (*love*) to the feeling.
Misattribution of arousal: When a person in a stage of physiological arousal (e.g., from exercising or being in a frightening situation), attributes these feelings to love or attraction to the person present.

not. And according to this theory, arousal is an important component of love or attraction.[3]

Now, of course, if the men (most of them heterosexuals) had been approached by an older man or a child, probably their responses would have been different. In fact, when the interviewer in the experiment was male, the effects discussed above did not occur. Society tells us what the appropriate objects of our love, attraction, or liking are. That is, we know for what kinds of people it is appropriate to have feelings of love or liking. For these heterosexual men, feelings toward an attractive woman could reasonably be labelled as love or attraction, whereas such labels would probably not be attached to feelings for a senior man.

The physical arousal that is important for love need not always be produced by unpleasant or frightening situations. Pleasant stimuli, such as sexual arousal or praise from the other person, may produce arousal and feelings of love. Indeed, Berscheid and Walster's theory does an excellent job of explaining why we seem to have such a strong tendency to associate love and sex. Sexual arousal is one method of producing a state of physiological arousal, and it is one that our culture has taught us to label as love. Thus both components necessary to feel love are present: arousal and a label. On the other hand, this phenomenon may lead us to confuse lust with love, an all-too-common error.

L07 Cross-Cultural Research

In the past two decades, researchers have studied people from various ethnic or cultural groups to see whether they experience attraction, intimacy, and love in similar ways. Three topics that have been studied are the impact of culture on how people view love, on whom people fall in love with, and on the importance of love in decisions to marry.

Cultural Values and the Meaning of Love

Cross-cultural psychologists have identified two dimensions on which cultures vary (Hatfield & Rapson, 1993a). The first is individualism–collectivism (Figure 12.10). *Individualistic cultures,* like those of Canada, the United States, and Western European countries, tend to emphasize individual goals over group and societal goals and interests. *Collectivist cultures,* like those of China, Africa, and Southeast Asian countries, emphasize group and collective goals over personal ones. Several specific traits have been identified that differentiate these two types of societies (Triandis et al., 1990). In individualistic cultures, behaviour is regulated by individual attitudes and cost–benefit considerations; emotional

Figure 12.10 Whether a culture is individualistic or collectivistic determines its views on love and marriage. In Canada, which is an individualistic culture, individuals choose each other and marry for love. In India, a collectivistic culture, marriages are arranged by family members to serve family interests.

detachment from the group is accepted. In collectivist cultures, the self is defined by group membership; behaviour is regulated by group norms; attachment to and harmony within the group are valued.

The two types of cultures have different conceptions of love. The majority group in Canadian society, for example, emphasizes passionate love as the basis for marriage (Dion & Dion, 1993b). Individuals select mates on the basis of such characteristics as physical attractiveness, similarity (compatibility), and wealth or resources. We look for intimacy in the relationship with our mate. In Chinese society, by contrast, many marriages are arranged; the primary criterion is that the two families be of similar status. The person finds intimacy in relationships with other family members.

The second dimension on which cultures differ is independence–interdependence. Many Western

---

[3] According to the terminology of Chapter 3, the Dutton and Aron study is an example of *experimental* research.

cultures view each person as independent and value individuality and uniqueness. Many other cultures view the person as interdependent with those around him or her. The self is defined in relation to others. Canadians value standing up for one's beliefs. The people of India value conformity and harmony within the group.

Dion and Dion (1993a) studied university students in Toronto from four ethnocultural groups. Students from Asian backgrounds were more likely to view love as companionate, as friendship, in contrast to those from English and Irish backgrounds. This tendency is consistent with the collectivist orientation of Asian cultures.

Cultural Influences on Mate Selection

Buss (1989) conducted a large-scale survey of 10,000 men and women from 37 societies. The sample included people from four cultures in Africa, eight in Asia, and four in eastern Europe, in addition to twelve Western European and four North American ones. Each respondent was given a list of 18 characteristics one might value in a potential mate and asked to rate how important each was to him or her personally. Regardless of which society they lived in, most respondents, male and female, rated intelligence, kindness, and understanding at the top of the list; note that these are characteristics of companionate love. Men worldwide placed more weight on cues of reproductive capacity, such as physical attractiveness; women rated cues of resources as more important. The results support the sociobiological perspective and suggest that there are not large cultural differences in mate selection.

Many people prefer mates who are physically attractive. We often hear that "beauty is in the eye of the beholder." This saying suggests that standards of beauty might vary across cultures. In one study, researchers had students from varying cultural backgrounds rate 45 photo graphs of women on a scale ranging from very attractive to very unattractive (Cunningham et al., 1995). The photographs portrayed women from many different societies. Overall, Asian, Hispanic, and white students did not differ in their ratings of the individual photographs. However, Asian students' ratings were less influenced by indicators of sexual maturity (such as facial narrowness) and expressivity (such as the vertical distance between the lips when the person smiled).

Love and Marriage

We noted earlier that individualistic cultures place a high value on romantic love, while collectivist cultures emphasize the group. The importance of romantic love in North American society is illustrated by responses to the question "If a man (woman) had all the other qualities you desired, would you marry this person if you were not in love with him (her)?" Over time, increasing

percentages of North American men and women answer no. The change has been greater for women.

Researchers asked this question of men and women in 11 different cultures (Levine et al., 1995). We would predict that members of individualistic cultures would answer no, whereas those in collectivist cultures would answer yes. Research has shown that, as predicted, many—about half of Indians and Pakistanis—would marry even though they didn't love the person (Levine et al., 1995). In Thailand, which is also collectivist, 19 percent said yes. In the individualistic cultures of Australia, England, and the United States, less than 7 percent of people would marry someone they did not love.

When we look at the findings of the cross-cultural research on love, attraction, and marriage, the pattern that emerges is one of *cross-cultural similarities and cross-cultural differences*, a theme we introduced in Chapter 1. That is, some phenomena are similar across cultures; for example, valuing intelligence, kindness, and understanding in a mate. Other phenomena differ substantially across cultures; for example, whether love is a prerequisite for marriage. However, even in Asian (collectivist) societies, young people are increasingly seeing love as a basis for marriage (Dion & Dion, 1993a). But they may also see love as developing after marriage rather than as a prerequisite for marriage.

What happens when an individual from a collectivist culture is raised in Canada? First Person tells the story of a Canadian man's decision to enter into an arranged marriage.

LO8

Communication

Consider the following situation involving Chris and Donna (we have purposely left Chris's gender ambiguous—Chris and Donna could be a same-sex or a mixed-sex couple.)

> Chris and Donna are undergraduate students who have been living together for about three years. Donna had had sex with only one other person before Chris, and she had never masturbated. Since they've been together, she has had orgasms only twice during lovemaking, despite the fact that they make love three or four times per week. She has been reading some magazine articles about female sexuality and is beginning to think that she should be experiencing more sexual satisfaction. As far as she knows, Chris is unaware that there is any problem. Donna feels lonely and a bit sad.

What should Donna do? She needs to communicate with Chris. They apparently have not communicated much about sex in the last three years, and they need to begin. The following sections will discuss the

Why I Chose to Have an Arranged Marriage

On my wedding day, I remember thinking that my choice of wanting an arranged marriage was rare for someone living in the West. I later realized that having an arranged marriage is not atypical for many individuals in North America and around the world.

I was born in Fiji Islands and immigrated at the age of seven to Vancouver with my parents and younger brother. Though I was raised in a traditional, Muslim home, I was nonetheless still affected by Western social ideals. The clash of cultures became more apparent as I matured.

My mother, a strong member of our religious community, travels the world in her efforts to spread Islam. Ever since I turned 18, she had been sending me photographs and "résumés" of girls (i.e., potential wives) she had met during her journeys. I would return the photos to my mother, with a lengthy explanation of what I considered to be the many limitations to an arranged marriage and how I would marry a girl I fall in love with and have known for some time.

Luckily for me, my denials and many "rejections" fell on deaf ears. In the spring of 1997, my mother sent me a package. It contained some souvenirs from her recent visit to Pakistan and four pictures of Ayesha, a young woman from Peshawar. As I looked carefully at the photos of this person, studying the softness of her complexion, the welcoming nature of her smile, the innocence of her gaze, something inside me wanted to know more about her.

I telephoned my mother and began asking her about the mysterious woman in the photos. At my very utterance of Ayesha's name, my mother let out a slightly audible sigh, one, which if given words to, would say, "Yes! I finally got him!"

This was one of the longest phone conversations I had with my mother. I learned that Ayesha was a caring, loving, and family-oriented person (qualities I admire), who, like me, also majored in English literature and psychology. The more I heard, the more I liked.

Of course, being raised in Canada, in a society where mothers and sons do not always prefer the same girl, I had to find out for myself. I asked my mother for Ayesha's phone number but was met with resistance: "Her parents will not allow a strange man to speak with her on the phone." Is this for real, I thought. Do the parents really expect me to marry their daughter without getting to know her? At this point I felt like abandoning this whole fantasy I had of meeting this "Pakistani Princess."

My mother then suggested that I fly to Peshawar to meet Ayesha and her family. Trusting my mother's good intentions and my own inner voice, I took time off from my practice and flew to Pakistan. Somewhere over the Atlantic Ocean, I remember thinking about stories I had heard of other men traveling overseas to meet women. The stories were similar. When they visited the home of the women, these women were adorned in their finest clothes, wore copious amounts of makeup and even cooked the meal, behaviour aimed at impressing their potential husbands.

I was no doubt surprised, then, when I met Ayesha, who greeted me with not a speck of makeup on. She had on clothes, which, while pleasant-looking, were not anything extraordinary. And she did not cook, nor help, with dinner. Ayesha was different from the rest. She was unique and real. In trying not to pique my interest, she did just that.

relationship between sex, communication, and relationships, and provide some suggestions on how to communicate effectively.

Communication and Relationships
A good deal of research has looked at differences in communication patterns between nondistressed (happy) couples and distressed (unhappy, seeking relationship counselling) heterosexual couples. This research shows, in general, that distressed couples tend to have communication deficits (Gottman, 1994). Further, research in Quebec has shown that heterosexual, gay male, and lesbian couples do not differ in their communication skills or in the contribution of communication deficits to their relationship adjustment (Julien et al., 2003). Research also shows that

Our interest in each other developed with our first conversation. I didn't want to tell Ayesha of my academic or professional achievements and question her on her domestic acumen (as is the typical queries in such meetings). I wanted to know about her interests, her passions, about her. As we felt more comfortable with each other, I asked her what types of books she liked to read, to which she responded with every relationship therapist's idea of romance—"love stories," she said, modestly looking at me for a response. I accepted Ayesha's openness and courage with an appreciative smile.

Realizing that my mother had told Ayesha's family that I was a psychologist, it was important for me that Ayesha know of my specialization. In telling her that I am a clinical sexologist, not only did she not judge me, she in fact grew curious about my career and later shared that I must be helping many people in need.

It was obvious to us that we had already begun to satisfy each other's needs. That night, the night of our first meeting, I shared with my mother my intentions of wanting to marry Ayesha. The next morning, my mother took a formal proposal to Ayesha's mother, who discussed the proposal with Ayesha. Ayesha accepted the proposal and we were wed ten days later.

I returned to Canada shortly after our wedding (our Nikka) and began the sponsoring process. Ayesha and I talked almost every day for about one year. In fact, we dated by phone and fell in love, long-distance, after we got married. Imagine that.

On May 2nd, 2007, Ayesha and I, along with our two beautiful daughters, Malaika and Alishba, celebrated our tenth year of wedded bliss. So, is having an arranged marriage the secret to our happiness? Maybe and maybe not. Our relationship is based on six key qualities: love, openness, a non-judgmental attitude, respect, commitment, and trust (I, till this day, have never broken a promise to her). When you consider that these same qualities also result in happy non-arranged marriages, it makes us wonder about the deeper meaning of the institution of marriage, regardless of how the individuals meet.

Her Perspective

I come from a traditional, yet open-minded family. Since it is typical for parents in Pakistan to arrange a marriage for their children, when my parents asked me if they could do the same for me, I had no objections. I trusted my parents and put my faith in God to find the "right" person for me.

When my parents told me that a family from Canada was coming to visit us, I sensed that they would be special because my parents had never asked me to meet any other families who were also interested in meeting me.

When I first met Faizal, I didn't even clearly see his face because it is a custom for women to not make eye contact with a man who is not related to them. However, from the way he spoke, I could sense his gentle personality and caring ways. Though we talked alone for an hour, I remember time just flying by—it was so easy and so much fun to talk to him that I could imagine my married life with him being full of love and happiness.

I hardly knew Faizal when we first got married. Soon afterward, I began to slowly fall in love with him, and ever since I am falling more and more in love with him every day.

Source: Faizal Sahukhan, Ph.D., sex therapist, university instructor, advice columnist, radio host, author. www.multiculturalromance .com

couples with sexual problems have poorer sexual and nonsexual communication than couples without sexual problems (Kelly et al., 2006). Of course, many other factors contribute to relationship conflict or sex problems, but poor communication patterns are certainly among them. Good communication skills are particularly important in negotiating the challenges of adjusting to life changes, positive or negative, such as a new job, the birth of a baby, parenting responsibilities, job loss, or retirement. The problem with this research is that it is correlational (see Chapter 3 for a discussion of this problem in research methods); in particular, we cannot tell whether poor communication causes unhappy relationships or whether unhappy relationships create poor communication patterns.

An elegant longitudinal study designed to meet this problem provides evidence that unrewarding, ineffective communication precedes and predicts later relationship problems (Markman et al., 2010). Couples who were planning to marry were recruited for the research. Each person completed a questionnaire, including a rating of the negativity (e.g., she or he criticizes, belittles me) of their communication. Each couple participated in a videotaped interaction, discussing the top problem in their relationship. Trained coders rated each person's communication during the discussion on 10 dimensions, including positive (e.g., problem solving skills, support, validation) and negative (e.g., denial, dominance, withdrawal). A composite positive score and negative score was calculated for each. Some 200 couples married, and were assessed near their fifth anniversary; at the time they were recruited they averaged 26 years of age and 16 years of education, and most were white (84 percent). Couples who divorced before the fifth year had rated their communication as significantly more negative at baseline. Among those who remained married, both observed and self-reported negative communication predicted lower marital adjustment at year five. Researchers considered couples with adjustment scores less than 100 distressed. These couples experienced significantly less decline in negative communication and significantly greater decline in positive communication over five years, compared with nondistressed couples.

On the basis of this notion that communication deficits cause communication problems, relationship counsellors and therapists often work on teaching couples communication skills. Research suggests that distressed couples do not always differ from nondistressed couples in their communication skills or ability; rather, some distressed couples use their skills as weapons, to send negative messages (Burleson & Denton, 1997; Gottman & Notarius, 2002). These results suggest that therapists should focus on the intent of the partners as they communicate with each other, not just on techniques.

But what are these negative messages? Gottman (1994) used audiotape, videotape, and monitoring of physiological arousal to answer this question. He identified four destructive patterns of interaction: criticism, contempt, defensiveness, and withdrawal. *Criticism* refers to attacking a partner's personality or character: "You are so selfish; you never think of anyone else." *Contempt* is intentionally insulting or orally abusing the other person: "How did I get hooked up with such a loser?" *Defensiveness* refers to denying responsibility, making excuses, replying with a complaint of one's own, and other self-protective responses, instead of addressing the problem. *Withdrawal* involves such activities as responding to the partner's complaint with silence, turning on the TV, or walking out of the room in anger. You can probably see that these types of communication are likely to lead to an escalation of the hostility rather than to a solution to the problem. In fact, a Quebec study found that a pattern of withdrawal was associated with a decrease in relationship adjustment (Guay et al., 2003).

On the other hand, positive communication is important in developing and maintaining intimate relationships (see First Person). In the following discussions, we describe some of the skills involved in positive sexual communication.

Sexual Self-Disclosure

As discussed earlier in this chapter, one of the keys to building a good relationship is self-disclosure. One of the keys to building a satisfying *sexual* relationship is *sexual* self-disclosure. **Sexual self-disclosure** involves telling personal sexual things about yourself. It may range from sharing your sexual likes and dislikes to disclosing about an unwanted sexual experience you had with a previous partner.

Unfortunately, most romantic partners have difficulty telling each other what pleases and displeases them sexually (Byers, 2011). How much do couples self-disclose about their preferences? In a survey of more than 3000 Canadian men and women, 97 percent said that they were sometimes or always able to discuss sex with their partner openly; however, only 28 percent had had one or more serious discussions in the past year (Auld & Brock, 2002). According to one New Brunswick study of individuals in heterosexual dating relationships, although people do talk to their dating partner about their sexual likes and dislikes, they do not fully reveal their personal feelings about them (Byers & Demmons, 1999). Both the men and the women in this study revealed more to their partner about their nonsexual feelings than about their sexual feelings and more about what they liked sexually than about what they didn't like. However, the more one member of the couple self-disclosed sexually, the more they reported that their partner did so too. That is, the sexual self-disclosure by one partner was reciprocated by the other partner, perhaps because self-disclosure by a partner assures us that he or she is comfortable talking about sex and shares similar values (Herold & Way, 1988). Researchers in Nova Scotia have shown that heterosexual, gay male, and lesbian couples do not differ in their levels of sexual self-disclosure (Holmberg & Blair, 2009).

Sexual self-disclosure leads to sexual satisfaction in two ways (MacNeil & Byers, 2005, 2009). First, it increases intimacy between partners. Talking about

Sexual self-disclosure: Telling personal sexual things about yourself such as your sexual likes and dislikes.

Sexuality and Disability: Constructing a Sexual Blueprint

For most people, coming out as a sexual being is just assumed. It isn't something they have to declare and take a stand for—that is, unless they live with a disability like I do. Whenever I talk about sexuality and disability, the "elephant in the room" that tends not to get named but is so very much part of the conversation is that sex for people with a disability is somehow not the "real thing" or that we really don't have the same feelings when we're kissed, touched, or fucked. I'm here to tell you that we do have the same sensations, wants and desires as anyone else, kink, vanilla, or otherwise. And when you have a disability and declare that you're queer, well, that's a whole other story!!

Part of my work in the community is that of a sexual health educator, and I have been educating people about sexuality and disability for more than 10 years. I began to do this work because of my own journey discovering how to be sexual in a world that overtly says that people with disabilities shouldn't have sex, relationships and all the trimmings or "trappings" that go with them. My interest in talking to groups about sexuality and disability is personal—it's important to me to remove the mystery and misconceptions that people have about what sex is like for disabled folks. I want to connect with people on a very real level that acknowledges the fragility of the body and that disability or difference is something that can enter into anyone's life whether through aging, illness, or accident. People with disabilities actually have lots to teach about pushing the boundaries surrounding conventional ideas about sex, how to make love, and notions of intimacy with oneself and with another person. I felt that it was so important to get the message out that I also coauthored a book on sexuality and disability entitled *The Ultimate Guide to Sex and Disability*.

In my own journey of sexual discovery, I experimented sexually with my male and female friends, all of whom lived with disabilities. My first sexual relationship was with a man when I was 18. We both lived with physical disability. Negotiating a sexual relationship was challenging but most of all it was fun, exciting, and very hot. I later had relationships with other men, some living with some form of physical disability and others not. I had to learn to create opportunities for communication because each sexual experience forced me and my partner to confront our assumptions. This meant that both of us had to ask questions about our desires as well as about what felt pleasurable and what didn't. Communication is important, although not easy, for everyone but particularly for people with a disability.

In one of the chapters of *The Ultimate Guide to Sex and Disability*, we wrote:

> Despite what people actually experience, many still view sex as something that is the same for everybody "normal," and inferior for the rest of us. Every person needs to discover what sex is to her/him, how it feels, what she/he respond to. Constructing a sexual blueprint, an understanding of where you have more or less sexual sensation, what your body looks like (inside and out), its textures and rhythms, leads to a healthier sexuality for anyone.

Whether my partner is someone living with disabilities or not, I am reminded that I can't rely on what I know from previous experiences. I have to be open to really exploring what's pleasurable and hot with this new person.

In my twenties through to my late thirties, my primary sexual relationships were with men. When I was 37, I fell in love and fell hard for a woman younger than myself. Although we were only together for a short period of time, I had previously never felt the depth of emotional and physical connection in a relationship that I had with her. I felt that I really had found where I belonged. Since then, my primary relationships have been with women, again some living with disability and others not. It really doesn't matter to me whether they have a disability. What does matter is how we feel together: whether the chemistry is there; whether we can make each other laugh; and, what we each bring to the relationship that keeps it alive, interesting, and hot.

The bottom line is that people with disabilities, straight or queer, *are* sexual—and as often as possible.

Source: Fran Odette is program manager of the Women with Disabilities and Violence Program at Springtide Resources (formerly Education Wife Assault) in Toronto.

sexual likes and dislikes allows partners to feel closer to each other and see themselves as compatible (Offman & Matheson, 2005). Feeling closer and more satisfied with the nonsexual aspects of the relationship leads to higher sexual satisfaction. Further, researchers in Nova Scotia have shown that there is a strong link between relational closeness and well-being and sexual satisfaction in both mixed-sex and same-sex relationships (Holmberg et al., 2010). Second, sharing what pleases and displeases us sexually with our partner allows him or her to learn about our sexual preferences. This kind of understanding helps partners to negotiate mutually enjoyable sexual interactions. That is, by telling our partner what we like and don't like sexually, we receive more of what we want and less of what we don't want during sexual interactions (Byers & Demmons, 1999; MacNeil & Byers, 1997; Purnine & Carey, 1997). In turn, having more pleasing sexual interactions is associated with enhanced sexual satisfaction.

Sexual self-disclosure is especially important for maintaining sexual satisfaction in long-term relationships. In contrast, early in a relationship, sex is new and exciting and may feel satisfying even though our partner is not fully aware of what pleases and displeases us sexually (Byers, 1999).

Being an Effective Communicator

Back to Donna and Chris: One of the first things to do in this type of situation is to decide to talk to one's partner, admitting that there is a problem. Then the issue is to resolve to communicate and particularly to be an *effective* communicator. Suppose Donna begins by saying,

> You're not giving me any orgasms when we have sex. (1)

Chris gets angry and walks away or gets upset. Donna meant to communicate that she wasn't having any orgasms, but Chris thought she meant that Chris was a lousy lover.

It is important to recognize the distinction between **intent** and **impact** in communicating (Gottman et al., 1976; Purnine & Carey, 1997). Intent is what you mean. Impact is what the other person thinks you mean. An **effective communicator** is one whose impact matches her or his intent. Donna wasn't an effective communicator in the above example because the impact on Chris was considerably different from her intent. Notice that effectiveness does not depend on the content of the message. One can be as effective at communicating contempt as communicating praise.

Intent: What the speaker means.
Impact: What someone else understands the speaker to mean.
Effective communicator: A communicator whose impact matches his or her intent.
"I" language: Speaking about yourself, using the word "I"; not mind reading.
Mind reading: Making assumptions about what your partner thinks or feels.

Many people value spontaneity in sex, and this attitude may extend to communicating about sex. It is best to recognize that to be an effective communicator, you may need to plan your strategy. It often takes some thinking to figure out how to make sure that your impact will match your intent. Planning also allows you to make sure that the timing is good—that you are not speaking out of anger, or that your partner is not tired or preoccupied with other things.

In the last few decades public communication about sex has become relatively open, but private communication remains difficult (Crawford et al., 1994). This doesn't mean that Donna can't communicate. But she shouldn't feel guilty or stupid if it is difficult for her. And she will be better off if she uses some specific communication skills and has some belief that they will work. The sections that follow suggest some skills that are useful in being an effective communicator and how to apply these to sexual relationships.

Good Messages

Every couple has problems. The best way to voice them is to complain rather than to criticize (Gottman, 1994). Complaining involves the use of **"I" language**, in which you speak about your own thoughts and feelings rather than about your partner. In contrast, "you" messages tend to be criticisms of the other person. Research has shown that nondistressed couples are more likely to self-disclose thoughts and feelings during problem-solving than to criticize their partner (Gottman & Notarius, 2002). When you use "I" language, your partner is less likely to become defensive. "I" language uses soft emotions, such as feelings of unhappiness or concern, rather than hard emotions such as anger. (Note that saying something like "I think you are a lousy lover" or "I feel that you're only interested in your own pleasure" are actually "you" messages not "I" language, even though they contains the word "I.") Thus, if Donna were to use this technique, she might say,

> I feel a bit unhappy because I don't have orgasms very often when we make love. (2)

Notice that she focuses specifically on herself. There is less cause for Chris to get angry, upset, or defensive than there was in message 1.

One of the best things about "I" language is that it avoids mind reading (Gottman et al., 1976). Suppose Donna says,

> I know you think I'm not much interested in sex, but I really wish I had more orgasms. (3)

She is engaging in **mind reading**. That is, she is making certain assumptions about what Chris is thinking. She assumes that Chris believes she is not interested in sex or having orgasms. Research shows that mind

Figure 12.11

reading is more common among distressed couples than among non-distressed couples (Gottman et al., 1977). Worse, Donna doesn't *check out* her assumptions with Chris. The problem is that she may be wrong, and Chris may not think that at all. "I" language helps Donna avoid this by focusing on herself and what she feels rather than on what Chris is doing or failing to do. Another important way to avoid mind reading is by giving and receiving feedback, a technique discussed in a later section.

Documenting is another important component of giving good messages (Brenton, 1972). In documenting you give specific examples of the issue. This is not quite so relevant in Donna's case, because she is talking about a general problem; but even here, specific documenting can be helpful. Once Donna has broached the subject, she might say,

> Last night when we made love, I enjoyed it and it felt really good, but I didn't have an orgasm, and then I felt disappointed. (4)

Now she has gotten her general complaint down to a specific situation that Chris can remember.

Suppose further that Donna has some idea of what Chris would need to do to bring her to orgasm: she would like more sensual touching or more oral stimulation of her clitoris. Then she might do specific documenting as follows:

> Last night when we made love, I enjoyed it, but I didn't have an orgasm, and then I felt disappointed. I think what I needed was for you to stimulate my clitoris with your mouth a bit more. You did it for a while, but it seemed so brief. I think if you had kept doing it for two or three minutes more, I would have had an orgasm. (5)

Now not only has she documented to Chris exactly what the problem was, but she has given a specific suggestion about what could have been done about it, and therefore what could be done in the future. A study of mixed-sex dating couples found that open communication about sex ("I tell my partner when I am especially sexually satisfied") was positively associated with satisfaction with sex and the relationship (Montesi et al., 2010).

Levelling and Editing

Levelling means telling your partner what you are feeling by stating your thoughts clearly, simply, and honestly—that is, self-disclosing your feelings (Gottman et al., 1976). This is often the hardest step in communication (Figure 12.11), especially when the topic is sex. It is especially difficult for adults to reach shared understandings about sex, since there is great secrecy about it in our society (Crawford et al., 1994). In levelling, keep in mind that the purposes are as follows:

1. To make communication clear
2. To clear up what partners expect of each other
3. To clear up what is pleasant and what is unpleasant
4. To clear up what is relevant and what is irrelevant
5. To notice things that draw you closer or push you apart (Gottman et al., 1976)

When you begin to level with your partner, you also need to do some editing. **Editing** involves censoring (not saying) things that would be deliberately hurtful to your partner or that would be irrelevant. You must take responsibility for making your communication polite and considerate. For example, details about past sexual relationships and comparison with past sexual partners are unnecessary and may be hurtful to your partner. Levelling, then, should not mean a "no-holds-barred" approach. Ironically, research indicates that married people are ruder to each other than they are

Documenting: Giving specific examples of the issue being discussed.
Levelling: Telling your partner what you are feeling by stating your thoughts clearly, simply, and honestly.
Editing: Censoring or not saying things that would be deliberately hurtful to your partner or that are irrelevant.

to strangers (Gottman et al., 1976). This is likely also true of all partners in long-term relationships.

Donna may be so disgruntled about her lack of orgasms that she's thinking of having sex with someone else to jolt Chris into recognizing her problem or perhaps to see if another partner would stimulate her to orgasm. Donna is probably best advised to edit out this line of thought and concentrate on the specific problem: her lack of orgasms. Having sex with someone else is not likely to magically solve her problem. If she and Chris can work it out together, not only will Donna be more sexually satisfied, but their relationship also will be stronger.

The trick is to balance levelling and editing. If you edit too much, you may not level at all, and there will be no communication. If you level too much and don't edit, the communication will fail because your partner will respond negatively, and things may get worse rather than better.

Listening

Up to this point, we have been concentrating on techniques for you to use in sending messages about sexual relationships. But, of course, communication is a two-way street, and you and your partner will exchange responses. It is therefore important for you and your partner to gain some skills in listening and responding constructively to messages. The following discussion will suggest such techniques.

One of the most important things is that you must really *listen*. This means more than just removing the headphones from your ears. It means actively trying to understand what the other person is saying. Often people are so busy trying to think of their next response that they hardly hear what the other person is saying. Good listening also involves positive non-verbal behaviours, such as maintaining eye contact with the speaker and nodding one's head when appropriate. Be a *nondefensive listener;* focus on what your partner is saying and feeling, and don't immediately become defensive or counterattack with complaints of your own.

The next step, after you have listened carefully and nondefensively, is to give *feedback*. This often involves giving brief vocalizations—"Uh-huh," "Okay"—nodding your head, or making facial movements that indicate you are listening (Gottman et al., 1998). It may involve the technique of **paraphrasing**—that is, repeating in your own words what you think your partner meant. Suppose, in response to Donna's initial statement, "You're not giving me any orgasms when we have sex," Chris hadn't gotten upset and instead had tried to listen and then

Paraphrasing: Saying in your own words what you think your partner meant.
Nonverbal communication: Communication not through words but through the body (e.g., eye contact, tone of voice, touching).

gave her feedback by paraphrasing. Chris might have responded,

> I hear you saying that I'm not very good at making love to you, and therefore you're not having orgasms. (7)

At that point, Donna would have had a chance to clear up the confusion she had created with her initial message, because Chris had given her feedback by paraphrasing. At that point she could have said, "No, I think you're a good lover, but I'm not having any orgasms, and I don't know why. I thought maybe we could figure it out together." Or perhaps she could have said, "No, I think you're a good lover. I just wish you'd do more of some of the things you do, like going down on me and stimulating my clitoris with your tongue."

It's also a good idea to *ask for feedback* from your partner, particularly if you're not sure whether you're communicating clearly.

Body Talk: Nonverbal Communication

Just as it is important to be a good listener to your partner's verbal messages, so too is it important to be good at reading your partner's nonverbal messages (Figure 12.12). Often the precise words we use are not as important as our **nonverbal communication**—the way we say them. Tone of voice, expression on the face, position of the body, whether you touch the other person—all are important in conveying the message. In fact, when verbal and nonverbal messages conflict, we tend to believe the nonverbal message (e.g., saying "I'm listening" while continuing to stare at the computer screen).

As an example, take the sentence "So you're here." If it is delivered as "So *you're* here" in a hostile tone of voice, the message is that the speaker is very unhappy that you're here. If it is delivered as "So you're *here*" in a pleased voice, the meaning may be that the speaker is glad and surprised to see you here in Newfoundland, having thought you were in Europe. "So you're here" with a smile and arms outstretched to initiate a hug might mean that the speaker has been waiting for you and is delighted to see you.

Suppose that in Donna and Chris's case, the reason Donna doesn't have more orgasms is that Chris doesn't stimulate her firmly enough or in the spot that feels best to her. During sex, Donna is worried that it is taking her too long to reach orgasm and that Chris is getting tired or bored stimulating her. (Notice that Donna is mind reading again.) As a result, Donna does not enjoy the stimulation she does get as much as she could, and her body language communicates that she's not really into it. Chris already believes that Donna does not really like sex and the response (or rather nonresponse) of her

(b)

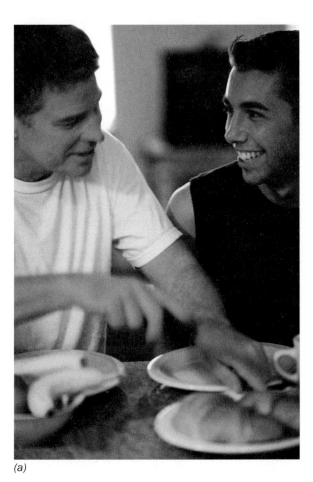

(a)

Figure 12.12 (a) A couple with good body language (good eye contact and body position); (b) A couple with poor body language (poor eye contact and body position).

body confirms these assumptions. Chris reads Donna's body language as communicating that she's not really enjoying having her clitoris stimulated. Although she would like to have an orgasm and for Chris to keep stimulating her, her body is saying, "I'm not into this. Let's get it over with." And that's exactly what Chris does.

To correct this situation, Donna might adopt a more active, encouraging approach. She might take Chris's hand and guide it to her clitoris, showing exactly where and how firmly she likes to have it rubbed. She might give Chris verbal feedback, saying "That's good" when Chris touches her in a way that she likes, or "Please don't stop" if she wants oral stimulation to continue.

The point is that in communicating about sex, we need to be sure that our nonverbal signals help to create the impact we intend rather than one we do not intend. It is also possible that nonverbal signals are confusing communication and need to be straightened out. "Checking out" is a technique for doing this that will be discussed in a later section.

Interestingly, research shows that distressed couples differ from nondistressed couples more in their nonverbal communication than in their verbal communication

(Gottman et al., 1977; Vincent et al., 1979). For example, even when a person from a distressed couple is expressing agreement with his or her partner, that person is more likely to accompany the verbal expressions of agreement with negative nonverbal behaviour. Distressed couples are also more likely to be negative listeners—while listening, the individuals are more likely to display frowning, angry, or disgusted facial expressions or tense or inattentive body postures. Contempt is often expressed nonverbally, by sneering or rolling the eyes, for example. In contrast, harmonious relationships are characterized by closer physical distances and more relaxed postures than are found in distressed couples (Beier & Sternberg, 1977). Once again, it is not only what we say verbally but also how we say it, and how we listen, that makes the difference.

Validating

Another good technique in communication is **validation** (Gottman et al., 1976), which means telling your partner that, given his or her point of view, you can see

Validation: Telling your partner that, given his or her point of view, you can see why he or she thinks a certain way.

why he or she thinks a certain way. It doesn't mean that you agree with your partner or that you're giving in. It simply means that you recognize your partner's point of view as legitimate, given his or her set of assumptions, which may be different from yours.

It is important to recognize that all couples have disagreements. What is important is how you handle these disagreements. If they lead to fights because one partner thinks the other is wrong, these will likely damage the relationship. It is much better to try to understand the other person's viewpoint. In a study of 76 couples, understanding of the partner's preferences for such things as sexual techniques, use of erotica, and use of contraception (not agreement with them) was associated with satisfaction with the sexual aspects of the relationship (Purnine & Carey, 1997).

Suppose that Donna and Chris have gotten into an argument about cunnilingus. Donna thinks it would bring her to orgasm. Chris doesn't want to do it and feels very uncomfortable with the idea. If Donna tried to validate Chris's feelings, she might say,

> I can understand the way you feel about going down on me, especially given the way you were brought up to think about sex. (8)

Chris might validate Donna's feelings by saying,

> I understand how important it is for you to have an orgasm. (9)

Validating hasn't solved their disagreement, but it has left the door open so that they can now make some progress.

Drawing Your Partner Out

Suppose it is Chris who initiates the conversation rather than Donna. Chris has noticed that Donna doesn't seem to get a lot of pleasure out of sex and would like to find out why and see what they can do about it. Chris needs to draw Donna out and might begin by saying,

> I've noticed lately that you don't seem to be enjoying sex as much as you used to. Am I right about that? (10)

That much is good because Chris is checking out an assumption. Unfortunately, the question leads to a "yes" or "no" answer, and that can stop the communication. So, if Donna replies "yes," Chris had better follow it up with an *open-ended* question like

> What can I do to help you enjoy it more? (11)

If Donna can give a reasonable answer, good communication should be on the way. One of the standard—and best—questions to ask in a situation like this is

> What can we do to make things better? (12)

Fighting fair: A set of rules designed to make arguments constructive rather than destructive.

Accentuate the Positive

We have been concentrating on negative communications, that is, communications in which some problem or complaint needs to be voiced. It is also important to communicate positive things about the relationship in general and sex in particular (Gottman & Notarius, 2002). If that was a great episode of lovemaking, or the best kiss you've ever experienced, say so. A learning theorist would say that you're giving your partner some positive reinforcement. As discussed earlier in this chapter, social psychologists' research shows that we tend to like people better who give us positive reinforcements. Recognition of the strengths in a relationship offers the potential for enriching it (e.g., Miller et al., 1975). And if you make a habit of positive communications about sex, it will be easier to initiate the negative ones, and they will be better received.

Most communication during sex is limited to muffled groans, or "Mmm," or an occasional "Faster, John" or "Did you, Michèle?" It might help your partner greatly if you gave frequent verbal and nonverbal feedback, such as "That was great" or "Let's do that again." This would make the positive communications and the negative ones far easier.

Research shows that nondistressed couples make more positive and fewer negative communications than distressed couples (Billings, 1979). In fact, Gottman's (1994) research with married couples found that there is a *magic ratio* of positive to negative communication. In stable marriages, there is five times as much positive interaction—verbal and nonverbal, including hugs and kisses, as there is negative. Not only do happy couples make more positive communications; they are more likely to respond to a negative communication with something positive (Billings, 1979). Distressed couples, on the other hand, are more likely to respond to negative communication with more negative communication, escalating into conflict. We might all take a cue from the happy couples and make efforts not only to increase our positive communications but even to make them in response to negative comments from our partner.

Fighting Fair

Even if you use all the techniques just described, you may still get into arguments with your partner. Arguments are a natural part of a relationship and are not necessarily bad. Given that there will be arguments in a relationship, it is useful if you and your partner have agreed to a set of rules called **fighting fair** (Bach & Wyden, 1969) so that the arguments may help and won't hurt (Figure 12.13).

Here are some of the basic rules for arguing that may be useful to you (Brenton, 1972; Creighton, 1992).

Figure 12.13 Arguments are not necessarily bad for a relationship, but it is important to observe the rules for fighting fair.

Many of them relate to the four destructive communication patterns identified by John Gottman (Gottman & Silver, 1999).

1. Edit what you say. Don't make sarcastic or insulting remarks about your partner's sexual adequacy. This generates resentment, opens you to counterattack, and is just a dirty way to fight.

2. Don't bring up the names of former partners, lovers, boyfriends, or girlfriends to illustrate how all these problems didn't happen with them. Stick to the issue: your relationship with your partner.

3. Don't play amateur psychologist. Don't say things like "The problem is that you're a compulsive personality" or "You acted that way because you never resolved your Oedipus complex." You really don't have the qualifications (even after reading this book) to do so. Even if you did, your partner is likely to think you are biased and would not be apt to recognize your expertise in the middle of an argument.

4. Don't engage in dumping. Don't store up gripes for six months and then dump them on your partner all at one time.

5. Don't hit and run. Don't bring up a serious negative issue when there is no opportunity to continue the discussion, such as when you're on the way out the door going to work or when guests are coming for dinner in five minutes.

6. Don't focus on who's to blame. Focus on looking for solutions, not on who's at fault. If you avoid blaming, it lets both you and your partner save face, which helps both of you feel better about the relationship.

Checking Out Sexy Signals

One of the problems with verbal and nonverbal sexual communications is that they are often ambiguous. This problem may occur more often with couples who don't know each other well, but it can cause uncertainty and misunderstanding in couples in long-term relationships as well.

Some messages are very direct. Statements like "I want to have sex with you" are not ambiguous at all. Unfortunately, such directness is not common in our society. Two New Brunswick studies show that only a minority of people in mixed-sex relationships—22 percent in dating relationships and 41 percent in long-term relationships—use a direct verbal statement to initiate sex (Byers & Heinlein, 1989; O'Sullivan & Byers, 1992). The rest use ambiguous verbal or nonverbal messages. Similarly, Ontario researchers found that men and women in same-sex relationships are more likely to initiate sex by using nonverbal than by using verbal behaviours (Beres et al., 2004). Consider George, who stands up, stretches, and says, "It's time for bed." Does he mean he wants to engage in sexual activity or to go to sleep?

Ambiguous messages can lead to feelings of hurt and rejection or to unnecessary anger and perhaps complaints to third parties. If George wants to have sex but his partner interprets his behaviour as meaning that George is tired, George may go to bed feeling hurt, unattractive, and unloved. A woman who casually puts her arm around the shoulders of a co-worker and gives him or her a hug may find herself explaining to her supervisor that it was a gesture of friendship, not a sexual proposition.

Ideally, each of us should be effective communicators, making sure our message clearly matches our intent. It helps to be clear yet also subtle and seductive as messages that are too direct or too polite may be a turnoff (Graham et al., 2004). As recipients of ambiguous messages, we need to make an effort to clear them up. In response to an invitation to a woman's apartment for coffee, a man might reply, "I would like some coffee, but I'm not interested in sex this time." Or he might draw her out with a question: "I'd like some coffee; is that all you have in mind?" Check out sexy signals. Don't make any assumptions about the meaning of ambiguous messages.

Gender Differences in Communication

Some authors argue that men and women have radically different verbal communication styles (Tannen, 1991). We should not be led astray by flashy claims that men and women are so different that they belong to different linguistic communities. Research generally has shown that there are some gender differences in communication. For example, as discussed in Chapter 13, women tend to self-disclose personal information about themselves and talk about their feelings more than men do, and women are generally better at reading another person's emotions and nonverbal behaviour (Hall, 1998; MacNeil & Byers, 2005). However, in general these differences are small and, contrary to gender stereotypes, both men and women place the highest value on communication that provides emotional support (Burleson, 2003). So whether an individual is in a relationship with a partner of the same gender or of the other gender, with a little effort couples should be able to engage in clear, accurate sexual communication. However, as noted earlier, for some couples poor communication leads to relationship distress or low sexual satisfaction. Not all these couples are able to improve communication on their own. For these couples, relationship or sexual therapy can be an effective way to improve communication and enhance relationship and sexual satisfaction.

Relationship Education

Because of the importance of good communication, a number of relationship or marital education programs have been developed; they include Better Marriages, Couple Communication, and Marriage Enrichment. Most of these programs focus primarily on developing better communication and problem-solving skills, and they include much of the material covered in this section, with many activities designed to encourage practice. A secondary focus may be on information and skills to improve a couple's ability to manage finances, raise children, and so on. A meta-analysis of evaluations of these programs found that they on average are somewhat effective, with larger effects for communication skills than marital quality. Programs lasting 9 to 20 hours were associated with larger effects than shorter programs (Hawkins et al., 2008). Another meta-analysis found that program effects lasted longer for well-functioning couples than for distressed ones (Blanchard et al., 2009). Most participants in this research are white, and there is little information about the effectiveness of these programs for couples in minority groups or low-income couples.

SUMMARY

For most people—heterosexual, gay, and lesbian—emotional passion and sexual passion are closely linked. Unfortunately, much of the research on love has been restricted to heterosexuals and has not included gay men, lesbians, or bisexuals.

Research indicates that mere repeated exposure to another person facilitates attraction. We tend to be attracted to people who are similar to us socially (age, race or ethnicity, economic status) and psychologically (attitudes, interests). In first impressions, we are most attracted to people who are physically attractive; we also tend to be attracted to people whom we believe to be within our reach, depending on our sense of our own attractiveness or desirability.

According to reinforcement theory, we are attracted to those who give us many reinforcements. Interaction with people who are similar to us is smooth and rewarding; they have similar outlooks and like the same things we do. According to sexual strategies theory, we prefer young, attractive people because they are likely to be healthy and fertile. Men prefer women who are sexually faithful; women prefer men with resources who will invest in them and their children.

Intimacy is a major component of a romantic relationship. It is defined as a quality of a relationship characterized by commitment, feelings of closeness and trust, and self-disclosure.

According to the triangular theory, love has three components: intimacy, passion, and decision or commitment. Love is a triangle, with each component as one of the points. Partners whose love triangles are substantially different are mismatched, and they are likely to be dissatisfied with their relationship.

According to the attachment theory of love, adults vary in their capacity for love as a result of their love or attachment experiences in infancy. The theory says that there are four types of lovers: secure lovers, preoccupied lovers, fearful lovers, and dismissing lovers.

Love can also be viewed as a story, with characters, a plot, and a theme. People use their love stories to interpret experiences in relationships. Falling in love happens when a person meets someone who can play a compatible role in his or her story.

Love may have a neurochemical component. Passionate love, a state of intense longing and arousal, may be produced by dopamine. Like all chemically induced highs, passionate love eventually comes to an end. It may be replaced by companionate love, a feeling of deep attachment and commitment to the partner. This type of love may be accompanied by elevated levels of prolactin and oxytocin, which may be produced by physical closeness and touch.

Passionate love is associated with brain activity in areas associated with reward and complex cognitive processing. Long-term love relationships are associated with brain areas related to maternal attachment. Brain activation by looking at photos of lovers differs from the activity associated with objects of sexual desire.

Hatfield and Sprecher have constructed a scale to measure passionate love. Such scales make it possible to do scientific research on complex phenomena like love. Scores on this scale were correlated with measures of commitment to and satisfaction with romantic relationships.

Researchers have hypothesized that there are two basic components of romantic love: being in a state of physiological arousal and attaching the label *love* to the feeling. Several studies report evidence consistent with the hypothesis.

Cross-cultural research indicates that individualistic cultures like that of Canada emphasize love as the basis for marriage and encourage intimacy between partners. Collectivist cultures emphasize intergroup bonds as the basis for marriage and discourage intimacy between partners. Culture influences the importance of

various characteristics in choosing a mate; it also affects our standards of beauty and the likelihood of marrying someone we don't love.

Research reveals clear differences in communication patterns between happy, nondistressed couples and couples who are unhappy, seeking counselling, or headed for divorce. Destructive patterns of interaction include criticism, contempt, defensiveness, and withdrawal. The key to building a good relationship is reciprocal self-disclosure. The key to maintaining a good relationship is being a good communicator.

Specific tips for being a good communicator include using "I" language, avoiding mind reading, documenting your points with specific examples, levelling and editing, being a nondefensive listener, giving feedback by paraphrasing, being aware of your nonverbal messages, validating the other's viewpoint, drawing your partner out, and engaging in positive verbal and nonverbal communication. When you do fight, fight fair. Finally, it is important to check out ambiguous sexy signals to find out what they really mean.

QUESTIONS FOR THOUGHT, DISCUSSION, AND DEBATE

1. If you are currently in love with someone, how would you describe the kind of love you feel, using the various concepts and theories of love discussed in this chapter?

2. Debate the following topic. Resolved: Selecting mates based on individualistic considerations, such as whether you love the person, contributes to the high rates of divorce and single-parent families.

3. Your best friend has been dating another person exclusively for the past year. One day you ask how the relationship is going. Your friend replies, "I don't know. We get along really well. We like to do the

same things, and we can tell each other everything. But I feel like something is missing. How do you know if you are in love?" How would you answer her question?

4. If you are in a long-term relationship, think about the kind of communication pattern you have with your partner. Do you use the methods of communication recommended in this chapter? If not, do you think that there are areas in which you could change and improve? Would your partner cooperate in attempts to improve your communication pattern?

Are YOU Curious?

1. What are some major ways in which men and women differ in their sexuality?

2. When heterosexual men report more sexual partners than heterosexual women do, is this accurate? How can this be?

3. How do surgeons create a penis or a vagina when they do gender-reassignment surgery?

Read this chapter to find out.

CHAPTER

Gender and Sexuality

LEARNING OBJECTIVES

After studying this chapter, you will be able to

LO1 Describe the various concepts related to gender.

LO2 Describe the gender role socialization process.

LO3 Discuss how ethnicity influences gender roles in general and in specific communities.

LO4 Identify and describe the primary gender differences seen in psychological functioning and sexuality.

LO5 Describe and evaluate the various explanations given for the reported gender differences in sexuality.

LO6 List and define the various terms used to describe sexualities that do not fit the traditional binary categories of female and male.

LO7 Describe the gender reassignment processes.

LO8 Describe research that addresses the possible causes of gender dysphoria.

The majority of women (happily for them) are not very much troubled with sexual feelings of any kind. What men are habitually, women are only exceptionally.*
The root of all men's desire is to have sex. When you brush your teeth, it's to have sex. When you eat, it's, well, I gotta have energy to have sex. When you get dressed, you think, oh, maybe if I wear these jeans I'll be more likely to have sex.**

* Dr. William Acton. (1857). *The functions and disorders of the reproductive organs.*
** Seth Rogen (2008).

When a baby is born, what is the first statement made about it? "It's a boy" or "It's a girl," of course. Children learn what gender they are early in development—by age two and a half, most children can correctly identify their own gender (Campbell et al., 2002; Thompson, 1975). Sociologists tell us that gender is one of the most basic of status characteristics. That is, in terms of both our individual interactions with people and the position we hold in society, gender is exceptionally important. Many people experience consternation in the rare cases when they are uncertain of a person's gender or when the individual is intersex and the eight variables of gender outlined in Chapter 5 are not all in agreement. They may not know how to interact with the person and may feel flustered, not to mention curious, until they can ferret out some clue as to whether the person is a man or a woman. This happens because the dominant culture in Canadian society adheres to a rigid two-gender system, male and female, which often excludes people who fall outside traditional conceptions of masculinity or femininity. Not all cultures define gender as a male–female dichotomy; some cultures have three or even four genders.

In this chapter we explore gender roles and the impact they may have on sexuality. As depicted in the quotes above, we have clear stereotypes about male and female sexuality. But, just how accurate are these stereotypes? We also discuss the phenomenon of transgender, which includes several variations on typical gender.

Gender Roles and Stereotypes

One of the basic ways in which societies codify this emphasis on gender is through gender roles.[1] A **gender role** is a set of norms, or culturally prescribed

expectations, that define how people of one gender ought to behave. A closely related phenomenon is a **stereotype**, which is a rigid set of beliefs about a group of people (e.g., men) that distinguishes those people from others (e.g., women) and is applied to all members of that group. Research shows that even in modern North American society, and even among university students, there is a belief that males and females do differ psychologically in many ways, and the stereotypes have not changed much since 1972 (Bergen & Williams, 1991).

Children as young as six are aware of these stereotypes. Researchers in Nova Scotia showed children pictures containing a man and a woman and told them brief stories about the pictures. Each story described a gender stereotype. The researchers then asked the children which person in the picture the story was about. The children responded with the appropriate stereotype most of the time. More than 85 percent of eight-year-olds identified the woman in the picture as appreciative, gentle, weak, soft-hearted, sentimental, emotional, excitable, and meek and mild. They identified the man in the picture as aggressive, strong, coarse, cruel, loud, and ambitious.

Heterosexuality is viewed as an important part of gender roles (Hyde & Jaffee, 2000). The "feminine" woman is expected to be sexually attractive to men and in turn to be attracted to them. Women who violate any part of this role—for example, lesbians because they are not attracted to men—are viewed as violators of gender roles and are considered masculine. Heterosexuality is equally important in the male role.

Gender Schema Theory
In Chapter 2 we discussed gender schema theory, a cognitive approach to understanding gender stereotypes. Recall that according to that theory, a gender schema is the set of ideas (about behaviours, personality,

Gender role: A set of norms, or culturally defined expectations, that define how people of one gender ought to behave.
Stereotype: A rigid set of beliefs about a group of people (e.g., men) that distinguishes them from others (e.g., women) and is applied to all members of that group.

[1] The distinction between sex and gender will be maintained in this chapter. Male–female roles–and thus gender roles–are being discussed here.

appearance, and so on) that we associate with males and females (Bem, 1981; Martin et al., 2002). Our gender schema influences how we process information. It causes us to tend to dichotomize information based on gender. It also leads us to distort or fail to remember information that is stereotype inconsistent. As a result, it is relatively difficult to change people's stereotyped notions because we tend to filter out information that contradicts stereotypes. Of course, people do not process information by using gender schema in every situation. Research in Ontario has shown that both our own gender roles (i.e., how traditional we are) and the situation we are in affect how likely we process information in terms of gender schema (McKenzie-Mohr & Zanna, 1990). In this study the researchers found that traditionally masculine men who were exposed to a nonviolent erotic film treated the female confederate in a *more sexist way* than did nontraditional men or men who saw a control film, suggesting that the erotic film activated a traditional gender schema for this group of men.

The Traditional Sexual Script

Scripts are cognitive frameworks for how people are expected to behave in social situations. The sexual script that is most pervasive in North America is a heterosexual script, termed the *traditional sexual script* or TSS. The TSS specifies how men and women are expected to behave in (heterosexual) sexual situations (Byers, 1996; Gagnon & Simon, 1973; Striepe & Tolman, 2003). Although young people often state that things have changed and that the gender roles are now egalitarian, research suggests that the traditional script is still the most common dating script (Laner & Ventrone, 2000). The following are some aspects of the TSS and the underlying gender schema:

1. Men are "oversexed" and women are "undersexed." As such, men are seen as having strong sexual needs and being highly motivated to engage in sexual activity at any opportunity. Women are depicted as being sexually reluctant, slow to arouse, and interested in sex only in the context of love and commitment.

2. High sexual experience enhances men's but decreases women's perceived status. That is, for men, sexual experience is perceived as reflecting positive characteristics, such as masculinity and attractiveness. In women, high sexual experience is attributed to undesirable characteristics, such as nonselectivity and lack of values. Think of the differences in the values attached to the words used to describe the sexually experienced man (*macho, stud*) compared with those used for the sexually experienced woman (*slut, whore*).

3. Men are expected to be "sexperts" and to take responsibility for both their own and their female partner's sexual pleasure and orgasm. Women are expected to be sexually naive. Thus, they may be afraid to share their sexual preferences with their partner out of fear that he will take this as evidence that they have had many sexual partners (something that is evaluated negatively in women). They also may fear that their partner will think they are criticizing him for not being the sexpert he is supposed to be.

4. Men, because of their greater sexual interest, are supposed to be the initiators in sexual situations.

5. To avoid being judged negatively by being too sexually available, women are expected to be sexual gatekeepers and place limits on sexual activity, particularly with a new partner. Thus, even when they are interested in engaging in sexual activity, females are expected to offer at least initial token resistance to their partner's sexual advances.

How much evidence is there that heterosexuals follow the TSS? Research conducted in New Brunswick sheds some light on this question (Byers, 1996). Participants in two studies (one of dating relationships, the other of long-term relationships) kept a diary in which they recorded sexual initiations and responses to initiations in their relationships (Byers & Heinlein, 1989; O'Sullivan & Byers, 1992). The results indicated that men initiate sex more often than women do in both mixed-sex dating and long-term relationships. This is consistent with the TSS. However, men are not always the initiators—on average women initiated sex more than once a week. Responses to initiations also did not follow the TSS. The research showed that men and women are equally likely to accept or refuse an initiation—they respond positively about 83 percent of the time in dating relationships and about 74 percent of the time in long-term relationships. Recent research also conducted in New Brunswick has found similar results (Simms & Byers, 2013; Vannier & O'Sullivan, 2011). Further, when one partner is reluctant to engage in sexual activity, men and women use the same strategies to try to change their partner's mind—most often flirting or touching and stroking the partner (O'Sullivan & Byers, 1996).

These results indicate that some aspects of the TSS, such as the expectation that it is the male role to initiate sex, continue to characterize heterosexual relationships. However, women regularly initiate sexual activity, albeit less frequently than their male partners. Further, research does not support other aspects of the TSS. Women are no more reluctant to engage in sexual activity than men are. To this extent, men's and

Figure 13.1 Children are very interested in imitating adult behaviour that entails gender.

women's roles in mixed-sex sexual interactions appear to be converging. Nonetheless, as discussed in Chapter 16, adherence to the TSS may be a cause of some men's use of sexually coercive behaviour with women (Byers, 1996).

L02 Socialization

Many adult women and men do behave as gender roles say they should. Why does this happen? Psychologists and sociologists believe that it is a result of gender-role socialization. **Socialization** refers to the ways in which society conveys to the individual its norms or expectations for his or her behaviour. Socialization occurs especially in childhood, as children are taught to behave as they will be expected to in adulthood. Socialization involves several processes. Children may be rewarded for behaviour that is appropriate for their gender ("What a brave little man he is"), or they may be punished for behaviour that is not appropriate to their gender ("Nice young ladies don't do that"). The adult models they imitate—whether these are parents of the same gender, teachers, or women and men on television—also contribute to their socialization (Figure 13.1). In some cases, simply telling children what is expected of boys/men and girls/women may be sufficient for role learning to take place. Children also engage in *self-socialization*, which operates in two ways. The more children come to identify with a particular gender (i.e., have a male or female gender identity), the more they are motivated to incorporate attributes associated with that gender into their self-concept. Conversely, seeing themselves as matching the stereotypes for their own gender strengthens children's gender identity (Tobin et al., 2010). Socialization continues in adulthood, as society conveys its norms of appropriate behaviour for adult women and men. These norms extend from appropriate jobs to who initiates sexual activity.

Gender socialization comes from multiple sources, including parents, peers, and the media (Leaper & Friedman, 2007). Certainly parents have an early, important influence, from buying dolls for girls and footballs or baseball bats for boys, to giving boys more freedom to explore. Research indicates that parents treat girls and boys similarly in many ways, with the exception that parents strongly encourage gender-typed activities (Blakemore et al., 2009).

The peer group also can have a big impact on socializing for gender roles. In an Ontario experiment, children in Grades 3 to 6 read stories about boys and girls who engaged in traditionally masculine, traditionally feminine, or a combination of masculine and feminine behaviours (Zucker et al., 1995). The boys preferred to be friends with the exclusively masculine boy, and girls preferred the exclusively feminine girl. Teenagers may be particularly effective at exerting pressure for gender-role conformity (Maccoby, 2002).

The media are also important socializing agents. Many people assume that things have changed a lot in the last 20 years and that gender stereotypes are a thing of the past. On the contrary, various media—from television to teen magazines—continue to show females and males in stereotyped roles. An analysis of gender stereotyping in children's picture books published from 1980 to 2001 showed no decline over time in stereotyping (Hamilton et al., 2006). For example, most of the adults in the books were shown engaged in gender-stereotyped occupations.

An analysis of advertising on the major television networks found that the "voice of authority"—the voice over—is male in 71 percent of ads (Messineo, 2008). In these commercials, men are more likely to be portrayed as assertive and employed, and women are more likely to be shown as parents and as sex objects.

Socialization: The ways in which society conveys to the individual its norms or expectations for his or her behaviour.

Dozens of studies show that gender stereotypes shown on television affect children's stereotyped ideas (Ward & Harrison, 2005). For example, in one study children in Grades 1 and 2 were exposed to television commercials in which all boys were playing with a gender-neutral toy (traditional condition), all girls were playing with it (nontraditional condition), or the commercials were not about toys (control) (Pike & Jennings, 2005). Afterward, children were asked to sort six toys into those that were for boys, those that were for girls, or those that were for both boys and girls. Among the six toys was the toy they had seen in the commercial. Children in the traditional condition were more likely to say that the toy was for boys, whereas children in the nontraditional condition were more likely to say that it was for both boys and girls. These results show not only the power of stereotyped television images but also that children can respond positively to nonstereotyped messages.

But picture books and TV are old-fashioned media. One might expect the new media to be less stereotyped. To the contrary, however, video games show patterns of extreme gender stereotyping (Dill & Thill, 2007). In *Grand Theft Auto,* the men are violent and the women are hookers. The average Grade 8 or 9 boy plays computer games 13 hours per week, compared with 5 hours for girls (Gentile et al., 2004). In short, boys' exposure to these games and their gender stereotypes is massive.

Although gender roles themselves are universal (Rosaldo, 1974)—that is, all societies have gender roles—the exact content of these roles varies from one culture to the next, from one ethnic group to another, and from one social class to another. Gender roles in the major ethnocultural Canadian communities are described next.

LO3 Gender Roles and Ethnicity

Ethnicity refers to a sizable group of people who share a common and distinct racial, national, religious, linguistic, or cultural origin or heritage. Although people of British and French backgrounds make up the largest ethnic groups in Canada, only 12 percent of Canadians report only British or French origins (Statistics Canada, 2008b). More than one in five (20.6 percent) Canadians were not born in Canada, and about two-thirds of these individuals (63 percent) live in Toronto, Montreal, or Vancouver. Indeed, between 23 and 46 percent of the population in Toronto, Vancouver, and Montreal were born outside Canada (Statistics Canada, 2013). Changing immigration patterns since the 1980s

Intersectionality: An approach that simultaneously considers the meaning and consequences of multiple categories of identity, difference, and disadvantage.
Acculturation: The process of incorporating the beliefs and customs of a new culture.

have increased the ethnocultural diversity of Canada and have introduced a wide range of attitudes and traditions surrounding gender roles.

As we consider variations in gender roles across variations in ethnic groups, it is crucial to understand how these gender roles are a product of *culture.* In the sections below, we consider some aspects of the culture of four ethnic groups and their relevance to gender roles and sexuality.

First, though, we will consider a key concept, **intersectionality**, which can be defined as an approach that simultaneously considers the meaning and consequences of multiple categories of identity, difference, and disadvantage (Cole, 2009). That is, according to this approach, we should not consider the effects of gender in isolation. Instead, we should consider the effects of gender, race, social class, and sexual orientation simultaneously. When we talk about the category "women," for example, we are talking about a complex group that differs by ethnicity, social class, sexual orientation, and many other identities, such as religion.

Within this framework, it becomes clear that some groups experience multiple disadvantages, such as poor Aboriginal women or lesbian women of colour. Others may be part of a disadvantaged group but also part of a privileged group, such as a middle-class Aboriginal person. In the sections that follow, we will look at the intersection of gender and ethnicity. In Chapter 14, we will also examine the intersection of gender, ethnicity, and sexual orientation.

In some ways, the gender roles of members of Canadian ethnocultural communities reflect the values and norms of their country of origin. However, gender roles are also influenced by the majority Canadian culture through the process of **acculturation**—the process of incorporating the beliefs and customs of a new culture. For example, in keeping with traditional values, immigrant parents may allow their sons but not their daughters to engage in unsupervised dating. However, the same parents may encourage their daughters to obtain professional degrees and take up careers even though women in their culture traditionally did not work outside the home (Mackie, 1991).

The study Ethnocultural Communities Facing AIDS examined sexuality within six Canadian ethnocultural communities (see Chapter 1 for a description of this study). Groups were chosen based on ethnicity, not race. The researchers chose large, cohesive communities with a large proportion of young people and people who had immigrated to Canada since 1986 (Cappon et al., 1996). They found a number of cross-cultural similarities in gender roles. Generally, men and women in these communities are seen as having distinct roles in that men are expected to be the head of the family, and women are expected to be the caregivers. However,

Figure 13.2 Gender roles in Canada's ethnocultural communities reflect aspects of the majority and aspects of the minority culture, such as this arranged Hindu marriage in Montreal.

economic realities often mean that women must work outside the home, and these role changes often create conflict within the family. There tends to be a double standard with respect to sexual behaviour. Dating and premarital sex are accepted and often encouraged in sons but not tolerated in daughters. Men are expected to be active in sexual relationships, whereas women are expected to be passive and to meet men's needs (Manson Singer et al., 1996).

There also are differences in gender role expectations between various ethnocultural groups (Figure 13.2), as the following descriptions of the Chinese, South Asian, and Caribbean communities in the aforementioned study demonstrate (Brabazon et al., 1993a, 1993b; Baxter et al., 1993a, 1993b; Gunter et al., 1993a, 1993b). As you will see, gender roles in Canada are not uniform. Different ethnic groups define gender roles differently. As with the majority Canadian culture, there also are variations in gender roles within each ethnocultural community. The following descriptions refer to the dominant views within these cultures.

The South Asian Communities

In 2006 there were 1,316,700 people who identified themselves as South Asian (e.g., Indians and Pakistanis)

living in Canada, the second-largest visible minority group in Canada. In South Asian communities, religion is a major focus of community life. Hard work, education, and achievement are seen as important. Respect for traditional values, which in some cases includes arranged marriages even for people born in Canada, is also highly valued (see First Person in Chapter 12). South Asian men and women tend to be assigned different roles, and women are expected to be submissive to men. Boys tend to be given privileges and freedom, dating is allowed, and it is expected that they will have some sexual experience. However, girls may not be allowed to date because female virginity before marriage is highly valued. Men are expected to take the lead in the sexual encounter; women are expected to be passive, submissive, and uninformed about sex. As a result of women's prescribed sexual passivity, some men visit sex workers for casual sex before and during marriage. The women are not supposed to question the behaviour of their husbands or to complain about extramarital sexual activity.

The Chinese Community

In the 2006 census, 1,346,510 people in Canada identified themselves as Chinese Canadians, the largest visible minority group in the country. Chinese culture

Figure 13.3 Gender roles in Canada's Asian community are becoming more diverse as people move away from their traditional background.

emphasizes responsibility to the family and the community over self-fulfillment and individualism as in the majority Canadian culture. Marriage is highly valued so that couples are reluctant to separate or divorce even when experiencing significant marital problems. In most families, the man is considered the head of the household; the woman is the primary caregiver and is expected to adopt a submissive role with her male partner. It is not acceptable for females to engage in premarital or extramarital sexual activity, and premarital sex is also discouraged for males. However, extramarital sexual activity by men may be accepted, particularly in "astronaut families" in which the man works away from home, for example, in Hong Kong or Taiwan. Today, gender roles within the community are becoming more diverse as people move away from their traditional roles. Because achievement and education are important within the Chinese community, women who pursue their education in Canada may experience conflict between the traditional gender roles of Chinese culture and those of Canadian culture, which increasingly prizes independence and assertiveness in women (Figure 13.3). Men may also experience conflict between family values and individual achievement.

English-Speaking Caribbean Communities

In 2006 there were 783,800 individuals in Canada who identified themselves as black, most with roots in the Caribbean. English-speaking Caribbean (e.g., Jamaican) communities have a strong sense of family and community. Traditionally, the man was expected to be the provider and the woman was expected to care for the children and the household while also working outside the home. Today there are many single-parent families in the Caribbean communities, usually headed by women. More restrictions are placed on girls than on boys, in part as an attempt to prevent adolescent

pregnancy. In adolescence and into adulthood, women's focus is on developing relationships, and they may engage in serial monogamy. Both having a male partner and having a child are considered important aspects of the female role and indicators of success. In contrast, young men are more likely to want to have many sexual partners. It also is not uncommon for married and cohabiting men to have multiple partners.

Aboriginal Communities

In the 2006 Canadian census, 1,678,235 people reported Aboriginal ancestry (Statistics Canada, 2008b). The Aboriginal peoples constitute important ethnocultural minority groups in Canada. Before contact with Europeans, at least some of the Aboriginal peoples in North America had relatively egalitarian gender roles (Kinsman, 1996; LaFromboise et al., 1990). That is, their roles were more egalitarian than those of the European culture of the same period. The process of acculturation and adaptation to the majority culture seems to have resulted in increased male dominance among North American Aboriginal peoples.

Among the more than 200 Aboriginal languages spoken in North America, at least two-thirds have a term that refers to a third (or third and fourth) gender beyond male and female (Tafoya & Wirth, 1996). European anthropologists termed this additional category *berdache,* a term rejected by many Aboriginal peoples who prefer the term *two-spirit* (Jacobs et al., 1997). These same anthropologists concluded that the people were homosexuals, transsexuals, or transvestites, none of which are accurate from an Aboriginal point of view (Kinsman, 1996). A man might be married to a two-spirit male, but the marriage would not be considered homosexual because the two are of different genders (Tafoya & Wirth, 1996).

There was also a role of the "manly hearted woman," a role that a woman who was exceptionally independent and aggressive could take on (Figure 13.4). There was a "warrior woman" role among the Apache, Crow, Cheyenne, Blackfoot, Pawnee, and Navajo tribes (e.g., Buchanan, 1986; House, 1997). In both cases, women could express masculine traits or participate in male-stereotyped activities while continuing to live and dress as women.

Gender Differences in Psychological Functioning

Gender differences in personality and behaviour have been studied extensively by psychologists (e.g., Hyde & Else-Quest, 2012). Here we will focus on gender

Figure 13.4 Among some First Nations there are three gender roles, the third being known as a "manly hearted woman" or "warrior woman." Chiricahua Tah-deste was a messenger and warrior in Geronimo's band. She participated in negotiations with several U.S. military leaders and surrendered with Geronimo in 1886.

differences in two areas that are particularly relevant to gender and sexuality: aggressiveness and communication styles.

Males and females differ in *aggressiveness.* Males are generally more aggressive than females, and this difference is found cross-culturally (Best, 2001). This is true for virtually all indicators of aggression (physical aggression, such as fighting; verbal aggression; and fantasy aggression) (Archer, 2004). It is also true at all ages; as soon as children are old enough to perform aggressive behaviours, boys are more aggressive, and men dominate the statistics on violent crimes. Researchers have found that there are some differences between men and women in their style of communicating, both verbally and nonverbally (Leaper & Ayres, 2007). Of particular relevance to sexuality, social psychologists have found gender differences in self-disclosure. Within dating relationships, women tend to self-disclose more than men do about both sexual and nonsexual issues (Byers & Demmons, 1999; MacNeil & Byers, 2005), and adolescent girls self-disclose to friends more than adolescent boys do (Rose & Rudolph, 2006).

Today, of course, males and females do much of their self-disclosure online. In one study of adolescents, girls'

online self-disclosure increased greatly between ages 10 and 13; boys displayed a similar increase, but it started about two years later (Valkenburg et al., 2011). Girls engaged in more online self-disclosure than boys did at all ages. Another study examined college students' self-disclosure on their Facebook pages (Special & Li-Barber, 2012). For both the male and female students, the top motive for using Facebook was maintaining relationships—that is, motives displayed gender similarities. Moreover, there was no gender difference in disclosure of personal information in this particular medium.

Norms about self-disclosure are changing, though. Traditional gender roles favoured emotional expressiveness for women but emotional repressiveness and avoidance of self-disclosure for men. There is a contemporary ethic, though, of good communication and openness that demands equal self-disclosure from males and females (Rubin et al., 1980). Research with university students in New Brunswick indicates that traditional gender roles persist in that women are more emotionally expressive than men are both in nonsexual and in sexual situations (Lawrance et al., 1996). However, this research also shows that we are moving toward a norm of greater emotional expressiveness for men. Men were described as ideally equally as expressive as women in sexual situations. Thus, the traditional expectation that men should not express their feelings seems to be gradually shifting toward the expectation that they be open and communicative.

There are gender differences in people's ability to understand the nonverbal behaviours of others. The technical phrase for this is "decoding nonverbal cues"—that is, the ability to read others' body language correctly. It might be measured, for example, by one's accuracy in interpreting facial expressions. Research shows that women are better than men are at decoding such nonverbal cues and at discerning others' emotions (Hall, 1998). Certainly, this is consistent with the gender-related expectation that women will show greater interpersonal sensitivity.

What are the implications of these gender differences in communication styles for sexuality? For example, if men are less able to disclose personal information about themselves, might this hamper their ability to communicate their sexual needs to their partners?

Gender Differences in Sexuality

In this section, the discussion will focus on areas of sexuality in which there is some evidence of male–female differences. As we will point out, differences do exist, but they are in a rather small number of areas—masturbation, attitudes about casual sex, arousal from erotica, consistency of orgasm during sex, and sex drive. There is a danger in focusing on these differences to the point of forgetting about gender similarities. Keep in mind that men and women are in many ways quite similar in their sexuality—for example, in the physiology of their sexual response (Chapter 9)—as you consider the evidence on male–female differences that follows.

Masturbation

A review of 730 studies of gender differences in sexuality found that one of the largest gender differences was the incidence of masturbation (Petersen & Hyde, 2010).

Recall that in the Kinsey data, 92 percent of the men had masturbated to orgasm at least once in their lives, as compared with 58 percent of the women. Not only did fewer women masturbate, but in general, those who did masturbate had begun at a later age than the men. Virtually all men said they had masturbated before age 20 (most began between ages 13 and 15), but substantial numbers of women reported masturbating for the first time at age 25, 30, or 35. This gender difference still appears in recent studies. For example, for adults between 25 and 29 in the National Survey of Sexual Health and Behavior (NSSHB), 94 percent of the men had masturbated at least once in their lives, compared with 85 percent of the women (Herbenick et al., 2010a). And 20 percent of the men masturbated four or more times per week, compared with 5 percent of the women (Herbenick et al., 2010b; Reece et al., 2010b). Similarly, 80 percent of male students but only 48 percent of female students at the University of British Columbia reported masturbating at least once (Meston et al., 1996). The data suggest, then, that there is a gender difference in the incidence of masturbation, with men more likely to have masturbated than women.

Attitudes About Casual Sex

In the review just mentioned, another substantial gender difference was in attitudes toward casual sex—that is, sexual intercourse in a situation, such as a one-night stand, in which there is no emotionally committed relationship between the partners (Petersen & Hyde, 2010; Yost & Zurbriggen, 2006). Men are considerably more approving of such interactions, and women tend to be disapproving (Figure 13.5). Many women feel that sexual intercourse is ethical or acceptable only in the context of an emotionally committed relationship. For many men, that is a nice context for sex, but it isn't absolutely necessary.

One study has gained legendary status as an illustration of men's greater interest in casual sex. Clark and Hatfield (1989) had female and male research assistants, who were confederates of the experimenters,

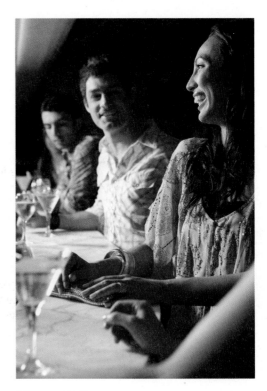

Figure 13.5 In pick-up situations, men are likely to be more interested in having the interaction lead to casual sex than women are.

approach people of the other gender and invite them to engage in casual sex. No women agreed to such a sexual encounter, whereas 70 percent of men agreed (see also Guéguen, 2011). Evolutionary theorists see these results as evidence of men's selection to have sex with many partners and women's selection to be choosy (Chapter 2). However, socialization explanations are equally plausible (Conley, 2011). Girls are socialized to perceive risk in the environment and, in particular, to be sensitive to the possibility of sexual assault. Boys, in contrast, are encouraged to ignore risk. Moreover, it may be more about the proposer than about the person receiving the proposal. Male proposers may be perceived as dangerous and female proposers as harmless. Then there is the issue of sexual pleasure. Doubtless men anticipate sexual pleasure from the encounter, whereas women would be less likely to think that the male proposer would give them pleasure. Several clever laboratory experiments support these socialization explanations (Conley, 2011).

In Canada, 68 percent of male adolescents but only 48 percent of female adolescents approve of having sex before marriage with someone you like (Bibby, 2001). Further, adolescent females are more likely to believe that sex without love is not satisfying. Gender differences in attitudes toward casual sex were even greater; in the Canada Youth Sexual Health and HIV/AIDS

Study, 66 percent of Grade 11 boys but only 32 percent of Grade 11 girls agreed that it was all right to have casual sex (Boyce et al., 2003).

One study asked male and female university students about their motives for having sex (Meston & Buss, 2007). Participants identified 237 reasons for having sex, ranging from wanting to experience physical pleasure to wanting to express love for the person, feel closer to God, improve their sexual skills, or make their partner happy. Twenty of the top 25 reasons were the same for the men and the women. Consistent with traditional gender roles, the men were more likely to have sex because of the physical desirability of their partner (e.g., "The person had a desirable body"), opportunity (e.g., "The person was available"), physical pleasure (e.g., "I wanted to achieve an orgasm"), and insecurity (e.g., "I felt obligated to"). Contrary to stereotypes, for the most part, the women were not more likely than the men were to endorse emotional and commitment motives for having sex, although the women were more likely to say that they had sex to express their love for their partner.

Use of Pornography

The third substantial gender difference found in the review noted above was in the use of pornography (Petersen & Hyde, 2010). Men were considerably more likely to report using porn than women were. Further, research in New Brunswick has shown that men are more likely to go online to view pornography than are women; they are also more likely to go online to engage in sexual activity with a partner (Shaughnessy et al., 2011). The gender difference in pornography use, in turn, is probably connected to the one discussed next.

Arousal from Erotica

Traditionally in our society most erotic material—sexually arousing pictures, movies, or stories—has been produced for a male audience. The corresponding assumption presumably has been that women are not aroused by such things. Does the scientific evidence bear out this notion?

Laboratory research shows that men are more aroused by erotic materials, but the gender difference is not large (Murnen & Stockton, 1997). A classic study by psychologist Julia Heiman (1975) provides a good deal of insight into the responses of men and women to erotic materials. The participants were sexually experienced university students, and Heiman studied their responses as they listened to tape recordings of erotic stories. Not only did she obtain the participants' self-ratings of their arousal, as other investigators have done, but she also got objective measures of their physiological levels of arousal. To do this, she used two instruments: a penile strain gauge and a vaginal photoplethysmograph (see

Figure 13.6 Two devices used to measure physiological sexual response in males and females. The penile strain gauge (left) consists of a flexible band that fits around the base of the penis. The photoplethysmograph (right) is an acrylic cylinder containing a photocell and a light source, which is placed just inside the vagina.

Figure 13.6). The **penile strain gauge** (which our students have dubbed the "peter meter") or *plethysmograph* is used to get a physiological measure of arousal in men; it is a flexible loop that fits around the base of the penis. The vaginal **photoplethysmograph**, or photometer, measures physiological arousal in the female; it is an acrylic cylinder, about the size of a tampon, that is placed just inside the entrance to the vagina. Both instruments measure vasocongestion in the genitals, which is the major physiological response during sexual arousal (see Chapter 9). A problem with these devices is that they are intrusive and neither can be used with both women and men. New technology has come to the rescue. Researchers in Quebec have shown that **thermal imaging** technology (i.e., changes in the temperature of the genital area because of sexual arousal are detected by a remote camera focused on the genital region) may be useful in assessing physiological genital arousal in both women and men (Kukkonen et al., 2007, 2010).

In the Heiman (1975) study, research participants heard one

Penile strain gauge: A device used to measure physiological sexual arousal in the male; it is a flexible loop that fits around the base of the penis.
Photoplethysmograph (foh-toh-pleth-ISS-moh-graf): An acrylic cylinder that is placed inside the vagina to measure physiological sexual arousal in the female. Also called a photometer.
Thermal imaging: A method of detecting genital arousal by using a remote camera focused on the genital region to measure its temperature.

of four kinds of tapes depicting heterosexual couples to test the stereotype that women are more turned on by romance, whereas men are more aroused by "raw sex." The tapes varied according to which of these kinds of content they contained. The first group of tapes was *erotic;* they included excerpts from popular novels giving explicit descriptions of heterosexual sex. The second group of tapes was *romantic;* a couple was heard expressing affection and tenderness for each other, but they did not actually engage in sex. The third group of tapes was *erotic-romantic;* they included erotic elements of explicit sex but also romantic elements. Finally, the fourth group of tapes served as a control; a couple were heard engaging in conversation but nothing else. The plots of the tapes also varied according to whether the man or the woman initiated the activity and whether the description centred on the woman's physical and psychological responses or on the man's. Thus, the tapes were either male-initiated or female-initiated and either female-centred or male-centred. Three important results emerged from the study:

1. Explicit heterosexual sex (the erotic and erotic-romantic tapes) was most arousing, both for women and for men. The great majority of both men and women responded most strongly, both physiologically and in self-ratings, to the erotic and erotic-romantic tapes. Women, in fact, rated the erotic tapes as more arousing than men did. Neither men nor women responded—either physiologically or in self-reports—to the romantic tapes or to the control tapes (except for a couple of men who were aroused by a discussion of the relative merits of an anthropology major versus pre-med—ah, well).

2. Both men and women found the female-initiated, female-centred tape to be most arousing. Perhaps the female-initiated plot was most arousing because of its somewhat forbidden or taboo nature.

3. Women were sometimes not aware of their own physiological arousal. Generally there was a high correlation between self-ratings of arousal and objective physiological measures of arousal for men. When men were physically aroused, they never made an error in reporting this in their self-ratings—it is pretty hard to miss an erection. But when the women were physically aroused, about half of them did not report arousal in their self-ratings. (One might assume that women who were sophisticated enough to volunteer for an experiment of this nature and who were willing to insert a photoplethysmograph into their vagina would not suddenly become bashful about reporting their arousal; that is, it seems likely that these women honestly did not perceive themselves to be aroused.)

In sum, then, Heiman's study indicates that women and men are quite similar in their responses to erotic materials but that women can sometimes be unaware of their own physical arousal. Researchers in New Brunswick measured men's and women's implicit attitudes (see Chapter 3) toward romantic and sexual stimuli and also found that men and women are similar in that both show a preference for romantic over sexual stimuli (Thompson & O'Sullivan, 2012). However, the women's preference was stronger than was the men's.

In statistical terms, Heiman found a low correlation between women's self-reports of arousal and the physiological measures of their arousal, a pattern that is still found in contemporary studies (Chivers et al., 2010; Suschinsky et al., 2009, 2011). In an interesting follow-up study, one group of women was instructed to attend to their genital signs of sexual arousal ("While rating these slides, I would like you to attend to various changes that may occur in your genital area, such as vaginal lubrication, pelvic warmth, and muscular tension"), and a second group was told to attend to nongenital signs of arousal ("While rating these slides, I would like you to attend to various changes that may occur in your body. These are heart rate increase, nipple erection, breast swelling, and muscular tension"), while a control group was given no instructions (Korff & Geer, 1983). Both experimental groups showed high correlations between self-reports and physiological measures of arousal, while the control group showed the same low correlation that Heiman found. This shows that women can be quite accurate in realizing their physical arousal if they are simply told to focus their attention on it. The broader culture, of course, does not give women such instructions but rather tells them to focus on the environment outside themselves—the love, romance, partner—so that many women have not learned to focus on their body. However, the experiment described here shows quite clearly that they can. A number of Canadian studies have also shown that there is better correspondence between women's subjective and physiological sexual arousal when blood flow is measured externally than when it is measured internally, but there is still a disconnect between subjective and physical arousal for some women (Kukkonen et al., 2007; Payne & Binik, 2006; Waxman & Pukall, 2009).

Heiman studied sexual arousal to preferred sexual stimuli. Recent research has shown that physiological sexual arousal is category specific in men but not in women. That is, heterosexual men are more physiologically aroused by stimuli depicting women than by stimuli depicting men, whereas gay men are more aroused by stimuli depicting men than by stimuli depicting women. In contrast, both heterosexual women and lesbians show similar arousal to male and female stimuli (Chivers, 2005; Chivers et al., 2004). This does not necessarily mean that women are inherently bisexual, just that there are a wide range of stimuli that can turn women on. In contrast, subjective arousal for both women and men was greatest in response to their preferred sex.

Recent studies have used fMRI brain scans to examine gender differences in response to erotic materials (Rupp & Wallen, 2008). The results show that the brain regions that fire, mostly in the limbic system, are the same in women and men. However, only men show increased activation in the hypothalamus, which, as we have seen in earlier chapters, is important to the release of testosterone.

Orgasm Consistency

Men are more consistent than women at having orgasms during sex. For example, according to the NSSHB, 91 percent of men but only 64 percent of women always have an orgasm during sex with their partner (Herbenick et al., 2010c). The gap is narrower for orgasm consistency during masturbation, but even here men seem to be more consistent: 80 percent of men, compared with 60 percent of women, report that they usually or always have an orgasm when masturbating (Laumann et al., 1994).

Sex Drive

Evidence from a number of sources indicates that men, on average, have a stronger sex drive than women do (Baumeister et al., 2001; Peplau, 2003). This is true for both individuals in mixed-sex and those in same-sex relationships (Holmberg & Blair, 2009). That is, men think about sex more often and have more frequent and varied fantasies than women do (Renaud & Byers, 1999). Further, compared with women, men desire more sexual partners and a greater frequency of intercourse. In a study across 52 nations, the gender difference in the preferred number of partners was found in all regions of the globe (Schmitt, 2003). It is important to remember, of course, that these are average differences. For a particular mixed-sex couple, it is quite possible that the woman's level of sexual desire would be higher than the man's.

Do men have sex on the brain? Do they think about sex constantly as the TSS suggests? And do women never think about sex? Flashy media reports suggest that this is true. However, a clever study indicates otherwise. Undergraduates were given golf tally counters and tallied their thoughts about sex for one week (Fisher et al., 2012). Men thought about sex on average 19 times a day, compared with 10 times a day for women, so men thought about sex more but not anything like 100 times per day. Moreover, other students tallied their thoughts about food and about sleep, and men thought about

both food and sleep more than women did, so it isn't just sex on their brains. Also, the range was enormous among men: one man thought about sex only once a day and, at the other end of the spectrum, another thought about it 388 times per day. One woman thought about sex 140 times per day. The differences from one man to the next, or from one woman to the next, are far greater than the average difference between women and men.

 What are some major ways in which men and women differ in their sexuality?

Why the Differences?

The previous section reviewed the evidence on differences in male and female sexuality. Four differences—the lower percentage of females, compared with males, who masturbate; women's more disapproving attitudes toward casual sex; women's lesser orgasm consistency; and men's greater sex drive—are fairly well documented. Thus, we need to explain them. What factors lead to these differences? Many possible explanations have been suggested by a wide variety of scholars. Before considering factors that may have resulted in gender differences, it is important to remember that these are differences in the average scores, and there is considerable variation among women and among men. Thus, these gender differences do not apply to all women and all men. For example, research in Ontario has identified a group of highly sexual women who report a high sex drive, high sexual desire, more frequent sexual thoughts and fantasies, and more positive attitudes toward casual sex and pornography (Wentland et al., 2009).

Are the Differences Bogus?

One possibility is that many of these gender differences, typically documented by self-report, are not true differences. Instead, it could be that people report what is expected of them, shaped by gender norms. Men are expected to want lots of sex, so they exaggerate their desire in self-reports, or women minimize theirs.

A clever study used the bogus-pipeline method to investigate this possibility (Alexander & Fisher, 2003; see also Conley et al., 2011; Jonason & Fisher, 2009). University students were brought to the lab to fill out questionnaires about their sexual attitudes and behaviours. They were randomly assigned to one of three experimental conditions. In the *bogus-pipeline condition*, the student was hooked up to a fake polygraph or lie-detector machine and told that the machine could detect false answers. People should respond very honestly in this condition. In the anonymous condition, the student simply filled out the questionnaire anonymously, as is typical of much sex research, and placed the questionnaire in a locked box when finished. In the exposure threat condition, respondents were instructed to hand their completed questionnaires directly to the experimenter, who was an undergraduate peer, and the experimenter sat in full view while the respondents completed their questionnaires, serving as a reminder that this other person would easily be able to see their answers. Figure 13.7 shows the results for reports of the number of sexual partners the respondents had had.

When people were in the bogus-pipeline condition and gave the most honest reporting, men's and women's reports of their number of partners were nearly identical—in fact, women's were slightly higher than men's. In the standard conditions of anonymity used in most sex research, women reported fewer partners than men did. Under a threat that responses would be made public, the largest gap between women and men appeared. In the anonymous condition and the exposure threat condition, differences emerged that were consistent with gender roles. Women confirmed the expectation that they have fewer partners.

What are the implications of this study? Does it mean that all the differences described in the previous section are bogus? Probably not, but it means that findings of gender differences obtained by self-reports are probably exaggerations of the truth. And it is important to note that findings obtained from physiological measures, such as those used in Heiman's study, are not vulnerable to these reporting biases.

Let's assume that the gender differences discussed in the previous section are real, although perhaps not as dramatically large as the research suggests. How can these differences be explained?

Biological Factors

Gender differences in sexuality might be created, in part, by two biological factors: anatomy and hormones.

Anatomy

Men's sexual anatomy is external and visible and has a very obvious response: erection. While a man is nude, he can easily see his sexual organs, either by looking down or by looking in a mirror. The female sexual organs, in contrast, are hidden. The nude woman looks down and sees nothing except pubic hair (which really is not very informative); she looks in a full-length mirror and sees the same thing. Only by using a hand-held mirror can she get a good view of her own genitals. To make matters worse, the word *clitoris*—but not *penis*—is often missing from books about sexuality, from parents'

> When heterosexual men report more sexual partners than heterosexual women do, is this accurate? How can this be?

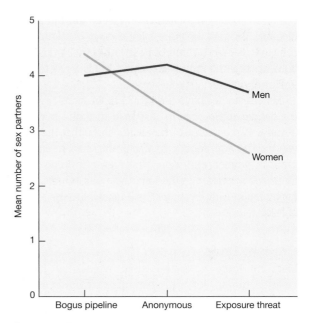

Figure 13.7 Mean number of sexual partners reported by men and women in the Bogus Pipeline Study (see text for further details).

talk about sex, and from students' knowledge about sexuality (Ogletree & Ginsburg, 2000). Furthermore, women's genitals do not have an obvious arousal response like the male's erection. As a result, women may be less aware of their own arousal, a notion that is supported by Heiman's research.

The anatomical explanation, then, is that because the woman's genitals are not in plain view and because their arousal response is less obvious than that of the man's genitals, she is less likely to masturbate and less likely to be fully aware of her own sexual response (Baldwin & Baldwin, 1997). If this explanation is correct, or at least part of the answer, could steps be taken to help women become more aware of their own sexuality? Perhaps parents can help their daughters to become more aware of their own sexual organs by naming the parts of their genitals including their clitoris and encouraging them to look at their genitals in the mirror. And parents might want to discuss the idea of masturbation with their daughters.

Hormones

The hormonal explanation rests on the finding that testosterone is related to sexual behaviour. This evidence was reviewed in Chapter 9. Basically, the evidence comes from studies in which male animals are castrated (and thus lose their natural source of testosterone), with the result that their sexual behaviour disappears, presumably reflecting a decrease in sex drive. If replacement injections of testosterone are given, the sexual behaviour returns.

Females generally have lower levels of testosterone in their tissues than males do. Women, for example, have about one-tenth the level of testosterone in their blood that men do (Janowsky et al., 1998).

The hormonal explanation, then, is that if testosterone is important in activating sexual behaviour and if women have only one-tenth as much of it as men have, this might result in a lower level of sexual behaviour such as masturbation in women or a lower sex drive.

There are at least two problems with this logic. First, it may be that cells in the hypothalamus or the genitals of women are more sensitive to testosterone than the comparable cells in men; thus a little testosterone may go a long way in women's bodies. Second, we must be cautious about making inferences to human males and females from studies done on animals. Although some recent studies have demonstrated the effects of testosterone on sexual interest and behaviour in humans, the effects are less consistent and more complex than in other species (Chapter 9).

Cultural Factors

Our culture has traditionally placed tighter restrictions on women's sexuality than it has on men's, and vestiges of these restrictions linger today. It seems likely that these restrictions have acted as a damper on female sexuality, and thus they may help to explain why some women do not masturbate, why some women have difficulty having orgasms, and why some women are wary about casual sex.

One of the clearest reflections of the differences in restrictions on male and female sexuality is the double standard. As we saw in Chapter 10, the double standard says that the same sexual behaviour is evaluated differently, depending on whether a male or a female engages in it. The sexual double standard gives women less sexual freedom than men (Crawford & Popp, 2003). An example is casual sex, which has been more acceptable for men than for women. Indeed, casual sex with multiple partners might be a status symbol for a man but a sign of undesirable characteristics for a woman. The sexual double standard is alive and well on prime-time television, where negative consequences (e.g., rejection or humiliation) are more common in scenes in which female characters initiate sex than scenes in which male characters initiate (Aubrey, 2004). In teen magazines, negative consequences of sex are associated more often with girls than with boys (Joshi et al., 2011)

Generally, there seems to be less of a double standard today than in the past, at least in terms of people's explicit attitudes—that is, the attitudes they self-report on questionnaires. The decline of the double standard may help to explain why some of the gender differences found in older studies of sexual behaviour have disappeared in more recent studies. When cultural forces do not make such a distinction between men and women, men and women become more similar in their sexual behaviour. Yet traces of the double standard remain today in regard to casual sex, which is considered less acceptable for women than for men (Bogle, 2008). For example, a Quebec study showed that university women rate women who have sex in an uncommitted relationship more negatively and believe male partners will see them more negatively if the women supply the condom than if the men supply the condom (Hynie & Lydon, 1995; Hynie et al., 1997). Also, students in Saskatchewan saw it as less normal for a man than a woman to be disinterested in sex, engage in same-sex sexual fantasies, and engage in sexual activities reflecting submission (Morrison et al., 2008). These results suggest that there is still a double standard in at least some areas of sexual behaviour.

Gender roles, particularly as prescribed by the traditional sexual script described earlier in this chapter, also contribute to differences in male and female sexuality (Sanchez et al., 2012). For example, the expectation is that in heterosexual relationships men are the initiators and women are the passive objects of men's advances. This makes the man responsible for both his own and his partner's response, and it may lead men to experience a lot of pressure. Further, the male role discourages men from expressing emotions such as tenderness or communicating feelings and teaches men that touching is a means to an end: sexual intercourse (Zilbergeld, 1999). Women have not been encouraged to be active in producing their own pleasure or bringing about their own orgasms.

In keeping with these gender role expectations, research has shown that men are more active in sexual situations than women are (Lawrance et al., 1996). In fact, women with traditional views of gender roles are the most passive in sexual situations. Women (and men) who are sexually passive have more difficulty becoming aroused and report lower sexual satisfaction (Kiefer & Sanchez, 2007; Sanchez et al., 2006).

Research in New Brunswick has shown that the cultural sexual script affects perceptions of a partner's sexual preferences (Miller & Byers, 2004). The researchers had 152 heterosexual couples report their actual and ideal duration of foreplay and intercourse, as well as their perceptions of their partner's desired duration of foreplay and intercourse. They found that men's estimates of their partner's ideals were more similar to their estimates of what the average woman would want than they were to the actual preferences stated by their partner. Similarly, women's estimates of their partner's ideals were more similar to their estimates of what the average man would want than they were to their partner's stated preferences. This suggests that people use stereotypes to guide their understanding of their partner's sexual preferences (and possibly the way they make love) more than they use explicit or implicit information provided by the partner. This is more evidence for the need for better sexual communication (see Chapter 12 for a discussion of good sexual communication).

Marital and family roles may play a part. When children are born, they can act as a damper on the parents' sexual relationship. The couple lose their privacy when they gain children. They may worry about their children bursting through an unlocked door and witnessing them making love. Or they may be concerned that their children will hear the sounds of lovemaking. Generally, the woman is assigned the primary responsibility for child-rearing, so she may be more aware of the presence of the children in the house and more concerned about the effects on them of witnessing their parents engaging in sex. Once again, her worry and anxiety do not contribute to her having a satisfying sexual experience.

Body image issues also contribute to gender differences in sexuality and, in particular, to women's sexual functioning (Woertman & van den Brink, 2012). Overall, there are gender differences in body esteem; compared with men, women feel more dissatisfied with their bodies. And sex is all about bodies. Research shows that women who are dissatisfied with their bodies report lower levels of sexual desire and arousal and more avoidance of sex (La Rocque & Cioe, 2011; Weaver & Byers, 2006, 2013). In part this is due to a kind of self-conscious monitoring of how one's body looks during sex. These are distracting thoughts and, as we will see in Chapter 17, distracting thoughts contribute to reduced enjoyment of sexual experiences. Why are women more dissatisfied with their bodies, and why do they monitor their appearance more? The major factor appears to be the media, which portray skinny women with airbrushed features that real women can't live up to, making them feel bad about their bodies (Grabe et al., 2008). Women's concerns that their body does not match their partner's ideals affect their sexual well-being (Weaver & Byers, 2013). Interestingly, researchers in Ontario have shown that women who focus more on appearance and who feel more pressure to fit the media ideal are more likely to consent to unwanted sexual advances rather than to use strategies to get out of the situation (Kennett et al., 2012).

Other Factors

A number of other factors, not easily classified as biological or cultural, may also contribute to differences between male and female sexuality.[2]

---

[2] Other possible causes of orgasm problems in women are discussed in Chapter 18.

Many Canadian adolescent girls who are sexually active do not use contraceptives or do not use them consistently—32 percent in one study (Fisher et al., 1999a; Levy et al., 1992). A woman who is worried about whether she will become pregnant—and, if she is single, about whether others will find out that she has been engaging in sexual activity—is not in a state conducive to the enjoyment of sex, much less the experience of orgasm (although this scarcely explains why fewer women than men masturbate).

Ineffective techniques of stimulating the woman may also be a factor, particularly in heterosexual relationships. The heterosexual techniques of intercourse, with the penis moving in and out of the vagina, may provide good stimulation for the man but not the woman, since she may not be getting sufficient clitoral stimulation. Perhaps the problem, then, is that women are expected to orgasm as a result of intercourse, when that technique is not very effective for producing orgasms in women. Although some lesbians also use ineffective techniques, Masters and Johnson (1979) found that lesbians benefited from stimulating another body like their own.

A relationship probably exists between the evidence that fewer women than men masturbate and gender differences in orgasm consistency. Childhood and adolescent experiences with masturbation are important early sources of learning about sexuality. Through these experiences we learn how our bodies respond to sexual stimulation and what the most effective techniques are for stimulating our own bodies. This learning is important to our experience of adult, two-person sex. For example, Kinsey's data suggested that women who masturbate to orgasm before marriage are more likely to orgasm in intercourse with their husbands;[3] 31 percent of the women who had never masturbated to orgasm before marriage had not had an orgasm by the end of their first year of marriage, while only 13 to 16 percent of the women who had masturbated had not had orgasms in their first year of marriage (Kinsey et al., 1953, p. 407).

Women's relative inexperience with masturbation may not only lead to a lack of sexual learning, but it also may create a kind of "erotic dependency" on men. Typically, boys' earliest sexual experiences are with masturbation, which they also hear about from other boys. More important, they learn that they can produce their own sexual pleasure. Girls typically have their earliest sexual experiences in mixed-sex touching and fondling. They therefore learn about sex from boys, and they learn that their sexual pleasure is produced by the male. As sex researcher John Gagnon (1977) commented:

---

[3] Note that this is in direct contradiction to the old-fashioned advice given in manuals that suggested that "getting hooked" on masturbation might impair later marital sexuality; if anything, just the reverse is true.

Young women may know of masturbation, but not know *how* to masturbate—how to produce pleasure, or even what the pleasures of orgasm might be. . . . Some young women report that they learned how to masturbate after they had orgasm from intercourse and petting, and decided they could do it for themselves. (p. 152)

Numerous factors that may contribute to shaping male and female sexuality have been discussed. Our feeling is that a combination of several of these factors produces the differences that do exist. The early differences in experiences with masturbation are very important. Although these differences may result from differences in anatomy, they could be eliminated by giving girls information on masturbation. Women may enter into adult sexual relationships with a lack of experience in the bodily sensations of arousal and orgasm, and they may be unaware of the best techniques for stimulating their own bodies. Put this lack of experience together with various cultural forces, such as the double standard and ineffective techniques of stimulation, and it is not too surprising that there are some gender differences in sexuality.

Beyond the Young Adults

One of the problems with our understanding of gender differences in sexuality is that so much of the research has concentrated on heterosexual university students or other groups of young adults (as is true of much behavioural research). This provides a very narrow view of male–female differences as female and male sexuality change in their nature and focus across the lifespan and differences may decrease as people age.

For example, psychiatrist Helen Singer Kaplan advanced an interesting view of differences between male sexuality and female sexuality across the lifespan (Kaplan & Sager, 1971). According to her analysis, the male teenager's sexuality is intense and almost exclusively genital in its focus. As a man approaches age 30, he is still highly interested in sex but not as urgently. He is also satisfied with fewer orgasms compared with when he was an adolescent. By the age of 50, he is typically satisfied with two orgasms a week, and the focus of his sexuality is not so completely genital; sex becomes a more sensuously diffuse experience and has a greater emotional component.

In women, the process is often quite different. Their sexual awakening may occur much later; they may, for example, not begin masturbating until age 30 or 35. While they are in their teens and 20s, their orgasmic response often is slow and inconsistent. However, by the time they reach their mid-30s, their sexual response has become quicker and more intense, and they orgasm

more consistently than during their teens and 20s. They initiate sex more frequently than they did in the past. Vaginal lubrication takes place almost instantaneously in women in this age group.

Most men, then, seem to begin with an intense, genitally focused sexuality and only later develop an appreciation for the sensuous and emotional aspects of sex. Most women have an early awareness of the sensuous and emotional aspects of sex and develop the capacity for intense genital response later. To express this in another way, we might use the terminology suggested by Ira Reiss: **person-centred sex** and **body-centred sex**. Adolescent male sexuality is body-centred, and the person-centred aspect is not added until later. Adolescent female sexuality is person-centred, and body-centred sex comes later.

It is important to remember, though, that these patterns may be culturally, rather than biologically, produced. In some other cultures—for example, the Mangaia in the South Pacific (see Chapter 1)—all females reportedly have orgasms during coitus, even when they are adolescents.

L06 Transgender

Most people experience their gender identity—that is, their internal sense of femaleness or maleness—as the same as or consistent with their physical sex. However, some individuals experience incongruity between their physical sex and their internal sense of gender. A person who feels uncomfortable with the assigned gender and wants to be seen as a member of the other gender is described as experiencing **gender dysphoria**. In the *Diagnostic and Statistical Manual of Mental Disorders* (American Psychiatric Association [APA], 2013), people may be diagnosed as having gender dysphoria if there is a strong and persistent (at least six months) incongruence between their experienced or expressed gender and their assigned gender and if it causes them distress. Keeping in mind the distinction between sex and gender, it is important to understand that this is an issue not of sexual behaviour but of gender and gender identity. (See A Sexually Diverse World in Chapter 5 for a discussion of the success of gender assignment for intersex and other individuals.)

Transgender, or **trans**, is an all-inclusive term that refers to people who cross the strict lines of the sex they were assigned

Person-centred sex: Sexual expression in which the emphasis is on the relationship and emotions between the two people.
Body-centred sex: Sexual expression in which the emphasis is on the body and physical pleasure.
Gender dysphoria (dis-FOR-ee-uh): A marked incongruence between people's experienced or expressed gender and their assigned gender.
Transgender (trans): A person whose behaviour, appearance, or identity crosses, transcends, or does not conform to culturally defined norms for a person of that biological sex.

at birth. It refers to a person's behavior, appearance or identity (APA, 2008). It is used to describe a number of different groups of people, including the following:

- Two-spirit persons. This term used by some Aboriginal peoples to describe people with alternative gender and sex expressions (discussed earlier in this chapter).
- Intersex persons. Persons born with mixed indicators of biological sex (discussed in Chapter 5).
- Individuals who **cross-dress**—that is, dress in clothing traditionally associated with the other sex. People cross-dress for a range of reasons. For trans-identified individuals, it is often to express their gender identity. However, most women can also identify situations when they prefer to express their more feminine side by dressing in more traditionally feminine clothing (e.g., dresses and high heels) and wearing makeup (in the queer community this is often referred to as *femme*) and other times when they prefer to express their more masculine side by dressing in more traditionally masculine clothing (e.g., jeans and a T-shirt) and look more *butch*. Indeed some people cross-dress to perform (drag queens and drag kings; discussed in Chapter 15). For some people, cross-dressing is not related to their sexual identity. Transvestites (discussed in Chapter 15) are men who dress in feminine clothing for purposes of sexual arousal, and their gender identity typically closely matches their biological sex.
- People who present both masculine and feminine characteristics.
- A **transsexual**: a transgender individual who wants to live and be accepted as a member of his or her preferred gender and wants to have surgical and hormonal intervention.

Many transgender individuals describe experiencing an incongruity between their gender identity and their physical sex from early childhood. They may experience particular difficulty when they reach puberty, feeling betrayed by their developing body. Further, adolescents are increasingly expected to conform to the gender role expected of their assigned gender. Given the lack of role models, information, and social support, many trans youth are likely to feel confused, isolated, and depressed. According to British Columbia sociologist Aaron Devor, recognizing and accepting oneself as transgender takes place over a number of years. He identified a series of stages in coming to terms with a new gender. In Stage 1,

Cross-dress: Dressing in the stereotypic clothing of the other gender.
Transsexual: A transgender individual who wants to live and be accepted as a member of his or her preferred gender and wants to have surgical and hormonal intervention.

Figure 13.8 Jenna Talackova is a transgender woman who competed in Miss Universe Canada.

individuals experience anxiety about their gender and sex, which leads them to question their assigned gender in Stage 2. In later stages, they change genders and sexes—some by undergoing gender reassignment surgery, others through taking hormones or just living as the other gender—and come to accept and experience themselves as the new gender (Figure 13.8).

Although many trans individuals regard their physical sex as inconsistent with their gender identity, others view the binary categories of female and male as restrictive and see themselves as neither female nor male, both female and male, or another gender altogether (Hill, 2000). In fact, researchers have proposed several alternatives to our current two-gender system. For example, Eyler and Wright (1997) conceptualized gender as occurring along a nine-point continuum with female-based identities on one end, male-based identities on the other, and *bigendered identities* in the middle. However, even this system leaves out people who do not identify with either gender. They considered people whose feelings and behaviours alternated between male and female as having a bigendered identity. Further, trans activists and authors, such as Aaron Devor (1989), Leslie Feinberg (1996), and Kate Bornstein (1994), have called for the recognition of identities that transcend current gender boundaries, putting forward terms such as *gender outlaw* and *hir* (rather than *him* and *her*) and *ze* (rather than *he* or *she*) to draw attention to the need for language that is more inclusive of all genders. In fact, Devor coined the term *gender blender*. Other new terms have emerged, including *gender bender* and *gender free* (Bockting, 1999). In an Internet sample, the largest number identified as genderqueer, followed by transgender, female, and male (Kuper et al., 2012).

What do we call everyone else, those who are not transgender? It would be tempting to call them "normal," but a new more equitable term has been introduced: **cisgender** (named after cis and trans isomers in organic chemistry).

Among transsexuals, some choose to present in accordance with their gender identity in only some situations, such as with a specific group of friends. Others may live in accordance with their gender identity without undergoing physical changes to make their body more in line with their gender. Many choose to alter their physical sex, a process known as sex change or more recently as *gender transition* or just *transitioning* (discussed shortly). They may take hormones to bring their physical sex more into alignment with their gender identity (see First Person). Further, some transsexuals pursue **gender reassignment**, in which their physical anatomy is surgically altered to reflect their gender identity. In the medical literature, individuals who do not pursue surgery are sometimes referred to as nonoperative; those who are planning surgery are called preoperative; and those who have had the surgery are described as postoperative. Many communities have organizations designed to provide a supportive and nonjudgmental environment for people to express their gender identity. One such organization is Gender Mosaic in Ottawa (www.gendermosaic.com).

There are no reliable estimates of how many people are transgender. However, recent estimates are that transsexualism is relatively rare—approximately 1 in 11,900 males and 1 in 30,400 females seek sex reassignment surgery (World Association for Transgender Health, 2001). The number of people who would fall on the transgender continuum but who do not seek surgery is likely considerably higher.

We use the terms "male-to-female" and "female-to-male" to identify the direction of the transition and the identity that the transsexual has shown. Thus, those born with male bodies whose identity is female are called **male-to-female transsexuals**, **transwomen**, or **MtFs**; those born with female bodies whose gender identity is male are called **female-to-male transsexuals**, **transmen**, or **FtMs.**

In addition to the distinction between MtF and FtM transsexuals, Ontario psychologist Ray Blanchard has proposed that we can also make a distinction between *gynephilic* and *androphilic* transgender individuals (Blanchard et al., 1985; Smith et al., 2005).[4] Those who are gynephilic are sexually attracted to women, and those who are androphilic are sexually attracted to men. For example, if we think of a female-to-male transsexual, he[5] would be classified as androphilic if he were attracted to men and as gynephilic if he were attracted to women. Androphilic MtFs tend to be shorter and lighter in weight compared with gynephilic MtFs and compared with men in the general population (Blanchard et al., 1995). This may be one reason why androphilic MtFs are more successful in their new gender—they are more convincing as women because they are smaller. Gynephilic MtFs, in contrast, often marry women and have children in young adulthood. They have a history of eroticized cross-dressing in childhood and adolescence. Masculine in appearance, they often make the transition to the new gender after they are 40. Among FtMs, those who are gynephilic are typically more interested in surgery to construct a penis (phalloplasty) compared with those who are androphilic (Chivers & Bailey, 2000). Some transsexuals, too, are bisexual. In one sample of MtFs recruited through the Internet, 32 percent said they were attracted to men, 31 percent to women, and 28 percent to both (Bockting, 2004).

References to transgender individuals are found in much of recorded history, although of course they are not referred to by this term (Devor, 1997a). For example, in the early centuries of Christianity, a number of women presented and lived as men. One example is Pelagia, a woman who declined marriage and, presenting as a man, entered a monastery. Pelagia became Pelagius, a man, and was later elected prior of a convent. A woman at the convent became pregnant and accused Pelagius of being the father. Of course, this was not possible; however, Pelagius was not in a position to offer his strongest defence. Consequently, he was expelled from the convent and died in disgrace. When he died, it was discovered that he had a female body.

Cisgender: A person whose gender identity matches the body he or she was born with.

Gender reassignment: The surgery done on transsexuals to change their anatomy to match their gender identity.

Male-to-female transsexual (MtF), transwoman: A person who is born with a male body but who has a female identity and wants to undergo gender reassignment.

Female-to-male transsexual (FtM), transman: A person born with a female body whose gender identity is male and who wants to undergo gender reassignment.

---

[4] A heated debate is being waged about the best terminology for these two types. Part of the complexity derives from the issue of, for example, describing a MtF's sexual orientation as homosexual. Does that refer to same-sex attraction according to the gender before or after surgery? *Gynephilic* and *androphilic* get around this problem.

[5] In keeping with the preferences of transgender individuals to use pronouns consistent with their gender identities, we refer to MtF individuals as "her" or "she" and FtM individuals as "him" or "he."

First Person

Matt: A Transman's Story

Matt is a 29-year-old man who lives in Ottawa. He describes himself as a "different kind of man" in that he was born and raised as a female.

Matt grew up in a small town in Southern Ontario. Unlike his sisters, Matt was not interested in being a Brownie or taking ballet. He had short hair and wore mainly T-shirts. He recalls feeling little pressure to behave like a girl until Grades 7 and 8, when he started to feel a need to conform to what was expected of him. Matt remembers thinking that he looked better as a boy than as a girl yet knowing that he would need to change to fit in. He started wearing more feminine clothing and grew his hair. As a teenager, Matt knew he was not interested in boys, yet living in a small town he had no idea of what it meant to be gay.

At 20, Matt moved to Ottawa to attend university. He became involved in the queer community and gradually began to change how he presented himself. He cut his hair, wore more masculine clothing, and expressed himself in more masculine ways. He felt comfortable with this gender presentation. More and more often, Matt was perceived and responded to as male. He recalled that one year he had two jackets. When he wore one of them, he would be perceived as female; when he wore the other, he would be perceived as male. It felt like society was presenting the idea of transitioning to him.

The decision to transition was very difficult for Matt. On the one hand, he did not find being a woman aversive and was concerned about the social consequences of not conforming to his biological gender and the physical consequences of taking testosterone. On the other hand, Matt felt more comfortable presenting as male. There was also the matter of how others responded to his gender presentation. Most often, people would initially perceive him as male, but then—often after noticing that Matt had breasts—see him as female. Some people were apologetic, which could be uncomfortable

Some societies consider transgender individuals to be members of a third gender, and they live comfortably in that category. Examples are the *two-spirit people* among Native North Americans, the *acault* from Burma, *hijras* and *jo-gappa* from India, *xaný-th* from Oman, *bantut* from the Phillipines, *kathoey* from Thailand, and *fa'afafine* from Somoa (Poasa et al., 2004). (See Milestones in Sex Research for a discussion of the *fa'afafine*). Australia now allows people to choose a third gender (X) on their passport instead of having to choose either male or female—some European countries are considering similar changes.

Most of our current understanding of transsexual issues is based on research with MtF transsexuals. This is because MtFs have been more than twice as likely as FtMs to seek sex reassignment surgery (Olsson & Moller, 2003). This may be because male prenatal development is more complex and error-prone or because preschool boys spend so much more time with their mothers than with their fathers. Alternatively, as about half of gender-dysphoric females do not make use of official gender clinics, the numbers may in reality be more equal (Devor, 1997a). There are several reasons for this. The surgery required to transform male into female genitalia is easier than the surgery required to transform female into male genitalia. In addition, transmen often pass as men more readily than transwomen pass as women. Finally, our society tends to be much more tolerant of women who cross-dress than men who cross-dress. As such, MtFs may be more strongly motivated to pursue surgery to live as their chosen gender.

LO7 The Gender Reassignment Process

Gender reassignment, sometimes called *sex change* or *gender transition,* is complex and proceeds in several stages (Sutcliffe et al., 2009). Some members of the transsexual community refer to the process as *crossing.* Programs in Montreal, Toronto, and Vancouver offer a range of services to transgender individuals; most of the gender-reassignment surgery is conducted at a private clinic in Montreal. Sex-reassignment surgery is either partially or fully funded in all provinces except New Brunswick and Prince Edward Island. The Canadian Professional Association for Transgender Health for Matt; others were hostile and, in many cases, verbally insulted him. He found public washrooms to be particularly difficult because of how others would respond to him. It was the fear for his physical safety and the stress associated with these daily interactions that prompted Matt to transition: "It took up so much energy not to conform to society's expectation that I present as one gender or the other. I had to choose."

At 25, Matt started taking testosterone. So that the changes would be gradual, he started on a low dose and slowly increased it. He grew facial hair and his voice deepened. Taking the testosterone enabled Matt to be more confident in his interactions with others. He did not have to be constantly vigilant about his personal safety or be concerned about how others would respond to him. Matt has since had a hysterectomy and a double mastectomy and now feels very happy with his body.

Matt feels like his family transitioned with him. Initially, they were concerned that he was transitioning only because he had been influenced by a friend's example. They worried that he would have difficulty

establishing a career, finding a long-term partner, and having a secure and happy future. However, when they recognized that Matt was becoming happier and healthier as he transitioned, they became less concerned. Matt feels his relationship with his parents is much closer than before he transitioned because they have become much more open with each other.

At present, Matt is completing the last year of an accounting diploma. He is in a four-year relationship with a woman, in which he is very happy. He feels that because of his experiences he is much more critical of society's messages about gender and other social categories. He has also developed much closer relationships with others as a result of his personal experiences of discrimination. Matt regards being trans and his decision to alter his body as a function of societal pressure to act in certain ways based on sex. He believes that we would all benefit from treating people in accordance with their personality, not their gender presentation.

Source: Based on an interview with Dr. Jacqueline Cohen.

---

provides detailed information about what procedures are covered in each province (www.cpath.ca).

Standards of care have been issued by professional organizations such as the American Psychological Association (2008), Endocrine Society (2009), and the World Professional Association for Transgender Health (2012). The first step is very careful counselling and psychological evaluation. It is important to establish that the person is a true transsexual—that is, someone whose gender identity does not match his or her body type. Some people mistakenly seek sex reassignment; for example, a man who is simply poorly adjusted, unhappy, and not very successful might think that things would go better for him if he were a woman. It is important to establish that the person is a true transsexual or has a core transgender identity before going ahead with a procedure that is irreversible.

Next comes the "real-life experience" in which the person live as a member of the preferred gender for three months or more. This is done to ensure that the person will be able to adjust to the role of the new gender; once again, the idea is to be as certain as possible that the person will not regret having medical procedures that

are not reversible. Many MtF transsexuals, even before consulting a physician, start dressing as women. Most transgender individuals encounter transphobia, sometimes to the point of violence (Monro, 2000; Lombardi et al., 2001).

Hormone therapy may begin during the real-life experience. The MtF is given estrogen and must remain on it for the rest of her life. The estrogen gradually produces some feminization. The breasts enlarge. The pattern of fat deposits becomes feminine; in particular, the hips become rounded. Balding, if it has begun, stops. Secretions by the prostate diminish, and eventually there is no ejaculate. Erections become less and less frequent, a phenomenon that pleases the transwoman, since they were an unpleasant reminder of the unwanted penis. The FtM is given androgens, which bring about a gradual masculinization. A beard may develop, to varying degrees. The voice deepens. The pattern of fat deposits becomes more masculine. The clitoris enlarges, although not nearly to the size of a penis, and becomes more erectile. The pelvic bone structure cannot be reshaped, and breasts do not disappear except with surgery. New MRI studies suggest that the brain may change as well. In FtMs given androgen treatment, the size of the hypothalamus enlarged from a typical female size to a typical male size (Hulshoff et al., 2006).

The final step for many people seeking gender reassignment is the surgery itself, which some transgender individuals decide to skip. For the MtF, the penis and testes are removed, but without severing the sensory nerves of the penis. The external genitalia are then reconstructed to look as much as possible like a woman's (see Figure 13.9). The glans of the penis is used to form a clitoris with sexual sensitivity. Next, an artificial vagina—a pouch 15 to 20 centimetres (6 to 8 inches) deep—is constructed. It is lined with the skin of the penis. For about six months afterward, the vagina must be dilated with a plastic device so that it does not reclose. Other cosmetic surgery may also be done, such as reducing the size of the Adam's apple.

> **How do surgeons create a penis or a vagina when they do gender-reassignment surgery?**

The FtM change is more complex and generally less successful. A number of types of surgery can be used to construct the penis (Figure 13.10) (Selvaggi & Elander, 2008). One, called metoidioplasty (see Figure 13.11), involves elongating the clitoris, which has already enlarged with testosterone treatments. Other techniques use a skin flap from the forearm, the lower abdomen, or the thigh to create a penis. One issue is whether the surgeon is also able to construct a urethra running the length of the constructed penis so that the transman can urinate standing up rather than sitting down, an important issue to many transmen. Generally the penis is not capable of erection, although some individuals choose to have a penile implant to enable erection (Hoebeke et al., 2010). (See Chapter 18 for a discussion of implants.) In addition, surgeons are experimenting with new techniques that would allow this to happen. Some FtMs choose not to have genital surgery and just go through breast removal and possibly hysterectomy.

An important experience for transgender individuals is *passing* (Bockting, 1999). For a MtF, this might mean going into a bank or supermarket dressed as a woman and having no one notice anything unusual, simply believing she is a woman.

LO8 What Causes a Person to Be Transgender?

Scientists have not found a definite cause of why some people are transgender. One likely reason is that there may be more than one path to it.

John Money (1986) has argued that the issue is a critical period during prenatal development. Some event, not yet known, may lead to atypical development of some brain structure—possibly the hypothalamus,

Daniel Greenwald, MD FACS

Figure 13.9   (*a*) The appearance of the genitals following MtF surgery. (*b*) Breast augmentation for the MtF transsexual.

corpus callosum, or anterior commissure. Other theorists, following this same line of thinking, have proposed that during prenatal development, the fetus, if it is to become a male, must be both defeminized and masculinized (Vasey et al., 2009). A failure of either process could produce a person with a male body but a female identity. To understand this distinction between defeminization and masculinization, at least for anatomy, recall from Chapter 5 that in a typically developing male

Figure 13.10 FtM surgery. (*a*) Skin on the forearm marked before transfer to the groin. (*b*) The penis is constructed (blood vessels and nerves shown on the left). (*c*) An inflatable prosthesis, wrapped in Goretex and ready for insertion. (*d*) Penis before insertion of the implant. (*e*) Erect penis.

the Müllerian ducts degenerate (defeminization) and the Wolffian ducts thrive (masculinization). If some process failed, though, both might thrive. The same might be true of cells in other brain regions having to do with gender identity. Consistent with this view, two studies have found differences between MtFs and typical men in the bed nucleus of the *stria terminalis* (BST), part of the limbic system (Kruijver et al., 2000; Zhou et al., 1995). As noted in other chapters, the limbic system is important in sexuality. In other MRI studies, FtMs display brain regions that are intermediate between cismales and cisfemales (Rametti et al., 2011).

Cutting-edge genetic research has identified several genes associated with transsexualism, and the genes are different for MtFs and FtMs (Bentz et al., 2008; Hare et al., 2008; Henningsson et al., 2005). MtFs, for example, are more likely than control men to have a mutation in the androgen receptor gene. However, not all MtFs carry this mutation.

An Ontario study found that the appearance of boys with gender dysphoria is less masculine and rugged, whereas girls with gender dysphoria appear more masculine and rugged than their cisgender peers (McDermid et al., 1998).

Milestones in Sex Research

Sex, Gender, and Sexual Orientation in Samoa

C anadians live in a culture that recognizes two genders: male and female; but, there are many places in the world where three or more genders are recognized. When I first learned about such places, my mind did somersaults. How was it possible that someone could be neither male nor female? It took me a while to realize that while male and female bodies are certainly grounded in biological reality, how these bodies are "gendered" varies historically and cross-culturally. If two gendered categories of personhood, such as "male" and "female," can be socially constructed, why not three . . . or more?

Since 2003, I have worked in Samoa, a culture where persons can be one of three genders: men, women, and *fa'afafine*. In the Samoan language, *fa'afafine* means "in the manner of a woman." Like men, *fa'afafine* are biological males. They differ from Samoa men, however, in that they are very feminine. From a Canadian perspective, many would be considered transgender. *Fa'afafine* are recognized in childhood, by their families and the members of their community, based on their tendencies to engage in feminine activities (e.g., playing with girls) and their aversion toward masculine activities (e.g., rough-and-tumble play) (Bartlett & Vasey, 2006). This process of recognition does not mean that boys

are made into *fa'afafine*. Rather, in Samoan culture, boyhood femininity is interpreted to mean that individuals simply are *fa'afafine* and it is understood that such individuals will not grow up to be "men." Some families react negatively to the presence of a *fa'afafine* child, with corporal punishment. However, the majority have a laissez-faire attitude, some even facilitate the child's feminine behaviour—sewing "him" dresses, for example (Vasey & Bartlett, 2007).

In Samoa, *fa'afafine* enjoy a high level of social acceptance that, while not absolute, stands in stark contrast to the overt discrimination experienced by Western transwomen. Indeed, *fa'afafine* are highly visible, active, and productive members of Samoa society. They occupy all manner of positions from stay-at-home caregivers to assistant chief executive officers in the government. The prime minister of Samoa, the Honourable Tuilaepa Sailele Malielegaoi, is Patron of the National Fa'afafine Association and has spoken publicly on many occasions about the value of *fa'afafine* for Samoan society.

My Samoan research has afforded me the opportunity to examine how human sexuality is expressed in a cultural system that recognizes two sexes and three genders. In adulthood, the vast majority of *fa'afafine* are androphilic (i.e., sexually attracted and aroused to adult

Figure 13.11 Metiodoplasty, one technique for female-to-male transsexual surgery.

Gender Variation in Children

Gender variation is found in children as young as two or three years of age. For example, research by Ontario psychologist Kenneth Zucker (Zucker et al., 1999; Zucker, 2000; Zucker et al., 2002) indicates that some children insist that they are the other gender, show a preference for dressing in the clothes of the other gender, demonstrate an intense desire to participate in the stereotypical play of the other gender, and express dislike for their sexual anatomy. According to the *Diagnostic and Statistical Manual of Mental Disorders* (APA, 2013a), children who experience a strong and persistent difference between their experienced or expressed gender and their assigned gender that is associated with distress have gender dysphoria. This diagnostic category, as well as the question of how and whether to treat children with gender dysphoria, has been very males). This fact might lead many to conclude, "Oh well, they're just gay, but in a different culture." I believe that would be a mistake. Remember, *fa'afafine* are identified in childhood, long before they have engaged in sexual activity. Moreover, *fa'afafine* do not consider themselves to be gay. At first, this was also difficult for me to grasp until I realized that "gay" is yet another culturally specific identity category with its own code of conduct. "Gays" as one of my *fa'afafine* friends pointed out to me, "have sex with other gays." "Ok," I thought, "I'm with you on that one." "But," my friend continued, "*fa'afafine* don't have sex with each other. They have sex with straight men." Huh? More mental somersaults. If *fa'afafine* have sex with "straight men," how could those men be "straight"? My *fa'afafine* friend regarded me as if I was a bit thick.

It took me a while to grasp that Samoans were obviously stretching the definition of the term "straight man" beyond its more narrow meaning as understood by most Canadians. In a Samoan cultural context, regardless of sexual orientation, "straight man" means a man who is masculine and who self-identifies as a "male" and as a "man." Some "straight men" in Samoa are gynephilic (i.e., sexually attracted and aroused to adult women) and only have sex with women. However, other gynephilic Samoan men have sex with *fa'afafine* when they are unable to access their preferred sexual partners (i.e., adult females). The majority of men who have sex with *fa'afafine* likely fall into this latter group.

Other men who have sex with *fa'afafine* appear to be attracted specifically to *fa'afafine*, to be bisexual, or to be androphilic (i.e., attracted to adult men). In short, the Samoan category of "straight man" is a very heterogeneous one with respect to sexual attraction and sexual orientation. All of this underscores the complex ways that sex, gender, and sexual orientation interact and how the pattern of interactions can vary from one culture to the next.

Much of the research I have conducted in Samoa involved interviewing *fa'afafine* about their behaviour in childhood (Bartlett & Vasey, 2006; VanderLaan et al. 2011; Vasey & Bartlett, 2007; Vasey et al., 2011). I have used this information to critically examine how Western psychologists characterize the mental health of gender-variant children. *Fa'afafine* don't grow up being constantly bombarded with the message that they're sick or that there is something wrong with them. Samoans simply acknowledge that "transgender" males are part of the cosmos and they move on. They don't try to "fix" them medically and, as a consequence, the society benefits as a whole. What a lesson Canada has to learn from these tiny islands.

Source: Written by Dr. Paul Vasey, a professor in the Department of Psychology University of Lethbridge.

controversial (Gender Identity Research and Education Society [GIRES], 2006). On the one hand, proponents of the diagnosis argue that cross-gender behaviour will result in social isolation and ostracism that, in turn, may lead to avoidance of school and participation in activities with peers, and may lead to depression, substance abuse, and suicide. Indeed, such advocates present a strong argument to intervene to help the child become more comfortable with his or her biological sex. Some parents allow their children to live as the other gender. Other experts note that if gender dysphoria persists throughout childhood and sex reassignment seems almost certain to be called for, then treatment will be much more effective if the youth does not go through the pubertal processes of his or her original gender (Delemarre-van de Waal & Cohen-Kettenis, 2006). Hormone treatments can suppress pubertal development

(Endocrine Society, 2009), giving the individual time to grow and make a mature, informed choice.

On the other hand, there are a number of problems with the gender dysphoria diagnosis. First, longitudinal studies suggest that most children who are diagnosed with gender dysphoria do not persist in identifying as the opposite to their biological sex in adulthood; rather, many children with gender dysphoria identify as gay or lesbian in adulthood (GIRES, 2006; Zucker, 2000; Zucker et al., 2002). In fact, as discussed in Chapter 14, many gays and lesbians recall engaging in cross-gender behaviours as children. Thus, these behaviours may be part of a normal developmental pathway for gays and lesbians. Giving children a diagnosis of gender dysphoria pathologizes them (Hill et al., 2007). Second, Canadian psychologist Nancy Bartlett and her colleagues have pointed out that even though the diagnosis of gender dysphoria is intended for children who experience strong discomfort with their biological sex, it may be misused to diagnose children who are dissatisfied with their gender role (Bartlett et al., 2000). As such, it may be more appropriate to regard such children as simply not fitting into the two gender categories prescribed by our culture rather than seeing them as having a disorder. Behaviour that violates cultural norms about how girls and boys are supposed to behave should not be considered disordered. Following this view, we should refer to these as cases of **gender variance** (Steensma et al., 2011). Such advocates argue that what is needed is not treatment for the children so much as support groups for the parents to help them accept and provide supportive guidance to their gender-variant children (Figure 13.12). Alberta researchers studying the *fa'afafine* in Samoa found that cross-gender behaviours or identities do not cause distress in children who are raised in cultures where they are accepted as members of a third gender (Vasey & Bartlett, 2007). Clearly, both sides are concerned with the welfare of the child. The key question appears to be whether the child benefits from a diagnosis of and treatment for gender dysphoria.

Other Issues

The phenomenon of transsexualism raises a number of interesting psychological, legal, and ethical questions for our contemporary society.

One case that attracted attention was that of Dr. Renée Richards, formerly Richard Raskind, a physician who had her gender reassigned to that of a woman. When she was a man, she was a successful tennis player. In 1976 she attempted to enter a women's tennis tournament. The women players protested that she was not a woman, and she protested that she was. Officials subsequently decided to use the **buccal smear** test for gender, which is a test of genetic gender. Richards protested that this was not the appropriate test to be used on her. Psychologically, she is a female, she has female genitals, and she functions socially as a female, and she felt that these are the appropriate criteria. She does, though, have a male pelvic bone structure and other bone structures that are masculine, and these may have important consequences for athletic performance. The important question raised by this case is, What should the criteria be for determining a person's gender? Should it be chromosomal gender (XX or XY) as tested by the buccal smear? Should it be the gender indicated by the external genitals? Should it be psychological gender identity? In 2000, the

Figure 13.12   Brandon Teena, a MtF who was murdered because of the ignorance and prejudice of those around him.

International Olympic Committee suspended its use of gender verification for female athletes (Genel, 2000). It seemed not to be accomplishing anything except to embarrass some women who turned out to have genetic anomalies.

Take the case of Spanish hurdler Maria Jose Martinez-Patiño. In 1985, her test revealed that she had sex chromosomes XY, and she was later found to have androgen-insensitivity syndrome (AIS, discussed in Chapter 5). The cells of her body do not respond to testosterone, and she has a female body. Should she have been allowed to compete as a woman? The issue surfaced again with the 2012 Olympics, and the International Olympic Committee decided to use blood testosterone level as the criterion; to compete in women's events, the person's testosterone level has to be in the typical female range. People with AIS would be allowed to compete as women. The more we know about the complexities of intersex and transgender conditions, the harder it makes it for the International Olympic Committee!

Another question that might be raised concerns institutions that are all male or all female. In 1999, a MtF transsexual who was receiving hormone therapy at the time of her conviction for murder was given permission

Gender variance: Cases in which the person does not have typical pairing of male gender identity and behaviour with a male body or female identity with a female body and behaviour.

Buccal smear: A test of genetic sex in which a small scraping of cells is taken from the inside of the mouth, stained, and examined under a microscope.

by Correctional Services Canada to undergo gender-reassignment surgery and be transferred to a women's prison. Similarly, in 2000 a member of the Canadian Armed Forces was probably the first soldier in the world to undergo a gender-reassignment operation while continuing to serve in the military.

Transsexuals also encounter a number of practical problems when undergoing gender reassignment. Official records, such as the social insurance number and birth certificate, must be changed to show not only the new name but also the new gender.

Transsexuals are able to give us, through their personal accounts, new insights into the nature of sex and gender.

Gender-Reassignment Surgery Outcomes

A number of criticisms of gender-reassignment surgery have been raised. The main one involves the question of whether the adjustment of transsexuals really improves following surgery. Transgender individuals do, of course, have adjustment problems, but much of this is due to the gender-related abuse that they suffer (Nuttbrock et al., 2010).

According to research, however, adjustment is significantly better following surgery. In one study, 86 percent of MtFs were satisfied with their surgery to create a vagina, and 89 percent of FtMs were satisfied with their surgery to create a penis (de Cuypere et al., 2005). In another study of 32 MtFs and FtMs, none expressed regret at having had the surgery (Johansson et al., 2010). A study of 49 FtMs in Belgium found that the transmen generally had a good quality of life and sexual functioning on average eight years following gender surgery (Wierckx et al., 2011). Further, most transsexuals report increased sexual satisfaction following surgery (Klein & Gorzalka, 2009). However, as society becomes increasingly aware of and accepting of the range of gender presentations, we may see fewer people pursuing surgery to fit into one of two discrete gender categories.

SUMMARY

A gender role is a set of norms, or culturally defined expectations, that specify how people of one gender ought to behave. Children are socialized into gender roles first by parents and later by other forces, such as peers and the media.

Gender roles are not uniform in Canada. They vary according to ethnic group and other factors, using the concept of intersectionality. Gender roles in ethnocultural communities, such as the Chinese, South Asian, and Caribbean communities, tend to reflect the traditional values of the country of origin. Although most Aboriginal people have adopted gender roles similar to those of the majority Canadian culture, some Aboriginal peoples traditionally had more egalitarian gender roles in comparison with European culture.

The traditional sexual script specifies how men and women are expected to behave in sexual situations. Research suggests that male and female roles in sexual situations differ in some respects but are converging.

Psychological gender differences have been documented in aggressiveness and communication styles, both of which have implications for sexuality.

Three substantial gender differences in sexuality are in the incidence of masturbation (men having the higher incidence), attitudes about casual sex (women being more disapproving), and the use of pornography (men reporting more use). Heiman's study of arousal from erotic materials illustrates how men and women are in some ways similar and in others different in their responses. Men are more consistent at having orgasms, especially during heterosexual intercourse, than women are, and men have a somewhat stronger sex drive.

One question is whether some of these gender differences, obtained through self-report, are accurate or whether they are the result of response biases, for example, with men exaggerating and women minimizing. Although some of the gender differences in sexuality may be due to biased reporting, some differences remain.

Three sets of factors have been proposed to explain gender differences in sexuality: biological factors (anatomy, hormones), cultural factors (gender roles, the double standard, body image), and other factors (fear of pregnancy, differences in masturbation patterns creating other gender differences).

Most research on gender and sexuality has been done with university-age samples. There is reason to believe that patterns of gender differences in sexuality change in middle age and beyond.

Transgender is a broad category of people whose gender identity does not match their anatomy. Transgender individuals respond in different ways, including some who seek surgery (transsexuals) and those who do not seek surgery or who see themselves as being in a third gender category. Generally, the adjustment of transsexuals following gender reassignment is good.

QUESTIONS FOR THOUGHT, DISCUSSION, AND DEBATE

1. Do you think that gender-reassignment surgery is the appropriate treatment for transsexuals? Why or why not?

2. Recalling your childhood, do you think you were socialized in a stereotyped masculine or feminine way? What impact do you think those socialization experiences have had on your current sexual attitudes and behaviours?

3. Do you think there is still a double standard for male and female sexuality today? Explain your answer.

4. Dominic is a strong advocate of equality between men and women, yet his six-year-old daughter's favourite television program shows both the parents and the children in very stereotyped roles. The mother is a secretary and the father is a physician. The teenage daughter is a cheerleader and thinks of nothing else, while the son plays football. What should Dominic do? Why?

Are YOU Curious?

1. What percentage of people are gay, lesbian, bisexual, or asexual?
2. How does growing up with two parents of the same gender affect children psychologically?
3. What causes people to be gay or heterosexual?
4. Are men or women more likely to be attracted to both genders?

Read this chapter to find out.

CHAPTER

14

Sexual Orientation and Identity: Gay, Lesbian, Bi, Straight, or Asexual?

LEARNING OBJECTIVES

After studying this chapter, you will be able to

LO1 Discuss the meanings of the various terms used to describe sexual identity.

LO2 Describe and evaluate the various ways in which sexual orientation can be defined and measured.

LO3 Describe the attitudes toward and stereotypes of gay men, lesbians, and bisexuals, and discuss the extent to which research supports these stereotypes.

LO4 Discuss the consequences of homonegativity.

LO5 Provide a brief history of the Canadian laws surrounding homosexuality.

LO6 Describe the life experiences of LGB individuals.

LO7 Evaluate the research on the mental health of LGB individuals and the success of therapies used to change a person's sexual orientation.

LO8 Evaluate the various theories used to explain sexual orientation.

LO9 Describe how culture affects attitudes toward and expression of sexual orientation.

The state has no business in the bedrooms of the nation.[*]

Jeffrey and i met when he responded to an online message i posted, seeking gay teenagers willing to discuss their online lives. . . . He made it clear that he could allow no overlap between his online gay life and the life he led in the "real world." . . . He feared that if word of his sexual orientation were to reach his parents, they might refuse to support him or pay for college. From his peers at school he dreaded violence.[**]

[*] Pierre Trudeau, 1967, when defending his bill to overhaul the *Criminal Code of Canada*, including statutes that had criminalized consensual same-sex sexual activity.
[**] Jennifer Egan. (2000). Lonely gay teen seeking same. *The New York Times Magazine*, December 10, 2000, p. 113.

Every summer, cities across North America hold a Gay Pride Day, usually including a parade (called *pride parade* or *pride festival*) to celebrate gay, lesbian, bisexual, and transgender culture. These events also commemorate the first time that gay, lesbian, and transgender individuals openly fought back against police harassment; this occurred in June 1969 in the Stonewall, a gay bar in New York City's Greenwich Village. Gay liberation was born. The first gay liberation group in Canada was formed in Vancouver in 1970 (Kinsman, 1996). Eight months later, 200 protesters on Parliament Hill demanded equal rights for gays and lesbians (Smith, 1999). In 1981, 3000 people rallied in Toronto to protest the arrest of 300 men during police raids on gay bathhouses (Kinsman, 1996).

LO1   The purpose of this chapter is to try to provide a better understanding of people's sexual orientations, whether to their own gender, the other gender, both genders, or neither gender. Note that both *cisgender* and *transgender* individuals (see Chapter 13) can be attracted to people of their own gender or of the other gender. First, though, several concepts need to be clarified. A distinction has already been made between sex (sexual behaviour) and gender (being male or female)[1] and between gender identity (the psychological sense of maleness or femaleness) and sexual orientation (heterosexual, gay, bisexual, or asexual).

Sexual identity: One's self-identity as gay, heterosexual, bisexual, or asexual.
Sexual orientation: A person's erotic and emotional orientation toward members of his or her own gender or members of the other gender.
Homosexual: A person whose sexual orientation is toward members of the same gender. Use of the terms gay or lesbian to refer to individuals is preferable.
Heterosexual: A person whose sexual orientation is toward members of the other gender.
Bisexual: A person whose sexual orientation is toward both men and women.
Asexual: A person who is not attracted to men or women.

[1] As discussed in Chapter 13, these two gender categories do not fit for some people who would identify as transgender.

To this, the concept of **sexual identity** should be added; this refers to one's self-label or self-identification as heterosexual, gay, lesbian, bisexual, asexual, or perhaps something else. (For a discussion of transgender, which refers to gender identity, not sexual identity or sexual orientation, see Chapter 13.)

There may be contradictions between people's sexual identity and their actual choice of sexual partners (Mathieson & Endicott, 1998). For example, a woman might identify herself as a lesbian yet occasionally have sex with men. Objectively, her choice of sexual partners is bisexual, but her identity is lesbian. More common are persons who think of themselves as heterosexuals but who engage in sex with both male and female partners. A good example of this is the tearoom trade–the successful, heterosexual married men who occasionally stop off at a public restroom to engage in oral sex with another man. Once again, the behaviour is objectively bisexual, in contradiction to the heterosexual identity. Another example is the group of women who report having bisexual identities but who have experienced only sex with men. These women claim bisexuality as an ideal they are capable of attaining at some later time. Once again, identity contradicts behaviour. Finally, some individuals identify as asexual but occasionally have sex with men or women.

Given these contradictions, **sexual orientation** is best defined by whom we are emotionally, romantically, and sexually attracted to (American Psychological Association, 2008). Thus a **homosexual** or gay person's sexual orientation is toward members of her or his own gender; a **heterosexual** person's sexual orientation is toward members of the other gender; a **bisexual** person's sexual orientation is toward both genders; and an **asexual** person does not have a sexual orientation toward either men or women. Again, however, a person's attraction may not match his or her behaviour or sexual identity. The word *homosexual* is derived from

Figure 14.1   Homosexuality has been found in many cultures and historical eras. Here we see male–male couples at a banquet in Roman art from the fifth century BCE.

the Greek root *homo*, meaning "same" (not the Latin word *homo*, meaning "man"). The term *homosexual* may be applied in a general way to people of both genders or specifically to men. The term **lesbian**, which is used to refer to women, can be traced to the great Greek poet Sappho, who lived on the island of Lesbos (hence "lesbian") around 600 BCE (Figure 14.1). She is famous for the love poetry that she wrote to other women.

Use of the term *homosexual* to refer to lesbians and gay men is problematic for three main reasons (American Psychological Association, 2009). First, in the past it has been associated with negative stereotypes,[2] such as deviance, mental illness, and criminal behaviour, and thus can be used as a derogatory label. Second, it emphasizes sexual behaviour rather than sexual identity. As discussed later in this chapter, many women and men engage in same-sex[3] behaviour, yet do not consider themselves to be lesbian, gay, or bisexual. Third, it is ambiguous because even though it is a general term, it has often been used to refer exclusively to gay men. For these reasons, it is preferable to use the terms lesbians, gay men, bisexual women, and bisexual. A heterosexual is then referred to as **straight**.

In recent years, some members of the gay, lesbian, and bisexual communities have reclaimed terms that

have historically been used as derogatory terms. Examples of such terms include *dyke, fairy, fag* or *faggot*, and *queer*. For example, the term **queer** has now been taken back by gay and lesbian activists, who use it as a proud term encompassing gay men, lesbians, and transgender persons—that is, all people who identify as outside the social norm with respect to gender and/or sexuality. As an umbrella term, it has the advantage of not forcing people to adopt a narrow, societally defined label that may not reflect their experience or the fluidity of sexual identity (Bower et al., 2002). Queer theory is prominent in LGB studies.

Another term that rejects societally imposed labels for sexual attraction and sexual orientation is *pansexual* (sometimes referred to as *omnisexual* or *polisexual*). Pansexual individuals are open to relationships with people of any sex, gender, or gender identity—that is, men, women, transgender, and intersex individuals. However, although some people are comfortable using these terms to refer to themselves, other people are not, perhaps because the terms have been used to belittle them in the past. Thus, while LGBs may use these terms themselves, it is probably not a good idea to impose these terms on them. *Sexual minority* is another term than encompasses all people who do not identify as heterosexual, regardless of their specific identity.

In this chapter, we will use the abbreviation "LGB" for lesbians, gay men, bisexual women, and bisexual men whenever possible because it is awkward to repeat the phrase "gay men and lesbians," and even that phrase omits bisexuals. Further, it omits the terms some individuals use to refer to themselves, such as

---

[2] A stereotype is a rigid set of beliefs about a group of people that distinguishes them from others and is applied to all members of the group.

[3] To be consistent with the definitions of gender and sex adopted in this book, we should use the terms "same-gender" or "other gender" when describing sexual behaviour or relationships. However, we have used the term "same-sex" because it is the term most people use—for example, there has been considerable public debate about same-sex marriage.

Lesbian: A woman whose sexual orientation is toward other women.
Straight: Heterosexual.
Queer: A self-label used by some LGBs and by some heterosexuals who want to identify as outside the social norm with respect to gender or sexuality.

queer, questioning, undecided, asexual. Of note, many organizations use more comprehensive abbreviations, such as LGBT or LGBTQ to represent all sexual and gender minorities.

L02

How Many People Are Gay, Lesbian, Bi, Straight, or Asexual?

Most people believe that homosexuality is rare. What percentages of people in North America are gay, lesbian, or bisexual? As it turns out, the answer to this question is complex. Basically, it depends on the definition we use. Determining how best to define and measure sexual orientation, particularly among adolescents, is quite complicated. Do we ask people about their attraction, identity, or behaviour? This is important because the three do not always go together (Saewyc, 2011).

Several well-sampled surveys in Canada, the United States, the United Kingdom, and France have given us estimates regarding sexual identity (Savin-Williams, 2006). Data from the (American) National Survey of Family Growth (NSFG) and the Canadian Community Health Survey (CCHS) are shown in Table 14.1. The 2003 and 2005 CCHS surveyed adults ages 18 to 59 and asked respondents to indicate whether they considered themselves to be homosexual, bisexual, or heterosexual; that is, it assessed sexual identity. Of the men surveyed, 1.4 percent considered themselves to be homosexual, 0.7 percent to

What percentage of people are gay, lesbian, bisexual, or asexual?

be bisexual. Of the women surveyed, 0.8 percent self-identified as homosexual, 0.9 percent as bisexual. However, people's sexual identities can change (Saewyc, 2011). For example, one longitudinal study followed, over 10 years, women who initially said that they were lesbian, bisexual, or "unlabelled" in their sexual orientation (Diamond, 2008b). At the start of the study, the women ranged in age between 18 and 25. Many women changed in their identity over time, often in response to relationship experiences. These changes occurred in all directions and thus were not just a result of a coming out process. Another study followed men and women in New Zealand from age 21 to 26 (Dickson et al., 2003). Women were more likely to report changes in their pattern of attraction than men were, but some men also reported changes in their attractions. Again, especially for women, attractions seemed to change in all possible directions, likely because women are more greatly influenced by relationship experience than are men when it comes to sexual identity.

The statistics from the NSFG are more complex because the survey asked several questions about sexual orientation and much depends on how *gay, lesbian,* and *bisexual* are defined. Should the definition be based on self-identification alone or also on behaviour? This is particularly important for adolescents who may not yet be involved in sexual relationships (Saewyc, 2011). In terms of behaviour, does the definition of gay or lesbian require someone to have had exclusively same-sex sexual experiences, or just some same-sex experiences, or perhaps just to have experienced sexual attraction to members of his or her own sex without ever acting on it? We will return to this point. What we can say here

Table 14.1 The NSFG and CCHS Statistics on Same-Sex Behaviour, Identity, and Attraction

	NSFG		CCHS	
	Men	**Women**	**Men**	**Women**
Behaviour				
Ever had sexual contact with same-sex partner	5.2%*	12.5%		
Sexual Identity				
Heterosexual	97.0	94.8	96.9%	98.3%
Bisexual	1.1	3.5	0.7	0.9
Homosexual/lesbian/gay	1.7	1.1	1.4	0.8
Something else**	0.2	0.6		
Sexual Attraction				
Only or mostly to same gender	1.9	1.4		
Equally to both	0.5	2.8		
Mostly to opposite sex	3.7	11.9		

* Different questions were used for men and women, and men's questions were narrower, so this percentage is an underestimate.

** The "something" else category may include people identifying as queer, questioning, and so on.

Sources: Chandra et al. (2011), Tjepkema (2008).

is that, according to the NSFG, 5 percent of men and 12 percent of women have had at least one same-sex sexual experience in adulthood, and about 4 percent of both men and women experience sexual attraction to members of their own sex. Roughly 2 percent of men and 1 percent of women have a gay identity.

Estimates based on the NSFG may not be perfectly accurate, however. We can expect underreporting on any kind of sensitive topic like sexual orientation, and the NSFG asked nonequivalent questions on behaviour to men and women, making gender comparisons inaccurate. The NSFG statistics are comparable to those found in a well-sampled international survey, which included the United Kingdom and France (Sell et al., 1995). So these results likely also apply to Canada.

Recently researchers have also started to assess how many people consider themselves to be asexual. According to a large British study, 1 percent of people reported that they have no sexual attraction to men or women although some did engage in a low level of sexual activity with a partner (Bogaert, 2004). In another study completed on the Internet, 3.6 percent of respondents chose to identify themselves as having an asexual sexual orientation (Prause & Graham, 2007). These persons reported less desire for partnered sex but not necessarily no desire for sex. (See Milestones in Sex Research in this chapter for more on asexuality).

What about youth? The CYSHHA survey asked Grade 7, 9, and 11 students whether they were attracted to males, to females, to both males and females, or to no one. Somewhat fewer than 3 percent indicated that they are attracted to members of their own gender. Interestingly, 9 percent of Grade 7 students but fewer than

2 percent of Grade 9 and 11 students said they were attracted to no one.

After reading these statistics, though, you may still be left wondering how many people are gay, lesbian, bisexual, and asexual. As Kinsey soon realized in trying to answer this question, it depends on how you count. A prevalent notion is that like the difference between the colours black and white, homosexual and heterosexual are two quite separate and distinct categories. This is what might be called a *typological conceptualization* (see Figure 14.2). Kinsey made an important scientific breakthrough when he decided to conceptualize mixed-sex and same-sex behaviour not as two separate categories but rather as variations on a continuum (Figure 14.2, section 2). The black and white extremes of heterosexuality and homosexuality have many shades of grey in between: people who have had some other-sex and some same-sex experience, in various mixtures. To accommodate all this variety, Kinsey constructed a scale running from 0 (*exclusively heterosexual experience*) to 6 (*exclusively homosexual experience*), with the midpoint of 3 indicating equal amounts of heterosexual and homosexual experience (see Figure 14.2 for the complete scale).

One problem with Kinsey's scale is that it refers only to behaviour and not to attraction. As discussed later in this chapter, some people engage in sexual activity with a person of the same-gender or of the other-gender because of circumstances rather than out of attraction. Conversely, some people do not engage in sexual activity with people of the same gender because of societal or their own negative attitudes. In addition, some theorists have suggested that Kinsey's one-dimensional scale is too simple (Sell, 1997; Storms, 1980). The alternative is

1. The typology

3. Two-dimensional scheme (Storms, 1980)

Figure 14.2   Three ways of conceptualizing homosexuality and heterosexuality.

Asexuality: A Sexual Dysfunction, a Sexual Orientation, or Something Else?

Although we generally think about the categories of heterosexual, homosexual, and bisexual when we consider a person's sexual orientation, more recently people have started identifying themselves as asexual. For example, in Kinsey's work that led to the development of the "Kinsey Scale." He found that 1.5 percent of the men sampled fit into the category described as "Asexual, Non-Sexual" and defined as individuals with "no socio-sexual contacts or reactions" (Kinsey, 1948). This figure was replicated nearly 60 years later when Anthony Bogaert (2004), a Canadian psychologist, examined data collected as part of a British national probability sample of 18,000 men and women. He found that 1.05 percent of people agreed with the following statement about sexual attraction: "I have never felt sexually attracted to anyone at all." This group had fewer sexual partners, a later debut of sexual activity (if it ever occurred), and less frequent sexual activity with a current partner.

Opinions differ about what exactly asexuality is. One view is that asexuality is about behaviour (or lack thereof). People who hold this view conclude that the lifelong lack of interest in sexual activity indicates that asexuality is really a sexual dysfunction related to a lack of sexual desire. Others conceptualize asexuality within the broader domain of sexual attraction. For them, asexual individuals' experience of not having sexual attraction raises many questions about whether sexual attraction indeed is evolutionarily hard-wired; it is usually assumed that there is such a mechanism that drives procreation. The observation that asexual individuals often retain "romantic attraction," or in other words, a desire to have a meaningful, committed, emotionally fulfilling relationship with a partner, also suggests that the processes underlying romantic attraction and sexual attraction may become uncoupled. Bogaert's study of the British probability sample found that 44 percent of the asexual sample had been or were currently in a serious relationship.

Asexuals themselves prefer to understand their asexuality from the perspective of it being a sexual identity/sexual orientation. This view holds that asexuality is genetic, lifelong, and not amenable to "treatment" in the same way that other sexual orientations (e.g., homosexuality) are. There is evidence to support this view that asexuality is likely biologically based. For example, Bogaert found that asexual individuals had a later onset of menarche, and were shorter and weighed less. This led him to conclude that asexuality was likely at least partly biologically based and determined before birth.

Although the Asexuality Visibility and Education Network (AVEN) online community had been established in 2001 (www.asexuality.org), the publication of Bogaert's paper led to a massive media blitz spotlighting asexuality. Critics doubted the possibility that people could be apathetic about sex—a basic biological drive necessary for the survival of our species. Moreover, the finding that almost half of asexual individuals were in committed relationships raised skepticism about the conclusion that romantic attachment can be preserved despite sexual attraction being deficient. Furthermore, the finding that many asexual individuals continued to masturbate also raised doubt that asexuality could even exist. That is, how could it be that, on the one hand, asexual individuals declared no interest in sex, yet on the other, they engaged in sexual acts with themselves?

What Does the Research on Asexuality Suggest?

Prause and Graham (2007) provide research evidence that supports the view that asexuality might be best construed as a sexual dysfunction. They conducted semi-structured individual interviews with four asexual individuals followed by online questionnaire completion by 1146 individuals, 41 of whom self-identified as asexual. The asexual individuals reported lower sexual desire and arousability than did the rest of the sample. However, they expressed no desire to speak to a health professional about their asexuality. The researchers also found that asexual individuals had lower excitatory processes but not necessarily higher inhibitory processes when compared with the sexual sample (see Chapter 9 for a discussion of excitatory and inhibitory processes in sexual response). Their low levels of sexual responding on validated questionnaires seemed to lead to the conclusion that asexuality might be a disorder of sexual response.

In 2010, Lori Brotto, a Canadian psychologist, and colleagues conducted a study of asexual men and women recruited from AVEN that sheds further light on this question. As would be expected, rates of sexual desire were low among the men and women in this study. However, they were not distressed about this. Because "distress or interpersonal impairment" is a fundamental component of the criteria for diagnosing a sexual disorder (see Chapter 18), asexual individuals do not meet the *DSM-V* definition of any sexual disorder. Further, follow-up in-depth interviews with 15 of the participants found that they strongly resisted the characterization of themselves as sexually dysfunctional. Rather, they sought to educate the public that asexuality may be better conceptualized as a sexual orientation or sexual identity (akin to homosexuality).

Is Asexuality Caused by Problems with Physiological Arousal?

Brotto and colleagues (2010) found that asexual individuals were as likely to masturbate as the general population. They rationalized their masturbation behaviour as an attempt to "clean out the plumbing" or as means of getting to sleep, rather than stemming from any intrinsic sexual need. This suggests that sexual arousal and ability to experience orgasm might be no different in asexual individuals than in the rest of the population. To explore this further, and to examine the critical position that suggests that asexuality is nothing more than an extreme sexual dysfunction, Brotto and Yule (2011) conducted a sexual psychophysiological study of asexual women. Equal numbers of asexual, heterosexual, bisexual, and homosexual women had their genital arousal measured with a vaginal photoplethysmograph while they watched an explicit film in a private room. Not surprising to the researchers, ratings of sexual attraction during the erotic film were lower in the asexual women compared with the other three groups

(which did not differ from each other). However, there were no significant group differences in genital sexual arousal, indicating that the asexual women became just as genitally engorged to the erotic film as did women in the sexual groups. The authors interpreted this finding as supporting their position that asexuality should not be characterized as a disorder of sexual response, given that, in the face of potent sexual stimuli, asexual individuals' bodies reflexively responded sexually in the same way as did sexual women.

Should Asexuality Be Considered a Sexual Orientation?

Much more research is needed before we can conclude that asexuality is a sexual orientation. One means of exploring this further is through the use of genetic marker and biological studies that allow one to test for the possibility that asexuality is associated with prenatal developmental factors and is not an adaptive response to early childhood trauma or extreme religiosity (as has been speculated by some). Yule (2011) studied 1200 men and women (315 of whom were asexual) and examined biological markers previously found to be associated with homosexual orientation. They found that the asexual individuals were significantly more likely than their heterosexual counterparts to be left-handed, and asexual men were significantly more likely to have older brothers than sexual men, but there were no significant group differences in their 2D:4D digit ratios (discussed later in the chapter). These data provide preliminary evidence of a neurodevelopmental basis to asexuality similar to the research found with homosexuality. Of course, more research is necessary.

Asexuality research may shed new light on the pathways toward the development of sexual and romantic attraction, potentially leading to new theories. This research may also lead to a better understanding of who is best suited for treatment of sexual difficulties versus those individuals who fully identify as asexual and are, essentially, not motivated to change.

Source: Written by Dr. Lori Brotto, University of British Columbia.

to form a two-dimensional scheme. The idea here is to have one scale for heteroeroticism (the extent of one's attraction to members of the other gender), ranging from low to high, and another for homoeroticism (the extent of attraction to members of one's own gender), ranging from low to high (see Figure 14.2, section 3). Thus if one is high on both heteroeroticism and homoeroticism, one is a bisexual; the person high on heteroeroticism and low on homoeroticism is heterosexual; the person high on homoeroticism and low on heteroeroticism is gay; and the person low on both scales is asexual. This two-dimensional scheme fits well for individuals who define themselves as asexual. Asexual individuals define asexuality in terms of a lack of attraction to men or women, not in terms of behaviour or desire (Brotto et al., 2010).

The answer to the original question—How many people are gay, lesbian, bisexual, and asexual?—is complex. Probably about 90 percent of men and 90 percent of women are exclusively heterosexual. About 10 percent of men and women have had at least one same-sex sexual experience in adulthood. About 2 percent of men and 1 percent of women identify themselves as gay. These figures are based on the NSFG and the NHSLS but adjusted somewhat to allow for concealment by some respondents.

LO3

Attitudes

Your sexual orientation has implications for the attitudes people have toward you. In Canadian culture there is the belief that all people are heterosexual, that heterosexuality is the norm. Furthermore, just as there are stereotypes about other minority groups, there are stereotypes (usually negative) about gay men and lesbians. These stereotypes and negative attitudes lead to discrimination and hate crimes against gay men and lesbians. In this section we will examine some of the scientific data on these negative attitudes.

Homophobia: A strong, irrational fear of gay men and lesbians; negative attitudes and reactions to gay men and lesbians.
Homonegativity: Negative attitudes and behaviours toward gay men and lesbians; sometimes called antigay prejudice or sexual prejudice.
Heterosexism: The belief that heterosexuality is the only legitimate, acceptable, and healthy way for people to be; homosexuality is denigrated.
Heteronormativity: The belief that heterosexuality is the norm.

Attitudes Toward Gay Men and Lesbians

What are Canadians' attitudes toward gay men and lesbians? Today, the vast majority of Canadians (80 percent) say that society should accept gays and lesbians (PEW Research, 2013). Note that the attitudes of Canadians toward gay men and lesbians are becoming increasingly accepting; for example, six years earlier only 70 percent of Canadians had this view. As shown in Table 14.2, most Canadians are also accepting of same-sex marriage and the rights of same-sex couples to adopt children, although women are more accepting than are men, and younger people are more accepting than are older people (Ipsos, 2013). Canadians also are more accepting of same-sex relationships than Americans are. For example, whereas 80 percent of Canadians say that society should accept gays and lesbians only 60 percent of Americans do. Similarly, whereas 76 percent of Canadians are accepting of same-sex marriage, only 65 percent of Americans are (Ipsos, 2013). The percentage for people living in the United Kingdom who favour same-sex marriage is about the same as in Canada. It's important to note that many Canadians accept same-sex relationships, same-sex marriage, and adoption by same-sex couples even if they are not "in favour" of them. For example, 13 percent of Canadians are in favour of some sort of legal recognition for same-sex couples, just not marriage.

Homophobia may be defined as a strong, irrational fear of gay individuals and, more generally, as fixed negative attitudes and reactions to gay men and lesbians. Some scholars dislike the term *homophobia* because, although certainly some people have antigay feelings so strong that they could be called a phobia, what are more common are negative attitudes and prejudiced behaviours. Therefore, some prefer the terms **homonegativity**, antigay prejudice, sexual prejudice, heterosexism, or heterocentrism (Herek, 2000; Morrison & Morrison, 2002). Interestingly, Canadian researchers have shown that traditional, or old-fashioned, homonegativity is less prevalent among Canadian students than is modern homonegativity (Morrison et al., 2009; Rye & Meaney, 2010). Traditionally, homonegativity was based on moral and religious views or beliefs that homosexuality is not "normal." Modern homonegativity reflects beliefs that gay men and lesbians exaggerate the importance of their sexual orientation or make unnecessary demands for social change. Research suggests that Canadian university students do not hold negative views toward homosexuality, although men's attitudes are more negative than are women's (Meaney & Rye, 2010). However, research in Saskatchewan still found that a substantial percentage of undergraduate students engaged in covert antigay behaviours. For example, 43 percent reported yelling insulting comments at gay men and 43 percent reported telling an antigay joke. **Heterosexism** is the belief that being heterosexual is "normal" and that heterosexuality is the only legitimate, acceptable, and healthy way for people to be; gay people and behaviours are denigrated (Berkman & Zinberg, 1997). It is closely connected to **heteronormativity**, the belief that heterosexuality is the norm. Some LGBs experience multiple forms of

Table 14.2 Attitudes of Adult Canadians Toward Homosexuality

	Strongly Agree	Somewhat Agree
Same-sex couples should be allowed to legally marry.	63	13
Same-sex couples should have the same rights to adopt children	45	25

Source: Ipsos (2013).

prejudice. Lesbians may face sexism as well as homonegativity. LGBs from visible minority groups may face racism as well as antigay prejudice. (See Chapter 13 for a discussion of intersectionality.)

Media and LGB Attitudes

What role do the media play in homonegativity/antigay attitudes? In previous decades there were almost no portrayals of gay men or lesbians, so they were invisible in the mass media. Current research, however, now finds more representations of sexual minorities in the media. In one study of television programming, content associated with sexual minorities occurred in 15 percent of programs overall, most of it in movies and sitcoms (Fisher et al., 2007).

So gays are now more visible in the media, but are they portrayed positively or negatively? Some argue that even successful programs increase stereotypes because they present the LGB characters in stereotypic ways, including lacking a stable relationship, being preoccupied with their sexuality, and laughable (Calzo & Ward, 2009). Others, though, argue that there are some programs that are positive because they use humour to expose and challenge stereotypes. For example, in shows such as *Glee* and *Modern Family*, sexual orientation still seems to be the defining feature of LGB characters or why they are funny. *The L Word* is a lesbian-centric show that is fairly realistic. And the main character in *Orange Is the New Black* is a queer character who does not define her sexuality.

These shows are doing a better job of addressing heterosexism and stereotypes head on as part of the plot lines. Research on the actual effects of the media on attitudes is very new and paints a complex picture (Calzo & Ward, 2009). For example, reading popular magazines is associated with more positive attitudes toward LGBs, but reading teen magazines is associated with less positive attitudes, probably because teen magazines tend to be conservative about sexuality.

LO4 Consequences of Homonegativity and Heterosexism

Homonegativity and heterosexism can have serious emotional and health consequences for LGB individuals (Maticka-Tyndale, 2008; Wells, 2009). This may be a particular problem for adolescents establishing their sexual identity. Antigay bullying and overt acts of antigay prejudice can cause significant pain and suffering. Sometimes the prejudice is subtle. The prevalence of antigay humour and the widespread insult "that's so gay" are hurtful to LGB youth who may be listening (go to www.thinkb4youspeak.com for a media campaign against this expression and others). The message is that there is something really bad about acting in any way that might suggest being gay (Adam, 2007). Some—but not all—LGB youth adopt the negative attitudes they see around them, called *internalized homonegativity*, and this may make it difficult for them to accept their sexual orientation. Cultural homonegativity, as well as internalized homonegativity, may also affect some LGB individuals' self-esteem. In some cases, LGB youth so devalue their self-worth that they contemplate or attempt suicide (D'Augelli, 2006). It may also affect their willingness to be open about their sexual identity (Figure 14.3).

The most extreme expressions of antigay prejudice occur in *hate crimes* against LGBs. One horrifying case occurred in Wyoming (Loffreda, 2000). Matthew Shepard, a University of Wyoming student, was found tied to a fence, savagely beaten, and comatose. Two young men had led Shepard to believe that they, too, were gay and lured him from a bar to ride in their pickup

Figure 14.3 Camp Fyrefly is a summer camp for LGB youth in Alberta and Saskatchewan.

truck, where they began beating him with a revolver. They later tied him to a fence, beat him more, and left him for dead. He died five days later. Similarly, in 2001, Aaron Webster, a prominent photographer and a gay man, was beaten to death in Vancouver by four men wielding baseball bats, a golf club, and a pool cue after they found him naked in an area widely known as a stroll for gay men looking for casual sex.

A survey of Canadian LGBs found high rates of violence (Faulkner, 1997). Seventy-eight percent had experienced verbal assaults, 21 percent had been physically assaulted, 21 percent reported harassment by the police, and 7 percent had been assaulted with a weapon. A study of LGBs in Vancouver found similar results: 74 percent had been verbally abused, 32 percent had been physically assaulted, and 9 percent had been physically and sexually assaulted. Indeed, according to Statistics Canada (Beauchamp, 2008), Canadians over the age of 15 who identify themselves as gay or lesbian are 2.5 times as likely to be victims of violent victimization as are heterosexual Canadians.

A survey of homophobia, biphobia, and transphobia in Canadian schools found that 55 percent of the sexual minority students had been verbally harassed and 21 percent had been physically harassed or assaulted about their gender expression or perceived sexual orientation (Taylor et al., 2011). The rates were even higher for trans youth. About a third of youth with LGBT parents (37 percent) also reported being harassed about their parents' sexual orientation or gender identity. More than 70 percent of participating students (LGBT and heterosexual) reported hearing homophobic expressions such as "that's so gay" *every day* in school; 48 percent heard the use of terms such as *faggot, lesbo,* and *dyke* as insults *every day* in school. The rates were higher among sexual minority students. Very few students had never heard these comments made at school. Sexual minority youth are more likely than their heterosexual counterparts to experience physical and sexual victimization, verbal harassment, and discrimination (McCreary Centre Society, 2007; Taylor et al., 2008). These studies show that hate crimes against and harassment of LGB youth are not rare, isolated incidents. These incidents exact a psychological toll and can affect adolescents' health, mental health, and development (Saewyc, 2007, 2011). LGB youth are less likely to feel safe at school.

But we should also recognize the other side of the coin. As we can see from the statistics in Table 14.2, most Canadians are tolerant or supportive of LGB individuals. For example, 67 percent of Canadians approve of overt gay and lesbian teachers in middle school, and 86 percent approve of openly gay MPs (Figure 14.4). Thus while some Canadians are bigots on the issue of homosexuality, most Canadians are not.

Figure 14.4   Kathleen Wynne, premier of Ontario, made history when she became the first openly gay premier in Canada.

Attitudes Toward Bisexuals

Bisexuals experience a different kind of stigma than do lesbians and gay men. If you are asked to imagine a lesbian or gay couple, you can likely come up with a mental image—two women kissing or two men holding hands or dancing together are easily recognizable as a lesbian or gay couple. Now what do you imagine when you are asked to think of a bisexual couple? The point is that we have few cultural images of bisexuality (Trynka & Tucker, 1995). As such, bisexuality is rarely even recognizable. A study of 22 self-identified bisexual Canadian women found that all participants felt that bisexuality was misunderstood by straight, lesbian, and gay communities (Bower et al., 2002).

There are a great many negative stereotypes about bisexuals (Herek, 2002). Bisexuals are often thought of as internally conflicted or psychologically immature (Rust, 2000a). They are stereotyped as nonmonogamous, needing both same-sex and other-sex partners to satisfy both the gay/lesbian and heterosexual sides of their sexualities (Yost & Thomas, 2012). In contrast, research has found that few bisexuals have both female and male partners at the same time (although some do), and bisexuals do not differ from lesbians and gay men in their relationship status and length (Balsam, 2004; Rust, 2000b). Further, few bisexuals report that they "need" both male and female partners to think of themselves as bisexual (Rust, 2001).

Similarly, bisexuals may be viewed with suspicion or downright hostility by the gay and lesbian communities (Bower et al., 2002; Rust, 2002). Bisexual-identified women are often told they are denying their true identity, which must be lesbian or heterosexual. Young women who have sexual involvements with other women are often regarded as heterosexuals who are merely experimenting with women because lesbianism is chic (Rust, 2000a). Bisexual women who are involved in lesbian communities may be told they are really lesbians who have not yet realized it. Bisexuality is sometimes seen as fence-sitting, a way to get the best of both worlds without having to commit to a particular identity. Some gay men and lesbians even argue that there is no such thing as a true bisexual (Rust, 2002).

In contrast, proponents of bisexuality argue that it has some strong advantages. It allows more variety in one's sexual and human relationships than does exclusive heterosexuality or exclusive homosexuality. The bisexual does not rule out any possibilities and is open to the widest variety of experiences.

L05 LGBs and the Law

Same-sex sexual activity used to be illegal in Canada. For example, in 1967 Everett Klippert was sent to prison as a "dangerous sex offender" after he told police that he had had sex with men over a 24-year period and was unlikely to change. However, consensual same-sex activity was decriminalized in 1969 when, under Prime Minister Pierre Trudeau, Parliament passed a bill introducing widespread changes to laws regulating sexual behaviour in the *Criminal Code of Canada*. Before 1969, "homosexual offences" included some outdated and derogatory terms, such as "buggery (anal intercourse), attempted buggery, indecent assault on a male by a male or female on a female, acts of gross indecency between men, procuring and attempting to procure acts of gross indecency between males" (Lahey, 1999, p. 135). These changes to the *Criminal Code* were a turning point in the recognition and increasing acceptance of LGBs in Canada. However, at that time, the offence of anal intercourse was added to the *Criminal Code*. Anal sex is illegal only if it involves children or is not done in private. However, the age of consent for anal sex is 18, whereas the age of consent for vaginal intercourse is 16. Further, anal sex is deemed not to be done in private (and therefore is illegal) if more than two persons are present. There is no similar provision for vaginal intercourse. This puts gay (and straight) youth who want to experiment sexually with anal intercourse

(many gay males do not engage in anal intercourse) in a difficult situation. Thus, the *Criminal Code* still discriminates against gay men in this way. However, recent court rulings have suggested that the higher age of consent for anal intercourse violates the equality provisions of the *Charter of Rights and Freedoms*.

Activists also argue that there has been more vigorous enforcement of the bawdy-house and obscenity laws (see Chapter 2 for a list of Canadian laws related to sexuality) against LGBs and same-sex erotic materials. For example, following the 1969 changes to the *Criminal Code*, police continued to lay "indecent act" and "bawdy-house" charges against men for engaging in consensual sex with other men. Nor were gay men and lesbians legally protected from discrimination (Kinsman, 1996). Before the *Charter of Rights and Freedoms*, virtually no human rights complaints by gay men and lesbians were successful (Lahey, 1999; Smith, 1999). For example, before 1992, homosexuality was grounds for dishonourable release from the military (Gouliquer, 2000). In the early 1980s, men and women who were suspected of being gay or lesbian were investigated, interrogated, and sometimes released by the military. However, in 1992 Canadian Forces policy concerning sexual orientation was found to violate the *Charter of Rights and Freedoms*. LGBs can no longer be denied the right to serve in the military.

In 1995, Parliament passed a hate crimes sentencing bill, which specifies longer sentences for hate-motivated crimes—that is, crimes motivated by hate, bias, and prejudice against specific groups. The list of unacceptable hate crimes includes those committed against gay men and lesbians. In 2004, Parliament passed a private member's bill introduced by former MP Svend Robinson that bans hate propaganda that targets gay men and lesbians. Although this is a step in the right direction of providing some legal protection to LGBs, it may seem like cold comfort to a person who has been the victim of such a crime. Further, police have some discretion in what charges are laid and do not always identify assaults against LGBs as motivated by hate.

Recent decisions by the Supreme Court of Canada recognize that the equality rights guaranteed in the Canadian *Charter of Rights and Freedoms* include sexual orientation and that provincial human rights codes must recognize sexual orientation as a prohibited ground for discrimination. In 1996, Parliament amended the *Human Rights Act* to specifically prohibit discrimination based on sexual orientation (the act already prohibited discrimination based on other characteristics, such as gender, race, and disability). The act also bans "hate speech" against gay men and lesbians. This means, among other things, that gay men and lesbians cannot be fired because of their sexual

Figure 14.5   Michael Stark and Michael Leshner of Toronto. Together for more than 20 years, this couple was instrumental in getting Ontario courts to recognize same-sex marriage. The federal government legalized same-sex marriage in June 2005.

orientation, they cannot be refused housing, and they are entitled to adopt children. In fact, Parliament recently passed the *Modernization of Benefits and Obligations Act*, which amended existing federal statutes to ensure that they apply equally to couples in same-sex and mixed-sex relationships. The majority of Canadians support such entitlement (refer to Table 14.2). In contrast, in the United States, gay men and lesbians do not have legal protection against discrimination, and fewer Americans support equal rights for gay men and lesbians.

The most recent area in which gay men and lesbians have attained equal rights is marriage. In 2003, courts in Ontario and British Columbia were the first to legalize same-sex marriage, ruling that federal laws restricting marriage to one man and one woman violated the *Charter of Rights and Freedoms* (Figure 14.5). In 2004, courts in Quebec, Manitoba, Nova Scotia, Saskatchewan, Newfoundland and Labrador, and Yukon made the same ruling. On June 28, 2005, the House of Commons passed a bill ensuring that marriage is a right for all Canadians regardless of sexual orientation so that all Canadians are treated as equal under the law; the bill was given royal assent and became law less than a month later, on July 20, 2005. Marriage is now defined as "the union of two people to the exclusion of all others." Canada was the fourth country in the world to legalize same-sex marriage; by 2014 a total of 15 countries had done so. In 2007, the Ontario Court of Appeal ruled that a child can have three parents—in this case, a biological mother and father and the mother's same-sex partner.

Gay Men, Lesbians, and Bisexuals as a Minority Group

From the foregoing discussion, it is clear that LGB people are the subject of many negative attitudes and stereotypes, just as other minority groups are (Meyer, 2003). Like members of other minority groups, they can experience discrimination, for example, in employment and housing, even though this is illegal in Canada. Only fairly recently have their rights been protected by law.

Discrimination goes hand in hand with stereotypes. One such stereotype is that gay men are child molesters. As with many stereotypes, this one is false. Research shows that the vast majority of child abusers have a heterosexual orientation; only 2 to 3 percent are gay (Jenny et al., 1994).

There is an important way in which LGBs differ from other minority groups, though. In the case of most other minorities, appearance is a fairly good indicator of minority-group status. It is typically easy to recognize a Chinese Canadian or a woman, for example, but one cannot tell simply by looking at a person what his or her sexual orientation is. Thus LGBs, unlike other minorities, can hide their status. There are certain advantages to this. It makes it fairly easy to get along in the heterosexual world—to "pass." However, it has the disadvantage of encouraging the person to conceal her or his true identity to avoid homonegativity; this hiding may be psychologically stressful (Meyer, 2003). Concealing a stigma—whether it is one's sexual orientation, mental illness, illiteracy, or history of child sexual abuse—exacts a psychological, and sometimes physical, toll (Pachankis, 2007).

We shouldn't leave this discussion of discrimination and prejudice against LGBs without asking a crucial question: What can be done to prevent or end this prejudice? Change must occur at many levels: the individual, the interpersonal, and the organizational levels (e.g., corporations, educational institutions), as well as society as a whole and its institutions (e.g., the federal government). At the individual level, all of us must examine our own attitudes toward LGBs to see if they are consistent with basic values we hold, such as a commitment to equality and justice. Some people may need to educate themselves or attend workshops to examine their attitudes. Research in Ontario has shown that workshops for university students that include imagery exercises, coming out stories, and discussion significantly reduce homonegativity and increase comfort with sexual matters (Rye & Meaney, 2009). These attitudes, though, were formed as we grew up—influenced by our parents, our peers, and the media. Parents must consider the messages they convey to their children about sexual minority groups. The adolescent peer group is strongly homophobic. What can be done to change it? How can the media change so as not to promote antigay prejudices and stereotypes? At the interpersonal level, people must recognize that LGBs are often a hidden minority. Eric, for example, just told a joke that ridiculed gay men. What he didn't know was that one of his three listeners is gay—just not "out" with Eric (for obvious reasons). We must examine our interactions with other people, recognizing the extent to which many of us assume that everyone is heterosexual until proven otherwise.

At the institutional level, how can education be changed to reduce antigay discrimination? A strong program of sex education across the grades, with open discussion of sexual orientation, would be a good start (see Chapter 19). In fact, schools have a responsibility to ensure that homophobic harassment and name-calling does not occur. Azmi Jubran filed a complaint against his school with the B.C. Human Rights Commission. Year after year he had been harassed verbally and physically by his school peers because they believed he was gay. In 2005, the B.C. Court of Appeal ruled that it is not enough for schools to discipline the offending students. Schools must provide preventive anti-homophobic education to prevent this kind of harassment. In addition, gay–straight alliances (GSAs) can work to combat heterosexism and antigay prejudice in organizations (see http://mygsa.ca for resources to support GSAs in Canadian schools). Such alliances have been established at many high schools and universities across Canada. They are open to all students and staff who want to work toward a more inclusive and supportive environment for LGB and trans students. A number of Canadian universities also have a Safe Spaces Projects (Figure 14.6), which involves supportive faculty, staff, and students displaying a sticker on their door to indicate that their space is open to and supportive of people with all sexual orientations and gender identities and that they will not tolerate homophobic or transphobic comments or jokes. It serves as a visible statement to sexual minority individuals that support is around them and provides an opportunity for education and discussion.

Life Experiences of LGB Individuals

In understanding the lives of LGBs, it is important to recognize that there is a wide variety of experiences. An important aspect of this variability is whether the person is a **covert homosexual** (in the closet) or an **overt homosexual** (out of the closet) about his or her sexual identity. As discussed earlier, some people may be in a mixed-sex marriage and have children but spend a few hours a month engaging in secret same-sex sexual behaviour or sexual fantasies.[4] Other gay men and lesbians may live almost entirely within an LGB community, particularly in a large city like Toronto or Vancouver where there is a large gay subculture. There are also various degrees of overtness (being "out") and covertness. Many lesbians and gay men are out with trusted friends but not with casual acquaintances or in some situations but not in others. The lifestyle of gay men differs from that of lesbians, perhaps as a result of the different roles assigned to men and women in our society and the different ways that boys and girls are reared. In addition, there is different discrimination against gay men than there is against lesbians. For example, it is considered quite natural for two women to share an apartment, but if two men over a certain age do so, eyebrows may be raised.

The lifestyles of LGBs are thus far from uniform. They vary according to whether one is male or female and overt or covert about one's sexual identity, and according to social class, occupation, personality, and a variety of other factors.

LGB Development

Some experts believe that sexual orientation is determined by age five or six or even prenatally, whereas others say that it is determined by age 10 or 12. Scientists don't have exact answers to this question, but without doubt it depends on the individual in ways that are discussed in the section that follows.

Covert homosexual: A gay man or lesbian who is "in the closet," who keeps his or her sexual orientation a secret.
Overt homosexual: A gay man or lesbian who is "out of the closet," who is open about his or her sexual orientation.

Figure 14.6 In a number of Canadian communities and institutions, Safe Spaces supports gay, lesbian, bisexual, transgender, two-spirit, and questioning individuals and their allies.

---

[4] Men who secretly have sex with other men while in a sexual relationship with a woman are sometimes said to be on the "down low" or "d" for short.

Some evidence indicates that gender variance in childhood predicts later LGB orientation (Steensma et al., 2012). That is, children who are rated by their parents as having characteristics such as "behaves like the opposite sex" and "wishes to be the opposite sex," at least somewhat, are more likely, in adulthood, to have same-sex attractions and behaviours. However, this prediction is far from perfect. In one study, the prevalence of homosexuality was 10 to 12 percent in adulthood among those who displayed gender variance in childhood, compared with 1 to 2 percent among those who did not display gender variance in childhood (Steensma et al., 2012). In fact, then, the majority of gender variant children did not turn out to be gay.

Sexual minority women report their first same-sex romantic attraction on average at age 12 and sexual minority men at age 11, but there is lots of variability around those averages (Katz-Wise, 2012). First questioning of one's sexual orientation occurs on average at age 12 for males and age 15 for females, and self-labelling as LGB occurs on average at age 16 for men and 17 or 18 for women. As we discussed in Chapter 10, a crucial task of adolescence is identity development, and sexual orientation is one important aspect of development that occurs over the adolescent years. Related to identity development is **coming out**, which involves acknowledging to oneself, and then to others, that one is gay or lesbian. Although many youth do not disclose their sexual orientation to their parents, if they do, they are more likely to tell their mothers than their fathers. Mothers also tend to react more positively to the disclosure than do fathers. Nonetheless, a study of 542 gay, lesbian, and bisexual youth found that 24 percent of mothers and 37 percent of fathers were intolerant or rejecting when they found out about their child's sexual orientation. Only 48 percent of mothers and 35 percent of fathers were accepting (D'Augelli, 2002). Whether the person experiences acceptance or rejection from family, friends, and others to whom he or she comes out can be critical to self-esteem and mental health. The Internet can also have a positive impact on the coming out process. For teenagers who are just realizing that they are gay or lesbian, the Internet provides boundless information and the opportunity to "chat" with others while remaining safe at home and not acknowledging the identity publicly in ways that could be embarrassing or even dangerous. Interactions with others on the Internet can foster a positive identity and self-acceptance (Schneider, 1991).

These developmental processes are complicated by the negative climate for sexual minority youth that exists in middle school, high school, and college or university. Many LGB youth report harassment by peers, especially in middle school (Robinson & Espelage, 2011). Indeed, as noted earlier, Canadian researchers found that 70 percent of students reported hearing expressions such as "that's so gay," and words like *faggot, lesbo,* and *dyke* every day at school. The use of homophobic epithets (name-calling) is common in middle school and high school (Poteat et al., 2012). Boys engage in this name-calling to each other more than girls do, and the frequency for boys actually increases from Grade 7 to Grade 12. Homophobic epithets are, in reality, a form of bullying and, among boys, they enforce the rules of masculinity (Poteat et al., 2011). Ironically, those who dish them out are also the most likely to receive them. And today, cyberbullying also occurs, often allowing perpetrators to remain anonymous and facilitating the "outing" of LGB adolescents to hundreds of peers with just a click (Robinson & Espelage, 2011). Harassment can lead sexual minority youth to skip school, which creates another set of problems. One Canadian high school student described one of his experiences of harassment in this way:

> At school I was attacked a couple of times in the hallway. Once I was walking down the hallway and a guy jumped on me and pretended to fuck me. It was a big joke for him and his friends. After throwing him off me, I collapsed. I couldn't believe that I had been violated in such a sexual way in front of the school. I had to deal with the students going around and saying I was going to take him to court. I had to deal with total strangers coming up to me and saying, "What are you doing to my friend? How come you are taking him to court?" These people didn't even recognize that I was the victim. I was not the one at fault. (Grace & Wells, 2007, p. 7)

Even at the undergraduate level, peer harassment can be intense (Figure 14.7), and this harassment has been linked to suicidal thoughts and suicide attempts (Robinson & Espelage, 2011). One much publicized example is the case of Tyler Clementi, a Rutgers University student, whose roommate used a webcam to record him kissing another man in the privacy of his room. The roommate then urged many others to view another encounter, and Clementi discovered what was happening. The next day, Clementi killed himself by jumping off the George Washington Bridge.

Support from adults, especially parents and adults at school, is crucial as sexual minority youth weather these storms (Darwich et al., 2012; Heatherington & Lavner, 2008). Often schools fail to address individual incidents and lack proactive policies to reduce negative climates. The case of Azmi Jubran, a B.C. high school student, described earlier, established that legally schools must provide preventive anti-homophobic education to prevent this kind of harassment. In addition, schools should provide professional development opportunities on LGB issues for all school staff. Schools can also

Coming out: The process of acknowledging to oneself, and then to others, that one is gay or lesbian.

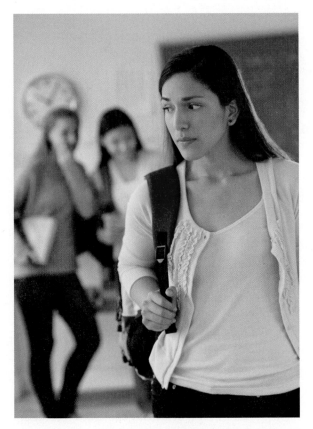

Figure 14.7 Peer harassment, such as spreading rumours, can be part of the school climate for LGB youth.

host gay–straight alliances, Safe Spaces programs, and wellness programs for sexual minority youth.

To this point, we have discussed sexual identity as something that develops during adolescence and then is fixed. That may be true for many people, but psychologist Lisa Diamond (2005, 2008a) has documented what she calls **sexual fluidity**, which refers to changes over time in sexual attractions, identity, or behaviour, which can occur with people in their 20s, 30s, or later (see First Person). Her research involved young women, followed longitudinally, over eight years. The women's attractions and identity shifted in all directions, for example, from bisexual to lesbian or from lesbian to heterosexual. Similar patterns have been documented in men as well (Katz-Wise, 2012). Some of these people report that they are attracted to the person, not the gender. As one man said,

> I find gender matters, but it's definitely not the first priority on the list for me. . . . In terms of attraction, I just like beautiful things, and I don't really classify those in men or women. I find both of them beautiful. (Katz-Wise, 2012, p. 122)

For some people, then, patterns of attraction and behavior can continue to develop and evolve well past adolescence.

Today, North American culture has a much wider variety of possible self-labels so that people don't have to fit themselves into just one of two boxes: heterosexual or homosexual. People can be bisexual, queer, questioning, or unlabelled. In one well-sampled American survey, 86 percent of women and 92 percent of men said that their sexual attractions were only to members of the opposite sex, but 10 percent of women and 4 percent of men said that their sexual attractions were "mostly" to the opposite sex (Chandra et al., 2011). They don't fit neatly into the heterosexual box or into the homosexual box.

Bisexual Identity

Bisexual men and women generally begin to think of themselves as bisexual in their early to mid-20s (Fox, 1995; Weinberg et al., 1994). There are some gender differences in the sequence of behaviours, though. Bisexual women typically have their first other-sex attraction and sexual experiences before their first same-sex ones. Bisexual men, in contrast, are more likely to have same-sex experiences first, followed by mixed-sex ones. What do bisexuals base their identity on? Sexual behaviour, feelings of attraction, or something else?

Research has shown that most bisexual men and women base their sexual identity on their feelings of sexual attraction or capacity to fall in love with either women or men regardless of whether they have expressed these feelings through sexual behaviour (Rust, 2001). Many describe their sexual attractions to women and men as different from each other. Those respondents who have had sexual experiences with both women and men generally report having these experiences serially over time, often including lengthy monogamous relationships. They indicate that they do not cease being bisexual when they became monogamously involved with either a woman or a man, just as heterosexuals do not cease being straight during a period of celibacy (Rust, 2000a). Some individuals adopt bisexual identities to reflect their politics. They may see bisexuality as a challenge to the importance of gender in defining sexuality, viewing their bisexual identity not as a combination of their attractions to women and men, but an attraction to specific people regardless of their gender.

Lesbian, Gay, and Bisexual Communities

A loose network of lesbian, gay, and bisexual communities extends around the world. As one woman put it,

> I have seen lesbian communities all over the world (e.g., South Africa, Brazil, and Israel) where the lesbians of that nation have

Sexual fluidity: Changes over time in a person's sexual attractions, identity, or behaviour.

First Person

Sexual Fluidity and Questioning

This case is taken from a series of interviews conducted by psychologist Lisa Diamond, author of *Sexual Fluidity* (2008).

At the very first interview, Eleanor described herself as "questioning." She has an outgoing, vivacious demeanor, with a broad, engaging smile and a self-deprecating sense of humour.

Eleanor flatly refused to characterize her same-sex attractions on a 0–100 percent scale. She threw up her hands and exclaimed, "I can't make any sense of that at all! There are too many variables involved when I'm attracted to someone, so there's no way for me to divide it up that way." Eleanor was 20 years old and had first begun to question her sexuality about a year earlier, when her boyfriend told her that he was bisexual. She had been aware of sporadic same-sex attractions since the age of 13, and, in her words, "they scared the hell out of me." Yet the attractions had always confused her. Most of her "gut level" urges were in response to men, but she found women more aesthetically and emotionally desirable. As she put it:

> I prefer to make out with men, but the idea of having sex with a man utterly repulses me. I would, however, like to marry a woman, and that's who I want to make a long-term commitment to.... When people ask me if I'm straight and I say yes, I know I'm being dishonest, and I can't tolerate that dishonesty. But if somebody asked me if I was a lesbian, I'd also feel dishonest saying yes. I guess I might be bisexual. I'm annoyed by the uncertainty. I know I'm not straight, it's just a matter of defining my not-straightness....

By the second interview Eleanor had settled on the compromise of a bisexual identification, despite the fact that her feelings for women remained relatively ambiguous. She was eager for more certainty about her sexuality.

> I still go through this whole explanation when I tell people I'm bisexual, because the truth is that my attraction to women isn't really all that sexual. It's more aesthetic. Women are just so much better looking than men. I guess I find women magnetic. That's not quite the same as a sexual attraction.... I thought that things would resolve themselves. I expected that over time I'd either feel clear sexual attractions and I'd identify as bisexual or I wouldn't feel them at all and I'd identify as heterosexual. But now I realize that won't happen—I still feel the same and I've accepted that.

At the third interview, at age 25, Eleanor had finally reconciled with the fact that her emotional and aesthetic appreciation for women did not really qualify as sexual attraction. Yet contrary to the notion that this might just be a rationalization for not identifying as lesbian or bisexual, Eleanor actually expressed great disappointment that she was not gay.

> I've kind of straightened out! I still call myself bisexual but I'm on the edge of heterosexual, which I'm not pleased about.... I never really wanted to be heterosexual but I don't have much choice in the matter.... I think sexuality definitely changes, because it's not that I'm just more aware of the straight parts of me, I've actually become more straight, but I don't have any idea what causes those changes.

Eleanor reported the same basic perspective at the 8-year and 10-year follow-up interviews, when she characterized herself as "reluctantly heterosexual." At the time of the 10-year interview, she described her emotional attraction as 70 percent to women, but her physical attraction as only 5 percent to women.

Source: Lisa M. Diamond, in *Sexual Fluidity: Understanding Women's Love and Desire*, pp. 155–158. Copyright © Harvard University Press. Reprinted with permission.

more in common with me (i.e., they play the same lesbian records, have read the same books, wear the same lesbian jewellery) than the heterosexual women of that nation have in common with heterosexual women in North America. (E. D. Rothblum, personal communication, 2007)

These links have been cemented in the past decade by increases in international travel, globalization, and the international reach of the Internet (Puar, 2001).

Distinct LGB communities became visible in Canada in the 1970s in Toronto, Vancouver, and Montreal (Kinsman, 1996). During this period, there was a flourishing of businesses catering to a gay clientele including bars, clubs, bathhouses, restaurants, bookstores, theatres, and social organizations. Many of these establishments also cater to a lesbian and bisexual clientele, although generally there are fewer businesses geared specifically toward lesbians. The lesbian community in particular has been involved in creating a lesbian culture, expressed in music and literature, and celebrated at festivals and women's sporting events. LGB residential areas grew up close to these commercial establishments, creating LGB neighbourhoods in these cities, although most gay men and lesbians do not live in these "gay villages" (Kinsman, 1996).

LGBs tend to be less visible in smaller Canadian communities, but they nonetheless tend to have strong social networks. Some people move to large urban centres seeking greater anonymity, acceptance, and perhaps distance from their families.

Several symbols are used as representations of gay, lesbian, and bisexual pride. That is, they are used to indicate that being gay is something to be proud of, not to hide. An upside-down pink triangle, which is what the Nazis used to label gay men, has been reclaimed by the gay community. The lowercase Greek letter lambda is also used. However, perhaps the most easily recognizable symbol is the rainbow flag, used by the gay community since 1978 and a representation of diversity and multiculturalism. A pink, purple, and blue striped flag is used to symbolize bisexual pride, with the pink representing attraction to members of the same gender, the blue representing attraction to people of the other gender, and the purple (the middle stripe) representing attraction to both men and women. Pride celebrations, which celebrate the anniversary of the Stonewall rebellion mentioned earlier, take place in various cities across Canada each summer. The Pride Parade, in particular, is considered an important celebration of what it means to be gay, lesbian, or bisexual (Figure 14.8). The use of slang is another sign of solidarity among LGBs.

Gay bars are one aspect of the LGB social life. These are gay-friendly clubs in which drinking, perhaps dancing, talking, socializing with friends, and, sometimes, the possibility of finding a romantic or sexual partner are important elements. In large cities, some gay bars cater to either gay men or lesbians. However, many gay bars, particularly in smaller Canadian cities, are mixed gender and mixed orientation. This means that they cater to both gay men and to lesbians, as well as to gay-positive heterosexuals. What makes them gay bars is not that they are different from other bars but that they are accepting of same-sex relationships. Thus, patrons can be open about their sexual orientation and feel free to socialize and dance with whomever they want without fearing verbal or physical harassment from other customers. Some gay bars look like any other bar from the outside, while others may have names—for example, The Open

Figure 14.8 Today many Canadian cities have an annual Pride Parade as part of Gay Pride Week, such as this June 2008 parade in Toronto. In the early 1990s, mayors of Fredericton, Hamilton, London, and Saskatoon refused to declare Gay Pride Week. In each case, the provincial Human Rights Commission found the mayors at fault, fined them, and ordered them to issue gay pride proclamations.

Closet—that indicate to the alert that they are gay bars. LGB-community dances and parties are other important avenues for socializing, particularly in small centres.

Gay baths are another aspect of some gay men's social and sexual lives (note that bathhouses, particularly in Toronto, were where the police raids took place that sparked numerous protests in the 1970s and 1980s). The baths are clubs with many rooms in them, generally including a swimming pool or whirlpool, as well as rooms for dancing, watching television, and socializing; most areas are dimly lit. Once a man has found a sexual partner, they go to one of a number of small rooms furnished with beds, where they can engage in sexual activity. The baths feature casual, impersonal sex, since a partner can be found and the act completed without the two even exchanging names, much less making any emotional commitment to each other.

In many parts of Canada, there are no or relatively few bathhouses (Myers et al., 1993). However, there are about seven in Montreal, eight in Toronto, and five in Vancouver. There is some controversy in the gay community about whether they encourage risky sexual practices. Some see the baths as an aspect of gay culture that spreads HIV and will continue to do so, killing thousands; they believe the baths must be closed and the destructive practices they encourage should stop (Rotello, 1997; Signorile, 1997). Others celebrate the liberated sexuality

Gay bar: A gay-friendly bar or club frequented by lesbians and gay men.
Gay baths: Clubs where gay men can socialize; features include a swimming pool or whirlpool and access to casual sex.

fostered by the baths and see it as an essential part of gay men's lifestyle. Today many bathhouses emphasize safe sex—for example, by supplying condoms and handing out safer sex information.

In keeping with the increased use of online dating websites by single individuals, a major way for LGB individuals to meet each other is through the Internet. Cyberspace is also a place where gay men and lesbians can find community when, geographically, they do not live in a place that has a gay community (Brown et al., 2005). Gay-related websites provide chat rooms and have ways for LGBs to form online relationships and perhaps find partners for casual sex or a long-term relationship (Brown et al., 2005; Ross et al., 2007).

Certainly, in the last three decades the *gay liberation movement* has had a tremendous impact on the gay lifestyle and community. In particular, it has encouraged LGBs to be more overt and to feel less guilty about their behaviour. The gay liberation movement has given rise to a number of provincial and national organizations committed to ending discrimination against LGBs. For example, EGALE (Equality for Gays and Lesbians Everywhere) is a national organization committed to advancing equality and justice for lesbian, gay, bisexual, and transgender individuals and their families across Canada. The organization does so by fighting for justice in the courts as well as by building communication and action networks. There are also many LGB organizations at the provincial and local levels. Some address social justice issues; others provide community service and education. For example, large Canadian cities and most Canadian universities have pride centres. The Canadian Lesbian and Gay Archives serves as a central clearinghouse for LGB information.

Figure 14.9 The comedic television series *Modern Family* is an example of a mainstream show that often deals with gay-friendly storylines.

There are thus many places for LGBs to socialize besides bars, including the Metropolitan Community Church (a network of gay and lesbian churches with three churches in Ontario), gay athletic organizations, and gay political organizations.

Among other accomplishments, members of the gay liberation movement have founded numerous gay newspapers, magazines, and Internet sites. These have many of the same features as other media: forums for political opinions, human-interest stories, and fashion news. Today there are many regional LGB publications, including *Wayves* published in Halifax, *Fugues* published in Montreal, *Outwords Inc.* published in Winnipeg, *Perceptions* published in Saskatoon, and *Outlooks* and *Xtra* published in Toronto, Ottawa (*Xtra*), and Vancouver (*Xtra West*). There are also several publications that list gay-owned or gay-friendly businesses, including information about bars, accommodations, shops, services, and tours. There is also a national GLB television station in Canada, OUTtv (Figure 14.9). The Canadian Gay, Lesbian, and Bisexual Resource Directory distributes information relevant to LGB communities across Canada through its website at www.gaycanada.com.

Same-Sex Relationships

Contrary to stereotypes, a substantial number of lesbians, gay men, and bisexuals form long-term relationships. Some bisexuals are in a relationship with a person of the other gender; others are in a relationship with someone of their same gender. Across numerous surveys, between 8 and 21 percent of lesbian couples had been together for 10 years or more, as had between 18 and 28 percent of the gay male couples (Kurdek, 2005) (Figure 14.10).

In the 2011 census, there were 21,015 same-sex married couples and 43,560 same-sex common-law couples in Canada (Statistics Canada, 2012). This is nearly three times the number of same-sex marriages than were reported in 2006. Of these, 55 percent were male couples and 45 percent were female couples. About 17 percent of female same-sex couples but only 4 percent of male same-sex couples have children living with them. One study asked same-sex Canadian couples why they wanted to be married (Alderson, 2004). For some, it was important to publicly declare their lifelong commitment to each other. For others marriage was part of a spiritual journey, including feeling that marriage brings greater depth to a relationship. Some felt that the legal protection provided by marriage (e.g., if their partner got sick) was important. Finally, for some it was about equality rights and making things better for gay and lesbian youth in the future. For example, here's what one 41-year-old woman said:

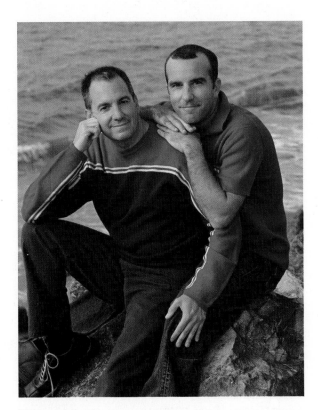

Figure 14.10 Many lesbians and gay men report currently being in a steady romantic relationship.

You can't represent the essence of it and that's the spiritual part that I'm talking about—that indescribable experience of being a family. And now that we're being recognized by the outside state as a family. It's very powerful to be recognized. (Alderson, 2004, p. 113)

All couples—gay or straight—must struggle to find a balance that suits both persons. Three aspects of the relationship typically have to be negotiated and can be sources of conflict: money, housework, and sex (Solomon et al., 2005).

What is striking about all the research on gay and lesbian relationships is how similar all relationships are, regardless of sexual orientation, in their satisfactions, loves, joys, and conflicts (Holmberg & Blair, 2009; Patterson, 2000) (see First Person). For example, in a Quebec study, gay, lesbian, and heterosexual couples were brought to the laboratory and told to discuss a problem (Julien et al., 2003). Each couple's interactions were videotaped and later coded for both positive and negative behaviours by each partner. The results showed no differences among lesbian, gay, and heterosexual couples on any of the interaction measures. Similarly, research in Alberta assessed the similarities and differences of the experiences of women who were currently in a same-sex relationship but had been married to a man in the past (Boon & Alderson, 2009).

The women reported that many of the issues they faced in the two relationships were similar. However, they also identified some differences including in the level of intimacy, communication style, and sharing of responsibilities. In addition, experiences of antigay prejudice, heterosexism, and homonegativity can affect same-sex relationships (Boon & Alderson, 2009; Cohen et al., 2008). Nonetheless, couples in which the partners were more out to the world tended to report higher relationship satisfaction (Clausell & Roisman, 2009).

Lesbian and Gay Families

Increasingly, gay and lesbian couples are creating families that include children (Bowe, 2006). In the past, the courts tended to grant custody to the nongay or nonlesbian parents and have often restricted visitation by the gay or lesbian parent (Barrett et al., 1997). However, legislation in most provinces allows same-sex adoption either by the partner of a parent or of an unrelated child. In provinces where there has not been such legislation, the courts have ruled that provincial acts that prevent same-sex couples from applying to adopt are unconstitutional. The Canadian *Charter of Rights and Freedoms* prohibits discrimination based on sexual orientation, and this applies to adoption, custody, and access (Figure 14.11). This legislation appears to recognize the result of research on the effects on children of living in a gay or lesbian family, which is reviewed below.

Of course, these families are not all the same. In some, the children were born to one partner in a previous mixed-sex relationship. In others, the children were adopted or, in the case of lesbian couples, born by means of assisted insemination. There is some preliminary evidence that use of donor sperm by lesbians in Canada has increased significantly since the legalization of same-sex marriage (Moskovtsev et al., 2013). Some are single-parent families, with, for example, a lesbian mother rearing her children from a previous mixed-sex marriage.

Heterosexuals often make the assumption, based on their homonegativity, that it is better for children to grow up in heterosexual families than in families with two parents of the same gender. Based on this assumption, they raise three questions about how children fare. First, will they be less healthy psychologically than children who grow up with two heterosexual parents? Second, will they have difficulties in relationships with their peers, perhaps being stigmatized or teased because of their unusual family situation? Third, will they show "disturbances" in gender identity or sexual identity? Will they become gay or lesbian? (Note the assumption that it would be better if they didn't.) What has research found?

How does growing up with two parents of the same gender affect children psychologically?

(a)

(b)

Figure 14.11 Lesbian and gay parents and their children. It is illegal to discriminate against gay men or lesbians in adoption, custody, or access decisions.

Medical model: A theoretical model in psychiatry in which mental problems are thought of as sickness or mental illness; the problems in turn are often thought to be due to biological factors.

Research on children growing up in lesbian or gay families, compared with those growing up in heterosexual families, dismisses these assumptions. For example, the adjustment and mental health of children in lesbian and gay families are no different from those of children in heterosexual families (Gartrell et al., 2005; Farr et al., 2010; Patterson, 2006). They fare about as well in terms of social skills and popularity as children growing up in heterosexual families (Patterson, 2009). This may be because, as shown by research in Quebec, the quality of the mother–child relationship is the same for heterosexual, lesbian, and bisexual mothers (Julien et al., 2008). Finally, the overwhelming numbers of children growing up in lesbian or gay households have a heterosexual orientation (Allen & Burrell, 2002).

In conclusion, although some people have raised concerns about children growing up in lesbian and gay families based on their negative assumptions, research consistently shows no difference between these children and those in heterosexual families in psychosocial development, gender identity, or sexual orientation (Canadian Psychological Association, 2003). Children need at least one loving, supportive parent and that can be found in many types of families. Nonetheless, these children may have to deal with the homonegativity of their peers. For example, a Canadian study found that 37 percent of youth with LGBTQ parents reported being verbally harassed about the sexual orientation of their parent (Taylor & Peter, 2011).

LO7

LGB Sexual Orientation and Mental Health

Some Canadians believe that homosexuality is a kind of mental illness. Is this really true? Do psychologists and psychiatrists agree that LGBs are poorly adjusted or deviant?

Sin and the Medical Model

The belief that homosexuality is a form of mental illness is something of an improvement over previous beliefs about homosexuality. Before the last century, the dominant belief in Europe and North America was that homosexuality was a sin or a heresy. During the Inquisition, people who were accused of being heretics were also frequently accused of being homosexuals and were burned at the stake. Indeed, in those times, all mental illness was regarded as a sin. In the twentieth century, this view was replaced by the **medical model**, in which mental disturbance, and homosexuality in particular, is viewed as a sickness or illness.[5]

---

[5] As one gay comedian quipped, "If homosexuality is an illness, hey, I'm going to call in queer to work tomorrow."

First Person

Carolyn and cj: A Same-Sex Couple

Carolyn is 29 and cj is 31. They have been together for eight years. They live in Ottawa, where Carolyn works for the federal government, and cj works as a researcher for an online activist organization.

Carolyn has always had close relationships with her parents and younger sister. They were her best friends when she was growing up, and she has many fond memories of working on family craft activities. In school, she was active in almost every nonsports extracurricular club. In middle school she wanted to have a boyfriend, mainly for the social status. In Grade 12, she had an impassioned relationship with a young man, and his openness about sexual identity influenced her own ideas on the subject. After this relationship, Carolyn wanted to balance her romantic experiences by having a relationship with a woman. She dated two women before cj and found that she was more able to be herself with women. Carolyn's nuclear family was supportive when she came out to them; they indicated that the gender of her partner was not an issue. She delayed coming out to her extended family, fearing that they would be less supportive. Carolyn identifies as a dyke: for her, the term *lesbian* assumes an attraction to women only, whereas the term *dyke* does not negate her past relationship with a man and recognizes her attraction to trans people.

cj's family is also close. She has two brothers and a sister. She had an active childhood and adolescence, spending much of it horseback riding and at the family cottage. Classism was a particular challenge for cj in school. She felt that there were certain expectations of her because she was from an upper-middle-class home. She rejected these expectations and purposefully sought out like-minded friends. Although cj had boyfriends in high school, including a couple of long-term relationships, she now recognizes that she was always attracted to women. In first-year university, cj had crushes on some of the women in her classes yet did not know how to act on her feelings. She dated one woman before Carolyn. When cj came out to her family, her father was immediately accepting. Her mother found it harder to come to terms with cj's sexual identity. Her minister and cj's sister were instrumental in helping her accept her daughter's identity. cj identifies as pansexual—that is, she is not exclusively attracted to women; rather, she is attracted to people regardless of their gender.

cj and Carolyn were both raised in Fredericton, where they attended the same high school. Although they knew each other by name, they travelled in different circles. When cj returned to Fredericton after university, she and Carolyn kept running into each other and had some awkward flirtatious moments. Yet they were not certain of each other's sexual identity or their mutual attraction until they saw each other at an LGBT event. Following this, they went on a coffee date, and within a few months were dating exclusively. Approximately 18 months later, they moved to Ottawa together so that Carolyn could complete a degree in art history and cj could do a master's degree in legal studies.

In spring 2000, three years before same-sex marriage was legalized in Ontario, Carolyn and cj applied for a marriage licence. Although they do not regard marriage as necessary to affirm their relationship, it was important for them to have the legal benefits and protections associated with marriage. They wanted to buy a house together and did not want to wait until same-sex marriage was legalized. So they took the necessary steps to ensure they would have as close to a legal equivalent to marriage as possible.

Most of Carolyn and cj's disagreements relate to household chores. Important aspects of their relationship are having similar politics and values, enjoying discussing such issues, and finding each other interesting. Their trust that the other person will be there to support them is also very important to them.

Source: Based on an interview by Dr. Jacqueline Cohen.

Research Evidence

What do the scientific data say? Early research compared a group of gay men and lesbians in therapy with a group of randomly chosen heterosexuals not in therapy. Not surprisingly, these studies tended to find more problems of adjustment among the gay and lesbian group than among the heterosexual group (Rosen, 1974). However, the reasoning was circular in assuming that LGBs were abnormal (in therapy) and that heterosexuals were normal (not in therapy), and then finding exactly that.

A major breakthrough came with the next group of studies, which involved nonpatient research. In these studies, a group of gay men and lesbians not in therapy (nonpatients) were compared with a group of heterosexuals not in therapy. The nonpatient gay men and lesbians were generally recruited through LGB organizations, advertisements, or word of mouth. Such nonpatient research has found no differences between the groups (Ross et al., 1988; Rothblum, 1994). That is, gay men, lesbians, and heterosexuals are equally well adjusted, a finding that is quite remarkable in view of the very negative attitudes that members of the general public tend to hold toward LGBs (Gonsiorek, 1996). This position has received official professional recognition by the American Psychiatric Association (APA). Before 1973, the APA had listed homosexuality as a disorder in its authoritative *Diagnostic and Statistical Manual of Mental Disorders* (which Canadian psychiatrists also use). In 1973, the APA voted to remove homosexuality from that listing so that it was no longer considered a psychiatric disorder by the APA or by the Canadian Psychiatric Association. Other countries were slower to make these changes. Homosexuality was removed from the list of mental disorders by the World Health Organization only in 1993, by Japan in 1995, and by China in 2001.

More recently, a new set of studies has emerged using even better designs that, for example, obtain a random sample of the general population and then compare the gay men and lesbians and the heterosexuals in the sample on indices of mental health (Cochran et al., 2003; Meyer, 2003; Roberts et al., 2010; Wichstrøm & Hegna, 2003). These studies find higher rates of depression, anxiety, and post-traumatic stress disorder among gay men and lesbians compared with heterosexuals, and suicide attempts are more common among LGB youth than among heterosexual youth (King et al., 2008; Mustanski et al., 2010; Roberts et al., 2010).

However, scientists vigorously debate the meaning of the statistics. One controversy concerns how big or meaningful the differences are. For example, in one study 9.1 percent of LGB adolescents had made a suicide attempt, compared with 3.6 percent for heterosexual adolescents (Wichstrøm & Hegna, 2003). We could focus on the fact that LGB youth were nearly three times as likely to attempt suicide. Alternatively, we could say that it's a gap of less than 6 percentage points and 90.9 percent of the LGBs had *not* attempted suicide (Savin-Williams, 2001; Savin-Williams & Ream, 2003). Should we view the glass as half full or half empty?

Conversion or reparative therapy: Any one of a number of treatments designed to turn LGBs into heterosexuals.

Beyond that, scientists agree that higher rates of depression and suicide among LGBs do not mean that homosexuality per se indicates mental illness. Rather, the higher rates reflect the following: (1) the exposure of LGBs to maltreatment and violence (Dunbar, 2006; Roberts et al., 2010), (2) the lack of support or downright rejection by family and friends that some LGBs experience (Ryan et al., 2009; Ueno, 2005), and (3) the stress of concealing their true identity (Meyer, 2003).

In contrast, high levels of social support from the LGB community and from family and friends are associated with better mental health (Fenaughty & Harré, 2003; Russell & Richards, 2003).

Can Sexual Orientation Be Changed by Psychotherapy?

Conversion therapy or **reparative therapy**—treatments designed to change LGBs into heterosexuals—have been around for more than 100 years (Shidlo et al., 2001; Haldeman, 1994). The latest versions come from far-right religious groups. Many earlier techniques were downright inhumane. They included crude behaviour therapy that involved giving gay men electrical shocks while they viewed slides of nude men, as well as surgeries ranging from castration to brain surgery. All these treatments rested on the assumption that homosexuality was an illness that should and could be cured.

Investigations of reparative therapies today reveal that many individuals undergoing reparative therapy do so because of pressures from their family. They also identify the personal agonies that people experience as they are forced into changing, or perhaps choose to change, their orientation. One man, who is now a psychologist, quoted from his diary:

> I am going to meet with the counselor tomorrow. I don't really know what to think. I feel that I need help but I also feel that I'm trying to do away with a part of myself. I know I should look at it as sinful and ugly, like a wart that needs to be burned off. Is it possible that those emotions are what allow me to be a sensitive caring male? Is it possible that God has allowed this in my life to build certain characteristics? Is it really ugly and sinful that I want to hold and be held by a man and that I want to have a relationship with a man that includes sex? It sure sounds ugly on paper. I don't like admitting these things. I really don't. What is it that causes me to think and feel this way? Is it Satanic? Am I possessed? (Ford, 2001, p. 77)

The consequences of reparative therapies can be ugly because they do not actually change people's sexual orientation but do make them feel awfully guilty about it. Thus, reparative therapy itself can create mental health problems. As a result, some gay men and bisexuals seek psychotherapy to help them recover from conversion therapies (Haldeman, 2001).

Given the evidence discussed earlier in this section supporting the argument that LGBs do not have a mental illness, reparative therapies make no sense. In addition, they do not work. Ethical issues are raised as well: Should a person be changed from gay to straight against his or her will? Why do we only try to change people from gay to straight and not the reverse? By 2000, the scandals associated with conversion therapies had become so great that the American Psychiatric Association issued an official position statement opposing them (American Psychiatric Association, 2000b).

What Determines Sexual Orientation?

A fascinating psychological question is, Why do people become gay, heterosexual, or bisexual? Several theoretical answers to this question, as well as the relevant evidence, are discussed in this section. You will notice that the older theorists and researchers considered it their task to explain homosexuality by reflecting a heteronormative approach; more recent investigators, realizing that heterosexuality needs to be explained as well, are more likely to consider it their task to understand the developmental pathways for all orientations, including heterosexuality.

Biological Theories

A number of scientists have proposed that sexual orientation is caused by biological factors. Interestingly, this is also the view of the majority of Canadians— 54 percent believe that homosexuality is something a person is born with and an additional 8 percent believe that it results from a combination of biological factors and environment (Mazzuca, 2004). The likeliest candidates for these biological causes are genetic factors, prenatal factors, differences in brain structure, and an endocrine imbalance.

Genetic Factors

One study recruited gay and bisexual men who had a twin brother or an adopted brother (Bailey & Pillard, 1991). Among the 56 gay men who had an identical twin brother, 52 percent of the co-twins were themselves gay (in the terminology of geneticists, this is a 52 percent concordance rate). Among the 54 gay men who had a nonidentical twin brother, 22 percent of the co-twins were themselves gay. Of the adoptive brothers of gay men, 11 percent were gay. The same research team later repeated the study with lesbians (Bailey

et al., 1993). Among the 71 lesbians who had an identical twin, 48 percent of the co-twins were also lesbian. Among the 37 lesbians who had a nonidentical twin sister, 16 percent of the co-twins were lesbian. Of the adoptive sisters of lesbians, 6 percent were lesbian. The statistics for women were therefore quite similar to those for men. Later studies using improved methods have found similar results (Kendler, Thornton, et al., 2000; Kirk et al., 2000).

The fact that the rate of concordance is substantially higher for identical twins than for nonidentical twins argues in favour of a genetic contribution to sexual orientation. If genetic factors absolutely *determined* sexual orientation, however, the concordance rate would be 100 percent for the identical twin pairs, and the rates are far from that. The implication is that factors other than genetics also play a role in influencing sexual orientation.

What causes people to be gay or heterosexual?

A milestone came in 2005 with the first full genome scan for sexual orientation in men, using modern genotyping methods (Mustanski et al., 2005). The sample consisted of 456 individuals from 146 different families, all of whom had two or more gay brothers. It included many heterosexual siblings and parents from those families, as well as the gay siblings. This design is ideal for spotting regions of DNA that are the same for two gay brothers but that differ from the heterosexual siblings or parents. The findings indicated possible influence by three genes, found on chromosomes 7, 8, and 10. It seems likely that multiple genes contribute to sexual orientation. This research is still in its infancy but should yield important findings in the next decade.

Prenatal Factors

Another possible biological cause is that homosexuality develops as a result of factors during the prenatal period. As we suggest in Chapter 5, exposure to inappropriate hormones during fetal development can lead a genetic female to have male genitals or a genetic male to have female genitals. It has been suggested that a similar process might account for homosexuality (and also for transgender—see Chapter 13).

According to one theory, homosexuality is caused by a variation in prenatal development. There is a critical time of fetal development during which the hypothalamus differentiates and sexual orientation is determined (Ellis & Cole-Harding, 2001). According to this theory, any of several biological variations during this period will produce homosexuality.

One line of animal research that supports this theory has found evidence that severe *stress to a mother* during pregnancy tends to produce homosexual offspring. For example, exposing pregnant female rats to stress produces male offspring that assume the female mating posture, although their ejaculatory behaviour is typical for males (Ward et al., 2002). The stress to the mother reduces the amount of testosterone in the fetus, which is thought to produce homosexual rats. Research with humans designed to test the prenatal stress hypothesis reports mixed results. Some studies find effects like those in the rat studies, and others do not (Bailey et al., 1991; Ellis & Cole-Harding, 2001).

Canadian researchers have been leaders in examining prenatal factors that may determine a person's sexual orientation. For example, Ontario psychologists Ray Blanchard and Anthony Bogaert have studied the birth order of gay men. Their research shows that consistently, across many samples, in a number of countries, compared with heterosexual men, gay men are more likely to have a late birth order and to have more older brothers but not more older sisters (Blanchard, 2004; Bogaert, 2003). This is termed the fraternal birth order effect. The researchers find no birth order or sibling effects for lesbians compared with heterosexual women. They believe that they have uncovered a prenatal effect, hypothesizing that, with each successive pregnancy with a male fetus, the mother forms more antibodies against an antigen (H-Y antigen) produced by a gene on the Y chromosome (Bogaert & Skorska, 2011). Because H-Y antigen is known to influence prenatal sexual differentiation, the hypothesis is that the mother's antibodies to this antigen may affect sexual differentiation in the developing fetal brain and subsequent sexual attraction. These researchers estimate that between 15 and 30 percent of gay men had their sexual orientation created in this manner (Blanchard & Bogaert, 2004; Cantor et al., 2002).

Other researchers have documented an odd but potentially important pattern concerning the 2D:4D finger-length ratio. This refers to the ratio of the length of the index finger (2D) to the length of the ring finger (4D). In general, men have lower 2D:4D ratios than women; that is, men's index fingers are relatively shorter than their ring fingers, compared with women's. Lesbians have a lower 2D:4D ratio than heterosexual women. There are no differences between gay men and heterosexual men (Grimbos et al., 2010). It is thought that the 2D:4D ratio is an indicator of prenatal androgen exposure, so these results suggest possible prenatal effects on women's sexual orientation. Ontario researcher Martin Lalumière has found that gay men and lesbians are more likely to be left-handed than are heterosexuals; gay men are about 40 percent more likely than straight men to be left-handed, and lesbians are nearly twice as likely as heterosexual women to be left-handed (Lalumière et al., 2000). Both patterns suggest some kind of prenatal hormone effect on the developing brain.

These theories of prenatal influence are intriguing, but none right now have enough scientific evidence behind them to be completely accepted (Gooren, 2006).

Brain Factors

Another line of theorizing argues that there are anatomical differences between the brains of gays and straights that produce the differences in sexual orientation. A number of studies have pursued this possibility, all looking at somewhat different regions of the brain (Swaab, 2005). A highly publicized study by neuroscientist Simon LeVay (1991) is an example. LeVay found significant differences between gay men and straight men in certain cells in the anterior portion of the hypothalamus. However, the study had a number of flaws. Other scientists who looked for this effect found no differences in this region of the hypothalamus as a function of the person's sexual orientation (Byne et al., 2000; Swaab, 2005). Yet animal researchers believe that they have identified a similar region in the hypothalamus of the rat that does seem to be involved in sexual behaviour (Swaab, 2005).

Using modern functional brain scanning methods, researchers exposed gay men, heterosexual men, and heterosexual women to human pheromones and recorded their brain responses (Savic et al., 2005). One of the pheromones, AND, is a "male" pheromone and is found in male sweat. The other, EST, is a "female" pheromone and is found in female urine. Gay men and heterosexual women showed activation of a region of the hypothalamus (the medial preoptic area, MPOA, of the anterior hypothalamus) in response to AND, whereas heterosexual men did not show the brain response to AND. As a control, the participants were also exposed to common odours, such as lavender oil; these odours did not activate the hypothalamus. In a second experiment, the researchers repeated the study with lesbians and found that EST stimulated their hypothalamus, as it does with heterosexual men (Berglund et al., 2006). What do these studies mean? They definitely don't mean that gay men have female brains and lesbians have male brains. What they do show is that both heterosexual men and lesbians are turned on (in their brains) by women's pheromones, and that gay men and heterosexual women are turned on by male pheromones.

Hormonal Factors

Investigating the possibility that endocrine factors are the cause of homosexuality, many researchers have tried to determine whether the testosterone levels of gay men differ from those of straight men. These studies have not found any hormonal differences between the two groups (Gooren, 2006).

Despite these results, in past decades some clinicians attempted to cure male homosexuality by administering testosterone therapy (Glass & Johnson, 1944). This therapy failed; indeed, it seems to result in even more same-sex sexual activity than usual. This is not an unexpected result, since, as we saw in Chapter 9, androgen levels seem to be related to sexual responsiveness. As a clinician friend of two of the authors replied to an undergraduate male who was seeking testosterone therapy for his homosexuality, "It won't make you heterosexual; it will only make you horny."

In conclusion, of the biological theories, the genetic theory has the best supporting evidence, but much more research is needed.

Learning Theory

Behaviourists emphasize the importance of learning in the development of sexual orientation. They note the prevalence of bisexual behaviour both in other species and in young humans, and they argue that rewards and punishments shape the individual's behaviour into predominant homosexuality or predominant heterosexuality. The assumption, then, is that humans have a relatively amorphous, undifferentiated pool of sex drive that, depending on circumstances (rewards and punishments), may be channelled in any of several directions. In short, people are born sexual, not heterosexual or homosexual. Only through learning does one of these behaviours become more likely than the other. For example, if early sexual experiences are with a same-sex partner and pleasant, the person may become gay. Same-sex sexual activity has essentially been rewarded and therefore becomes more likely.

Another possibility, according to a learning-theory approach, is that a person who has early heterosexual experiences that are very unpleasant might develop toward homosexuality. Heterosexuality has essentially been punished and therefore becomes less likely. This might occur, for instance, in the case of a girl who is sexually assaulted by a male at an early age; her first experience with a male was extremely unpleasant, so she avoids it and turns to homosexuality.

The learning-theory approach treats same-sex sexual activity as a normal form of behaviour and recognizes that both heterosexuality and homosexuality are not necessarily inborn but must be learned.

The evidence on learning-theory's explanation of sexual orientation is mixed. A comprehensive study of the influences on sexual orientation in humans disconfirmed some essential arguments. The idea that homosexuality results from early unpleasant heterosexual experiences was not supported by the data. Lesbian women, for example, were no more likely to have been sexually assaulted than were heterosexual women (Bell et al., 1981). Yet recent research using an animal model does point to the importance of early learning. Zebra finches are small birds that are monogamous, mate for

life, and are almost invariably heterosexual. If the fathers are removed from the cages, though, so that the young birds grow up without adult males or male–female pairs, in adulthood these birds pair with either males or females (Adkins-Regan, 2002). That is, their behaviour, which is bisexual, is a result of early experience.

In contrast to the bird research, research with humans indicates that the great majority of children who grow up with a gay or lesbian parent identify themselves as heterosexual (Allen & Burrell, 2002; Gartrell et al., 2011; Patterson, 2006). In this sense, then, sexual orientation is not "learned" from one's parents.

Interactionist Theory

Psychologist Daryl Bem (1996) proposed a theory of the development of sexual orientation that encompasses the interaction of biological factors and experiences with the environment best described as the exotic becomes erotic. Bem's theory is diagrammed in Figure 14.12.

The theory begins with biological influences, relying on the evidence discussed earlier about biological contributions to sexual orientation (box A in Figure 14.12). However, Bem does not believe that genes and other

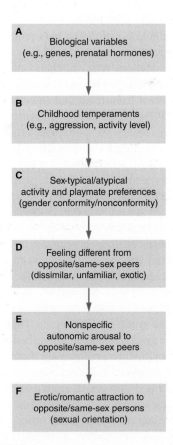

Figure 14.12 Daryl Bem's theory of the development of sexual orientation: the exotic becomes erotic.

biological factors directly and magically determine a person's sexual orientation. Rather, he theorized that biological factors exert their influence on sexual orientation through their influence on temperament in childhood (box A to box B). Psychologists have found abundant evidence that two aspects of temperament have some biological basis: aggression and activity level. Moreover, these two aspects of temperament show reliable gender differences. According to Bem, most children show levels of aggression and activity that are typical of their gender; boys are generally more aggressive and more active than girls are. These tendencies lead children to engage in gender-conforming activities (boxes B to C). Most boys play active, aggressive sports, and most girls prefer quieter play activities. These play patterns also lead children to associate almost exclusively with members of their own gender. The boy playing tackle football is playing in a group that consists either entirely or almost entirely of boys. This chain of events will eventually lead to a heterosexual orientation in adulthood.

A minority of children, however, have temperamental characteristics that are not typical of their gender: some boys are not particularly active or aggressive and some girls are. These children are then gender-nonconforming in their play patterns. The boys prefer quieter, less active play and have more girls as friends, and the gender-nonconforming girls prefer aggressive sports and have more boys as friends.

These experiences with childhood play and playmates create a feeling in children that certain other children are different from them and therefore are exotic (boxes C to D). For the boy who spends most of his time playing active, aggressive sports with other boys, girls are different, mysterious, and exotic. For the gender-nonconforming girl who plays active sports with boys, most girls, too, seem different and exotic to her.

The presence of an exotic other causes a person to feel generalized arousal, whether in childhood, adolescence, or adulthood (boxes D to E). Those of you who are heterosexual certainly remember many instances in your past when you felt ill at ease and nervous in the presence of a member of the other gender.

In the final link of the model, this generalized arousal is transformed into erotic or romantic attraction. Essentially, the exotic becomes erotic. This transformation may be a result of processes described in Berscheid and Walster's (1974) two-component theory of arousal, discussed in Chapter 12. Generalized arousal can easily be transformed into sexual arousal and attraction if the conditions are right. For heterosexual persons, the exotic people are members of the other gender, with whom they had less contact in childhood and who have become eroticized. For gay men and lesbians, the exotic people are members of their own gender, from whom they felt different in childhood and who have become eroticized. For most individuals, then, members of the other gender are exotic. Thus, one virtue of the theory is that it is designed to explain both gay and heterosexual sexual orientations.

One body of evidence that is consistent with Bem's theory indicates that gay men and lesbians, on average, are more likely than heterosexuals are to have had a childhood history of gender nonconformity. In one intriguing study, researchers recruited gay men, lesbians, heterosexual men, and heterosexual women (Rieger et al., 2008). They asked the participants for home movies or videos taken of them when they were children. The videos were then coded by trained raters who were unaware of the adult sexual orientation of the child shown in the video. For each video, they rated the child's behaviour on a seven-point scale ranging from more masculine to more feminine. The results showed that, as early as age four, the "pre-homosexual" children differed significantly from the "pre-heterosexual" children. The pre-homosexual children were less gender conforming—that is, the boys were, on average, more feminine in their behaviour than the pre-heterosexual boys were, and the pre-homosexual girls were more masculine, on average, than the pre-heterosexual girls were. It is fascinating that gender nonconformity can be detected at such an early age, and the study provides support for Bem's theory, although it is also consistent with the biological theories.

At the same time, Bem's theory and evidence have been criticized (Peplau et al., 1998; for Bem's response, see Bem, 1998). Two criticisms have been raised: (1) evidence not discussed by Bem contradicts some central propositions of the theory, and (2) the theory reflects male experience and neglects female experience. Regarding the evidence, Bem noted that, in one major study, lesbians (70 percent) were significantly more likely than were heterosexual women (51 percent) to recall feeling somewhat or very different from other girls their age (Bell et al., 1981). The difference is significant but perhaps more important is the finding that a majority of heterosexual women also felt different from other girls. Other girls seemed different or exotic to them. Why didn't they become lesbian, then?

Sociological Theory

Sociologists emphasize the effects of *labelling* in explaining homosexuality. The label "homosexual" has a big impact in our society. For example, one of the biggest insults used by middle-school students is calling a classmate a "fag" (McFarland, 2001). The label "homosexual" often has derogatory connotations, reflecting our society's predominantly negative attitudes toward homosexuality.

But the label "homosexual" might also act as a self-fulfilling prophecy. Suppose that a young boy—possibly because he is gender nonconforming or poor in sports, or for no reason at all—is called "gay." He reacts strongly and becomes more and more anxious and worried about his problem. He becomes painfully aware of the slightest same-sex attraction in himself. Finally, he convinces himself that he is gay. He begins engaging in same-sex sexual activity and associates with a gay group. In short, a gay man has been created through labelling.

Recall that in Chapter 2 we discussed Reiss's sociological theory of human sexuality. In his theorizing, he addresses the issue of sexual orientation, focusing particularly on gay men. Recognizing the need to explain cross-cultural differences in sexual patterns, he contends that it is male-dominant societies with a great rigidity of gender roles that produce the highest incidence of homosexuality. In such societies, there is a rigid male role that must be learned and conformed to, but young boys have little opportunity to learn it from adult men precisely because the gender roles are rigid: women take care of children, and men have little contact with them. It is therefore difficult to learn the heterosexual component of the male role. In addition, because the male role is rigid, there will be a certain number of males who dislike it and reject its heterosexual component. Cross-cultural studies support his observations (Reiss, 1986). Societies that have a great maternal involvement with infants and low father involvement with infants and that have rigid gender roles are precisely those that have the highest incidence of same-sex sexual behaviour in males.

This pattern describes the negative pathway to becoming gay or lesbian. Reiss argues that there is also a positive pathway. It exists in less gender-rigid societies with more permissiveness about sexuality. In such societies, individuals feel freer to experiment with same-sex behaviour and may find it satisfying. Examples are provided by several First Nations peoples in which three gender roles have been recognized (see Chapter 13).

The Bottom Line

We have examined a number of theories of sexual orientation and the evidence supporting or refuting them. What is the bottom line? Which theory is correct? The answer is, we don't know yet. We do not know what causes sexual orientation. Several theories have strong evidence supporting them, but no one theory accounts for all cases. We believe that a good lesson can be learned from this conclusion.

It has generally been assumed not only that LGBs form a distinct category (which, we have already seen, is not very accurate) but also that they form a homogeneous category; that is, that all LGBs are fairly similar.

Not so. Probably there are many different kinds or types of gay men, lesbians, bisexuals, and heterosexuals. If this is the case, then one would not expect a single cause of sexual orientation but rather many causes, each corresponding to its type. The next step in research, then, should be to identify the various types of LGBs and heterosexuals and the different pathways of development that lead to each.

Differences Between Gay Men and Lesbians

Although gay men and lesbians are commonly lumped together in one category based on their attraction to individuals of their same gender, evidence from a number of sources indicates that there are some important differences between the two groups that go beyond one group being male and the other female.

Women are more likely to be bisexual and less likely to be exclusively homosexual than men are. In the NSFG data set, 2.8 percent of women and 0.5 percent of men indicated that they were sexually attracted to both women and men (Chandra et al., 2011).

In related research, among both individuals who identify as both straight and gay, women show more flexibility or change over time in their sexual orientation (Kinnish et al., 2005). As noted earlier in this chapter, this is what Diamond (2008a) called *sexual fluidity*. In laboratory research, men are specific in their sexual arousal whereas women tend not to be (Chivers et al., 2004). That is, heterosexual men tend to be aroused, physiologically, by female stimuli and not male stimuli, and gay men show the reverse pattern. Women, however, whether lesbian or heterosexual, show arousal to both male and female stimuli.

Some of the theories discussed earlier in this chapter seem to work for gay men or for lesbians but not for both. For example, the fraternal birth order effect has been found repeatedly; compared with heterosexual men, gay men are more likely to have a late birth order and an excess of older brothers. Lesbians, however, are no more or less likely to have a late birth order compared with heterosexual women (Blanchard, 1997; Bogaert, 2003).

Are men or women more likely to be attracted to both genders?

We will almost certainly need somewhat different theories to explain the development of sexual orientation in women and in men (Hyde & Jaffee, 2000). This does not mean that any one theory will apply to all gay men or all lesbians; we likely will need different theories to explain development of sexual orientation within each gender as well.

Sexual Orientation in Multicultural Perspective

Different cultures around the world hold different views of homosexuality. A survey of attitudes in 39 countries, found that there is general acceptance in North America, the European Union, and much of Latin America. However, there is widespread rejection in predominantly Muslim countries, Africa, Russia, and parts of Asia (Pew Research, 2013). In some other countries opinions are divided. Countries in which religion is more central to people's lives tend to be less accepting.

Different cultures also hold different views of same-sex sexual behaviour. For example, as described in Sexuality in a Diverse World in Chapter 2, among the Melanesians of the southwest Pacific same-sex behaviour is ritualized such that boys are expected to engage in exclusively same-sex sexual activity for about ten years but then marry women and become exclusively heterosexual. As one anthropologist observed about the Sambia of Papua New Guinea:

> Semen is also necessary for young boys to attain full growth to manhood. . . . They need a boost, as it were. When a boy is eleven or twelve years old, he is engaged for several months in homosexual intercourse with a healthy older man chosen by his father. (This is always an in-law or unrelated person, since the same notions of incestuous relations apply to little boys as to marriageable women.) Men point to the rapid growth of adolescent youths, the appearance of peach fuzz beards, and so on, as the favorable results of this child-rearing practice. (Schieffelin, 1976, p. 124)

Similarly, various Canadian ethnic minority groups differ in their cultural definitions for same-sex behaviours.

Generally, members of Canadian ethnocultural communities have less tolerance for homosexuality than members of the majority culture do. There tends to be a stigma attached to being a gay man, a denial of the existence of homosexuality within the community, and considerable pressure to conform to community norms. As a result, many LGBs feel forced to stay in the closet with respect to their sexual orientation to be accepted within their family and community (Manson Singer et al., 1996). Thus, ethnic minority LGBs have a double minority status and may experience racism within the gay community, as well as antigay prejudice within their ethnic group (Ibañez, et al., 2009). Perhaps as a result, in the Canadian Community Health Survey, members of ethnocultural minorities were less likely to identify themselves as homosexual than were Canadians from the majority culture (Tjepkema, 2008).

For example, in both the Caribbean and African communities in Canada, gay and bisexual men may keep their activities secret for fear of being ostracized if they are open about their sexual orientation (Health Canada, 1994a, 1994b). Similarly, because of strong negative attitudes in the community, many gay and bisexual men in the South Asian community keep their same-sex relationships hidden. They may comply with family pressure to get married to avoid causing conflict in the family. South Asian men who were born in Canada are more likely to be open about their sexual orientation (Health Canada, 1994c).

Members of some ethnic groups, including men from the Caribbean and Latin American communities, may engage in extensive same-sex sexual behaviour while still considering themselves to be heterosexual (Manson Singer et al., 1996). An interesting example of these different cultural definitions comes from a study of Mexican and Mexican-American men (Magaña & Carrier, 1991). In Mexico, there is a dichotomizing of same-sex sexual behaviours that parallels traditional gender roles. Anal intercourse, because it most resembles penis-in-vagina intercourse, is the preferred behaviour, and fellatio is practised relatively little. A man adopts the role of either receptive partner or inserting partner and does this exclusively. Those who take the receptive role are considered unmanly, feminine, and homosexual. Those who take the inserting role are considered masculine, are not labelled as homosexual, and are not stigmatized. Research with Latin American men living in Montreal also found that men who take the inserting role during anal intercourse with men often consider themselves to be heterosexual (Health Canada, 1994d). In contrast, men who take the receptive role are considered gay and are marginalized in the community. This approach differs substantially from that in the gay Canadian majority, where men commonly switch roles and both are considered gay.

Such different definitions of homosexuality are not limited to Latin American cultures. One researcher described the scene in contemporary Egypt as follows:

> In Egypt, because there was so little sense of homosexuality as an identity, what position you took in bed defined all. Between men, the only sex that counted was anal sex. . . . In the minds of most Egyptians, "gay," if it meant anything at all, signified taking the receptive position in anal sex. On the other hand, a person who took the insertive role—and that seemed to include virtually all Egyptian men, to judge by what my acquaintances told me—was not considered gay. . . . Many of the insults in the Arabic language concern being penetrated anally by another man. (Miller, 1992, p. 76)

As for lesbians, Latin American women and Caribbean women experience conflicts in the complexities of ethnicity and sexual orientation (Espin, 1987; Gonzalez & Espin, 1996; Silvera, 1990). In both cultures, emotional and physical closeness among women is

Figure 14.13 Ethnicity and sexual orientation. Among Latin American and Caribbean women, warmth and physical closeness are very acceptable, but there are strong taboos against female–female sexual relationships.

considered acceptable and desirable. However, attitudes toward lesbianism are extremely restrictive (Figure 14.13). Familism, the special emphasis on family—defined as mother, father, children, and grandparents in Latin American cultures—and the emphasis on attracting a man and bearing a child in Caribbean cultures makes the lesbian even more of an outsider. Women who are openly lesbian may be stigmatized and ostracized in these communities.

Among Asian communities in Canada, two features of the culture shape attitudes toward homosexuality and its expression: (1) a strong distinction between what may be expressed publicly and what should be kept private, and (2) a stronger value placed on loyalty to one's family and on the performance of family roles than on the expression of one's own desires (Chan, 1995; Cochran et al., 2007). Sexuality is something that must be expressed only privately, not publicly. And having an identity, much less a sexual identity or a gay lifestyle, apart from one's family is almost incomprehensible to traditional Asians. As a result, a relatively

small proportion of LGB members of the Asian communities in Canada are "out" in their community. Nonetheless, there is an active gay Asian community in Vancouver. However, these individuals often remain in the closet within Asian communities because of fear of bringing shame to their families (Health Canada, 1994e). As with other ethnocultural communities in Canada, members of Asian communities who are out tend to be more acculturated—that is, influenced by Canadian culture.

In sum, when we consider sexual orientation from a multicultural perspective, two main points emerge. First, the very definition of homosexuality is set by culture. In Canada, we would say that a man who is the inserting partner in anal intercourse with another man is engaging in homosexual behaviour, but other cultures (such as Mexico and Egypt) would not agree. Second, many ethnocultural communities are more disapproving of homosexuality than is the majority Canadian culture. In those cases, LGBs feel conflicts between their sexual identity and loyalty to their ethnic group.

A Final Note

As we have seen in this chapter, most theory and research rests on the assumption that sexual orientation is determined by conditions in childhood or by prenatal or genetic factors. Yet some people have their first mixed-sex and then their first same-sex experience in their 20s. It is difficult to believe that these behaviours were determined by some pathological condition at age five. **Deprivation homosexuality**, or situational homosexuality, is also a good example of the influence of late-occurring experience. A heterosexual man may engage in same-sex sexual behaviour while in prison but return to exclusive heterosexuality after his release (Kunzel, 2008). Once again, it seems likely that such a man's same-sex sexual behaviour was determined by his circumstances (being in prison) rather than by some influence years before.

Unlike gender identity, which seems to be fixed in the preschool years, sexual identity continues to evolve. This contradicts some scientists' assertion that sexual orientation is determined before

Deprivation homosexuality: Same-sex sexual activity that occurs in certain situations, such as prisons, when people are deprived of their regular mixed-sex activity.

adolescence (Bell et al., 1981). We think that when sexual orientation is determined is still an open question. For some it may be determined by genetic factors or experiences early in life, but for others it may be determined in adulthood or continue to be fluid.

A question is raised as to whether heterosexuality is really the "natural" state. The pattern in some theories has been to try to discover the pathological conditions that cause a person to become gay (e.g., a father who is an inadequate role model or an unusual dose of prenatal hormones)—all on the basis of the assumption that heterosexuality is the natural state and that homosexuality must be explained as a deviation from it. As we have seen, this approach has failed; there appear to be multiple causes of homosexuality, just as there may be multiple causes of heterosexuality. The important alternative to consider is that bisexuality is the natural state, a point acknowledged by Freud, the learning theorists, and sociological theorists (Weinberg et al., 1994). This chapter will close, then, with some questions. Psychologically, the real question should concern not the conditions that lead a person to become gay but rather the causes of exclusive attraction to members of one's own gender or to members of the other gender. Why do we eliminate some people as potential sex partners simply based on their gender? Why isn't everyone bisexual?

SUMMARY

Sexual orientation refers to a person's erotic and emotional attraction toward members of his or her own gender, toward members of the other gender, both, or neither.

Well-sampled surveys indicate (when corrected for some underreporting) that about 2 percent of men and 1 percent of women have a gay identity. Kinsey devised a scale ranging from 0 (exclusively heterosexual experience) to 6 (exclusively homosexual experience) to measure this diversity of experience. A person's sexual identity may be discordant with his or her actual behaviour.

Although some Canadians believe that homosexuality is wrong, the vast majority are in favour of equal rights for LGBs, and most favour same-sex marriage. In some cases homonegativity and antigay prejudice may be so strong that they result in maltreatment and harassment.

Lesbian, gay, and bisexual communities can be found around the world. These communities are defined by a common culture and social life and by rituals, such as pride marches. In surveys, the majority of

gay men and lesbians report being in a steady romantic relationship. Although people with negative attitudes toward LGBs have voiced concerns about the psychological well-being of children who grow up in lesbian and gay families, these concerns are unfounded, according to the available studies.

Well-conducted research indicates that homosexuality per se is not a sign of poor adjustment. Research does show somewhat elevated rates of depression and suicide among LGBs, mainly because of exposure to prejudice and hate crimes and the failure of family and friends to support the person. Although some groups claim success in reparative therapy to change the sexual orientation of LGBs, there is no scientific evidence that one's sexual orientation can be changed and many indications that these therapies are psychologically harmful. Most therapists believe that it is impossible to change a person's sexual orientation (that is, their erotic and emotional attraction), although people can and do change their sexual identity.

In regard to the causes of sexual orientation, biological explanations include genetic factors, hormone imbalance, prenatal factors, and brain factors. The genetic explanation has some support from the data. Learning theorists stress that the sex drive is undifferentiated and is channelled, through experience, into heterosexuality or homosexuality. Bem's interactionist theory proposes that homosexuality results from the influence of biological factors on temperament, which in turn influences whether a child plays with boys or girls; the less familiar (exotic) gender becomes associated with sexual arousal. Sociologists emphasize the importance of roles and labelling in understanding homosexuality. Available data do not point to any single factor as a cause of sexual orientation but rather suggest that there may be many types of homosexuality and heterosexuality with corresponding multiple causes.

Gay men and lesbians differ in some important ways. Women are more likely to be bisexual, and theories that are effective in explaining men's sexual orientation are not supported for women. Bisexuality may be more "natural" than either exclusive heterosexuality or exclusive homosexuality.

Different ethnic groups in Canada, as well as different cultures around the world, hold diverse views of same-sex sexual behaviours.

QUESTIONS FOR THOUGHT, DISCUSSION, AND DEBATE

1. Do you feel that you are homonegative or homophobic, or do you feel that your attitude toward gays and lesbians is positive or tolerant? Why do you think your attitudes are the way they are? Are you satisfied with your attitudes or do you want to change them?

2. Does your university, in addition to prohibiting discrimination based on race and sex, have a proactive policy to prevent discrimination based on sexual orientation? Do you think it should?

3. Imagine that you are a gay man employed at a managerial level in an advertising agency in Calgary. You and your partner have been together for 11 years and intend to stay that way. It is becoming increasingly awkward for you to pretend that you have no partner and that you are straight when you attend parties for the staff or when people ask you how your weekend was. Should you come out to your colleagues at work? Why or why not?

connect | LEARNSMART | SMARTBOOK™

For more information on the resources available from McGraw-Hill Ryerson, go to **www.mheducation.ca/he/solutions**.

Are **YOU** Curious?

1. How can I tell if sexual behaviour is problematic?
2. Are men or women more likely to engage in problematic sexual behaviour?
3. What is kinky sex?
4. Is my online sexual activity compulsive?

Read this chapter to find out.

CHAPTER

15

Variations in Sexual Behaviour

LEARNING OBJECTIVES

After studying this chapter, you will be able to

LO1 Differentiate between normal and abnormal sexual behaviour.

LO2 Define and describe sexual addictions and compulsive sexual behaviour, and apply these concepts to online sexual activity.

LO3 Discuss the different forms of fetishism and the mechanism by which they develop.

LO4 Define transvestism and the four possible motivations for it.

LO5 Define and compare the various components of BDSM.

LO6 Define and describe the similarities and differences between voyeurism and exhibitionism, and outline possible causes of these behaviours.

LO7 Describe hypersexuality and its relationship to other paraphilias.

LO8 Identify and define some of the less common sexual variations.

LO9 Describe the ways in which harmful sexual variations can be prevented and treated.

ariety's the spice of life
    That gives it all its flavor.*

---

* William Cowper (1785).

Most laypeople, as well as most scientists, have a tendency to classify behaviour as normal or abnormal. There seems to be a particular tendency to do this with regard to sexual behaviour. Many terms are used for abnormal sexual behaviour, including *sexual deviance*, *perversion*, *sexual variance*, and *paraphilia*. The term *sexual variations* will be used in this chapter because it is currently favoured in scientific circles.

This chapter will deal with some behaviours that many people consider to be abnormal, so it seems advisable at this point to consider exactly when a sexual behaviour is abnormal. Which of the following would you consider abnormal? A man has difficulty getting aroused unless he is wearing women's panties. A woman enjoys being tied up as part of sex play. A man gets turned on watching someone undress without that person's knowledge.

L01

When Is Sexual Behaviour Abnormal?

Defining Abnormal

As we saw in Chapter 1, sexual behaviour varies a great deal across cultures. There is a corresponding variation in what is considered to be "abnormal" sexual behaviour. Given this great variability, how can anyone come up with a reasonable set of criteria for what is abnormal?

One approach is to use a *statistical definition*. According to this approach, an abnormal sexual behaviour is one that is rare or not practised by many people. Following this definition, then, standing on one's hands while having intercourse would be considered abnormal because it is rarely done, although it does not seem very abnormal in other ways. This definition, unfortunately, does not give us much insight into the psychological or social functioning of the person who engages in the behaviour.

In the *sociological approach*, the problem of culture dependence is explicitly acknowledged. A sociologist might define a sexual behaviour that violates the norms

of society as a deviant (or abnormal) sexual behaviour. Thus, if a society says that a particular sexual behaviour is deviant, it is—at least in that society. This approach recognizes the importance of the individual's interaction with society and of the problems that people face if their behaviour is labelled "deviant" in the culture in which they live.

A *psychological approach* was stated by Arnold Buss in his text entitled *Psychopathology* (1966). He says, "The three criteria of abnormality are discomfort, inefficiency, and bizarreness." The last of these criteria, bizarreness, has the problem of being culturally defined; what seems bizarre in one culture may seem normal in another. However, the first two criteria are good in that they focus on the discomfort and unhappiness sometimes felt by the person with a truly abnormal pattern of sexual behaviour and on inefficiency. For example, a male clerk in a Minneapolis supermarket was having intercourse with willing shoppers in their cars several times a day. This apparently compulsive behaviour led to his being fired. This is an example of inefficient functioning, a behaviour that can reasonably be considered abnormal.

The *medical approach* is exemplified by the definitions included in the *Diagnostic and Statistical Manual of Mental Disorders* (*DSM-5*) (American Psychiatric Association, 2013a). It recognizes eight specific paraphilic disorders: voyeuristic disorder, exhibitionist disorder, frotteuristic disorder, sexual masochism disorder, sexual sadism disorder, pedophilic disorder, fetishistic disorder, and transvestic disorder. There is also a category for paraphilias that are not listed because there are many other paraphilias. A **paraphilia** is an intense and persistent sexual interest, manifested by fantasies, sexual urges, or behaviour, in unusual objects, situations, or individuals. Canadian psychologist Peggy Kleinplatz and her colleague Charles Moser argue that because there is no agreed-on definition of healthy sexuality, it is difficult to be clear about what behaviours should be classified as paraphilic. They believe that behaviours that involve unusual sexual interests but not coercion, such as sexual sadism and sexual masochism, may be healthy expressions of sexuality for some individuals. They argue

Paraphilia (par-uh-FILL-ee-uh): Intense and persistent sexual interest in unusual objects, situations, or individuals.

that the fact that they are labelled as paraphilias is due to sociopolitical and historical factors (Moser & Kleinplatz, 2005).

The *DSM-5* distinguishes between paraphilias and paraphilic disorders. A **paraphilic disorder** is a paraphilia that causes distress or impairment to the individual or whose satisfaction has entailed personal harm or risk of harm to others (American Psychiatric Association, 2013a, p. 685). That is, not all paraphilias are disorders and many do not require clinical intervention. Diagnostic criteria are stated for each specific paraphilic disorder; these generally include that (1) the fantasies, urges, or behaviours are recurrent and intense; (2) they have occurred for at least six months; and (3) they have negative consequences for the individual (i.e., distress, impairment, or harm to others).

Note that some paraphilias and most atypical sexual behaviours are not against the law (e.g., fetishism and sexual masochism). However, some are. For example, pedophilia, the most serious paraphilia, is against the law because it involves exploitation and force. It is discussed in Chapter 16. Other behaviours do not involve exploitation or force but do violate community standards of taste. In this area we find laws against **indecent exposure**, voyeurism, indecent acts in a public place, and public nudity (refer to Table 2.1 for a list of sex crimes contained in the *Criminal Code of Canada*).

An interesting case that demonstrates how community standards of taste can affect laws regulating sex crimes arose when Gwen Jacobs walked topless through the city of Guelph in Ontario in 1991. She was charged with committing an indecent act in a public place. However, in 1996, the Ontario Court of Appeal ruled that women have a right to go topless as long as it is not for commercial gain or sexual purposes. What are the attitudes of Canadians toward women going topless? One study found that 72 percent of Canadians think it should be illegal for women to go topless on city streets, and 48 percent think it should be illegal for them to go topless on a public beach (Fischtein et al., 2005). This does not necessarily mean they think it constitutes abnormal behaviour, however.

In this chapter we discuss a number of atypical sexual behaviours, including seven of the behaviours that can be diagnosed as paraphilias—all except pedophilia, which is discussed in Chapter 16. We also discuss several other atypical sexual behaviours, including hypersexuality, asphyxiophilia, and compulsive online sexual activities. As discussed next, all these behaviours occur along a continuum from normal to abnormal.

Paraphilic disorder: A paraphilia that causes distress or impairment to the individual or that harms or would harm other people.
Indecent exposure: Showing one's genitals in a public place to passersby; exhibitionism.

The Normal–Abnormal Continuum

Each approach just described provides criteria that attempt to distinguish what is "normal" from what is "abnormal." Although such distinctions may be made in theory, they are often difficult to make in reality. For example, lingerie is often sexually arousing for both men and women (Figure 15.1). For a woman who is wearing a low-cut bra and silk thong panties, the sensuous feel of the material against her skin may be arousing; for a man it might be the sight of the woman wearing the lingerie. At the same time, lingerie is a common sexual fetish object. This is an excellent example of the continuum from normal to abnormal sexual behaviour. That is, normal sexual behaviour and abnormal sexual behaviour—like other normal and abnormal behaviours—are not two separate categories but rather gradations on a continuum. Many people have mild fetishes, finding such things as silk underwear arousing,

Figure 15.1   Wearing lingerie is an excellent example of sexual behaviour that falls on a continuum from normal (sexually arousing for both men and women) to abnormal (being a common sexual fetish object).

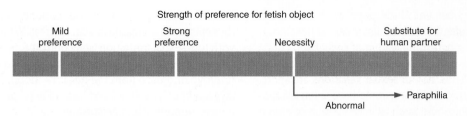

Figure 15.2   The continuum from normal to abnormal behaviour in the case of fetishes.

and that is well within the range of normal behaviour; only when the fetish becomes extreme is it abnormal. Indeed, in one sample of university men, 42 percent reported that they had engaged in voyeurism and 35 percent had engaged in *frottage* (sexual rubbing against a woman in a crowd) (Templeman & Stinnett, 1991). But the point is that many of these behaviours are common even in "normal" populations.

This continuum from normal to abnormal behaviour might be conceptualized by using the scheme shown in Figure 15.2. A mild preference, or even a strong preference, for the fetish object (say, silk panties) is within the normal range of sexual behaviour. When the silk panties become a necessity—when the man cannot become aroused and engage in sexual activity unless they are present—we have crossed the boundary into abnormal behaviour. When the man becomes obsessed with white silk panties and shoplifts them at every opportunity so that he will always have them available, the fetish has become a paraphilia. In extreme forms, the silk panties may become a substitute for a human partner, and the man's sexual behaviour consists of masturbating with the silk panties present. In these extreme forms, the man may commit burglary or even assault to get the desired fetish object, which would certainly fit our definition of abnormal sexual behaviour.

The continuum from normal to abnormal behaviour holds for many of the sexual variations discussed in this chapter, such as voyeurism, exhibitionism, and sadism. So when does a behaviour become abnormal? Putting it simply, a sexual behaviour is likely to fall on the abnormal end of the continuum when it interferes with having healthy relationships or completing day-to-day activities or causes harm to other people.

 LO2

Sexual Addictions and Compulsions

Patrick Carnes (1983) advanced the theory that some sexual variations are a result of an addictive process much like alcoholism. One definition of alcoholism

or other drug dependency is that the person has a pathological relationship with the mood-altering substance. In the case of sexual addiction, the person has a pathological relationship to a sexual event or process, substituting it for a healthy relationship with others. However, there are some differences between chemical addictions that create a physiological dependency and behavioural "addictions." For example, if a person suddenly abstains from an addictive sexual behaviour, there are no physiological withdrawal symptoms as there are from abstaining from using alcohol. A second criticism is that use of the term *addiction* may affect perceptions of these behaviours and thus become an excuse for illegal, destructive behaviour. For example, a sex offender might say, "I'm sexually addicted to forced sex and can't stop myself." Therefore, some experts recommend that we use the term *compulsive sexual behaviour* instead of *sexual addiction* (e.g., Coleman, 1991).

How can I tell if sexual behaviour is problematic?

Compulsive Sexual Behaviour

How do we define compulsive sexual behaviour? **Compulsive sexual behaviour**

> is a disorder in which the individual experiences intense sexually arousing fantasies, urges, and associated sexual behaviors that are intrusive, driven, and repetitive. Individuals with this disorder (a) are lacking in impulse control, (b) often incur social and legal sanctions, (c) cause interference in interpersonal and occupational functioning, and (d) create health risks. (Coleman et al., 2001, p. 326)

A sexual compulsion can be paraphilic (i.e., involve the sexual behaviours listed in the *DSM-5*) or nonparaphilic (involve conventional sexual behaviours, such as compulsive masturbation or compulsive use of the Internet for sexual purposes) (Coleman et al., 2003). Note that this perspective differs from the addiction approach in emphasizing that the person may experience social and legal sanctions and take health risks. Coleman et al. (2003) estimate that

Compulsive sexual behaviour: A disorder in which the person experiences intense sexually arousing fantasies, urges, and associated sexual behaviour.

approximately 5 percent of the population—more men than women—suffer from compulsive sexual behaviour.

The chief distinguishing feature of sexual addictions or compulsions is that the person has lost control over the behaviour. Thus, not all sexual variations are addictions or compulsions. Some people have intense urges to engage in behaviours, such as masturbation or online sexual activity, that in and of themselves are normal. Thus, for example, the man who masturbates every day in the privacy of his own home while looking at pornographic magazines or at pornography on the Internet is probably not experiencing a compulsion or an addiction, and the behaviour is well within the normal range. However, the married man who (and this is based on a real person) rushes from his desk at work several times a day to lock himself in the supply closet to masturbate and can think of little else than the next time he will masturbate, probably does have a sexual compulsion or addiction. The key is the compulsiveness, the lack of control, the obsession (constant thoughts of the sexual scenario), and the obliviousness to danger or harmful consequences.

Several studies have used a 10-item sexual compulsivity scale (Kalichman & Rompa, 1995) in research on persons at risk for HIV/AIDS. High scorers on the Kalichman Sexual Compulsivity Scale (KSCS) report more sexual partners and more one-time or casual partners (Kalichman & Cain, 2004). Similarly, students with high scores are more likely to report unprotected oral, anal, and vaginal intercourse, and engaging in sex in public places (Dodge et al., 2004).

Some researchers emphasize the out-of-control aspects of problematic sexual behaviour (Bancroft & Vikadinovic, 2004; Figure 15.3). Whereas most people lose interest in sex when anxious or depressed, a minority experience increased sexual interest. When coupled with low sexual inhibition (self-control), the person may engage in compulsive sexual behaviour in an attempt to improve or escape from the negative mood. This intensive study of 31 self-defined "sex addicts" provided evidence supporting this perspective.

A study of sexually compulsive men in New York City who identified as gay or bisexual also found that depression, low self-esteem, a need for validation and affection, and stress release were associated with their behaviour (Parsons et al., 2008). The men also pointed to relationship issues, the ready availability of male sex partners in New York City (bars, bathhouses, meeting areas) and on the Internet, and childhood sexual abuse. Other studies report that the percentage of people with sexual compulsivity who have been sexually abused ranges from 30 to 78 percent, suggesting it is an important factor.

People who have sexual compulsions or addictions—like alcoholics—often hold faulty beliefs that can contribute to the problem because they involve a denial or distortion of reality. These beliefs allow these people to justify their behaviour before engaging in it. For example, they may deny the possibility of contracting a sexually transmitted infection. They also engage in self-justification, such as "If I don't have it every few days, the pressure builds up." Like alcoholism, the compulsive behaviour leads to many self-destructive behaviours. The person with a sexual compulsion or addiction may spend money that he or she doesn't have (e.g., to pay prostitutes), may neglect work or family to engage in the behaviour (e.g., by spending many hours on the Internet), or may risk arrest (e.g., for indecent exposure).

Figure 15.3 Tiger Woods, who was linked in media reports with at least 15 women, several of them claiming long-term affairs with him, entered treatment for sex addiction in 2010.

According to Carnes's (1983) analysis, each episode of the sexually compulsive behaviour proceeds through a four-step cycle, which intensifies each time it is repeated:

1. *Preoccupation.* The person can think of nothing other than the sexual act to which he or she is addicted.
2. *Rituals.* The person enacts certain rituals that have become a prelude to the addictive act.
3. *Compulsive sexual behaviour.* The sexual behaviour is enacted and the person feels that he or she has no control over it.
4. *Despair.* Rather than feeling good after the sexual act is completed, the addict falls into a feeling of hopelessness and despair.

For example, consider the story of a man who engaged in compulsive exhibitionism—let's call him Sam. Often, after a stressful interpersonal event, Sam would become preoccupied with (unrealistic) thoughts of women's positive reactions if he exposed himself. He would then put on certain clothes, go for a walk, "just happen" to walk by a coffee shop, and "just happen" to stop for coffee, all without acknowledging to himself that he intended to expose himself. Sam would look around until he identified a woman who did some small thing that he could misinterpret as indicating that she was interested in him sexually. He would follow her out to the parking lot and expose himself, feeling he had no control over the behaviour. He would feel good at the time but shortly after would feel bad about himself and about his lack of control over his behaviour. Interestingly, there is often a history of alcoholism or other types of addictions in the families of people with compulsive sexual behaviour. Sometimes, too, there is a family history of the same compulsive sexual behaviour.

Fetishism

Fetishism is characterized by sexual fantasies, urges, or behaviours involving the use of nonliving objects to produce or enhance sexual arousal with or in the absence of a partner. In extreme cases the person is incapable of becoming aroused and having an orgasm unless the fetish object is present. Typically, the fetish item is something closely associated with the body, such as clothing. Inanimate-object fetishes can be roughly divided into two subcategories: media fetishes and form fetishes.

Media Fetishes and Form Fetishes

In a **media fetish**, the material out of which an object is made is the source of arousal. An example would be a

Figure 15.4 A common fetish is for leather, often in association with sexual sadism and masochism. This store caters to clientele interested or involved in those activities.

leather fetish, in which any leather item is arousing to the person (Figure 15.4). Media fetishes can be subdivided into hard media fetishes and soft media fetishes. In a hard media fetish, the fetish is for a hard substance, such as leather or rubber. Hard media fetishes may often be associated with sadomasochism (discussed later in this chapter). In a soft media fetish, the substance is soft, such as fur or silk.

In a **form fetish**, it is the object and its shape that are important. An example would be a shoe fetish, in which shoes are highly arousing (see First Person). Some shoe fetishes require that the shoes be high-heeled; this fetish may be associated with sadomasochism, in which the fetishist derives sexual satisfaction from being walked on by a woman in high heels. Other shoe fetishes require that the shoes be leather boots that have been worn. Other examples of form fetishes are nylon stockings, garters, and lingerie.

Fetishism: A person's sexual fixation on some object other than another human being and attachment of great erotic significance to that object.
Media fetish: A fetish whose object is anything made of a particular substance, such as leather.
Form fetish: A fetish whose object is a particular shape, such as high-heeled shoes.

Why Do People Develop a Fetish?

Psychologists are not sure what causes fetishes to develop. Here we will consider three theoretical explanations: learning theory, cognitive theory, and the sexual addiction model. These theories can be applied equally well to explaining many of the other sexual variations in this chapter.

According to learning theory (e.g., McGuire et al., 1965), fetishes result from classical conditioning, in which a learned association is built between the fetish object and sexual arousal and orgasm. In some cases, a single learning trial might serve to cement the association. For example, one adult male recalled:

> I was home alone and saw my uncle's new penny loafers. I went over and started smelling the fresh new leather scent and kissing and licking them. It turned me on so much that I actually ejaculated my first load into my pants and have been turned on ever since. (Weinberg et al., 1995, p. 22)

In this case, shoes were associated with sexual arousal as the result of an early learning experience. Another example of a shoe fetishist is described in First Person. This case clearly exemplifies the *DSM-5* criteria for paraphilia. The youth/man experienced sexual fantasies and urges associated with women's shoes for years, experienced arousal and ejaculation only when they were present, and experienced significant impairment in his academic and social life as a result. In an experiment, it was even demonstrated that men could, in the laboratory, be conditioned to become sexually aroused when viewing pictures of shoes (Rachman, 1966).

A second possible theoretical explanation comes from cognitive psychology, discussed in Chapter 2 (Walen & Roth, 1987). According to cognitive theorists, people with fetishes (or other paraphilias) have a serious cognitive distortion in that they perceive an unconventional stimulus—such as black leather boots—as erotic. Further, their perception of arousal is distorted. They feel driven to the sexual behaviour when aroused, but the arousal may actually be caused by feelings of guilt and self-loathing. Thus, there is a chain in which there are initial feelings of guilt at thoughts of the unconventional behaviour, which produces arousal, which is misinterpreted as sexual arousal, which leads to a feeling that the fetish ritual must be carried out; it is, and there is orgasm and temporary feelings of relief, but the evaluation of the event is negative, leading to further feelings of guilt and self-loathing, which perpetuates the chain.

A third theory that has been advanced to explain some sexual variations, especially those that seem compulsive, is the theory of sexual addiction, discussed earlier in this chapter.

Whatever the cause, fetishism typically develops early in life. In one sample of foot or shoe fetishes, the mean age at which respondents reported first being sexually aroused by feet or shoes was 12 years (Weinberg et al., 1995).

 L04

Transvestism

Cross-dressing refers to wearing clothes stereotypically associated with the other gender. **Transvestism** (*trans* meaning "cross"; *vest* meaning "dressing") refers to cross-dressing for erotic purposes (Moser & Kleinplatz, 2002).

Cross-dressing may be done by a variety of people for a variety of reasons. As discussed in Chapter 13, transgender individuals cross-dress to express a more feminine or masculine side of themselves and to live as the other gender as part of transitioning. Some gay men—**drag queens**—dress up as women, and some lesbians dress in masculine clothes (drag kings); these practices, though, are basically caricatures of traditional gender roles. **Female impersonators** are men who dress as women, often as part of their jobs as entertainers (Figure 15.5). For example, Robin Williams in *Mrs. Doubtfire* and Dustin Hoffman in *Tootsie* won praise from critics and big box office profits for their impersonations of women. Finally, many boys try on the clothes or accessories (hair bands, barrettes, necklaces) of a sister who is close in age out of curiosity or as part of gender-role socialization. As with many behaviours in childhood (see Chapter 10), these boys are primarily motivated by curiosity or wanting to feel special. Some adolescent boys cross-dress,

Transvestism: The practice of deriving sexual gratification from dressing as a member of the other gender; transvestic fetishism.

Drag queens: Gay men who dress in women's clothing.

Female impersonators: Men who dress up as women as part of a job in entertainment.

Figure 15.5 Michelle Ross at the Carlu.

First Person

A Case History of a Shoe Fetishist

The following case history is taken directly from the 1886 book *Psychopathia Sexualis*, by Richard von Krafft-Ebing, the influential early investigator of sexual deviance. It should give you the flavour of his work.

Case 114. X., aged twenty-four, from a badly tainted family (mother's brother and grandfather insane, one sister epileptic, another sister subject to migraine, parents of excitable temperament). During dentition [teething] he had convulsions. At the age of seven he was taught to masturbate by a servant girl. X. first experienced pleasure in these manipulations when the girl happened to touch his member [penis] with her shoe-clad foot. Thus, in the predisposed boy, an association was established, as a result of which, from that time on, merely the sight of a woman's shoe, and finally, merely the idea of them, sufficed to induce sexual excitement and erection. He now masturbated while looking at women's shoes or while calling them up in imagination. The shoes of the schoolmistress excited him intensely, and in general he was affected by shoes that were partly concealed by female garments. One day he could not keep from grasping the teacher's shoes—an act that caused him great sexual excitement. In spite of punishment he could not keep from performing this act repeatedly. Finally, it was recognized that there must be an abnormal motive in play, and he was sent to a male teacher. He then revelled in the memory of the shoe scenes with his former school mistress and thus had erections, orgasms, and, after his fourteenth year, ejaculation. At the same time, he masturbated while thinking of a woman's shoes. One day the thought came to him to increase his pleasure by using such a shoe for masturbation. There after he frequently took shoes secretly and used them for that purpose.

Nothing else in a woman could excite him; the thought of coitus filled him with horror. Men did not interest him in any way. At the age of eighteen he opened a shop and, among other things, dealt in ladies' shoes. He was excited sexually by fitting shoes for his female patrons or by manipulating shoes that came for mending. One day while doing this he had an epileptic attack, and, soon after, another while practicing onanism in his customary way. Then he recognized for the first time the injury to health caused by his sexual practices. He tried to overcome his onanism, sold no more shoes, and strove to free himself from the abnormal association between women's shoes and the sexual function. Then frequent pollutions, with erotic dreams about shoes occurred, and the epileptic attacks continued. Though devoid of the slightest feeling for the female sex, he determined on marriage, which seemed to him to be the only remedy.

He married a pretty young lady. In spite of lively erections when he thought of his wife's shoes, in attempts at cohabitation he was absolutely impotent because his distaste for coitus and for close intercourse in general was far more powerful than the influence of the shoe-idea, which induced sexual excitement. On account of his impotence the patient applied to Dr. Hammond, who treated his epilepsy with bromides and advised him to hang a shoe up over his bed and look at it fixedly during coitus, at the same time imagining his wife to be a shoe. The patient became free from epileptic attacks and potent so that he could have coitus about once a week. His sexual excitation by women's shoes also grew less and less.

Source: Von Krafft-Ebing (1886).

usually only once or a few times (Green, 1975). This behaviour does not necessarily mean that the boy will continue to cross-dress throughout his life; it may simply reflect exploration of his gender or sexuality; it may also reflect the sexual drives, confusions, and frustrations of adolescence.

In contrast to people who engage in cross-dressing for the reasons just discussed, a transvestite is a

heterosexual man who dresses in female clothing to produce or enhance sexual arousal (American Psychiatric Association, 2000).[1] Note that the key here is that cross-dressing is used to produce or enhance sexual arousal not, for example, to express one's true gender.

---

[1] A common abbreviation for transvestism, used both by scientists and by members of the transvestite subculture, is TV.

If the man's fantasies, urges, or behaviours meet the *DSM-5* diagnostic criteria, the man is said to have a transvestic fetish disorder. The cross-dressing is often done in private, perhaps by a married man without his partner's knowledge. An online article tells the story of a married man who has crossed-dressed in women's satin lingerie for 19 years (Clark-Flory, 2011). He reports that it mentally brings a sense of relief and arousal.

Are men or women more likely to engage in problematic sexual behaviour?

Transvestic fetishism is almost exclusively a male sexual variation; it is essentially unknown among women. There may be a number of reasons for this difference, including our culture's tolerance of women who wear masculine clothing and intolerance of men who wear feminine clothing. Also, traditionally women's clothing is by design sensual and erotic, whereas men's clothing is functional (Wheeler et al., 2008).

The phenomenon illustrates a more general point, namely, that many sexual variations are defined for, or practised almost exclusively by, members of one gender; the parallel practice by members of the other gender is often not considered deviant. Most sexual variations are practised mainly by men. Several theories have been proposed to explain why there are so many more men than women with paraphilias (Finkelhor & Russell, 1984). Sociobiologists believe that the difference lies in the evolutionary selection of males to inseminate many partners and to be aroused by sexual stimuli devoid of emotional content (Wilson, 1987). Sociologists point to gender role socialization, which teaches males to be instrumental and to initiate sexual interactions. Females, on the other hand, are taught to be nurturing and to empathize with others; for example, with the vulnerability of children (Traven et al., 1990). Psychoanalytic theory (see Chapter 2) suggests that paraphilias result from castration anxiety, which is relieved by a forceful sexual act; because women do not fear castration, they are not subject to paraphilias. Moser and Kleinplatz (2005) argue that diagnosis of certain paraphilias, such as transvestism, results from the tendency in our culture to define masculinity very narrowly and to pathologize unconventional behaviour. The social construction perspective suggests that because we consider paraphilias a male phenomenon, a woman with the same behaviours (e.g., compulsive extradyadic sex) will not consider herself to have a paraphilia or an addiction. If she is concerned about her behaviour, she will define it as a relationship problem.

A survey of a national sample in Sweden asked each participant whether she or he had ever dressed in clothing of the other gender and experienced sexual arousal (Långström & Zucker, 2005). Almost 3 percent of men and 0.4 percent of women reported at least one such experience. Among men, this behaviour was associated with being easily sexually aroused (in general, not just by cross-dressing), more frequent masturbation, and same-sex sexual experience.

A common means of studying persons with atypical sexual behaviour patterns is to place ads in specialty newsletters and magazines, and to solicit participants at meetings and conventions attended by such persons. Using these procedures, researchers gathered survey data from 1032 cross-dressers (Docter & Prince, 1997). The sample did not include drag queens or female impersonators. The vast majority of the men (87 percent) were heterosexual, 60 percent were married, 65 percent had a university education, and 76 percent reported being raised by both parents through age 18. Sixty-six percent reported that their first cross-dressing experience occurred before age 10. About 40 percent reported that they often or always associated sexual excitement and orgasms with cross-dressing. This indicates that this sample included men who cross-dress for a variety of reasons—not just men who do so to enhance sexual arousal. Almost all (93 percent) preferred complete cross-dressing, but only 14 percent frequently went out in public dressed as a woman.

Another survey was conducted by mailing questionnaires to 1200 members of a U.S. cross-dressing organization (Bullough & Bullough, 1997). There were 372 questionnaires returned. The median age at which the men began to cross-dress was 8.5; 32 percent reported that they first dressed as a female before they were six. Most of them reported cross-dressing as children, and 56 percent said they were never caught.

How do the partner and children of the cross-dresser react to his unusual behaviour? In one sample of 50 heterosexual cross-dressers, 60 percent of the wives were accepting of their husband's cross-dressing (Talamini, 1982). Most of these women commented that he was a good husband. Some of the wives felt fulfilled being supportive of the husband, and some even helped him in dressing and applying makeup. In the same sample, 13 of the couples had told their children about the cross-dressing. They claimed that the relationship with the children was undamaged and that the children were tolerant and understanding. However, given societal attitudes toward cross-dressing and gender roles, the partner may have problems with it—particularly if she did not know about the cross-dressing before they became involved.

Like other sexual variations, transvestism occurs on a continuum. For many people, it occurs in a mild form and so is one of the harmless, victimless sexual variations. Like other fetishes, it is a problem only when it becomes so extreme that it is the person's only source of erotic gratification or when it becomes a compulsion the person cannot control and therefore causes distress in other areas of the person's life.

BDSM

Definitions

A **sexual sadist** is a person who derives sexual excitement and satisfaction from inflicting pain, suffering, or humiliation on another person. The term *sadism* derives from the name of the Marquis de Sade, who lived around the time of the French Revolution. Not only did he practise sexual sadism—several women apparently died from his attentions (Bullough, 1976)—but he also wrote novels about these practices (the best known is *Justine*), thus assuring his place in history.

A **sexual masochist** is a person who is sexually aroused by fantasies, urges, or behaviours involving being beaten, humiliated, bound, or tortured to enhance or achieve sexual excitement. This variation is named after Leopold von Sacher-Masoch (1836–1895), who was himself a masochist and who wrote novels expressing masochistic fantasies. Notice that the definitions of these variations make specific their sexual nature; the terms are often loosely used to refer to people who are cruel or to people who seem to bring misfortune on themselves, but these are not the meanings used here. These two are often referred to as a pair since the two behaviours or roles (giving and receiving pain) are complementary.

There are two styles of interaction that are related to sadism-masochism (S-M). These are bondage and discipline (B-D) and dominance and submission (D-S) (Ernulf & Innala, 1995). **Bondage and discipline** refers to the use of physically restraining devices or psychologically restraining commands as a central aspect of sexual interactions. These devices or commands may enforce obedience and servitude without inducing any physical pain. **Dominance and submission** refers to interaction that involves a consensual exchange of power; the dominant partner uses his or her power to control and sexually stimulate the submissive partner. Both B-D and D-S encompass a variety of specific interactions that range from atypical to paraphilic (see First Person for one man's account of BDSM).

There is considerable overlap between these variance terms. Thus, collectively they are often referred to as BDSM. That is, B and D, interpreted together, refer to bondage and discipline, D and S together refer to dominance and submission, and S and M together refer to sadism and masochism.

Sexual Sadism and Masochism

Sadomasochism (S-M) is a rare form of sexual behaviour, although in its milder forms it is probably more common than many people think. In fact, discussion of spanking and use of handcuffs during sexual activity has made it to such prime-time television shows as *Friends*, *Sex and the City*, and *Seinfeld*. Kinsey found that about one-quarter of both males and females had experienced definite or frequent erotic response as a result of being bitten during sexual activity (Kinsey et al., 1953). Sadistic or masochistic sexual fantasies are more common; a New Brunswick study found that 65 percent of university students have sexual fantasies of being tied up and 62 percent have fantasies of tying someone up (Renaud & Byers, 1999).

Another study administered questionnaires to 130 men and 52 women who responded to ads placed in S-M magazines (Breslow et al., 1985). Thirty-three percent of the men and 28 percent of the women preferred the dominant role; 41 percent of the men and 40 percent of the women preferred the submissive role; and 26 percent of the men and 32 percent of the women were versatile. The majority of these S-M respondents were heterosexual. Men involved in S-M frequently report having been interested in such activity since childhood; women are more likely to report having been introduced to the subculture by someone else (Weinberg, 1994). Women prefer bondage, spanking, and master-and-slave role-playing (Levitt et al., 1994). A review of several studies concluded that 13 to 30 percent of the participants are women (Hucker, 2008).

Thus, a spectrum of activities constitute S-M. People who become involved in it often have tried a variety of these behaviours and find only some of them satisfying. They develop a script of activities (recall the concept of scripts in Chapter 2) that they prefer to enact each time they engage in S-M. One group of researchers (Santilla et al., 2002) identified 29 individual sexual behaviours associated with S-M. They administered questionnaires to 184 Finnish men and women who were members of S-M clubs. Each participant was asked which of the behaviours he or she had participated in during the preceding year. Four clusters or themes were identified: hypermasculinity (e.g., dildo, enema), administering and receiving pain (e.g., clothespins attached to nipples, caning, hot wax), physical restriction (e.g., handcuffs, straitjackets), and humiliation (e.g., verbal humiliation, face slapping).

Sexual sadist: A person who derives sexual satisfaction from inflicting pain, suffering, or humiliation on another person.
Sexual masochist: A person who derives sexual satisfaction from experiencing pain.
Bondage and discipline: The use of physical or psychological restraint to enforce servitude, from which both participants derive sensual pleasure.
Dominance and submission: The use of power consensually given to control the sexual stimulation and behaviour of the other person.

First Person

The Pleasure of Kinky Sex: Trevor Jacques, a BDSM Practitioner and Advocate

T revor Jacques is 52 years old, is single, and lives in Toronto. He was born in England, the eldest of four children of middle-class parents. As a child, he was the "good son," even serving as an altar boy for a while. His parents raised him to ask questions and "do the right thing." This allowed him to chart his own course in life, both in his career and, in his words, his "kink."

In terms of his career, Trevor is a physicist who became an engineer. He worked on avionic missile systems in Great Britain, on infrared surveillance technology for the Canadian and U.S. navies, and as a database consultant. However, he identifies a strong passion for educating people about safer BDSM and conducting research about the experiences of members of the BDSM community. (Note how Trevor uses "safer" rather than "safe," in that nothing, even breathing, is entirely safe.)

Trevor uses the term BDSM to describe the practices of the community because it encompasses multiple meanings and roles, and is almost free of the baggage that comes with words used in clinical diagnosis. Trevor also subscribes to the term *kinky*, because he feels it describes what BDSM practitioners like to do, while making it clear that they only are interested in consensual partners and do not want to hurt anyone who does not clearly want and consent to it. For Trevor "hurt" refers to the application of intense stimulation, which may or may not include pain but does not entail injury.

What is kinky sex?

As an adolescent, Trevor does not recall being particularly interested in girls and sex, yet his father assured him "it would come." He had his first sexual experience when he was 21, with a woman. He describes it as conventional and very enjoyable, yet "missing something." Trevor came out as gay at 26. He also realized that he was attracted to more than conventional sex when he found himself gravitating toward erotica that depicted hypermasculine men and men representing or engaged in BDSM activities. He describes coming out as kinky as a far faster process than coming out as gay, because he had already been through the coming out process once. He realized that being kinky was "simply who he is and how he was born," in the same way he is gay.

Since openly identifying as kinky, Trevor has been very active in the BDSM community, which he regards as one of his two chosen families (the other being his "LGBTIQ" family). He finds "vanilla" (non-BDSM) sex enjoyable yet also looks for opportunities for BDSM play. He particularly enjoys social events organized by and for the BDSM community. Many of these are social functions that raise money for local charities. Some are similar to any other reception or dinner; others have people "dressed to the gills in leather/rubber/PVC or other role-playing clothes and accessories." There are other categories of BDSM gatherings that he likes, including BDSM conferences and sex events—the former referring to open public events, and the latter being very private events, limited to self-identified members of BDSM organizations.

Further analyses of participation in the behaviours within each cluster identified a continuum in frequency from very common to very rare, with the order of the behaviours suggesting that this continuum reflects a dimension from least to most intense. For example, the humiliation continuum ranges from flagellation (reported by 81 percent; least intense) to verbal humiliation (70 percent) to gagging (53 percent) and face slapping (37 percent) to using knives to make surface wounds (11 percent; most intense). The results suggest that the S-M activities within each cluster are *scripted*, with the less intense behaviours being much more common.

Some observers note that S-M is about play, as in the theatre. S-M sexual activities are organized into *scenes*; one *plays* with one's S-M partners. In addition to the activities such as those just discussed, roles, costumes, and props are an important part of each scene. The

What does Trevor like about these events? He enjoys the opportunity to meet new people who share his interests. He does not feel a need to have sex or BDSM play during (in the case of the private sex/BDSM events) or after the event, although he certainly enjoys it when it does happen. He also enjoys being able to express what he refers to as the "exhibitionist" and "voyeuristic" parts of himself at these events. Note that what he is referring to as exhibitionism is the desire to show off and be admired by other men when he is dressed up in his BDSM gear and, potentially, showing off his kinky prowess (e.g., by flogging a consenting partner). This is very different from exhibitionism that involves displaying one's genitals, for example, to a *non*consenting person in a public venue. (All of Trevor's teaching of BDSM strongly stresses consent and the avoidance of harm. He practises what he teaches.) Similarly, Trevor enjoys being able to see and watch other men, who know they are being watched, dressed up and engaging in the activities that turn him on.

Trevor describes himself as a "fetishistic switch." This means that he has a fetish for specific clothing/gear—in his case, leather, rubber, and other clothing—and that he likes to switch between being the top (the dominant/disciplining/sadistic partner) and the bottom (the submissive/receiving/masochistic partner). Pain may be part of his play; however, it is not essential. Indeed, he is very uncomfortable with the myth that "BDSM necessarily equals pain," and that all pain is undesired (e.g., stubbing one's toe during a heavy flogging is a good example of unwanted pain during desired pain). He enjoys many kinky pleasures, such as bondage, "artfully applied pain" for sexual pleasure, fetishes, control, and so on. However, consistent with the basic tenets of safer BDSM play, his limits extend to the agreed play, respect for his partner(s), and the assurance that harm does not occur. Like most BDSM practitioners, he is a proponent of what is termed safe, sane, and consensual (SSC) play. What Trevor enjoys at any point in time depends, among other factors, on the person with whom he's playing, how he and the person(s) feel at the time, and what his day has been like. One of the things he likes about BDSM is that he becomes immersed in the play and that his brain switches off the minutiae of daily life.

In 1991, Trevor and his co-authors of the bestselling *On the Safe Edge: A Manual for SM Play* designed and began to deliver a series of seminars on SM safety, under the auspices of the AIDS Committee of Toronto (ACT). Since that time, more than 3500 people have attended these courses. He also is frequently invited to talk about BDSM on television and radio and to university classes. One of his main messages is that people need to be honest with themselves and others about their practices and the pleasure they get from them: they should not let other people define them. Otherwise, they may miss out on years of pleasure and enjoyment. Further, people interested in BDSM need to learn what is safe. And they need informed consent while having their own kind of fun.

Source: As told to Sandra Byers.

roles include slave and master, maid and mistress, and teacher and pupil. The costumes range from simple to elaborate. The props may include tight leather clothing, pins and needles, ropes, whips, and hot wax. In S-M clubs, which may be heterosexual or homosexual, there are often rules governing the social and S-M interaction, particularly the creation and enactment of scenes. According to one website, the rules include no touching of another's body without consent, giving players the room they need to enact a scene, not intruding physically or verbally on a scene in progress, and sometimes no sexual penetration.

As you might expect, Canadian researchers have shown that male sexual sadists show greater subjective and genital arousal to sexual stimuli involving mutually consenting violence and injury than do other men (Seto et al., 2012). Nonetheless, sexual sadists and masochists do not consistently find experiencing pain and giving pain to be sexually satisfying. For example, the masochist who smashes a finger in a door will yell and be unhappy just like anyone else. Pain is arousing for such people only when it is part of a carefully scripted ritual. As one woman put it,

> Of course, he doesn't *really* hurt me. I mean quite recently he tied me down ready to receive "punishment," and then by mistake he kicked my heel with his toe as he walked by. I gave a yelp, and he said, "Sorry love—did I hurt you?" (Gosselin & Wilson, 1980, p. 55)

Causes of Preference for Sexual Sadomasochism

Most experts view sexual sadomasochism as a variation on other forms of healthy sexuality. The causes of why people come to prefer sexual activities that involve sexual sadism and masochism (and equally most other sexual preferences) are not precisely known. The theories in our discussion of fetishes can be applied here as well. For example, learning theory points to conditioning as an explanation. A little boy is being spanked over his mother's knee; in the process, his penis rubs against her knee, and he gets an erection. Or a little girl is caught masturbating and is spanked. In both cases, the child has learned to associate pain or spanking with sexual arousal, possibly setting up a lifelong career as a masochist.

A related theory points to childhood sexual abuse that causes sadistic fantasies, for example, of revenge, as the root of at least sadistic violence. For the child experiencing abuse, these fantasies are functional, helping them cope with the abuse. If sexual arousal is paired with the fantasies, they may influence sexual behaviour (MacCulloch et al., 2000).

Another psychological theory has been proposed to explain sexual masochism specifically, although not sadism (Baumeister, 1988a, 1988b). According to the theory, the masochist is motivated by a desire to escape from self-awareness. That is, the masochistic behaviour helps the individual escape from being conscious of the self in the same way that drunkenness and some forms of meditation do. In an era dominated by individualism and self-interest, why would anyone want to escape from the self? Probably because high levels of self-awareness can lead to anxiety as a result of a focus on pressures on the self, added responsibilities, the need to keep up a good image in front of others, and so on. Sexual masochistic activity allows the person to escape from being an autonomous, separate individual. Sexual masochism may be an unusually powerful form of escape because of its link to sexual pleasure. This theory can also explain why sexual masochism is more common among men than among women (Baumeister, 1988b). According to the theory, the male role is especially burdensome because of the heavy pressures for

autonomy, separateness, and individual achievement. Sexual masochism accomplishes an escape from these aspects of the male role. Some men cross-dress while engaging in sexual masochistic activity, a finding that tends to support this theory (Chivers & Blanchard, 1996).

Bondage and Discipline

Sexual bondage, the use in sexual behaviour of restraining devices that have sexual significance, has been a staple of erotic fiction and art for centuries. Current mainstream and adult films and videos portray this activity. In some communities, individuals interested in B-D have formed clubs. There are many B-D sites on the Internet that may also advertise BDSM "play parties," as well as BDSM *munches*. A BDSM munch is an informal gathering of people who are interested in BDSM, often at a restaurant (hence the term *munch*), so they can eat, socialize, and meet other people with similar interests.

We noted earlier the difficulty of gathering data on participation in variant forms of sexual expression. One innovative study downloaded all the messages about bondage mailed to an international computer discussion group (Ernulf & Innala, 1995). Of the messages in which senders indicated their gender, 75 percent were men. Of those indicating a sexual orientation, most were heterosexual; 18 percent said they were gay, and 11 percent said they were lesbian. The messages were coded for discussion of what the person found sexually arousing about B-D. Most frequently mentioned (12 percent) was play: "sex is funny, and sex is lovely, and sex is PLAY." Next was the exchange of power (4 percent): "It is a power trip because the active is responsible for the submissive's pleasure." The next most common themes were intensified sexual pleasure, tactile stimulation associated with the use of ropes and cuffs, and the visual enjoyment experienced by the dominant person.

There is a marked imbalance in preferences for the active ("top") and passive ("bottom") roles. Most men and women, regardless of their sexual orientation, prefer to be "bottom." This may be the reason why there are an estimated 2500 professional dominatrices in the United States.

Dominance and Submission

Sociologists emphasize that the key to S-M is not pain but rather dominance and submission (D-S) (Weinberg, 1987). Thus it is not an individual phenomenon but rather a social behaviour embedded in a subculture and controlled by elaborate scripts.

Sociologists feel that to understand D-S, one must understand the social processes that create and sustain it (Weinberg, 1987). There is a distinct D-S subculture, involving DVDs, clubs, and bars. It creates culturally defined meanings for D-S acts. Thus a D-S act is not a

Figure 15.6   Sexual bondage involves restraining devices and discipline, such as in this scene.

wild outbreak of violence but rather a carefully controlled performance with a script. One woman reported,

> we got into dominance and submission. Like him giving me orders. Being very rough and pushing me around and giving me orders, calling me a slut, calling me a cunt. Making me crawl around . . . on all fours and beg to suck his cock. Dominance-submission is more important than the pain. I've done lots and lots of scenes that involve no pain. Just a lot of taking orders, being humiliated. (Maurer, 1994, pp. 253, 257)

Within the play, people take on roles such as master, slave, or naughty child. Thus men can play the submissive role in D-S culture, even though it contradicts the male role, because it is really not they who are the naughty child, just as an actor can play the part of a murderer and know that he is not a murderer (Figure 15.6).

One interesting phenomenon, from a sociological point of view, is the social control over risk taking that exists in the D-S subculture (Weinberg, 1987). That is, having allowed oneself to be tied up or restrained and then whipped, one could be seriously injured or even murdered, yet such outcomes are rare. Why? Research shows that complex social arrangements are made to reduce the risk (Lee, 1979). First, initial contacts are usually made in protected territories, such as bars or meetings, which are inhabited by other people involved in D-S who play by the same rules. Second, the basic scripts are widely shared so that everyone understands what will and will not occur. When the participants are strangers, the scenario may be negotiated before it is enacted. Third, as the activity unfolds, very subtle nonverbal signals are used to control the interaction (Weinberg, 1994).

By using these signals, the person playing the submissive role can influence what occurs. Thus, as two people enact the master and slave script, the master is not in complete control and the slave is not powerless. So it is the *illusion* of control, not actual control, that is central to D-S activity for both the master and the slave.

 LO6

Voyeurism and Exhibitionism

Voyeurism and exhibitionism are often discussed together because they seem complementary. However, they are rather different, and a voyeur would not find watching an exhibitionist arousing.

Voyeurism

There are two types of **voyeurism** (*Peeping Tom*).[2] In **scoptophilia**, sexual pleasure is derived from observing sexual acts and the genitals; in *voyeurism*, technically, the sexual pleasure comes from viewing nudes, often while the observer is masturbating. The most recent strategy of people who engage in voyeurism is to install small video cameras secretly so that they can observe women using

> **Voyeurism:** A sexual variation in which the person becomes sexually aroused from secretly viewing nudes.
> **Scoptophilia:** A sexual variation in which the person becomes sexually aroused by observing others' sexual acts and genitals.

---

[2] *Voyeur* comes from the French word *voir*, meaning "to see." *Peeping Tom* comes from the story of Lady Godiva; when she rode through town nude to protest the fact that her husband was raising his tenants' taxes, none of the townspeople looked except one, Tom of Coventry.

the washroom or changing their clothes. Surreptitiously observing or recording a naked person who is in a private place are both criminal offences (see Table 2.1).

Voyeurism provides another good illustration of the continuum from normal to abnormal behaviour. Although voyeurism can be a paraphilia, it is also of interest to many individuals without paraphilias. The appeal of watching is illustrated by an Ontario study that asked university students whether they would watch an attractive person undress and an attractive couple having sex (Rye & Meaney, 2007b). The likelihood of being caught was specified as 0, 10, or 25 percent. Two-thirds said they would watch someone undress; 45 percent said they would watch the couple. The likelihood of watching the person undress increased as the risk decreased; the likelihood of watching the couple did not vary by risk. There were no differences between the men and the women in the study. Note that voyeurism is considered problematic behaviour when the other person involved is an unwilling participant. A man who derives erotic pleasure from watching his partner or a willing participant (e.g., on the Internet) undress is not engaging in criminal or paraphilic behaviour.

People who engage in voyeurism are typically men who want the woman they view to be a stranger and do not want her to know what they are doing. The element of risk is also important; while one might think that a nudist camp would be heaven to a voyeur, it is not, because the elements of risk and forbiddenness are missing (Sagarin, 1973).

A survey of 2540 randomly selected 18- to 60-year-old Swedes found that almost 8 percent reported one or more experiences of having been sexually aroused by watching others have sex. About three-quarters of them were men. Note that this is a very broad question and could include watching consenting others. People who reported these experiences tended to report more psychological problems and alcohol and drug use, as well as greater sexual interest, activity, and novelty-seeking (Långström & Seto, 2006).

A study of 561 men who sought treatment for paraphilias included 62 voyeurs (Abel & Rouleau, 1990). One-third reported that their first experience occurred before they were 12 years old. One-half said they recognized their interest before age 15. These men estimated that, on average, they had peeped at 470 persons.

These studies point out one of the major problems with the research on sexual variations: much of it has been done only on people who have been arrested for their behaviour or sought treatment. One analyst suggests that only a small minority of people who engage in voyeurism are distressed by their behaviour and thus likely to seek treatment (Lavin, 2008). The "respectable"

Exhibitionism: A person derives sexual gratification from exposing his genitals to others in situations in which this is inappropriate.

person with a paraphilia who has the behaviour under somewhat better control or who is skilled enough or can pull enough strings not to get caught is not studied in such research. Thus, the picture that research provides for us of these variations may be very biased.

Exhibitionism

The complement to voyeurism is **exhibitionism** (*flashing*), in which the person derives sexual pleasure from exposing his genitals to others in situations where this is clearly inappropriate (Figure 15.7). In the *Criminal Code of Canada*, this is referred to as indecent exposure. The pronoun "his" is used advisedly, since exhibitionism is primarily associated with men. When a man exposes himself, his behaviour is likely to be considered offensive. On the other hand, a man who notices that a woman wearing a skirt is not wearing panties is more likely to be turned on than offended. Here again, whether a sexual behaviour is considered abnormal depends greatly on whether the person doing it is a male or a female. (Recall our discussion of the social constructionist view of paraphilias and gender). Homosexual exhibitionism is also quite rare; so the prototype we have for exhibitionism is a man exposing himself

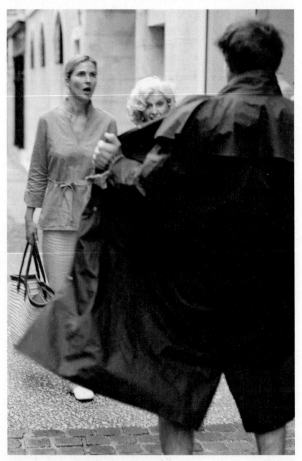

Figure 15.7 Exhibitionism.

to a woman. Research in New Brunswick found that in 1996, 6 percent of male sex offenders were convicted of indecent exposure (Byers et al., 1997). Many of the men convicted of indecent exposure, 48 percent in one Canadian study, commit another similar offence within the next few years (Marshall et al., 1991). In addition, 6 percent of the exhibitionists in an Ottawa study were subsequently convicted of a hands-on sexual offence, such as sexual touching or sexual assault (Greenberg et al., 2002). According to one survey, 33 percent of university women have been the objects of indecent exposure (Cox, 1988). As with voyeurism, exhibitionism is considered a problematic behaviour only when the other person involved is an unwilling participant. A woman who is aroused by exhibiting her body in new lingerie to her partner or to willing others (e.g., on the Internet) is obviously not engaging in criminal or paraphilic behaviour.

According to the benchmark study of men seeking treatment for paraphilias (Abel & Rouleau, 1990), 15 percent of the exhibitionists had exposed themselves at least once by age 12; half had done so by age 15. According to other research (Blair & Lanyon, 1981), exhibitionists generally recall their childhoods as being characterized by inconsistent discipline, lack of affection, and little training in appropriate forms of social behaviour. An analysis of 10 studies of the social skills of sexual offenders (rapists, child molesters, incest offenders, pedophiles, and exhibitionists) found that sexual offenders possess fewer social skills than non-offenders (Emmers-Sommer et al., 2004).

The study of Swedish adults found that 3 percent reported ever being aroused by exposing their genitals to a stranger; about two-thirds were men. The same variables associated with reports of watching others were associated with exhibitionism (Långström & Seto, 2006).

The causes of exhibitionism are not known, but a social learning-theory explanation offers some possibilities (Blair & Lanyon, 1981). According to this view, the parents might have subtly (or perhaps obviously) modelled such behaviour to the person when he was a child. In adulthood, there may be reinforcements for the exhibitionistic behaviour because the man gets attention when he performs it. In addition, even if he is married, the man may lack the social skills to form an intimate adult relationship (Marshall et al., 1991). As a result he receives little reinforcement from interpersonal sex.

Many women, understandably, are alarmed by exhibitionists. But since the exhibitionist's goal is to produce shock or some other strong emotional response, the woman who becomes extremely upset is gratifying him. Probably the best strategy for a woman to use in this situation is to respond calmly and walk away.

A study of 62 female sex offenders in Great Britain identified five women who had exhibited themselves (O'Connor, 1987). For example, one 21-year-old woman stripped off her clothes and masturbated in public on several occasions. All five women had histories of unusual behaviour and had been diagnosed with alcohol or psychiatric problems. A study in Ontario of persons seeking treatment for paraphilias included three women who were diagnosed with exhibitionistic paraphilia (Federoff et al., 1999). In all eight cases, their atypical sexual behaviours appear to reflect other problems rather than sexual motivations.

Extended online interviews with six women who exhibited themselves found that they rejected the paraphilic, deviant characterization of their behaviour (Hugh-Jones et al., 2005). Instead, they promoted and normalized it, saying that it provided self-confidence, that they were sensitive to the audience and would not exhibit to seniors or children, and that they received positive support from family, friends, and co-workers (consistent with learning theory). Four of the six women exhibited by posting nude photos online; it is not clear that any exposed themselves to unsuspecting strangers.

The term *exhibitionism* is also used to refer to people who get sexually aroused by having other people watch them engage in sexual activity, although this is not the way the term is used in the *DSM-5*. Conversely, the *voyeurs* are turned on by watching people engaging in sexual activity. Thus, this is a consensual activity between exhibitionists and voyeurs and may occur in a private home or in an outdoor location. In Britain, the term used to describe all kinds of outdoor sexual activity watched by others is *dogging*.

L07 ━━━━━━━━━━━━━━━━━━━━━━━

Hypersexuality

We turn now to several variations that are not explicitly listed in the *DSM-5*; however, each of these also may vary from atypical through compulsive to paraphilic, depending on their frequency, duration, and consequences.

Hypersexuality includes **nymphomania** and **satyriasis**, conditions in which there is an extraordinarily high level of sexual activity and sex drive; the person is apparently insatiable and, at the extreme, sexuality overshadows all other concerns and interests. When it occurs in women, it is called nymphomania; in men, it is called satyriasis[3] (or Don Juanism; Figure 15.8). Although this definition seems

> **Nymphomania (nimf-oh-MANE-ee-uh):** An excessive, insatiable sex drive in a woman.
> **Satyriasis (sat-ur-EYE-uh-sis):** An excessive, insatiable sex drive in a man.

---

[3] *Satyriasis* is named for the satyrs, who were part-human, part-animal beasts in Greek mythology. A part of the entourage of Dionysus, the god of wine and fertility, they were jovial and lusty and have become a symbol of the sexually active male.

Figure 15.8   Historical painting of a satyr, which gives the name to satyriasis, a sexual variation in which a man has an excessive, insatiable sex drive.

fairly simple, in practice it is difficult to say when a person has an abnormally high sex drive. As we saw in Chapters 10 and 11, there is a wide range in the frequencies with which people engage in sexual activity; therefore, the range we define as "normal" should also be broad. In real life, nymphomania or satyriasis is often defined by the partner who thinks his or her partner wants sex too frequently. In particular, our society is not accepting of highly sexual women, and they are likely to be labelled in negative ways (Blumberg, 2003).

Because these two terms are imprecise, some researchers prefer the term hypersexuality. **Hypersexuality** refers to an excessive, insatiable sex drive in either a man or a woman—not just to a high level of sexual desire or of sexual activity. It leads to compulsive sexual behaviour in the sense that the person feels driven to it even when there may be very negative consequences (Goldberg, 1987). The person is also never satisfied by the activity, and she or he may not be having orgasms, despite all the sexual activity. Such cases meet the criteria for abnormal behaviour discussed at the beginning of this chapter. The compulsiveness of the behaviour leads it to become extremely inefficient, with the result that it impairs functioning in other areas of the person's life. Although most people use sexuality sites on the Internet in healthy ways, some people feel driven toward online sexual pursuits. Compulsive cybersex use is discussed shortly.

Researchers in Ontario have identified different types of hypersexuality that may require psychological interventions based on referrals to the Sexual Behaviours Clinic of the Centre for Addiction and Mental Health in Toronto (Cantor et al., 2013). The two largest groups were those with

Hypersexuality: An excessive, insatiable sex drive in either men or women.

paraphilic hypersexuality and those with *avoidant masturbation*. The individuals with paraphilic hypersexuality had extremely high frequency of one or more sexual behaviours (such as chronic adultery, use of prostitutes, viewing of pornography) leading to distress. They also tended to report several low-grade paraphilic interests. Individuals who engaged in avoidant masturbation spent extreme amounts of time viewing pornography and masturbating, which often led to negative social consequences. Unlike those with paraphilic hypersexuality (who also sometimes spend extreme amounts of time masturbating), they do not report any paraphilic interests. Some of the individuals seen were distressed (or had a partner who was distressed) about their behaviour but did not actually engage in extreme behaviour.

One study recruited women from volunteers at presentations about highly sexual women and via newspaper ads in alternative newspapers (Blumberg, 2003). The authors used the term *highly sexual* to refer to women who desire sexual stimulation to orgasm six or seven times per week or who think of themselves as highly sexual and their sexuality frequently strongly affects their lives. Forty-four women were interviewed, ranging in age from 20 to 82, from such diverse occupations as janitor and corporate CEO. Twenty-five percent were married; 48 percent were separated or divorced. The preferred weekly frequency of sexual episodes—again, not orgasms—ranged from 3 to 70. The women reported that the internal demand for sexual excitement and satisfaction was too strong to be ignored; for many of them, it shaped their daily lives. This demand led to challenges in their feelings about themselves, their relationships with partners, and their relationships with female friends. Some of the women found it impossible to form a single relationship that could fulfill their needs, leading to multiple partners or the frequent forming of new relationships. The researcher believed that neither the term *sexual addiction* nor *compulsive sexual behaviour* should be applied to this behaviour. These women did not feel that their behaviour was out of control, and they did not report an increase in frequency of behaviour or the impact of it on their lives over time.

Researchers have developed a scale to assess hypersexuality, the Hypersexuality Behavior Inventory or HBI (Reid et al., 2011). The scale includes 19 items asking respondents to report the relative frequency of a variety of experiences related to sexuality during the past 90 days. The scale was validated by using two samples of male outpatients drawn from several states, including men reporting compulsive masturbation, habitual solicitation of commercial sex workers, extramarital affairs, and multiple anonymous partners. Analyses indicate three underlying factors: control ("My attempts to change my sexual behavior fail"), consequences ("My sexual activities interfere with . . . work or school"), and coping ("I use sex . . . [to] deal with my problems"). They propose the use of the HBI as an objective diagnostic tool compared with, for example, number of orgasms per week. The HBI is highly correlated with measures of compulsive sexual behaviour.

Experts on hypersexuality have concluded that there is no specific, agreed-on definition or diagnosis (Kaplan & Krueger, 2010). This condition has been linked to a wide variety of behaviours and frequencies of behaviours. There is some support for the sexual addiction model. In addition, the authors proposed that organic causes, specifically those involved with the dopaminergic system, and stimulant drugs, be researched.

Online Sexual Activity Use and Abuse

Online sexual activity (OSA) refers to the use of the Internet for any activities of a sexual nature (Cooper & Griffin-Shelley, 2002; Shaughnessy, Byers, & Walsh, 2011). For some people this involves solitary activities; for other people this involves sexual activity with a partner, which is also called *cybersex* (Shaughnessy, Byers, & Thornton, 2011). A major concern in recent years, particularly in the media, has been whether the use of the Internet to access sexually oriented materials, chat rooms, and bulletin boards (Figure 15.9) can become compulsive, addictive, or paraphilic. Recall that compulsive behaviour involves (1) a lack of impulse control, (2) a tendency to lead to social and legal sanctions, (3) interference in interpersonal and occupational functioning, and (4) the creation of health risks. This concern has been raised by therapists and clinicians, who report cases of Internet use leading to job loss, relationship difficulties leading to divorce, and other adverse consequences (Galbreath et al., 2002).

If we think about Internet sexual behaviour as falling on a continuum from healthy and normal to unhealthy and abnormal, most people who engage in OSA are recreational users, not abusers, addicts, or compulsives (Cooper et al., 1999a, 1999b). Indeed, a study in New Brunswick found that university students who engage in OSA did so infrequently, on average less than once a week (Shaughnessy, Byers, & Walsh, 2011). However, the Internet is thought to be especially likely to be involved in leading to addictive or compulsive behaviour because it is characterized by the three A's: anonymity, accessibility, and affordability. Unlike in face-to-face behaviours, such as cruising for a partner or buying or renting X-rated DVDs, Internet users are anonymous. The Net is available 24/7, and its use is relatively cheap—you can download almost any kind of sexual material, often for free.

British psychologist Mark Griffiths (2000, 2001) has argued that OSA becomes an addiction or compulsion when it has the following six characteristics. These characteristics are similar to those proposed by Carnes (1983) for sexual addictions more generally:

1. *Salience.* OSA becomes the most important activity in the person's life, and he or she becomes preoccupied with thinking about it.
2. *Mood modification.* The person reports that OSA alters his or her negative mood by producing either an arousing buzz or high or a calming feeling of escape or numbing and thus is used as a coping strategy.
3. *Tolerance.* The person requires greater and greater amounts of OSA to achieve the former changes in mood. As a result, he or she spends more and more time engaging in OSA.
4. *Withdrawal symptoms.* The person experiences unpleasant feelings and physical effects when he or she stops engaging in OSA or suddenly decreases its use.
5. *Conflict.* As a result of spending a great deal of time on the Internet, the person experiences conflicts with the significant people in his or her life (e.g., not spending time with his or her partner), with other activities (such as a job, a social life, school), or within himself or herself.
6. *Relapse.* If the person begins to engage in OSA again after a period of not doing so, he or she quickly returns to his or her most extreme pattern of use.

Research on Internet use has used convenience samples of persons who respond to invitations on websites and agree to complete an online questionnaire. Obviously, such samples consist of persons with access to computers who possess basic online skills. Thus, these samples may underrepresent lower income persons and those from minority groups, although they may be representative of people engaging in OSA. Of concern is the 8 percent of participants who report spending 11 or more hours per week in OSA (Cooper et al., 1999b). These heavy users were more likely than were recreational users to go online both at home and at work and to report that their online sexual behaviour interfered with their lives. A study based on more than 40,000 users assessed the relationship between the frequency and duration of Internet use and mental health. The results indicated that the number of months that had passed since participants first went online and the number of hours per week online were associated with a history of mental health problems and treatment (Mathy & Cooper, 2003).

Online sexual activity (OSA): Use of the Internet for any activities of a sexual nature, including sexual activities with a partner, called cybersex.

(a)

http://www.clarkslist.org

Guy looking for dominant lady – m4w – 42 (Montreal)

Hi…

If you like to be the dominant in the encounter and you want to use your toys on me, let me know. I don't have experience but I want a lady to be my "macho" in bed. I'm a standard guy eager to please you. Please: No professionals. I want a real lady who wants to free this dark side of her.

Kisses.

ID: 3301328934

[Reply To This Post]

You lay down watch good porn and get sucked by cute couple - m4m - 23 (Vancouver)

We are a cute couple of to guys 25 and 21. You lay down, watch good porn and get sucked by us. We are cute clean and serious. Please under 35 and send a facepic in first email.

ID: 2644997727

[Reply To This Post]

Girl for girl if my bf can watch - 18 (Calgary)

I'm young white, sexy, in shape c cup but I'm small and skinny, dark hair blue eyes, I'm looking for a girl to fool around with while my bf watches, must be clean.

ID: 2583531178

[Reply To This Post]

Looking for feminine boy who i can dress up and put makeup on - w4m - 22 (Halifax)

I want a skinny pretty boy who I can dress in my clothes and completely makeover in to a girl. I'd like to get fucked while both of us are wearing skirts. I'm not a crossdresser or a tv but a real girl so you have to be attracted to women for this to work. You also can't be over a size 5 in women's clothes unless you want to buy your own. I have a thing for nail polished fingers and toes so please don't have extremely hairy hands unless you're willing to wax. Send a picture so I can see what I'm going to be working with.

ID: 2600447786

[Reply To This Post]

Bi-ker Babe (Regina)

Wanted! Couple 30s, who like to ride. She's: sensuous, lewd. He's: fine, driving and lasting, You're: lovely in leather or lace. On bikes, bars, or candlelight dining, friends sharing what we like best. We're open!

ID: 6256001766

[Reply To This Post]

(b)

Figure 15.9 (a) Advertising for partners with similar kinky interests. Many websites, newspapers, and magazines carry such personal ads. (b) Shoe-New Business @ 1982 NcNelly. Distributed by King Features Syndicate. Reprinted by permission.

A Swedish study focused on cybersex—that is, OSA with a partner (Daneback et al., 2005). Researchers placed a banner soliciting participation on a Web portal. The banner appeared randomly during a two-week period; 1835 persons completed the survey. Almost one-third reported that they had engaged in cybersex; the most common location was in a chatroom. Participants in cybersex were young, and gay men were four times as likely to report cybersex as were heterosexual men. Those who reported cybersex spent more time online and reported more offline sexual partners than did people who did not report cybersex.

Research using a sexual compulsivity scale sought to determine what percentage of users were compulsive users (Cooper et al., 2000). The study found that 83 percent of the participants were not problematic users. Eleven percent attained moderate scores on the scale, 4.6 percent were sexually compulsive, and 1 percent were OSA compulsives—that is, they attained the highest scores on compulsivity and spent more than 11 hours per week in online sexual pursuits. Persons in the OSA compulsive group were more likely to be male, to be single and dating, and to report that they were bisexual; they reported spending 15 to 25 hours per week in OSA. Twenty-one percent of the respondents reported that their online activities had jeopardized at least one area of their life, the most common being personal relationships. The researchers concluded that bisexuals, and perhaps other sexually marginalized groups, may be especially at risk for online sexual compulsivity.

The criteria used to define "problematic" OSA vary widely (Aboujaoude, 2010). Some researchers emphasize increasing time spent online over time and withdrawal symptoms—irritability, preoccupation—if prevented from accessing the Internet. Others emphasize behaviours and view problematic use as an impulse-control (or inhibition) disorder (recall our discussion of the dual control model of sexual arousal in Chapter 9). Others, for example, Cooper and colleagues in the study just discussed, emphasize compulsivity. Obviously, we get different estimates when using these different criteria. The research also suggests high rates of co-occurrence with other disorders; people whose Internet use is problematic are more likely to be depressed (by standard measures), report sleep disturbances, and report alcohol and drug abuse. The question is which came first: the Internet use, which then led to depression and substance abuse (because the Internet use was causing problems), or the depression and substance abuse, which led to the person finding escape online? A meta-analysis of studies of Internet "addiction" also noted the inconsistent criteria and indicated that online samples may result in biased estimates of the prevalence of the problem (Byun et al., 2009).

Other Sexual Variations

A review of the literature identified more than 100 sexual variations (Federoff, 2007). Some of these just describe unusual sexual interests; the individual involved may not actually have a paraphilia. Participation in others may be fatal (e.g., asphyxiophilia) or against the law (e.g., frotteurism, zoophilia). Most of the paraphilias are too rare to have had much research devoted to them. Nonetheless, some of them are described here. The Internet provides an avenue for individuals with even rare sexual interests to find like-minded individuals.

Asphyxiophilia

Asphyxiophilia or *hypooxyphilia* is the desire to induce in oneself a state of oxygen deficiency to create sexual arousal or to enhance sexual excitement and orgasm (Zaviačič, 1994). A variety of techniques are used, including temporary strangulation by a rope around the neck, a pillow against the face, or a plastic bag over the head or upper body. Obviously, this is very dangerous behaviour; a miscalculation can lead to death.

Little is known about asphyxiophilia. Most of the deaths attributed to the practice involve men, about three men for every woman (Sauvageau & Racette, 2006). There were 118 recorded deaths from asphyxiophilia in Alberta and Ontario (the only provinces that record this information) between 1974 and 1987; only one was female (Hucker & Blanchard, 1992). The average age of death was 26 but ranged from 10 to 56 years. Such cases are often obvious to the trained investigator. Characteristics that distinguish these deaths from intentional suicides include a male who is nude, cross-dressed, or dressed with genitals exposed, and evidence of sexual activity at the time of death (Hucker & Blanchard, 1992). Pornography or other props, such as mirrors, are often present (Zaviačič, 1994).

Some cases have been identified involving women (Byard et al., 1993). A review of eight fatal cases among women found that only one involved unusual clothing, and none involved pornography or props. Two of the cases were initially ruled homicide, one suicide, and five accidental death. The investigators suggest that death from asphyxiophilia may be much more common among women than we realize, because these deaths are less often recognized for what they are.

Men and women engage in asphyxiophilia in the belief that arousal and orgasm are intensified by reduced oxygen. There is no way to determine whether this

Is my online sexual activity compulsive?

Asphyxiophilia: The desire to induce in oneself a state of oxygen deficiency to create sexual arousal or to enhance excitement and orgasm.

is true. If the experience is more intense, it may be due to heightened arousal created by the risk rather than by reduced oxygen. Some believe that certain women may experience an orgasm accompanied by urethral ejaculation; this belief has been identified as one reason women engage in asphyxiophilia. Again, there is no evidence.

An online survey collected data from practitioners and found that 71 percent reported masochistic activities, and 31 percent reported sadistic ones. Sixty-six percent reported using bondage, and 14 percent reported using electrical stimulation. Forty-one percent engaged in it alone (Hucker, 2008).

Zoophilia

Zoophilia is sexual contact with an animal; this behaviour is also called *bestiality* or *sodomy*, although the latter term is also sometimes used to refer to anal intercourse or even mouth–genital sex between humans. About 8 percent of the men in Kinsey's sample reported having had sexual experiences with animals. Most of this activity was concentrated in adolescence and probably reflected the experimentation and diffuse sexual urges of that period. Not surprisingly, the percentage was considerably higher among boys on farms; 17 percent of boys raised on farms had had animal contacts resulting in orgasm. Kinsey found that only about 3 to 4 percent of all women have had some sexual contact with animals. Contemporary therapists report cases of men and women engaging in sexual activity with household pets. Activities include masturbating the animal, oral–genital contact, and intercourse. A preference for sexual contact with animals over humans is extremely rare and usually starts in adolescence (Earls & Lalumière, 2002, 2009; Milner et al., 2008). Here is the experience of a male physician with a preference for mares:

> As I grew into adolescence my sexual ideation was different than it was supposed to be. I looked at horses the same as other boys looked a girls. I watched cowboy movies to catch glimpses of horses. I furtively looked at pictures of horses in the library. . . . When I was first married, I tried so hard to be good and didn't have any contact with equines for about a year. After that, I couldn't suppress it anymore and my contact with horses rose while my relations with my wife declined. I tried to be a normal husband but human sex always felt wrong, I could do it but I couldn't learn to like it. (Earls & Lalumière, 2009, p. 606)

Researchers posted a questionnaire online and recruited participants through a letter to members of a network of people with sexual interests in animals (as we said, you can find anything on the Internet—that's accessibility). Those who volunteered were asked to refer others who had interests similar to those assessed by the questionnaire (Williams & Weinberg, 2003). Data were obtained from 114 men, all white, with a median age of 27; 64 percent were single, never married, and 83 percent had at least some university education. These characteristics undoubtedly reflect in part the fact that the sample was obtained via the Internet. Ninety-three percent defined themselves as "zoophiles" and said this identity involved a concern for the animal's welfare and an emphasis on consensual sexual activity. They compared themselves favourably with "bestialists," whom they said were not concerned about an animal's welfare. Given a list of possible reasons for sexual interest in animals, the two most common were a desire for affection and pleasurable sex. The type of sexual contact reported by the men varied by the type of animal. Receiving oral sex and receiving anal intercourse were the most frequent activities with dogs, whereas performing vaginal and anal intercourse were most frequent with horses. Only one man preferred sheep. Many of the men had not had a human partner of either sex in the preceding year. The researchers suggest that a preference for sexual activity with animals can be explained by learning theory in that the rewards offered by sex with animals are immediate, easy, and intense, and thus extremely reinforcing. They suggested that the respondents' choice of animal is explained by their early conditioning; most men preferred the type of animal they first had sex with.

The paraphilic form appears to be rare, with onset in adolescence (Milner et al., 2008).

Other Variations

Frotteurism is the seventh paraphilia identified by the *DSM-5*. It is defined as sexual fantasies, urges, or behaviours involving touching or rubbing one's genitals against the body of a nonconsenting person, usually in a crowded public place (Figure 15.10). It must occur over at least six months and cause marked distress or interpersonal difficulty. Milder forms of this activity are common and often intentional. A man may approach a woman from the rear and press his penis against her buttocks; or a woman may approach a man from the side and rub her genitals against his leg or hip. The target may be unaware of it, if it occurs in a crowded elevator or subway train or in the crush of a crowd at a sports event or concert. We noted earlier that 35 percent of a sample of university men reported having engaged in this activity. A variation is *toucherism*, which involves grabbing or rubbing the hands against an unsuspecting person.

Limited evidence from clinical samples suggests that about 10 percent of persons with a history of paraphilia

Zoophilia: Sexual contact with an animal; also called bestiality or sodomy.
Frotteurism: Rubbing one's genitals against the body of a nonconsenting person.

Figure 15.10 Frotteurism may involve touching or rubbing one's genitals against the body of a nonconsenting person, usually in a crowded public place.

or paraphilic-related behaviour have engaged in acts of frotteurism. These activities tend to start in early adulthood (Lussier & Piché, 2008).

Saliromania is a variation found mainly in men; there is a desire to damage or soil a woman or her clothes or the image of a woman, such as a painting or statue. The man becomes sexually excited and may ejaculate during the act.

Coprophilia and **urophilia** are both variations having to do with excretion. In coprophilia the feces are important to sexual satisfaction. In urophilia it is the urine that is important. The urophiliac may want to be urinated on as part of the sexual act. Insiders refer to urination as "golden showers."

Necrophilia is sexual contact with a dead person. It is a very rare form of behaviour and is considered by experts to be psychotic and extremely deviant. Necrophiliacs derive sexual gratification from viewing a corpse or actually having intercourse with it; the corpse may be mutilated afterward (Thorpe et al., 1961).

Feederism consists of the eroticization of weight gain and feeding (Terry & Vasey, 2010). Individuals can be either *feeders*, becoming sexually aroused by feeding their partner and encouraging them to gain weight, or *feedees*, becoming sexually aroused by eating, being fed, and the idea or act of gaining weight. Feeders are more often men and feedees are more often women (Terry & Vasey, 2010).

Sexsomnia, or sleep sex, refers to automatic, unintentional sexual behaviours during sleep (Williams & Lettieri, 2012); the term was introduced in 2003 (Shapiro et al., 2003). The behaviour occurs during nonrapid eye movement sleep, usually in the first hours of sleep, and is related to an abnormal transition between sleep and wake states. It typically arises from slow-wave sleep, which is characterized by reduced cortical control by the brain leading to uninhibited behaviour. The person is unaware of the behaviour or his or her surroundings, and if awakened has no memory of what happened.

The range of reported sexual behaviours is broad, from sexual sounds like moaning to fondling, masturbation, cunnilingus, sexual intercourse with or without orgasm, and sexual assault (Schenck et al., 2007). About 80 percent of the reported cases involve men. Partnered behaviours typically involve another person in the same bed. Partners may experience physical injuries. Both the actor and the partner report various negative psychosocial after-effects, including guilt, shame, embarrassment, alarm, and low self-esteem. Sexsomnia obviously may cause relationship problems. Sexsomnia has features in common with other sleep somnias (sleepwalking, sleep eating); the distinguishing feature is persistent sexual arousal—erection, lubrication, ejaculation—during the episode.

Causes or contributing features include things that can disrupt normal sleep cycles, including sleep apnea, sleep deprivation, stress, alcohol use or abuse, and some medications. Sexsomnia is considered a sleep disorder rather than a paraphilia, but some reported cases involve paraphilic behaviour (e.g., genital fondling of a minor) repeated over a long time. Other sexual behaviours are also related to sleep disorders, for example, sexual acts related to seizures during sleep.

 LO9

Prevention and Treatment of Paraphilic Disorders

For many of the variations discussed in this chapter, there is a continuum from normal to abnormal. People whose behaviour falls at the normal end enjoy these activities at no expense to themselves or others. Some may need reassurance that there is nothing wrong with engaging in these behaviours but do not need treatment to change their behaviour. They may, however, benefit from treatment aimed at helping them accept themselves and question pressure by family members or society to fit a narrow definition of normality. It is important that therapists are able to accept that there are a range of normal sexual behaviours. Individuals with atypical sexual interests may be reluctant to see a therapist out of fear that their interests will be pathologized. As a result, some therapists in Canadian cities are advertising themselves as "kink friendly" or "kink positive" to communicate their accepting attitudes.

However, some people engage in behaviours that fall at the

Saliromania: A desire to damage or soil a woman or her clothes.

Coprophilia (cop-roh-FILL-ee-uh): Deriving sexual satisfaction from contact with feces.

Urophilia (YUR-oh-fill-ee-uh): Deriving sexual satisfaction from contact with urine.

Necrophilia: Deriving sexual satisfaction from contact with a dead person.

Feederism: Deriving sexual pleasure from weight gain or feeding.

Sexsomnia: Automatic, unintentional sexual behaviours during sleep; also called sleep sex.

abnormal end. Some people engage in sexual variations that they find highly distressing, causing them significant unhappiness. Their sexual interests (e.g., in the case of a person with a sexual compulsion or addiction) may interfere with having healthy relationships or completing their day-to-day responsibilities. Yet they may find these sexual interests extremely difficult to change or control. Other sexual variations—for example, pedophilia—cause significant harm to other people. However, some pedophiles do not see their behaviour as harmful. Thus, the issue of whom to treat is extremely complex. Nonetheless, it is important to develop programs to prevent and treat these types of abnormal or harmful sexual variations.

Prevention of Paraphilic and Nonparaphilic Disorders

In preventive medicine, a distinction is made between primary prevention and secondary prevention. Applied to the sexual variations, primary prevention would mean intervening in home life or in other factors during childhood to help prevent problems from developing or trying to teach people how to cope with crises or stress so that problems do not develop. In secondary prevention, the idea is to identify people who are at high risk to develop a problem as early as possible, so that difficulties are minimized.

It would be highly advantageous to do primary prevention of harmful or distressing sexual variations—that is, to head them off before they even develop. Unfortunately, this method is proving to be difficult, for a number of reasons. One problem is the diagnostic categories. The categories for the diagnosis of sexual variations are not nearly as clear-cut in real life as they may seem in this chapter, and multiple diagnoses for one person are not uncommon. If it is unclear how to diagnose sexual variations, it is going to be rather difficult to figure out how to prevent them. Further muddying the waters is the co-occurrence of paraphilia and other psychiatric conditions. A study of 120 men (88 diagnosed with paraphilias, 38 with paraphilia-related disorders) systematically assessed co-occurrence (Kafka & Hennen, 2002). More than two-thirds had mood disorders, such as major depression; 38 percent had anxiety disorders; and 34 percent abused psychoactive substances. Men with paraphilias were significantly more likely to abuse cocaine. One-third of the men had retrospectively diagnosed attention-deficit hyperactivity disorder.

An alternative approach that seems promising—rather than figuring out ways to prevent each separate variation—is to analyze the *components of sexual development*. Disturbance in one or more of these components in development might lead to different sexual variations. Two such components are arousal to appropriate stimuli and formation of relationships with others (Bancroft, 1978). Thus, for example, a disturbance in attachment relationships in childhood might lead to exhibitionism or to compulsive OSA. The idea would then be to try to ensure that as children grow up, their development in each component is healthy (primary prevention). We might have specific programs for children who demonstrate characteristics or behaviour that is known to lead to abnormal or harmful sexual variations (secondary prevention). Ideally, these types of sexual variations would then not occur. However, this task is made more difficult by the fact that we have little scientific knowledge about either what constitutes unusual sexual behaviours among children or what components of development lead to abnormal or harmful sexual variations (Moser et al., 2004).

The review presented in this chapter makes it clear that childhood sexual abuse is a risk factor for paraphilic behaviour and paraphilias later in life. Indeed, individuals with paraphilias are more likely to have experienced both sexual and nonsexual abuse in childhood, as well as neglect and disturbed family relationships (Brotto & Klein, 2007). It is obvious that adults are responsible for sexual violence against children, so prevention (and treatment) must be targeted at adults and at preventing child sexual abuse.

Two factors have increased interest in developing prevention programs targeting children. First, paraphilias often first occur when individuals are in their mid-teens, although for other individuals they occur in their mid-20s (Brotto & Klein, 2007). Second, each year a number of youth are charged with sexual offences. For example, in 2008 in Canada 534 youth were convicted of sexual assault, and 228 youth were charged with other sexual offences in youth court (many more youth were charged with other crimes, such as physical assault and theft, than were charged with sexual offences). Research with 45 adolescent sex offenders in Toronto indicated that 42 percent showed equal or greater arousal to film clips of children than to film clips of adults—that is, they had pedophilic interests (Seto et al., 2003). One study of American adolescents incarcerated for sexual offences found that 46 percent committed their first offence before the age of 12 (Burton, 2000). Childhood victimization was positively associated with later sexual aggression by the youth, suggesting that social learning can help explain the development of sexual offending. Of course, most individuals who have experienced childhood abuse do not develop paraphilias. We have a long way to go in preventing abnormal or harmful sexual variations, to say the least.

Treatment of Paraphilic and Nonparaphilic Disorders

Despite our best efforts, it is unlikely that we will be successful in preventing all abnormal sexual variations. Treatments are needed for this category of variations. Many different treatments have been tried, each based on a different theoretical understanding of the causes of sexual variations. We will look at four categories of treatments: medical treatments, cognitive-behavioural therapies, skills training, and AA-type 12-step programs.

Medical Treatments

Inspired by the notion that sexual variations are caused by biological factors, several medical treatments for sexual variations have been tried over the last century. Some of them look today like nothing other than cruel and unusual punishment. Nonetheless, people would love to have a "pill" that would cure some of these complex and painful or dangerous paraphilias, so the search for such treatments continues.

Surgical castration has never been commonly used in Canada as a treatment for various kinds of uncontrollable sexual urges, although it was used extensively in Europe. However, a few sex offenders in Canada do voluntarily undergo surgical castration. Indeed, a study of 134 men interested in castration found that 41 percent of them indicated that the reason that they wanted to be castrated was to have more control over their sexual urges (Wassersug et al., 2004). Such treatments are based on the notion that removing a man's testosterone by removing the testes will lead to a drastic reduction in sex drive, which will in turn erase urges to commit sex offences. However, as we saw in Chapter 9, a reduction in testosterone levels in humans does not always lead to a reduction in sexual behaviour (Federoff & Moran, 1997). Surgical castration cannot be recommended as a treatment for sex offenders either on ethical grounds or on grounds of effectiveness.

Hormonal treatment involves the use of drugs to reduce sexual desire. Sexual arousability is heavily dependent on maintaining the level of androgen in the bloodstream above a given threshold. Two ways to reduce this level are to administer (1) drugs that reduce the production of androgen in the testes (*chemical castration*), or (2) anti-androgens that bind to androgen receptors in the brain and genitals, blocking the effects of androgen. The use of either should produce a sharp decline in sexual desire. Several drugs have been tried in the past 40 years. Medroxyprogesterone acetate (MPA), which binds to androgen receptors, was commonly used in Canada for some years. However, the drug has serious, adverse side effects, and its use has been discontinued in Europe (Thibaut et al., 2010). Cyproterone acetate (CPA) is replacing MPA; it acts as both a progestin and an anti-androgen. It binds to all androgen receptors, including those in the brain, and blocks testosterone uptake. It is taken daily as a tablet (the usual dosage is 100 mg) or injected weekly or biweekly. In studies involving 900 men, its use was associated with significant decreases in sexual fantasy, activity, and masturbation. Problematic sexual behaviour disappeared in 80 to 90 percent of the men in 4 to 12 weeks. One study reported efficacy for up to eight years. One problem associated with CPA in pill form is poor compliance by patients.

Clinicians also use leuprolide acetate, a synthetic analogue of gonadotropin-releasing hormone (GnRH; see Chapter 5); its continued use suppresses androgen production and reduces sexual fantasies and sex drive. One study reported its use with 12 adults with paraphilic or other sexual disorders (Krueger & Kaplan, 2001). These individuals were followed for between six months and six years. Treatment resulted in significant suppression of deviant sexual interests and behaviour. Similar results were found in a study of six young juveniles/young adults (Saleh et al., 2004). A review of research concluded that GnRH analogues may be needed for paraphilias that involve intense and deviant sexual desire and arousal or predispose the person to severe abnormal behaviour (Thibaut et al., 2010).

The use of alternative *psychopharmacological treatment* increased dramatically in frequency in the 1990s. Here, psychotropic medications are administered to offenders. These medications influence patients' psychological functioning and behaviour through their action on the central nervous system. The newness of the drugs being used means there is little research on the effectiveness of this technique. There is a great deal of interest in the use of the newer antidepressants known as selective serotonin reuptake inhibitors (SSRIs). Case reports indicate that SSRIs reduce paraphilic fantasies and urges (Raymond et al., 2002). They appear to change the compulsive sexual behaviour rather than sexual desire (Bradford, 2000; Federoff, 1995). Because these drugs have been successfully used to treat nonsexual compulsive behaviours, their success with paraphilias suggests that these conditions may be a type of obsessive-compulsive disorder (Miner & Coleman, 2001).

Both hormonal and psychopharmacological treatment should be used as only one element in a complete program of therapy, which would include therapy and treatment for other emotional and social deficits (Bradford, 2000; Saleh & Berlin, 2003). For example, Eli Coleman (Coleman et al., 2003) recommends that in addition to psychopharmacological treatment, individuals with compulsive sexual behaviour should (1) receive psychotherapy to deal with issues from the families of origin and learn to better deal with the stress, anxiety, and depression that can trigger the compulsive sexual behaviour; (2) participate in group therapy to learn from others with similar problems and overcome feelings of shame and guilt; and (3) receive couples therapy aimed at improving the couple's intimacy and sexual functioning. The best results are obtained with men who are highly motivated to change their behaviour and therefore comply with the prescribed treatment regimen. If the man with the paraphilia stops taking the drug or stops participating in other aspects of treatment, the program will fail. Unfortunately, one of the limitations of research on the effectiveness of these treatments is the high dropout rate, which was 46 percent in one study.

Cognitive-Behavioural Therapies

Compared with other therapeutic approaches, cognitive-behavioural therapy (CBT) is effective at reducing recidivism among sex offenders (Hanson et al., 2002; Marshall et al., 1991; Marshall et al., 2006). CBT is used extensively to treat incarcerated sex offenders in Canadian prisons (Byers et al., 1997). Comprehensive programs target offender needs and risk factors. However, they also aim to reduce the need to reoffend by helping the offender attain the skills and self-beliefs (including self-esteem) needed to attain a "good life" (Marshall et al., 2006). As such, most programs include the following:

1. Behaviour therapy to reduce inappropriate sexual arousal and enhance appropriate arousal
2. The learning of more effective ways of coping and managing moods
3. Social skills training to increase skills that are needed to form satisfying and effective interpersonal relationships
4. The learning of ways to increase the capacity to accept responsibility for one's actions, for example, through modification of distorted thinking and challenging the rationalizations that the person uses to justify the undesirable behaviour
5. Relapse prevention: helping the person identify and control or avoid whatever triggers the behaviour and to identify sources of support
6. A search for other, less problematic ways of meeting the needs and desires fulfilled by the behaviour

An evaluation of the effectiveness of programs for adult offenders reports that high-quality CBT programs for sex offenders in prison reduce recidivism 15 percent; for offenders on probation, the reduction is 31 percent (Aos et al., 2006).

One technique that is used in CBT is *covert sensitization*. It involves pairing aversive imagery (thoughts) with fantasies of the target behaviour. In the treatment of an exhibitionist, for example, he repeatedly practises a vivid fantasy in which, just as he imagines getting ready to expose himself, he experiences waves of nausea and vomiting. The details, of course, are individualized to the person and his particular problem. Reports indicate that this approach has been effective in some cases of sexual sadism, exhibitionism, and pedophilia (Barlow et al., 1969; Walen & Roth, 1987). However, although it may stop people from engaging in paraphilic behaviour, it is unlikely to alter their sexual interests and urges.

One program designed for female offenders combined CBT with psychodynamic techniques and relied on one-on-one rather than group therapy (Traven et al., 1990). Male offenders typically deny responsibility for their behaviour, so the initial stage of treatment may focus on acknowledging his behaviour and its consequences. Women in this program readily acknowledged what they had done and were overwhelmed by guilt and shame, so the initial stage focused on self-esteem. Thus, different treatment programs may be needed for men and women with paraphilias. A meta-analysis found that recidivism rates for women convicted of sexual offences (only some of which would be paraphilias) were much lower than rates for men (Cortini et al., 2010).

Skills Training

According to yet another theoretical understanding, persons with paraphilias engage in their behaviour because they have great difficulty forming relationships and so do not have access to appropriate forms of sexual gratification. This perspective is consistent with data on IQ differences between sex offenders and controls. A meta-analysis included results from 75 studies involving 236 independent samples and more than 25,000 persons (Cantor, Blanchard, et al., 2005). Men who committed sex offences scored significantly lower on IQ than nonoffenders did and lower than those who committed nonsexual offences. Among sex offenders, the younger the age of the victims, the lower the IQ score of the offender. Many of these people do not have the skills to initiate and maintain conversation. They may find it difficult to develop intimacy (see Chapter 12) (Keenan & Ward, 2000). Such people may benefit from a treatment program that includes social skills training. Such training may include how to carry on a conversation, how to develop intimacy, how to be appropriately assertive, and how to identify irrational fears that are inhibiting the person (Abel et al., 1992). These programs may also include basic sex education.

If a person needs to learn and practise sexual interaction skills, one approach would be to have him interact with a trained partner. This is the basis for a controversial practice: the use of *sex surrogates* as part of a treatment program. The surrogate works with the therapist, interacting socially and sexually with the client to provide opportunities for using the newly acquired information and skills. Some therapists believe that the use of surrogates is ethical, but others see it as a type of prostitution. Just as the definition of abnormal depends on one's point of view, so does the definition of sex therapy.

We noted earlier that some sex offenders are adolescents. A therapeutic program targeting this group by using CBT and skills training has been shown to be effective (LeTourneau et al., 2009). The program, multisystemic therapy (MST), involves family therapy, behavioural (skills) parent training, and CBT. The intervention is individualized to the specific offender and his or her caregivers, and is presented in the home and at school. It addresses (1) overcoming youth and caregiver denial about the offence, (2) minimizing the youth's access to potential victims, and (3) promoting age-appropriate and normative social experiences with peers. Youth (median age 14, all but three male) were randomly assigned to MST or the usual treatment prescribed for juvenile offenders in that jurisdiction: one-a-week group treatment session following a standard protocol. At 12-month follow-up, youth in MST showed significant reductions in problematic sexual behaviour (77 percent compared with zero decline), delinquency (60 percent compared with 18 percent), and substance abuse (50 percent decrease compared with 65 percent increase). Such programs are more effective with juveniles than adults and most effective with high-risk juvenile offenders, that is, those with prior arrests (Ward et al., 2008).

12-Step Programs

Sexual addictions theory argues that many people who engage in compulsive, inappropriate sexual patterns are addicted to their particular sexual practice. The appropriate treatment, according to this approach, is one of the 12-step programs modelled on Alcoholics Anonymous (AA). Several groups have adapted the AA program for sexual addictions, among them Sexaholics Anonymous (SA), Sexual Addicts Anonymous (SAA), Sexual Compulsives Anonymous (SCA), and Sex and Love Addicts Anonymous (SLAA). These groups can usually be found by calling the local phone number for Alcoholics Anonymous or by looking up their websites on the Internet. Some of the programs are run by group members, whereas others are affiliated with professional health care facilities.

Twelve-step programs combine cognitive restructuring, obtaining support from other members who have the same or similar problem behaviours, and enhancing spirituality (Figure 15.11). This last aspect involves

Figure 15.11   The centrepiece of 12-step programs such as Sex Addicts Anonymous are group meetings in which participants confront their addiction with the support of other group members.

increasing one's awareness of a "higher power" that can be relied on to help in recovery. The first step is admitting that one is sexually addicted, that the behaviour is out of control, and that life has become unmanageable. These are hard admissions for someone who has spent years denying the existence of a problem. There are frequent meetings with a support group, and there is a strong emphasis on building feelings of self-worth. AA for alcohol or drug addiction demands that the addict abstain from contact with the substance. Similarly, programs for sexual addicts adopt a definition of "sexual sobriety." They cannot adopt an abstinence model, however, because sexual expression is a basic human need. Thus, they attempt to differentiate addictive sexual behaviour from healthy sexual behaviour. For some groups, although not all, only marital sex (and not other partnered sex or masturbation) is considered to fit the definition of sexual sobriety.

Groups using 12-step programs are generally unwilling to cooperate with researchers, believing that to do so would prevent group members from concentrating on recovery. As a result, there is little research data on the effectiveness of these programs.

What Works?

Meta-analyses of the effectiveness of treatment programs for sex offenders consistently find that some programs are more effective than others. A systematic review of controlled outcome evaluations of psychosocial and hormonal treatment programs found that, overall, such programs reduced sexual recidivism by 37 percent compared with those in control groups (Schmucker & Losel, 2008). Use of hormonal medications showed the largest effect. Of various psychosocial treatments, only CBT was associated with reduced recidivism. Classical behavioural programs, including skills training, were associated with the smallest significant effect. Programs are more effective with some types of offenders than others are. The programs had the largest effect in treating sexual assault, the second largest with exhibitionism, and the smallest with intra-familial child sexual offenders. Importantly, the programs were effective only when participation was voluntary.

SUMMARY

It seems reasonable to define *abnormal sexual behaviour* as behaviour that is uncomfortable for the person, inefficient, bizarre, or physically or psychologically harmful to the person or others. The American Psychiatric Association defines *paraphilias* as recurrent, intense, sexually arousing fantasies, urges, or behaviours that are obsessive and compulsive. A behaviour is compulsive if the person is obsessed with it, feels compelled to engage in it, and has experienced personal, relationship, medical, or legal difficulties as a result of it. Some of these behaviours are against the law, but most are not.

Four theoretical approaches have been used in understanding the paraphilias: learning theory, cognitive theory, the sexual addiction or compulsion model, and sociological theory. Several explanations have been proposed for the fact that there are many more men than women with paraphilias.

A fetishist is a person who becomes erotically attached to some object other than another human being. Most likely, fetishism arises from conditioning, and it provides a good example of the continuum from normal to abnormal behaviour.

The transvestite derives sexual satisfaction from dressing as a member of the other gender. Like many other sexual variations, transvestism is much more common among men than among women. Survey data suggest that many men who later become transvestites begin cross-dressing in childhood.

Three interrelated styles of sexual interaction, jointly termed BDSM, involve differences in control over sexual interactions. Dominance and submission involve a consensual exchange of power and the enacting of scripted performances. Bondage and discipline involve the use of physical restraints or verbal commands by one person to control the other. Both D-S and B-D may occur without genital contact or orgasm. Sexual sadism and masochism involve deriving sexual gratification from giving and receiving pain. Both are recognized as paraphilias if they become compulsive.

The voyeur is sexually aroused by looking at nudes. The exhibitionist displays his or her sex organs to others. Both are generally harmless.

Nymphomania, satyriasis, and hypersexuality are terms used to describe women and men with an extraordinarily high sex drive. Nymphomania and satyriasis are ambiguous and subject to misuse. The term hypersexuality is potentially more precise, particularly if it is defined behaviourally.

Use of the Internet to engage in sexual activity may become compulsive or addictive. The Internet may facilitate sexual compulsion because of the three A's—anonymity, accessibility, and affordability.

Other sexual variations include asphyxiophilia, use of oxygen deprivation in an attempt to enhance sexual sensations; zoophilia, sexual contact with animals; and frotteurism, touching or rubbing ones genitals against the body of a nonconsenting person. Others include coprophilia, urophilia, and necrophilia. Programs to prevent sexual variations are being developed and evaluated.

Four types of programs to treat sexual variations are medical treatments, including hormonal and psychopharmacological interventions; cognitive-behavioural therapies; social skills training; and AA-type 12-step programs. Controlled evaluation studies find that hormonal treatments, CBT, and skills training are effective at treating some kinds of variations.

QUESTIONS FOR THOUGHT, DISCUSSION, AND DEBATE

1. What do you think of the idea about preventing sexual variations presented in this chapter? Do you think the schools or some other agency should institute a program to screen children, trying to detect those with characteristics that might indicate they would develop a sexual variation later in life and then give therapy to those children?

2. A common phenomenon in medical school is for medical students to think they have contracted one of the diseases they are studying. The analogous phenomenon would be for students who read this chapter to think that they have one or more of the paraphilias. Did you notice yourself becoming sexually aroused as you read about one (or more) of the

variations? If so, do you think you are abnormal? Why, or why not?

3. Most persons who seek treatment or are arrested for atypical or paraphilic behaviours are white men. Do you think that this is an accurate picture of our society, or are we just unaware of non-whites who engage in these behaviours? Based on the data presented and the causes discussed, would you expect black, Asian, or Aboriginal men to engage in these behaviours? Why, or why not?

4. Which of the behaviours in this chapter would you consider to be abnormal? Which would you consider to be atypical but normal?

1. What percentage of middle school and high school students in Canada have experienced sexual coercion?
2. What factors predispose men to be sexually aggressive?
3. When child molesters are released from prison, how likely are they to reoffend?
4. What behaviours in the workplace count as sexual harassment?

Read this chapter to find out.

CHAPTER

16

Sexual Coercion

LEARNING OBJECTIVES

After studying this chapter, you will be able to

LO1 Describe the offences in the *Criminal Code of Canada* that relate to sexual assault, and contrast these with the statute on rape before 1983.

LO2 Discuss the Canadian data on the reported frequency of sexual assault and sexual coercion.

LO3 Describe theories used to explain and factors that contribute to sexual assault.

LO4 Describe the emotional reactions and common physical injuries of victims of a sexual assault.

LO5 Profile men as victims of sexual assault.

LO6 Identify strategies that can prevent sexual assault and child sexual abuse.

LO7 Describe the offences in the *Criminal Code of Canada* that relate to child sexual abuse.

LO8 Summarize the Canadian data on the prevalence of child sexual abuse.

LO9 Describe the impact of child sexual abuse on the victim.

LO10 Differentiate child molesters from pedophiles, and discuss the characteristics of pedophiles.

LO11 Give examples of the treatment options available for sex offenders, and explain the controversy surrounding the National Sex Offender Registry.

LO12 Define and discuss, with examples, the different forms of sexual harassment.

Eboni's basic education about sex came from what she saw and the direct experiences that she had. When she was 5, she and her brother were wrestling with their uncle. Suddenly her uncle locked her brother out of the room and began taking off Eboni's clothes. He held her down on the bed and began to penetrate her but stopped abruptly. Eboni was frightened of him from then on. She didn't really understand what he intended to do or why he wanted to do it, but she knew that his behavior was unexpected and strange. . . .

Eboni's grandmother and father insisted that she not talk to strangers or take money from them. Eboni understood why—she knew that being molested meant being raped. But strangers were not the predators.[*]

[*] Wyatt (1997, pp. 72–73).

This chapter is about sexual activity that involves coercion and is not between consenting adults; specifically, we will consider sexual assault, child sexual abuse, and sexual harassment at work, in education, and by professionals. All these topics have been highly publicized in the last 20 years, and much good scientific research on them has appeared.

 LO1

Sexual Assault

In the last two decades, there has been a movement toward seeing crimes involving force in sexual relations as crimes of violence and victimization rather than as sex crimes. In 1983, the *Criminal Code of Canada* was amended to accommodate this different understanding and to protect victims. Before 1983, the *Criminal Code* had four sections that prohibited forced sexual activity: rape, attempted rape, indecent assault against a female, and indecent assault against a male. At that time, the legal definition of rape was forced heterosexual intercourse by a man with a woman who was not his wife (see Table 16.1). The rape law was criticized on a number of grounds. First, rape was limited to forced heterosexual intercourse. Second, it defined the assailant as male and the victim as female. Thus, women could not be charged with rape, and men could not be victims of rape. Third, husbands could not be charged with raping their wives, meaning that a woman could not legally refuse her husband's demands. Fourth, the victim's prior sexual activities could be considered as evidence of her consent and of the credibility of her testimony, effectively putting her past on trial. In addition, the law had a number of provisions that made the criminal justice system unresponsive to sexual assault complaints. It specifically required corroboration that the crime of rape actually took place. The judge was obliged to inform the jury that they should not convict only based on the complainant's testimony (Los, 1994). Finally, rape

Table 16.1 The Offence of Rape in the *Criminal Code of Canada* in 1968

In 1983 three sexual assault offences replaced this offence (see Table 2.1 for a description of the current offences).

A male person commits rape when he has sexual intercourse with a female person who is not his wife,

a. Without her consent, or
b. With her consent if the consent
   (i) Is extorted by threats or fear of bodily harm
   (ii) Is obtained by impersonating her husband, or
   (iii) Is obtained by false and fraudulent representations as to the nature and quality of the act.

complaints that were not made immediately after the attack were invalidated. These provisions meant that it was extremely difficult to get a conviction if there was no physical evidence (such as physical injury) or when the complaint was not filed immediately. In fact, the majority of complaints of rape did not result in a conviction (Clark & Lewis, 1977; Siegel & McCormick, 1999).

In 1983, the *Criminal Code* was amended so that the offences of rape and indecent assault were replaced with three gender-neutral crimes of sexual assault. The differences in these crimes depend on the amount of force used to carry out the assault and the degree of injury sustained by the victim, not on the nature of the forced sexual activity. The purpose of these changes was to de-emphasize the sexual nature of the offence, stress their violent nature, encourage victims to report these crimes to the police, and improve the court procedure to reduce trauma to victims and increase the rate of convictions (Roberts & Gebotys, 1992). The three levels of sexual assault parallel the three levels of physical assault in the *Criminal Code*: (simple) sexual assault, sexual assault with a weapon causing serious injury or endangering the life of the victim or causing bodily harm, and aggravated sexual assault (refer to Table 2.1 for a description of these offences).

Sexual assault[1] includes a variety of nonconsensual sexual experiences ranging from unwanted touching to forced oral, anal, or vaginal intercourse and sexual violence causing serious physical injury or disfigurement to the victim. In keeping with the equality provisions of the *Charter of Rights and Freedoms*, the law is written in gender-neutral terms so that either men or women can be the victim of a sexual assault and can be charged with sexual assault, and the statute no longer discriminates against married people. The crucial point is that the activity is nonconsensual—that is, the victim did not consent to it. The *Criminal Code* also defines *consent* for the purposes of sexual assault offences. Consent must be actively established. Silence, inaction, or ambiguous conduct is not consent. There is no consent if the complainant is drunk or unconscious, if the complainant shows by his or her actions that he or she is not in agreement, or if the complainant consents to engage in sexual activity and then changes his or her mind. Children under age 16 cannot be considered to have consented to sexual activity with an adult as this is considered child sexual abuse (discussed later in this chapter).

There were also some provisions that related to court proceedings, such as limiting the questioning of victims about their sexual history in sexual assault trials (often referred to as the *rape shield laws*) and no longer requiring corroboration of the victim's testimony. However, because of court challenges, there are now some conditions under which the judge can admit the victim's sexual history as evidence. Advocacy groups, such as the Women's Legal Education and Action Fund (LEAF), argue that myths and stereotypes about sexual assault still influence many judges, such as the mistaken belief that many women make false allegations about sexual assault, and thus, contrary to the will of Parliament, judges frequently permit sexual history evidence (Busby, 1999).

What percentage of middle school and high school students in Canada have experienced sexual coercion?

L02 Statistics

The 2009 Canadian General Social Survey asked both women and men under age 65 about their experiences of criminal sexual assault: 3.4 percent of the women and 1.5 percent of the men reported that they had experienced sexual assault in the previous 12 months (Perreault & Brennan, 2010). Most of the

Sexual assault: Any nonconsensual sexual activity ranging from unwanted touching, to forced oral, anal, or vaginal intercourse, to sexual violence in which the victim is wounded or maimed or his or her life is endangered or when the victim is incapable of giving consent.

---

[1] Although many Canadians still use the term *rape* in everyday conversation—usually meaning forced sexual intercourse—in keeping with the *Criminal Code of Canada* we have chosen to use the term *sexual assault* in this chapter, except when studies specifically used the term *rape*.

perpetrators (87 percent) were male. Most of these sexual assaults (81 percent) were the least serious type of sexual assault; the remainder involved threats or actual violence. In about half of these incidents, the perpetrator was someone the victim knew.

Few of these individuals had reported their experience to the police. Thus, statistics from police reports represent only a small proportion of sexual assaults in Canada. In 2011, there were 14,436 sexual assaults reported to the police (Sinha, 2013). The rate of reported sexual assault has been decreasing since the 1990s. Some of the reasons that women choose not to report their sexual assault to the police were believing that the police could not do anything, wanting to keep the event private, feeling ashamed or embarrassed, being afraid of not being believed, fearing the perpetrator, and not wanting the perpetrator to be arrested (Kong et al., 2003; Lievore, 2003).

Individuals with disabilities are at greater risk of experiencing sexual assault than are individuals without disabilities—more than four times as likely in one study (Martin et al., 2006).

The following discussion starts with sexual assault by men against women because this is the most common type of sexual assault.

L02 L03 Sexual Assault of Women by Acquaintances

Sexual assault by someone who is known to the victim, often called *date rape* (although it often doesn't occur on dates) or sexual assault by an acquaintance, is much more frequent than sexual assault by a stranger. How many women report these types of unwanted sexual experiences? Few if we go by police reports; for example, in 2011 in Canada, 75 percent of the assaults that women reported to the police (10,680 women) were by someone they knew (Sinha, 2013). These figures likely underestimate the true rate of sexual assault because many women do not report their sexual assault to the police, particularly if it involves an acquaintance.

Indeed, research that examined sexual coercion in university or community samples found considerably higher numbers. These studies typically ask respondents about a range of unwanted sexual activity not only from threats or physical force but also from verbal coercion, such as continual arguments and pressure. Thus, some but not all of these unwanted experiences would meet a legal definition of sexual assault. A study in Ontario found that 48 percent of university women reported having experienced coerced sexual activity involving pressure or force (Hartwick et al., 2007). Similarly, 44 percent of middle school and high school girls in New Brunswick reported having had a sexually coercive experience with a boyfriend; 17 percent of boys reported that they had been sexually abusive (Sears & Byers, 2010; Sears et al., 2007). More than half of these girls (57 percent) were upset by the experience. Many women do not recognize that what happened to them was sexual assault because it occurred in a dating situation, often after the couple had engaged in consensual sexual activity at a lower level (e.g., kissing). Nonetheless, research in Ontario has demonstrated that sexual coercion by a dating partner is associated with depression, lower self-esteem, and more negative sexual self-perceptions (Offman & Matheson, 2004).

Miscommunication may contribute to sexual assault in dating relationships. Research has shown that many men still hold to the traditional view that a woman who says "no" really means "yes" (Osman, 2003). Others believe that because a woman gave consent to, for example, kissing at the beginning of a sexual encounter, she has given consent to engaging in sexual intercourse. Films that portray women as enjoying sex resulting from sexual coercion by men reinforce this myth. Men need to learn that no means no whether it occurs before or during the sexual encounter. Consider this example of miscommunication and different perceptions in a case of sexual assault by an acquaintance:

Bob: Patty and I were in the same statistics class together. She usually sat near me and was always very friendly. I liked her and thought maybe she liked me, too. Last Thursday I decided to find out. After class I suggested that she come to my place to study for midterms together. She agreed immediately, which was a good sign. That night everything seemed to go perfectly. We studied for a while and then took a break. I could tell that she liked me, and I was attracted to her. I was getting excited. I started kissing her. I could tell that she really liked it. We started touching each other and it felt really good. All of a sudden she pulled away and said "Stop." I figured she didn't want me to think that she was "easy" or "loose." A lot of girls think they have to say "no" at first. I knew once I showed her what a good time she could have, and that I would respect her in the morning, it would be OK. I just ignored her protests and eventually she stopped struggling. I think she liked it but afterward she acted bummed out and cold. Who knows what her problem was?

Patty: I knew Bob from my statistics class. He's cute and we are both good at statistics, so when a tough midterm was scheduled, I was glad that he suggested we study together. It never occurred to me that it was anything except a study date. That night everything went fine at first, we got a lot of studying done in a short amount of time, so when he suggested we take a break I thought we deserved it. Well, all of a sudden he started acting really romantic and started kissing me. I liked the kissing but then he started touching me below the waist. I pulled away and tried to stop him but he didn't listen. After a while I stopped struggling; he was hurting me and I was scared. He was so much bigger and stronger than me. I couldn't believe it was happening to me. I didn't know what to do. He actually forced me to have sex with him. I guess looking back on it I should have screamed or done something besides trying to reason with him but it was so unexpected. I couldn't believe it was happening. I still can't believe it did. (Hughes & Sandler, 1987, p. 1)

Two factors seem to explain why sexually aggressive men misperceive women's communications. First, men in general tend to misperceive women's warmth and friendliness as indicating sexual interest, a pattern found in numerous studies (Farris et al., 2008; Perilloux et al., 2012). Second, sexually aggressive men are likely to have a "suspicious schema," meaning that they generally believe that women do not communicate honestly, particularly when the woman communicates clearly and assertively that she is rejecting an advance (Malamuth & Brown, 1994). These men choose to ignore verbal and nonverbal refusals, even when they are clear (Senn, 2013). The second finding has important implications for prevention and treatment programs for sexual aggressors. Cognitive therapy using cognitive restructuring is probably necessary, the goal being to get the man to change his suspicious schema. Such programs might be used with incarcerated sex offenders, but they might also be used in prevention programs with high school or college and university men who have been identified as being prone to sexual violence.

A frightening problem today is the emergence of the so-called date-rape drugs. There are three major types: Rohypnol, GHB, and ketamine. Numerous cases have been reported of men who slipped the drug into a woman's drink and then sexually assaulted her. Rohypnol (row-HIP-nawl; *roofie, roachie, La Rocha, forget pills, pasta, peanuts, whiteys, ropes*) is the drug name for flunitrazepam. The drug causes drowsiness or sleep, and the man sexually assaults the woman while she is incapacitated. The drug also causes the woman not to remember the event the next day. GHB (*liquid G, G, Georgia home boy, easy lay, grievous bodily harm*), the drug name for gamma hydroxyl butyrate, produces similar effects to alcohol but can cause hallucinations in larger doses and when mixed with alcohol can lead to loss of consciousness. Ketamine (*K, vitamin K, special K*) causes a combination of amnesia and hallucinations. Ecstasy (*Adam, XTC, bean, E, M, roll*) and Foxy Methoxy are also sometimes used as date-rape drugs. Several strategies for avoiding this situation have been suggested, including, especially, not accepting a drink from a stranger and never leaving your drink unattended. In addition to these drugs, there are a number of other substances that have been used to facilitate sexual assault, often termed *drug-facilitated sexual assault* because they result in disinhibition, drowsiness, or amnesia. These drugs include alcohol, marijuana, and tranquilizers (du Mont et al., 2009).

Partner Sexual Assault of Women

The definition of sexual assault in the *Criminal Code of Canada* includes nonconsensual sex with a spouse, common-law partner, or other intimate partner. How common is **partner sexual assault**? Community-based surveys indicate that, of women who have experienced forced intercourse, more than half (51 percent) were assaulted by an intimate partner (Black et al., 2011). However, few of these women report the assault to the police; for example, in 2011 only 17 percent of sexual assaults reported to police were by an intimate partner (spouse or dating partner (Sinha, 2013). The trauma to the woman who is sexually assaulted by an intimate partner is, of course, no less severe than other forms of sexual assault (Bennice & Resick, 2003; Brousseau et al., 2011).

One phenomenon that emerges from the research is an association between nonsexual and sexual violence in long-term relationships—that is, the man who batters his female partner is also likely to force her to have sex (Centers for Disease Control and Prevention, 2004).

A man might sexually assault his female partner from many motives, including anger, power and domination, sadism, or a desire for sex regardless of whether she is willing (Russell, 1990). In some cases the man is extremely angry, perhaps in the middle of a family argument, and he expresses his anger toward his partner by sexually assaulting her. In other cases, power and domination of the female partner seem to be the motive; for example, the woman may be threatening to leave him. Finally, some sexual assaults occur because the man believes his female partner "owes" him sex.

The Impact of Sexual Assault on Women

Compared with nonvictimized women, women who have experienced sexual assault are more likely to show several types of psychological distress, including anxiety, depression, suicide ideation and attempts, and **posttraumatic stress disorder (PTSD)** (Martin et al., 2011). This is true of both women sexually assaulted by a stranger and those sexually assaulted by an acquaintance or a date (Koss, 1993; Neville & Heppner, 1999). PTSD is defined as the long-term psychological distress suffered by someone who has experienced a terrifying, uncontrollable event (Figure 16.1). Originally developed to describe the long-term psychological distress suffered by war veterans, most of whom are men, it later became clear that female survivors of sexual assault show these same symptoms characteristic of PTSD (Koss & Figueredo, 2004). Typical symptoms can include anxiety, depression, nightmares, and not feeling safe.

Partner sexual assault: The sexual assault of a person by his or her current or former marital or common-law spouse or other intimate partner.
Posttraumatic stress disorder (PTSD): Long-term psychological distress suffered by someone who has experienced a terrifying event.

Figure 16.1 Many women experience severe emotional distress after a sexual assault, and it is important that crisis counselling be available to them.

According to the cognitive-behavioural view of PTSD, people who have experienced a terrifying event form a memory schema that involves information about the situation and their responses to it (Foa et al., 1989). Because the schema is large, many cues can trigger it and thereby evoke the feelings of terror that occurred at the time; the schema is probably activated at some level all the time. The consequences can be far-reaching and long-lasting.

Most women who experience a sexual assault have negative psychological reactions immediately afterward. Many, but not all, show significant recovery within a year (Martin et al., 2011). A number of factors are associated with worse psychological outcomes: whether the woman has experienced sexual violence previously (i.e., this is a revictimization), the severity of the violence (more severe violence is associated with worse outcomes), and the reactions of others when the woman discloses the assault (negative reactions from others produce worse psychological outcomes). See First Person for one woman's account of these effects on her life. The good news is that psychotherapeutic treatments for PTSD are available and they are successful in treating sexual assault survivors (Resick et al., 2012).

Some women experience self-blame (Cairns, 1993). A woman may spend hours agonizing over what she did to bring on the sexual assault or what she might have done to prevent it: "If I hadn't worn that tight sweater . . .", "If I hadn't been dumb enough to walk on that dark street . . .", "If I hadn't been stupid enough to trust that guy. . . ." Or she may *know* that she is not to blame but nonetheless feel guilty—that is, experience emotional self-blame but not cognitive self-blame (Glenn & Byers, 2009). Self-blame is a result of a tendency on the part of society to *blame the victim* and excuse the perpetrator and is linked to worse long-term psychological outcomes for victims (Glenn & Byers, 2009; Koss & Figueredo, 2004). People are particularly

A Sexual Assault Victim Tells Her Story

During my second year at university, I realized that I wanted to socialize more. I broke up with my hometown honey, began attending parties, started drinking, and dated other guys at my school. I was a virgin and didn't want to be anymore. I met my second boyfriend in physics. "G" was a football player and a big, handsome man, the best-looking man I'd ever met. We began to date and at first it was wonderful. He even carried me home once from a party, and I thought, "This is the one." Our first attempt at intercourse was difficult, and I began to beg him to stop, but he just kept trying until he was successful and there was blood everywhere. It was awful.

I continued to date G, but he began to act very differently. When he drank, he became extremely violent, and on different occasions I watched him break a vending machine and pull a toilet out of a wall at a university residence. He was unhappy with the way he was treated on the football team. He demanded to know where I was at all times and accused me of cheating on him. I wanted to break up with him, especially since sex was rough and not always consensual, but I was scared of him. I tried avoiding him but he always found me.

One night, G arrived very drunk at a party I was attending. I tried to sneak out of the party. He noticed I left and ran out after me. I didn't want trouble so I drove him to his dorm. He claimed he was too drunk to walk to his dorm, so I tried to help him into his room. When I turned around to leave, he sprang up and locked me in. He attacked me. I tried fighting him, but he wouldn't listen or stop. He hit my head into the wall several times and tried to force me to perform oral sex. I bit him, and that made him more angry. He then tried to force anal sex, and I fought as hard as I could. I finally started crying, and he stopped when he lost his erection. The rest of the night, I felt completely trapped in his dorm room. I lay awake all night and tried to leave, but he would wake up and stop me. I've never forgotten how scared I felt that entire night. He got up that morning and showered and acted as if nothing had happened. He was in all my classes for the rest of my university career.

I began to drink very heavily afterward. I told my roommate, J, and another woman on my floor, D. I never thought to report it, since he was my "boyfriend."

A year and a half later, I began to hear voices. It was a male voice calling me a fucking bitch, whore, and other names. I thought I was going crazy and became very depressed. I decided I must be schizophrenic and decided to kill myself.

Soon after, I was shopping in a bookstore. I saw this title staring right at me, *I Never Called It Rape*. I started reading it right there in the store, and I began crying and thinking, "This is what happened to me." I spoke with a faculty member, who arranged for immediate counselling.

The first time I went to see the counsellor, I couldn't even speak. I sat in her office and cried for the entire hour. She kept saying, "It's not your fault, it's not your fault." I couldn't believe it. Later we discussed how most of the times G and I had sex had actually been sexual assault, including the first and the last. I participated in a "Take Back the Night March." Members of one male residence threw bottles at us.

I went through medical school and residency. During my first year of residency, I was assaulted again, this time by a man in a stairwell during a New Year's Eve party at a hotel. I started screaming, "You're raping me, you're raping me!" He stopped and I got away! But I didn't go to the ER, I just went home and crawled in bed. My old shame came back. I began to drink heavily again. One night I drank all night and never showed up to work that next morning. I finally rolled into my director's office, depressed, hung over, and still smelling of alcohol, and my boss said I had to stop and straighten up right away or he wouldn't let me back for the next year. So I stopped drinking. I also made two very good friends around the same time. Through their support, I really turned my life around.

Three years later, I moved to a different city. I was living alone for the first time and had a great deal of anxiety. I joined a Sexual Assault Survivors Support Group. Then in the spring, I was invited to speak at my old university for Career Day for high school students, so I went back there ten years after the incidents. I was finally successful in my career, had strong, loving relationships with my friends and parents, and was happy. I look back at what happened now and think that I really survived a lot. I feel it helps me to be a better physician because I can empathize with how bad life can be for people.

Source: Based on an interview conducted by Janet Hyde.

likely to blame the victim if she voluntarily used alcohol or drugs, even when the perpetrator used physical force (Girard & Senn, 2008).

Researchers are finding increased evidence of the damage to women's *physical health* that may result from sexual assault (de Visser et al., 2007; Golding, 1999; Paras et al., 2009). Women may suffer physical injuries, such as cuts and bruises and vaginal pain and bleeding. Women who have been forced to have oral sex may suffer irritation or damage to the throat. Women forced to have anal intercourse report rectal bleeding and pain. A sexually assaulted woman may contract a sexually transmitted infection, such as HIV/AIDS or herpes. In about 5 percent of cases involving forced intercourse, pregnancy results (Koss et al., 1991). Women who have been sexually or physically assaulted at some time in the past visit their physician twice as often per year as nonvictimized women (Koss et al., 1991).

Sexual assault affects many people in addition to the victim—women in general, partners of victims, and the victim's friends. For example, most women routinely do a number of things that stem from fears of sexual assault even though they have never experienced sexual assault. That is, many women, when getting into their car at night, almost reflexively check the back seat to make sure no one is hiding there. In addition, most university women avoid walking alone through dark parts of the campus at night. In the Violence Against Women Survey (Statistics Canada, 1993), 60 percent of women reported feeling worried when walking alone in their neighbourhood after dark. Most women experience the fear of sexual assault, if not sexual assault itself, and this fear restricts their activities (Parrot & Cummings, 2006; Senn & Dzinas, 1996).

Spouses or partners of victims and the victim's friends may also be profoundly affected. At the same time, they can provide important support for the woman as she recovers (see First Person).

New research in psychology indicates that not everyone who experiences a serious traumatic event develops PTSD. Some, in fact, display **posttraumatic growth**—that is, positive life changes and psychological development following exposure to trauma (Tedeschi et al., 1998). Research with sexual assault survivors confirms that some do report positive life changes, such as an increased ability to take care of themselves, a greater sense of purpose in life, and greater concern for others in similar situations (Frazier et al., 2004).

 Causes of Sexual Assault Against Women

Posttraumatic growth: Positive life changes and psychological development following exposure to trauma.

To provide a perspective for the discussion that follows, we can distinguish among three major theoretical views of the nature of sexual assault (Baron & Straus, 1989; Zurbriggen, 2010).

1. *Psychopathology of sex offenders.* This theoretical view holds that sexual assault is an act committed by a psychologically disturbed man. His deviance is responsible for the crime occurring.

2. *Feminist.* Feminist theorists and learning theorists view sexual assault as the product of gender-role socialization in our culture, which reinforces and legitimizes male aggression in general and sexual coercion specifically. Feminists also have theorized about the complex links between sex and power: In some assaults, men use sex to demonstrate their power over women; in other assaults, men use their power over women to get sex. Feminists also point to the eroticization of violence in our society. Gender inequality is both the cause and the result of sexual assault in this view.

3. *Social disorganization.* Sociologists believe that crime rates, including sexual assault rates, increase after disruption to the social organization of a community. Under such conditions the community cannot enforce its norms against crime.

You personally may subscribe to one or more of these views. It is also true that researchers in this area have generally based their work on one of these theoretical models, which may influence their research. Keep these models in mind as you read the rest of this chapter.

What do the data say? Research indicates that a number of factors contribute to sexual assault, ranging from forces at the cultural level to factors at the individual level. These factors include the following: cultural values, sexual scripts, early family influences, peer-group influences, characteristics of the situation, miscommunication, sex and power motives, and masculinity norms and men's attitudes. The data on each of these factors are considered here.

Cultural values can serve to support sexual assault. In the International Dating Violence Study, researchers collected data from university students at 38 sites around the world, including several states in the United States and sites in Asia, Europe, Latin America, and the Middle East (Hines, 2007). The results indicated that the more hostility that men from a culture expressed toward women on questionnaires, the higher the rate of women reporting being sexually coerced.

Sexual scripts play a role in sexual aggression as well (Byers, 1996; Krahé et al., 2007). Adolescents quickly learn society's expectations about dating and sex through culturally transmitted sexual scripts. These scripts support sexual assault when they convey the message that the man is supposed to be oversexed and be the sexual "aggressor." By adolescence, both girls

What Should I Do After a Sexual Assault?

If You Have Been Sexually Assaulted

Tell someone you trust. Sexual assault is a traumatic violation of the person. Especially in the beginning it is helpful to be with someone who will listen to your feelings and help you carry out your decisions. If you can't tell a friend or a family member, call a sexual assault crisis line.

Decide whether to report the assault to the police. This is your decision. If you decide to report, call the police as soon as possible and preserve evidence of the crime. Do not wash, change your clothes, bathe, shower, or douche until you have a medical exam. Save anything that was involved as it may be needed as evidence.

Seek medical attention. Whether or not you decide to report the assault to the police, it is important that you see a doctor to treat any physical injuries and check for STIs and pregnancy. If pregnancy seems likely, emergency contraception can be used (see Chapter 7). You have the right to have forensic evidence collected, whether or not you choose to report the sexual assault to the police at that time, so that the evidence is available if you later decide to report it. The hospital will use a sexual assault forensic kit to collect evidence such as scrapings, semen, blood, and hair. It is important that this be done within 72 hours of the assault.

Understand that it is normal to experience a wide range of emotions. Emotions such as anger, sadness, detachment, depression, fear, and being out of control are normal responses to sexual assault. It will take time to recover. Taking control over the little things in your life, and later the bigger things, can be one step on the road to recovery.

Understand that the assault was not your fault. You may feel guilty or that the attack was somehow your fault. Sexual assault is a crime, and it was not your fault.

If Someone You Know Has Been Sexually Assaulted

Believe them. Sexual assault survivors may fear not being believed. Accept their version of the facts and be supportive. Sexual assault survivors react differently; not having an emotional reaction may indicate that they are in shock.

Listen to them. Find somewhere to be alone with them, and let them talk. Be patient. Let them tell their story at their own speed and in their own way. They may need to talk at odd hours or a great deal in the beginning.

Comfort them and provide security. Try to calm and ground them if they are anxious or upset. Do this in a soothing, not a disapproving, way. They may not want to be held or touched, but you can still nurture them by offering tea, a blanket, a comfortable chair, a favourite object, and so on. Help them feel safe by offering to find them a secure place to sleep and companionship when they return home.

Tell them it was not their fault. Do not judge. Avoid questions that seem to blame them for their actions. Avoid "why" questions such as "Why didn't you fight harder?" or "Why did you go to their room?" Let them know that it was the aggressor's fault, not theirs.

Encourage action. Suggest calling a sexual assault crisis centre. A sexual assault crisis worker is experienced in talking to survivors and can understand the survivors' needs and offer useful resources. Medical assistance also may be important, depending on the nature of the assault. If they agree to medical assistance, go with them to the hospital, clinic, or doctor's office. Stay during the examination if they want you to.

Let them make the decisions. Sexual assault survivors need to regain their feeling of control. You can help with this by giving referrals and resources but letting them make the decisions.

Help them decide whether to report the assault. If they decide to report the assault, encourage them to preserve any evidence. They should not take a shower or remove their clothes until they are examined at a hospital. However, even if the person did take a shower and then decided to be examined, evidence may still be collected.

Recognize your own limitations. Take time out when you need it. Recognize when you have reached the limits of your abilities. Help them create a network of support and referrals. Put aside your feelings and deal with them elsewhere. If you have strong feelings, talk to another friend or a local hotline.

Source: Condensed from Hughes and Sandler (1987) and from materials developed by the Fredericton Sexual Assault Crisis Centre.

and boys endorse scripts that justify sexual aggression. A New Brunswick study of almost 1700 middle school and high school students found that about 11 percent of boys believe that it is acceptable for boys to be sexually coercive with a girlfriend (Price & Byers, 1999; Sears et al., 2007). Boys who were sexually abusive but not abusive in other ways (i.e., physically or psychologically) were more accepting of sexual dating violence and had friends who were sexually abusive. This suggests that these boys see sexual coercion as a normal part of the sexual script.

Early family influences may play a role in shaping a man into becoming a sexual aggressor. Specifically, young men who are sexual aggressors are more likely to have been sexually abused themselves in childhood (Seto et al., 2010).

The peer group can be a powerful factor in men's sexually aggressive behaviour. For example, a national study of 1300 Canadian male college and university students found that men who had abusive friends were more likely to have used sexual aggression (DeKeseredy & Kelly, 1993; DeKeseredy & Schwartz, 1998). It may be that aggressive friends encourage men to be sexually aggressive. It also may be that sexually aggressive men choose friends who have similar attitudes.

Characteristics of the situation play a role. Sexual assault is more likely to occur in secluded places or at parties at which excessive alcohol is used (Koss et al., 1994). Another situational factor is social disorganization, as noted earlier. An extreme example is war, in which sexual assault of women is common (Zurbriggen, 2010). We see graphic examples in Darfur, Sudan, where roving units called Janjaweed (armed men on horses) terrorize the local civilians, including through sexual assault of the women (Parrot & Cummings, 2006).

Miscommunication between women and men is a factor. In our discussion of sexual assault in dating relationships, we saw a case in which the man and the woman had totally different understandings of what had occurred. Because many people in Canada find it difficult to discuss sex, they most often do not ask their partner for sexual consent directly but rather try to infer sexual interest from subtle nonverbal cues, a process that is highly prone to errors (Humphreys & Brousseau, 2010). For example, some men may interpret a woman's friendly or affectionate behaviour or sexy clothing as carrying a sexual message that she did not intend (Farris et al., 2006; Lindgren et al., 2008).

Sex and power motives are involved in sexual assault. Feminists have stressed that sexual violence is an expression of power and dominance by men over women (Parrot & Cummings, 2006; Zurbriggen, 2010). Current theory emphasizes that sexual motives and

What factors predispose men to be sexually aggressive?

power motives are both involved and interact with each other. For example, using phallometric assessment, researchers in Ontario examined differences in physiological arousal to consensual and nonconsensual sexual scenarios between a group of men convicted of sexual assault, a group of men convicted of nonsexual crimes, and a group of men from the community. The violent nonsexual criminals and men from the community were more aroused by hearing about consensual sex than by hearing about forced sex. However, the sex offenders showed little difference in their arousal to consenting and sexual assault scenarios (Lalumière et al., 2003).

Finally, *masculinity norms and men's attitudes* are another factor (Abram et al., 2003; Zurbriggen, 2010), as we will see in the next section. Supporting the feminist theoretical view, research shows that men who have more hypermasculine attitudes are more likely to have a history of sexual aggression (Murnen et al., 2002).

Thus, research has supported the theories that propose that socialization, social inequality, and social disorganization contribute to sexual assault. However, research has not found that women cause their own sexual assault (victim-precipitated theory) or that most men who commit sexual assault have psychological disorders. The very commonness of sexual assault, especially in dating relationships, argues against the psychopathology of sexual offenders. Hypermasculinity is a far more common cause than psychopathology.

LO3 Men Who Are Sexually Aggressive Against Women

There is no typical sexually aggressive man. Men who commit sexual assault against women vary tremendously in occupation, education, relationship status, previous criminal record, and motivation for committing sexual assault.

One thing we do know about sexually aggressive men is that they tend to be repeat offenders. In one study of men who admitted to sexual assault on a survey but had never been prosecuted, the majority had committed the crime more than once (Lisak & Miller, 2002). Those who were repeat offenders averaged about six sexual assaults each.

Compared with other men, men who commit sexual assault tend to have the following characteristics (Gannon & Ward, 2008; Thakker et al., 2008):

1. They hold a number of social cognitions or *implicit theories* that support sexual assault. They believe that women are sexual objects, that women are dangerous and deceptive, that the world in general is dangerous, that certain behaviours are uncontrollable in the face of strong urges, and

they have a sense of entitlement involving male superiority and control.

2. They are more likely to have had brain injuries as a child, which may be related to the next deficit. Nonetheless, only about 4 percent of men who have committed sexual assault have had traumatic head injuries.

3. They are characterized by poor inhibition and self-regulation. In particular, they are unable to inhibit aggressive impulses.

4. They lack empathy (Senn et al., 2000). Specifically, they fail to understand the suffering that a sexual assault victim experiences.

5. They may have experienced environmental triggers, such as being in a war.

6. They are more likely themselves to have been victims of child sexual abuse (Jesperson et al., 2009).

These research findings have important implications for programs of therapy aimed at reducing the chance of men convicted of sexual assault reoffending (Marshall, 1993; Pithers, 1993; Thakker et al., 2008). They need training in empathy. In addition, therapy must challenge their cognitive distortions and denial that they did anything wrong.

L02 L03 Ethnicity and Sexual Assault Against Women

We have seen how cultural context can promote or inhibit sexual assault. The cultural heritages of various ethnocultural groups in Canada provide different cultural contexts for people of those groups, so it is important to consider the incidence of sexual assault in Canadian ethnocultural communities. Participants in three of the communities that participated in the Ethnocultural Communities Facing AIDS study were asked whether they had ever been coerced or forced to have sex with someone against their will. The incidence of sexual coercion differed markedly from one community to the other. In the English-speaking Caribbean communities, 37 percent of the women and 19 percent of the men reported that they had experienced sexual coercion, compared to 8 percent of the women and 1 percent of the men in the Latin American communities, and 5 percent of the men from the South Asian communities (Maticka-Tyndale et al., 1996). Interestingly, in the English-speaking Caribbean communities, people who had been in Canada longer were more likely to indicate that they had experienced sexual coercion. This suggests that sexual coercion is a more common experience in Canada than it is in the Caribbean.

Sometimes ethnic heritage can help. In Asian cultures, saving face is very important. For men from Asian communities in Canada, the potential for loss of face by

committing sexual assault is a deterrent to such activity (Hall et al., 2005).

Historical factors may also affect the meaning of sexual assault. For example, many recent Canadian immigrants are refugees from places such as Bosnia, where invading military forces instituted systematic campaigns of sexual violence against women (Valentich, 1994). Similarly, sexual assault has a highly charged meaning in the history of African Americans (Sommerville, 2004). In the period following the American Civil War, a black man convicted of rape or attempted rape of a white woman was typically castrated or lynched. In sharp contrast, there was no penalty for a white man who raped a black woman.

In some cultures, it is considered a wife's duty to have sex with her husband when he wants to. Might these cultural expectations affect how sexual assault—particularly spousal assault—is defined in these countries?

L03 L05 Sexual Assault Against Men

The sexual assault provisions in the *Criminal Code of Canada* apply equally to men and to women as victims. However, men were the victims of only 8 percent of sexual assault reported to the police (Sinha, 2013). Some authors believe, based on self-report studies, that there are more female sex offenders than indicated by police reports (Denov, 2003). Further, gay men also experience sexual coercion from their sexual partners (Gavey et al., 2009). For example, in one study 20 percent of a sample of gay and bisexual men reported having experienced unwanted sexual intercourse resulting from threats or use of force as an adult (Kalichman et al., 2001). It is important for counsellors and others in helping professions to recognize the possibility of male victims of sexual assault.

As with the statistics for women, estimates of the number of men who have experienced sexual coercion are higher when the data are based on university and community samples than when they are based on police reports. For example, research in New Brunswick has investigated men's and women's experiences of unwanted sexual activity through pressure or force (Byers & O'Sullivan, 1998; O'Sullivan et al., 1998). The results showed that sexual coercion of men by women is not rare—19 percent of men had experienced unwilling sexual activity in the previous year; 9 percent of women reported having used sexual coercion. Further, 14 percent of the men who had experienced sexual coercion were extremely upset by the incident. In a study of New Brunswick middle school and high school students, 33 percent of the boys reported that they had experienced sexual coercion; 5 percent of the girls reported that they had been sexually abusive (Sears & Byers, 2010; Sears et al., 2007). Only 19 percent of these boys were upset by the experience, however. Although both these studies showed that girls and women are more likely to experience sexual coercion than are boys and men, they also indicate that sexual coercion of men by women is not that infrequent.

These experiences are very upsetting for some men. For example, some men (straight and gay) who have been sexually assaulted experience symptoms of PTSD (Dunmore et al., 2001; Gold et al., 2007). Men who have been sexually assaulted also experience self-blame, guilt, and shame (Byers & Glenn, 2012). Research in Quebec has shown that in 20 percent of couples, sexual coercion is reciprocal (Brousseau et al., 2011).

Some of the same factors that contribute to sexual aggression by men also contribute to sexual aggression by women. They occur in similar heterosexual dating situations, and men and women use similar strategies to influence their partner to engage in the unwanted sexual activities, most often verbal forms of pressure or ignoring requests to stop (Byers & Glenn, 2012; Hartwick et al., 2007; O'Sullivan et al., 1998). Sexual scripts play a role as well. Research in Ontario has shown that many women believe the stereotype that men are always interested in sex (Clements-Schreiber et al., 1998). Thus, they may not believe that when a man says no he really means no. For example, in a study of sexual coercion in a sample of university students, 58 percent of the men (and 78 percent of the women) reported being the objects of sexual persistence after they had refused sexual advances (Struckman-Johnson et al., 2003). Sexual persistence included using any of a number of tactics to have sexual contact with the respondent despite their initial refusal of the sexual advances. The persistence tactics assessed included persistent kissing and touching, the perpetrator taking off his or her own clothes, telling lies, and using physical restraints. One man said,

> At a party, she came up and began talking to me. I was already drinking some at the time. While playing cards, she talked me into finishing several of her drinks and beers. She said there was another party and convinced me to go. I was too drunk to drive so she drove us. The "party" seemed to lack other people. After about a half-hour of kissing/making out, I was tired and wanted to go home. She said no and told me she wanted to have sex. I said no, but she continued to kiss me and try to talk me into it. When she produced a condom, I gave in. (Struckman-Johnson et al., 2003, p. 83)

Research in Ontario found that male victims tend to be blamed more harshly for their victimization than female victims and female perpetrators blamed more leniently for their behaviour than male perpetrators (Rye et al., 2006). Men may be particularly unlikely to report a sexual assault if they are aware that they may be blamed for their own victimization.

Having recognized that some men are sexually coerced by women, it is important to note that the great majority of male victims of forced intercourse are sexually assaulted by men, not women (Calderwood, 1987). In particular, sexual coercion is a pervasive problem in the relationships of men who have sex with men (Kalichman et al., 2001). Men who have been sexually assaulted by other men can experience very negative behavioural and psychological consequences (Walker et al., 2005). Sexual coercion also exists in women's same-sex relationships. This suggests that we need programs, as we have for heterosexual individuals, aimed at reducing sexual coercion in same-sex relationships (Kalichman et al., 2001).

LO2 LO3 LO5 Sexual Assault in Prison

According to a study of 516 male and female prisoners in U.S. prisons, 22 percent of the men and 7 percent of the women had been the objects of sexual coercion while in prison (Struckman-Johnson et al., 1996). Prison staff were the perpetrators in 18 percent of the cases, fellow prisoners in the remainder. Among the male victims, 53 percent had been forced to have receptive anal sex, sometimes with multiple male perpetrators, and 8 percent were forced to have receptive oral sex. The men reported severe emotional consequences. Inmates offered a number of suggestions for ending prison sexual violence. The most frequent was to segregate the most vulnerable: those who are young, nonviolent, new to prison, and white. Many also favoured allowing conjugal visits.

Sexual assault in prison is a particularly clear example of the way in which sexual assault is an expression of power and aggression; prisoners—most of whom would identify as heterosexual—use it as a means of establishing a dominance hierarchy.

LO6 Preventing Sexual Assault

Strategies for preventing sexual assault need to be aimed at both men and women. Although most programs are aimed at teaching women ways to avoid victimization, it is perhaps more important to develop programs for men. To eliminate sexual assault of women, our society would need to make a radical change in the way it socializes males (Hall & Barongan, 1997). If little boys were not so pressed to be aggressive and tough, and were encouraged to express their feelings and to be nurturant to others there would be far fewer sexually aggressive men. If adolescent boys did not have to demonstrate that they are hypersexual, perhaps there would be few sexually aggressive men.

We also need prevention programs aimed at changing attitudes that contribute to sexual assault. These programs need to stress the importance of obtaining verbal consent and to provide behavioural strategies for doing so. Research in Ontario has shown that women more than men stress a need for active verbal consent in both new and ongoing relationships (Humphreys, 2007; Humphreys & Herold, 2007). Programs need to foster a climate in which sexually coercive behaviour is seen as unacceptable in such a way that men do not perceive the presenters to be "male bashing" (Figure 16.2) These types of perceptions can result in a backlash that increases attitudes and statements justifying men's use of sexual coercion. An infamous example is the response of some men to a "No Means No" campaign at Queen's University in Kingston—they hung banners out of the windows of male residences that read "No means more beer" and "No means tie her up."

Unfortunately, until society makes large changes, we still need to teach women to be vigilant and to empower women be more assertive in communicating their lack of consent (Humphreys & Kennett, 2010). A sexual assault resistance program recently developed by Charlene Senn at the University of Windsor is designed to enhance women's ability to physically, verbally, and psychologically resist sexual coercion and assault (Senn et al., 2011; Senn, 2011, 2013). It has three three-hour units. Unit 1 focuses on increasing women's awareness of personal risk, helping them become more aware of situations that pose risk, and helping them develop problem-solving strategies to reduce risk and avoid the assault. Unit 2 helps women more quickly admit to themselves when they are in a coercive situation and deal with their emotional barriers to taking strong action in those situations. Unit 3 teaches women about the most successful tactics for resisting sexual coercion in different situations, including self-defence training (Figure 16.3). More recently the authors have added Unit 4, which provides sexuality education to broaden women's sexual assertiveness. Preliminary results with female high school and undergraduate students showed that the program led to significant attitude change, greater confidence that they could defend themselves if attacked, and use of more effective methods of self-defence in hypothetical situations. We will have to wait on the full evaluation to find out whether it is actually successful at helping women avoid sexual assault.

Research shows that fighting back—fighting, yelling, and fleeing—increases a woman's likelihood of thwarting a sexual assault attempt (Ahrens et al., 2008; Brecklin & Ullman, 2005; Zoucha-Jensen & Coyne, 1993). However, we also need to change how we socialize girls so that women are more comfortable being assertive and using self-defence.

Finally, to prevent sexual assault of men, we need to combat the cultural stereotype that men are always interested in sex. This belief may make it difficult for men to clearly and repeatedly refuse a sexual invitation,

Figure 16.2 Young people today are challenging stereotypes about female weakness and passivity. This photo shows a protest by more than 800 students in Welland, Ontario, against violence against women.

Figure 16.3   Self-defence classes for women. Many experts believe that all women should take such classes to gain the skills necessary to defend themselves in the case of an attempted sexual assault.

and may make men's partners less likely to believe men when they do say no. However, for people to be honest and open about their sexual interests, they will first need to become more comfortable talking about sex and less reliant on nonverbal communication.

A variety of types of sexual assault prevention programs have been tested, often in academic settings, such as with incoming first-year postsecondary students. The programs generally are based on one of several strategies (Gidycz et al., 2011):

1. *Awareness-based programs* aim to raise people's awareness of the prevalence of sexual assault and thereby create community change.

2. *Empathy-based programs* seek to increase the audience's understanding of the consequences for victims, thereby increasing empathy for them.

3. *Social norms-based programs* encourage individuals to question the gender-role norms that support violence against women.

4. *Skills-based programs* teach people, especially women, skills that will decrease their risk of being the objects of sexual violence (e.g., avoid excessive drinking).

5. *Bystander intervention programs* encourage people to intervene if they see violence occurring.

A crucial aspect of effective programs involves having the participants actively practise skills (Gidycz et al., 2011). Passive programs with an expert lecturing to a class are less effective. Peer-led programs that focus on a single gender in a small group (e.g., an athletic team) and for multiple sessions seem to be most effective.

 L07

Child Sexual Abuse

In this section we discuss the broad category of child sexual abuse and one specific subcategory, intrafamilial sexual abuse—sexual abuse that occurs within the family.

There are currently several statutes in the *Criminal Code of Canada* related to the sexual exploitation of children, including sexual assault, sexual interference, invitation to sexual touching, and sexual exploitation (refer to Table 2.1). These offences apply to any type of sexual contact with a child by a man or a woman, showing pornography to a child, having a child witness sexual intercourse, or using a computer to facilitate committing a sexual offence against a child. Making, possessing, and distributing child pornography is also illegal and is discussed in Chapter 17.

The laws that seek to prevent the sexual exploitation of children and young people were amended in 1985, and new laws have been added since then. Many of the criticisms of the repealed rape law discussed earlier in this chapter also applied to the laws pertaining to sexual exploitation of children. For example, in most cases

Figure 16.4 Ages of Consent

Consent laws can often be confusing to understand, and are subject to change. The chart below may be useful when deciding if a particular relationship is consensual in the eyes of the law.

Can consent be given if . . .

The youth is . . . → And the other person is . . . ↓	Under 12	12	13	14	15	16	17	18	19	20
Under 12	*	No	No	No	No	No	No	No	No	No
Same Age	No	Yes**	Yes**	Yes**	Yes**	Yes**	Yes**	Yes	Yes	Yes
Less Than 1 Year Older	No	Yes**	Yes**	Yes**	Yes**	Yes**	Yes**	Yes	Yes	Yes
Less Than 2 Years Older	No	Yes**	Yes**	Yes**	Yes**	Yes**	Yes**	Yes	Yes	Yes
Less Than 3 Years Older	No	No	No	Yes**	Yes**	Yes**	Yes**	Yes	Yes	Yes
Less Than 4 Years Older	No	No	No	Yes**	Yes**	Yes**	Yes**	Yes	Yes	Yes
Less Than 5 Years Older	No	No	No	Yes**	Yes**	Yes**	Yes**	Yes	Yes	Yes
More Than 5 Years Older	No	No	No	No	No	Yes**	Yes**	Yes	Yes	Yes

Other considerations: The law also provides for the protection of persons with mental or physical disabilities without any age restrictions.

* Children under the age of 12 cannot consent to any sexual activity with any other age. However, it is not an offence if two children under 12 engaged in sexual activities.

** This does not apply if one of the individuals is in a position of trust or authority over the other, one is in a relationship of dependency with the other, or if the relationship between them is found to be exploitative.

they applied only to girls (Busby, 1999). In contrast, the current provisions are gender-neutral and based on a combination of age, whether the accused is in a position of trust, and the specific activities that occurred. The age of consent is normally 16. This means that an adult accused of engaging in sexual activity with someone under 16 cannot defend himself or herself on the basis that the child agreed to the sexual activity. However, as shown in Figure 16.4, there are what are called "close in age" exceptions: a child who is 14 or 15 years old can legally have sex with someone who is less than five years older; a child of who is 12 or 13 years old can consent to nonexploitative sexual activity with adolescents less than two years older. A study conducted in British Columbia found that very few adolescents who had engaged in first intercourse at 14 or 15 years old had had a partner who was not "close in age"; however, 25 percent of the boys and 49 percent of the girls who had engaged in first intercourse at 12 or 13 had a first partners who would not fit the "close in age" exemption (Miller et al., 2010). The age of consent for anal intercourse is 18 and thus is higher than for vaginal intercourse, although the Supreme Court has ruled that this constitutes discrimination against gay youth. The age of consent is also higher if the adult is in a position of trust or authority with a child, such as a teacher or sports coach. Under the sexual exploitation provision, it is an offence for a person in a position of trust to have sex with a child who is under 18 years old, whether or not the child consents to it.

The *Criminal Code* includes a law against incest. This statute prohibits sexual intercourse with a person who is a blood relative—that is, a parent, child, brother, sister, grandparent, or grandchild. Most prosecutions are cases involving children and adult relatives, although the incest statute is not specific to child sexual abuse. The nearly universal taboo against incest seems to have as its purposes the promise to children that the home will be a place where they can be free from sexual pressure and the prevention of the genetic problems of inbreeding.

The latest form of child sexual abuse involves **Internet sexual solicitation of youth** (Wolak et al., 2008). In such cases, a sexual predator meets a child or adolescent online, gains the youth's confidence, and arranges a face-to-face meeting. A well-sampled survey of youth between the ages of 10 and 17 found that 18 percent of girls and 8 percent of boys had received a sexual solicitation on the Internet (Mitchell et al., 2007). Only a few of those incidents resulted in an actual meeting, but the sexual solicitation itself can be distressing.

The court process can be stressful for the child who discloses the abuse. A number of Child Advocacy Centres have been established across Canada to help children through the aftermath of reporting the abuse.

(L08) Patterns of Child Sexual Abuse

How common is child sexual abuse in Canada? A survey of 9953 individuals ages 15 and above living in Ontario found that 11 percent of the women and 4 percent of the men reported that they had experienced severe sexual abuse as children (threats, touching, or intercourse) (MacMillan et al., 1997).

Internet sexual solicitation of youth: Cases in which a sexual predator meets a child or adolescent online, gains the youth's confidence, and arranges a face-to-face meeting.

Similarly, research in Quebec using a telephone survey of 1002 adults found that 22 percent of the women and 10 percent of the men reported unwanted sexual activities by an adult or a child three or more years older than them before the age of 18 (Hébert et al., 2009). It seems clear that child sexual abuse is not rare and that girls are more often its victims than boys are. Worldwide, roughly 20 percent of women and 5 to 10 percent of men report sexual contact with an adult when they were a child (Freyd et al., 2005).

Most cases of child sexual abuse are never reported. For example, in the National Population Survey, only about 20 percent of the victims had told anyone. Similarly, in the Quebec survey described above, 21 percent of respondents (and more men than women) had never told anyone about the abuse; only 21 percent had disclosed the abuse within a month of its occurrence (Hébert et al., 2009). How many of these incidents are reported to the authorities? In 2010, there were 4.1 reported sexual offences against children per 1000 children in Canada (Sinha, 2012). Reported sexual assaults for girls were more than four times as high as for boys; reports for youth between the ages of 12 to 17 were twice as high as for younger children. Of those complaints substantiated by police, most involve touching and fondling of the genitals (68 percent), attempted or completed sexual activity (35 percent), or adults exposing their genitals (12 percent) (Trocmé et al., 2001). Thus, in the great majority of cases, both for boys and girls, the sexual activity involves touching of the genitals without penetration.

The great majority of perpetrators of child sexual abuse are men. According to the National Health and Social Life Survey (NHSLS), for girls almost all the reported cases involved sexual contact with men; for boys, most cases involved men although some cases involved women. A number of factors probably account for this great imbalance. Men in our culture are socialized more toward seeing sexuality as focused on sexual acts rather than as part of an emotional relationship. The sexual script for men involves partners who are smaller and younger than them, whereas women's sexual script involves partners who are larger and older than they are.

Reports from 155 police departments in 2008 provide information regarding reported cases of sexual assault of children and youth in Canada (Ogrodnik, 2010). Most (82 percent) of the child and youth victims of sexual offences were girls. Some of the sexual abuse was of children at very young ages (some under three years old), although the rates for youth between the ages of 12 and 17 were higher than those of children between the ages of 3 and 11. Table 16.2 shows the relationship between these adults and their victims. Notice that sexual assault by a stranger is least common,

Intrafamilial sexual abuse: Sexual contact between a child and an adult who is the child's relative or caregiver, such as a stepfather.

accounting for only 9 percent of sexual assaults of girls and 6 percent of sexual assaults of boys. In contrast, 35 percent of the girls and 40 percent of the boys were sexually assaulted by a family member, including parents, siblings, and extended family members, such as stepparents or grandparents.

Of particular concern is sexual abuse of children by a person in a position of trust or authority (Figure 16.5). One of the most publicized cases of this type of abuse was that of eight Roman Catholic priests and ten lay members of the Christian Brothers of Ireland in Canada, who were convicted of sexually abusing 77 boys at Mount Cashel Orphanage in St. John's, Newfoundland, in the 1970s. A number of priests in other parts of Canada and in the United States, as well as coaches, Scout leaders, teachers, and so on, have also been convicted of child sexual abuse. Many First Nations children attending residential schools and Aboriginal and non-Aboriginal boys in youth detention centres were sexually abused by persons charged with their care. In all these situations, individuals who had responsibility to protect the welfare of children used their power and authority to coerce children into engaging in sexual activity with them.

Patterns of Intrafamilial Sexual Abuse

Incest is defined in the *Criminal Code of Canada* as sexual contact between blood relatives. Of particular concern is sexual abuse of children by an adult family member, often called **intrafamilial sexual abuse**. Intrafamilial abuse includes child sexual abuse both by a blood relative and by a nonrelative who is the child's caregiver (e.g., by a stepfather) and is typically prosecuted under the sexual assault provisions of the *Criminal Code* (see Table 2.1).

The overwhelming majority of cases of intrafamilial child sexual abuse go unreported to authorities and so are not prosecuted. Nonetheless, court statistics (see Table 16.2) show that in 2009 family members were accused of 34 percent of the sexual assaults against children (Brzozowski, 2007). Data from the NHSLS based on adult recollections of incidents of sexual abuse in childhood, most of which were never reported, also show that a large percentage of cases are perpetrated by family members. Researchers found that 54 percent of the women and 20 percent of the men reported that the perpetrator was a family member.

LO9   ## Impact on the Victim

Child sexual abuse can have serious and long-lasting effects on the victim (Kendall-Tackett et al., 1993; Figure 16.5). Children who have experienced child sexual abuse are more likely to experience a variety of symptoms including anxiety, depression, health complaints, and thoughts of suicide (Brabant et al., 2013; Cyr & Hébert, 2011; Kendall-Tackett et al., 1993).

(a)

(b)

Figure 16.5   Sexual abuse outside the family is most often perpetrated by a person in a position of trust, such as (a) in the sexual abuse of Theo Fleury by his junior hockey coach, and (b) the sexual and physical abuse of Aboriginal children attending residential schools run by several different Christian churches—the subject of an Edmonton-to-Ottawa walk for justice by Robert Desjarlais in June 2000.

Table 16.2 Categories of People Who Were Accused of Child Sexual Offences in 2009		
	Percentage of Victims	
Perpetrators	**Girls**	**Boys**
Acquaintance*	44%	43%
Family	35	40
Stranger	9	6
Unknown	12	10

*Acquaintance includes any relationship in which the perpetrator and victim were familiar with each other but were not related or in a legal guardianship arrangement.

Source: Statistics Canada (2011c).

For example, research in Quebec has shown that sexually abused children experience more symptoms associated with PTSD than do children who have experienced other life stressors, such as an orthopedic problem (Collin-Vézina & Hébert, 2005; Tremblay et al., 2000). Boys who have experienced child sexual abuse are also more likely to engage in risky sexual behaviour in adolescence (Homma et al., 2012). Note that although children who have experienced sexual abuse are more likely to experience each of these symptoms, some sexually abused children do not experience any severe negative consequences. (See Milestones in Sex

Figure 16.6   A counsellor holds art depicting the before and after feelings of an abused child. On the limbs of the after image, words such as *mad*, *hate*, *scared*, *upset*, and *angry* are written.

Milestones in Sex Research

False Memory Syndrome? Recovered Memory?

A topic that is extremely controversial concerns the issue of what some call *recovered memory* and others call *false memory syndrome*. The issue is whether the child victim of sexual abuse or other severe trauma can forget (suppress) the memory of the event and later recover that memory.

On one side of the argument, the *recovered memory* side, psychotherapists see adult clients who display serious symptoms of prior trauma, such as severe depression and anxiety. Sometimes these clients have clear memories of being sexually abused in childhood and have always remembered the events but have never told anyone until they told the therapist. In other cases, the client does not remember that any abuse occurred but, during the process of therapy, or sometimes spontaneously before therapy, something triggers the memory and the client then recalls the sexual abuse.

On the other side, some psychologists believe that these memories for events that had been forgotten and then are remembered are actually *false memories*; that is, the events never occurred. They argue that unscrupulous or overzealous therapists may induce these memories by hypnotizing clients or strongly suggesting to clients that they had been abused in childhood. Even subtle suggestions by a well-intentioned therapist can produce false memories in susceptible individuals.

What do the data say? Research on the issue of child sexual abuse provides support for the idea that forgetting does occur in some cases. In one study, 129 women who were known to have been sexually abused as children—they had been brought to a hospital for treatment at the time and the abuse had been medically verified—were interviewed 17 years later; 38 percent did not remember the abuse (Williams, 1994). The possible flaw in this study is that some of the respondents may have remembered but not have reported it to the interviewer. However, they were reporting many other intimate sexual experiences, so it seems likely that they would report accurately about this one, too. In a study of adult women who reported to a researcher that they had been a victim of child sexual abuse, 30 percent said that they had completely blocked out any memory of the abuse for a full year or more (Gold et al., 1994). In an especially elegant study, children who were sexually abused and the cases prosecuted were studied at the time. A follow-up study more than 10 years later, when the individuals were in their twenties, tested their memory for the earlier events (Alexander et al., 2005). Frequency of abuse was associated with worse memory for the events. Poor support from the mother at the time was also associated with worse memory.

Therefore, the evidence seems to indicate that in 30 to 40 percent of cases, memories of childhood sexual abuse are forgotten for a period and then remembered again. In fact, it has been theorized that amnesia

Research for a discussion of whether children who were victims of sexual abuse or other severe trauma can forget or suppress the memory.)

If a case is reported and prosecuted, the child may be as traumatized by testifying in court as by the abuse itself. Repeatedly testifying about severe abuse is associated with worse mental health outcomes (Quas et al., 2005). Interestingly, the perpetrator receiving a light sentence is also associated with worse mental health outcomes for the child.

Research has demonstrated that many of the negative effects of child sexual abuse persist into adulthood. Canadian research has shown that, compared with controls, adults who were sexually abused as children display more depression, anxiety, eating disorders, psychological distress, and alcohol and drug dependence (Gold, 1986; LeClerc et al., 2010; Runtz & Roche, 1999). They also have more negative feelings about sexuality, more sexual difficulties, and difficulty forming stable, safe romantic relationships (Lacelle et al., 2012a, 2012b; Leclerc et al., 2010; Lemieux & Byers, 2008; Testa et al., 2005). The risk of these difficulties is greater if attempted or completed intercourse occurred, if the abuse was by a relative, and if the victim told for traumatic events of this kind, particularly when the child has been betrayed by someone in a position of trust like a parent, is an adaptive response that helps the child survive in a terribly distressed family situation (Freyd, 1996).

The other question is, can memories of events that did not occur be implanted in someone? In one study, the researcher was able to create false memories of childhood events in 25 percent of the adults given the treatment (Loftus, 1993). Certain conditions seem to increase the chances that people will think they remember things that did not actually occur, including suggestion by an authority figure and suggestion under hypnosis.

Two studies shed additional light on this debate. One was a study of women admitted to a hospital unit specializing in the treatment of trauma-related psychological disorders (Chu et al., 1999). Among those reporting childhood sexual abuse, 26 percent had partial amnesia for it and 27 percent had complete amnesia for a period of time before recalling it. These patients also displayed dissociative symptoms. *Dissociative amnesia* is an inability to recall important personal information, usually of a traumatic nature (American Psychiatric Association, 2000a). The great majority of those who suffered child sexual abuse had been able to corroborate the occurrences by some method, such as medical records. Importantly, most of them first remembered the abuse while at home, and about half were not involved in any kind of treatment or counselling at the time they remembered, ruling out the possibility of suggestion by a therapist.

In another study, normal participants' brains were scanned by using fMRI (functional magnetic resonance imaging) while they were suppressing unwanted memories (Anderson et al., 2004). Neural systems underlying suppression were clearly identified and included a region in the prefrontal cortex and the hippocampus. From this study we can see that suppression of memories is not just hocus-pocus but has a real basis in the brain.

What is the bottom line? There is evidence that some people do forget childhood sexual abuse and remember it later. There is also evidence that some people can form false memories based on suggestions made by another person. It seems likely that most of the cases of recovered memory of child sexual abuse are true but that some are false and the product of suggestion. It is also probably true that false accusations of past child abuse are made, often by a well-intentioned "victim" who is highly suggestible to press reports of other cases or who has been influenced by a therapist. This may result in an arrest of an innocent person. There are errors of justice on both sides. Nonetheless, there are many more cases of unreported and unpunished perpetrators than of falsely convicted persons.

Sources: Alexander et al. (2005); Anderson et al. (2004), Chu et al. (1999), Dalenberg et al. (2012), Freyd (1996), Gold et al. (1994), Loftus (1993), Williams (1994).

someone and received a negative response from that person (Bulik et al., 2001; Feiring et al., 2009; Lemieux & Byers, 2008; Rellini & Meston, 2011). Adult survivors of child sexual abuse are also more likely to experience sexual assault as an adult and sexual disorders, such as fears of sex (sexual aversion), lack of sexual desire, and lack of arousal (Meston et al., 2006; Najman et al., 2005). Women who were sexually abused as children are also more likely to be preoccupied with sex, younger at the time of their first voluntary intercourse, and more likely to be teen mothers (Noll et al., 2003). Their sexuality is ambivalent—they experience both sexual aversion and a preoccupation with sex.

Again, though, not all adults who report sexual contact with an adult as a child show these long-term negative consequences.

Child sexual abuse has effects not only on mental health but on physical health as well. Adults who were sexually abused as children are one and a half times as likely as those who were not abused to have had health problems in the past year (Sachs-Ericsson et al., 2005).

In most cases child sexual abuse is psychologically damaging and may lead to symptoms such as depression and PTSD. The evidence indicates that the extent of distress is associated with a number of factors including,

Milestones in Sex Research

What Causes Pedophilia?

I t is very difficult to think of a group more hated than pedophiles—people who are sexually aroused by children (Cantor et al., 2009). This anger is fuelled by the media, which tend to focus on alarming cases of sexual offences against children. It is also fuelled by the commonly held view that anyone sexually attracted to children is invariably a sexual predator who will act on that attraction and harm children. Not all pedophiles are also child molesters, however; not all act on their sexual attraction. The proportion of people who experience a sexual attraction to children and never act on it at all is not known. Activist and sex/relationship columnist Dan Savage (2010) referred to pedophiles remaining celibate for their whole lives rather than risk harm to a child as "gold star pedophiles" and suggested that society should be helping rather than automatically demonizing such people.

In contrast, and counterintuitively, most people who sexually abuse children are *not* pedophiles. That is, most cases of child sexual abuse are committed by people who actually prefer adults as sexual partners. This phenomenon is common in cases of intrafamilial

sexual abuse (e.g., parent–child) and in sexual activity (both consensual and coercive) between siblings. Typically, nonpedophiles who sexually abuse children also exhibit generally antisocial behaviour, use drugs and alcohol, or have histories of childhood adversity themselves, such as violence and neglect (but only sometimes sexual abuse).

What causes pedophilia? For most of the twentieth century, pedophilia was believed to be the result of having been sexually abused as a child. This has often been called the *abused-abuser hypothesis*. But does experiencing sexual abuse as a child cause a person to become a pedophile? There is evidence that children who experience adversity in childhood—whether sexual abuse, nonsexual physical abuse, or neglect—are more likely to engage in criminal behaviour in adulthood. However, there is little solid evidence for any specific association between having been sexually abused and becoming a sexual abuser (U.S. General Accounting Office, 1996). Also, almost all child molesters are male, whereas the majority of their victims are female. If the abused-abuser hypothesis of pedophilia were true, one would expect the sex ratio to be the same among victims and

especially, the severity of the abuse (Kallstrom-Fuqua et al., 2004). Patterns of sexual abuse can range from five minutes of fondling by a neighbour to repeated forced intercourse by a father or stepfather over a period of several years. The effects of sexual abuse are most severe when it involved intercourse, occurred repeatedly over years, and was committed by a father or stepfather (Fleming et al., 1999; Kendler & Bulik et al., 2000). In addition, Canadian studies have shown that adjustment is affected by both the abused child's coping style and the quality of family relationships (Hébert et al., 2006; Runtz & Schallow, 1997; Tremblay et al., 1999).

Treatments such as cognitive-behavioural therapy are available and effective in treating adults with PTSD following child sexual abuse (McDonagh et al., 2005).

Pedophilia: Paraphilia in which an adult has a sexual preference for prepubescent children.

 The Offenders

Many child molesters abuse more than one child. In particular, child sexual abusers who abuse boys outside the family are likely to have multiple victims (Abel et al., 1987). For example, in 2000, Carl Toft came up for parole after serving 8 years of a 13-year sentence for molesting more than 200 boys at the New Brunswick Training Centre. In 2005, he was released into the community after completing 10 years of that 13-year sentence. Critics argued that he should be denied parole because, by his own admission, he was not cured.

What do the data say about child sexual abusers? Are they likely to repeat the offence? Are there effective treatments for them?

Pedophilia involves an adult who has a sexual preference for prepubescent children, generally ages perpetrators—that is, that most abusers would be female not male.

More recently, researchers have used neuroimaging and other procedures to show that there are differences in the brains of pedophiles compared with men who commit nonsexual crimes and with healthy noncriminals. The evidence suggests that at least some of these biological differences existed before birth. First, relative to sex offenders against adults and to people with atypical sexualities other than pedophilia, pedophiles score lower on IQ and memory tests (Blanchard et al., 2007; Cantor et al., 2004; Cantor, Blanchard, et al., 2005). Because pedophilic sexual offenders against children score lower than nonpedophilic sexual offenders (i.e., sex offenders who offend against adults), we cannot attribute the difference merely to less intelligent people getting caught. Second, more than one-third of pedophiles are not right-handed (they are left-handed or ambidextrous), compared with approximately 10 percent in the mainstream population (Cantor, Klassen, et al., 2005). Because handedness results from prenatal brain organization, this difference suggests that whatever chain of events leads to pedophilia, the first links of that chain were present before birth.

Third, MRI and fMRI studies have compared the brain structure and brain function of pedophiles with both healthy controls and people who have committed nonsexual offences. Pedophiles demonstrate significant differences from nonsexual offenders in white matter tissue (Cantor et al., 2008; Cantor & Blanchard, 2012), the bundles of axons that connect neurons with each other. The affected tissues appear to be those that connect the brain areas that respond to sexual stimuli. Interestingly, fMRI studies have shown that in both pedophiles and nonpedophiles, the same areas of the brain respond to people they find sexually attractive. They only differ in whom they find sexually attractive (Polisois-Keating & Joyal, 2013).

This growing body of research suggests that people do not choose to be sexually attracted to children. However, they do remain entirely in control of their behaviour. When it comes to pedophilia, almost all of society's attention is on punishment to help prevent a second offence. The more we learn about what causes pedophilia, however, the better we might prevent the first offence.

Sources: Blanchard et al. (2007), Cantor et al. (2004, 2008, 2009), Cantor & Blanchard (2012), Cantor, Blanchard, et al. (2005); Cantor, Klassen, et al. (2005), Savage (2010), U.S. General Accounting Office (1996). Written by James M. Cantor, PhD, Centre for Addiction and Mental Health, Toronto.

13 or younger. A *pedophilic disorder* (one of the paraphilic disorders identified in the *DSM-5*; see Chapter 15 for more information on paraphilic disorders) can be diagnosed when an individual experiences recurrent intense fantasies or urges involving children and the person has either acted on these urges or the urges cause marked distress or interpersonal difficulties (American Psychiatric Association, 2013). (See Milestones in Sex Research for a discussion of the causes of pedophilia.) Although the vast majority of pedophiles are male, some women also sexually abuse young children (Seto, 2004). An Alberta study of convicted adolescent sex offenders showed a high frequency of deviant sexual fantasies (Aylwin et al., 2005). Not all pedophiles are child molesters—that is, not all have sex with children. Some experts distinguish between pedophilia as a sexual attraction to children versus acting on those urges. At least some people who experience pedophilic urges never act on them (Seto, 2009). In addition, not all child molesters are pedophiles—that is, not all have a sexual preference for prepubescent children. Research in Ontario has shown that most men convicted of child pornography offences are pedophiles; they show a preference for prepubescent children (Seto et al., 2006). Child pornography is discussed in Chapter 17.

Pedophiles fall into a number of categories, depending on the gender of the children they are attracted to and other factors. In one study of 678 pedophiles, all of them men, 27 percent were attracted to boys, 47 percent to girls, and 25 percent to both (Blanchard et al., 1999). Child molesters also differ in whether their victims are their biological children, stepchildren, children they know, or children they do not know

(Guay et al., 2001). Pedophiles who molest children tend to be repeat offenders and their patterns of preference tend to be stable over time.

Pedophiles score low on measures of heterosocial competence (Dreznick, 2003). That is, they lack the interpersonal skills to function well in adult heterosexual relationships. They are more likely to have experienced sexual and nonsexual abuse as children (Brotto & Klein, 2007). Canadian research shows that pedophiles have poorer cognitive functioning than controls and are more likely than controls (11 percent compared with 5 percent) to have had accidents involving head injury and unconsciousness before the age of six (Blanchard et al., 2002; Cantor et al., 2004; Cantor, Blanchard, et al., 2005). This suggests that problems with early brain development or some injury to the developing brain may create this disorder in some cases.

Researchers are very interested in developing measures that might identify pedophiles who have not been arrested and perhaps have not even offended yet (Seto, 2004). Sophisticated cognitive tests using reaction times indicate that pedophiles have a strong mental association between children and sex, whereas non-pedophiles have an association between adults and sex (Gray et al., 2005). Research in Ontario using phallometric measures, such as those discussed in Chapters 3 and 11, indicate that men who are attracted to child pornography but have not sexually offended against children show greater arousal to child photos than to adult photos, and their arousal to child photos is even greater than the arousal of men who have actually sexually offended against children (Seto et al., 2006). Possession of child pornography itself might be an indicator of pedophilia (Seto, 2004). Measures such as these may provide ways to identify men who are likely to offend even before they commit their crime.

When child molesters are released from prison, how likely are they to reoffend?

One study that attempted to answer the question of recidivism (repeat offending) followed a sample of 206 child molesters and found a recidivism rate of 23 percent (Moulden et al., 2009). This is no doubt an underestimate of the actual rates of reoffending, because so much child sexual abuse goes unreported (Hanson, 2000). Ontario researchers have shown that recidivism is much higher for sex offenders who had not received treatment (participation in treatment was voluntary) (Hanson & Bussière, 1998). It was also higher for certain subgroups of child molesters, such as those men who had committed previous sexual offences, had begun sexual offending at an early age, and had targeted male victims. Ontario researchers have also demonstrated that the recidivism rate is higher for extrafamilial offenders than for intrafamilial offenders, as well as for offenders with general feelings of hostility (Firestone et al., 2000, 2005; Greenberg et al., 2000). Several Canadian studies have found that men who show greater sexual arousal to children as measured through phallometric assessment are more likely to commit another sexual offence (Firestone et al., 2000; Proulx et al., 1997; Seto et al., 2000).

Most experts believe that pedophilia itself—the sexual attraction to children—cannot be changed; the best that we can hope for with treatment is to increase the individual's voluntary control over acting on those urges (Seto, 2009).

LO11 Treatment of Sex Offenders

Canadian researchers have been leaders in the development of assessment and treatment strategies for child sexual abusers (Bradford & Greenberg, 1996; Hall, 1995; Marshall & Barbaree, 1988; Marshall & Pithers, 1994). Among the treatments in use in Canada are anti-androgen drugs, hormones, antidepressant drugs (SSRIs, such as Prozac), and cognitive-behavioural therapy. Cyproterone acetate (CPA) is an anti-androgen drug—it reduces the action of testosterone in the body with the hope of a corresponding reduction of the sexually aggressive behaviour—that has been used in the treatment of child sexual abusers and other sex offenders. It does seem to be effective in reducing sexual urges (Seto, 2009). Other anti-androgen drugs seem to be less effective. One problem is that sex offenders have to agree voluntarily to this treatment. Few sex offenders are willing to continue to take anti-androgens because they also suppress normal sexual arousal. Between 30 and 100 percent of men who start hormonal treatment later drop out (Barbaree & Seto, 1997). One class of antidepressants (the SSRIs, which include Prozac and Zoloft) has also been tried in the treatment of sex offenders (Bradford & Greenberg, 1996). Its use is based on the assumption that sex offending can be a particular kind of obsessive-compulsive disorder, and such disorders generally respond well to these antidepressants. Although there have not yet been any blind clinical trials, there is some research evidence that use of SSRIs can be a helpful addition to other interventions, such as therapy (Hall & Hall, 2007).

Behavioural treatment generally aims to teach pedophiles to control their sexual arousal to children (Seto, 2009). One method involves aversive classical conditioning, in which an unpleasant stimulus (e.g., the smell of ammonia) is repeatedly paired with sexual pictures of children. This method does seem to increase the individual's voluntary control of his sexual arousal to children. Behavioural treatments to increase pedophiles' positive, appropriate sexual arousal to adults—which would be another important component to the solution—have been less successful. Correctional Services Canada uses *cognitive-behavioural treatment* that targets not only behaviours but also attitudes and beliefs.

Canadian researchers conducted a follow-up of high-risk sex offenders (high risk because they had a history of multiple offences or violent offences) (Abracen & Looman, 2004). They found that the recidivism rate was 52 percent for untreated sex offenders and 24 percent for treated sex offenders, a significant improvement with treatment. The treatment was cognitive-behavioural therapy (CBT). A more recent well-controlled study by these authors found that the rate of sexually reoffending over more than a nine-year period were low (about 10 percent) for both offenders who received sex offender treatment and those who received other treatment programs (Abracen et al., 2010). Other studies, however, have found that CBT is ineffective with sex offenders (Camilleri & Quinsey, 2008). Some experts question whether, at present, there are any successful treatments for pedophiles (Camilleri & Quinsey, 2008; Seto, 2009).

LO11 Mandatory Notification of the Release of Sex Offenders

Many Canadians are concerned that sex offenders released into the community after serving their sentence will reoffend—that is, commit another sexual assault or molest another child. Media coverage of high-profile cases in which offenders have reoffended after their release adds to public fears and has resulted in calls for mandatory public notification of the release of sex offenders. The rationale is that if people are aware that there is a released sex offender in their community, they can protect themselves and their children from sexual violence.

Since 1994, organizations (but not individuals) have been able to have potential employees and volunteers screened by police to ensure that they do not have a prior conviction for child sexual abuse. In addition, in December 2004 the federal government, with unanimous support of the provinces and territories, implemented the National Sex Offender Registry, which is available only to law enforcement officials and is intended to help them investigate unsolved crimes of a sexual nature. In 2011, the National Sex Offender Registry was strengthened in several ways, including automatic inclusion of all convicted sex offenders, mandatory DNA sampling, and proactive use of the registry by police to help prevent sexual crimes.

Some people argue that there should be a comparable national registry of child molesters available to the public (Canadian Centre for Justice Statistics, 1999). Most authorities raise a number of concerns with doing this, including misidentification of innocent people and sex offenders' rights to privacy if they do not pose a risk to the public. They also fear that some citizens might take the law into their own hands. Finally, public notification may drive sex offenders underground so that it becomes more difficult for police to keep track of them. The issue of public warnings about the release of sex offenders pits the rights of the community to be informed about the risk of significant harm against the privacy rights of the offender (Canadian Centre for Justice Statistics, 1999). Therefore, at present community notification is restricted to offenders believed to pose an immediate risk to the public. The police use a great deal of discretion in determining which offenders pose such a risk, leaving the issue open to continued public debate.

Is the National Sex Offender Registry working? That is, does it help to reduce the likelihood that convicted sex offenders will reoffend? We do not know because there has been no published research evaluating its effectiveness at reducing recidivism (Murphy et al., 2009).

LO6 Preventing Child Sexual Abuse

With increasing awareness of the prevalence and potential negative consequences of child sexual abuse, most elementary schools in Canada have implemented sexual abuse prevention programs (these often go by names such as *personal safety*). The goal of these programs is to empower children and to provide them with the necessary skills to resist people who attempt to abuse them sexually. Most programs share certain concepts (Hébert et al., 2001; Hébert & Tourigny, 2004). For example, they help children to distinguish between good touches and bad touches, as well as to recognize potentially abusive situations. They teach them strategies to deal assertively with potential abuse, such as yelling no. They emphasize the importance of the child telling a trusted adult about the abuse or attempted abuse. Finally, they reassure children that they are not to blame in the event that sexual abuse does occur. However, the programs differ in their length, the way the program is delivered (e.g., video, puppets, books), and who delivers it (teachers, parents, police officers) (Hébert & Tremblay, 2000; Hébert et al., 2001). A few programs offer concurrent programs for parents to assist them in talking to their children about sexual abuse. Researchers in Quebec evaluated the impact of such a parent workshop (Hébert et al., 2002). They found that the workshop had a positive impact on parents' knowledge and on their reactions to a hypothetical situation involving child sexual abuse, compared with parents who did not attend the workshop. However, only 20 percent of the invited parents chose to attend the workshop.

How effective are these programs? Do children learn the concepts? Do they remember them? A review of studies on the effectiveness of child sexual abuse prevention programs found that these programs do increase elementary school children's knowledge (Hébert & Tourigny, 2004). Further, in role-play scenarios, the children are better able to identify potentially abusive situations and implement the skills that they learned. Older children tend to show greater gains than younger children do. However, the gains are sometimes small and tend to decrease over time. Further, more recent research in Quebec suggests they may not be effective with children who are from low-socioeconomic-status immigrant families who have little knowledge of sexual abuse (Daigneault et al., 2012). This suggests that children will need to have booster sessions—that is, have sexual abuse prevention skills reviewed regularly—if they are to retain their skills. Longer programs and programs that allow children to practise and role-play their self-protection skills, rather than relying only on instruction, tend to be more effective. Evaluation of child abuse prevention programs in Quebec and Calgary found that the children who received the program increased their knowledge and skills at the end of the program more than a control group (Hébert et al., 2001; Tutty, 1997).

There are some concerns that are often raised about child abuse prevention programs. First, are children able to put the skills they learn into practice (Finkelhor & Daro, 1997)? That is, how many children actually use the skills they learned in a sexual abuse prevention program when faced with a sexual abuser, particularly when the abuser is a family member? Second, will the program have negative effects on the children, such as increasing their anxieties or their fear of appropriate physical affection (Reppucci et al., 1999)? Although some children do show these types of responses, according to parental reports most children do not (Hébert et al., 2001; Tutty, 1997).

What behaviours in the workplace count as sexual harassment?

LO12

Sexual Harassment

Under Canadian federal and provincial law, sexual harassment is a form of sex discrimination. However, unless it involves sexual assault, it is not a *Criminal Code* offence and is not dealt with in a court of law. Rather, victims can lodge a complaint with the Human Rights Commission. The issue is a powerful one—it can interfere with a person's ability to do a job or obtain a service. It may force a victim out of a job, but it can also force a perpetrator from a job.

Canadian courts and human rights tribunals have used the following definition of sexual harassment developed by the U.S. Equal Employment Opportunity Commission (Aggarwal, 1992):

> Unwelcome sexual advances, requests for sexual favors, and other verbal or physical conduct of a sexual nature constitute sexual harassment when
> A. Submission to such conduct is made either explicitly or implicitly a term or condition of an individual's employment or academic advancement,
> B. Submission to or rejection of such conduct by an individual is used as the basis for academic or employment decisions affecting that individual, or
> C. Such conduct has the purpose or effect of unreasonably interfering with an individual's work or academic performance or creating an intimidating, hostile, or offensive working or educational environment.

According to the New Brunswick Human Rights Commission, sexual harassment is any "vexatious comment or conduct of a sexual nature, that is known or ought reasonably to be known to be unwanted"—that is, that a reasonable person should have known was unwelcome. Sexual harassment can be divided into two categories: sexual coercion and sexual annoyance (Aggarwal, 1992). The key ingredient for sexual coercion is that compliance with the sexual advances has some direct link to employment or educational status or opportunity, or to receipt of a public service. This is termed "quid pro quo harassment" (*quid pro quo* meaning "I'll do something for you if you do something for me"). Sexual annoyance or environmental harassment is sexually related behaviour that creates a hostile, intimidating work environment so that the person cannot work effectively, such as constant lewd innuendoes, verbal intimidation, or practical jokes that cause embarrassment. Gay men and lesbians are particularly likely to experience sexual harassment based on their sexual orientation. In one study, more than half of gay and lesbian youth had experienced verbal abuse on more than three separate occasions (D'Augelli, 2006).

Sexual harassment can occur at work and in education, as well as in other contexts, such as psychotherapy or on the street.

Sexual Harassment at Work

Sexual harassment at work may take a number of different forms (Figure 16.7). A prospective employer may make it clear that sexual activity is a prerequisite to being hired. Stories of such incidents are rampant among actors. Once on the job, sexual activity may

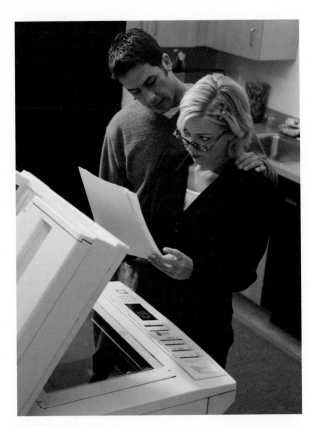

Figure 16.7 Sexual harassment at work: This man is engaging in inappropriate touching, but if he is her supervisor, she may be hesitant to protest.

become a condition for continued employment, for a promotion, or for other benefits, such as a raise. Or it can involve creating a hostile work environment. Here is one case:

> I work at a family-owned restaurant. Because I am a bartender, it is often just me behind the bar. On numerous occasions, I have caught one of the owners staring at my backside as I am getting things out of the refrigerator behind the bar. He has also blatantly stared at my legs, if I am wearing a skirt, while I am trying to speak with him. He has also shown me how to clean the nozzle used to foam milk for coffee drinks, but does so in a fashion that looks much like someone manually stimulating a certain piece of the male anatomy, and then looks at me with a grin on his face. There have been times when the dishwasher wasn't working and he made comments to the male bartender, as I was standing right there, such as, "Be gentle with her . . . you have to go slowly so you don't hurt it . . . it needs lubrication." He has walked up behind me and blown on my neck. All of the comments and actions are very unnerving. (From a student essay)

It is clear how psychologically damaging such environments are to the victim.

Surveys indicate that sexual harassment at work is far more common than many people realize, although the estimates vary depending on the definition of sexual harassment. In 1991, an Angus Reid-Southam News telephone survey found rates of harassment at work of 37 percent for women and 10 percent for men (Aggarwal, 1992). A more recent survey of 1990 Canadian women between the ages of 18 and 65 found that 56 percent had experienced sexual harassment in the last year; the overall lifetime rate was 77 percent (Crocker & Kalemba, 1999). Averaging many studies, between 25 and 50 percent of women have been sexually harassed at work, counting harassment both by supervisors and by co-workers (Ilies et al., 2003). The preponderance of harassers are male.

Both female and male victims report that harassment has negative effects on their emotional and physical health, their ability to work with others on the job, and their feelings about work (Chan et al., 2008; Willness et al., 2007). However, men are more likely to feel that the overtures from women ended up being reciprocal and mutually enjoyable. Women, on the other hand, are more likely to report damaging consequences, including being fired or quitting their job (Gutek, 1985). There is evidence linking the experience of sexual harassment to depression, anxiety, and PTSD (Rederstorff et al., 2007). Even subtle sexual harassment, such as asking, "Do you have a boyfriend?" in a job interview, can damage women's performance in the interview (Woodzicka & LaFrance, 2005).

Why does sexual harassment at work occur? According to one theory proposed, it results from a combination of gender stereotyping and men's ambivalent motives (Fiske & Glick, 1995; Krings & Facchin, 2009). Stereotypes of women in our culture are complex and include three distinct clusters: *sexy, nontraditional* (e.g., feminist), and *traditional* (e.g., mother). Many men have ambivalent motives in their interactions with women because they desire both dominance and intimacy. Fiske and Glick (1995) argue that there are four types of harassment of women by men. With the first, *earnest harassment*, the man is truly motivated by a desire for sexual intimacy, but he will not take no for an answer and persists with unwelcome sexual advances. He stereotypes women as sexy. With the second type, *hostile harassment*, the man's motivation is domination of the woman, often because he perceives her as being in competition with him in the workplace. He holds the stereotype of women as nontraditional and therefore competitive with him. His response to rejection by a woman is increased harassment. The third and fourth types of harassment involve ambivalent combinations of the two basic motives: dominance and a desire for intimacy. In the third type, *paternalistic-ambivalent harassment*, the man is motivated by a desire for sexual intimacy but also by a paternalistic desire to be like a father to the woman. This type of harassment may be particularly insidious because the man thinks of himself as acting benevolently toward the woman. Finally, the fourth type, *competitive-ambivalent harassment*, mixes real sexual attraction and a stereotype of women as sexy with the man's hostile desire to dominate the woman, which is based on his belief that she is nontraditional and competitive with him. This theory gives us an excellent view of the complex motives that underlie men's sexual harassment of women.

Social psychologists have developed a clever method for studying sexual harassment experimentally in the laboratory, called the Computer Harassment Paradigm (Maass et al., 2003). In one study, university men were first exposed to a female confederate of the experimenters, who expressed either strong feminist beliefs (intentions to get a high-level career in an area usually reserved for men and involvement in an organization for women's rights) or traditional beliefs. The men then had the opportunity to harass the woman by sending her pornographic material on a computer (she did not actually receive it). The men exposed to the feminist sent significantly more pornography than did men in the control group. However, not all men in the feminist-threat condition responded with harassment; those who did so were mainly men who identified strongly with the male role. The findings of this experiment are consistent with the type of harassment known as hostile environment harassment.

Sexual harassment at work is more than just an annoyance. Particularly for women, because they are more likely to be harassed by supervisors, it can make a critical difference in career advancement. For the woman who supports her family, being fired for sexual noncompliance is a catastrophe. The power of coercion is enormous.

Sexual Harassment in Education

Sexual harassment on campus is not rare (Pyke, 1996). For example, a 1989 survey at the University of Prince Edward Island found that 29 percent of the female students reported that a faculty member had sexually harassed them personally (Mazer & Percival, 1989). Harassment ranged from sexual teasing and jokes to unwanted touching and offers of favours for sex. More than 85 percent of male and female students had experienced sexual harassment in class, most commonly sexual jokes and other remarks by faculty that put down women, men, gay men, or lesbians. Women report dropping courses, changing majors, or dropping out of university because of sexual harassment (Fitzgerald, 1993). Many Canadian universities have

sexual harassment policies and have set up reporting and grievance procedures for dealing with sexual harassment cases.

Sexual harassment in an educational context is not confined either to universities or to teachers harassing students. One survey of 14- and 15-year-olds in the Netherlands found that 24 percent of the girls and 11 percent of the boys had been the objects of sexual harassment (Timmerman, 2003). Of those cases, 73 percent represented harassment by peers and 27 percent harassment by teachers (or other school-related adults, such as a tutor or principal). Of the teachers who were harassers, 90 percent were men. The psychological consequences were more severe when the harassment was done by a teacher than by a peer. An Ontario study of 1213 youth in Grades 6 to 8 found that 36 percent of boys and 21 percent of girls reported have perpetrated sexual harassment; 42 percent of boys and 38 percent of girls reported have experienced sexual harassment (McMaster et al., 2002). The two most common sexually harassing behaviours were homophobic name-calling and sexual comments, jokes, gestures, and looks. Indeed, Canadian research has shown that 49 percent of trans students, 41 percent of male sexual minority students, and 36 percent of female sexual minority students reported that they had experienced sexual harassment (Taylor & Peter, 2011).

Sex Between Health Care Professionals and Clients or Patients

There is another category of coercive and potentially damaging sexual encounters—those between a client or patient and a health care professional, such as a psychotherapist, physician, physiotherapist, or chiropractor (Plaut, 2008). Professional associations, such as the Canadian Psychological Association (1995), state clearly in their codes of ethics that such behaviours are unethical. Nonetheless, professional sexual misconduct does occur and can be extremely damaging.

Experts regard this kind of situation as having the potential for serious emotional damage to the client (Pope, 2001). Like the cases of sexual harassment discussed earlier, it is a situation of unequal power, in which the more powerful person, the health care professional, imposes sexual activity on the less powerful person, the patient or client. The situation is regarded as particularly serious in psychotherapy because clients have opened themselves up emotionally to the therapist and therefore are extremely vulnerable. Some provinces, such as Ontario and New Brunswick, have passed legislation that defines sexual contact between a patient or client and any health professional in a position of trust as sexual abuse or misconduct. How do professionals accused of sexual misconduct respond? According to two Quebec researchers, they generally fall into three groups: *deniers, rationalizers,* and *repentants.* Deniers refuse to acknowledge that the sexual activities occurred. Rationalizers tend to avoid responsibility for their behaviour by minimizing its impact. Those in the repentant group take full responsibility for their action, are sincerely sorry that it occurred, and take steps to ensure that it will not occur again (Assalian & Ravart, 2003).

SUMMARY

In the *Criminal Code of Canada*, sexual assault is any activity to which the victim did not consent, ranging from unwanted touching to forced oral, anal, or vaginal intercourse. There are three levels of sexual assault, depending on the amount of force used not on the nature of the sexual activity. The law is gender-neutral in that it applies equally to men and women as victims.

The Violence Against Women Survey found that 39 percent of Canadian women reported having been sexually assaulted. Other surveys have found that some men report having experienced sexual coercion, although a smaller percentage of men than women report these experiences. Victims may experience posttraumatic stress disorder (PTSD) as a result of the assault.

Sexual assault by a dating or romantic partner or spouse is quite common. There are four major theoretical views of sexual assault: victim precipitated, psychopathology of sex offenders, feminist, and social disorganization. Compared with other men, men who commit sexual assault tend to hold beliefs that support forced sex and to lack empathy. The incidence of sexual assault differs markedly between the various ethnocultural communities in Canada.

Approximately 18 percent of women and 8 percent of men report that they had experienced unwanted sexual contact with an adult or an older adolescent by age 16. There are currently several offences related to the sexual abuse of children in the *Criminal Code of Canada*, including sexual assault, sexual interference, invitation to sexual touching, and sexual exploitation. Most sexual abuse of children is committed by a relative or by a family friend. People who were sexually abused as children are more likely than other people to have symptoms such as anxiety, PTSD, depression, and health complaints. More severe psychological consequences are likely to occur when the perpetrator is a close family member who is an adult (sibling incest seems less likely to be harmful) and when the sexual contact is extensive and involves penetration. Pedophiles are more likely to be attracted to girls than to boys. Some types of child molesters have a low rate of recidivism, but certain types are highly likely to repeat their offence. Experts debate whether treatments for pedophiles are effective. There is a controversy among professionals over whether adults can recover memories of child sexual abuse that they had forgotten (recovered memory) or whether these are cases of false memory syndrome, in which the supposedly remembered incidents never actually occurred. Most schools offer child abuse prevention programs. Their goals are to provide children with the knowledge and skills to resist people who attempt to abuse them.

Sexual harassment, whether on the job or in education, involves unwelcome sexual advances when there is some coercion involved, such as making the sexual contact a condition of being hired or receiving an A grade in a course. In another form of sexual harassment, the work or educational environment is made so hostile on a sexual and gender basis that the employee cannot work effectively. Surveys show that sexual harassment at work is fairly common. In severe cases it can lead to damaging psychological consequences, such as PTSD for the victim. In education, the data indicate that about one-third of female students have been individually harassed by professors, although many more have experienced sexual harassment in class. This abuse can lead to negative consequences for the student, such as being forced to change majors or drop out of school. Sex between health care professionals and patients or clients is a violation of professional ethics.

QUESTIONS FOR THOUGHT, DISCUSSION, AND DEBATE

1. On your campus, what services are available for sexual assault victims? Are these services adequate, given what you have learned about victim responses to sexual assault? What could improve the services?

2. What procedures are available on your campus to deal with sexual harassment of a student by a professor?.

3. Apply the four theoretical views of sexual assault to child sexual abuse.

4. Your friend Angie has just confided in you that she was sexually assaulted last night at a party. Her assailant was a man she had met previously in one of her classes. Should she report the assault to the police?

Are **YOU** Curious?

1. Why do some men and women pay for sex?
2. What types of pornography are illegal in Canada?
3. What are the effects of viewing erotica and pornography on sexual behaviour?

Read this chapter to find out.

CHAPTER

17

Sex for Sale

LEARNING OBJECTIVES

After studying this chapter, you will be able to

LO1 Describe Canadian laws regarding prostitution and pornography and why they are controversial.

LO2 Describe and compare various kinds of sex workers and sex work.

LO3 Outline the role of third parties in the lives of sex workers.

LO4 Describe the "career development" (or history) and well-being of a typical sex worker.

LO5 Describe the customers of sex workers and their motivations.

LO6 Discuss the primary issues surrounding sex tourism.

LO7 Distinguish between pornography, obscenity, and erotica, and explain the community standards of tolerance test.

LO8 Outline the various types of pornography and the typical consumer.

LO9 Identify the reasons some people object to pornography and evaluate research on the effects of pornography on its users.

Parliament has the power to regulate against nuisances, but not at the cost of the health, safety, and lives of prostitutes. . . . The prohibitions all heighten the risks [to prostitutes]. . . . They do not merely impose conditions on how prostitutes operate. They go a critical step further, by imposing *dangerous* conditions on prostitution; they prevent people engaged in a risky—but legal—activity from taking steps to protect themselves from the risks.[*]

[*] Chief Justice Beverley McLachlin, Supreme Court of Canada, December 20, 2013.

The exchange of sexual gratification for money is a prominent feature of many contemporary societies and one that involves large amounts of money. In this chapter, we consider two ways in which sex can be bought and sold: commercial sex work and pornography. Both involve complex legal issues and public controversy, but both also attract a steady stream of eager customers. Other commercial ventures related to sexuality—such as the selling of sex toys and fetish objects—are discussed elsewhere in this book (e.g., Chapters 9 and 15).

 LO1

Commercial Sex Work

Sex workers are individuals who work as prostitutes, escorts, erotic dancers, phone sex workers, pornographic models and actors, and in nontherapeutic massage parlours. According to Ontario sociologist Eleanor Maticka-Tyndale and her colleagues (2000b), what is common to all these types of activities is that they involve the sale of a service to "satisfy a sexual fantasy, produce sexual excitement or arousal, and/or provide sexual satisfaction to the customer" (p. 88). We use the term *sex worker* as much as possible throughout this chapter because the term focuses on the activity and does not imply that a person's identity is determined by the activities he or she engages in. **Commercial sex workers** who engage in prostitution (*hookers*) receive money, material gifts, or some other form of payment (such as drugs) for engaging in partnered sexual activities or interactions. As social critics have pointed out, some dating and living arrangements, and some long-term relationships, including certain marriages, also fall in this category. For example, a Quebec study found that 3 percent of adolescents reported that they had received "money, drugs, alcohol, or gifts" for sex, and 4 percent reported that they had provided something for sex at least once

Commercial sex workers: Persons who engage in sexual acts in return for money or drugs and do so in a fairly nondiscriminating fashion; prostitutes.

Common bawdy house: A place kept, occupied, or used by one or more persons to engage in prostitution or indecency.

(Lavoie et al., 2010). Most of the time (95 percent of buys and 88 percent of sellers) the other person was a friend or an acquaintance. Similarly, a B.C. study found that, among youth who had every used alcohol or drugs, 2 percent of the boys and 3 percent of the girls had exchanged sex for substances (Homma, Nicholson, et al., 2012).

Although prostitution per se—that is, the buying and selling of sex—has never been illegal in Canada, various activities related to prostitution are criminal offences (Shaver, 1996b). These offences are listed in Table 2.1. The *Criminal Code of Canada* prohibits stopping cars, impeding the flow of traffic, or communicating in public for the purposes of engaging in prostitution or obtaining the sexual services of a prostitute. These offences are often called "communication offences." The statute clearly states that a prostitute can be a person of either gender and that both the sex workers and their customers can be charged. In addition, cities attempt to control sex work through bylaws pertaining to zoning, traffic, and licensing of businesses.

Enforcement of these statutes has largely been aimed at street sex workers and their customers to make sex workers less visible and less of a nuisance. Prostitution is considered a minor offence, punishable usually by a fine or by a short jail term for repeat offenders. Keeping or being found in a **common bawdy house** (the legal term for a place in which prostitution occurs), procuring (pimping), and living on money made from prostitution are also illegal, and the maximum sentences for these offences are significantly higher than for the communication offences. It is also illegal to keep a common bawdy house for performance of "indecent acts," although what is considered indecent is determined by community standards. Performing sexual services in a massage parlour may be illegal if the police can prove that the purpose of the massage parlour is to engage in prostitution (i.e., if the massage parlour is a common bawdy house) or if communication occurred about the price of sexual services (a communication offence). In reality, both of these are difficult to prove.

One criticism of the current law is that although prostitution is legal, there are no clear guidelines on where it can take place. Further, these laws are difficult to enforce, and the probability of arrest is low. Thus, the laws do little to discourage prostitution.

How are the prostitution laws enforced? The answer is with great inconsistency (Gemme, 1998; Shaver, 1993, 1994, 1996b). Almost all charges are for communication offences involving street prostitution—people working within massage parlours, escort services, brothels, and call operations rarely get charged. More sex workers than customers are charged, and their sentences are more severe. In addition, more men who pay for sex with women are charged than men who pay for sex with men, in part because male police officers do not like to pose as prostitutes to entrap clients. Charges are disproportionately laid against female sex workers. As Quebec sociologist Frances Shaver concluded:

> The women and men involved are both culpable under the law—as are all persons engaged in any form of prostitution—nevertheless, the enforcement patterns penalize women more often and more severely than men; they penalize prostitutes more than customers, procurers, or pimps; and they penalize on-street prostitution more than off-street prostitution. (Shaver, 1993, p. 165)

In 2013 the Supreme Court unanimously struck down the sections of the *Criminal Code* dealing with prostitution as violating the *Charter of Rights and Freedoms* (Figure 17.1). However, they gave the government until December 2014 to amend the legislation, so the laws did not immediately change. The Court was asked to decide whether the laws put vulnerable women at increased risk of violence. They ruled that, although Parliament has the power to impose conditions on how prostitutes operate, the current conditions prevent sex workers from protecting themselves from the risks associated with their work and therefore violate Canadians' basic values. The court cited specific harms caused by

each of the prostitution laws: the ban on brothels, the law against living off the avails of prostitution, and the ban on street soliciting.

How do Canadians view sex work? According to a 2007 Angus Reid Poll, only 38 percent of Canadians believe that prostitution is morally acceptable; however, more Canadians believe prostitution is moral than believe that having an extramarital affair (17 percent) or using illegal drugs (20 percent) are moral. Another Angus Reid Poll (2009) asked Canadians about the current laws related to prostitution. Canadians were evenly split with 41 percent indicating that the current provisions protect the public good and 41 percent indicating that they are unfair because they force prostitutes into unsafe situations. Almost half of Canadians (48 percent) felt that neither clients nor sex workers should be punished with fines or jail sentences for engaging in consensual prostitution. Men tended to be more accepting of prostitution than were women.

Some people argue that prostitution is a victimless crime and that because both parties in prostitution are consenting, prostitution should not be illegal. The argument against the criminalization of prostitution assumes that if prostitution-related activities were legal or at least decriminalized, they could be regulated and the problems of crime, public offence, and the spread of sexually transmitted infections associated with prostitution would be reduced. Enhancing the safety of sex workers is a particularly important issue (Young, 2008). Researchers interviewed women engaged in sex work in Vancouver (Farley et al., 2005). Almost all had had been physically assaulted (90 percent) or sexually assaulted (78 percent) in the course of their work. Further, an average of seven prostitutes are killed each year while practising their trade in Canada (Beattie & Cotter, 2010). Under decriminalization, prostitution is viewed as a personal choice and therefore a private matter between adults rather than a crime. The law could still be involved to ensure that people, particularly children, are not forced into prostitution and to penalize pimps and other people who profit from sex work.

Quebec sexologist Robert Gemme argued that while we need to eliminate the legal consequences of prostitution, we also need to remove the negative effects that result from the social stigma attached to prostitution—thus the term *sex worker*. From this perspective, prostitution is sex *work* (emphasis on the word "work") and is a trade to be regulated like any other trade. Thus, sex workers should be entitled to all the benefits and protection given to other workers, such as freedom from harassment, proper pay, humane living and working conditions, the right to be treated with respect, and worker compensation (MacDonald & Jeffrey, 2000; Lewis et al., 2005). In several Canadian cities, there are movements to unionize sex workers.

Figure 17.1 In 2013 the Supreme Court of Canada struck down Canada's prostitution laws as violating the *Charter of Rights and Freedoms*.

Other Canadians do not favour decriminalizing the activities related to prostitution. They argue that the activities of prostitution have turned some areas of large cities into unpleasant and possibly dangerous places for many citizens, because prostitution brings with it added traffic, loitering, noise, illegal drugs, and exposure of children and residents to discarded condoms and needles. Thus, they want better enforcement of current laws to contain prostitution to nonresidential areas and reduce the visibility and the nuisance aspects of prostitution (Duchesne, 1999). Still other Canadians want stronger laws and stiffer sentences imposed by the courts.

L02 Female Sex Workers
Venues

Commercial sexual activity occurs in a number of settings or venues. The nature of the venue or of the social or sexual context influences the type of sex worker and client found there (e.g., race, social class), the activity that occurs, and its associated risks. In New Brunswick, 80 percent of sex workers work the streets; the remainder work for an escort agency or strip club (Lee & Coates, 2007). In Vancouver, on the other hand, most sex workers work in a variety of venues, sometimes more than one at a time (Benoit & Millar, 2001). The discussion that follows focuses on female workers and their male clients, but keep in mind that there are male, female, gay, lesbian, bisexual, and transgender sex workers and clients.

The **call girl** (notice the diminutive "girl") works out of her own residence, making appointments with clients by a landline, cellphone, or the Internet. She is often from a middle-class background and may be a university graduate. She dresses expensively and lives in an upscale neighbourhood. A call girl in a medium-sized city may charge a minimum of $150 per hour and more if she engages in atypical activities; call girls in major metropolitan areas charge $200 or more per hour. A call girl can earn a great deal of money. But she also has heavy business expenses: an expensive residence, an extensive wardrobe, bills for makeup and hairdressers, online marketing, and tips for porters and landlords.

A call girl may have a number of regular customers and may accept new clients only on referral. Because she makes dates by telephone or over the Internet, she can exercise close control over whom she sees and over her schedule. She usually sees clients in her residence, which also allows her to control the setting in which she works. In addition to sexual gratification, she often provides an illusion of intimacy (Leaver & Dolnick, 2010). She may provide other services, such as accompanying clients to business and social gatherings. Call girls have considerable autonomy, and their physical and health risks are reduced by the setting in which they work. Many call girls advertise on specialized websites (Bernstein, 2007).

Another venue for commercial sex work is the **brothel**. In the nineteen century and the early twentieth century, there were many successful brothels in North America. They varied from storefront clip joints, where the customer's money was stolen while he was sexually occupied, to elegant mansions where the customer was treated like a distinguished dinner guest. Brothels declined in number after World War II. In the past 20 years, they have been replaced by **in-call services**, which employ women working regular shifts in an apartment or condominium, servicing clients who come to the apartment. In major cities the charge is $150 or $200 per hour; in exchange, the client can participate in standard sexual activity including fellatio, cunnilingus, and vaginal intercourse. Many in-call services also require initial contact by telephone, although others advertise their location in specialized media or even telephone books. A sex worker in this setting generally has less autonomy than a call girl has; there is usually a manager or madam (discussed shortly) who determines the conditions of work and the fees to be charged, and collects a substantial percentage of each fee. In-call workers have less choice of clients and may be expected to service several per shift. Brothels and in-call services are illegal in Canada under the *Criminal Code* provision that it is illegal to be involved in a common bawdy house.

Another contemporary setting for commercial sex is the **massage parlour**. Some massage parlours provide legitimate massage therapy. In others, the employees sell sexual services; these often advertise "sensual massage" or "erotic massage," making it pretty clear which type of parlour they are. Some parlours offer a standard list of services and prices; others allow the masseuse or masseur to decide what she or he will do with a particular client and possibly how much of a "tip" is required for that activity. Massage parlours vary greatly in decor and price. Some are located in professional buildings, are expensively decorated, and provide food and drinks in addition to sexual gratification. Charges may range from $100 to $300 or more. Such parlours may accept charge cards, with the business listed on the monthly statement as a restaurant. At the other end of the scale, storefront parlours, often located in commercial sex districts, offer no amenities and charge rates of $40 to $100.

Another venue for a sex business is the *escort service*. These services have revealing names, such as

Call girl: The most expensive and exclusive category of sex workers.
Brothel (BRAH-thul): A house of prostitution where sex workers and customers meet for sexual activity.
In-call service: A residence in which sex workers work regular shifts, selling sexual services on an hourly basis.
Massage parlour: A place where massages and sexual services can generally be purchased.

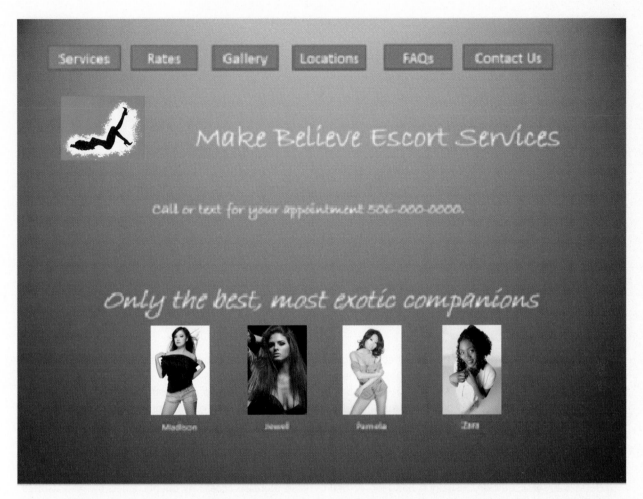

Figure 17.2 Escort services are another venue for a sex work and provide a range of services. They are frequently advertised online. (NOTE: The models whose photos are shown here are being used for illustrative purposes only.)

Alternative Lifestyle Services, First Affair, All Yours, Versatile Entertainment, and Hubbies for Hire (Figure 17.2). Most escort services employ both men and women who will engage in sexual activity; like massage parlours, the service may have a standard menu, or the escort may have the autonomy to decide what activities he or she will do with a client. Sex work in this setting is referred to as an **out-call service** since the escorts go to the clients. This is obviously a more risky business in that the escort cannot control the setting in which the services are provided. Escorts are usually required to telephone the service when they arrive and when they leave the client's location. This not only contributes to their safety but also allows the service to monitor how long the escort spent with the client and therefore the amount owed the service. Several Canadian cities license escorting, including Calgary, Edmonton, Winnipeg, and Windsor. The bylaw in Windsor differs from that in other Canadian cities because it allows escorts to work out of their own homes instead of requiring them to set up offices in specially zoned areas of the city. This was an attempt to treat escorts the same as

other independent business people (Maticka-Tyndale et al., 2005).

In major Canadian cities, there are upscale (and very expensive) escort services, such as Executive's Choice in Windsor, Diamonds Escorts in the Niagara Region, A Touch of Class Escorts in Alberta, and VIP Escorts for Eastern Canada. These services provide male and female companions, and their websites include disclaimers that sexual services are not being offered. (Compare that with the poses and dress of the companions shown in the online photo galleries!) As a result, charges are a single rate and do not depend on what services the companion provides. Often the companion is providing the GFE/BFE (boyfriend/girlfriend experience), including personalized attention, conversation, and ego-stroking. Rates are by the hour, with many agencies offering discounts for multihour appointments. Hourly rates are between $150 and $350; daily rates are between $1000 and $2500. They also offer rates for weddings, weekends, and dinner dates. The reach of the Internet

Out-call service: A service that sends a sex worker to a location specified by the client to provide sexual services.

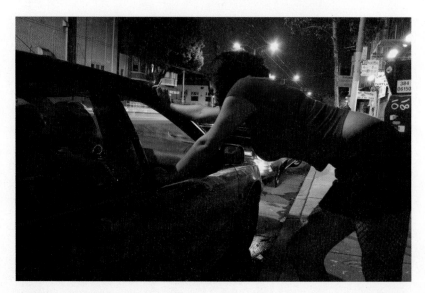

Figure 17.3   Streetwalkers have little control over the conditions in which they work and are at risk of assault, sexual assault, and arrest.

allows these agencies to develop ties to companions and clients all over the world. Some agencies provide or encourage communication via Skype.

In most communities, the most visible sex worker is the **streetwalker**. She sells her wares on the streets of cities (Figure 17.3). She is generally less attractive and less fashionably dressed than the call girl, and she charges correspondingly less for services, perhaps as little as $20 for a "quickie," usually a hand-job or oral sex. She is more likely to impose strict time constraints on the customer. In one study, female street sex workers in Montreal earned between $1800 and $2000 per week. On the other hand, a study in Vancouver found that the median annual income of the sex workers they interviewed was only $18,000 (Benoit & Millar, 2001). Because her mode of operation is obvious, she is most likely to be arrested; 95 percent of prostitution-related charges in Canada are for street prostitution (Wolff & Geissel, 1994). Because streetwalkers have relatively little control over the conditions in which they work, they are at greater risk of disease and of violence at the hands of their customers, pimps, and even police officers. In one study of 30 female sex workers in Montreal, 14 had been sexually assaulted and 22 had been physically assaulted in the previous 12 months (Shaver, 1996b). In Vancouver, more than 50 women, most of them sex workers, were murdered between 1983 and 2001.

Child or juvenile sex workers also work as street prostitutes. About one-half of sex workers enter the trade when they are under 16 years old (Badgley, 1984). There has been an increasing demand in recent years for child prostitutes. In 1988 Parliament passed specific legislation prohibiting the purchase of sexual services from someone under 18 years old. The Federal/Provincial/Territorial Working Group on Prostitution has recommended that youths involved in prostitution be treated as persons in need of assistance and not as offenders (Canadian Centre for Justice Statistics, 1999).

The Internet and cellphones have made entry into work as an out-call worker or call girl much easier. They also increase access by clients, aided by Web listings. In some cities these technologies have remarkably reduced demand for and provision of services by streetwalkers (Venkatesh, 2011).

Research on commercial sex workers in a large Canadian city has found that the same person may work in several different venues over time (Lewis et al., 2004). For example, in areas with cold winters, people who work on the streets in the summer and fall may work in in-call services or bars during the winter. Women also may move back and forth between an escort service and working as a call girl.

L03   **The Role of Third Parties**

Research in Ontario, Quebec, and the Maritimes has shown that most sex workers work with third parties, whether working for themselves or working for an agency (Clamen et al., 2013). A third party is anyone involved who is neither the client nor the worker. These third parties take a variety of different roles. They may be supervisors, owners, managers, receptionists, security, drivers, personal assistants, advertisers, or webmasters. They may hire, work with, or work for, third parties. Sex workers themselves can be third parties if they facilitate another sex worker's activities. The researchers found that these relationships are complex

Streetwalker: A lower status sex worker who works on the streets selling sexual services.

and that they challenge the stereotypes about third parties involved with commercial sex workers. That is, they found that many of these relationships are not abusive or exploitative and provide important services that increase safety, security, and well-being. Of course, some relationships are abusive and exploitative.

Many people associate sex workers with a **pimp** ("The Man"), portrayed as the companion-master. If a sex worker has a pimp, she supports him with her earnings, and in return he may provide her with companionship and sex, bail her out of jail, and provide her with food, shelter, clothing, and drugs. If he keeps an eye on her when she is working, he may provide some protection against theft and violence because a sex worker is scarcely in a position to go to the police if a customer robs her. But the same pimp also may exercise considerable control over her and engage in verbal, physical, and sexual abuse if she fails to do what he tells her. The stereotype of all sex workers having pimps is not accurate. In Canada, a majority of adult sex workers work *without* a pimp (Shaver, 1994). For example, in New Brunswick 74 percent of sex workers work for themselves (Lee & Coats, 2007) (see Milestones in Sex Research for some of their stories). However, many child prostitutes do have pimps.

Just as many call girls and exotic dancers have day jobs, so do pimps. Many are in the food trades or services (Venkatesh, 2011). Some are students. One pimp worked his way through university connecting male students with women to go on dates, dance at parties, and provide sexual services in a variety of places, or deliver the GFE (Adshade, 2010). He knew many of the men and women from school; a man would request a service, and he kept asking women until one agreed. His take depended on the woman's attractiveness and skill, the service, the venue, and the client's willingness to pay—from $20 (for a hand job in a car) to $700 (all night in a luxury hotel). He described his role as helping "women, friends of mine, to find paying customers."

Another third party in commercial sex work is the **madam**, a woman who manages or owns an in-call service, out-call service, brothel, or escort service. A madam is usually experienced and skilled at managing sex workers and businesses. Sometimes she also is socially skilled with a network of contacts in the community.

In other venues there may be other third parties. Massage parlours employ managers who are on the premises at all times and may exercise close control of their employees. The importance of these third parties is that they reduce the autonomy of the sex workers they supervise and may coerce them to perform activities or work with clients that they do not want to. There is sharp disagreement among observers over the extent to which a sex worker can exercise choice with regard to his or her activities. Some argue workers choose who they serve and what acts they perform; others argue that they have little choice if they need the money. The reality depends, in part, on the involvement of the third parties in the worker's daily life.

Sex trafficking refers to the recruitment and control of persons, by threat or use of force or deception, for purposes of sexual exploitation (Hynes & Raymond, 2002). In one scenario, girls and young women are recruited in developing countries by ads or by people who promise them education, a good job (as a dancer, nanny, secretary), or a husband in a developed country. Recruiters may even supply forged travel documents, often for a price. When the women arrive in the destination country, they find themselves captives; often their travel documents are taken away, the money they earn goes to those who control them, and their controllers threaten physical harm to the women or their families if they disobey or run away. The women often work in bars, brothels, and massage parlours, and they may be moved every few weeks. It is estimated that trafficking produces $7 billion profit per year (Parrot & Cummings, 2006). The United Nations estimates that tens of thousands of young women and girls are trafficked each year; half are children, with most of these victims ending up in Germany, the United States, and Italy. Thousands of these women are brought to Canada every year to work in the sex trade; some are kept as virtual prisoners (McClelland, 2001).

Another image is of the child sex slave, an image vigorously railed against by some celebrities (e.g., Ashton Kutchner) and numerous media including the *New York Times*, *Fox News*, and *CNN*. Here the scenario is a girl age 10 or 11 to 17 seduced or kidnapped by an older man and forced into prostitution in various venues—strip clubs, brothels, massage parlors, private homes. Their exploiters use threats of and actual physical violence, and threats to their families to control them. The usual quoted figure is "100,000 to 300,000 child sex slaves in the United States today" (Cizmar et al., 2011). The problem is that the number is false. It began as a "guestimate" by researchers at the University of Pennsylvania in 2001, of the number of children *at risk in all of North America*.

Three American studies using three different methods do not support the assertion that there are even 100,000 "child sex slaves" in the United States or that the number of foreign nationals trafficked for sexual exploitation is equally large (Banks & Kyckelhahn, 2011; Hinman, 2011). It shouldn't really matter whether the number is large or small, or the victims are children or adults, male or female. Sexual

Pimp: A sex worker's companion, protector, and master.
Madam: A woman who manages a brothel, in-call, out-call, or escort service.
Sex trafficking: The recruitment and control of persons for sexual exploitation.

Milestones In Sex Research

Talking Back: Stories of Sex Work in the Maritimes

One really does not expect a sex worker to be articulate, to resist, or to "talk back" to dominant stereotypes of her or his work, but that is what we found when we started asking for and recording the words of sex workers in the Maritimes.

Many of us have stereotypes of people in sex work. Sex workers are often depicted by the media, some police, and certain conservative religious groups as victims or as deserving of a certain fate. Rarely are sex workers depicted as the people they are—mothers, friends, sisters, brothers, fathers, grandparents, lovers, or workers. Equally problematic is the view that sex workers are passive and lacking agency, the ability to act in the social world, to make choices, or to resist dominant, negative beliefs about their lives. In our study, we asked 62 sex workers (men, women, and transgender) in three Maritime cities about their perceptions and attitudes about the work they do, as well as about others' views of them. In answering our questions, they were articulate, witty, and courageous. They did not hesitate to "talk back" to dominant, erroneous images of them. Their words were the most important part of our study because we saw ourselves as engaged in a politics of solidarity rather than a politics of saving. Here we share some of their insights.

We asked about the best and worst aspects of sex work that they encountered. The best parts of the work they claimed were "the money, honey." Colleen from Moncton could not understand why anyone would not do her work, given the amount of money she makes compared with other service work:

> There's one woman at my work (call centre), she's a psychology major, and she has her master's. And she's working at a call centre for $8.00 an hour. I think she's making a little bit more now 'cause she's been there for a long time. I think she's making $8.40 an hour. Like, still, you spent $50,000 on university, to make $8.40 an hour?

On the other hand, Eric from Moncton claimed he'd never go back to sex work, and that he'd "rather work for twelve hours a day than go out and stand for an hour in the cold. It's degrading." Money was talked about in terms of refusal to "budget" according to what the state (read social assistance) was demanding. As Jacqueline of Saint John said: "It's cash in my pocket. Welfare doesn't know. It gives my son better clothes, better food. . . . I spend all my money on him." Sex workers' refusal to "be poor" and to accept "handouts," and their desire to be their own boss was a common theme as well.

Violence was the worst part of sex work; all participants reported an increase in violence. Dana, of Halifax, blamed the increase in violence as being squarely connected to people's stereotypes:

> The reason I feel that [clients have become more violent] is because the media portrays us as non-people. And yeah, they do, they make us more . . . like the word *prostitute*, this is where I have the big problem, it dehumanizes people . . . they use the word "prostitute" or

exploitation is wrong, a crime, and very damaging to the victim. We need to increase efforts to eradicate it based on a realistic picture of the problem. Vastly exaggerated estimates do not help.

Some girls are definitely forced into prostitution in Canada, although it is impossible to know how many. The Canadian Women's Foundation is funding grassroots organizations across the country to help prevent trafficking and help girls and women escape sex trafficking.

 The Career of a Sex Worker

The first step in a sex worker's career is entry. Women enter sex work for a variety of reasons (Vanwesenbeeck, 2001). For sex workers in Western countries, the most important one is economics. Some women, for various reasons, are attracted by a desire for money, material goods, and an exciting lifestyle. These women are attracted by the image of the call girl, a status that some of them are fortunate enough to attain. For some women—for example, a poor but attractive woman—sex "hooker" as opposed to "a woman who was working as a prostitute." It's a job—it's not a person.

They've made it a person and they've made it a stereotypical low-life person and a disposable person and the more that the media continues to do that, the more the tricks feel that they are allowed to be violent.

Stigma was also cited by Jason in Moncton:

Okay, how can I put this? We're not scum because you're the ones paying. . . . You guys are looking down on us . . . yeah, but who's paying us? It's you guys. How do we make our money? You guys.

Stigma extends beyond behaviour on the street. Many reported the kind of experience that Jill, from Saint John, had when she went to emergency services at the local hospital:

I've gone in for a coffee burn, and you know what I mean, all of a sudden it's turned into my drug use, and the way I was dressed and stuff: "Well, you're just a prostitute, you know and you probably deserved it." And it was a coffee burn, so you know what I mean, so . . . . They make you feel like you're diseased or something.

Others, such as Denise, an ex-worker in Halifax, spoke of how much they grew in the experience of sex work, how much they learned:

I learned a lot. I learned a lot about myself: how strong I really could be. I met a lot of other people, like girls like myself. We were all normal, and then things happened. And I learned a lot about people in general. . . . I can survive, and I have survived. I have become strong. You look into the face of death every day and you're either gonna make it or break it. You're gonna be found dead, or you're gonna survive. . . . But I never forget the times and I'm not embarrassed. I learned a lot about society, and the law.

Felicity from Halifax reported that her clients were one of the best parts of her job and that she deplored any kind of discrimination they might face:

They [her clients] are missing something, whether they don't have a wife at home that's giving them enough attention, or they have no one in their lives. You know, some of them just need to be close to someone, or they just need somebody to love them even if it's a half-hour or an hour at a time. . . .

In sum, the world of sex workers is far from the usual stereotypes that people create. It isn't always safe, it isn't always pretty, but as they point out, many other jobs have similar types of stories—of exploitation, of addiction, and of liberation and independence.

The last words belong to Alexis, a 17-year-old former sex worker from Moncton:

If I had a chance to tell the media so that they—so the world would hear what I had to say, something I'd tell them is, "Don't speak. You want to know about a whore, you get to know a whore and you'll see that she's just like you." That's what I'd tell them.

Source: Written by Gayle MacDonald, based on interviews conducted by Leslie Ann Jeffrey and Gayle MacDonald for *Sex Workers in the Maritimes Talk Back* (2006).

work can be a means of upward economic mobility. Other women enter out of economic necessity, in order to survive. The importance of the money, which can amount to hundreds of dollars per day or shift, is illustrated by the dramatic increase in applicants for positions in strip and sex clubs and other establishments in the U.S. during the recession of 2008–2009 ("More Women," 2009). A poorly educated single mother may have no alternative means of earning a living. For example, a sex worker in Vancouver said,

I worked for a couple of months as a house cleaner, scrubbing floors and toilets to survive and make money to afford an apartment. From that amount, I couldn't survive . . . so I started to work in an escort agency. (Benoit & Millar, 2001, p. 12)

Some women become sex workers to support a drug addiction.

Force or coercion is another factor. Some women report being coerced physically or psychologically by a husband or lover into selling sex for money. As noted earlier, coercion is a major factor in sex trafficking. Some women become involved in prostitution through a family member or friend who is already a sex worker and can teach them the ropes (Miller, 1986).

On entering prostitution, most sex workers go through an apprenticeship in which they learn the skills of the trade. The apprentice learns sexual techniques, especially fellatio, since many customers want oral sex. She learns how to hustle, to successfully negotiate her services and price with potential customers. She learns how to maintain control over the interaction so that she can protect herself as much as possible from being hurt or robbed by clients (and many sex workers are hurt or robbed). She learns values, like "the customer is always right," and fairness to other "working girls." Women who are recruited into the life by a pimp may be trained by one of his more experienced "wives." Some women are trained by an experienced madam, in exchange for a large percentage of their fees.

There has been relatively little research on the "mid-career" sex worker. We have noted that a sex worker may work in several different venues over time. After learning the ropes, women may work in the in-call or out-call services and try to establish a list of regular clients. If successful, they usually begin to work independently (Bernstein, 2007). A woman might move from in-call to out-call as she becomes more experienced at managing clients. She might move from the street into work in bars or at truck stops in response to changes in the weather or her health. Sex workers who are addicted to drugs may be forced to work long hours and service many customers in more than one venue to support their habit. Again, some of these changes may result from coercion or exploitation by a pimp or a sex trafficker.

Research in New Brunswick and Nova Scotia found that when asked "What is the best part of sex work?" almost all sex workers replied "the money" (Jeffrey & MacDonald, 2006a, 2006b). This did not mean that they were forced into sex work by economic factors but rather that they chose sex work over their other alternatives, such as a minimum-wage job or social assistance. They also identified independence and flexibility of work as a positive part of their work. Thus, these sex workers chose sex work as a way of earning a better income (between $30 and $300 per night for outdoor work and between $50 and $150 per hour for indoor work) in a relatively short period while being able to set their own schedule. "Squaring up" or "leaving the life" refers to giving up sex work. Financially and psychologically it is a difficult thing to do, particularly for the woman with no job skills. As Gwen wrote,

> When you can't understand why a woman can't leave the sex trade or why she goes back or why she can't just get a job, I want you to remember that her life is not like yours. I want you to remember that your experiences are as foreign to her as hers are to you. She can no more become a bureaucrat tomorrow than you can become a sexually exploited youth tonight. (Field & Rabinovitch, 2003)

Recognizing this, some analysts call for comprehensive programs that provide education and job training, shelters, and counselling for women (and men) who want to leave commercial sex work (Hynes & Raymond, 2002). For example, PEERS, which stands for Prostitutes, Empowerment, Education, and Resource Society, has branches in several Canadian cities and provides support, training, and resources to help male and female sex workers leave the trade. Stella is an organization in Quebec that provides support and information to sex workers and is working to educate the public, fight discrimination against sex workers, and promote decriminalization of their work (chezstella.org).

The major hazards associated with being a sex worker are being a victim of a "bad trick" (i.e., physical or sexual assault or even murder), drug addiction, sexually transmitted infections, and arrest by police (Church et al., 2001; Jeffrey & MacDonald, 2006a, 2006b). However, there are variations across the country in how vigorously laws pertaining to prostitution are enforced and in the sentences (fines compared with prison terms) given to women who are convicted of prostitution-related offences (Wolff & Geissel, 1994). The worst risk is of being murdered.

 Sex Workers' Well-Being

There are a variety of images of the contemporary sex worker: young, attractive, autonomous, healthy, "the happy hooker"; young, brazen, aggressive, "the tough chick"; not-so-young, bruised emotionally and physically, a victim. Which one is valid?

According to a landmark study (Vanwesenbeeck, 1994), all these images are accurate. Researchers in the Netherlands recruited 100 women who had been working for at least one year for a study of "sex and health"; these women were interviewed and completed several measures of coping style and well-being. The samples included women who worked on the street, in windows, in clubs and brothels (Figure 17.4), for escort services, and in their own homes. The results indicated that one-quarter of the women were doing well. They had few physical or psychosocial complaints, used problem-focused coping strategies, and were satisfied with their lives. Another quarter were at the opposite end. They complained of headaches, backaches, anxiety, and depression; their coping strategies involved dissociation (seeing problems as unrelated to the self) and denial, and they were dissatisfied with sex work. The remaining women were in the middle.

Figure 17.4 Brothels in a few cities around the world display available workers in windows on the sidewalk. These workers have cleaner and safer working conditions.

The risks to a woman and thus her well-being varied according to the venue in which she worked. In the Netherlands, where sex work is legal, women who worked in windows and on the streets were at greater risk. Similarly, research in Canada has found that working the streets is associated with greater risk of arrest and of violence by clients (Lewis et al., 2005; Shaver, 2005). This obviously influences physical and mental health. Women who worked in windows or on the streets worked faster, had more clients, and earned less per customer than those working in in-call and out-call services. In a more recent study of indoor sex workers in the Netherlands, workers reported having an average nine-hour workday; more than one-third worked more than 40 hours per week, and half had taken no holidays in the preceding year (Venicz & Vanwesenbeeck, 2000). The scores of indoor sex workers on measures of burnout—depersonalization and emotional exhaustion—were compared with the scores of female health care workers and persons in treatment for work-related problems. Sex workers scored significantly higher on depersonalization, which was mainly explained by contextual factors: working because of coercion,

experiences of violence, and lack of control in interaction with clients (Vanwesenbeeck, 2005). An important caveat in interpreting these studies is that they were conducted in the context of legalized prostitution in the Netherlands. Doubtless the health outcomes would be worse in countries in which prostitution was illegal and therefore sex workers have little recourse if, for example, they are assaulted.

A unique study of the geography of sex worker victimization used reports filed by sex workers in New South Wales in Australia (Prior et al., 2012). An outreach project there encourages workers to voluntarily report instances of victimization they experience. An analysis of 333 reports filed over eight years identified 528 criminal acts. One-fifth involved theft including stealing, defrauding, and nonpayment. One-sixth involved harassment including stalking, nuisance behaviour, and threats. Other actions included disorderly conduct, assault, and abduction. Most incidents occurred indoors, regardless of the venue; victimization occurred in the assailant's car (street work), the premises (brothels), the assailant's home (out-call), or the worker's residence (in-call). The authors concluded that privacy and the worker's lack of control are major situational contributors to victimization.

Risks are especially high for women who are being trafficked because they are at risk of suffering abuse and injury by both clients and masters, experiencing illness and infection, and facing medical neglect (Hynes & Raymond, 2002).

There is also the risk of exposure to sexually transmitted infections, especially HIV/AIDS. Sex workers infected with HIV are often workers who are also injecting drugs; research indicates that the injection is the greater risk. In the Western world, studies show that the sex worker's risk of HIV infection is greater in his or her private sex life than in the sex work. The risk varies greatly in other parts of the world, with high rates of HIV/AIDS in some cities and countries but low rates in others (Vanwesenbeeck, 2001).

Some suggest that the high levels of violence and of psychological distress found among sex workers are not due to the nature of the sex work per se, but instead reflect the stigma associated with sex work (Bernstein, 2007). Sex workers are at risk of sexual assault because of attitudes such as the view that prostitutes cannot be sexually assaulted so no harm is done if you do force them to have sex (Miller & Schwartz, 1995). The risk of arrest and mistreatment by law enforcement personnel, and the resulting anxiety and distress, reflect the fact that some aspects of sex work are illegal.

Sex workers use a variety of strategies to cope with the risks of their work. Some use drugs and alcohol to increase their confidence and decrease their guilt. Others use a strategy of shutting down their feelings and focusing narrowly on the task. The consequences of this distancing are often referred to as *depersonalization* (not, of course, an experience unique to sex work). Independent women may view themselves as professionals, providing therapy, "sexual healing," or sex education. They may take courses to enhance their skills, such as massage certification, or use prior training as a therapist or social worker. These women perceive their work as offering opportunities for personal growth (Bernstein, 2007). Some emphasize the rewarding aspects of the work, perhaps that it supports their children. Many sex workers use as a coping technique the careful management of time and place, locating their sex work in a specific physical and temporal place separated from their private sexual and familial relationships (also not unique to sex work). Sex workers also may use the network of contacts with other sex workers as a source of support; workers on one "stroll" worked together to protect a pregnant colleague by giving her all the customers who wanted a blow job and protecting her from clients known to be rough (M. Anderson, personal communication, 2004).

The Role of Early Abuse

The study of women working in the Netherlands found that, in addition to their work venue, having a history of victimization and trauma as children or adolescents before they entered prostitution was associated with poorer well-being (Vanwesenbeeck, 1994). Much of the research literature before 1990 reported that a high percentage of sex workers had been physically or sexually abused as children, which was then often taken as the cause of their entry into sex work (Vanwesenbeeck, 2001). It was often suggested that childhood abuse leads to feelings of stigmatization that in turn results in early sexual activity and/or drug use, running away from home, and a drift into sex work. There is no doubt that some men and women do enter commercial sex work via this path. But the research on which this view is based used samples of streetwalkers, women in jail, or former sex workers located through social service agencies. These respondents are not representative of all sex workers, so these results cannot be generalized. Further, according to Quebec sociologist Frances Shaver (2005), much of this research has failed to use an appropriate comparison group—that is, a comparison group that is similar to the group of sex workers in age and socioeconomic status. We do not, in fact, know how important a history of abuse might be in any individual's entry into sex work. Clearly, any adult who has experienced childhood victimization may have poor well-being.

Customers

At the time of the Kinsey research, about 69 percent of all white males had had some experience with sex workers (Kinsey et al., 1948). In 1992, the National Health and Social Life Survey (NHSLS) asked all respondents whether they had had sex with someone they paid or who paid them (Laumann et al., 1994). Only 17 percent of men and 2 percent of women reported that they had had sex with such a partner since age 18. According to the National Survey of Sexual Health and Behavior (NSSHB), in the United States in 2009, 4.3 percent of men ages 18 to 59 and 0.8 percent of women ages 18 to 59 reported paying or being paid for sex in the last year (Herbenick et al., 2010c). Thus, the use of prostitutes has declined dramatically in the past 50 years. This likely reflects the increased frequency of nonmarital and casual sexual activity during this same period (see Chapters 10 and 11).

Sex workers refer to their customers as "johns." A Canadian study of johns developed a detailed questionnaire; it could be filled out on the Internet, printed and returned by mail, or completed in-person, by telephone, or through an Internet interview (Atchison, 2010). Participants were recruited by ads placed in newspapers, magazines, newsletters, adult clubs and businesses, and online discussion boards. Participants had to be at least 19, have paid for sex at least once in their lifetime, and reside in Canada. The author analyzed completed questionnaires from 861 people. The mean age was 42, and 99.4 percent were male. At the time of the survey, one-half were married or in a common-law relationship, and 39 percent were single. Of those who were not married, 25 percent had regular sex partners. Two-thirds earned at least $50,000 in 2007. On average, participants had purchased sex 100 times in their lives and had visited indoor sex establishments 4.8 times in the previous 12 months. Eighty-six percent preferred female workers and 10.5 percent preferred male workers. The most recent time they paid for sex, they paid for multiple activities (25 percent), half-oral and half-vaginal sex (17 percent), the GFE (16 percent), and vaginal intercourse (16 percent). Thus, most of these johns were heterosexual, in a relationship, middle class by income (and occupation), and visited commercial sex workers several times per year. Some johns are occasional johns; they may be businessmen who seek only occasional contacts with sex workers, perhaps while on business trips; some are compulsive johns, who use sex workers for their major sexual outlet. They are driven to them and cannot stay away (see Chapter 15).[1] Nearly 50 percent of johns are repeat clients who seek a regular relationship with one particular sex worker or a small group of them (Freund et al., 1991).

---

[1] Some Canadian cities have implemented programs designed to increase johns' awareness of the risks of street prostitution. Instead of receiving criminal charges, the johns attend a full-day seminar that provides information on community concerns, health risks, and sexual addictions and compulsions (Symbalauk & Jones, 1999).

Research in Quebec indicates that men use the services of sex workers for a variety of reasons (Gemme et al., 1984). Some have long-term partners but want sex more frequently than their partner does or want to engage in practices—such as fellatio—that they feel their partner would not be willing to do. Some use sex workers to satisfy their exotic sexual needs, such as being whipped or having sex with a woman who pretends to be a corpse. Others, particularly adolescents, may have sex with sex workers to prove their manhood or gain sexual experience. Finally, for some men it is a way to engage in discreet same-sex activity. A survey of visitors to a commercial sex event in Australia found that 23 percent of the men had paid for sex at least once. These men reported that their main reasons were to satisfy sexual needs, that it was easy, and that it would be entertaining (Pitts et al., 2004).

For many clients, a major appeal is the clear and bounded nature of the sexual interaction. Money is paid and services are received. The exchange is limited in time and space, and requires no effort to develop or maintain a relationship. The client wants "bounded authenticity"—real sex, a sense that she or he matters and is desirable, without the effort, expense, and hassles of commitment (Bernstein, 2007).

LO2 Male Sex Workers

Although under the *Criminal Code of Canada* a person engaging in prostitution can be male or female, male sex workers are less likely to be charged than are female sex workers (Shaver 1994, 1996b). Most male sex workers serve a male clientele—97 percent of clients of Canadian sex workers are male (Badgley, 1984). However, some sell their services to women or to both women and men.

Male sex workers serving a female clientele work in three settings. These male sex workers virtually never work in the street, in contrast to female streetwalkers and male *hustlers* (discussed shortly). This reflects gender-role socialization; female clients are unlikely to cruise the streets and pick up a sex worker, because they have been taught to let the male take the initiative and because women are not supposed to be that interested in sex, especially not interested enough to be willing to pay for it. Some male sex workers work for escort services and provide companionship and sexual gratification on an out-call basis. Some men work in massage parlours, under the same conditions as female employees. A third type is the **gigolo**, a man who provides companionship and sexual gratification on a continuing basis to a woman in exchange for money. A gigolo often, though not always, has only one client at a time. The demand for gigolos reflects the fact that women, like men, desire sexual gratification on a

continuing basis and will pay for it when circumstances require or allow them to do so. On the other hand, most women prefer their sexual activity to be part of an ongoing relationship.

Hustlers are male sex workers who cater to men (Figure 17.5). Interestingly, some of them consider themselves to be straight, not gay. In one study of male sex workers in Canada, 23 percent reported that they were heterosexual (Badgley, 1984). They may have strict rules for their customers to follow, such as only permitting the customer to perform fellatio on them.

There are male escort services for a more upscale male clientele. Male escorts may place advertisements in gay newspapers or, increasingly, online (Logan, 2010).

Male hustlers seem to fall into three main categories (Allen, 1980). First are the full-time street and bar hustlers, who operate much as female streetwalkers do except that they rarely have a pimp (Logan, 2010). They tend to be younger than other sex workers, and there is a market for "chickens" (young boys) as sex workers. They are less likely to experience violence from pimps or customers. Increasingly, male sex workers are working from indoor locations by using telephones or the Internet, and working as licensed escorts and masseurs rather than as street sex workers, particularly in small Canadian cities (Allman, 1999). Second are full-time call boys or kept boys. They tend to have a more exclusive clientele and to be more attractive and more sexually versatile than the streetwalkers. Surprisingly, by far the largest group is the third: part-time hustlers, who are typically students or individuals employed in another occupation. They engage in sex work only when they need money. The part-time hustlers are notable because unlike those in the other groups, they are less likely to come from dysfunctional families. They also have the best long-term chance for acquiring an education and a stable job and achieving a good social adjustment.

One study investigated gay and bisexual Internet-based male escorts in New York City. Their primary reasons for engaging in escorting were monetary gains, a bolstering of their sense of self, and sexual pleasure (Uy et al., 2004). For example, one man said,

> It's a very big ego trip. And you can get addicted to it very easily. You're getting paid by somebody who's giving you a lot of attention for an hour. . . . most of the guys I know that do this full-time, they can't get out because they are addicted to the sex and the ego and some of the power they get. (Uy et al., p. 17)

Similarly, in one study of male sex workers in Montreal between the ages of 16 and 29, the main reason for engaging in sex work,

> **Why do some men and women pay for sex?**

Gigolo (JIG-uh-loh): A male who provides companionship and sexual gratification on a continuing basis to a woman in exchange for money.
Hustlers: Male sex workers who sell their services to men.

Figure 17.5 Sex for sale on Jarvis Street in Toronto.

stated by 88 percent, was money, although some said they engaged in sex work as a way to meet people (Earls & David, 1989). Many of these young men came from troubled home environments, often leaving home at an early age. The majority (78 percent) reported using drugs on a regular basis.

 Transgender Sex Workers

Some transwomen work as sex workers. They are typically taking estrogen, which feminizes their body, including giving them breasts. Transgender sex workers serve a male clientele. A study of 46 cisgender women, 46 cisgender men, and 48 transwomen working as street sex workers found that the transgender sex workers were more similar to the female sex workers than to the male sex workers in keeping regular hours and spending less time with each client (Weinberg et al., 1999). Most reported that they enjoyed sexual activities with clients at least sometimes; in this way they were more similar to the male than to the female sex workers in the study. The transgender sex workers typically provided oral sex, manual stimulation, and receptive anal intercourse. More than half never or rarely told their customers that they were male; they would deceive their customers by

Sex tourism: Leisure travel with the purpose of purchasing sexual services.

restricting services (e.g., to oral sex), taping or tucking their penis back between their legs, and providing an excuse not to remove their skirt or panties (e.g., having their period).

Sex Tourism

An increasingly important type of commercial sex is **sex tourism**, which refers to varieties of leisure travel that have as their purpose the purchase of sexual services (Wonders & Michalowski, 2001). Both men and women engage in sex tourism, although women may be more likely to identify their behaviour as *romance tourism* resulting in sexual activity (Jacobs, 2009; Perrott, 2012). Sex tourism is made possible by three large-scale social forces: the migration of men and women from less developed nations, or from rural to urban areas, in search of jobs; the commodification of sexual intimacy, making all types of sex a commodity or service for sale; and increased travel for recreational purposes. All three of these forces are tied to increasing globalization, the movement of information and people freely across national boundaries.

The migration of people in search of economic opportunities provides a large group of young men and women in search of work. In some locales, they are aggressively recruited into sex work by pimps or persons with ties to sex trafficking. In other places, they enter into the life more or less voluntarily, often because there are few other opportunities for persons of their racial or ethnic background. In Amsterdam, where the attitude toward sex work can be described as regulated tolerance, a few individuals control much of the commercial sex work, recruiting foreign migrants to work in windows and brothels. In contrast, in Havana, Cuba, commercial sex work is decentralized, with many men and women working independently. They contact potential clients in hotels, bars, and on the street, hoping to connect with someone who will employ them perhaps for several days.

In some countries, sex tourism is the most rapidly growing economic sector and a major source of hard currency; in such places, governments have little incentive to reduce or eliminate it. One estimate places the value of the global sex industry at $20 billion per year.

The tourists who can purchase sexual services are obviously wealthy enough to travel, which in turn often means they are citizens of developed countries and members of the middle and upper classes in their home societies. The sex workers are often from a different national and ethnic background. One of the attractions for the tourist is sex with this "dark-skinned other," perhaps someone from a group stereotyped as sexually free and uninhibited. The encounter is appealing because it is a sharp contrast to the tourist's usual sexual experience (Brennan, 2010; Padilla, 2007). Unfortunately, one such appeal for men is sex with a young girl, and in some Asian cities girls as young as 12 and 13 are available in brothels, where they are tightly controlled by their managers. Of importance, Canadian citizens and permanent residents who engage in sexual activities with children in a foreign country that are against the law in Canada (see Table 2.1) can be charged and prosecuted in Canada.

The search for the type of sex workers—gender, age, sexual orientation—and experience that the tourist seeks is facilitated by the Internet (Padilla, 2007). Websites publish information about sex work, cruising areas and meeting places, and prices; past visitors review their experiences. Sex workers advertise on some of these sites, and some have their own web pages.

Pornography

A debate over pornography has been raging for decades. Some conservatives, religious fundamentalists, and some feminists (strange bedfellows, indeed!) agree that some kinds of pornography should be made illegal. Each group has overlapping but also different reasons

for taking this position (Cowan et al., 1989; Luff, 2001). In contrast, some civil liberties groups, liberals, and some other feminists argue that freedom of expression, guaranteed in the *Charter of Rights and Freedoms*, must be preserved and therefore pornography should not be restricted by law. Meanwhile, Joe Brown downloads *All New Beaver Hunt, v. 13* for a pleasurable evening's entertainment. Here we will examine what the issues are, paying particular attention to social scientists' research on the effects of pornography on people who are exposed to it. First, we need to clarify some terminology.

Terms

We can distinguish among pornography, obscenity, and erotica. Pornography comes from the Greek words *porneia*, which means, quite simply, "prostitution," and *graphos*, which means "writing." In general usage today, **pornography** refers to magazines, films, and so on, that are intended to be sexually arousing (Malamuth, 1998). The term is often used by people to refer to any image they don't like.

The *Criminal Code of Canada* uses the term *obscenity*, not pornography, in defining what sexual explicit material involving adults is illegal. It is a crime to sell or possess for the purposes of distribution any material that is obscene. It is also illegal to present an "immoral, indecent, or obscene" play, film, or other live performance. **Obscenity** refers to "any publication a dominant characteristic of which is the undue exploitation of sex." Because "undue exploitation" is rather vague, the courts have used the **community standards of tolerance test** to determine whether material is obscene. Community standards of tolerance do not refer to what Canadians would look at themselves; they refer to what Canadians would accept other Canadians being exposed to. Using the community standards of tolerance test means that standards can and do change over time as societal attitudes change. In 2005, the Supreme Court of Canada ruled that the test for indecency should not just be whether an activity violates community standards but whether it actually causes harm.

In the debate over pornography, some people make the distinction between pornography (which is unacceptable to them) and erotica (which is acceptable to them). According to this distinction, *pornography* depicts sexually explicit activities that are coupled with violence, are degrading or dehumanizing (usually to women), or include children (Russell, 1980). In contrast,

> **What types of pornography are illegal in Canada?**

Pornography: Sexually arousing art, literature, or films.
Obscenity: Something that is offensive according to accepted standards of decency; the legal term for pornography.
Community standards of tolerance test: The test used by courts to determine whether something is obscene based on what Canadians would accept other Canadians being exposed to and whether it causes harm.

erotica depicts explicit sex that is not violent and is neither degrading nor dehumanizing. According to this definition, a movie of a woman being sexually assaulted would be pornography, whereas a movie of two mutually consenting adults who are both enjoying having intercourse together would be considered erotica.

In keeping with this distinction, the Supreme Court of Canada in the *Butler* case ruled in 1992 that sexually explicit material depicting adults engaging in consensual sexual activity that does not depict violence, and that is not degrading or dehumanizing, is not obscene. This decision divided pornography into three categories: (1) explicit sex with violence, (2) explicit sex without violence but in which people are treated in a way that is degrading or dehumanizing, and (3) explicit sex that is neither degrading nor dehumanizing. The Court ruled that the first category, sex with violence, constitutes "undue exploitation of sex" and thus fits the definition of obscenity in the *Criminal Code*. The Court indicated that the third category (erotica) is generally accepted in Canadian society (unless it involves children) and thus is not obscene. However, explicit sex that is degrading or dehumanizing may or may not be obscene depending on the risk of harm involved and whether the material has artistic merit. Although the Supreme Court decision gave a good deal of guidance to the courts, there is still ambiguity in the law. For example, what exactly constitutes degrading or dehumanizing sex? What criteria should be used to determine whether material has artistic merit? Should material depicting sadomasochistic activity in which partners consensually participate in some types of pain rituals or degrading activities (see Chapter 15) be considered obscene?

Another complication is that Canada Customs officials have the power to refuse to allow books, magazines, DVDs, and other materials deemed to be obscene to enter Canada without having to lay criminal charges or have the materials reviewed by the courts. In 1994, the Little Sisters Bookstore and Art Emporium in Vancouver challenged the right of Customs officials to do so. They argued that Customs officials specifically target gay and lesbian bookstores and that they deem material that does not include violence or degradation to be obscene just because it depicts gay or lesbian sex. Ultimately, the Supreme Court of Canada upheld the Customs Act but criticized Customs inspectors for unfairly targeting the store.

 L08   ## Types of Pornography

Pornography is a multibillion-dollar business in North America. Included in this business are many different products and services: computer porn, including

Erotica: Sexually arousing material that is not violent, degrading, or demeaning and does not include children.

adult websites, chat rooms, news groups, and bulletin boards; DVDs, videos, and films; magazines; live entertainment; and child pornography. Some of this activity is legal (e.g., publishing *Playboy*), some of it is illegal (e.g., producing videos of children engaged in sex); and some is legal depending on the city you live in (e.g., strip clubs). It is impossible to obtain precise data on the economics of pornography in Canada. However, it is estimated that in 2006 retail sales of all types of pornography in the United States totalled about $13 billion (Mandese, 2007). The global market for Internet pornography alone is worth almost $5 billion.

Pornography Online

In the past 15 years, the Internet has made available a wide variety of sex-related services for every computer in Canada with a connection to a DSL, satellite, or modem, whether at work, school, or home. According to Trekkie Monster in the musical *Avenue Q*, "The Internet is for porn!" Is that really true? Well, in 2010, 4 percent of the most-trafficked websites in the world were sex related (Ruvalo, 2011). From July 2009 to July 2010, 13 percent of Web searches were for erotic content. The most common sex-related search term? Something related to youth (e.g., teen) (Ogas & Gaddam, 2011). Interestingly, the third most popular search was for women in their 40s and 50s (e.g., MILF). The day on which the most people look at pornography on the Internet? Monday. The busiest month? January. About 40 million Americans (13 percent of the population) regularly visit porn sites, and one out of three visitors is a woman. A technical analysis of the infrastructure needed to service such sites suggests that porn certainly drives Internet technology. The most visited site has 4.4 billion page views per month, three times the size of CNN. And each viewer spends an average of 15 to 20 minutes (Anthony, 2012). The storage needed for the thousands of videos, and the bandwidth needed to meet the download demand is huge. Downloads of porn videos at peak may absorb the equivalent of one-fifteenth of the bandwidth available between New York and London.

The services provided online include access to sexually arousing videos, photos and stories; an array of goods (sex toys, lingerie, even panties worn by porn stars) and services for sale; online chats with like-minded others; and access to bulletin boards with a variety of specialized materials.

Adult Websites

Adult websites display and sell a variety of sexual materials and services. According to websitetrafficspy .com, in 2012 the most visited sites were xvideos.com, xhamster.com, livejasmin.com, and pornhub.com. All are in the top 100 most-visited sites on the Internet. Sites like xvideo specialize in sexually explicit videos that can be viewed online or purchased, explicit photos, profiles of the women, and message forums for communicating about each woman. Livejasmin provides live sex online and the opportunity to chat with the actors. There are hundreds of other sites with names like Amateurs Gone Wild, Asian Pleasures, Lovely Cheerleaders, and Lydia Lashes. Each site typically includes thousands of photos organized by content, pornographic videos that can be viewed on your computer screen, stories, links to live sex shows, and links to live video cameras in such places as men's and women's locker rooms. Some also sell videos, CD-ROMs, sex toys, and costumes. Some also include interactive sex shows where the viewer can request that the actor perform specific acts. Many of these sites specialize, featuring "teenagers" (if the actors are under 18, the material violates the law), Black, Asian or Hispanic women, gay men, lesbians, pregnant women, and on and on (Figure 17.6). Each site charges a daily, weekly, or monthly membership fee for access; the fee can usually be paid by supplying a valid credit card number.

Viewing pornography on the Internet can be a positive alternative sexual outlet. Further, it allows people access to sexually explicit images in privacy, letting them explore their individual interests without experiencing shyness or shame (Nosko et al., 2007). However, Internet pornography may also be a cause for

concern, for several reasons. One is that the large and ever-increasing number of chat rooms, news groups, and websites lead to some people becoming dependent on or addicted to (see Chapter 15) this type of sexual content (Yellowlees & Marks, 2007). None of these involves face-to-face social interaction, which is central to most sexual relationships; the risk is that these encounters become a substitute. However, only a small percentage of people who use the Internet for sexual activities (1 percent in one study) develop a sexual addiction or compulsion (Griffiths, 2001).

There is also a great deal of concern that children will access these materials. All sites include a printed notice that one must be over 18 to access the site and that anyone who is offended by sexually explicit material should not enter the site. This honour system is not an effective control. It is true that to access a website or download photographs from bulletin boards the user must supply a valid credit card number, but this is not a major deterrent for many adolescents. A telephone survey of Internet users ages 10 to 17 in 2005 found that 42 percent had been exposed to online pornography in the preceding year. Sixty-six percent of these youth reported that the exposure was unwanted (Wolak et al., 2007). To date, there has been little guidance from Canadian courts on the issues involved in Internet pornography.

Figure 17.6 The newest innovation in the porn business is computer porn.

Finally, the Internet facilitates the distribution of child pornography, which is illegal in Canada. Existing Canadian laws governing child pornography apply to the Internet, and some law enforcement agencies seek out and arrest offenders. However, this material can be easily transferred across borders and may be legal in the country where it originated, making enforcement of the child pornography laws difficult (Canadian Centre for Justice Statistics, 1999).

Chat Rooms

Chat rooms, or Internet relay chat groups, provide a location where individuals can meet and carry on conversations electronically. These rooms are often oriented toward persons with particular sexual interests, often captured by their names. The conversations often involve graphic descriptions of sexual activities or fantasies. The telephone sex conversation reproduced later in the chapter could have taken place electronically, with the words displayed on a computer screen or through audio connections instead of spoken over a phone line. In this context, an interesting feature of these chats can be that the other person cannot see you. This allows you to present yourself in any way you desire, to rehearse or try out a broad range of identities (Turkle, 1995).

News Groups

People can also log on to sex-oriented news or discussion groups, read messages posted by others, and post messages themselves. The messages may include personal information, or they may be a story or a file containing pornographic pictures in digital format. Stories can be printed by the user; picture files can be downloaded and viewed through a plug-in. Often, the messages are simply advertisements for or links to sex-oriented websites that sell pornographic material.

Commercial Bulletin Boards

There are numerous commercial bulletin boards that contain sexually explicit photographs in digital form. Users may log on to these bulletin boards and download images for a fee. Each image is listed in an electronic catalogue with a short description. Table 17.1 displays the results of a large-scale analysis of images on bulletin boards. Hard-core images (sample description: "Girl with big tits gets fucked by guy") made up 38 percent of the downloaded images. Another 33 percent were images of paraphilias ("Girl with big tits gets fucked by horse"). Of particular concern is the popularity of pedophilic images, which accounted for 15.6 percent of the downloaded images. Possessing such images is illegal in Canada (see Table 2.1) and not readily available elsewhere. The researchers concluded: "The adult Bulletin Board System (BBS) market is driven largely by

Table 17.1 Total Surveyed Adult Usenet Files and Downloads by Classification

Classification	Total Files	Total Downloads
Hard core	133,180 (45.6%)	2,102,329 (37.9%)
Soft core	75,659 (25.9%)	760,009 (13.7%)
Paraphilia	63,232 (21.6%)	1,821,444 (32.8%)
Pedophilia	20,043 (6.9%)	864,333 (15.6%)

Source: Martin Rimm, "Marketing Pornography on the Information Superhighway," in Georgetown Law Journal, Vol 83, 1995, p. 1891. Georgetown Law Journal © 1995. Reprinted by permission of the publisher.

the demand for paraphilic and pedophilic imagery. The availability of, and the demand for, vaginal sex imagery is relatively small" (Rimm, 1995, p. 1890). Canadian and U.S. authorities continue to debate what, if anything, can be done to regulate the flow of these materials on computer networks.

DVDs, Videos, and Films

Sexually explicit movies were made as early as 1915. The technology remained primitive and distribution very limited until the 1960s. The *hard-core film* industry began to emerge in a big way around 1970. Two films were especially important in this breakthrough. *I Am Curious (Yellow)*, appearing in the late 1960s, showed sexual intercourse explicitly. In part because it was a foreign film with an intellectual tone, it became fashionable for people, including married couples, to see it. The other important early film was *Deep Throat*, appearing in 1972. With its humour and creative plot, it was respectable and popular among the middle class. After the success of *Deep Throat*, many more full-length, technically well-made hard-core films appeared. *Deep Throat* had made it clear that there were big profits to be made. It cost US$24,000 to make, yet by 1982 it had yielded US$25 million in profits.

Loops are short (10-minute) hard-core videos. They are set up in coin-operated computers in private booths, usually in adult bookstores. The patron can enter and view the film in private and perhaps masturbate while doing so. They cater to both the straight and gay communities.

In the early 1980s, X-rated videocassettes for home viewing began to replace porn theatres. For example, *Deep Throat* became available on cassette in 1977, and by 1982, 300,000 copies had been sold (Cohn, 1983). Cable and satellite television also entered the arena, with porn channels thriving in some areas (Figure 7.17). The latest advance is the DVD. This *privatization* of pornography was furthered by the development of the Internet, which vastly expanded the potential market.

Figure 17.7 Anne-Marie Losique recently launched Canada's first adult channels in English and French, Vanessa TV, which shows the softer and more erotic side of sex.

There are also increasing numbers of adult videos made for gay men and lesbians. Canadian gay men criticize pornography aimed at gay men for depicting hyper-masculine men, being nonegalitarian, and simulating a heterosexual model (Morrison, 2004). Research with lesbian women in Canada identified two types of lesbian pornography: "pseudo-lesbian" pornography, which is actually created to cater to meet the erotic interests and fantasies of male viewers, and lesbian pornography, which is created by and designed for lesbians. In lesbian-created pornography, performers do not necessarily have "ideal" bodies, there is a greater attempt to convey intimacy and emotion, and there is a focus on the body rather than on genitals and penetration (Morrison & Tallack, 2005). However, even in lesbian-created pornography women's bodies are still unrealistic in terms of weight and breast size. Further, too much focus on intimacy and emotion sometimes results in depictions that are not sexually arousing.

Many hard-core films and X-rated DVDs are made for a heterosexual audience. In the United States, adult videos earn US$4 billion per year and account for more than 700 million rentals annually (Rich, 2001). Based on an informal survey, an adult video distributor estimated that in 1998 more than 38,000 adult videos were rented each day in Ontario, resulting in annual revenue of more than $52 million. There are no national data available. These videos portray couples engaging in both fellatio and cunnilingus, and in vaginal and anal intercourse in various settings and positions. Less often,

films and videos show sexual activity involving three or more people, or two women (Davis & Bauserman, 1993). First Person offers a look at the making of X-rated videos from the perspective of the actors.

On university campuses, viewing pornography is gendered. A study in New Brunswick found that 89 percent of male students and 39 percent of female students had looked at sexually explicit pictures or videos online in the previous month (Shaughnessy, Byers, & Walsh, 2011). Other research suggests that the main reasons for viewing it are curiosity and to experience sexual arousal. Salmon (2012) suggested that women are not attracted to pornography because it emphasizes impersonal sex and sexual variety. Women, she argues, are aroused by an emphasis on relationships, and women are aroused by finding Mr. or Ms. Right. For heterosexual women, they can find both of these in romance novels. Romance novels account for 13 percent of paperback book sales in the United States and attract 29 million readers (compared with 40 million viewers of Internet porn).

A rapidly expanding part of the porn industry is the amateur video. The development of the home video camera has enabled anybody with a willing partner, friends, or neighbours to produce homemade porn. Such videos cost virtually nothing to make, and distributors are eager to purchase them. These films account for at least 20 percent of all adult videos made in the United States ("Sex Industry," 1998). Amateur videos are available free on numerous Internet sites. Perhaps as a result, sales and rentals of adult videos fell 30 percent

FIRST PERSON

Behind the Scene: Making X-Rated Videos

Dave Cummings bounces out of bed. He's working today, so he goes through his routine: he showers, shaves extremely close to get a smooth face, trims his fingernails and his pubic hair, applies lotion to his groin, and finishes with hand lotion. He dresses casually and drives to a large, expensive home in Beverly Hills rented for the shoot. When he arrives, he greets the other performers, mostly young women and men in their 20s and 30s. In this group, Dave is the odd man out. He is 59 years old, balding, and looks like your doctor, not the typical male performer in an X-rated video. It is that appearance that gets him work. Dave provides the realism in the video; he is believable as a doctor, lawyer, judge, or schoolteacher in roles where a hard-bodied, bronzed guy in his 20s is not credible (Kikuras, 2004).

Dave points to one of the most important qualifications for a male actor in the world of X-rated videos: the ability to perform sexually. Many videos budget for a three-day shoot. The script calls for six to nine episodes of sex, each requiring one or more erect penises; the majority are to end with visible ejaculation. In other words, these videos place a premium on male sexual performance, perhaps not surprising in a performance-oriented culture. It costs money and frustrates everyone involved if a male actor has a long refractory period (see Chapter 9). To make it in the industry, a man has to demonstrate that he is up to the demands. Dave is lucky; he has good genes and stamina. In his own words, he can "get it up, keep it up, not come before [I am] told to, and can climax on cue." In years past, a man without Dave's

talents would not last in this line of work. But a pharmaceutical breakthrough—Viagra—changed all that. Many male porn actors routinely use Viagra or similar medications, which enable them to get and keep an erection. As a result, there are hundreds of men competing for the available jobs.

One consequence of this competition is pressure to perform acts and take risks that the actor might prefer to avoid. Even in this era of widespread knowledge of HIV/AIDS, condom use is rare in the porn industry; some viewers don't like to see them, some directors and producers don't allow them, some actors and actresses don't like the resulting hassle or change in sensation. The risk became very real in May 2004, when it was announced that five performers had positive HIV tests. One of these performers was Lara Roxx, who was from Quebec. A Canadian documentary about her, *Inside Lara Roxx*, was recently released.

Another consequence of the competition is low pay. Men may be paid as little as $500 for a video. The industry is built primarily around women (even older women; Figure 17.8). It is the women who achieve a kind of stardom, whose names appear in the publicity and on the video boxes, and whose bodies are featured in the videos. Relatively new performers may be paid $350 to $1000 for a film featuring conventional sex. Engaging in unconventional or rough sex brings a higher fee. Needless to say, there are no royalties paid to the performers. The typical film is budgeted at $5000 to $35,000 (Huffstutter & Frammolino, 2001). A typical release sells 1000 to 2000 copies; only the rare hit brings in $1 million

from 2004 to 2006 (Baram, 2007). Sales fell an additional 50 percent from 2006 to 2010 (Johansmeyer, 2010).

In the 1990s, a number of companies began marketing videos designed to educate people about various aspects of human sexuality. With names like the "Better Sex" video series, these include explicit portrayals of a wide variety of consenting heterosexual activities. As such, these are erotica, not pornography. They often include commentary by a psychologist or sex therapist,

reassuring viewers that the activities portrayed are normal and providing factual information. These series are advertised in national magazines and some daily newspapers.

There is a continuum from the subtle to the explicit in portrayals of sex. The subtle end is found in *music videos*. The sexual content of many videos is unmistakable (Figure 17.9). A content analysis of lead performers in 34 music videos found significant gender differences

("How Big," 2001). Thus, there is constant pressure to keep costs to a minimum.

Just as there are a variety of pathways into commercial sex work, individuals enter the porn industry in different ways. Dave Cummings voluntarily entered the industry at age 54. Once he had demonstrated his prowess, he found himself in continuing demand. In fact, he is now producing his own line of videos. Cummings says he does it because he enjoys sex and for the opportunity to have sex with lots of attractive young women. A 21-year-old starlet, Sienna, drifted into performing in adult videos. She had worked in a fast-food outlet and bagel shop; she saw an ad in the newspaper for "nude modelling" and tried it. For the first year she did still photo shoots, $350 to $400 for a few hours. Then she moved to working for an Internet company, engaging in masturbation while clients watched her via the Net. After a few months she thought, "If I'm gonna do this, I might as well do porn and make more money." Sienna says she may leave the industry soon; "I've just been pounded so much in these movies that I'm starting to get tired" (Petkovich, 2004). Some performers report being coerced into performing for stills or movies through the use of alcohol, drugs, or physical force by others on camera.

The emphasis on sexual performance reflects the larger North American culture, and it is often chemically enhanced, as are many other performances in the contemporary world. The distribution and sale of the DVDs reflects the commercialization of sex, turning access to sexual images and sexual gratification into a commodity to be sold for cash or credit.

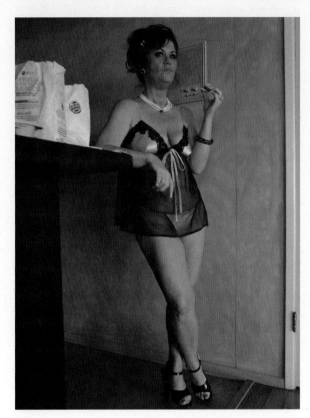

Figure 17.8 The greying pornography: as baby boomers get older, the demand for older performers is increasing. Here De'Bella, 50, waits for the director's call for her closeups; her male costars are usually in their 20s.

in how men and women are portrayed (Wallis, 2011). The authors divided the videos that appeared on MTV and MTV2 over a three week period into 30-second segments. They coded behaviours such as suggestive dancing, sultry looks, showing force, and sexual self-touch. The authors found that that portrayals reinforced male and female stereotypes. That is, women tended to be portrayed as subordinate whereas the men tended to be portrayed as aggressive. In addition, the women engaged in more sexually suggestive behaviour, such as sexual self-touch, suggestive dancing. Other research on music videos, including rap music videos, has found that men are portrayed as dominant over women, as wanted by women, and as having sex with attractive women (Conrad et al., 2009; Ward et al., 2005). Women are portrayed wearing revealing clothing and are valued almost exclusively for their physical appearance and sex appeal—that is, as sex objects.

Figure 17.9 The sexual content of many music videos and live performances is unmistakable. Clothing, body language, and physical contact between performers evoke sexual images.

Magazines

A declining share of the pornography market consists of magazines, ranging from *soft-core* (genital display, such as in *Playboy*) to *hard-core* (penetrative sex, threesomes, such as in *Hustler*). The number and sales of slick, colour magazines mushroomed in the 1970s and 1980s following the success of *Playboy*. Launched in 1953, *Playboy*'s circulation peaked in 1972 at 7.2 million. In the 1980s, *Penthouse* and *Hustler* provided stiff competition with more graphic and daring photo and editorial content, and there were dozens of less well-known competitors. Fierce legal and public-relations battles were fought in the 1980s and 1990s over the display and sale of these magazines, forerunners of today's battles over sexual content on the Internet. The development of the high-quality mass-produced videos available on VHS and later DVD caused the magazine market to go into a long decline, *Penthouse* declared bankruptcy in 2003; by 2010, *Playboy*'s circulation had declined to 1.6 million, and it no longer publishes every month.

Magazines catering to specialized tastes remain on the market. They include material designed for gay men, leather fetishists, swingers, people interested in interracial sex, and people interested in girl-on-girl sex.

Hard-core magazines have a no-holds-barred approach to content. Photographs may include vaginal fisting, anal intercourse and fisting, dual penetration, sadomasochism, bondage, and sex with animals. A study of the titles of magazines and books found in adult bookstores in the United States revealed that 17 percent were about a paraphilia or sexual variation (see Chapter 15) (Lebeque, 1991). Of those, 50 percent featured sadomasochism. An additional 21 percent dealt with incest.

The profit on magazines is high. Photos are often outtakes from commercial or amateur videos. Sets and lighting are minimal. The markups may be as high as 600 percent. The number of outlets selling these magazines appears to have declined in the past decade. Repeat, frequent customers account for a substantial percentage of the sales in such stores.

Live Entertainment

Shows providing live, sexualized entertainment are yet another part of the sex industry. Burlesque, which featured women seductively undressing on a stage in a theatre, has been transformed into strip clubs. These provide seminude (i.e., with pasties and a G-string) or nude dancing in a lounge setting; often dancers circulate among the patrons when not on stage. These clubs range in style from converted neighbourhood bars to upscale gentlemen's clubs. Participant observation research, supplemented by interviews, indicates that many of the customers are regulars; they come not for sexual release but for the opportunity to interact with attractive young women and the pleasure of a sexualized interaction without the need to perform sexually (Frank, 2005).

The Lion's Den, a club in a New England town, is typical of how strip clubs are run. There is a gendered division of labour. Men, in the roles of manager, bartenders, deejays, and bouncers, run the club and manage the women—the waitresses and strippers. The club employs as many as 51 strippers, mostly white, mostly with a high school education. The strippers work seven-hour shifts, dividing their time between stage performances lasting 15 to 30 minutes and circulating to solicit private or table dances. A number of the dancers are single mothers; working at night allows them to spend the days with their children (Price-Glynn, 2010).

In 1997, there were 2478 licensed exotic dancers in Toronto alone (Maticka-Tyndale et al., 1999). Dancers perform stage shows, table dances, and lap dances. Dancers earn only a small wage for dancing on stage and are typically expected to offer table dances or lap dances if requested. Lap dances can be performed either in public or in private areas of the club. In the private areas the stripper allows the patron to touch her body, excluding her genitals, as she dances. Most often she

Figure 17.10   Canadians are divided in their opinions about lap dancing. The Supreme Court of Canada banned lap dancing in public areas because it inflicts "attitudinal harm" to those watching but ruled that lap dancing in private cubicles, where people passing by can't see it, is not indecent.

will gyrate in his lap and rub herself against him. An Ontario study found that lap dancers made between $10 and $20 per dance, although customers pay more for dances in private rooms (Lewis & Maticka-Tyndale, 1998). Some strip clubs also offer VIP rooms in which a greater level of sexual activity takes place, although not all strippers provide these services. Typically, this involves fellatio and manual stimulation to ejaculation, as well as a lap dance. The price is typically between $100 and $150.

The question of whether lap dancing is legal or constitutes an "indecent performance," particularly when done in a private room, has not been fully settled by the courts (Figure 17.10). However, in general, the courts have ruled that the community's level of tolerance can be quite high when activities occur in private. This is complicated by the fact that lap dancing is safest for dancers if it is done in a public area of the club where they are less likely to be assaulted or forced to go beyond dancing (Lewis & Maticka-Tyndale, 1998; Maticka-Tyndale et al., 2000b). There is also more protection for the customer in these public areas from pressure to engage in activities beyond watching the dancer. Some cities, such as Toronto, have enacted

bylaws that prohibit physical contact, including touching, between patrons and persons providing services in adult entertainment parlours as a way of restricting table dancing and lap dancing.

The blog lettersfromstripclubs contain posts by men who visit the clubs. One poster, engaged to a "knockout," goes to the club to indulge his fetish for large, fake breasts; he frequents clubs where the women allow him to fondle them. A gay man goes with male friends to celebrate events in their lives and to people watch. A third man considers it therapy; where else can you talk completely openly to someone who won't judge you?

Male strippers catering to a female audience are less common but perform periodically in many communities. In the commercial sex districts of large cities there are also live sex shows featuring couples or groups engaging in sexual acts onstage. These shows are second cousins to the elaborately staged reviews in major casinos and hotels, which often feature nudity and simulated sexual activity in a lavish setting.

Telephone Sex

Telephone sex provides another example of enlisting technology to provide sexual excitement. It refers to sexually explicit conversations between one or more persons; often the participant(s) engage in masturbation. Note "one or more"; one type of commercial phone sex involves listening to prerecorded narratives. Another type involves live conversations with a paid phone sex operator. Of course, phone sex may be noncommercial, involving separated lovers; in this case, both may masturbate. And, of course, lovers can now add video, in what might be called Skype sex.

A study of a sample of prerecorded messages identified several patterns (Glascock & LaRose, 1993). The typical recording was of a female voice describing a series of sexual activities in which the caller was a participant. Callers were likely to hear fantasies involving masturbation, vaginal intercourse, and oral sex. Few descriptions included violence or forced sex.

There are a number of companies that provide phone sex services. They employ dispatchers who direct calls and may process payment information, and erotic performers who provide conversation. Performers may work in company office suites or from their home. The Sexy Smart Girls Agency (a pseudonym) employs 40 workers, some part time and some full time (Guidroz & Rich, 2010). It is mostly night work, since most calls come between 11 p.m. and 5 a.m. Callers may want to discuss straight sex, anal sex, adult baby/diaper lover, incest (with the operator playing mom or sis), BDSM, bestiality, and fetishism. Some companies/workers limit topics they will discuss; others advertise "no taboos." Sexy Smart Girls advertises in men's sex magazines. Operators who were interviewed were 21 to 45, but all presented in calls as 20 to 23. All were white, with at least a high school education. Most had worked in phone sex less than 18 months, suggesting a high turnover. They typically concealed their phone sex work from family, friends, and other employers. Most had unconventional sexual/intimate relationship arrangements; this is also true of some strippers. Live sex work in clubs and on the telephone undoubtedly creates stress in many intimate relationships.

In some cases, phone sex workers work for themselves rather than for a company. For example, a student who needed money for tuition and books set up a 1-900 line in her home after reading an advertisement for phone sex operators in a Winnipeg newspaper (Schroeder, 2000). Callers were charged by the minute.

Here is a phone sex call recounted to an interviewer:

I say, "When you give a guy a blow job, what's your favorite way to do it?" She says, "Well, I love being on my knees, cause being on my knees with him standing is so submissive." I said, "Do you like looking at his cock in his pants, does

Child pornography: Visual depictions of explicit sexual activities or genitalia involving children.

that really turn you on?" She says, "I love that." I say, "I would love to be standing in front of you." She says, "Oh, that would really turn me on." "Do you like having your breasts played with when you're giving a blow job?" "Yes, I like it very much. I also like to be fingered." "How many fingers do you like inside you?" "I love two fingers." "And why do you like blowing a guy so much?" "Because I'm getting him excited and I know I can't wait for him to fuck me." "Do you like to fuck for a long time?" "Yes, I get lost in it." So then I said, "Well, I've really been thinking about you on top of me, and while you're riding me, I'll be spanking you." She said, "Oh God, I love that." I was masturbating and I came. It was great. (Maurer, 1994, pp. 349–350)

Child Pornography

Child pornography refers to any visual depiction—photo, film, video, audio—of sexually explicit conduct involving a person under 18 years of age; it may include images of nude genitalia, or even clothed genitals if the images are sexual. It is viewed by many as the most reprehensible part of the porn industry because it produces such an obvious victim: the child model. Children, by virtue of their developmental level, cannot give truly informed consent to participation in such activities, and the potential for doing psychological and physical damage to them is great.

The *Criminal Code of Canada* prohibits people from possessing, making, or distributing child pornography. Child pornography is defined as any representation of a person who is or is depicted to be under the age of 18 engaging in explicit sexual activity or that depicts their genitals for sexual purposes; any written or audio material that advocates sexual activity with someone under 18; and any written material or audio recordings that describes, for sexual purposes, sex with someone under 18 (see Table 2.1). The sections of the statute use the term "pornography" rather than "obscenity" as with the adult provisions, and they specifically prohibit the making, sale, or possession of child pornography. The purpose of these laws is to protect children from harm by ensuring that they are not involved in the making of pornography and by preventing child sexual abuse by users of child pornography. Indeed, research in Ontario has shown that most men convicted of child pornography offences are pedophiles—that is, they show a preference for prepubescent children and thus are at risk to offend against children (Seto et al., 2006). A child is defined as anyone under the age of 18. These statutes also outlaw "pseudo-child pornography"—that is, pornography that uses adults but makes them look like children.

Child pornography offences differ from offences governing adult pornography in three primary ways.

Displaying or offering to sell pornography to persons under 16 is an offence, whether or not these materials would be viewed as obscene under the *Criminal Code*. In addition, the sentences for child pornography offences are greater than for obscenity offences. Finally, it is an offence to be in the possession of child pornography, whereas it is only illegal to sell or distribute obscene material involving adults.

In 2001, the Supreme Court upheld the law criminalizing the possession of child pornography with two narrow exceptions. It ruled that possessing private works of imagination that have artistic merit and photographic depictions of oneself are legal. Thus, it is legal to write or draw sexually explicit depictions of children for one's own personal pleasure. In response to this ruling, Parliament passed amendments to the child pornography legislation in 2002 that broadened the definition of child pornography, prohibited advertising child pornography, increased penalties, and ensured that people using the artistic merit defence will have to show that they have a legitimate purpose for possessing the child pornography.

A major study of people who produce child pornography found that all of the 69 offenders studied were male. They ranged in age from 20 to 70, with an average age of 43. Thirty-eight percent had an already established relationship with the child before the illicit activity began—they were family friends or relatives, neighbours, teachers, or counsellors (Burgess, 1984). Interpol, the International Criminal Police Organization, has an office in Ottawa and tracks Internet child pornography cases in Canada. In 2001, it identified 500 cases. Some producers are pedophiles and are motivated by their own sexual interest in children, but others are motivated by profit (Quayle, 2008).

Advertising

Let's close our discussion of the types of pornography by considering a mating of sex and money that all of us encounter every day—*sex in advertising*. Both subtle and obvious sexual promises are used to sell a wide variety of products. A muscular young man wearing low-slung jeans and no shirt sells Calvin Klein. Abercrombie & Fitch catalogues feature photos of nude young people in bed or in pools. Perfumes promise that they will make women instantly sexually attractive. One brand of coffee seems to guarantee a warm, romantic, sensuous evening for the couple who drink it.

How much sexual content is there in advertising? One study analyzed the sexual content of magazine advertising in 1983 and 2003 (Reichert & Carpenter, 2004). Sexual clothing and portrayals of intimate contact became more frequent. In 2003, for example, 78 percent of women in ads in men's magazines were

Figure 17.11   Sex in advertising. Many advertisers, including Calvin Klein, use sexual images to sell products. Do you consider this image lascivious? Some people do.

attired in sexually suggestive clothing. Sexually provocative behaviour is another aspect of sex found in magazine advertising; in ads portraying heterosexual couples, 53 percent engage in sexual contact (passionate kissing, simulated intercourse) (Reichert, 2002).

Television advertising uses not only bodily display or nudity and sexually suggestive interaction but also context (a Caribbean beach, a bed or bedroom), language including double entendre (a message with two meanings, one being sexual), and talk about sexual activity. Some advertisers, such as Victoria's Secret and Calvin Klein, cultivate a sexually suggestive image (Figure 17.11). A study of prime-time commercials broadcast on NBC found that 12 percent of the female models and 2 percent of the male models were dressed to be sexually suggestive. Network promotional ads were more likely to include sexual content. Sexual contact in ads increased from 12 percent in 1990 to 21 percent in 1998. A review of the research on the effects of advertising concludes that sexual information attracts attention, and viewers are more likely to remember the sexual image; paradoxically, however, they are less likely to remember the brand name (Reichert, 2002). Beyond the effects of ads on brand images and purchasing, there is concern that continuing exposure to ads that contain gender-stereotyped ideas and images, such as thin, attractive females and taut, buff males, may affect attitudes toward one's body. In one study, male and female university students were shown either 15 sexist and 5 neutral ads, 20 neutral ads, or no ads. The results indicated that exposure to the sexist ads was associated with dissatisfaction with one's own body among *both* men and women (Lavine et al., 1999).

The Customers

What is known about the consumer of pornography? As shown in Table 17.2, most people using pornography are men between the ages of 18 and 40. Studies consistently find that the typical customer in an X-rated bookstore is an educated, middle-class male between the ages of 22 and 34 (Mahoney, 1983). That is, the use of the materials sold in such stores is "typical" or "normal" (in the statistical sense) among males. But the range is wide. The manager of one store said,

> We get everyone in here from millionaires to scum of the earth. The blue-collar and white-collar men come for the tapes. Married couples come in for things to help their sex life. The gay crowd cruises the booths in back. Groups of women come in for gag items. (Moore, 1994)

Table 17.2 Do You Use Porn? A Survey by the Kinsey Institute ($N = 10,453$)	
Sex	
Male	80%
Female	17
Viewed sexual images in the past month?	
Never have viewed them	3%
Not once, but I have in the past	20
One or two times	16
Once a week	10
A few times a week	27
Once a day	9
Several times a day	10
How much time per week in the past month?	
I did not use porn in the past month	11%
Less than one hour	18
1 to 5 hours	37
6 to 15 hours	16
16 to 25 hours	6
26 to 50 hours	3
More than 50 hours	3
Why do you use porn? (Top five answers)	
To masturbate/for physical release	72%
To sexually arouse myself and/or others	69
Out of curiosity	54
To fantasize about things I would not necessarily want in real life	43
To distract myself	38

Source: Frontline, courtesy of WGBH-TV Boston.
Copyright © 1995–2010 WGBH Educational Foundation.

Women do purchase and watch pornographic videos. Research conducted in Australia in 1999 reported that a woman or a heterosexual couple purchased 65 percent of X-rated videos. In data from 280 women in the Australian study, 20 percent said they selected the video, 50 percent said both selected it, 18 percent said the partner selected it with both their preferences in mind, and 9 percent said the partner selected it (C. Contessini, personal communication, 2003). Female interest in erotica was recognized 30 years ago by Candida Royalle, then a film star; she became a producer and director and has made more than a dozen films for women. A growing number of men and women are attempting to market to women, producing what is called "female-empowered" adult entertainment, including films, cable TV programs, sex-toy stores, and websites (Figure 17.12).

In female strip clubs, most women who enter are with male customers, but increasingly a single woman or groups of two or more women are in the audience. Participant observation research found that even if women actively demonstrated interest, such as by tipping dancers on the stage, dancers often *pass over* (avoid) them as the dancers circulated on the floor (Wosick-Correa & Joseph, 2008). Some dancers acknowledged them as women, by complaining to them about costumes or male customers. Some more experienced dancers treated them as customers and gave them lap dances; these dances are *tailored* to a woman's body (e.g., involved breast play) and individualized.

Repeat customers are a crucial part of the success of the porn business: "There are people who come in here three to five times a day for their fix. Before work. At lunch. After work. Late at night. Their addiction isn't to the perversion of it, just the pornography" (Moore, 1994). Adult retail stores are potentially important as sources of sexual health information and products (Reece et al., 2004). A survey of employees of 80 stores in the United States found that most sold condoms and lubricants, and up to half provided written health information. Partnerships with sexual health professionals and training for employees could enhance this potential.

Internet pornography attracts a more varied clientele. Chat rooms and news groups attract both men and women of diverse ages (assuming that those who describe themselves are doing so accurately). Some of these people are married. Depending on the focus of the room or group, participants may be from different racial or ethnic backgrounds. For the most part, bulletin boards and adult websites probably attract the same types of clients as adult bookstores—young, middle-class, white men. However, Nielson/NetRatings found that one-quarter of visitors to adult websites are women. Table 17.2 presents results from an online survey that

Figure 17.12 While there are differences between men and women in their response to pornography, some women enjoy watching a stripper as much as some men do.

assessed the number of times and hours per month that users view sexually explicit materials. Participants ranged in age from 18 to over 70.

Feminist Objections to Pornography

Some—though not all—feminists are very critical of pornography (e.g., Griffin, 1981; Jensen, 2007; Lederer, 1980). Why would feminists, who prize sexual liberation, be opposed to pornography?

There are four basic reasons why some feminists object to pornography. First, they argue that pornography debases women. In the milder, soft-core versions it portrays women as sex objects whose breasts, legs, and buttocks can be purchased and then ogled. In the hard-core versions women may be shown being urinated on or being chained. To what extent does mainstream pornography objectify women? The answer depends in part on how one defines the term. That is, objectification can include using a person as an object for someone else's

purposes, as if they are owned by someone else, as if their feelings and experiences do not matter, or primarily in terms of how they look. McKee (2005) performed a content analysis of the 50 bestselling pornographic videos in Australia to examine objectification. Objectification was defined as treating another person as an object, one partner dominating another, and penis worship. Many of the videos were imports from the United States and Europe. Seven measures allowed direct comparison of portrayals of men and portrayals of women. On one measure, *not having an orgasm*, women were significantly higher than men were, that is, men were portrayed as having an orgasm while the women were not. On three measures, *less time spent looking at the camera*, *less time spent talking to the camera*, and *less likely to initiate sex*, men were significantly higher than women were. On three measures, *having a name*, *being a central character*, and *time spent talking*, there were no significant differences. These results suggest that women were more likely to be objectified in pornography than men were.

Second, feminists argue that pornography associates sex with violence toward women. As such, some feminists believe it contributes to sexual assault and other forms of violence against women and girls. Robin Morgan has put it bluntly: "pornography is the theory and rape is the practice" (1980, p. 139). This is a point that can be tested with scientific data, producing evidence that will be covered shortly.

Third, pornography shows, indeed glamorizes, unequal power relationships between women and men. A common theme in pornography is men forcing women to have sex, so the power of men and subordination of women are emphasized. Consistent with this point, many feminists do not object to sexual materials that portray women and men in equal, humanized relationships—what we have termed *erotica*.

Finally, feminists object to the structure of the pornography industry. Anti-pornography feminists believe that many models and actors in the pornography industry are physically, sexually, and emotionally abused in doing their work.

Feminists also note the intimate relationship between pornography and traditional gender roles. Pornography is enmeshed as both cause and effect. That is, pornography in part results from traditional gender roles that make it socially acceptable for men to use and require hyper-sexuality and aggressiveness as part of the male role. In turn, pornography may serve to perpetuate traditional gender roles. By seeing or reading about dominant men and submissive, dehumanized women, each new generation of adolescent boys is socialized to accept these roles. On the other hand, the female-oriented videos discussed earlier attempt to equalize

Figure 17.13   Not all producers of pornography are men. Women are increasingly involved in the production of sexually explicit video and Internet materials.

the power relationships between the male and female characters and are often filmed from the woman's point of view (Figure 17.13).

LO9   The Effects of Pornography

Some of the assertions just summarized[2]—for example, that using violent pornography may predispose men toward committing violent crimes against women—can be tested by using the methods of social science. A number of social psychologists have been collecting data for 35 years to test such assertions.

Four questions can be asked about the effects of using pornography. First, does it produce sexual arousal? Second, does it affect users' attitudes, particularly about sexual and nonsexual violence toward women? Third, does it affect the sexual behaviour of users? Fourth, does it affect the aggressive or criminal behaviour of users, particularly aggressive behaviour toward women?

Many studies have examined the effect of sexually explicit material on sexual arousal. This research consistently finds that exposure to *material that the viewer finds acceptable* does produce arousal (Davis & Bauserman, 1993). Exposure to portrayals that the

> **What are the effects of viewing erotica and pornography on sexual behavior?**

viewer finds objectionable produces a negative reaction. Most people disapprove of paraphilic behaviours (see Chapter 15), sexual assault, and sexual activity involving children, so they react negatively to hard-core and child pornography.

There are gender differences in self-reports of response to sexually explicit materials. Men report higher levels of arousal to such portrayals than do women (Kingston et al., 2009; Malamuth, 1998). The differences are larger in response to pornography than to erotica, and the difference is much larger among university students than among older persons (Murnen & Stockton, 1997). This difference between men and women is often attributed to the fact that most erotica and pornography is male oriented. The focus is almost exclusively on sexual behaviour, with little character development or concern for relationships. There is limited foreplay and afterplay; the male typically ejaculates on some part of the woman's body (the *cum shot*) rather than inside her. Former porn film star Candida Royalle produces videos made for women. An experiment found that male university students responded positively to and were aroused by videos made for men and for women; females reported negative responses to the videos intended for men and positive responses and sexual arousal to the videos designed for women (Mosher & MacIan, 1994).

How does pornography affect attitudes? The research indicates that a single exposure to stories, photographs, or videos has little or no effect. Massive exposure (such

---

[2] Note that this discussion refers primarily to violent pornography. There are many other sexually explicit images that are not of concern.

as viewing videos for five hours) does lead to more permissive attitudes. In this situation, viewers become more tolerant of the behaviour observed and less in favour of restrictions on it (Davis & Bauserman, 1993). What about attitudes toward aggression against women? Some studies show that exposure to portrayals of forced intercourse lead men to be more tolerant of sexual assault, but other studies do not find a relationship between exposure and attitudes (Fisher & Grenier, 1994). Men exposed to portrayals of sexual aggression against women do not report a greater willingness to sexually assault a woman (Davis & Bauserman, 1993). On the other hand, individuals classified as high risk to commit sexual aggression are particularly influenced by exposure, showing negative attitudes toward women (Kingston et al., 2009).

There is particular concern about the effects of exposure to child pornography. It would be illegal (and therefore unethical) to show research participants sexual images of persons under 18. So researchers exposed college students to "barely legal" images, of persons who are over 18 but look (much) younger (Paul & Linz, 2008). Images were either in web page format, or in the same format on the page but with Web banners, ads, and so on, removed. The researchers wondered whether exposure would create an association or schema relating sex and eroticism to youth. To test for such an association they used the *priming paradigm*, where target words are tested for speed of recognition, images are viewed, and then speed of recognition is measured again. Men and women exposed to "barely legal" images exhibited faster recognition of the words "erotic" and "beautiful" than men and women exposed to similar images of models over 21 years of age, suggesting that exposure to the images did create an association.

With regard to sexual behaviour, the research shows that, in response to erotic portrayals of consenting heterosexual activity, both men and women may report an increase in sexual thoughts and fantasies and in behaviours such as masturbation and intercourse. A survey of early adolescents in the United States questioned them about exposure to sexually explicit content in adult magazines, X-rated movies, and the Internet (Brown & L'Engle, 2009). Two-thirds of the boys and 39 percent of the girls had seen at least one sexually explicit medium in the past year. Being black, older, having a lower socioeconomic status, and having less-educated parents were related to greater exposure for both boys and girls. Follow-up data were collected two years later. For both boys and girls, early exposure predicted less progressive gender-role attitudes, having oral sex, and having intercourse; among boys, it also predicted more permissive attitudes about sex. Exposure to portrayals of behaviour the person has not personally engaged in did *not* lead to an increase in these behaviours (Davis & Bauserman, 1993).

Finally, there has been great interest in whether exposure to portrayals of sexual aggression (which almost always involve men behaving aggressively toward women) increase aggressive behaviour. A number of laboratory studies have shown that men who are insulted or provoked by a woman and have been exposed to violent pornography are significantly more aggressive toward the woman in the experimental situation compared with men exposed to sexually explicit but nonviolent material. If the comparison group is men exposed to nonsexual violent films, many studies find no difference between the two, but some find that exposure to sexual violence increases aggression toward a woman more than exposure just to violence (Davis & Bauserman, 1993). Laboratory exposure has greater negative impact on men who report high levels of use compared with men with low levels of use (Kingston et al., 2009). Research in Ontario suggests that men with lower IQs may be more influenced by violent pornography than men with higher IQs (Bogaert et al., 1999). However, few men (5 to 6 percent in one Ontario study) choose to watch violent pornography when given the opportunity (Bogaert, 1993, 2001).

Ontario psychologists William Fisher and Guy Grenier have questioned the extent to which these laboratory studies capture the relationship between pornography and aggression in the real world (Fisher & Grenier, 1994). They point out that, in these laboratory studies, the men are told by the experimenter to send some level of shock to the female confederate. Although they can choose the level of shock to administer, they are not given the opportunity to engage in a nonaggressive response. However, in a real-life situation, a man could choose to speak to a woman who angered him or to walk away from the situation, instead of engaging in an aggressive response. The researchers found that when given the choice, 86 percent of the men chose not to make an aggressive response. Thus, it is not clear that exposure to pornography causes sexual aggressive behaviour in men who are not already predisposed to sexual violence (Seto et al., 2001).

The research reviewed above examined effects of exposure on individuals. An alternative approach is to assess the effects of making sexually explicit materials more widely available, for example by legalizing their sale and distribution in a city, province or territory, or country. Diamond (2009) has been studying this issue for some time, examining the effects of increased availability on sex-crime rates. If exposure to such materials causes sexual aggression, we would expect an increase in rates of sexual assault and other sexual offences, and perhaps in prostitution, in the jurisdiction after such materials become available. In fact, every methodologically sound investigation finds that "as pornography has increased in availability, sex crimes have either decreased or not increased" (p. 304).

In sum, then, we can conclude that exposure to sexually explicit material that the viewer finds acceptable is arousing to both men and women. Exposure to aggressive pornography does increase men's aggression toward women under certain laboratory conditions. The extent to which these results are generalizable to a real-life situation is not known, however. Exposure to aggressive pornography may also affect men's attitudes, making them more accepting of violence against women, particularly men at high risk. Researchers in Ontario have concluded that men who are already predisposed to sexual aggression are the most likely to be affected by pornography; men who are not predisposed toward violence are unlikely to be affected (Seto et al., 2001).

What about the effects of pornography on women? Researchers in Ontario found that exposure to violent and dehumanizing pornography, but not to erotica, has a negative emotional impact on women (Senn & Radtke, 1990). Of particular interest is that women who reported having had more forceful sexual experiences in the past were particularly negative in their evaluations of pornography but not of erotica. It may be that, for these women, violent sexual images bring back painful memories.

LO8 What Is the Solution?

Some of the conclusions about pornography (not about erotica), particularly violent pornography, are disturbing. What is the solution? Should pornography be censored or made illegal? Or would this only make it forbidden and therefore more attractive and still available on the black market? Or should all forms of pornography be legal and readily available, and should we rely on other methods—such as education of parents and students through the school system—to abolish its use? Or should we adopt some in-between strategy, making some forms of pornography—such as child pornography and violent porn—illegal, while allowing free access to erotica? Note that the 1992 Supreme Court decision in the *Butler* case and child pornography legislation adopted this last approach.

Our own opinion is that legal restrictions of sexually explicit material depicting adults—known less politely as censorship—are probably not the solution. We agree with the view of Donnerstein and his colleagues that a better solution is education (Donnerstein et al., 1987; Linz et al., 1987). In their experiments, they debrief male participants at the conclusion of the procedures. They convey to the participants that media depictions are unreal and that the portrayal of women enjoying forced sex is fictitious. They dispel common myths about sexual assault, especially any that were shown in the film used in the experiment. Participants who have been debriefed in this way show less acceptance of myths about sexual aggression and more sensitivity to victims of sexual assault than participants shown a neutral film (Donnerstein et al., 1987). More recently, researchers in Ontario examined the effects of a similar intervention on men's responses to Internet pornography (Isaacs & Fisher, 2008). This intervention reduced the men's attraction to and enjoyment of violent pornography compared with men who did not get the intervention. The experimental group was also more able to recognize and reject violent pornography.

Subsequently, some researchers introduced *pre*briefing of participants in research involving exposure to sexually explicit materials. The typical briefing (pre or post) consists of a short audiotape or a printed handout pointing out that the material is fictional. It reminds participants that women do not enjoy forced sex and that sexual assault is a serious crime. Researchers identified 10 studies that included prebriefing or post debriefing and measured the effects of exposure to the material. All 10 found that there were no negative effects of exposure accompanied by an educational briefing; in six of the studies, participants were less accepting of rape myths at the conclusion of the study than at the beginning (Allen et al., 1996). This research provides solid evidence that education can eliminate at least negative effects on attitudes. This suggests that sex education needs to highlight the reality of sexual assault for the victim and challenge myths that are prevalent in pornography, particularly violent pornography.

SUMMARY

Commercial sex is a major industry in Canada and increasingly around the world. Two prominent aspects of it are sex work and pornography. Although sex work is not illegal in Canada, various activities related to it are. It is also a crime to see or distribute any material that is obscene. Obscenity is determined by using the community standards of tolerance test. Possession of child pornography is also illegal.

Commercial sex workers engage in partnered sexual activity in return for payment, such as money, gifts, or drugs. There are several venues in which they work in Canada, including their own homes, in-call services, out-call services, and massage parlours. The working conditions, risks, and income of a sex worker depend on the setting. Third parties who may be involved include a pimp, madam, or manager; the involvement of these people generally limits a worker's autonomy. Sex trafficking involves exploitation and is a major problem. Research suggests that a female sex worker's well-being depends on the risk level of the setting in which she works, the reasons she entered sex work, and whether she experienced victimization as a child or an adolescent.

Data indicate that the use of sex workers has declined substantially in North America in the past 50 years. About one-half of the clients of female sex workers are occasional johns; the other 50 percent are repeat clients. Some men rely on sex workers for their sexual outlet.

Some male sex workers serve a female clientele. They may work as escorts, employees of massage parlours, or gigolos. More common are hustlers who cater to a male clientele.

Distinctions are made among pornography (sexually arousing art, literature, or film), obscenity (material offensive to Canadians), and erotica (sexual material that shows men and women in equal, humane relationships). Pornography on the Internet has mushroomed in the past 20 years; people can discuss explicit sexual activity online, read sexually arousing stories, download sexually explicit images, or purchase a variety of goods and services at adult websites. Pornographic magazines, films, and DVDs, both soft-core (erotica) and hard-core, are a multibillion-dollar business. Children are the victims in child pornography.

Some feminists object to pornography on the grounds that it debases women, encourages violence against women, and portrays unequal relationships between men and women.

Social psychological research indicates that exposure to portrayals that the viewer finds acceptable is arousing to both men and women. Men are more likely to report arousal than women. Massive exposure leads to more favourable attitudes toward the behaviour observed. Some studies find that exposure to violent pornography creates more tolerant attitudes toward violence against women, but others find no such effect. Exposure of heterosexuals to portrayals of consenting heterosexual activity leads to an increase in sexual thoughts and behaviour. Exposure to portrayals of sexual or nonsexual violence toward women increases men's aggression against women in the laboratory, although the extent to which these results generalize to real-life situations is not known. Education about the effects of pornography is probably the best solution to the problems created by violent and dehumanizing pornography.

QUESTIONS FOR THOUGHT, DISCUSSION, AND DEBATE

1. What is your position on the issue of censoring pornography? Do you think that all pornography should be illegal? Or should all pornography be legal? Or should some kinds—such as child pornography and violent pornography—be illegal, but not other kinds? What reasoning led you to your position?

2. In Canada, sex work is not illegal, but many of the activities associated with sex work, such as communicating for the purposes of sex work, are illegal. Some people argue that we should have stricter laws and tougher sentences to deter the exchange of sex for money. Other people argue that sex work should be decriminalized, as it is a private matter between consenting adults. Based on what you know about sex workers and their clients, what approach would you suggest? Should the act of sex work be a criminal offence? If sex work-related activities were legal, in what ways should the sex trade be regulated, if at all?

3. Many of the streetwalkers in major cities are black or Asian women. Adult websites often prominently display photographs, stories, and videos about "interracial sex." Yet most of the customers of both sex workers and adult websites are white males. What attracts white men to materials featuring women from other ethnic groups?

Are **YOU** Curious?

1. What counts as premature (early) ejaculation?
2. What can a woman do if she has trouble having orgasms?
3. How does Viagra work?

Read this chapter to find out.

CHAPTER

18

Sexual Disorders and Sex Therapy

LEARNING OBJECTIVES

After studying this chapter, you will be able to

LO1 Describe each of the sexual disorders listed in the *DSM-5*.

LO2 Discuss the physical (organic), drug, and psychological factors that may cause or maintain sexual disorders.

LO3 Compare and contrast the different approaches to sex therapy.

LO4 Describe the specific therapeutic and biomedical treatments for specific sexual disorders.

LO5 Discuss the primary criticisms of sex therapy techniques.

LO6 Contrast the traditional diagnoses of female sexual disorders with the New View of women's sexual problems.

LO7 Describe ways to prevent sexual dysfunctions, and list strategies for choosing a sex therapist.

Telling it in plain words makes me see how I feared the wrong thing.[*]

* Margaret Avison. (1982). The Agnes Cleves Papers, *In Winter Sun/The Dumbfounding: Poems 1940–66*, Toronto: McClelland & Stewart.

Many people experience occasional sexual problems and concerns that go away without treatment. When a problem with sexual response causes significant psychological distress or interpersonal difficulty, it is called a *sexual disorder*. The term *sexual dysfunction* is also used. Examples are a man's difficulty getting an erection and a woman's difficulty having an orgasm.

This definition seems fairly simple. As we will see, however, in practice it can be difficult to determine exactly when something is a sexual disorder. Indeed, whether we define something as a sexual disorder is affected by the social and cultural context in which we live. In addition, there is a tendency to think in terms of only two categories, people with a sexual disorder and "normal" people. In fact, there is a continuum. Most of us have had, at one time or another, a sexual problem that went away in a day or a few months without treatment. In one New Brunswick study, 59 percent of the men and 68 percent of the women reported experiencing a sexual problem in the previous 18 months, but none had sought treatment (MacNeil & Byers, 1997). Another New Brunswick study showed that sexual problems can start at a young age—on average almost all university students had experienced one or more sexual problems (six different problems on average), although most problems were not chronic (O'Sullivan & Majerovich, 2008). Students from the Chinese and other Asian ethnocultural community groups are more likely than Euro-Canadian students to experience sexual problems (Woo & Brotto, 2008). These cases represent the shades of grey that lie between absolutely great sexual functioning and long-term difficulties that require sex therapy.

Long-term sexual difficulties can cause a great deal of psychological distress to individuals and their partners, and many of these people seek out treatment. Until the 1960s, the only available treatment was long-term psychoanalysis, which was costly and not particularly effective. A new era in understanding and treatment was ushered in with the publication, in 1970, of *Human Sexual Inadequacy* by Masters and Johnson. This book reported on the team's research on sexual disorders, as well as on their rapid-treatment program of behavioural therapy. Since then, many additional developments have taken place in the field, including cognitive-behavioural therapy and medical (drug) treatments.

Sexual disorders and treatments for them are the topics of this chapter. First we will consider the kinds of sexual disorders. Following that, we will review the causes of these disorders and then the treatments for them.

Sexual Disorders

In this section we will consider seven categories of **sexual disorders** listed in the *DSM-5* (American Psychiatric Association [APA], 2013b): delayed ejaculation, erectile disorder, female orgasmic disorder, female sexual interest/arousal disorder, genito-pelvic pain/penetration disorder, male hypoactive sexual desire disorder, and premature (early) ejaculation. Notice that some of the disorders refer to men and some of them refer to women. Of course, sexual disorders do not always fall so neatly into these distinct categories. For example, a person who has difficulty with orgasm or who experiences sexual pain is likely to develop low desire as a result. In this case, a person can have more than one disorder. Although each disorder corresponds to different aspects of the sexual response cycle (see Chapter 9), in all disorders the person is not able to respond sexually or to feel sexual pleasure because of the disorder and experiences distress because of it. The *DSM-5* also includes substance/medication-induced sexual dysfunction and a category for other sexual disorders. Of note, a number of Canadian researchers were instrumental in spearheading needed changes to the *DSM* diagnostic categories for sexual dysfunctions in the recent update to the *DSM-5*—indeed, Dr. Ken Zucker from the Centre for Addiction and Mental Health was the chair of the committee reviewing needed changes.

Each disorder can be seen to vary along two dimensions. It can be a **lifelong sexual disorder** or it can be an **acquired sexual disorder**. A lifelong sexual disorder occurs when the individual has always had that disorder (e.g., the person has never had an orgasm). An acquired sexual disorder occurs when the individual currently has the problem but did not have the problem in the past (e.g., has had orgasms in the past but is currently unable to orgasm).

Sexual disorders: Problems with sexual response that cause a person mental distress.
Lifelong sexual disorder: A sexual disorder that has been present since the person began sexual functioning.
Acquired sexual disorder: A sexual disorder that develops after a period of normal functioning.

Sexual disorders can also be either *generalized*, that is, occurring in all situations, or *situational*. A **situational sexual disorder** is a disorder that occurs in some situations but not in others. Many sexual disorders are not absolute. They may occur with one partner (e.g., the spouse) but not another (e.g., the lover) or in one situation (e.g., at home) but not another (e.g., on vacation). Sexual disorders can occur with a partner of the same or other gender. The clinician needs to assess a number of factors that may be affecting the problem before deciding whether the individual has a sexual disorder—such as whether the person is receiving effective stimulation and what the relationship between the partners is like. These are discussed in more detail below.

Disorders in Men

Desire disorders include hypoactive sexual desire and sexual aversion disorders. The disorders that can be diagnosed for men include male hypoactive sexual desire disorder, erectile disorder, premature (early) ejaculation, and delayed ejaculation.

Male Hypoactive Sexual Desire Disorder

Sexual desire, or *libido*, refers to an interest in sexual activity, leading the individual to seek out sexual activity or to be pleasurably receptive to it. The term **hypoactive sexual desire disorder** (HSDD; the prefix *hypo* means "low") is used when an individual does not have spontaneous thoughts or fantasies about sexual activity and is not interested in sexual activity (Basson, 2004; Brotto et al., 2010). It is also sometimes termed *inhibited sexual desire* or *low sexual desire*. This disorder is diagnosed in men because in women desire and arousal are often linked and thus are part of the same disorder. The defining characteristics are persistent or recurrent low or lack of sexual thoughts or fantasies and low or absent interest in sex that is distressing to the individual. For many people, desire occurs before sexual activity begins and leads them to initiate sex; other people begin to feel desire after their partner initiates or after sexual activity starts. This latter pattern is called *responsive desire*. It is not uncommon for men to report problems with sexual desire: about 6 percent of young men and 41 percent of men over the age of 65 report this problem (APA, 2013b). However, less than 2 percent of men meet the criteria for a diagnosis of male hypoactive sexual desire disorder.

Like other sexual disorders, HSDD poses complex problems of definition. There are many

Situational sexual disorder: A sexual disorder that a person has in some situations but not in others.

Hypoactive sexual desire (HSDD): A sexual disorder in which there is a lack of interest in sexual activity; also termed inhibited sexual desire or low sexual desire.

Discrepancy of sexual desire: A sexual problem in which the partners have considerably different levels of sexual desire.

Erectile (eh-REK-tile) disorder: The inability to have or maintain an erection.

Premature (early) ejaculation: A sexual disorder in which the man ejaculates too soon and feels he cannot control when he ejaculates.

circumstances when it is perfectly normal for a person not to experience sexual desire. For example, one cannot be expected to be turned on by every potential partner. Men who experience anxiety about erection or ejaculation may lose interest in sex. (See Chapter 14 for a discussion of the difference between asexuality and hypoactive sexual desire disorder.)

It is also often true that the problem is not the individual's absolute level of sexual desire but a discrepancy between the partners' levels (Willoughby & Vitas, 2012). That is, if one partner wants sex considerably less frequently than the other partner does, there is a conflict, even if neither partner is experiencing a sexual disorder. This problem is termed a **discrepancy of sexual desire** and is a couple problem, not a sexual disorder.

Erectile Disorder

Erectile disorder (ED) is the inability to have an erection or maintain one on almost all or all occasions. Other terms for it are *erectile dysfunction* and *inhibited sexual excitement*. Although erectile disorder used to be called *impotence* (a term many laypeople still use), many professionals prefer not to use this term because of the negative connotations associated with it. One result of erectile disorder is that the man cannot engage in sexual intercourse. Using terminology discussed earlier, cases of erectile disorder can be classified as either *lifelong erectile disorder* (which is quite rare) or *acquired erectile disorder*, depending on whether the man has ever been able to have and maintain an erection that is satisfactory for penetration in the past. It can also be *generalized* or *situational* (i.e., it happens only with certain types of stimulation or types of partners).

According to surveys in North America and Europe, erectile disorder occurs in fewer than 10 percent of men under 40 but then increases to about 30 percent for men in their 60s (Lewis et al., 2010). Erectile disorder is the most common of the disorders among men who seek sex therapy, particularly since the introduction of Viagra.

Psychological reactions to erectile disorder may be severe. For many men, it is one of the most embarrassing things they can imagine. Depression may follow from repeated episodes. The man may avoid sexual encounters. It may also cause embarrassment or worry to the man's partner.

Premature (Early) Ejaculation

Premature (early) ejaculation occurs when a man persistently has an orgasm and ejaculates sooner than desired during sexual activity with a partner and is significantly distressed about the problem (APA, 2013b). For individuals who engage in penile–vaginal intercourse, ejaculation must occur within one minute following penetration; although premature (early) ejaculation also applies to men with a same-sex partner, specific time criteria have not been specified for other sexual activities. This definition is similar to the definition adopted by the International Society for Sexual Medicine to create consistency in both research and diagnosis (Althof et al., 2010). Both definitions involve three parts: (1) ejaculation that always or almost always occurs before or within one minute of vaginal penetration (note the heteronormativity of both of the definitions); (2) the inability to delay ejaculation; and (3) distress about the problem. This definition therefore includes a time component, a lack of control component, and a distress component. Premature (early) ejaculation can be lifelong or acquired and situational or generalized.

In extreme cases, ejaculation may take place so soon after erection that it happens before penetration can occur. In other cases, the man is able to delay the orgasm to some extent, but not as long as he would like or not long enough to meet his partner's preferences. This definition is an improvement over previous definitions because it specifies what is meant by "premature" or "early"—at least for penile–vaginal intercourse. In the past, the definitions used by clinicians and researchers in the field varied widely (Bettocchi et al., 2008; Grenier & Byers, 1995, 2001).

Psychiatrist and sex therapist Helen Singer Kaplan (1974; Grenier & Byers, 2001; McCarthy, 1989) believed that the key to defining rapid ejaculation is the absence of voluntary control of orgasm; that is, the real problem is that the man with premature (early) ejaculation has little or no control over when he orgasms. Another good definition is self-definition, even if the man does not meet the criteria for a formal diagnosis: if a man finds that he has become greatly concerned about his lack of ejaculatory control or that it is interfering with his ability to form intimate relationships, or if a couple agree that it is a problem in their relationship, it is entirely legitimate to seek professional assistance for these concerns.

Estimates are that between 1 and 3 percent of men would be diagnosed with premature (early) ejaculation (APA, 2013b). However, many more men report poor ejaculatory control. Our research has shown that 24 percent of Canadian men report having a current problem with climaxing "too early" (Grenier & Byers, 2001). Although the average time to ejaculation after penetration reported by the men in this study was about eight minutes, 7 percent reported ejaculating within one minute (which would fit within the *DSM-5* guidelines), and 17 percent reported ejaculating within two minutes. Not all of the men who reported that they had a problem with early ejaculation actually ejaculated quickly; some had unrealistic expectations about how long intercourse should last. It might be some relief for them to know that their female partners were less likely to see the timing of their ejaculation as a problem—only

10 percent of the partners felt the man had a problem related to early ejaculation compared with 24 percent of the men (Byers & Grenier, 2003). Further, early ejaculation was associated with lower sexual satisfaction for the men but not for their partners, and it was not associated with relationship satisfaction for either partner. In another study, 53 percent of university men in New Brunswick reported limited ejaculatory control; 59 percent were very concerned about ejaculating sooner than they wanted to (Grenier & Byers, 1997). Very few of these men had ever sought therapy for the problem.

Like erectile disorder, premature ejaculation may create a web of related psychological problems. Because the ability to postpone ejaculation and "satisfy" a partner is so important in our concept of a man who is a competent lover, early ejaculation can cause a man to become anxious about his sexual competence. Furthermore, the partner may become frustrated because she or he is not having a satisfying sexual experience either. So the condition may create friction in the relationship.

> **What counts as premature (early) ejaculation?**

The negative psychological effects of early ejaculation are illustrated by a young man in one of our sexuality classes who handed in an anonymous question. He described himself as a premature ejaculator and said that after several humiliating experiences during intercourse with dates, he was now convinced that no woman would want him in that condition. He no longer had the courage to ask for dates, so he had stopped dating entirely. He wanted to know how the women in the class would react to a man with such a problem. The question was discussed in class, and most of the women agreed that their reaction to his problem would depend a great deal on the quality of the relationship they had with him. If they cared deeply for him, they would be sympathetic and patient and help him overcome the difficulty. The point is, though, that the early ejaculation had created problems so severe that the young man not only had stopped having sex but had also stopped dating.

Men have developed (mostly ineffective) home remedies for dealing with early ejaculation, such as doubling up on condoms and using desensitizing creams. Perhaps the most common is to think of something else. We had university men in New Brunswick report the thoughts they used to delay ejaculation (Grenier & Byers, 1997). These thoughts fell into five categories: sex negative (thinking of an unattractive TV personality); sex positive (thinking "we're in no hurry" or visualizing a past episode of prolonged intercourse); nonsexual and negative (thinking of a sad event, unpaid debts); sex neutral (counting backward from 100); and sexually incongruous (thinking of your grandmother, reciting the Lord's Prayer). Of these options, we recommend the sex-positive alternative because it not only delays ejaculation but also allows both partners to remain in the moment. However, to some extent, any distraction technique may detract from attention to the sensations, and the proximity to the "point of no return." Thus, many clinicians encourage men to remain focused on sensations and the stop-start technique (described later in the chapter) to maintain arousal at manageable levels.

Delayed Ejaculation

Delayed ejaculation (also sometimes called *retarded ejaculation*) is the opposite of rapid (early) ejaculation. The man is consistently (for a period of at least six months) unable to orgasm or orgasm is greatly delayed when engaging in sexual activity with a partner, even though he has a solid erection and has had more than adequate stimulation, and he is distressed about this (APA, 2013b; Perelman & Rowland, 2006). In the most common version, the man is incapable of orgasm during intercourse but may be able to orgasm as a result of hand or mouth stimulation.

Male orgasmic disorder is far less common than premature ejaculation. In the National Health and Social Life Survey (NHSLS), 8 percent of the male respondents had had a problem in the last 12 months with being unable to orgasm (Laumann et al., 1999). However, likely less than 1 percent of men would meet the criteria for a diagnosis of delayed ejaculation, although it is more common among men over 50 than among younger men (APA, 2013b). As discussed later, some medications can result in delayed ejaculation (APA, 2013b).

Male orgasmic disorder is, to say the least, a frustrating experience for a man. In addition, some people react negatively to this condition, seeing their partner's inability to have an orgasm as a personal rejection. Some men, anticipating these negative reactions, have adopted the practice of faking orgasm. In other cases, the couple engages in prolonged thrusting so that the man can orgasm, which results in exhaustion or genital discomfort.

Delayed ejaculation: A sexual disorder in which the man cannot have an orgasm or the orgasm is greatly delayed, even though he has an erection and has had a great deal of sexual stimulation.
Female sexual interest/arousal disorder: A sexual disorder in which the woman's sexual interest or arousal is significantly reduced.
Female orgasmic disorder: A sexual disorder in which the woman is unable to have an orgasm or experiences orgasms that are less intense.

Disorders in Women

The disorders that can be diagnosed for women include female sexual interest/arousal disorder, female orgasmic disorder, and genitopelvic pain/penetration disorder.

Female Sexual Interest/ Arousal Disorder

Female sexual interest/arousal disorder refers to a lack of or significantly reduced sexual interest or arousal (APA, 2013b). To meet the criteria for this disorder, the woman would experience at least three of the following persistent symptoms that cause clinically significant distress: lack of interest in sexual activity; lack of sexual thoughts; lack of desire as demonstrated by not initiating sex with a partner and not being responsive to the partner's initiations (i.e., responsive desire); absent or reduced sexual excitement or pleasure in all or almost all sexual encounters; absent or reduced response to sexual stimuli; and absent or reduced physiological response during all or almost all sexual encounters. The disorder cannot be due to psychological or relationship distress. This definition takes into account that different women may experience female sexual interest/arousal disorder differently and may exhibit different symptoms. For some women, the disorder may primarily affect her sexual interest and thoughts—that is, her sexual desire. In fact, about 39 percent of Canadian women report diminished sexual desire (Fisher et al., 1999b). This varies by age though. Roughly 8 percent of women up to age 49 meet the criteria for female HSDD; rates increase to 10 percent in women between the ages of 50 and 59 (Rosen, Connor, et al., 2012). An additional, 20 percent of the women in that study reported distressing symptoms of low desire, although they did not meet the criteria for female HSDD.

In other women, female sexual interest/arousal disorder may primarily affect their ability to become aroused and respond sexually—that is, their arousal. In still other women, it may affect both.

Note that, as with male HSDD, a *discrepancy of sexual desire* between members of the couple (in which the woman has lower desire than her partner) is not sufficient to diagnose female sexual interest/arousal disorder.

Difficulties with arousal and lubrication are common. However, most are not persistent and, particularly in older women, they may not cause distress (APA, 2013b). These problems become particularly frequent among women during and after menopause (Rosen, Connor, et al., 2012). As estrogen levels decline, vaginal lubrication decreases. The use of sterile lubricants is an easy way to deal with this problem. The absence of subjective feelings of arousal is more complex to treat.

Female Orgasmic Disorder

Female orgasmic disorder refers to a woman's recurrent difficulty having an orgasm or reduced orgasm intensity during almost all sexual activity (APA, 2013b). As with the other disorders, the woman must be distressed about the situation (see First Person for one woman's story). This condition goes by a variety of other terms, including *orgasmic dysfunction*, *anorgasmia*, and *inhibited female orgasm*. Laypersons may call it *frigidity*, but sex therapists reject this term because it has derogatory connotations and is imprecise because it may refer to a variety of conditions ranging from total lack of sexual arousal to arousal without orgasm. Therefore, the term *female orgasmic disorder* is preferred.

Like other sexual disorders, cases of female orgasmic disorder may be classified into *lifelong* and *acquired* depending on whether the woman has ever had orgasms in the past (APA, 2013b). A common pattern is *situational orgasmic disorder*, in which the woman has orgasms in some situations but not others. For example, she may be able to have orgasms while masturbating but not while being stimulated by a partner. Orgasmic disorders are common among women (Heiman, 2007). Younger women are more likely to report infrequent orgasms than are older women (Fisher et al., 1999b).

Worldwide, approximately 10 percent of women never experience an orgasm in their lifetime (APA, 2013b). However, 21 percent of Canadian women report that they do not usually have an orgasm during intercourse (Fisher et al., 1999b). These women don't necessarily have a disorder (APA, 2013b). Consider the case of the heterosexual woman who orgasms as a result of masturbation or hand or mouth stimulation by a partner but who does not orgasm during penile–vaginal intercourse. Is this really a sexual disorder? The notion that it is a disorder can be traced to sexual scripts and beliefs that there is a "right" way to have sex—with the penis inside the vagina—and a corresponding "right" way to have orgasms. Because this pattern of situational orgasmic disorder is so common, the *DSM-5* explicitly states that women who need clitoral stimulation to reach orgasm should not be diagnosed with this disorder. Often the woman who orgasms as a result of hand or mouth stimulation, but not penile thrusting, is simply having orgasms when she is adequately stimulated and is not having them when she is inadequately stimulated.

Nonetheless, there should be room for self-definition of sexual concerns and problems as deserving of attention, even if not a diagnosis. If a woman is truly distressed that she is not able to orgasm during vaginal intercourse and wants therapy, then it may be appropriate to provide it even if she does not meet the criteria for having a disorder. The therapist, however, should be careful to explain to her the problems of cultural definition just raised to be sure that her request for therapy stems from her own dissatisfaction with her sexual responding rather than from an overly idealistic sexual script. Therapy in such cases probably is best viewed as an effort to enrich the client's experience rather than to fix a problem.

Genito-Pelvic Pain/Penetration Disorder

Genito-pelvic pain/penetration disorder refers to any one of four symptoms that typically occur together: difficulty having intercourse/penetration; marked genital and/or pelvic pain during penetration attempts (sometimes termed **dyspareunia**); fear of pain associated with vaginal penetration; and marked tension or tightening of the pelvic floor muscles during attempts at vaginal penetration (APA, 2013b). The symptoms must occur for more than six months and must cause the woman significant distress. Difficulty having intercourse may be situational or generalized, although it is more typical for women who experience pain with a partner to also experience pain in other situations, such as during a gynaecological exam. Approximately, 15 percent of women report recurrent pain during sexual intercourse. Of particular concern, research in Quebec found that dyspareunia is common in girls between the ages of 12 and 19 who are engaging in intercourse— 20 percent of these girls reported experiencing regular pain during intercourse for at least six months (Landry & Bergeron, 2009). Although complaints of occasional pain during intercourse are fairly common among women, persistent genito-pelvic pain is not as common. The location of the pain, its nature, and its intensity may vary. It may be felt in the vagina, around the vaginal entrance and clitoris, or deep in the pelvis. It may be generalized or localized to a particular area (Damsted-Petersen et al., 2009). The pain may also differ in quality and in intensity (Pukall et al., 2003). Some women describe a burning sensation, others a sharp pain or an aching feeling. To put it mildly, dyspareunia decreases a woman's enjoyment of the sexual experience, frequently causes problems with arousal and orgasm, and may even lead one to avoid sexual situations. Some women experience reflexive muscle spasm of the outer third of the vagina making penetration impossible; this is often referred to as *vaginismus*. For other women, whose pelvic floor muscles tighten involuntarily, penetration may be possible if they learn to relax their muscles. Although there is no equivalent male disorder in the *DSM-5*, men sometimes also experience pain during intercourse.

Quebec psychologist Yitzchak Binik and his colleagues have criticized the notion of a sexual pain disorder (Binik et al., 2007; Meana et al., 1997; Pukall et al., 2000). They point out that just because pain interferes with sexual activity such as intercourse, this does not make it a sexual disorder. They use the analogy of lower back pain that interferes with work. Although lower back pain may prevent a person from working, this pain is classified by its location (i.e., lower back pain) rather than by the activity it interferes with (i.e., work pain). Further, the pain associated with intercourse often also occurs in nonsexual situations, such as inserting a tampon or physical exercise. Thus they argue that painful intercourse should be reclassified and treated as a pain disorder that interferes with sexual activity rather than as a sexual disorder (Binik, 2005; Payne, Reissing, et al., 2005).

Genito-pelvic pain/penetration disorder: Any one of four symptoms that typically occur together related to genital pain during actual or attempted sexual intercourse.
Dyspareunia (dis-pah-ROO-nee-uh): Painful intercourse.

First Person

A Case of Female Orgasmic Disorder

Jane was a self-employed, attractive, divorced woman who came to the clinic at the age of 43, with an acquired inability to reach orgasm, which had then led to a decline in her sexual desire. She had been divorced from her husband, Tom, for 5½ years after a 17-year marriage. Even though she was not in love with him, Jane had married Tom because he was the first man with whom she had sexual intercourse. Jane and Tom had two sons from this marriage, ages 13 (Bruce) and 18 (Dean). Bruce was attending a costly private school paid for by Jane. Dean had a history of emotional and behavioral problems.

At the time she sought help at our clinic, Jane was in a three-year-long relationship with Frank, a 45-year-old divorced man. Frank directed their sexual relationship. Jane was compliant with Frank's sexual requests, never asking that her needs be met. She reported having an orgasm only once with Frank, although she still reported becoming aroused during their sexual interactions. This lack of orgasm was in contrast to the pattern during her marriage, when she was able to have an orgasm at least half of the time by rubbing her clitoris against her husband's pelvic area when she was on top (her husband did not always have an erection). This difficulty having an orgasm, along with the lack of a supportive response from her partner, affected Jane's sexual desire, which declined precipitously.

Jane came to therapy believing that there was something wrong with her physically—that she was broken sexually. This belief originated from her boyfriend's assertion that she had a small clitoris, which interfered with her ability to orgasm. She lacked an adequate sexual vocabulary and experienced difficulty talking about sex, often becoming red-faced or tearful. These problems with sexual communication were partially the result of her upbringing in a small rural town in a fundamentalist religious family, where sex was rarely discussed. Jane grew up with her biological parents, two brothers, and two sisters. She described her family as "fundamentally religious," her father as the dominant decision-maker, and her mother as "puritanical." In therapy, it emerged that she had been sexually abused by both older brothers, beginning when she was 12 years old.

Jane's treatment proceeded over several years because of the need to help her recover from the child sexual abuse and the PTSD and depression that resulted from it. Treatment used the Sexual Health Model developed at the University of Minnesota and involved multiple treatment methods described in this chapter, including individual, couple, and group therapy and psychiatric care. Jane found a new partner who was more supportive, and treatment ended with Jane feeling sexually confident.

Source: Robinson et al. (2011). Names have been changed to preserve anonymity. Read the article by Robinson et al. if you want the full details of the therapy.

As with other pain disorders, psychological and cognitive factors, such as the fear of pain, increase the intensity of the pain experienced (Desrochers et al., 2008, 2009).

 L02

What Causes Sexual Disorders?

Biopsychosocial model: A general model that argues that physical, psychological, and social factors all contribute to sexual disorders.

There are many causes of sexual disorders, varying from person to person and from one disorder to another. Several categories of factors may be related to sexual disorders: physical factors, drugs, individual psychological factors, and interpersonal factors. These factors interact with each other so that the causes of most disorders can best be understood from a biopsychosocial perspective. According to the **biopsychosocial model**, biological, psychological, and social factors all play a role in the development and maintenance of sexual disorders. For example, disorders that are largely due to physical factors affect people's thoughts, feelings, and relationships; in turn, their thoughts and feelings may make the problem worse (or better). Conversely, disorders that are primarily due to psychological or social factors nonetheless affect nerves and blood vessels in a physical way. Each of these categories is discussed separately.

Physical Causes

Physical factors that cause sexual disorders include **organic factors of sexual disorders** (physical factors, such as diseases) and drugs.

Erectile Disorder

Diseases associated with the heart and the circulatory system are particularly likely to be associated with erectile disorder, since erection itself depends on the circulatory system (Rosen, 2007). Any kind of vascular pathology (problems in the blood vessels supplying the penis) can produce erection problems. Erection depends on having a great deal of blood flowing into the penis via the arteries, with simultaneous constricting of the veins so that the blood cannot flow out as rapidly as it is coming in. Thus, damage to either these arteries or the veins may produce erectile disorder.

Erectile disorder is associated with diabetes mellitus. Several aspects of diabetes are involved including circulation problems and peripheral nerve damage (Sáenz de Tejada et al., 2004). In fact, in some cases erectile disorder may be the earliest symptom of diabetes. Of course, not all diabetic men have erectile disorders; indeed, the majority do not. One estimate is that 28 percent of men with diabetes have an erectile disorder (Sáenz de Tejada et al., 2004). Diabetes is also associated with sexual disorders in women (Giraldi & Kristensen, 2010)

Hypogonadism—an underfunctioning of the testes so that testosterone levels are very low—is associated with ED (Morales & Heaton, 2001). ED is also associated with a condition called hyperprolactinemia in which there is excessive production of prolactin (Johri et al., 2001).

Any disease or injury that damages the lower part of the spinal cord may cause erectile disorder, since that is the location of the erection reflex centre (see Chapter 9). Finally, some—though not all—kinds of prostate surgery may cause the condition (Libman & Fichten, 1987; Libman et al., 1989).

With erectile disorders, as with most sexual disorders, it is important to recognize that the distinction between organic causes and psychological causes is too simple (Rosen, 2007). In keeping with the biopsychosocial model, most sexual disorders result from a complex interplay of the two causes. For example, a man who has circulatory problems that initially cause him to have erection problems is likely to develop anxieties about erection, which in turn may create further difficulties. This notion of dual causes has important implications for therapy. A comprehensive approach to treatment should include attention to physical, psychological, and interpersonal factors.

Premature (Early) Ejaculation

Premature (early) ejaculation is more often caused by psychological than physical factors. However, for some men rapid ejaculation may be due to a malfunctioning of the ejaculatory reflexes (Grenier & Byers, 1995). These men have a physiological hypersensitivity that results in faster ejaculation. (See Chapter 9 for a discussion of ejaculation.) Physical factors may also be involved in cases of acquired premature ejaculation, in which the man at one time had ejaculatory control but later lost it. A local infection, such as prostatitis, may be the cause, as may degeneration in the related parts of the nervous system, which may occur in neural disorders, such as multiple sclerosis.

An intriguing explanation for early ejaculation comes from the sociobiologists (Hong, 1984). Their idea is that rapid ejaculation has been selected for in the process of evolution—what we might call "survival of the fastest." Monkeys and apes (and humans) who copulated and ejaculated rapidly, the argument goes, would be more likely to survive and reproduce in that the female would be less likely to get away, and the male would be less likely to be attacked by other sexually aroused males while he was copulating. In fact, the average time from intromission (insertion of the penis into the vagina) to ejaculation among chimpanzees is rapid—about seven seconds (Tutin & McGinnis, 1981). However, primates engage in lengthy courtship and foreplay behaviours that would not be predicted by sociobiologists (Bixler, 1986). Nonetheless, according to sociobiologists, the genes for rapid ejaculation are still around.

Delayed Ejaculation

Delayed ejaculation may be associated with a variety of medical or surgical conditions, such as multiple sclerosis, spinal cord injury, and prostate surgery (Rosen & Leiblum, 1995b). Most commonly, though, it is associated with psychological factors.

Female Orgasmic Disorder

Orgasmic disorder in women may be caused by severe illness, general ill health, or extreme fatigue. Injury to the spinal cord can cause orgasm problems (Sipski et al., 2001). However, most cases are primarily caused by psychological factors.

Genito-pelvic Pain/Penetration Disorder

Although genito-pelvic pain in women is often caused by organic factors, research suggests that psychosocial and interpersonal factors also contribute (Bergeron et al.,

Organic factors of sexual disorders: Physical factors, such as disease or injury, that cause sexual disorders.

2010; Rosen & Leiblum, 1995a). Further, the experience of pain during sexual activity is influenced by psychological factors (Bergeron et al., 2010; Desrochers et al., 2008; Desrochers et al., 2009).

Organic factors for genito-pelvic pain/penetration disorder include the following:

1. *Disorders of the vaginal entrance.* Irritated remnants of the hymen; painful scars, perhaps from an episiotomy or sexual assault; or infection of the Bartholin glands

2. *Disorders of the vagina.* Vaginal infections; allergic reactions to spermicidal creams or the latex in condoms or diaphragms; a thinning of the vaginal walls, which occurs naturally with age or chemically induced menopause; or scarring of the roof of the vagina, which can occur after hysterectomy

3. *Pelvic disorders.* Pelvic infection, such as pelvic inflammatory disease; endometriosis; tumours; cysts; or tearing of the ligaments supporting the uterus

4. *Dysfunction of the pelvic floor muscles.* Higher pelvic floor muscle tone; lower vaginal flexibility; higher mucosal sensitivity; lower muscle strength (Bergeron et al., 2010)

Sexual pain in men is typically caused by a variety of organic factors. It may be caused by infection. For an uncircumcised man, poor hygiene may be a cause; if the penis is not washed thoroughly with the foreskin retracted, material may collect under the foreskin, causing infection. An allergic reaction to spermicidal creams or to the latex in condoms may also be involved. Finally, various prostate problems may cause pain during intercourse, after intercourse, or on ejaculation (Smith et al., 2007).

Drugs
Some drugs may have side effects that cause sexual disorders (APA, 2013b; Ashton, 2007; Segraves & Balon, 2003, 2010). For example, hormonal contraceptives interfere with sexual desire and arousal in some women. Some drugs used to treat high blood pressure increase problems with erection in men and decrease sexual desire in both men and women. Similarly, many antidepressants can have a range of sexual side effects. Indeed, there are so many substances and drugs that can cause problems with sexual functioning that the *DSM-5* includes a diagnostic category for *substance/medication-induced sexual dysfunction*. Although it would be impossible to list every drug effect on every aspect of sexual functioning, a list of some of the major drugs that may cause sexual disorders is provided in Table 18.1.

Here we will consider the effects of alcohol, illicit drugs, and prescription drugs.

Alcohol
The effects of alcohol on sexual responding vary considerably. We can think of these effects as falling into three categories: (1) short-term pharmacological effects, (2) expectancy effects, and (3) long-term effects of chronic alcohol abuse. In the last category, people who abuse alcohol, particularly in the later stages of alcoholism, frequently have sexual disorders, typically including erectile disorder, orgasmic disorder, and loss of desire (Segraves & Balon, 2003). These sex problems may be the result of any of a number of organic effects of long-term alcoholism. For example, chronic alcoholism in men may cause disturbances in sex hormone production because of atrophy of the testes or liver damage. Chronic alcohol abuse, too, generally has negative effects on the person's interpersonal relationships, which may contribute to sexual disorders.

What about the person who is not an alcoholic but has had one or many drinks on a particular evening and then proceeds to a sexual interaction (Figure 18.1a)? As noted earlier, there is an interplay of two effects: expectancy effects and actual pharmacological effects (George & Stoner, 2000; George et al., 2006). Many people have the expectation that alcohol will loosen them up, making them more sociable and sexually uninhibited. These expectancy effects in themselves produce increased physiological arousal and subjective feelings of arousal. Expectancy effects, though, interact with the pharmacological effects and work mainly at low doses, that is, when only a little alcohol has been consumed. At high dosage levels, alcohol acts as a depressant and sexual arousal is markedly suppressed, in both men[1] and women.

Illicit or Recreational Drugs
There is a widespread belief that marijuana (*cannabis, pot, weed*) has aphrodisiac properties. Scientific research is limited. Therefore, we can provide only tentative ideas about the effects of marijuana on sexual functioning. In surveys of users, many respondents report that it increases sexual desire and makes sexual interactions more pleasurable (McKay, 2005a). In regard to potential negative effects, there is concern that marijuana use contributes to risky sexual behaviour, such as unprotected sex (Collins et al., 2005). Chronic users report decreased sexual desire (Segraves & Balon, 2003). In community studies, marijuana use has been associated with orgasmic disorder (Johnson et al., 2004).

To make matters more complicated, B.C. researchers have found that the effects of cannabinoids (the active

---

[1] Some refer to the resulting erection problems as "whisky dick."

Table 18.1 Drugs That May Impair or Improve Sexual Response

Drug	How It Affects Sexual Functioning	Common Medical Uses
1. Psychoactive Drugs		
Antianxiety drugs/tranquillizers		Anxiety, panic disorders
Buspirone	Enhanced desire, orgasm	
Benzodiazepines (Librium, Valium, Ativan)	Decreased hypoactive desire, improvement of premature ejaculation	
Antidepressants I: Tricyclics and MAO inhibitors	Desire disorders, erection problems, orgasm problems, ejaculation problems	Depression
	May treat hypersexuality, premature ejaculation	
Antidepressants II: Serotonin reuptake inhibitors (Paxil, Prozac, Zoloft)	Desire disorders, erection problems, orgasm problems	Depression, obsessive-compulsive disorder, panic disorders
Lithium	Desire disorders, erection problems	Bipolar disorder
Antipsychotics (Thorazine, Haldol)	Desire disorders, erection problems, orgasm problems, ejaculation problems	Schizophrenia
2. Antihypertensives		
Reserpine, methyldopa	Desire disorders, erection difficulties, orgasm delayed or blocked	High blood pressure
ACE inhibitors (Vasotec)	Erection difficulties	
3. Substance Use and Abuse		
Alcohol	At low doses, increases desire	
	At high doses, decreases erection, arousal, orgasm	
	Alcoholism creates many disorders and atrophied testicles, infertility	
Nicotine	Decreases blood flow to penis, creates erectile disorder	
Opioids		
Endogenous: Endorphins (neurotransmitter, not a drug)	Sense of well-being and relaxation	
Heroin	Decreased desire, orgasm, ejaculation, replacement for sex	
Marijuana	Enhanced sexual pleasure but not actual "performance"; chronic use decreases desire	

Sources: Ashton (2007), Meston et al. (2004), Segraves & Balon (2003).

drugs in marijuana) depend on gender (Gorzalka et al., 2010). In women, low doses of cannabis are associated with increased sexual desire and sexual pleasure. It is possible that cannabis boosts the production of androgens in women, leading to the positive sexual effects. At higher doses, though, cannabis creates sexual problems. In men, moderate doses of cannabis appear to increase sexual desire while at the same time creating erection problems.

Among drug users, cocaine is reported to be one of the drugs of choice for enhancing sexual experiences (Figure 18.1b). It is said to increase sexual desire, enhance sensuality, and delay orgasm. Chronic use of cocaine, however, is associated with loss of sexual desire, orgasmic disorders, and erectile disorders

(Segraves & Balon, 2003). The effects also depend on the means of administration—whether the cocaine is inhaled, smoked, or injected. The most negative effects on sexual functioning occur among those who regularly inject the drug. Crack cocaine is highly addictive and the crack epidemic, especially in city downtown areas, often involves the exchange of sex for drugs (Green et al., 2005).

Stimulant drugs, notably amphetamines, are associated with increased sexual desire and better control of orgasm in some studies (Segraves & Balon, 2003). Injection of amphetamines itself causes a physical sensation that is described by some as a total-body orgasm. In some cases, though, orgasm becomes difficult or impossible when using amphetamines.

Figure 18.1 Alcohol and cocaine are popular recreational drugs that many people believe enhance sexual experience. Research shows, though, that high levels of alcohol suppress sexual arousal, and repeated use of cocaine is associated with loss of sexual desire, orgasm disorders, and erection problems.

Crystal methamphetamine (also known as *ice* or *crystal meth*) is a popular recreational drug. This drug is of particular concern because, while high on it, people have a tendency to engage in risky sexual behaviours (Semple et al., 2004; Semple et al., 2009; Urbina & Jones, 2004; Wohl et al., 2002). One study of heterosexual, HIV-negative adults using crystal meth indicated that, over a two-month period, they averaged 22 acts of unprotected vaginal sex and 9 different sex partners (Semple et al., 2004). Crystal meth can also lead to paranoia, hallucinations, and violent behaviour (Brecht et al., 2004).

The opiates, such as morphine, heroin, and methadone, have strong suppression effects on sexual desire and response (Segraves & Balon, 2003). Long-term use of heroin, in particular, leads to decreased testosterone levels in males.

Prescription Drugs

Some *psychiatric drugs*—that is, drugs used in the treatment of psychological disorders—may affect sexual functioning (Segraves & Balon, 2003). In general, these drugs have their beneficial psychological effects because they alter the functioning of the central nervous system (CNS). But these CNS alterations in turn affect sexual functioning. For example, the drugs used to treat schizophrenia may cause delayed orgasm or "dry orgasm" in men—that is, orgasm with no ejaculation. Tranquillizers and antidepressants often improve sexual responding by improving the person's mental state. However, there may also be negative effects.

Many of the antidepressants, especially selective serotonin reuptake inhibitors (SSRIs) are associated with desire, arousal, and delayed orgasm problems in men and women. This is a problem because, according to Health Canada, there were over 15 million prescriptions for SSRI antidepressants filled in Canada in 2003, and these are very common side effects—between 30 and 60 percent of people taking SSRIs experience a sexual disorder (Gregorian et al., 2002; Hemels et al., 2002). On the other hand, they are sometimes used to treat premature ejaculation precisely because they delay orgasm. A few antidepressants—most notably bupropion (Wellbutrin)—have fewer sexual side effects and are becoming popular for that very reason.

The list of other prescription drugs that can affect sexual functioning is long, so we will mention just two examples. Some of the antihypertensive drugs (used to treat high blood pressure) can cause erection problems in men (Segraves & Balon, 2003). Most of the research on antihypertensive drug effects has been done with men, so we know less about their effects on women, although sexual problems have been reported among women using antihypertensive medication. Some of the medications used to treat epilepsy appear to cause erection problems and decreased sexual desire, although epilepsy by itself also seems to be associated with sexual disorders.

Psychological Causes

The psychological sources of sexual disorders can be separated into predisposing factors and maintaining or ongoing causes (Wincze & Carey, 2001). **Predisposing factors** are people's prior life experiences—for example, things that happened in childhood—that now inhibit the sexual response. **Maintaining factors** are ongoing life circumstances, personal characteristics, and characteristics of lovemaking that help explain why the problem continues.

There are eight factors that are often maintaining psychological causes of sexual disorder. Six of these factors are within the individual: myths or misinformation; negative attitudes; anxieties or inhibition; cognitive interference; individual psychological distress, such as depression; and behavioural or lifestyle factors. Two of the factors are interpersonal: failure to engage in effective, sexually stimulating behaviour, often caused by failure of the partners to communicate; and relationship distress. To be effective, treatment needs to address these maintaining factors.

Maintaining Individual Causes

Myths or misinformation can be a source of sexual dysfunction. Many people have beliefs about lovemaking that are incorrect, or they are unaware of sexual information (such as the effects of aging on the sexual response) that is important to sexual functioning. For example, some couples seek sex therapy because of a woman's failure to orgasm; the therapist soon discovers that neither partner is aware of the location of the clitoris, much less its fantastic erotic potential. Misinformation can lead to a sexual script that does not fully enhance sexual arousal and pleasure or to anxiety and worry. These cases can often be cleared up by simple educational techniques.

A second possible source of sexual dysfunction is *negative attitudes* about sexual activity, one's own body, or one's partner's body. For example, the beliefs that "good" people do not enjoy sex or that one is ugly or fat may result in anxiety or other negative feelings during sexual activity that may affect sexual functioning. Researchers in B.C. found that sex guilt—feeling that one is violating "proper" sexual conduct—is associated with lower sexual desire in women, and sex guilt accounts for why South Asian women tend to report lower sexual desire than Euro-Canadian women (Woo et al., 2011, 2012).

Anxiety during sexual activity can be a source of sexual disorders. Anxiety may be caused by negative or traumatic experiences in the past, such as child sexual abuse. Indeed, experiences of child sexual abuse have been linked to a range of sexual problems and disorders (Desrochers et al., 2008; Lemieux & Byers, 2008). However, anxiety also may be caused by fear of failure—that is, fear of being unable to perform. Anxiety itself can block sexual response in some people. Often anxiety can create a vicious circle of self-fulfilling prophecy in which fear of failure produces a failure, which produces more fear, which produces another failure, and so on. For example, a man may have one episode of erectile dysfunction, perhaps after drinking too much at a party. The next time he has sex, he anxiously wonders whether he will "fail" again. His anxiety is so great that he cannot get an erection. At this point he is convinced that the condition is permanent, and all future sexual activity is marked by such intense fear of failure that erectile disorder results. The prophecy is fulfilled. The effects of anxiety, though, are complicated and depend on the individual, as we will see in the research of David Barlow described later in this section.

In Chapter 9, we discussed the sexual excitation-inhibition model, or the dual control model of sexual response (Bancroft et al., 2009). In brief, the model proposes that two basic processes underlie human sexual response: excitation (responding with arousal to sexual stimuli) and inhibition (inhibiting sexual arousal, not responding to sexual stimuli). This model can be applied directly to understanding the origins of sexual disorders. In general, the idea is that people who are low on sexual excitation, high on sexual inhibition, or both, are likely to develop sexual disorders. For example, in research with a community sample of men, scores on the sexual inhibition scale correlated strongly with the men's reports of difficulties in obtaining or maintaining an erection (Bancroft et al., 2009). Similarly, research with a community sample of women showed that sexual inhibition scores were correlated with their reports of sexual problems (Sanders et al., 2008).

Cognitive interference is a fourth maintaining cause of sexual disorders. Cognitive interference refers to thoughts that distract the person from focusing on the erotic experience. The problem is basically one of attention (de Jong, 2009). Is the person focusing his or her attention on erotic thoughts and feelings or on distracting thoughts? (Will my technique be good enough to please her? Will my body be beautiful enough to arouse him?) Research in Ontario asked undergraduate students about the nonerotic thoughts

Predisposing factors: Experiences that people have had in the past—for example, in childhood—that now affect their sexual response.
Maintaining factors: Various ongoing life circumstances, personal characteristics, and lovemaking patterns that inhibit sexual response.
Cognitive interference: Negative thoughts that distract a person from focusing on the erotic experience.

they had during their most recent sexual encounter that took away from their sexual experience (Purdon & Holdaway, 2006; Purdon & Watson, 2011). More than 90 percent of participants reported having at least one such nonerotic thought. These thoughts most often related to performance concerns; concerns related to external consequences (e.g., STIs) and emotional consequences (e.g., for relationship); and body image. Men are more likely to have thoughts related to performance and the women were more likely to have thoughts related to body image (Nelson & Purdon, 2011; Purdon & Watson, 2011). Students who reported more nonerotic thoughts, particularly nonerotic thoughts that caused anxiety, had poorer sexual functioning. Similarly, research in New Brunswick has shown that poor body image is associated with poorer sexual functioning in women, beyond the effects of actual body size (Weaver & Byers, 2006, 2013). This is likely because poor body image leads to nonerotic thoughts and anxiety about the body in sexual situations. Researchers in Quebec have shown that, among women with dyspareunia, negative thoughts about the meaning of pain is associated with experiencing more intense pain (Desrochers et al., 2010; Rosen, Bergeron, Lambert, et al., 2012).

Spectatoring, a term coined by Masters and Johnson, is one kind of cognitive interference. The person behaves like a spectator or judge of his or her own sexual "performance." People who do this are constantly (mentally) stepping outside the sexual activities in which they are engaged to evaluate how they are doing, mentally commenting, "Good job," or "Lousy," or "Could stand improvement." These ideas on the importance of cognition in sexual disorder derive from the cognitive theories of sexual responding discussed in Chapter 2.

Sex researcher David Barlow (1986; Wiegel et al., 2007) ran an elegant series of experiments to test the ways in which anxiety and cognitive interference affect sexual functioning. He studied men with and without sexual disorders, particularly erectile disorder, whom he calls the "dysfunctionals" and the "functionals." He found that functionals and dysfunctionals respond very differently to stimuli in sexual situations. For example, anxiety (induced by the threat of being shocked) *increases* the arousal of functional men but *decreases* the arousal of dysfunctional men while watching erotic films. Similarly, demands for performance (e.g., the experimenter says the research participant must have an erection or he will be shocked) increase the arousal of functionals but are distracting to (create cognitive interference in) and decrease the arousal of dysfunctionals. When both self-reports of arousal and physiological measures of arousal (the penile strain gauge) are used, dysfunctional men consistently

Spectatoring: Masters and Johnson's term for acting as an observer or judge of one's own sexual performance; hypothesized to contribute to sexual disorders.

underestimate their physical arousal, whereas functional men are accurate in their reporting.

From these laboratory findings, Barlow (1986) constructed a model that describes how anxiety, positive and negative emotions (affect), and cognitive interference act together to produce sexual disorders, such as erectile disorder. When dysfunctionals are in a sexual situation, there is a performance demand. This causes them to feel anxiety and other negative emotions. They then experience cognitive interference and focus their attention on nonerotic thoughts, such as thinking about how awful it will be when they don't have an erection. This increases arousal of their autonomic nervous system. To them, that feels like anxiety and generates more negative affect, whereas a functional person would experience it as sexual arousal. For the dysfunctionals, the anxiety creates further cognitive interference, and eventually the sexual performance is dysfunctional—they don't manage to get an erection. The situation is amplified because the dysfunctionals have various negative cognitive biases. For example, they expect to perform poorly. All this leads them to avoid future sexual encounters or, when they are in one, to experience negative feelings, and the cycle repeats itself. This model recognizes the importance of cognitive processes, such as cognitive interference and the effect of emotion.

Research in Quebec suggests there may be a similar process in women who experience sexual pain. That is, anxiety and fear about sexual pain lead women who experience pain to focus their attention on possible pain cues rather than on erotic stimuli (Payne, Binik, et al., 2005). In turn, this cognitive interference may interfere with the sexual response over and above any pain experienced.

It is important to note that anxiety produces sex problems only in some men. For the majority of men, who function well sexually, anxiety does not impair sexual responding, at least in the lab. The same is true for women (Elliott & O'Donohue, 1997).

A fifth possible cause of sexual disorders is individual *psychological distress*. That is, sexual disorder may be one symptom of a more general psychological disorder. For example, individuals who are depressed often experience low sexual desire or have difficulty becoming aroused (Brotto & Klein, 2010; Frohlich & Meston, 2002; McCabe et al., 2010). Emotions such as anger and sadness (as well as anxiety, as we saw earlier) can interfere with sexual responding in some people (Araujo et al., 2000; Brotto & Klein, 2010). These are examples of the mind–body connection.

Behavioural and lifestyle factors can also affect sexual functioning. Smoking, alcohol consumption, and obesity are all behaviours that are associated with higher rates of sexual disorders (Derby et al., 2000; Segraves & Balon, 2003). However, these behaviours are quite modifiable. A study of obese men between the ages of

35 and 55 showed that regular physical exercise reduced their body mass index (BMI) and the incidence of erectile disorder (Esposito et al., 2004). A stressful lifestyle, such as a difficult work environment, long work hours, or a lack of privacy in the home, may also affect sexual functioning. Surprisingly, couples often fail to recognize how their lifestyle impairs their sexual functioning.

Maintaining Interpersonal Factors

The last two maintaining factors relate to the couple's interactions and relationship. Sexual disorders may be caused by *failure to engage in effective sexually stimulating behaviour.* Sometimes this is a result of simple ignorance—that is, myths and misinformation. More often poor technique is due to the failure of the partners to communicate with each other about their sexual preferences. We often expect our partners to read our minds (which most of us are not particularly good at) to determine what we like and don't like. In fact, a survey of more than 3000 Canadian men and women found that only 28 percent had had even one serious discussion about sex in their relationship in the previous year (Auld et al., 2002). New Brunswick researchers examined whether sexual self-disclosure does, in fact, enhance sexual functioning in dating and long-term relationships (MacNeil & Byers, 2005, 2009). They had 74 heterosexual couples independently complete measures of their sexual likes and dislikes, their partner's sexual likes and dislikes, and their own sexual satisfaction. They found that, for both the men and the women, individuals who self-disclosed more about their sexual preferences had partners who had a better understanding of what pleased them sexually. In turn, the more the partner understood their sexual likes, the more the couple engaged in mutually pleasing and the less they engaged in displeasing sexual activities during lovemaking; the more pleasing and less displeasing the sexual script, the more sexually satisfied they were.

In short, you are the leading expert in the field of what feels good to you, and your partner will never know what turns you on or what you desire at a particular moment unless you make this known, either verbally or nonverbally. But many people do not communicate their sexual desires. For example, a woman who needs a great deal of clitoral stimulation to have an orgasm may never tell her partner this; as a result, her partner provides some clitoral stimulation but not the amount of stimulation she needs. Consequently, she does not orgasm.

Relationship distress, that is, disturbances in a couple's relationship, is another leading cause of sexual disorders (Althof et al., 2004; McCabe et al., 2010). That is, the relational context in which sex occurs is key to understanding an individual's sexual functioning and interest in and ability to respond sexually. Frequent arguments or anger and resentment toward one's partner do not

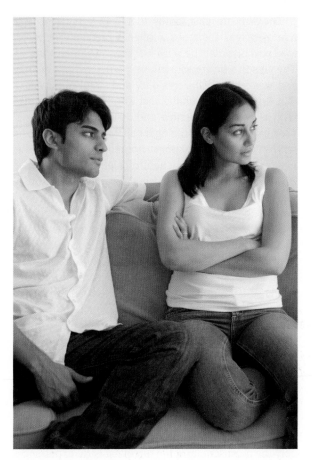

Figure 18.2 Relationship distress is a leading cause of sexual disorders.

create an optimal environment for sexual enjoyment (Figure 18.2). Intimacy problems in the relationship can be a factor in sexual disorders. Poor communication, not feeling understood, a lack of common interests, and a lack of trust may interfere with the feelings of closeness and intimacy that are important to quality lovemaking and to being able to respond sexually (Basson, 2001b). Researchers in Ontario have shown that individuals who have a partner who respond negatively when they experience a sexual difficulty, experience poorer sexual functioning and lower sexual satisfaction (Fallis et al., 2013). A lack of quality time together because of an overly hectic lifestyle can also contribute to reduced feelings of intimacy and closeness and thus to relationship distress. In turn, relationship distress may result in a sexual disorder.

Predisposing Factors

The immediate or maintaining causes of sexual dysfunction are often a result of things that were learned or experienced in childhood, adolescence, or even adulthood. These early events result in negative attitudes, misinformation, cognitive interference, difficulty communicating, and so on.

Growing up in a family that communicates negative messages about sex is often a predisposing factor to sexual disorders because it creates negative attitudes. The person who grew up in a very strict, religious family and was taught that sex is dirty and sinful may believe that sex is not pleasurable, that it should be gotten over with as quickly as possible, and that it is for purposes of procreation only. It is the rigid belief in sexual rights and wrongs (particularly wrongs), not religiosity per se, that likely impacts sexual functioning (Kleinplatz & Krippner, 2000). The child who is punished severely for masturbating and told never to "touch herself" again may develop negative attitudes about her genitals and about genital touching. Parents who teach their children the double standard may contribute to sexual disorders, particularly in daughters who were told that no nice woman is interested in sex or enjoys it. Growing up in a homonegative family or culture may contribute to internalized homonegativity among gays and lesbians, which in turn may affect their sexual functioning. Such learning inhibits the enjoyment of a full sexual response.

In some cases, the person's first sexual act was traumatic. An example would be a young man who could not get an erection the first time he attempted penetration and was laughed at by his partner. Such an experience sets the stage for future erectile disorder.

Child sexual abuse by parents or other adults is probably the most serious of the traumatic early experiences that lead to later sexual disorders (Najman et al., 2005). A history of sexual abuse is frequently reported by people seeking therapy for problems with sexual desire, arousal, or aversion (Leonard & Follette, 2002; Loeb et al., 2002). For example, researchers in Quebec have shown that young women with chronic dyspareunia were more likely than young women without pain to have experienced sexual abuse (Landry & Bergeron, 2011).

Combined Cognitive and Physiological Factors

According to the cognitive–physiological model of sexual functioning and dysfunction, we function well sexually when we are physiologically aroused and we interpret it as sexual arousal rather than something else, like nervousness (Palace, 1995a, 1995b). As Barlow's research shows, people with sexual disorders tend to interpret their arousal as anxiety. In addition, the physiological processes and cognitive interpretations form a feedback loop. That is, interpreting arousal as sexual arousal increases arousal further.

In a clever experiment, British Columbia women with sexual disorders were exposed, in a laboratory setting, to a frightening movie that increased their general autonomic arousal (Palace, 1995b). The women were then shown a brief erotic video and given feedback (actually false) that their genitals had shown a strong

arousal response to it. This feedback created a cognitive interpretation for the way they were feeling. The combination of general autonomic arousal and the belief that they were responding with strong sexual arousal led these women, compared with the controls, to greater vaginal arousal responses and subjective reports of arousal in subsequent sessions. This demonstration of the effectiveness of combined physiological and cognitive factors is particularly striking because the women began with problems in sexual responding.

 ## A New View of Women's Sexual Problems and Their Causes

Over the past decade, a group of sex therapists specializing in treating women's sex problems worked together to formulate what they call a New View of the nature of women's sexual problems and their causes (Tiefer, 2001). The New View was critical of the categories of disorders formulated by the American Psychiatric Association in the *DSM-IV-TR*, the diagnostic manual that has just recently been up-dated to the *DSM-5*. It argues that these diagnostic categories had three flaws: (1) they treat male sexuality and female sexuality as totally equivalent, when they differ in some important ways; (2) they ignore the relational context of sexuality and desires for emotional intimacy; and (3) they ignore differences among women and naturally occurring variations in women's sexuality.

In keeping with the New View critique of the *DSM* and emphasis on contextual factors that influence sexual functioning, the *DSM-5* stipulates that clinicians need to consider a number of factors in arriving at a diagnosis, including partner factors, relationship factors, individual vulnerability factors, cultural or religious factors, and medical factors. In some cases, the *DSM-5* specifically prohibits diagnosing a disorder when one of these factors is present—for example, severe relationship distress. Still, many of the New View criticisms of the *DSM* approach are still relevant. They also have changed some of the diagnostic categories to better fit women's experience so that, as you saw earlier in the chapter, the diagnostic categories for men and women are not parallel.

What did these experts propose instead of the approach taken in the *DSM*? As described below, they defined a sexual problem as dissatisfaction with any emotional, physical, or relational aspect of sexual experience. Their definition takes social, cultural and relationship factors into account.

Sexual Problems Due to Sociocultural, Political, or Economic Factors

The category of sociocultural, political, or economic factors includes problems that are due to (1) ignorance and anxiety because of inadequate sexuality education, lack of access to health services, or other social constraints;

(2) sexual avoidance or distress because of perceived inability to meet cultural norms regarding ideal sexuality (e.g., anxiety about one's body or about sexual orientation); (3) inhibitions caused by conflict between the norms of one's culture of origin and those of the dominant culture; and (4) lack of interest or fatigue caused by family and work obligations.

Sexual Problems Relating to Partner and Relationship

Problems in the category relating to the partner and relationship involve (1) sexual inhibition or distress arising from betrayal or fear of the partner because of abuse; (2) discrepancies in desire or preferences for sexual activities; (3) ignorance or inhibition about sexual communications; (4) loss of sexual interest as a result of conflicts over issues, such as money, or resulting from traumatic experiences, such as infertility; and (5) loss of arousal because of a partner's health or sexual problems.

Sexual Problems Due to Psychological Factors

The category of psychological factors includes the following problems: (1) sexual aversion or inhibition of sexual pleasure because of past experiences of physical, sexual, or emotional abuse; (2) personality problems with attachment or rejection, or depression or anxiety; and (3) sexual inhibition caused by fear of sexual acts or their possible consequences, such as pain during intercourse or fear of pregnancy or STIs.

Sexual Problems Due to Medical Factors

When sexual problems arise despite a supportive interpersonal situation, adequate sexual knowledge, and positive attitudes, they may be a result of (1) any number of medical conditions that affect neurological, circulatory, endocrine, or other systems of the body; (2) pregnancy or STIs; (3) side effects of medications.

As you can see, this way of thinking about sexual disorders and their causes in women is considerably different from the dominant ways of thinking and the categories listed in the *DSM-IV-TR* or *DSM-5*. New research is beginning to support this alternative view (King et al., 2007). For example, official diagnoses of disorders do not correlate well with women's perception that they have a problem or with their psychological distress. This suggests that the traditional diagnostic categories are missing the mark for some women.

Therapies for Sexual Disorders

A variety of therapies for sexual disorders are available, each relying on a different theoretical understanding of what causes sexual disorders. Here we examine four major categories of therapies: behaviour therapy, cognitive-behavioural therapy, couple therapy, and biomedical therapies. Effective treatments for sexual disorders focus on factors that are currently maintaining the sexual disorder rather than on predisposing factors.

Behaviour Therapy

Behaviour therapy has its roots in learning theory. The basic assumption is that sex problems are the result of prior learning and that they are maintained by ongoing reinforcements and punishments (immediate causes). It follows that these problem behaviours can be unlearned by new conditioning. One of the key techniques is in vivo desensitization, in which the client is gradually led through exercises that reduce anxiety.

In 1970, Masters and Johnson reported on their development of a set of techniques for sex therapy with heterosexual couples and ushered in a new era of sex therapy. They operated from a behaviour therapy model because they saw sexual disorders as learned behaviours rather than as symptoms of psychiatric illness. Masters and Johnson used a rapid two-week program of intensive daily therapy that consisted mainly of education and specific behavioural exercises, or "homework assignments."

Often the first step in behavioural sex therapy is to help clients learn more about their own bodies and what they like and do not like sexually. Because each person is unique, this is often done by assigning an exercise, sometimes called *body mapping*, which the client does alone (that is, without their partner present). Clients map out their own sensations by touching their body all over (usually first excluding breasts and genitals) to find out what parts of the body and what ways of touching produce pleasure. They later communicate what they have learned to their partner.

One of the basic goals of Masters and Johnson's therapy was to eliminate goal-oriented sexual performance. Many clients believe that in sex they must perform and achieve certain things. If sex is an achievement situation, it also can become the scene of failure, and perceived failures lead people to believe that they have a sexual problem. In one technique used in behaviour therapy to eliminate a goal-oriented attitude toward sex, the couple is forbidden to have sexual intercourse until they are specifically permitted to by the therapists. They are assigned sensate focus exercises that reduce the demands on them. As the couple successfully completes each of these exercises, the sexual component of subsequent exercises is gradually increased. The couple chalk up a series of successes until eventually they are having intercourse and the disorder has disappeared. This exercise also works to condition a new response to sexual stimuli that

Behaviour therapy: A system of therapy based on learning theory, in which the focus is on the problem behaviour and how it can be modified or changed.

were previously experienced as anxiety-producing by pairing relaxation and intimacy with these stimuli.

Sensate focus exercises are based on the notion that touching and being touched are important forms of sexual expression and that touching is also an important form of communication; for example, a touch can express affection, desire, understanding, or a lack of caring. In the exercises, one member of the couple plays the giving role (touches and strokes the other), while the other person plays the receiving role (is touched by the other). The giving partner is instructed to massage or caress the other, while the receiving partner is instructed to communicate to the giver what is most pleasurable. Thus the exercise fosters communication. The partners switch roles after a certain period. In the first exercises, the giver is not to stroke the genitals or breasts (nor should the receiver ask for this) but may touch any other area. As the couple progress through the exercises, they are instructed to begin touching the genitals and breasts. These exercises also encourage the partners to focus their attention on the sensuous pleasures they are receiving. Many people's sexual response is dulled because they are distracted; they are thinking about how to solve a family financial problem or are spectatoring their own performance. They are victims of cognitive interference. The sensate focus exercises train people to concentrate only on their sexual experience, thereby increasing the pleasure of it. In addition to these exercises, behaviour therapists provide simple education. The couple is given thorough instruction in the anatomy and physiology of the male or female sexual organs (depending on whether the couple are of the same sex or not). Some couples, for example, have no idea what or where the clitoris is. These instructions may also clear up myths and misinformation that either member of the couple may have had since childhood. For example, a man with an erectile disorder may have been told as a child that men can have only a fixed number of orgasms in their lifetime. As he approaches middle age, he starts to worry because his erections may come and go during lovemaking (see Chapter 11) or about whether he may have used up almost all of his orgasms, and this creates the erectile disorder. It is important for such men to learn that nature has imposed no quota on them.

Masters and Johnson collected data on the success and failure rates of their therapy. In their book *Human Sexual Inadequacy*, they reported on the treatment of 790 persons. Of these, 142 still had a disorder at the end of the two-week therapy program. This translates to a failure rate of 18 percent or a *success rate of 82 percent.*

Sensate focus exercises: A part of the sex therapy developed by Masters and Johnson in which one partner caresses the other, the other communicates what is pleasurable, and there are no performance demands.

Cognitive-behavioural therapy: A form of therapy that combines behaviour therapy and restructuring of negative thought patterns.

Although the failure rate ran around 18 percent for most disorders, there were two exceptions: Therapy for rapid ejaculation had a very low failure rate (2.2 percent), and therapy for lifelong erectile disorder had a high failure rate (40.6 percent). That is, rapid ejaculation was quite easy to cure, and lifelong erectile disorder very difficult. Masters and Johnson's success rate is impressive, although their results have been called into question, as we shall see later in this chapter.

In Masters and Johnson's initial development of their therapy techniques, all the couples were mixed-sex. They later used the same techniques in treating sexual disorders in same-sex couples, with a comparable success rate (Masters & Johnson, 1979).

Cognitive-Behavioural Therapy

Paralleling the increased importance of cognitive theories in psychology (see Chapter 2) is the increased importance of cognitive approaches to psychotherapy. Today, many sex therapists use a combination of the behavioural exercises pioneered by Masters and Johnson and cognitive therapy (Heiman, 2007). This is termed **cognitive-behavioural therapy**.

Cognitive restructuring is an important technique in a cognitive approach to sex therapy (Wincze & Carey, 2001). In cognitive restructuring, the therapist essentially helps the client restructure his or her thought patterns, helping him or her to become more positive (for an example, see First Person). Cognitive restructuring is particularly useful in addressing two of the maintaining causes of sexual disorders described earlier in this chapter—negative attitudes and cognitive interference. In one form of cognitive restructuring, the therapist challenges the client's negative attitudes. These attitudes may be as general as a woman's distrusting attitudes toward all men or as specific as a man's negative attitudes toward masturbation. The client is helped to reshape these attitudes into more positive ones.

Cognitive therapists also like to address cognitive interference. The general idea is to reduce the presence of interfering thoughts during sex. First the therapist must help the client identify the presence of such thoughts. The therapist then suggests techniques for reducing these thoughts, generally by replacing them with erotic thoughts—perhaps focusing attention on a particular part of one's body and how it is responding with arousal, or having an erotic fantasy. Out go the bad thoughts, and in come the good thoughts.

Recently some therapists have added mindfulness training as part of sex therapy. Mindfulness training helps individuals focus their attention on the present moment and create nonjudgmental present-moment sexual awareness (Brotto & Heiman, 2007;

First Person

A Case of Low Sexual Desire

Sarah, age 27, was referred to a sex therapist by an endocrinologist, to be considered for testosterone treatment for her complaints of low sexual desire. Sarah had no ovarian tissue. One ovary that had a large cyst had been removed when she was 13, and her other ovary had undergone torsion (twisting that cut off the blood supply) and had to be removed when she was 16. She had been given estrogen and progesterone replacement immediately so that her menstrual periods never stopped.

When Sarah met with the therapist, she explained that sex with her partner Carl was enjoyable. They had been together four years and were sexual approximately once a week. Carl would have preferred to be sexual every day, but Sarah resisted. She said that even though sex was enjoyable and satisfying, if she never had sex again, it would be fine with her. She reported that Carl thought that she was very abnormal and so did her endocrinologist.

Sarah had very few sexual thoughts about arousal or anticipating sexual activity. Her sexual thoughts were instead troubling and focused on her guilt that their sexual interactions were infrequent and that she was abnormal. During sexual interactions with Carl, she was aroused, she enjoyed the experience, and had orgasms. She found arousing Carl to be pleasurable and arousing for her.

Using the New View of women's sexual problems described earlier in the chapter, the therapist explained to Sarah that her experience was within normal limits. In a meeting with Carl, the therapist described the range of women's sexual experiences. The next question was whether some factors were causing Sarah's behaviour to be toward one end of the spectrum. Both biological and psychological factors seemed to be involved. Because of the removal of her ovaries, she was manufacturing no testosterone, although androgens manufactured by the adrenal gland were present. Sarah's life history also gave clues regarding possible psychological factors. Sarah grew up with an alcoholic father who was prone to shouting, arguing, and engaging in emotional abuse; Sarah coped by retreating to her bedroom. She suppressed her feelings of anger and did not rebel even when she was a teenager. This coping style worked well at the time. However, as an adult, she was still in the habit of suppressing emotions generally. Sarah agreed that her sexual emotions were probably also suppressed.

The therapist decided against testosterone treatment and instead focused on encouraging Sarah to deliberately attempt to feel more (nonsexual) emotion throughout the day. In addition, she was to deliberately allow more sexual stimuli in her life, such as music, movies, dancing, and erotic conversations.

The therapist met with Carl to explain the situation and assess his own family history. His parents had a bitter divorce when he was just ten. He felt that neither parent had really loved him. For Carl, having sex with his partner was a sign that he was loved. Carl was able to realize that pressuring Sarah did not help the situation and he ceased doing so, which Sarah appreciated. In addition, when Sarah realized the origins and extent of Carl's need to feel loved, she became strongly motivated to find the triggers that were able to make her feel more sexual. Salsa dancing proved to be one of those triggers, combined with encouraging Carl to flirt with her more often. Sarah's sexual self-image increased markedly, as did her sexual desire.

Source: Rosemary Basson, "Sexual Desire/Arousal Disorders in Women," in S. Leiblum (Ed.), *Principles and Practice of Sex Therapy* 4e, 2007, pp. 42–43. Reprinted by permission of the Guilford Press.

Brotto, Heiman, et al., 2008). For example, Canadian psychologist Lori Brotto explains to clients,

> Many of us go through life not living in the present moment. We fluctuate between thinking in the future (worrying, planning, thinking) and living in the past (reviewing events, conversations, plans). We miss out on valuable and meaningful experiences in the present. . . . In instances when we want to be present, such as the sexual scenario, it is difficult if not impossible for us to turn off the cerebral chatter. The net effect is a reduction in arousal, thereby making the sexual experience less rewarding and pleasurable.

She then assigns clients a series of exercises, first in nonsexual situations and then in sexual situations, that help them learn to be fully present (Brotto, Heiman, et al., 2008).

Couple Therapy

As we noted earlier, poor communication and relationship distress are important maintaining causes of sexual disorders. Accordingly, many sex therapists use couple therapy as part of the treatment. This approach rests on the assumption that there is a reciprocal relationship between interpersonal conflict and sex problems. Sex problems can cause conflicts, and conflicts can cause sex problems. In couple therapy, the relationship itself is treated, with the goal of reducing antagonisms and tensions between the partners and improving communication. As the relationship improves, the sex problem should be reduced. Canadian researchers have shown that, for women with dyspareunia, their partner's response to their pain can either help alleviate it or can make it worse (Rosen et al., 2010; Rosen, Bergeron, Glowacka, 2012). This suggests that it would be helpful to involve the partner in the therapy.

For certain disorders and certain couples, therapists may use a combination of cognitive-behavioural and couple therapy. For example, sex therapists Raymond Rosen, Sandra Leiblum, and Ilana Spector (1994) used a five-part model in treating men with erectile disorder:

1. *Sexual- and performance-anxiety reduction.* Individuals with sexual disorders, particularly men with erectile disorder, often have a great deal of performance anxiety. This can be treated using such techniques as sensate focus exercises.

2. *Education and cognitive intervention.* As noted earlier, people with sexual disorders often lack sexual information. Many also have unrealistic expectations about sexual functioning and satisfaction. Cognitive interventions may help men with erection problems to overcome "all or nothing" thinking—that is, the belief that if any aspect of his sexual performance is not perfect, the whole interaction is a disaster. An example is the belief that "I failed sexually because my erection was not 100 percent rigid."

> **What can a woman do if she has trouble having orgasms?**

3. *Script assessment and modification.* All couples have a sexual script that they enact together. People with sexual disorders typically have a restricted, repetitive, and inflexible script, using a small number of techniques that they never change. Novelty is one of the greatest turn-ons, so therapy is designed to help the couple break out of their restricted script and develop a new, mutually pleasurable sexual script.

4. *Conflict resolution and relationship enhancement.* As we have discussed, conflicts in a couple's relationship can lead to sexual disorders. In therapy, these conflicts are identified and the couple works to resolve them. Couples also work to increase their positive interactions.

5. *Relapse prevention training.* Sometimes a relapse—a return of the disorder—occurs following therapy. Therapists have developed techniques to help couples avoid or deal with such relapses. For example, they are told to engage in sensate focus sessions at least once a month.

Notice that part 1 represents the behaviour therapy techniques pioneered by Masters and Johnson; parts 2 and 3 are cognitive therapy techniques; and part 4 is couple therapy. Most skilled sex therapists today use combined or integrated techniques such as these, tailored to the specific disorder and situation of the couple.

LO4 Specific Treatments for Specific Problems

Some very specific techniques have been developed for the treatment of certain sexual disorders. Of course, each of these techniques is typically only one part of a comprehensive treatment approach.

The Stop-Start Technique

The stop-start technique is used in the treatment of premature (early) ejaculation (see Figure 18.3). The man first learns to identify sensations before the point of ejaculatory inevitability (see Chapter 9). The partner manually stimulates the man to erection and then stops the stimulation before that point. Gradually the man loses his erection. The partner resumes stimulation, the man gets another erection, the partner stops, and so on. After doing this three or four times, the man can allow himself to orgasm. The man learns that he can have an erection and be highly aroused without having an orgasm. Using this technique, the couple may extend their sex play to 15 or 20 minutes, and the man gains control over his orgasm. Another version of this method that is occasionally used is the squeeze technique, in which the partner adds a squeeze around the coronal ridge, which also stops orgasm.

Masturbation

The most effective form of therapy for women with orgasmic disorder is a program of directed masturbation (LoPiccolo & Stock, 1986; Meston et al., 2004). The data indicate that masturbation is the technique most likely to produce orgasm in women; it is therefore a logical treatment for women who have problems with having orgasms, many of whom have never masturbated. Women can use a vibrator to learn to bring themselves to orgasm. Masturbation is sometimes recommended as

Figure 18.3 The stop-start technique for treating rapid ejaculation and the position of the couple while using the stop-start technique.

therapy for men as well, for example, in learning to have greater control over the timing of ejaculation.

Kegel Exercises

One technique that is used with women is **Kegel exercises**, named for the physician who devised them (Kegel, 1952). They are designed to exercise and strengthen the *pubococcygeal muscle*, or PC muscle, which runs along the sides of the entrance of the vagina. The exercises are particularly helpful for women who have had this muscle stretched in childbirth, who have poor muscle tone, or who have vaginismus. The woman is instructed first to find her PC muscle by sitting on a toilet with her legs spread apart, beginning to urinate, and stopping the flow of urine voluntarily. The muscle that stops the flow is the PC muscle. After that, the woman is told to contract the muscle 10 times during each of six sessions per day. Gradually, she can work up to more.[2] These exercises seem to enhance arousal and facilitate orgasm by increasing women's awareness of and comfort with their genitals (Heiman, 2007). They also permit the heterosexual woman to stimulate her partner more because her vagina can grip his penis more tightly, and they are a cure for women who have problems with involuntarily urinating as they orgasm.

Pelvic floor muscle exercises and therapy can be used on their own and should be used as part of the comprehensive, multidisciplinary treatment of genito-pelvic pain/penetration disorder that includes both pelvic floor rehabilitation and cognitive-behavioural therapy (Bergeron et al., 2010; van Lankveld et al., 2010). Physiotherapists provide physical assistance to make sure that the woman is doing the exercises correctly—about half of women do not do them correctly with just verbal instructions (Rosenbaum, 2005, 2007a). Often physiotherapists use biofeedback to help women learn to isolate and contract the correct muscles of the pelvic floor. Research in Ontario has shown that pelvic floor physiotherapy is effective at treating genito-pelvic pain and vaginismus in women (Gentilcore-Saulnier et al., 2010; Goldfinger et al., 2009; Reissing et al., 2013). A variation on the Kegel exercises is reverse Kegels, in which the focus is on learning to relax the muscles in the pelvic area. Women who have genito-pelvic pain accompanied by tensing or tightening of the pelvic floor muscles during attempted penetration can use vaginal dilators to help them overcome their involuntary muscle contraction (see Figure 18.4). The set of dilators are graduated in size so that women can start with inserting a very small dilator and then build up to larger dilators. Some women prefer to use their own or their partner's fingers (starting with the tip of the little finger) instead of dilators.

> **Kegel (KAY-gul) exercises:** A part of sex therapy for women with orgasmic disorder, in which the woman exercises the muscles surrounding the vagina; also called pubococcygeal or PC muscle exercises.

---

[2] Students should recognize the exciting possibilities for doing these exercises. For example, they are a good way to amuse yourself in the middle of a lecture, and no one will ever know you are doing them.

Figure 18.4 This is a set of vaginal dilators that vary in size. Women who have genito-pelvic pain accompanied by tensing or tightening of the pelvic floor muscles during attempted penetration can use them to help overcome their involuntary muscle contraction.

Pelvic floor muscle exercises are sometimes also used in treating men with premature ejaculation.

Bibliotherapy

Bibliotherapy refers simply to the use of a self-help book to treat a disorder. Research shows that bibliotherapy is effective for orgasmic disorders in women (van Lankveld, 1998). Julia Heiman and Joseph LoPiccolo's *Becoming Orgasmic: A Sexual Growth Program for Women* (1988) has been used extensively for this purpose. Bibliotherapy has also been shown to be effective for couples with a mixture of male and female sexual disorders (van Lankveld et al., 2001, van Lankveld, 2009). In addition, many people describe Bernie Zilbergeld's self-help book *The New Male Sexuality* (1999) and Michale Metz and Barry McCarthy's book *Coping with Premature Ejaculation: How to Overcome PE, Please Your Partner and Have Great Sex* (2003) (among others) as helpful. Other couples find sex therapy videotapes to be helpful. Interestingly, as early as 1973, Steven Neiger, a Canadian pioneer in sex therapy and sex education, developed a series of 12 audiotapes to help couples overcome sexual problems (Alexander, 1990). It may be that in the future the Internet will replace bibliotherapy as self-help methods for treating sexual disorders. The advice columns at self-help websites can provide accurate, explicit, and nonjudgmental information. Specialized message boards and chat rooms for people who share a common interest (e.g., bisexuals, persons with disabilities) can help to create a sense of community and provide useful information,

How does Viagra work?

Bibliotherapy: The use of a self-help book to treat a disorder.
Viagra: A drug used in the treatment of erectile disorder; sildenafil.

especially for those who are geographically isolated or in countries where sex therapy is unknown.

LO4 Biomedical Therapies

Beginning in the 1990s, there was increased recognition of the biological bases of some sexual disorders. Consistent with this emphasis, many developments in medical and drug treatments and even surgical treatment have occurred. From the biopsychosocial perspective, biomedical therapies need to be used in conjunction with other interventions that address the psychosocial factors associated with the sexual disorder. The medicalization of sexuality, with its emphasis on performance and medical treatment, is discussed later in this chapter.

Drug Treatments

Many promising advances have been made in the identification of drugs that cure sexual disorders or work well when used together with cognitive-behavioural therapy or other psychological forms of sex therapy (Ashton, 2007; Rosen, 2007; Rowland & Burnett, 2000). Some are drugs that have direct sexual effects, whereas others are psychotherapeutic drugs (such as antidepressants) that work by improving the person's mood but, as discussed earlier in this chapter, may also affect sexual functioning.

Certainly the most widely publicized breakthrough among these treatments was the approval of **Viagra** (sildenafil) for the treatment of erectile disorder (Figure 18.5). Earlier biomedical treatments, such as intracavernosal injections, were unsatisfactory for various reasons (these are discussed in the next section). Viagra is taken by mouth approximately one hour before anticipated sexual activity. It does not, by itself, produce an erection. Rather, when the man is stimulated sexually after taking Viagra, the drug facilitates the physiological processes that produce erection. Specifically, it relaxes the smooth muscles in the corpora cavernosa, allowing blood to flow in and create an erection. Averaged over 27 clinical trials, about 57 percent of men respond successfully to Viagra, compared with 21 percent responding to the placebo (Fink et al., 2002). Men have generally been quite satisfied with Viagra. Side effects are not common; if present, they included headache, flushing, and vision disturbances (Ashton, 2007).

On balance, Viagra seems to be quite safe (Morales et al., 1998; Rosen & McKenna, 2002). It does not seem to cause priapism (an erection that just won't go away). Yet the very ease of its use may lead physicians to overprescribe it and men to demand it in inappropriate circumstances. Today it is easily available on the Internet. If the erection difficulties are due to relationship problems or individual issues, Viagra will provide at most a temporary solution. It is not helpful for sexual disorders other than erectile disorder. And there is no evidence that it

Figure 18.5 Viagra, one of the prescription drugs available for treating erectile disorder.

enhances sexual performance in men who function sexually within the normal range. In addition, its recreational or high-performance uses are causes for concern (Harte & Meston, 2011).

Viagra was such a success, financially and otherwise, that drug companies immediately sought successors—drugs that would be more convenient or would work in cases that were not effectively treated with Viagra. One of these, Cialis (tadalafil), is very much like Viagra in that it relaxes the smooth muscle surrounding the arteries to the penis, facilitating engorgement (Brock et al., 2002; Montorsi et al., 2004; Padma-Nathan et al., 2001). Whereas Viagra lasts only a maximum of 8 to 10 hours, Cialis can be effective for as long as 24 to 36 hours. Drugs such as Cialis have been shown to have no negative effects on sperm production or sex hormone production (Hellstrom et al., 2003a).

Levitra and staxyn (vardenafil) are different versions of another new drug that works much like Viagra but has a slightly different formulation (Hatzichristou et al., 2004; Hellstrom et al., 2003b; Rosen & McKenna, 2002). A particularly important success story is that these drugs can be effective in treating erectile dysfunction that results from complete surgical removal of the prostate (Brock et al., 2003).

Viagra, Cialis, and Levitra each act peripherally—that is, they act on sites in the penis. Another alternative is centrally acting drugs, meaning drugs that act on regions of the brain involved in arousal. One of these is Uprima

(apomorphine SL;[3] Heaton, 2001). It acts in about 20 minutes and, like other drugs, does not produce a spontaneous erection. Rather, it has to be accompanied by sexual stimulation. Uprima acts by boosting levels of the neurotransmitter dopamine in the brain, particularly in the hypothalamus, and is effective in about 55 percent of cases (Heaton, 2001; Montorsi et al., 2003a, 2003b).

And what about a Viagra for women? The drug company Pfizer, as well as many scientists, hoped that Viagra also would work for women—that is, it would cure their desire and orgasm problems. The problem is that Viagra works by increasing vasocongestion, and insufficient vasocongestion is probably not what causes most women's sexual difficulties. After many failed clinical trials, Pfizer announced in 2004 that it would give up on testing Viagra for women (Harris, 2004). For example, British Columbia researcher Rosemary Basson and her colleagues found that Viagra does not increase either arousal or orgasm in either premenopausal or postmenopausal women with sexual dysfunction (Basson & Brotto, 2003; Basson et al., 2002).

In another attempt at a female Viagra, German pharmaceutical company Boehringer developed the drug flibanserin (proposed trade name Girosa). It had originally been developed to be an antidepressant, but it didn't work very well for that purpose. It acts to reduce levels of the neurotransmitter serotonin and increase levels of dopamine and norepinephrine. To use terms from the dual control model discussed in Chapter 9, serotonin is thought to have an inhibitory effect on sexual desire and dopamine and norepinephrine are thought to have excitatory effects. All that sounds good on paper, but the U.S. Food and Drug Administration investigated it and issued a negative report in 2010 and again in 2013, based on clinical trials that showed no actual increase in sexual desire in women taking it, compared with controls.

Women's sexual problems most commonly involve orgasm difficulties and low sexual desire/arousal, the latter being a problem particularly as women age and their ovaries decline in production of testosterone. One possibility is administration of testosterone or some other androgen (Basaria & Dobs, 2006; Baulieu et al., 2000), although use of testosterone in women is still quite controversial. For example, researchers in B.C. found no difference in testosterone levels between women with and without hypoactive sexual desire disorder (Basson et al., 2010). Intrinsa is a testosterone patch designed for postmenopausal women experiencing low sexual desire. However, initial results have not been sufficiently positive to receive approval to market the patch in Canada or the United States.

---

[3] The *SL* means "sublingual"; that is, you take it by putting it under your tongue and letting it dissolve rather than by swallowing it. It gets to the brain more efficiently that way. Previously, apomorphine had been used to treat Parkinson's disease.

The other issue concerning women and Viagra involves the partners of men with Viagra-aided erections. Not all partners, some of whom had adjusted to a relationship without intercourse, welcome the man's new capacity, an issue that has been ignored in the medical fix approach (Potts et al., 2003; Rosen & McKenna, 2002). For example, for a couple with relationship problems, it may create additional problems if taking Viagra results in pressure to engage in unwanted sexual activity. Often it is important to combine couple therapy with drug therapy. Some women, of course, are absolutely delighted with the results (Montorsi & Althof, 2004).

Intracavernosal Injection

Intracavernosal injection (ICI) is a treatment for erectile disorders (Hsiao et al., 2011; Shabsigh et al., 2000). It involves injecting a drug (such as alprostadil, or Edex) into the corpora cavernosa of the penis. The drugs used are vasodilators—that is, they dilate the blood vessels in the penis so that much more blood can accumulate there, producing an erection.

Since the introduction of Viagra, ICI is now used mainly in cases in which the erection problem is organic and the man does not respond to Viagra or its successors (Shabsigh et al., 2000). It can also be used in conjunction with cognitive-behavioural therapy in cases that have combined organic and psychological causes. Like Viagra, ICI can have positive psychological effects because it restores the man's confidence in his ability to get erections. It also reduces his performance anxiety because he is able to engage in intercourse successfully. However, according to research in British Columbia, about 50 percent of men who begin using ICI discontinue its use (Basson and VHHSC Centre, 1998). ICI can also result in a prolonged erection that does not go away, even in the absence of stimulation, called *priapism*. This condition is painful and requires medical treatment. There are also potential abuses. Men who have normal erections should not use ICI in an attempt to produce a "super erection."

Alprostadil is now also available as a suppository to place inside the urethra or as a cream to rub on, eliminating the need for the needle. This system is often called MUSE, which stands for "medicated urethral system for erections." However, MUSE is not as effective as ICI.

Vacuum Devices

Vacuum devices are another treatment for sexual arousal disorders. Essentially, they pump you up! A tube is placed over the penis (see Figure 18.6). With some devices, the mouth can produce enough suction; with others, a small hand pump is used. Once a reasonably firm erection is present, the tube is removed and a rubber ring is placed around the base of the penis to maintain the

Penile prosthesis (prahs-THEE-sis): A surgical treatment for erectile dysfunction, in which inflatable tubes are inserted into the penis.

Suction

Figure 18.6 A treatment for erectile disorder. An external tube, with a rubber ring around it, is placed over the lubricated penis. Suction applied to the tube produces erection, which is maintained by the constricting action of the rubber ring once the plastic tube has been removed.

penis's engorgement with blood. These devices have been used successfully with, for example, diabetic men. They can also be helpful in combination with cognitive-behavioural couple therapy for cases of erectile dysfunction that are mainly psychological in origin (Wylie et al., 2003).

There is also now a vacuum device to assist women with clitoral engorgement called EROS. However, there is little research supporting the effectiveness of this device; for most women the subjective aspects of arousal are at least equally important as is clitoral engorgement per se.

Surgical Therapy

There is promising evidence that surgery (e.g., vestibulectomy) can help women with some types of genito-pelvic pain (Bergeron et al., 2001; Lambert et al., 2012; Landry et al., 2008). Nonetheless, most surgical treatments are currently focused on male sexual problems.

For severe cases of erectile disorder, surgical therapy is possible. The surgery involves implanting a **prosthesis** into the penis (Hellstrom, 2003). A sac or bladder of sterile fluid is implanted in the lower abdomen, connected to two inflatable tubes running the length of the corpus spongiosum, with a pump in the scrotum. Thus the man can literally pump up or inflate his penis so that he has a full erection.

It should be emphasized that this is a radical treatment that should be reserved only for those cases that have not been successfully treated by sex therapy or drug therapy. The patient must understand that the surgery itself destroys some portions of the penis, so that a natural erection will never again be possible. Although the treatment is radical and should be used conservatively, it is right for some men who have been incapable of erection because of organic difficulties.

In another version of a surgical approach, a semirigid, silicone-like rod is implanted into the penis (Fathy et al., 2007; Ferguson & Cespedes, 2003). This noninflatable device is less costly than the inflatable version and has a lower rate of complications (Rosen & Leiblum, 1995b).

Critiques of Sex Therapy

One of the most basic questions we must ask about sex therapy is: Is it effective?

Psychologists Bernie Zilbergeld and Michael Evans (1980) did an extensive critique of the research methods used by Masters and Johnson in evaluating the success of their sex therapy. Zilbergeld and Evans concluded that there are a number of substantial problems. In brief, the criticisms suggest that we really do not know what the success rate of Masters and Johnson's therapy was. A discussion of the specific criticisms follows. These points are important to bear in mind when evaluating any type of sex therapy.

First, Masters and Johnson never actually reported a *success* rate for the therapy. Instead, they reported a *failure* rate of about 18 percent. The rest apparently included a mixture of clear successes and cases that were ambiguous as to whether they were successes or failures—in short, they had 80 percent nonfailures, but that does not mean 82 percent successes.

Furthermore, Masters and Johnson never defined what they meant by a "success" in therapy. This is an important issue. How improved does a person have to be to be counted as a success? Suppose a woman seeks help for anorgasmia; she has never had an orgasm. By the end of therapy, she is able to orgasm from a vibrator but not from hand stimulation or mouth stimulation by her partner, nor by penetration. Is this case a success? How would Masters and Johnson have classified her?

Zilbergeld and Evans (1980) initiated their critical appraisal after finding that they and other sex therapists were unable to obtain success rates as dramatic or relapse rates as low as the ones Masters and Johnson reported. One possibility is that other sex therapists have been using definitions of therapy success that are stricter and more precise than the definition used by Masters and Johnson. Another possibility is that current therapists are seeing clients who are significantly different from the clients seen by Masters and Johnson. For example, today individuals with straightforward problems can often resolve the problem with information they find in books or on the Internet. These options were not available when Masters and Johnson were doing their work.

More recently researchers conducted a meta-analysis to determine whether, across all studies that have compared psychological interventions for sexual dysfunction to waiting list controls, there is evidence that these interventions work (Frühauf et al., 2013). They found that psychological treatment both decreased symptom severity and increased sexual satisfaction. There also is sufficient evidence evaluating certain treatments for certain disorders to reach the following conclusions (Althof, 2007; Heiman, 2007; McCabe et al., 2010; Rosenbaum, 2007b):

- Lifelong orgasmic dysfunction is successfully treated with directed masturbation, and the treatment can be enhanced with sensate focus exercises.
- Treatments for acquired orgasmic dysfunction are somewhat less successful. Therapy that combines some or all of the following components seems to be most effective: sex education, sexual skills training, communication skills training, and body image therapy. The problem here, most likely, is that there are many different patterns of secondary anorgasmia, with a need to match treatment to the pattern of the disorder, something that research has not been able to untangle.
- Vaginismus can be successfully treated with progressive vaginal dilators; relaxation and Kegel exercises may also be helpful, but the evidence is not as strong. A recent study compared cognitive-behavioural therapy including these and other components to a control group and found that 14 percent of the treated participants but none of the control participants reported successful intercourse (van Lankveld et al., 2006)—a significant but small effect for treatment.
- Cognitive-behavioural therapy (CBT) is effective for treating premature ejaculation. Drugs, specifically some antidepressants (e.g., SSRIs), also may be effective combined with CBT (Hellstrom, 2011).
- Erectile disorder can be treated successfully with a combination of CBT and couple therapy, as described in the section on couple therapy.
- For some disorders—male sexual desire disorder, genito-pelvic pain/penetration disorder, female desire/arousal disorder, and delayed ejaculation in men—research is insufficient to conclude that there is an effective treatment. Of course, this does not mean that current treatments are not effective; just that the research has not been done to determine one way or the other.

Another critique points out the *medicalization* of sexual disorders (Kleinplatz, 2003a; Tiefer, 1994, 2000). Research has increasingly identified organic sources of male erectile disorder, and with these advances have come attempts to identify drugs and surgeries, rather than psychotherapies, to treat problems. In part, political and financial issues are involved, as physicians try to seize the treatment of sexual disorders from psychologists and other therapists. But there is also a cost to the patient as the disorder may be given a quick fix with drugs while the patient's anxieties and relationship problems are ignored. That is, we treat the symptoms, not the problem (Kleinplatz, 2003b). For biomedical treatments to be successful over the long term, the cognitive, affective, and interpersonal issues must also be addressed (Basson and VHHSC Centre, 1998). The New View of women's sexual problems, discussed earlier in this chapter, was proposed in part as an alternative to medicalization; of importance, it takes sociocultural and relationship factors into account.

In contrast to these scientific criticisms, sex therapy has also been criticized on philosophical grounds. Ottawa psychologist and sex therapist Peggy Kleinplatz (1992, 1998) has argued that the current approach to sex therapy is goal-oriented rather than pleasure-oriented. By defining problems in terms of sexual disorders, sex therapists and their clients may focus on physiological and mechanical outcomes (getting an erection, having an orgasm) rather than on clients' subjective experience of sexuality, sexual satisfaction, and eroticism (Kleinplatz, 2003b). Sexual satisfaction is not just the absence of a sexual disorder (Byers, 1999). Often individuals get aroused and have orgasms but experience disappointment with the quality of their sexual encounters with their partner. Evaluation of the success of sex therapy should include more attention to whether therapy has resulted in enhanced sexual satisfaction (Handy et al., 1985). Resolving a sexual disorder often results in a decrease in sexual *dissatisfaction*, but it does not necessarily result in increased sexual satisfaction.

Psychiatrist Thomas Szasz (1980) argued that sex therapists have essentially produced a lot of illness by creating the (somewhat arbitrary) diagnostic categories of sexual disorder. This criticism may especially apply to individuals with disabilities. Ontario researcher Gina Di Giulio (2003) has argued that the diagnostic categories for sexual dysfunction do not fit for such persons. In particular, the focus on genital response may imply that persons with disabilities cannot experience a highly pleasurable and satisfying sex life. Yet a woman with a spinal cord injury who has little genital sensation might get great pleasure from having her breasts or other parts of her body stroked, and reach orgasm from this type of pleasuring. That is, she has adapted her lovemaking to meet her own needs and situation. It is important for sex therapists to communicate to their clients with disabilities that they are fully sexual and that there is no right way to make love.

Where do these criticisms leave us? In our opinion, they do not invalidate the work of sex therapists. Rather, they urge us to be cautious. Most sexual disorders will not have success rates of 80 percent (but then, most therapies for other disorders do not either) but they may well turn out to have success rates of 60 percent or more, which is still pretty good. Many other clients may feel that their sexual functioning has been enhanced by sex therapy (Kaplan, 1979). A single method of therapy, such as Masters and Johnson's behaviour therapy, will not be effective with every disorder. Finally, we must be sensitive to the values expressed in labelling something as being, or someone as having, a "disorder."

Some Practical Information

Avoiding Sexual Disorders

People can use some of the principles that emerge from sex therapists' work to avoid having sexual disorders in the first place. As the saying goes, an ounce of prevention is worth a pound of cure. In Chapter 1, we introduced the concept of sexual health. The following are some principles of good sexual mental health:

1. *Communicate with your partner.* Don't expect him or her to be a mind reader concerning what is pleasurable to you. One way to do this is to make it a habit to talk to your partner while you are having sex; verbal communication then does not come as a shock. Some people, though, feel uncomfortable talking at such times; nonverbal communication, such as placing your hand on top of your partner's and moving it where you want it, works well too although not as well (see Chapter 12 for more detail about good sexual communication).

2. *Concentrate on giving and receiving sexual pleasure.* Don't be a spectator, feeling as if you are putting on a sexual performance that you constantly need to evaluate. Concentrate as much as possible on the giving and receiving of sensual pleasures, not on how well you are doing.

3. *Relax and enjoy yourself.* Don't set up goals for sexual performance. If you have a goal, you can fail, and failure can produce disorders. Don't set your heart on having simultaneous orgasms or, if you are a woman, on having five orgasms before your partner has one. Just relax and enjoy yourself.

4. *Be choosy about the situations in which you have sex.* Don't have sex when you are in a terrific hurry or are afraid you will be disturbed. Also, be choosy about who your partner is. Trusting your partner is essential to good sexual functioning; similarly,

a partner who really cares for you will be understanding if things don't go well and will not laugh or be sarcastic.

5. *Accept that disappointments will occur.* They do in any sexual relationship. What is important is how you interpret them. It is important that you don't see yourself as a failure and don't let them ruin the relationship. Instead, try to think, "How can we make this turn out well anyhow?"

Choosing a Sex Therapist

No provinces or territories require specific licensing or certification to practise sex therapy. This means that anyone can hang out a shingle saying "sex therapist," and some people with no training in the field have done so.

How do you go about finding a good, qualified sex therapist? Since 2013, Quebec has required sexologists to be licensed, as they do other professions (see www.opsq.org). Although they are not required by law to do so, some Ontario sex therapists choose to become certified by the Board of Examiners in Sexual Therapy and Counselling (BESTCO). These organizations ensure that people who identify themselves as sex therapists have the knowledge and training to effectively treat sexual disorders (Kleinplatz, 2009). However, the other provinces and territories do not have such boards. A very few Canadian sex therapists choose to be certified by a U.S. organization. However, most sex therapists in Canada operate under their discipline licences—such as psychology, clinical social work, or psychiatry—and therefore do not seek additional certification as a sex therapist even if they have training in sex therapy. Your local medical or psychological association can provide a list of therapists in your area and may be able to tell you which ones have special training in sex therapy. Unfortunately, most therapists have only limited training in assessing and treating sexual difficulties (Miller & Byers, 2009, 2010; Reissing & Di Giulio, 2010). As a result, many are not confident in their abilities to provide treatment for sexual concerns and, as a result, do not routinely address their clients' sexual issues and concerns (Miller & Byers, 2012). Thus, it is important to ask potential sex therapists about their specific training in sex therapy and about their approach to it to make sure that they are qualified to provide sex therapy. Choose a therapist or clinic that offers an individualized *integrated biopsychosocial approach* that recognizes the potential biological, psychological, and relationship influences on any sexual disorder and is prepared to address all these and work in conjunction with professionals from other disciplines if needed.

What about people who live in an area where there are no sex therapists? Some therapists provide sex therapy online. What are its advantages and disadvantages (McCabe et al., 2010)? Proponents of sex therapy online argue that it is more affordable than traditional in-person therapy and that its anonymity is a major advantage. Interactions with a therapist online can break the wall of isolation surrounding a person with a sexual disorder. There are disadvantages, too. Currently, there is no system for licensing online sex therapists, so unqualified and perhaps unethical persons could easily present themselves as therapists. In fact, it is difficult to find legitimate sex therapy websites because searching for terms such as "sex therapy" leads to a deluge of porn sites. Moreover, online sex therapists probably will not be able to give true intensive therapy of the kind one would get in multiple in-person sessions with a therapist. However, qualified online therapists can affirm that a behaviour is not problematic and provide positive encouragement as well as accurate information, and that's enough to solve many people's problems. Unfortunately, many people who would benefit from sex therapy are unlikely to seek help, even over the Internet, for religious or cultural reasons, because they are embarrassed about it, or because they are erotophobic.

SUMMARY

There are seven main sexual disorders according to the *DSM-5*: male hypoactive sexual desire disorder, erectile disorder, premature (early) ejaculation, delayed ejaculation, female sexual interest/arousal disorder, female orgasmic disorder, and genito-pelvic pain/penetration disorder.

Sexual disorders may be caused by physical factors, individual psychological factors, and interpersonal factors. Organic causes include some illnesses, infections, and damage to the spinal cord. Certain drugs may also create problems with sexual functioning.

Psychological causes are categorized into predisposing factors and maintaining causes including myths and misinformation, negative attitudes, anxiety and inhibition, cognitive interference, psychological distress, and behavioural or lifestyle factors. Interpersonal factors include failure to engage in effective stimulation, often cause by poor sexual communication, and relationship distress caused by, for example, conflict in the couple's relationship or lack of intimacy.

Therapies for sexual disorders include behaviour therapy based on learning theory (pioneered by Masters and

Johnson), cognitive-behavioural therapy, couple therapy, specific treatments for specific problems (e.g., stop-start for premature ejaculation), and a variety of biomedical treatments, which include drug treatments (e.g., Viagra).

A number of criticisms of sex therapy have been raised, including concerns about the research methods used to evaluate the success of Masters and Johnson's therapy, the medicalization of sexual disorders, focusing on physiological outcomes rather than on sexual pleasure and satisfaction, and the entire enterprise of identifying and labelling sexual disorders. Steps to prevent the occurrence of sexual disorders include good couple communication and not setting up sexual performance goals. When choosing a sex therapist, it is important that the person is licensed or certified in their field and has specific sex therapy training.

QUESTIONS FOR THOUGHT, DISCUSSION, AND DEBATE

1. When (or if) you engage in sexual activity with a partner, do you feel that you are under pressure to perform and that you engage in spectatoring? If so, what might you do to change this pattern?

2. Considering the predisposing causes of sexual disorders, what are the implications for parents who want to raise sexually healthy children? Could parents do certain things that would avoid or prevent sexual disorders in their children?

3. Your best friend, Steve, who is 22, discloses to you a recent history of erectile difficulties, which has been very embarrassing and frustrating for him. He has heard about Viagra and, knowing that you are taking a human sexuality course, comes to you for advice about whether he should go to a doctor to get a prescription for it. What advice would you give him?

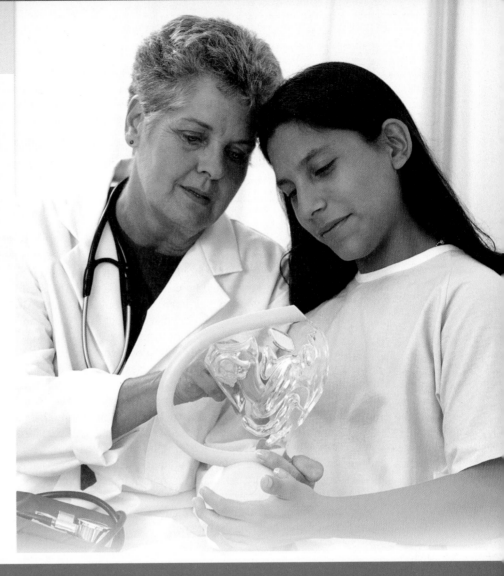

Are YOU Curious?

1. What do Canadians think about sex education in schools?
2. What kinds of sex education programs work?
3. Why don't parents provide sex education for their kids?

Read this chapter to find out.

CHAPTER

19

Sexuality Education

LEARNING OBJECTIVES

After studying this chapter, you will be able to

LO1 Outline the purpose and desired positive outcomes of the *Canadian Guidelines for Sexual Health Education*.

LO2 Discuss the attitudes of Canadian parents, teachers, and students toward sex education in school and at home.

LO3 Describe what sexual information should be taught to children at different ages and how this relates to children's knowledge and sexual interest.

LO4 Discuss and evaluate the components of the various types of sex education curriculum available.

LO5 Outline the controversies surrounding condom distribution in schools and the inclusion of sexual orientation issues in sex education programs.

LO6 Describe the qualities necessary to be a good sexuality education teacher.

LO7 Explain why parents do not provide much explicit sex education to their children and how parents can prepare themselves to communicate with their children about sexuality topics.

LO8 Describe the role that the media, health professionals, and the Internet can play in providing sex education in the community.

LO9 Discuss the pertinent issues surrounding teaching sexual health education to persons from different cultures and to persons with developmental disabilities.

Formal sex education in Canadian schools goes back at least to the early 1900s when Arthur W. Beall gave his "Advanced Purity Lectures." . . . Those involved in public and school sex education saw themselves at the forefront of "modern thinking." Nevertheless, their message strongly reinforced conventional morality. . . . [T]hey appear to have been 100% successful in eliminating masturbatory insanity as a social problem. You hardly hear about that these days.*

* Michael Barrett (1990), Chair, Sex Information and Education Council of Canada (SIECCAN).

As we look to the future, a top priority for society has to be comprehensive sexuality education. If you have studied this textbook, you should be prepared to be a good sex educator for your own children. You should also be a well-informed citizen who can make thoughtful decisions about sexuality education. However, it is not just children who require sex education. Most people need additional information about sexuality throughout their lives so that they can adapt to changes in their life circumstances (e.g., becoming single again, physical changes caused by aging and illness). This chapter concerns **sexuality education**. Sexuality education is the lifelong process of acquiring information about sexual behaviour and forming attitudes, beliefs, and values about identity, relationships, and intimacy (SIECUS, 1991). Sex education can occur in many settings: home, school, church or synagogue, youth programs, relationships, and via the Internet.

L01

Purposes of Sexuality Education

The goal of sexuality education is to promote healthy sexuality. What is healthy sexuality? The Public Health Agency of Canada (PHAC, 2008a) has adopted the definition of sexual health put forward by the World Health Organization (see Chapter 1):

> Sexual health is a state of physical, emotional, mental, and social well-being in relation to sexuality; it is not merely the absence of disease, dysfunction, or infirmity. Sexual health requires a positive and respectful approach to sexuality and sexual relationships, as well as the possibility of having pleasurable and safe sexual experiences, free of coercion, discrimination, and violence. For sexual health to be attained and maintained, the sexual rights of all persons must be respected, protected, and fulfilled.

Sexuality education: The lifelong process of acquiring information about sexual behaviour and forming attitudes, beliefs, and values about identity, relationships, and intimacy. **SIECCAN:** The Sex Information and Education Council of Canada, a national resource for up-to-date information, research, and publications on human sexuality, including sexual health.

Notice that this definition emphasizes positive sexuality, not just freedom from disease or dysfunction. The Sex Information and Education Council of Canada (**SIECCAN**) is active in promoting high-quality sex education in Canada and coordinated the development of the *Canadian Guidelines for Sexual Health Education* (PHAC, 2008a). The Guidelines provide a framework for sexual health education for persons of all ages and from diverse populations that balances the well-being and desires of the individual with the needs and rights of others and of society. According to the Guidelines, sexuality education should help people both to achieve positive outcomes and to avoid negative ones. Positive outcomes include self-esteem, respect for self and others, nonexploitative sexual satisfaction and sexual pleasure, rewarding human relationships, and the joy of desired parenthood. Negative outcomes include unwanted pregnancy, sexually transmitted infection, sexual coercion, and sexual dysfunction. Effective sexual health education integrates four key components through a variety of activities. These allow individuals to develop the following:

1. A deeper understanding that is relevant to their specific health needs and concerns
2. The confidence, motivation, and personal insight needed to act on that knowledge
3. The skills necessary to enhance sexual health and to avoid negative sexual health outcomes
4. A safe, secure, and inclusive environment that is conducive to promoting optimal sexual health (PHAC, 2008a, p. 14)

To achieve these goals, youth need to have an opportunity to explore attitudes, feelings, and values that may influence their decisions and behaviour. Sex education should emphasize the self-worth and dignity of the individual, and encourage respect for diversity in values, background, and sexual orientation. The Guidelines recognize that students need to make their own informed and responsible choices rather than have choices imposed on them. For example, some adolescents will choose abstinence over sexual involvement; others will choose to have sexual relationships. However, research in New Brunswick has shown that abstinence means different things to different people (Byers et al., 2009). Almost all students agreed that a person can engage in deep kissing and still be abstinent. However, students are quite mixed on whether a person can engage in oral sex or genital fondling and still consider themselves to be abstinent.

The Sexuality Information and Education Council of the United States, in partnership with Advocates for Youth and Answers, has developed specific standards for comprehensive and responsible sexuality education in their document *National Sexuality Education Standards: Core Content and Skills* (Future of Sex Education Initiative, 2012). This document identifies seven topics as the minimum, essential content: anatomy and physiology, puberty and adolescent development, identity, pregnancy and reproduction, sexually transmitted infections and HIV, healthy relationships, and personal safety. It also identifies key indicators that students have mastered content and skills in each area for Kindergarten through Grade 12.

In the Home, in the School, or Somewhere Else?

Invariably some people object to providing sexuality education in schools. They might say that sex education promotes sexual intercourse, teenage pregnancy, or HIV/AIDS, and they are sure that it should take place only in the home (or possibly the church), but certainly not in the schools. Other people accept sexuality education in schools but object to specific aspects of the curriculum or the grade level at which topics are covered (for example, you might recall the controversy in 2010 about the Ontario sexuality education curriculum).

As shown in Table 19.1, school is the main source of sexuality education for Grade 9 students in Canada; 41 percent of the girls and 51 percent of the boys gave this response (Boyce et al., 2003). In contrast, only 6 percent of the boys and 14 percent of the girls identified parents or other family members as their main source of sexuality information. The fact is that many children are given little or no sexuality education at home; of course, not talking about sex with one's children is also a form of communication and sends a variety of negative messages. Further, individuals for whom sex was not discussed at home may have difficulty talking about sex with their partner or children, may develop negative attitudes about their own sexuality or about sex in general, or may not be equipped to make good

Table 19.1 Main Sources of Grade 9 Students' Information About Sex		
	Boys	**Girls**
Parents or other family members	6%	14%
Friends	9	17
Internet	12	3
School	51	41
Magazines, newspapers, books	5	12
Television/movies	9	5
Physician or nurse	5	5

Source: Boyce, W., Doherty-Poirier, M., Fortin, C., MacKinnon, D. (2003). Canadian youth, sexual health and HIV/AIDS study. Council of Ministers of Education.

sexual choices for themselves. Notice that TV, movies, printed materials such as magazines, and the Internet are important sources of information for many youth, as are friends. In many cases the information provided on TV and in movies is sensationalized and unrealistic (see Milestones in Sex Research in Chapter 10). Relying on friends for information is unwise; they likely know no more than you do. Teens are increasingly turning to the Internet for information about sex. More than 50 percent of students in grades 7 to 12 report that they have searched for health information online (Rideout et al., 2010). The problem with the Internet as the primary source of sexuality information for youth is that there is no quality control; there are some sites with excellent and accurate information but others that promote misinformation. For example, one study of 177 sites found that 46 percent of those discussing contraception and 35 percent of those discussing abortion contained inaccurate information (Buhi et al., 2010). One of the best sites is www.sexualityandu.ca. Possibly the worst source? Pornography; some teens say they got their information from watching pornography on the Web. Thus, it is fortunate and appropriate that school has become the main and preferred source of information (McKay & Holowaty, 1997). Of concern, though, is that youth who have immigrated to Canada within the previous three years are more likely than other youth to report not having received sex education (Salehi et al., 2010).

Sex education in the school is not "instead of" education in the home. Most Canadian parents, teachers, and students feel that both parents and schools have a role to play in providing sex education (Byers et al., 2003a, 2003b; Cohen et al., 2004; McKay & Holowaty, 1997; McKay et al., 1998; Weaver et al., 2002). For example, in a survey of parents in New Brunswick, 95 percent felt that responsibility for sexual health education should be shared by parents and schools (Weaver et al., 2002); somewhat fewer high school students (77 percent) and

DENNIS the MENACE

"THAT'S FUNNY... MY DAD CAN TELL IF IT'S A BOY OR A GIRL JUST BY LOOKIN' AT THE BOTTOM OF ITS FEET."

Figure 19.1   Children often have inaccurate ideas about sex.

Source: Reprinted with permission of Torstar Syndication Services. Dennis the Menace cartoon by T.M. 1983. Dennis the Menace®: used by permission of Hank Ketcham and © North American Syndicate.

middle-school students (69 percent) shared this view (Byers et al., 2003a, 2003b). Some sexuality education programs actively involve parents by including homework to be done jointly by parent and child. The evaluation of one program of this type found that students receiving classroom instruction plus homework felt more able to refuse high-risk behaviours and more often intended to delay initiation of intercourse compared with students receiving only classroom instruction (Blake et al., 2003). The homework assignments appeared to reinforce the school-based program, and resulted in greater parent–child communication about sex.

How well are parents and schools doing in providing sex education (Figure 19.1)? According to parents and students who participated in four New Brunswick studies, only between 24 percent (according to middle-school students) and 38 percent (according to the parents) of children are getting excellent or very good sex education at home. According to the teachers

and students, the schools are not doing much better: between 13 percent (according to high school students) and 37 percent (according to middle-school students) rated the sexual health education they had received in school as very good or excellent. One study involved interviews with 40 rural and urban youth in Nova Scotia and British Columbia about their sexual experiences, including their experiences with sexual health education (Shoveller et al., 2004). The youth indicated that neither schools nor parents promoted meaningful discussions about sex. Rather they perceived that both sexual health education and discussion with parents (if they had any) focused on prevention of pregnancy and STIs; what was missing for these youth was discussion of issues related to sexual relationships, especially the emotional and potentially positive aspects of sexual relationships. For example, one male youth described the sexual health education he had received in school:

> It [sex] was only talked about in Sex Ed . . . it was very *technical* and, of course, you couldn't ask *real* questions about your own experience. I think I understand the physical stuff but it's so emotional. And, it's the emotional stuff that you are always fucked up about when you are young. So, that's the part that was difficult. There's no question-and-answer period for that. You would never do that [emotional stuff] in a science class. (Shoveller et al., 2004, p. 480)

Similarly, youth indicated that they picked up subtle and not-so-subtle messages from their parents that certain kinds of questions and discussions about sex were off limits.

The goal of this chapter is to describe effective sex education, with particular focus on sex education in school and at home. We will also look at the potential of the Internet for providing sexual education. However, we first examine what research can tell us about what children should be taught about sex at different ages.

What to Teach at Different Ages

Sexuality education, whether at home or at school, is not something that can be carried out all at once in one week during Grade 5 or by having "the talk." Like teaching math or life skills, it is a process that must begin when children are small. They should learn simple concepts first, progressing to more complex ones as they grow older. Although sex education should always come before experience, what is taught at any particular age depends, in part, on the child's sexual behaviour (see Chapter 10), sexual knowledge, and sexual interests at that age. This section will concentrate on theories and research that provide information on the last two points.

Children's Sexual Knowledge

A few researchers have investigated what children in Western countries know about sex and reproduction at various ages. Children begin to develop an understanding of pregnancy and birth at a very early age. Very young children may believe that a baby has always existed, that it existed somewhere else before it got inside the mother. The following dialogue demonstrates this:

> (How did the baby happen to be in your Mommy's tummy?) It just grows inside. (How did it get there?) It's there all the time. Mommy doesn't have to do anything. She waits until she feels it. (You said that the baby wasn't in there when you were there.) Yeah, then he was in the other place . . . in America. (In America?) Yeah, in somebody else's tummy. (Bernstein & Cowan, 1975, p. 86)

As children get older, they develop—we hope—a more accurate understanding!

By age seven or eight, children have a more sophisticated understanding of reproduction. They may know that three things are involved in making a baby: a social relationship between two people, such as love or marriage; sexual activity; and the union of sperm and egg. However, they may not understand that the sexual activity involves intercourse. At age 12, some children can give a good physiological explanation of reproduction that includes the idea that the embryo begins its biological existence at the moment of conception and is the product of genetic material from both parents. As one preteen explained:

> The sperm encounters one ovum, and one sperm breaks into the ovum which produces, the sperm makes like a cell, and the cell separates and divides. And so it's dividing, and the ovum goes through a tube and embeds itself in the wall of the, I think it's the fetus of the woman. (Bernstein & Cowan, 1975, p. 89)

Some 10- and 11-year-olds understand that one of the reasons parents want to be alone is to have sex; others are reluctant to recognize the sexual dimension of their parents' relationship (De La Vega Salas & Thériault, 2001).

As we discussed in Chapter 10, research suggests that many children engage in sexual play and exploration. How does sexual behaviour relate to sexual knowledge? One review of the literature concluded that young children often engage in sexual behaviour without having a clear understanding of what it means (Gordon & Schroeder, 1995). These findings have important implications for sex education. Educators need to be aware of the level of the child's understanding and should not inundate him or her with information inappropriate for his or her age. Instead, the educator should attempt to clarify misunderstandings in the child's beliefs. For example, if a child believes a baby has always existed, the educator might say, "To make a baby, you need two grownups: a man and a woman."

Children's Sexual Interests

Children's knowledge of and interest in sex are reflected in the questions they ask. At age five, kids may be asking where babies come from. At age nine, a boy or girl may ask about sexual behaviours: "What's oral sex?" Such questions are often stimulated by hearing the term in conversation or in the media. A ten-year-old may be interested in bodily processes and ask, "What's a period?" By age 11, many kids are asking questions related to puberty, such as "When will I get breasts?" or "When will I grow taller?" Such questions typically reflect an awareness that other youth are experiencing such growth. At age 13 or 14, many youth have specific questions about sexual activity. One young man asked, "Do girls move a lot when they have sex?" A 14-year-old girl asked her mom, "Where do people have sex?" (Blake, 2004). It is important that sex education for a particular age group address the questions of that age group, rather than questions children of that age thought about but answered long ago.

High school students agree that sex education should begin in early elementary school and should progress from the simple to the complex (Byers et al., 2003a). They believe that it should cover a wide range of topics, including reproduction, pregnancy, abortion, birth control options, disease prevention, sexual violence, relationships and gender roles, sexual pleasure, sexual orientation and attraction, and sexual decision making. They would like all these topics presented by Grade 8 but then revisited in high school. In particular, they want sexual health education that talks more about sex—feelings, arousal, foreplay, contraception, condoms, weighing alternatives, healthy relationships, sexual pleasure, sexual communication (that is, not just biological topics)—and is respectful of their choices (Caputo, 2000; Causarano et al., 2010; Langille, 2000; Maticka-Tyndale, 2001).

The sexual knowledge of preschool children in the United States was assessed by interviewing 147 two- to six-year olds (Volbert, 2000). Drawings were used to initiate discussion. The results indicated that sexual knowledge evolves during the preschool years. At age two, children can identify the sex of others and use slang to refer to the genitals. At age three, children explain gender differences using cultural characteristics (clothing, earrings). At age five, children explain gender identity based on genital differences; and at age six, children have some knowledge of vaginal or Caesarian birth. There were no significant differences in knowledge between boys and girls.

Table 19.2 Responses of Parents, Teachers, and Students

	Percentage Agreeing with Each Statement			
	Parents	**Teachers**	**Middle-School Students**	**High School Students**
Sexual health education should be provided in the schools.	94%	93%	93%	92%
The schools and parents should share responsibility for providing children with sexual health education.	95%	95%	69%	77%
Sexual health education should start in Grades K–5.	65%	78%	30%	23%

Sources: Byers et al. (2003a, 2003b), Cohen et al. (2004), Weaver et al. (2002).

An analysis of questions emailed to a reproductive health website found that 23 percent of the questions involved misconceptions about reproduction (Wynn et al., 2009). The authors suggest that two causes of this lack of information are poor sex education and confusing media messages.

LO2
Attitudes Toward School-Based Sexuality Education

Surveys in Ontario, Nova Scotia, and New Brunswick have found very high levels of support for sex education in schools among parents, teachers, and students (Langille et al., 1996; McKay, 1996; McKay et al., 1998; Weaver et al., 2002). For example, we surveyed 4206 parents, 336 teachers, 745 middle-school students, and 1666 high school students in New Brunswick about their ideas about sex education. Some of the results are presented in Table 19.2. The four groups were consistent with each other in many of their views. For example, all four groups were strongly in support of sexual health education in the schools—more than 90 percent agreed that sexual health education should be provided in schools. Further, they were in favour of a broadly based curriculum that covers a wide range of topics, including HIV/AIDS and other STIs, sexual decision making, sexual communication, sexual assault, birth control, abortion, and homosexuality. Similar results were found in the other provinces. The point is that there is strong support for broad-based sex education in schools, beginning in the primary grades.

What do Canadians think about sex education in schools?

You may be surprised to learn that most adults favour sex education. The media regularly publicize controversies, cases in which parents are protesting sex education in the schools. There are three things to keep in mind about such episodes. First, they are rare. The vast majority of schools with sex education programs have not experienced such conflict. Second, the protesters are usually in a minority. Third, the controversy is often not over whether there should be a program but over the use of a particular curriculum, book, or video.

LO4
The Curriculum

The term *sexuality education* has been used to refer to a wide variety of programs. With the exception of Quebec, all Canadian provinces and territories have, as part of their health programs, province-wide, school-based sexual health curricula (Health Canada, 2003; Joint Consortium for School Health [JCSH], 2007). In 2005, Quebec changed its health curriculum and removed sexual health education. Instead, all teachers are asked to incorporate teaching of sexual health into other subjects such as math, science, or history. Critics say this is not working; students are not getting the sex education they need and are campaigning to bring sex education back as part of the health curriculum. In addition, there are major differences in how fully these curricula are implemented in different communities (Barrett, 1990). The comprehensiveness of the curriculum that is taught varies considerably across schools, school boards, and provinces and territories. For example, a study in British Columbia concluded that sexual health education in that province does not meet the criteria set out by the *Canadian Guidelines for Sexual Health Education* and that it is "hit or miss" as to whether students get quality sexual health education (Options for Sexual Health, 2004).

Other problems with the curricula are that they tend to only go up to Grade 8 or 9 even though students in Grades 10 to 12 are the most likely to be engaging in sexual activity, there is little discussion of the positive and pleasurable aspects of sexual relationships, and there are few resources tailored for specific groups, such as GLBT youth, youth with disabilities, or youth from specific ethnocultural communities or the Aboriginal community (JCSH, 2007). There is also considerable controversy over specific aspects of the curriculum. These controversies reflect cultural attitudes toward children and sexuality, with people who object often arguing that sexuality education should not provide specific types of information too early, in order to protect "the innocence of children" (Figure 19.2). Of course, children are not really "innocent" and know a lot more about sex than some parents may suspect (see Chapter 10 for a discussion of childhood sexuality). Also, having sexual knowledge is helpful and not harmful to children.

One area that is particularly controversial is whether the curriculum should address homonegativity. Toronto's Human Sexuality Program was developed following the fatal beating of a gay student in Toronto in 1985 and provides classroom presentations on sexual-minority issues. However, there was a strong public outcry in 1997 in some parts of British Columbia when the B.C. Teachers Federation announced a decision to develop resources to help teachers address homonegativity in the classroom. For example, the conservative Citizens Research Institute developed a pamphlet to help parents demand that children not "be exposed to and/or involved in any activity or program which: discusses or portrays the lifestyle of gays, lesbians, bisexual and/or transgendered individuals as one which is normal, acceptable or must be tolerated" (Dwyer & Farran, 1997). They do not represent the majority; most Canadian parents, teachers, and students want sexual orientation included in sex education programs (Byers et al., 2003a, 2003b; Cohen et al., 2004; McKay et al., 1998; Weaver et al., 2002). Most classrooms will have one or two students who are not heterosexual. Thus, discussion of sexual orientation helps to meet their needs as well as to increase acceptance of diversity among their classmates (McKay, 2000).

We will focus in the next section on the more substantial programs.

Early Sex Education

The first programs, developed 30 years ago, were concerned with the transmission of knowledge. The goal of these programs was to reduce the number of teen pregnancies. Accordingly, the emphasis was on teaching students about sexual intercourse, pregnancy and birth control, and the consequences of having a baby. Later programs retained the informational content of the first ones, but the emphasis was placed on values clarification and decision-making skills. Proponents of these programs believed that young people engage in sexual risk taking because they are unsure of their values and

Figure 19.2 Although some parents claim that sex education belongs in the home, it is rarely conducted there effectively.
Source: margulies/The Journal/Rothco.

have difficulty making decisions. These programs also taught skills designed to improve communication with partners. Subsequent evaluations demonstrated that these programs were not particularly effective at reducing teenage pregnancy or sexual risk-taking behaviour (Kirby, 1992).

HIV/AIDS Risk Education

In the 1990s, the focus of sex education shifted from pregnancy prevention to HIV/AIDS and other STIs. All provinces and territories (with the exception of Quebec) have school-based programs that include information about HIV and AIDS (Barrett, 1994). Research has shown that more than 99 percent of Canadian parents approve of HIV/AIDS education in the schools (Weaver et al., 2002).

Programs of this type are often sharply focused on disease prevention. They have a variety of goals, including removing myths about HIV/AIDS and other STIs, encouraging delay of sexual intercourse, and supporting condom use or abstinence from unprotected intercourse. Each curriculum relies on lectures and class discussion facilitated by a teacher, a public health nurse or, more recently, a peer educator (Dunn et al., 1998). On occasion, someone with HIV/AIDS is brought in to talk with the class. These programs were usually short, often lasting only one or two class periods. A review of the effectiveness of these programs found that they improved knowledge significantly (Kim et al., 1997). In addition, many studies reported positive changes in respondents' intentions to use condoms.

One example of an HIV/AIDS education program in Canadian schools is the 20-hour Skills for Healthy Relationships program developed jointly by the federal and provincial governments. This program is designed for Grade 9 students and includes components aimed at delaying sexual activity, increasing condom use, creating compassion for persons living with HIV/AIDS, combating homonegativity, and improving communications and negotiating skills. It is based on a theoretical model that includes acquiring knowledge, developing responsible attitudes, increasing motivation, and developing skills (Fisher & Fisher, 1998). The program uses students as peer-group leaders and encourages parental involvement. An evaluation of the effectiveness of the program found that, compared with the regular program, students gained significantly in knowledge, became more positive in their attitudes toward people living with HIV/AIDS, increased their intentions to communicate assertively in sexual situations, and improved their skills in being able to use condoms correctly. However, the program did not affect the likelihood that students would engage in sexual intercourse or use a condom when they did engage in intercourse (Boyce et al., 2000).

The Canada Youth Sexual Health and HIV/AIDS Study (CYSHHAS) found that students in 2002 had *less* knowledge about HIV/AIDS than students who participated in the 1989 Canada Youth and AIDS Study (Boyce et al., 2003). This may be because of decreased focus on the disease in schools and in the media, and it is of concern because it might increase the risk of acquiring an infection (Brooke et al., 2010).

Abstinence-Only Programs

Abstinence-only programs of sex education developed out of opposition to sex education in the schools. Some people were opposed to any sex education in the schools; others felt that the existing programs were too liberal or permissive. The concerns led to passage by the U.S. Congress of an act that limits the use of U.S. federal funds to abstinence-only programs that "promote sexual abstinence as the sole means of preventing pregnancy and exposure to sexually transmitted diseases" (Wilcox & Wyatt, 1997, p. 4). Millions of dollars have been spent by U.S. state and federal governments to support the development and widespread use of these programs. The two most widely known of these curricula are called Sex Respect and Teen Aid. Sex Respect is designed for middle-school students (Figure 19.3) and includes catchy slogans for children to chant in class, such as "Don't be a louse, wait for your spouse!"; "Do the right thing, wait for the ring!"; and "Pet your dog, not your date!"

Abstinence-only programs of sex education: Programs that promote sexual abstinence until marriage as the sole means of preventing pregnancy and exposure to sexually transmitted infections.

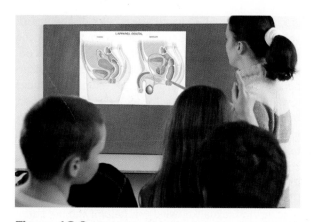

Figure 19.3 In a sexual health education class for middle-school students, the questions range from "How do you know when you need a bra?" to "Can you have sex at 12?"

All students take a "chastity pledge," and there is a chart of physical intimacy in which a prolonged kiss is characterized as the "beginning of danger." The curriculum teaches that condoms can be the road to ruin because many fail, resulting in pregnancy (which as you know from Chapter 7 is not accurate).

Sex Respect throws in a lot of gender-role stereotypes as well, characterizing boys as "sexual aggressors" and girls as "virginity protectors." It presents the two-parent, heterosexual couple as "the sole model of a healthy, 'real' family." Another problematic characteristic of abstinence-only programs is that sexual diversity is not accepted or respected.

Neither the federal nor the provincial governments in Canada have supported the development or implementation of abstinence-only sexuality education in the schools. In general, school-based sexuality education in Canada has taken the approach of not promoting a particular set of values; that is, teaching about both abstinence and about birth control and safer sex (JCSH, 2007; PHAC, 2008a; SIECCAN, 2009). Nonetheless, these abstinence-only programs are being offered in some Canadian schools (Figure 19.4). For example, in 1992 Teen Aid was taught to more than 20,000 students in 203 Saskatchewan schools, even though the Department of Education in that province offers a broadly based sexuality education curriculum. School boards paid $150 to $250 a day to the Teen Aid organization for it to offer the program. More often the programs are offered in the community, by church groups, for example.

So, how effective are these curricula? Researchers who assessed the content of Sex Respect concluded that it omits a number of important topics, including sexual anatomy (!), sexual physiology, sexual response, contraception, and abortion (Goodson & Edmundson, 1994). We noted earlier that high school students say that all of these topics should be included in sex

Figure 19.4 Reacting to controversy, in 2010 Dalton McGuinty, who was premier at the time, postponed the launch of a revamped school curriculum in Ontario that was developed after two years of work and extensive discussion. Some religious leaders and parents objected to children being taught about masturbation, homosexuality, and anal sex. The curriculum has still not been updated.

education. There have been many evaluations of these programs' effects on student attitudes and behaviour. A review of 52 evaluations concluded that, for the most part, the research shows these programs do not delay the onset of sexual activity or reduce the percentage of students having sex, getting pregnant, or acquiring an STI (Wilcox & Wyatt, 1997). That is, contrary to claims, these programs are not effective at delaying intercourse or reducing the rates of teenage pregnancy (Bennett & Assefi, 2005; Technical Working Group, 2002; Trenholm et al., 2007). In fact, data indicate that an emphasis on abstinence-only curricula is associated with higher teen pregnancy rates (Stanger-Hall & Hall, 2011). These programs also put youth at greater risk when they do start having sex, because they are less likely to use condoms.

Comprehensive, Theoretically Based Programs

The newest programs are comprehensive and are explicitly based on social science theories of health promotion, including social inoculation theory, social learning theory, the information–motivation–behavioural skills approach, and the health belief model (McKay, 1993). *Social inoculation theory* proposes that people are better able to resist social pressure when they recognize the pressure, are motivated to resist it, and have rehearsed resisting it. These programs include discussion of the

social pressures to engage in sex, and ways to resist these influences (based on inoculation theory). *Social learning theory* emphasizes the importance of practising new skills that can be easily translated into behaviour, so these curricula include rehearsal and role-playing activities. The *information–motivation–behavioural skills model* not only emphasizes the importance of health-related information but also enhances both skills and the motivation to use those skills. The *health belief model* includes attitudes, expectations, and self-efficacy—that is, the confidence that one can enact needed behaviours. The Sexuality Information and Education Council of the United States has developed a curriculum based on social science theories of health promotion (SIECUS, 1991).

In light of the continuing high levels of teenage pregnancy—about 2.8 percent of Canadian teenagers became pregnant in 2010 (McKay, 2012)—the sharp increases in rates of STIs among persons 15 to 24 years of age, and the increasing rate of HIV infection in adolescents, it is imperative that we identify sex education programs that are effective in reducing sexual risk-taking behaviour. Although most programs increase students' knowledge, many programs are not effective at changing behaviour. Unfortunately, there are few published studies evaluating school-based sex education programs in Canada (Barrett, 1990; DiCenso et al., 2002). The effectiveness of school-based programs in the United States has been reviewed, however (Kirby et al., 1994).

Researchers identified six characteristics that, according to the scientific evidence, are associated with delaying the initiation of intercourse, reducing the frequency of intercourse, reducing the number of sexual partners, and increasing the use of condoms and other contraceptives:

- *Effective programs focus on reducing risk-taking behaviour.* Such programs have a small number of specific goals. They do not emphasize general issues, such as gender equality and dating.
- *Effective programs are based on theories of social learning.* Programs that use theory in designing the curriculum are more effective than nontheoretical programs. The theories suggest that, to be effective, the program must increase knowledge, elicit or increase motivation to protect oneself, demonstrate that specific behaviours will protect the person, and teach the person how to use those behaviours effectively.
- *Effective programs teach through experiential activities that personalize the messages.* Such programs avoid lectures and videos; instead they use small-group discussions, simulation and games, role-playing, rehearsal, and similar educational techniques. Some of these programs rely on peer educators.
- *Effective programs address media and other social influences that encourage sexual risk-taking behaviours.* Some programs look at how the media use sex to sell products. All the effective programs analyze the lines that young people use to try to get someone else to engage in sex and teach ways of responding to these approaches.
- *Effective programs reinforce clear and appropriate values.* These programs are not value-free. They emphasize the values of postponing sex and avoiding unprotected sex and high-risk partners. The values and norms must be tailored to the target population. Different programs are needed for middle-school students, for white middle-class high school students, and for ethnic-minority-group high school students.
- *Effective programs enhance communication skills.* Such programs provide models of good communication and opportunities for practice and skill rehearsal.

What kinds of sex education programs work?

The length of the program and teacher training are also important. Effective programs are long enough to complete all these components and activities and are delivered by teachers or peers who believe in the program and have received training in how to deliver it (Kirby, 2002).

A review of the impact of 55 curriculum-based programs found that two-thirds of the programs that emphasized condoms and contraceptives as well as abstinence had positive effects. Youth who receive these programs are more likely to delay initiation of sexual activity, reduce sexual activity, and increase condom or contraceptive use (Kirby & Laris, 2009). Similar results were found in a review of the effectiveness of sexuality education programs by the United Nations Program on HIV/AIDS, with data from countries as diverse as Mexico, France, Thailand, and the United States (UNAIDS, 1997). The review focused on 53 studies that measured the impact of educational programs on behaviour. Three studies found an increase in sexual behaviour following a program. Twenty-two of the studies reported that the program delayed the initiation of sexual activity, led to a reduction in the number of partners, or reduced rates of unwanted pregnancy and STIs. The characteristics of the most effective programs were similar to those just identified.

We need to ensure that such programs are fully implemented and that teachers receive adequate training and support. Provincial and territorial governments and school boards also need to stand firm against vocal opponents of these programs. We also need to make sure that the curriculum is aimed not only at reducing negative outcomes, such as unwanted teenage pregnancies, STIs, and HIV/AIDS, but also at helping youth achieve positive outcomes, such as sexual self-esteem, sexual comfort, and fulfilling interpersonal relationships.

L05 Condom Distribution

One visible conflict has been over whether schools should distribute condoms to students (Figure 19.5). Different schools and school districts in Canada have widely differing policies on making condoms available in the schools. In some schools, condoms are available through the sex education program. In other schools, clinics providing health care services to adolescents dispense condoms. In still other schools, condoms are sold in vending machines—one high school in Ottawa and two on Vancouver Island were the first to install condom machines, in 1989. Again, data indicate widespread support in Canada for the distribution of condoms in schools (Ornstein, 1989).

The most visible opposition to condom distribution programs is by the Roman Catholic Church and other religious groups. These groups oppose such programs on the grounds that they will encourage sexual intercourse outside of marriage. However, research does not support their fears. For example, in a study comparing students in Massachusetts high schools that did and did not have such programs, students in schools with condoms available were *less* likely to report having ever

Figure 19.5 Research indicates that sex education programs are most effective when they include experiential and skill-building activities that personalize the message. Here students learn how to use a condom.

had intercourse and *less* likely to report recent intercourse (Blake et al., 2003). In addition, sexually active students in schools that made condoms available were twice as likely to use condoms.

Research indicates that condom distribution programs are associated with reductions in teenage pregnancies and abortions. For example, making condoms available through specialized health units in high schools in one county in rural Ontario resulted in a 21 percent drop in the pregnancy rate and an 11 percent drop in the number of abortions among teenagers ages 18 years and younger.

 Sexual Diversity

Whether or not they are out to teachers and classmates, it is likely that in every classroom there are at least one or two gay, lesbian, bisexual, or transgender students (PHAC, 2010c; SIECCAN, 2009). Other students have sexual-minority family members or friends. It is important that sex education programs address the needs of all students, including students who are members of sexual minorities, and include discussion of sexual diversity (SIECCAN, 2009). A study of LGB youth in Ontario found that they perceived that the sex education they received neglected them and their experiences (Brooke et al., 2010). Because bullying and harassment of LGBT youth in Canadian schools is so common (see Chapter 14), it is important that sex education address heterosexism, homonegativity, transphobia, and discrimination on the basis of sexual orientation and gender identity (Grace & Wells, 2001; McKay, 2005b; Taylor et al., 2011; Wells, 2009). In fact, in 2005 the B.C. Court of Appeal ruled that schools have a duty to take strong action to address homonegativity to ensure that no students experience discrimination and harassment at school.

This ruling was the result of a complaint by Azmi Jubran, a student in North Vancouver's Handsworth Secondary School, who was the victim of homophobic bullying, including being called names like "faggot" and "queer" and being pushed, punched, and spat on because the other students thought he was gay. The court ruled that it was not enough that the school punished the offending students. Instead, the school had a duty to provide "anti-homophobia" education to all students. This is important because although more and more high school students are coming out and there are more gay–straight alliance clubs in schools, LGBT students frequently experience psychological and physical harassment from other students, as well as a lack of support from homophobic school teachers and principals (Grace & Wells, 2001). A lesbian high school student in Alberta living in a safe house described her experience:

> The high school I went to in Grades 10 and 11 was awful. It was very, very homophobic. It's funny. When I got involved in going to gay bars, I even saw some of my teachers that are gay. But why aren't they out in school? I don't know, but I wish they were. Then at least I could have gone to them. But I can understand why they're not because it is a really homophobic high school. If I ever did hear a queer-related topic, it was always something negative. So I always had to shut up because I was too scared. (Grace & Wells, 2001, pp. 138–139)

In a tragic case, 15-year-old Jamie Hubley, a gay Ottawa teenager, committed suicide as a result of homophobic bullying. What changes are needed? First, sex education needs to include discussion of sexual orientation, including being gay, bisexual, and transgender. In this way, straight and questioning students would learn about being gay, lesbian, or bisexual. Second, LGBT students need to see themselves represented throughout the curriculum. For example, elementary school children could read books that feature same-sex parents. Math problems might feature a same-sex couple (e.g., Jim wanted to give David an engagement ring that cost . . ."). Third, schools need to be supportive of LGBT teachers so that these teachers can serve as respected role models for LGBT and questioning students. Fourth, all schools need to be proactive in establishing a gay-positive environment. This would mean hanging gay-positive posters where all students can see them. Schools could hand out student bookmarks that list contact information for a number of support groups including LGBT youth groups. All schools should establish **gay–straight alliance clubs** (Figure 19.6). These are school-based clubs run by students and, importantly, supported by teachers, that work to create a safe, caring, and inclusive environment for LGBT students. They are open to all students, regardless of sexual orientation. There are currently 150 Canadian GSA clubs registered on Egale Canada website (check them out at www.myGSA.ca). Research legislation in Ontario requires schools to allow students to form groups to raise awareness and understanding of sexual orientation and

Gay–straight alliance clubs: School-based clubs run by students and, importantly, supported by teachers that work to create a safe, caring, and inclusive environment for LGBT students.

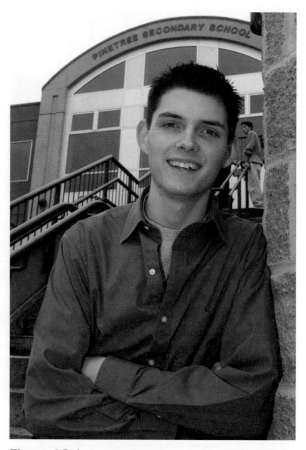

Figure 19.6 While a Grade 12 student in Coquitlam, British Columbia, Brent Power formed a gay–straight alliance club to combat homophobia; some B.C. parents strongly objected to discussion of homosexuality in the classroom.

gender identity; in the past some schools did not allow such organizations. Finally, schools must have clear policies that protect students from discrimination on the basis of sexual orientation (Grace & Wells, 2001, 2006, 2007).

The Teacher

Suppose you have decided to start a program of sexuality education. You have found a curriculum that is consistent with your objectives. Wherever the program is to be carried out—in the home, the school, the place of worship, or someplace else—the next resource you need is the teacher. There are two essential qualifications: the person must be educated about sexuality, and he or she must be comfortable and skillful in interacting with learners about sexual topics (Health Canada, 2003). Interviews with female high school students in Amherst, Nova Scotia, identified teacher discomfort and lack of knowledge as important barriers in sex education (Langille et al., 1999). This is in large part because many of the teachers providing sexual health education have had no training to teach the subject (Cohen et al., 2012). Students also see as important the ability of teachers to personalize the information; that is, to relate the material to the students' lives (Eisenberg et al., 1997).

Sex education teachers need to be educated about sex. Reading a comprehensive text, such as this one, or taking a college or university course in sexuality are good ways to acquire the needed information. The teacher does not have to have a degree in sexology; the important qualifications are a good basic knowledge, a willingness to admit when he or she does not know the answer to a question, and the patience to look things up. A survey of Canadian BEd programs found that only 16 percent of them included sexuality as part of a required course (10 to 13 hours on average); about a quarter had an optional sexuality course (McKay & Barrett, 1999). In contrast, undergraduate students in the Department of Sexology at the University of Quebec in Montreal take 28 courses related to sexuality, and the department offers a master's degree in sexual health education (Dupras, 2001). A national survey found that only about half of school districts regularly offer in-service training in sexuality education, and teachers do not feel comfortable or competent in teaching sex (McCall et al., 1999). A survey of junior high school teachers in Newfoundland and Labrador who were responsible for sexual health education found that none had received specific training to teach sex education (Ninomiya, 2010). Perhaps as a result, most teachers do not cover the more sensitive issues associated with sexuality and do not use active learning strategies, such as role-playing and small-group discussions (Cohen et al., 2004; Ninomiya, 2010). Clearly, there is a need for more training in sexuality to prepare teachers to teach sex education.

Equally important is the teacher's comfort with sexual topics. Even when parents or other adults willingly give factual information about sex to a child or an adolescent, they may convey negative attitudes because they become anxious or blush or because they use euphemisms rather than explicit sexual language. According to one 16-year-old girl, "The personal development classes are a joke. Even the teacher looks uncomfortable. There is no way anybody is going to ask a serious question" (Stodghill, 1998). Teachers who are comfortable with the subject matter are willing to ask students questions to determine what they know

and to find out about any myths and misinformation they may have. They will encourage students to ask questions and be able to answer the questions asked. They will use a variety of active and interactive teaching techniques.

Some people are relaxed and comfortable in discussing sex. Others must work to learn this attitude. There are a number of ways to do this. For example, the teacher can role-play, with another adult, having sexual discussions with children. Some communities periodically offer programs designed to increase the comfort of the sexuality teacher or to enhance awareness of his or her own sexual values and attitudes. A good teacher is also a good listener who can assess what the learner knows from the questions asked and who can understand what a child really wants to know when she or he asks a question. As one joke had it, little Billy ran into the kitchen one day after Kindergarten and asked his mother where he had come from; she gritted her teeth, realized the time had come, and proceeded with a 15-minute discussion of intercourse, conception, and birth, blushing the whole time. Billy listened, but at the end he appeared somewhat confused and walked away shaking his head, saying, "That's funny. Jimmy says he came from Winnipeg."

Finally, it is important that teachers receive training and professional development to address their own homonegativity, to learn how to help make schools safe for and inclusive of LGBT students, and to learn to be supportive of students questioning their sexual orientation or going through the coming-out process (Grace & Wells, 2006; PHAC, 2010c).

How are Canadian teachers doing? A survey of university students in Ontario found that students gave the sexual health education teachers they had in middle school and high school a rating between average and good in terms of their confidence, knowledge, approachability, and comfort with sexual topics (Meaney et al., 2009). Middle school students in New Brunswick on average rated their teachers as doing a "good" rather than a "very good" or "excellent" job of providing them with sex education (Byers, Sears, et al., 2013). Boys and girls in lower grades and with less sexual experience tended to rate their teachers more highly, suggesting that the content focused on pubertal development rather than issues related to sexuality within romantic relationships. Students who perceived their teacher as covering sexual health topics that matched their interests more adequately, as more comfortable talking about these topics, and as doing a better job of answering their questions rated the quality of the sex education they received more positively. That is, student perceptions of both the content and the delivery of sex education affected their views of its quality.

Home-Based Sexuality Education

Some Canadian youth identify their parents as an important source of sexuality information (Frappier et al., 2008). Others are given little or poor sex education at home. For example, a New Brunswick study asked parents of elementary and middle-school students about the extent to which they had discussed a number of sexual topics with their child (Weaver et al., 2002). The topics they had discussed in the most detail were child sexual abuse and the correct names for genitals, but even these topics most parents had discussed only in some detail but not in a lot of detail. On average, the parents said that they had discussed the other topics, including puberty, STIs, birth control, and sexual decision making, in general terms or not at all. Few parents of even the middle-school students had discussed these topics in a lot of detail. Perhaps as a result, less than half of parents (38 percent), middle school students (42 percent), and high school students (36 percent) indicated that the quality of sex education provided by parents was very good or excellent (Byers, 2011). Similarly, in a more recent New Brunswick study, 29 percent of mothers had engaged in sexual discussions with their middle school adolescent in some detail and an additional 22 percent intended to do so in the next six months (Byers & Sears, 2012). Of concern is that 49 percent did not intend to discuss sexuality with their adolescent in the next six months even though these adolescents likely will be going through puberty and starting to date.

The results of these studies also point to four major reasons why parents do not provide much explicit education to their children. First, many people are embarrassed about discussing sexuality. We see few models of how to have an explicit, matter-of-fact discussion; we are much more likely to see people discussing sex indirectly, with euphemisms and innuendo, or telling dirty jokes. (As a partial corrective, we have tried to write this book in an explicit, straightforward way.) Parents who are more comfortable talking about sex do a better job providing their children with sex education, including encouraging their children to ask questions more frequently (Byers et al., 2008; Foster et al., 2011).

Second, many parents lack *self-efficacy*—that is confidence that they can talk to their child about these topics. This may be because they perceive themselves as not knowing enough about various sexual topics. Many parents did not have good sexuality education themselves, and they may be painfully aware of their ignorance. In one Canadian survey, 76 percent of mothers indicated that they were not able to find some of the information

Why don't parents provide sex education for their kids?

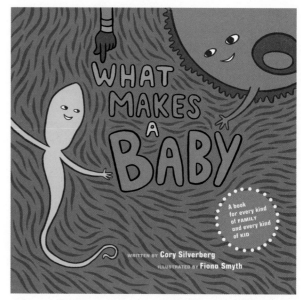

Figure 19.7   Parents who want to communicate with their children about sex can use books like this one to open the discussion. *What Makes a Baby* is notable because it is written and illustrated to include all kinds of kids, adults, and families.

they needed to have these discussions with their adolescent (Frappier et al., 2008). Interestingly, parents who had good sex education themselves in high school or university tend to talk more to their children about sexuality than do parents who did not take a human sexuality course. Parents who are more satisfied with the sex education they received from their own parents also provide better sex education to their own children (Byers et al., 2008). It appears that parents tend to replicate the sex education they received themselves (Byers, 2011).

Third, parents do not know how to provide sex education to their children (Figure 19.7). They also do not know at what ages they should discuss various topics. Of course, whether or not sexuality is openly discussed in the home (and many of our students say that it was never talked about in their home), parents communicate to their children about sex. Thus, just as parents convey a positive attitude toward sexuality by, for example, providing children with the correct names for their genitals and comfortably answering their sexual questions, parents convey their negative attitudes toward sex by not doing these things and by not talking about sex. As such, sexual education starts at birth through the nonverbal messages we give that lead to children feeling either good about their bodies or uncomfortable with their bodies and genitals.

Fourth, some parents have attitudes that are not supportive of sex education. Some are not convinced that parent–child sexual communication (particularly with

Talking to Your Children About Sex

Many parents want to be able to communicate with their children about sexuality but feel nervous about doing so. Here are a few guidelines for parents taken in part from the materials prepared by SIECCAN for the Canadian Health Network.

Be prepared. This means that you should educate yourself about sexuality. If you are fortunate and had a good sex education course in high school or university, you may already feel knowledgeable enough to answer your children's questions. However, many parents do not feel that they know as much as they should and are afraid that their children will ask them questions that they can't answer. It's okay not to know everything about sex; after all, most children can get the facts from the sex education they receive at school. Besides, sharing your feelings and values, not teaching facts, is the most important contribution that you can make to your children's sexuality education. Nonetheless, you may want to take steps to fill in some of the gaps you have in your knowledge about sexuality. To do this you can read books, such as this textbook on human sexuality or books on talking to children about sexuality, or you can attend a workshop for parents on that subject. You can also find out what is in your child's sex education curriculum at school. Remember, you need to talk to your children about both the positive aspects of sex (e.g., pleasure, sexual self-esteem) and the negative aspects of sex (e.g., sexual abuse, sexual coercion, and STIs).

Work to increase your comfort level. One of the most important contributions you can make to your children's sex education is increasing their comfort in talking about and asking questions about sex. Children's comfort will largely reflect the parents' comfort (Figure 19.8). You need to acknowledge to yourself the areas and topics that make you uncomfortable and take steps to increase your comfort level. Books and workshops about talking to your children about sexuality are good ways to increase your comfort level. Planning what to say and practising saying it (preferably in front of the mirror or with a partner) may also help to increase your comfort.

Plan ahead. Most of us did not have parents who talked to us about sex, so we can't base our own approach to educating our children about sexuality on our own experiences. As a result, it is important for you to decide how you want to approach sex education with your children. For example, you need to

Figure 19.8 It is important to be prepared, proactive, and honest when talking with your child about sex.

decide what you want to tell your children at various ages, how you plan to share your values with them, how you want to respond to questions about things your child hears at school, and so on. Remember that positive messages are more likely to have an influence than are lectures and threats. Also, you need to plan for what you might say if your teenager tells you something that you find upsetting. It is important for you to discuss these matters with your teen calmly, without yelling, or you will close the doors to further discussions. (For examples of key topics that you should cover at different stages of development, you can check out www.sexualityandu.ca/parents/sexuality-child-development.)

Be proactive. Too many parents wait for their children to ask them questions. Children are naturally curious about sex, but they are unlikely to ask questions if they have been getting nonverbal messages that you are uncomfortable talking about sex, or you never mention it at all. If you take the first steps, it will be easier for your children to raise questions and concerns at a later date. Opening the lines of communication is as important as the information you provide.

A good way to start talking to your children about sex is to use what we often call "teachable moments." For example, bath time is a good opportunity to provide your children with the correct term for their genitals just as you provide them with the correct name for their other body parts—nose, knee, and toes. Other teachable moments occur when someone your child knows becomes pregnant or gives birth, when something sexual is mentioned on television, or when a sexually related story is on the news. You can use these teachable moments to raise the topic of where babies come from, under what circumstances it is okay for teenagers to have sex, whether a couple in a movie are engaging in safer sex, and so on.

Another way to be proactive is to provide children and youth with books and DVDs about sexuality. For example, children's author Robie Harris has written excellent illustrated books for parents to read with children ages four and up (*It's Not the Stork!*, 2006), seven and up (*It's So Amazing!*, 2004) and ten and up (*It's Perfectly Normal*, 1994). You will need to read the books or watch the DVDs with your young and pre-adolescent children. Each page or DVD segment can lead to interesting discussions on the topics raised in the book or video. Your teen likely will prefer to read books on his or her own, but you should nonetheless initiate a discussion about the material to answer

questions or concerns that the teenager has. You also need to initiate discussions with your teen on sexual decision making and to try to ensure that they have the skills to apply their decisions in real-life situations. For example, you can help your teen become more comfortable talking to a partner about their sexual decisions or, if they do decide to have sex, about safer sex and birth control.

Listen first and then answer all questions truthfully, honestly, and accurately. Before answering their question, listen carefully to what your child is saying so that you are clear about what he or she is asking. For young children, answering questions truthfully, honestly, and accurately will involve providing short answers containing direct explanations. As your children grow older, they will want and need more detail and will be more likely to ask questions if you've created an open environment. You do not need to worry about providing your children with too much information too early. Children take the information they need and tend to ignore the rest. Unless you are a sex educator yourself, it is likely that your children will eventually ask you a question and you will not know the answer. It's okay not to know everything about sex. By admitting that you don't know the answer, you give your children permission not to have to know everything about sex, and communicate that having to seek out answers is normal and healthy at any time in life. Of course, it's important for you to then try to find the answer with your child.

younger children) will have positive outcomes and not negative outcomes for them and for their child. Some believe that the people who are significant in their lives would not approve of these discussions. As a result, they do not initiate these conversations. Changing parents' attitudes would likely change their intentions to talk to their children and their behaviour (Byers & Sears, 2012).

Many Canadian parents want to talk to their children about sex. However, they feel that they need to be more knowledgeable about sexuality and more comfortable

talking about sex before they can do so. They also feel that they need guidance on when and how to communicate with their children about sexuality (Byers, 2011). First Person provides some suggestions to parents who want to communicate with their children about sexuality.

What are the results of better parent–child sexual communication? Research suggests that more extensive sexual communication between parents and their adolescent is associated with a number of positive outcomes for the adolescent, including increased sexual knowledge, greater confidence about using condoms, and later initiation of sexual intercourse (DiIorio et al., 1999; Hutchison & Cooney, 1998). Researchers in Ontario also have shown that young women who had more conversations with their parents about dealing with unwanted sexual advances were more *sexually resourceful*—that is, they had more skills to resist, say no, or leave situations involving noncoercive unwanted sexual activity rather than give in to them (Kennett et al., 2012). Women who are more sexually resourceful give in to unwanted sexual behaviour less frequently.

Sexuality Education in the Community

The need for accurate sexual information does not end when people graduate from high school. For example, about 15,000 students in Canadian colleges and universities take a human sexuality course, perhaps like the one you are taking, each year—this number likely could be higher, but some schools do not offer courses in human sexuality. In addition, people need additional information about sexuality throughout their lives as they reach different life stages. The pregnant woman may need to learn about pregnancy and childbirth. New parents may want to increase their understanding of sexuality in childhood or of child sexual abuse. LGBT individuals may want information about other people's coming-out process. The middle-age woman may want to learn more about menopause. Older adults may need to learn about the effects of aging on the sexual response. Even for children and youth, sex education can and does occur outside the home and the classroom. For example, HIV/STI prevention interventions occur in public health clinics, in community settings, or through the media. These efforts can be directed at the population at large, or at specific subgroups with specific needs—for example, men who have sex with men, street youth, or members of specific ethnocultural minority groups. Community groups, health care professionals, and the Internet can all provide sex education outside the school or home setting.

Sex Education by Health Care Professionals

Physicians and other health professionals have an important role to play in educating youth about sexual health (McCall & McKay, 2004). For example, by routinely asking about sexual involvement in a non-judgmental way, physicians make it more likely that teenagers will approach them for advice on contraception when they do begin having sexual intercourse. However, many physicians are not comfortable talking about sex with their patients, particularly their adolescent patients, and thus do not routinely ask these questions. Others do not feel knowledgeable about sexuality. A survey of Canadian medical schools indicated that 14 of 18 sexual topics listed were covered in the curriculum, mostly through lecture and clinical experience (Barrett et al., 2012). However, two-thirds of programs in Canada and the United States provide medical students with less than ten hours of instruction related to sexual issues (Solursh et al., 2003). Perhaps as a result, a Nova Scotia study found that few high school students had ever discussed with their family doctor whether they were sexually active. Even among students who were engaging in intercourse, only 56 percent of the girls and 16 percent of the boys had discussed this with their family physician (Langille et al., 2001). A notable exception to the dearth of sexuality instruction in medical schools is l'Université de Québec à Sherbrooke, where medical students attend a four-day retreat related to sexuality. At the retreat they examine their attitudes and biases related to sexuality, with the goal of making it more comfortable to discuss sexual concerns with their clients (Solursh et al., 2003).

Even some specialists who are routinely consulted about sexual issues do not feel confident in their sexuality training. For example, researchers in Ontario found that obstetrics and gynaecology residents had significant knowledge gaps in some, but not all, areas (Garcia & Fisher, 2007). To fill this gap in physician training related to sexuality, the Society for Gynaecologists and Obstetricians recently released two sets of guidelines for physicians who treat women's sexual health concerns (Burnett et al., 2011; Lamont et al., 2012). However, studies of patients diagnosed with an illness that affected their sexual functioning (e.g., cancer) indicate that they were not fully educated by their health care providers about the sexual changes they might experience (Archibald et al., 2006; Letts et al., 2010). For example, one woman with breast cancer commented about changes to her sexual functioning resulting from treatment:

> I would have liked to have known ahead of time to know what to expect. Like is this normal? Is it just something I am feeling? . . . I would have been prepared for it. Like I wouldn't have been as worried about it, or as concerned about it. (Archibald et al., 2006)

It is important that health care workers ensure that their patients' information and support needs are met with respect to the sexual changes they experience as a result of their disease or treatment.

Therapists also have a role in providing sexual health information to their clients (Miller & Byers, 2009, 2010). To do so, therapists need to be knowledgeable about topics about which their clients might have sexual concerns (Fisher & Holzapfel, 2014). As one example, they need to be knowledgeable about STI transmission and prevention so that they can help their clients make decisions that do not put them at risk for infection. They also need knowledge about issues related to the sexual response, sexual orientation, gender identity, and aging, to name just a few. Yet Canadian researchers have shown that many lack confidence that they can relay accurate sexual health information (Miller & Byers 2012).

Sex Education on the Internet

The media can be used to increase awareness of specific sexual issues, such as prenatal nutrition, sexual minorities, or sexual violence. In particular, the Internet may be useful in providing information about sexuality. This can be an addition to formal school-based sex education, or a way of providing sexual information to people throughout their lives. Certainly, many Canadians already seek out sexuality information on the Internet. For example, in an online survey of 760 university students in British Columbia, about half (52.5 percent) had looked for sexuality information on the Internet within the past year (Boies, 2002). Further, 21 percent of the students reported that their first sexuality education material had come from the Internet. A New Brunswick study found that 18 percent of male university students and 31 percent of female students had looked for sexuality information online in the previous month (Shaughnessy, Byers, & Walsh, 2011). The Internet is particularly attractive because it is an affordable, available, anonymous, and acceptable way to access sexuality information, and people can do so without being observed (Barak & Fisher, 2001; Cooper, 1998). There are several other advantages to sex education on the Internet (Barak & Fisher, 2001):

- Materials are easily revised so all users can have access to the most up-to-date information.
- Websites can use multimedia communications, including text, sound, pictures, animation, and videos.
- The material can be accessed from any computer, at any time.
- Users can exchange information with other users.
- A website can provide access to information and services outside its own site by providing links to other sites.

- Potentially, information and programs provided can be individualized to the needs of each user based on responses to prescreening questions administered on the site.

There are also potential problems with sex education on the Internet. Anybody can establish an Internet site, and nobody monitors these sites for the accuracy of their content, so the unsuspecting user may be getting incorrect information (Fisher & Barak, 2000). Indeed, as noted earlier, there is also a great deal of misinformation provided on the Web, which is a huge problem. Finally, not everybody has access to the Internet; people who are socioeconomically disadvantaged and who belong to ethnocultural minority groups tend to have less access. Nonetheless, the Internet certainly has the potential to enhance traditional approaches to sex education.

Effective Multicultural Sexuality Education

Much of the discussion in this chapter has assumed that the participants in a sexuality education program are homogeneous, that they are all from the same ethnocultural community. In some situations that assumption is valid, but in other settings the learners may be from diverse ethnocultural backgrounds.

Cultures vary in a number of ways that may affect the success or failure of a sexuality education program (Irvine, 1995). There are cultural differences in sexual practices; some of these were discussed in Chapter 1. The acceptability of explicit sexual language or of particular types of language, such as street slang, varies from one cultural community to another. Cultures vary in the meaning they attach to sexuality. The majority cultures in Europe and North America have emphasized sex for the purpose of reproduction and thus tend to regard vaginal intercourse as the norm (see Chapter 20 on Connect™ Online). Other cultures place greater emphasis on the pleasure that can be derived from sexual stimulation. Finally, cultures vary in the definition of and the roles expected within the family.

Of necessity, sexuality education programs use language. Street slang might enhance rapport with street youth but deeply offend recent immigrants. Curriculum developers and teachers base their programs on assumptions about the prevalence of specific sexual practices, such as vaginal and anal intercourse. They implicitly or explicitly identify some practices as desirable, for example, condom use. They also reflect assumptions about the purposes of sexual intimacy; for example, abstinence-based programs assume that sexual intercourse is most or only meaningful within marriage.

If sexuality education is to be successful, it must reflect, or at least accept, the cultures of the participants. The educator must assess the audience, the intended messages, and the context, and target the program accordingly (Irvine, 1995). Educators must recognize their own sexual culture, learn about the sexual cultures of the participants, and be aware of the power differences between groups in our society. In the classroom, they should use this knowledge to enhance the effectiveness of the presentation. The use of communication styles and media common to the cultures of the participants—for example, music—can be a valuable tool. Finally, it is important that the program not advocate beliefs and practices that are incompatible with participants' cultures. Such programs are doomed to failure. This is true for school-based sexuality education and for workshops and outreach programs. For example, researchers in Toronto documented a need for educational outreach and services specifically for East Asian and Southeast Asian men who have sex with men. They used the results of a needs assessment to make specific recommendations about how to best provide culturally appropriate services (Poon et al., 2001). It also means that sex education programs developed in one country will not necessarily be accepted or be effective in another country (Figure 19.9). Rather, they typically will have to be modified to fit the culture of that country.

The First Nations HIV/TB Training Kit is designed to train community health educators to deliver culturally based training sessions on HIV and TB (tuberculosis) (Association of Iroquois and Allied Indians, 1997). Training emphasizes cultural sensitivity to distinct rituals, cultural practices, and methods within each First Nations community, such as storytelling, the talking circle, traditional medicines, and the medicine wheel. Resources like this one, and the programs that result from this type of training, respond to the call for sexuality education that incorporates the family and community context in which our sexuality is grounded (PHAC, 2008a; Maddock, 1997; Young, 1996).

Another group that needs to have sexuality education tailored to its needs is those with disabilities. We cannot assume that curricula designed for students in Grade 6 can be presented to 12-year-olds with disabilities (Di Giulio, 2003). Instead, these youth need sex education programs that are tailored to their unique learning needs, concerns, and styles. This includes individuals with intellectual disabilities (see First Person). It also includes youth on the autism spectrum who may need sex education that integrates core social

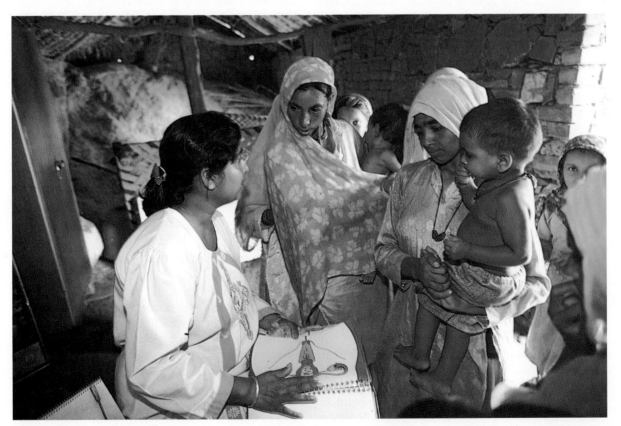

Figure 19.9 Sex education around the world. At this family-planning clinic in India, an educator explains the female reproductive system to these mothers.

First Person

Sex Education for Persons with Developmental Disabilities LO9

Persons with IQs below 70 are generally classified as having an intellectual or a developmental disability. There is a great range of capacities among individuals with developmental disabilities, from some who require constant care to those who function quite well in the community, who can read and write and hold simple jobs. It is important to recognize that the great majority of persons with intellectual disabilities in the moderate range (IQs between 50 and 70) are in the category of near-normal functioning. Programs need to assess the cognitive and emotional abilities of each child and adolescent and then present developmentally appropriate materials.

In the past, society has regarded persons with disabilities, including developmental disabilities, as asexual. Although many of these attitudes remain, society, parents, and caregivers are increasingly recognizing that persons with developmental disabilities have normal sexual desires. However, because these children are often slower to learn the norms of society, they may express themselves sexually in ways that are not acceptable to others, such as masturbating in public. Further, persons with developmental disabilities may be particularly vulnerable to sexual exploitation and abuse.

Unfortunately, not all youth with developmental disabilities have access to adequate sex education; in fact, many receive little or no such education. For students enrolled in regular classes, the sexual health education curriculum may not fit their learning style or level of understanding. For these reasons and others, careful sexuality education for persons with intellectual disabilities is essential. Fortunately, there are now a number of comprehensive guides and curricula that have been developed precisely to teach youth with developmental disabilities about their sexuality.

It is important that persons with developmental disabilities be educated about contraception and that contraceptives be made available to them (Figure 19.10). Because persons with developmental disabilities have normal sexual desires, they may engage in sexual activity, including intercourse. In one study, 24 percent of boys and 8 percent of girls with developmental delays had engaged in intercourse by age 16 (Cheng & Udry, 2003). If these youth lack sexuality education, they may not realize that pregnancy and STIs can result. An unwanted pregnancy for a woman or couple with developmental disabilities may be a difficult situation; they may be able to function well when taking care of themselves but not with the added burden of a baby. On the other hand, some persons with developmental disabilities do function sufficiently well to care for a child. The important thing is that they make as educated a

and relationship skills development with more traditional sexuality content (Byers et al., 2012). Youth with physical disabilities may need additional information in addition to the mainstream sex education pertaining to self-esteem and body image (Krupa & Esmail, 2010; Parrott & Esmail, 2010).

As we increasingly recognize diversity both within Canada and around the world, creating developmentally and culturally effective sexuality educational programs should be an important priority. Happily, research has consistently shown that, internationally, a large majority of parents support the provision of school-based sexual health education—for example, 75 percent of parents in

Tanzania and 92 percent of parents in Nigeria (Mkumbo & Ingham, 2010; Ogunjimi, 2006). Another important priority is helping parents from diverse cultures talk to their children about sexuality in ways that promote the children's sexual health. For example, research in Pakistan has found that youth do not consider their parents to be reliable sources of information about sex (Khan & Pine, 2003). Similarly, few parents in a study conducted in rural Nigeria had discussed sexual issues with their children; the ones that had done so typically had provided incorrect, frightening information in an attempt to prevent them from engaging in sexual activity (Izugbara, 2008).

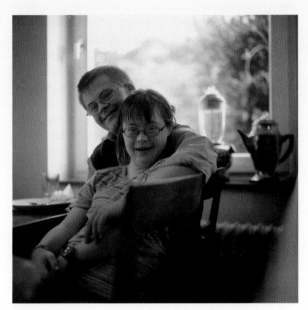

Figure 19.10 There is a need to provide sex education to children and adults with disabilities.

decision as possible and that they have access to contraceptives. Many experts recommend an IUD or other methods that do not require memory or forethought for effective use for women with developmental disabilities.

Information about forms of romantic and sexual expression may have to emphasize social norms about what is appropriate, and discourage inappropriate behaviours in public. Also, programs for persons with disabilities must recognize their vulnerability to exploitation and make special efforts to teach them self-protection skills.

In the 1920s, both Alberta and British Columbia passed laws allowing sterilization without consent of people deemed to have "mental retardation." While we now view this as a violation of human rights, the law was not repealed in Alberta until 1972, after 2900 such operations had been performed. In 1996, an Alberta woman successfully sued the government for damages related to her involuntary sterilization. She had been sterilized at the age of 14 without her knowledge or consent.

In summary, persons with developmental disabilities have sexual needs and desires. Because of their special needs, it is especially important that they receive appropriate sexual health education.

Sources: Ames (1991), Baladerian (1991), Di Giulio (2003), Kempton & Kahn (1991), Nemeth (1995).

SUMMARY

School is the primary source of sexuality information in Canada. However, many children receive their sex education from their peers or other sources, not from their parents. The vast majority of Canadians support sex education in the school. Cases of opposition to sex education involve a small number of people.

The purposes of sexuality education include providing children with adequate knowledge of the physical and emotional aspects of sex, with an opportunity to develop their own values and interpersonal skills, and

with the maturity to take responsibility for their sexuality. Sex education should help people achieve positive outcomes and avoid negative outcomes.

What is taught at each age should depend on what children are thinking about at that age. Children pass through various stages in their understanding of sexuality. For example, at first they believe that a baby has always existed. Later, they realize that the parents caused the baby's creation, but they don't know exactly how. Older children acquire a more scientific understanding of reproduction. Children's sexual play seems to precede rather than follow the development of sexual knowledge.

Sexuality education curricula have evolved a great deal over the past three decades. The early programs focused on preventing adolescent pregnancy and HIV/AIDS through knowledge, values clarification, and decision-making skills. They resulted in increased knowledge and intentions to use condoms. Conservative programs, such as Sex Respect, emphasize abstinence and are limited in content. The evidence indicates they are not effective and may lead to increased risk. Contemporary, broadly based programs are based on social science theory and emphasize the importance of not only providing information but also allowing students to practise new behaviours such as communication skills. Research suggests that sexuality education programs that are effective at delaying the onset of intercourse, reducing the frequency of intercourse and the number of partners, and increasing condom use share several characteristics: they focus on specific risk-taking behaviours, are based on theory, use experiential activities, address social influences on sexual behaviour, reinforce values, and provide opportunities to practise new skills.

There is a good deal of conflict over the distribution of condoms in high schools. There is widespread support among both high school students and their parents for such programs, but the Catholic Church, among others, is a vocal opponent.

It is important that sex education programs address the needs of LGBT students as well as heterosexism, homonegativity, and discrimination on the basis of sexual orientation.

A good sexuality education instructor must have accurate knowledge about sexuality, be comfortable discussing it, and be good at listening to the questions learners ask. Students say that the instructor's ability to relate the material to their lives is also important.

It also is important that parents talk to their children about sexuality. Some guidelines for parents are (1) be prepared, (2) work to increase your comfort level, (3) plan ahead, (4) be proactive, and (5) answer all questions truthfully, honestly, and accurately.

People have a need for continuing sex education throughout their lives. Physicians, other health professionals, and the Internet are all important sources of ongoing sex education.

To be effective, multicultural sexuality education must reflect or be consistent with the culture(s) of participants. It should present messages that are compatible with their beliefs and practices. Such programs should use language and styles of communication that are appropriate.

QUESTIONS FOR THOUGHT, DISCUSSION, AND DEBATE

1. Design a sample sexuality education curriculum for the schools, indicating what topics you think would be important to teach at various age levels and what your reasoning is behind your choices.

2. Debate the following topic. Resolved: A sexuality education unit, at least a week long, should be included in all grades in all schools.

3. The mass media are a major source of information about sexuality for young people, but we saw in Chapter 1 and Milestones in Sex Research in Chapter 10 that media portrayals are generally unrealistic. How would you deal with access to media portrayals of sexuality for your child at ages 5, 10, and 15? What would you do and tell your child at each age?

References

Aasheim, V., Nilsen, A. B. V., Lukasse, M., Reinar, L. M. (2011). Perineal techniques during the second stage of labour for reducing perineal trauma. *Cochrane Database of Systematic Reviews, 12,* CD006672.

Abbott, A. (2010). Baby boom bags Nobel prize. *Nature, 467,* 641–642.

Abdool Karim, Q., Abdool Karim, S. S., Frohlich, J. A., Grobler, A. C., Baxter, C., Mansoor, L. E., . . . CAPRISA 004 Trial Group. (2010). Effectiveness and safety of tenofovir gel, an antiretroviral microbicide, for the prevention of HIV infection in women. *Science, 329,* 1168–1174.

Abel, G. G., Becker, J. V., Mittelman, M., Cunningham-Rathner, J., Rouleau, J. L., & Murphy, W. D. (1987). Self-reported sex crimes of nonincarcerated paraphiliacs. *Journal of Interpersonal Violence, 2,* 3–25.

Abel, G. G., Osborn, C., Anthony, D., & Gardos, P. (1992). Current treatments of paraphiliacs. *Annual Review of Sex Research, 3,* 255–290.

Abel, G., & Rouleau, J.-L. (1990). The nature and extent of sexual assault. In W. L. Marshall, D. R. Laws, & H. E. Bartarce (Eds.), *Handbook of sexual assault* (pp. 9–21). New York, NY: Plenum.

Aboujaoude, E. (2010). Problematic internet use: An overview. *World Psychiatry, 9,* 85–90

Abracen, J., & Looman, J. (2004). Issues in the treatment of sexual offenders: Recent development and directions for future research. *Aggression and Violent Behavior, 9,* 229–246.

Abracen, J., Looman, J., Ferguson, M., Harkins, L., & Mailloux, D. (2010). Recidivism among treated sexual offenders and comparison subjects: Recent outcome data from the Regional Treatment Centre (Ontario) high-intensity sex offender treatment programme. *Journal of Sexual Aggression.* doi:10.1080/13552600903511980

Abram, D., Viki, G., Masser, B., & Bohner, G. (2003). Perceptions of stranger and acquaintance rape: The role of benevolent and hostile sexism in victim blame and rape proclivity. *Journal of Personality and Social Psychology, 84,* 111–125.

Acevedo, B., Aron A., Fisher, H. E., & Brown, L. (2012). Neural correlates of long-term intense romantic love. *Social Cognitive and Affective Neuroscience, 7,* 145–159.

Acker, M., & Davis, M. (1992). Intimacy, passion and commitment in adult romantic relationships: A test of the triangular theory of love. *Journal of Social and Personal Relationships, 9,* 21–50.

Acton, W. (1857). *The functions and disorders of the reproductive organs in childhood, youth, adult age, and advanced life, considered in their physiological, social, and moral relations.* Philadelphia, PA: Lindsay and Blakiston.

Adam, B. D. (2007). Why be queer? In G. Pavlich & M. Hird (Eds.), *Questioning sociology* (pp. 71–79). Don Mills, Canada: Oxford University Press.

Adam, B. D., Elliott, R., Husbands, W., Murray, J., & Maxwell, J. (2008). Effects of the criminalization of HIV transmission in Cuerrier on men reporting unprotected sex with men. *Canadian Journal of Law and Society, 23,* 143–159.

Adam, B. D., Betacourt, G., & Serrano-Sánchez, A. (2011). Development of an HIV prevention and life skills program for Spanish-speaking gay and bisexual newcomers to Canada. *Canadian Journal of Human Sexuality, 20,* 11–17.

Adams, M. A., Banting, J. D., Maurice, D. H., Morales, A., & Heaton, J. P. W. (1997). Vascular control mechanisms in penile erection: Phylogeny and the inevitability of multiple and overlapping systems. *International Journal of Impotence Research, 9,* 85–91.

Addiego, F., Belzer, E. G., Comolli, J., Moger, W., Perry, J. D., & Whipple, B. (1981). Female ejaculation: A case study. *Journal of Sex Research, 17,* 13–21.

Adkins-Regan, E. (2002). Development of sexual partner preference in the zebra finch: A socially monogamous, pair-bonding animal. *Archives of Sexual Behavior, 31,* 27–34.

Adoya-Osiguwa, S. A., Markoulaki, S., Pocock, V., Milligan, S. R., & Fraser, L. R. (2003). 17B-estradiol and environmental estrogens significantly affect mammalian sperm function. *Human Reproduction, 18,* 101–107.

Adshade, M. (2010). Confessions of a college pimp. Retrieved from http://www.bigthink.com/ideas/24377

Afifi, M. (2009). Women's empowerment and the intention to continue the practice of female genital cutting in Egypt. *Archives of Iranian Medicine, 12,* 154–160.

Aggarwal, A. P. (1992). *Sexual harassment: A guide for understanding and prevention.* Toronto, Canada: Butterworths.

Agnew, T. (1997). *A multicultural perspective of breast-feeding in Canada.* Ottawa, Canada: Minister of Public Works and Government Services Canada.

Ahlborg, T., Rudeblad, K., Linnér, S., & Linton, S. J. (2008). Sensual and sexual marital contentment in parents of small children—A follow-up study when the first child is four years old. *Journal of Sex Research, 45,* 295–304.

Ahluwalia, I. B., Merritt, R., Beck, L. E., & Rogers, M. (2001). Multiple lifestyle and psychosocial risks and delivery of small for gestational age infants. *Obstetrics and Gynecology, 97,* 649–656.

Ahmadi, N. (2003). Rocking sexualities: Iranian migrants' views on sexuality. *Archives of Sexual Behavior, 32,* 317–326.

Assisted Human Reproduction Canada. (2011). Risks associated with AHR. Retrieved from http://www.ahrc-pac.gc.ca

Ahrens, C. E., Dean, K., Rozee, P. D., & McKenzie, M. (2008). Understanding and preventing rape. In F. L. Denmark & M. Paludi (Eds.), *Psychology of women: A handbook of issues and theories* (pp. 509–554). Westport, CT: Praeger.

Ainsworth, C. (2005). The secret life of sperm. *Nature, 436,* 770–771.

Aksglaede, L., Sørensen, K., Petersen, J. H., Skakkebæk, N. E., & Juul, A. (2009). Recent decline in age at breast development: The Copenhagen Puberty Study. *Pediatrics, 123,* e932–e939.

Albanesi, H. P. (2010). *Gender and sexual agency: How young people make choices about sex.* Lanham, MD: Lexington Books.

Albright, J. M. (2008). Sex in America online: an exploration of sex, marital status, and sexual identity in Internet sexseeking and its impacts. *Journal of Sex Research, 45,* 175–186.

Alderson, K. G. (2004). A phenomenological investigation of same-sex marriage. *Canadian Journal of Human Sexuality, 13,* 107–122.

Alexander, E. (1990). Sexual therapy in English-speaking Canada. *SIECCAN Journal, 5*(1), 37–43.

Alexander, K. W., Quas, J. A., Goodman, G. S., Ghetti, S., Edelstein, R. S., Redlich, A. D., Cordon, I. M., & Jones, D. P. H. (2005). Traumatic impact predicts long-term memory for documented child sexual abuse. *Psychological Science, 16,* 33–40.

Alexander, M. G., & Fisher, T. D. (2003). Truth and consequences: Using the bogus pipeline to examine sex differences in self-reported sexuality. *Journal of Sex Research, 40,* 27–35.

Allen, D. M. (1980). Young male prostitutes: A psychological study. *Archives of Sexual Behavior, 9,* 399–426.

Allen, K. R., & Goldberg, A. E. (2009). Sexual activity during menstruation: A qualitative study. *Journal of Sex Research, 46,* 535–545.

Allen, M., & Burrell, N. A. (2002). Sexual orientation of the parent: The impact on the child. In M. Allen, R. W. Preiss, B. M. Gayle, & N. A. Burrell (Eds.), *Interpersonal communication research: Advances through meta-analysis* (pp. 125–143). Mahwah, NJ: Erlbaum.

Allen, M., D'Alessio, D., Emmers, T., & Gebhardt, L. (1996). The role of educational briefings in mitigating effects of experimental exposure to violent sexually explicit material. *Journal of Sex Research, 33,* 135–141.

Allman, D. (1999). *M is for mutual A is for acts: Male sex work and AIDS in Canada.* Ottawa, Canada: Health Canada.

Almroth, L., Almroth-Berggren, V., & Hassanein, O. M. (2001). Male complications of female genital mutilation. *Social Science & Medicine, 53,* 1455–1460.

Al-Sahab, B., Ardern, C. I., Hamadeh, M. J., & Tamim, H. (2010). Age at menarche in Canada: Results from the National Longitudinal Survey of Children & Youth. *BMC Public Health, 10,* 736.

Al-Sahab, B., Saqib, M., Hauser, G., & Tamim, H. (2010). Prevalence of smoking during pregnancy and associated risk factors among Canadian women: A national survey. *BMC Pregnancy and Childbirth, 10,* 24.

Althof, S. E. (2007). Treatment of rapid ejaculation: Psychotherapy, pharmacotherapy, and combined therapy. In S. Leiblum (Ed.), *Principles and practice of sex therapy* (4th ed., pp. 212–240). New York, NY: Guilford.

Althof, S. E., Abdo, C. H. N., Dean, J., Hackett, G., McCabe, M., McMahon, C. G., . . . Tan, H. M. (2010).

International Society for Sexual Medicine's guidelines for the diagnosis and treatment of premature ejaculation. *Journal of Sexual Medicine, 7,* 2947–2969.

Althof, S. E., Leiblum, S. R., Chevret-Measson, M., Hartmann, U., Levine, S. B., McCabe, M., Plaut, M., Rodrigues, O., & Wylie, K. (2004). Psychological and interpersonal dimensions of sexual function and dysfunction. In T. F. Lue, R. Basson, R. Rosen, F. Giuliano, S. Khoury, & F. Montorsi (Eds.), *Sexual medicine: Sexual dysfunctions in men and women* (pp. 73–115). Paris, France: Editions 21.

Ambert, A. (2009). Divorce: Facts, causes, and consequences (3rd ed.). *Contemporary Family Trends.* Vanier Institute of the Family. Retrieved from http://www.vifamily.ca

American Academy of Pediatrics Committee on Genetics. (2000). Evaluation of the newborn with developmental anomalies of the external genitalia. *Pediatrics, 106,* 138–142.

American Academy of Pediatrics. (2010). Policy statement—sexuality, contraception, and the media. *Pediatrics, 126,* 576–582.

American Cancer Society. (2009). *Cancer facts and figures.* Atlanta: American Cancer Society.

American Cancer Society. (2012). Cancer facts and figures 2012. Retrieved from http://www.cancer.org

American Congress of Obstetricians and Gynecologists. (2007, September 1). ACOG advises against cosmetic vaginal procedures due to lack of safety and efficacy data. Retrieved from http://www.acog.org

American Psychiatric Association. (2000a). Position statement on therapies focused on attempts to change sexual orientation (reparative or conversion therapies). *American Journal of Psychiatry, 157,* 1719–1721.

American Psychiatric Association. (2000b). *Diagnostic and statistical manual of mental disorders* (4th ed.). Washington, DC: Author.

American Psychiatric Association. (2010b). *The American Psychiatric Publishing Textbook of Psychiatry* (5th ed.). Arlington, VA: Author. Retrieved from http://www.psychiatryonline.com

American Psychiatric Association. (2013a). *Diagnostic and statistical manual of mental disorders* (5th ed.). Washington, DC: Author.

American Psychiatric Association. (2013b). Sexual dysfunctions. *Diagnostic and Statistical Manual of Mental Disorders* (5th ed., pp. 423–450.) Washington, DC: Author.

American Psychological Association, Task Force on the Sexualization of Girls. (2007). *Report of the APA Task Force on the Sexualization of Girls.* Washington, DC: Author. Retrieved from http://www.apa.org/pi/wpo/sexualization.html

American Psychological Association. (2008). *Answers to your questions: For a better understanding of sexual orientation and homosexuality.* Washington, DC: Author. Retrieved from http://www.apa.org/topics/sorientation.pdf

American Psychological Association. (2009). *Publication manual of the American Psychological Association* (6th ed.). Washington DC: Author.

American Urological Association Practice Guidelines Committee. (2003). AUA guideline on management of benign prostatic hyperplasia (2003). Chapter 1: Diagnosis and treatment recommendations. *Journal of Urology, 170,* 530–547.

Ames, T.-R. (1991). Guidelines for providing sexuality-related services to severely and profoundly retarded individuals: The challenge for the 1990s. *Sexuality and Disability, 9,* 113–122.

Anderson, A. (2001). The perfect woman. *The Weekend Post.* Retreived from http://www.nationaldream.ca/2001Feb10.pdf

Anderson, K., Kaplan, H., & Lancaster, J. (2001). *Men's financial expenditures on genetic children and stepchildren from current and former relationships* (Report No. 01–484). Ann Arbor, MI: Population Studies Center.

Anderson, M. C., Ochsner, K. N., Kuhl, B., Cooper, J., Robertson, E., & Gabrieli, S. W. (2004). Neural systems underlying the suppression of unwanted memories. *Science, 303,* 232–235.

Anglican Bishops of Canada. (1997). Human sexuality: A statement by the Anglican bishops of Canada. Retrieved from http://www.anglican.ca/faith/identity/hob-statement.htm

Anglican Church of Canada. (1989). *Abortion in a new perspective: Report on the task force on abortion.* Toronto, Canada: Anglican Book Centre.

Angus Reid Public Opinion. (2009a). Gender shapes views on debate over prostitution in Canada. Retrieved from http://www.visioncritical.com/category/global-opinions-and-trends

Angus Reid Public Opinion. (2009b). Household income levels define what is morally acceptable for Canadians. Retrieved from http://www.visioncritical.com/category/global-opinions-and-trends

Angus Reid Strategies. (2007, December 20). Canada open-minded on relationships and sexual behaviour, but not drugs. Retrieved from http://www.angusreidstrategies.com

Anthony, S. (2012). Just how big are porn sites? Retrieved from http://www.extremetech.com/computing/123929

Aos, S., Miller, M., & Drake, E. (2006). *Evidence-based adult corrections programs: What works and what does not.* Olympia, WA: Washington State Institute for Public Policy.

Appleby, B. M. (1999). *Responsible parenthood: Decriminalizing contraception in Canada.* Toronto, Canada: University of Toronto Press.

Aquinas, St. Thomas. (1968). *Summa theologica* (Vol. 43). In T. Gilly (Trans.). New York, NY: McGraw-Hill.

Araujo, A. B., Johannes, C. B., Feldman, H. A., Derby, C. A., & McKinlay, J. B. (2000). Relation between psychosocial risk factors and incident erectile dysfunction: Prospective results from the Massachusetts Male Aging Study. *American Journal of Epidemiology, 152,* 533–541.

Archer, J. (2004). Sex differences in aggression in real-world settings: A meta-analytic review. *Review of General Psychology, 8,* 291–322.

Archibald, S. A., Lemieux, S., Byers, E. S., Tamlyn, K., & Worth, J. (2006). Chemically-induced menopause and the sexual functioning of breast cancer survivors. *Women and Therapy, 29,* 83–106. doi:10.1300/J015v29n01_05

Armstrong, E. A., England, P., & Fogarty, A. C. K. (2012). Accounting for women's orgasm and sexual enjoyment in college hookups and relationships. *American Sociological Review, 77,* 435–462.

Arnold, A. P. (2003). The gender of the voice within: The neural origin of sex differences in the brain. *Current Opinion in Neurobiology, 13,* 759–764.

Arnow, B. A., Desmond, J. E., Banner, L. L., Glover, G. H., Solomon, A., Polan, M. L., Lue T. F., & Atlas, S. W. (2002). Brain activation and sexual arousal in healthy, heterosexual males. *Brain, 125,* 1014–1023.

Ashby, S. L., Arcari, C. M., & Edmonson, M. B. (2006). Television viewing and risk of sexual initiation by young adolescents. *Archives of Pediatric & Adolescent Medicine, 160*(4), 375–380.

Ashton, A. K. (2007). The new sexual pharmacology: A guide for the clinician. In S. Leiblum (Ed.), *Principles and practice of sex therapy* (4th ed., pp. 509–542). New York, NY: Guilford Press.

Assalian, P., & Ravart, M. (2003). Management of professional sexual misconduct: Evaluation and recommendations. *Journal of Sexual & Reproductive Medicine, 3,* 89–92.

Assisted Human Reproduction Canada. (2011). Risks associated with AHR. Retrieved from http://www.ahrc-pac.gc.ca

Association of Iroquois and Allied Indians. (1997). *First Nations HIV/TB training kit.* Ottawa, Canada: Medical Services Branch-Health Canada.

Atchison, C. (2010). *Report of the preliminary findings for John's voice: A study of adult Canadian sex buyers.* Vancouver, Canada: ORCHID.

Aubrey, J. S. (2004). Sex and punishment: An examination of sexual consequences and the sexual double standard in teen programming. *Sex Roles, 50,* 505–514.

Aucoin, M. W., & Wasserug, R. J. (2006). The sexuality and social performance of androgen-deprived (castrated) men throughout history: Implications for modern day cancer patients. *Social Science & Medicine, 63,* 3162–3173.

Auld, B. R., & Brock, G. (2002). Sexuality and erectile dysfunction: Results of a national survey. *Journal of Sexual & Reproductive Medicine, 2,* 50–54.

Autry, A. M., Hayes, E. C., Jacobson, G. F., & Kirby, R. S. (2002). A comparison of medical induction and dilation and evacuation for secondtrimester abortion. *American Journal of Obstetrics and Gynecology, 187,* 393–397.

Avis, N. E., & McKinlay, S. M. (1995, March–April). The Massachusetts Women's Health Study: An epidemiological investigation of the menopause. *Journal of the American Medical Women's Association, 50,* 45–63.

Aylwin, A. S., Reddon, J. R., & Burke, A. R. (2005). Sexual fantasies of adolescent male sex offenders in residential treatment: A descriptive study. *Archives of Sexual Behavior, 34,* 231–239.

Bach, G., & Wyden, P. (1969). *The intimate enemy: How to fight fair in love and marriage.* New York, NY: Morrow.

Bachmann, G. A., & Leiblum, S. R. (1991). Sexuality in sexagenarian women. *Maturitas, 13,* 43–50.

Backstrom, L., Armstrong, E. A., & Puentes, J. (2012). Women's negotiation of cunnilingus in college hookups and relationships. *Journal of Sex Research, 49,* 1–12.

Badeau, D., & Bergeron, A. (1997). *Bien vieillir. En santé sexuelle. Pour une approche globale des adultes agés.* Montreal, Canada: Meridien.

Badgley, R. (1984). *Sexual offences against children: Report of the Committee on Sexual Offences Against Children and Youths.* Ottawa, Canada: Canadian Government Publishing.

Bagemihl, B. (1999). *Biological exuberance: Animal homosexuality and natural diversity.* New York, NY: St. Martin's Press.

Bailey, J. M., & Pillard, R. C. (1991). A genetic study of male sexual orientation. *Archives of General Psychiatry, 48*, 1089–1096.

Bailey, J. M., Pillard, R. C., Neale, M. C., & Agyei, Y. (1993). Heritable factors influence sexual orientation in women. *Archives of General Psychiatry, 50*, 217–223.

Bailey, J. M., Willerman, L., & Parks, C. (1991). A test of the maternal stress theory of human male homosexuality. *Archives of Sexual Behavior, 20*, 277–294.

Bailey, J., Kim, P. Y., Hills, A., & Linsenmeier, J. W. (1997). Butch, femme, or straight acting? Partner preferences of gay men and lesbians. *Journal of Personality and Social Psychology, 73*(5), 960–973.

Bailey, R. C., Moses, S., Parker, C. B., Agot, K., Maclean, I., Krieger, J. N., Williams, C. F., Campbell, R. T., & Ndinya-Achola, J. O. (2007). Male circumcision for HIV prevention in young men in Kisumu, Kenya: A randomised controlled trial. *Lancet, 369*, 643–656.

Bain, J. (2007). The many faces of testosterone. *Clinical Interventions in Aging, 2*(4), 1–10.

Bain, J. (2010). Testosterone and the aging male: To treat or not to treat? *Maturitas, 66*, 16–22.

Baird, T. L., & Flinn, S. K. (2001). *Manual vacuum aspiration: Expanding women's access to safe abortion.* Chapel Hill, NC, Ipas.

Baker, F. C., Driver, H. S., Paiker, J., Rogers, G. G., & Mitchell, D. (2002). Acetaminophen does not affect 24-h body temperature or sleep in the luteal phase of the menstrual cycle. *Journal of Applied Physiology, 92*, 1684–1691.

Baker, M. (2008). Embryonic-like stem cells from a single human hair. *Nature Reports Stem Cells.* doi:10.1038/stemcells.2008.142

Baladerian, N. J. (1991). Sexual abuse of people with developmental disabilities. *Sexuality and Disability, 9*, 323–335.

Baldwin, J. D., & Baldwin, J. I. (1989). The socialization of homosexuality and heterosexuality in a non-Western society. *Archives of Sexual Behavior, 18*, 13–30.

Baldwin, J. D., & Baldwin, J. I. (1997). Gender differences in sexual interest. *Archives of Sexual Behavior, 26*, 181–210.

Baldwin, S. B., Wallace, D. R., Papenfuss, M. R., Abrahamsen, M., Vaught, L. C., & Giuliano A. R. (2004). Condom use and other factors affecting penile human papillomavirus detection in men attending a sexually transmitted disease clinic. *Sexually Transmitted Diseases, 31*, 601–607.

Balsam, K. F. (2004, August). *Identity, community, and outness: Comparing bisexual and lesbian/gay adults.* Paper presented at the 111th Annual Convention of the American Psychological Association, Toronto, Canada.

Bancroft, J. (1978). The prevention of sexual offenses. In C. B. Qualls, J. P. Wincze, & D. H. Barlow (Eds.), *The prevention of sexual disorders* (pp. 95–116). New York, NY: Plenum.

Bancroft, J. (2004). Alfred C. Kinsey and the politics of sex research. *Annual Review of Sex Research, 15*, 1–39.

Bancroft, J. (2010). Sexual desire and the brain revisited. *Sexual and Relationship Therapy, 25*(2), 166–171.

Bancroft, J., & Vikadinovic, Z. (2004). Sexual addiction, sexual compulsivity, sexual impulsivity, or

what? Toward a theoretical model. *Journal of Sex Research, 41*, 225–234.

Bancroft, J., Graham, C., Janssen, E., & Sanders, S. A. (2009). The dual control model: Current status and future directions. *Journal of Sex Research, 46*, 121–142.

Bancroft, J., Herbenick, D., & Reynolds, M. (2003). Masturbation as a marker of sexual development. In John Bancroft (Ed.), *Sexual development in childhood.* Bloomington, IN: Indiana University Press.

Bandura, A. (1982). Self-efficacy mechanism in human agency. *American Psychologist, 37*, 122–147.

Bandura, A. J. (1977). *Social learning theory.* Englewood Cliffs, NJ: Prentice-Hall.

Bandura, A., & Walters, R. H. (1963). *Social learning and personality development.* New York, NY: Holt.

Bang, A. K., Carlsen, E., Holm, M., Petersen, J. H., Skakkebæk, N. E., & Jørgensen, N. (2005). A study of finger lengths, semen quality and sex hormones in 360 young men from the general Danish population. *Human Reproduction, 20*, 3109–3113.

Banks, D., & Kyckelhahn, T. (2011). Characteristics of suspected human trafficking incidents, 2008–2010. Washington, DC: U. S. Department of Justice, Bureau of Justice Statistics, NCJ 233732.

Barak, A., & Fisher, W. A. (2001). Toward an Internet-driven, theoretically based, innovative approach to sex education. *Journal of Sex Research, 38*, 324–332.

Baram, M. (2007). Free porn threatens adult film industry. *ABC News.* Retrieved from http://abcnews.com

Barash, D. P. (1982). *Sociobiology and behavior* (2nd ed.). New York, NY: Elsevier.

Barbaree, H. E., & Seto, M. C. (1997). Pedophilia: Assessment and treatment. In D. R. Laws & W. O'Donohue (Eds.), *Sexual deviance: Theory, assessment, and treatment* (pp. 175–193). New York, NY: Guilford Press.

Barlow, D. H. (1986). Causes of sexual dysfunction: The role of cognitive interference. *Journal of Consulting and Clinical Psychology, 54*, 140–148.

Barlow, D. H., Leitenberg, H., & Agras, W. S. (1969). Experimental control of sexual deviation through manipulation of noxious scenes in covert sensitization. *Journal of Abnormal Psychology, 74*, 596–601.

Baron, L., & Straus, M. A. (1989). *Four theories of rape in American society.* New Haven, CT: Yale University Press.

Barr, H. M., Streissguth, A. P., Darby, B. L., & Sampson, P. D. (1990). Prenatal exposure to alcohol, caffeine, tobacco and aspirin: Effects on fine and gross motor performance in 4-year-old children. *Developmental Psychology, 26*, 339–348.

Barrett, J. R. (2006). Fertile grounds of inquiry: Environmental effects on human reproduction. *Environmental Health Perspectives, 114*, A644–A649.

Barrett, M. (1990). Selected observations of sex education in Canada. *SIECCAN Journal, 5*(1), 21–30.

Barrett, M. (1994). Sexuality education in Canadian schools: An overview in 1994. *Canadian Journal of Human Sexuality, 3*, 199–225.

Barrett, M., King, A., Levy, J., Maticka-Tyndale, E., & McKay, A. (1997). *The international encyclopdia of sexuality* (Vol. 1, pp. 221–343). New York, NY: Continuum Publishing.

Barrett, M., McKay, A., Dickson, C., Seto, J., Fisher, W., Read, R., Steben, M., Gale-Rowe, M., & Wong, T. (2012). Sexual health curriculum and training in Canadian medical schools: A study of family medicine, obstetrics and gynaecology and undergraduate medicine programs in 2011 with comparisons to 1996. *Canadian Journal of Human Sexuality, 21*, 63–73.

Bartels, A., & Zeki, S. (2004). The neural correlates of maternal and romantic love. *Neuroimage, 21*, 1155–1166.

Bartholomew, K., & Horowitz, L. M. (1991). Attachment styles among young adults: A test of a 4-category model. *Journal of Personality and Social Psychology, 61*, 226–244.

Bartlett, N. H., Vasey, P. L., & Bukowski, W. M. (2000). Is gender identity disorder in children a mental disorder? *Sex Roles, 43*, 753–785.

Bartlett, N. B., & Vasey, P. L. (2006). A retrospective study of childhood gender-atypical behavior in Samoan *fa'afafine*. *Archives of Sexual Behavior, 35*, 559–566.

Basaria, S., & Dobs, A. (2006). Controversies regarding transdermal androgen therapy in postmenopausal women. *Journal of Clinical Endocrinology and Metabolism, 91*, 4743–4752.

Basson, R. (2001a). Human sex-response cycles. *Journal of Sex & Marital Therapy, 27*, 33–43.

Basson, R. (2001b). Using a different model for female sexual response to address women's problematic low sexual desire. *Journal of Sex & Marital Therapy, 27*, 395–403.

Basson, R. (2004). Summary of the recommendations on women's sexual dysfunctions. In T. F. Lue, R. Basson, R. Rosen, F. Giuliano, S. Khoury, & F. Montorsi (Eds.), *Sexual medicine: Sexual dysfunctions in men and women* (pp. 975–990). Paris, France: Editions 21.

Basson, R. (2005). Women's sexual dysfunction: Revised and expanded definitions. *Canadian Medical Association Journal, 172*, 1327–1333.

Basson, R. (2006). Sexual desire and arousal disorders in women. *New England Journal of Medicine, 354*, 1497–1506.

Basson, R. (2007). Sexual desire/arousal disorders in women. In S. Leiblum (Ed.), *Principles and practice of sex therapy* (4th ed., pp. 25–53). New York, NY: Guilford.

Basson, R., & Brotto, L. A. (2003). Sexual psychophysiology and effects of sildenafil citrate in oestrogenised women with acquired genital arousal disorder and impaired orgasm: A randomised controlled trial. *BJOG: International Journal of Obstetrics and Gynaecology, 110*, 1014–1024.

Basson, R., & VHHSC Centre for Sexuality, Gender Identity, & Reproductive Health. (1998). Integrating new biomedical treatments into the assessment and management of erectile dysfunction. *Canadian Journal of Human Sexuality, 7*, 213–229.

Basson, R., Berman, J., Burnett, A., Derogatis, L., Ferguson, D., Fourcroy, J., . . . Whipple, B. (2001). Report of the International Consensus Development Conference on female sexual dysfunction: Definitions and classifications. *Journal of Sex & Marital Therapy, 27*, 83–94.

Basson, R., Brotto, L. A., Petkau, A. J., & Labrie, F. (2010). Role of androgens in women's sexual dysfunction. *Menopause, 17*, 1–10.

Basson, R., McInnes, R., Smith, M., Hodgson, G., & Koppiker, N. (2002). Efficacy and safety of sildenafil citrate in women with sexual dysfunction associated with female sexual arousal disorder. *Journal of Women's Health & Gender-Based Medicine, 11*, 367–377.

Baulieu, E. E., Thomas, G., Legrain, S., Lahlou, N., Roger, M., Debuire, B., ... Forette, F. (2000). Dehydroepiandrosterone (DHEA), DHEA sulfate, and aging: Contributions of the DHEAge study to a sociobiomedical issue. *Proceedings of the National Academy of Sciences, 97*, 4279–4284.

Baumeister, R. F. (1988a). Masochism as escape from the self. *Journal of Sex Research, 25*, 28–59.

Baumeister, R. F. (1988b). Gender differences in masochistic scripts. *Journal of Sex Research, 25*, 478–499.

Baumeister, R. F., Catanese, K., & Vohs, K. (2001). Is there a gender difference in strength of sex drive? Theoretical views, conceptual distinctions, and a review of relevant evidence. *Personality and Social Psychology Review, 5*, 242–273.

Baxter, J., Brabazon, C., Gunter, K., & Willms, D. (1993a). *Many voices: HIV/AIDS in the context of culture: Report for the communities from the Horn of Africa. Ethnocultural communities facing AIDS: A national study.* Ottawa, Canada: National Health Research and Development Program (Health Canada)/AIDS Education and Prevention Unit (National AIDS Strategy) Health Canada.

Baxter, J., Brabazon, C., Gunter, K., & Willms, D. (1993b). *Many voices: HIV/AIDS in the context of culture: Report for the English-speaking Caribbean communities. Ethnocultural communities facing AIDS: A national study.* Ottawa, Canada: National Health Research and Development Program (Health Canada)/AIDS Education and Prevention Unit National AIDS Strategy) Health Canada.

Bazelon, E. (2007, January 21). Is there a post-abortion syndrome? *New York Times Magazine.*

Beach, F. A. (Ed.). (1976). *Human sexuality in four perspectives.* Baltimore, MD: Johns Hopkins University Press.

Beall, A., & Sternberg, R. (1995). The social construction of love. *Journal of Social and Personal Relationships, 12*, 417–438.

Beattie S., & Cotter, A. (2010). Homicide in Canada, 2009. *Juristat, 30*(3). Retrieved from http://www.statcan.gc.ca/pub/85-002-x/2010003/article/11352-eng.pdf

Beauchamp, D. L. (2008). Canadian Centre for Justice Statistics profile series: Sexual orientation and victimization 2004. Retreived from http://www.mtroyal.ca/cs/groups/public/documents/pdf/psc_orientation_victimisation.pdf

Beaulieu, M. (1994). Screening for D (Rh) sensitization in pregnancy. *The Canadian guide to clinical preventive health care.* Ottawa, Canada: Public Health Agency of Canada.

Beaupré P. (2008). I do. Take two? Changes in intentions to remarry among divorced Canadians during the past 20 years. *Matter of Fact, 5*, 1–3.

Beier, E. G., & Sternberg, D. P. (1977). Marital communication. *Journal of Communication, 27*, 92–103.

Bell, A. P., Weinberg, M. S., & Hammersmith, S. K. (1981). *Sexual preference.* Bloomington, IN: Indiana University Press.

Belzer, E. G. (1981). Orgasmic expulsions of women: A review and heuristic inquiry. *Journal of Sex Research, 17*, 1–12.

Bem, D. J. (1996). Exotic becomes erotic: A developmental theory of sexual orientation. *Psychological Review, 103*, 320–335.

Bem, D. J. (1998). Is EBE theory supported by the evidence? Is it androcentric? A reply to Peplau et al. (1998). *Psychological Review, 105*, 395–398.

Bem, S. L. (1981). Gender schema theory: A cognitive account of sex typing. *Psychological Review, 88*, 354–364.

Bem, S. L. (1989). Genital knowledge and gender consistency in preschool children. *Child Development, 60*, 649–662.

Bem, S. L. (1993). *The lenses of gender: Transforming the debate on sexual inequality.* New Haven, CT: Yale University Press.

Bennett, S., & Assefi, N. (2005). School-based teenage pregnancy prevention programs: A systematic review of randomized controlled trials. *Journal of Adolescent Health, 36*, 72–81.

Bennice, J. A., & Resick, P. (2003). Marital rape: History, research, and practice. *Trauma, Violence, & Abuse, 4*, 228–246.

Benoit, C., & Millar, A. (2001). *Dispelling myths/understanding realities: Working conditions, health status and exiting experiences of sex workers.* Report prepared for the Prostitutes Empowerment and Resource Society. Vancouver, Canada: British Columbia Health Research Foundation.

Benoit, C., Jannson, M., Millar, A., & Phillips, R. (2005). Community-academic research on hard-to-reach populations: Benefits and challenges. *Qualitative Health Research, 15*, 263–282.

Bentz, E., Hefler, L., Kaufmann, U., Huber, J., Kolbus, A., & Tempfer, C. (2008). A polymorphism of the CYP17 gene related to sex steroid metabolism is associated female-to-male but not male-to-female transsexualism. *Fertility and Sterility, 90*, 56–59.

Ben-Ze'ev, A. (2004). *Love online: Emotions on the Internet.* Cambridge, England: Cambridge University Press.

Berenbaum, S. A. (2006). Psychological outcome in children with disorders of sex development: Implications for understanding typical development. *Annual Review of Sex Research, 17*, 1–38.

Beres, M. A., Herold, E., & Maitland, S. B. (2004). Sexual consent behaviours in same-sex relationships. *Archives of Sexual Behavior, 33*, 475–486.

Berg, B. L. (2007). *Qualitative research methods for the social sciences.* Boston, MA: Allyn and Bacon.

Berg, J. H., & Derlega, V. J. (1987). Themes in the study of self-disclosure. In V. J. Derlega & J. H. Berg (Eds.), *Self-disclosure: Theory, research and therapy* (pp. 1–8). New York, NY: Plenum.

Bergen, D. J., & Williams, J. E. (1991). Sex stereotypes in the United States revisited: 1972–1988. *Sex Roles, 24*, 413–423.

Bergeron, S., Binik, Y. M., Khalifé, S., Pagidas, K., Glazer, H. I., Meana, M., & Amsel, R. (2001). A randomized comparison of group cognitive-behavioral therapy, surface electromyographic biofeedback, and vestibulectomy in the treatment of dyspareunia resulting from vulvar vestibulitis. *Pain, 91*, 297–306.

Bergeron, S., Morin, M., & Lord, M. (2010). Integrating pelvic floor rehabilitation and cognitive-behavioural therapy for sexual pain: What have we learned and where do we go from here? *Sexual and Relationship Therapy, 25*, 289–298.

Berglund, H., Lindström, P., & Savic, I. (2006). Brain response to putative pheromones in lesbian women. *Proceedings of the National Academy of Sciences, 103*, 8269–8274.

Bergman, K. M., Sarkar, P., O'Connor, T. G., Modi, N., & Glover, V. (2007). Prenatal stressful life events predict child cognitive outcomes. *Early Human Development, 83*, 136.

Bergstrand, C., & Williams, J. B. (2000, October 10). Today's alternative marriage styles: The case of swingers. *Electronic Journal of Human Sexuality, 3*. Retrieved from http://www.ejhs.org

Berkman, C., & Zinberg, G. (1997). Homophobia and heterosexism in social workers. *Journal of the National Association of Social Workers, 42*, 319–332.

Berman, J. R., Adhikari, S. P., & Goldstein, I. (2000). Anatomy and physiology of female sexual function and dysfunction. *European Urology, 38*, 20–29.

Berman, L., Berman, J., Miles, M., Pollets, D., & Powell, J. A. (2003). Genital self-image as a component of sexual health: Relationship between genital self-image, female sexual function, and quality of life measures. *Journal of Sex & Marital Therapy, 29*, 11–21.

Bermant, G., & Davidson, J. M. (1974). *Biological bases of sexual behavior.* New York, NY: Harper & Row.

Bernstein, A. C., & Cowan, P. A. (1975). Children's concepts of how people get babies. *Child Development, 46*, 77–92.

Bernstein, E. (2007). *Temporarily yours: Intimacy, authenticity, and the commerce of sex.* Chicago, IL: University of Chicago Press.

Bersamin, M. M., Paschall, M. J., Saltz, R. F., & Zamboanga, B. L. (2012). Young adults and casual sex: The relevance of college drinking settings. *Journal of Sex Research, 49*, 274–281.

Berscheid, E., & Hatfield, E. (1978). *Interpersonal attraction* (2nd ed.). Reading, MA: Addison-Wesley.

Berscheid, E., & Walster, E. (1974). A little bit about love. In T. L. Huston (Ed.), *Foundations of interpersonal attraction.* New York, NY: Academic.

Best, D. L. (2001). Gender concepts: Convergence in cross-cultural research and methodologies. *Cross-Cultural Research, 35*, 23–43.

Bettocchi, C., Verze, P., Palumbo, F., Arcaniolo, D., & Mirone, V. (2008). Ejaculatory disorders: Pathophysiology and management. *Nature Clinical Practice Urology, 5*, 93–103.

between social inequality, teenage births and STDs. *Canadian Journal of Human Sexuality, 8*(22), 77–90.

Bhattacharya, S., Townend, J., Shetty, A., Campbell, D., & Bhattacharya, S. (2008). Does miscarriage in initial pregnancy lead to adverse obstetric and perinatal outcomes in the next continuing pregnancy? *BJOG, 115*, 1623–1629.

Bibby, R. (1987). *Fragmented gods: The poverty and potential of religion in Canada.* Toronto, Canada: Irwin.

Bibby, R. (1993). *Unknown gods: The ongoing story of religion in Canada.* Toronto, Canada: Stoddart.

Bibby, R. W. (1995). *The Bibby report: Social trends Canadian style.* Toronto, Canada: Stoddart.

Bibby, R. W. (2001). *Canada's teens: Today, yesterday, and tomorrow.* Toronto, Canada: Stoddart.

Bibby, R. W. (2002). Homosexuality in Canada: A national reading. Retrieved from http://www.reginaldbibby.com/images/PCReleaseHomosexualityMay02.pdf

Bibby, R. W. (2004). *The future families project.* Vanier Institute of the Family. Retrieved October 16, 2007, from http://www.vifamily.ca

Bibby, R. W. (2006). The boomer factor: What *Canada's most famous generation is leaving beind.* Toronto, Canada: Bastian Books.

Bibby, R. W., Russell, S., & Rolheiser, R. (2009). *The emerging millennials: How Canada's newest generation is responding to change & choice.* Lethbridge, Canada: Project Canada Books.

Biggs, M. L., & Schwartz, S. M. (2007). Cancer of the testis. In L. A. G. Ries, J. L. Young, G. E. Keel, M. P. Eisner, Y. D. Lin, & M.-J. D. Horner, (Eds.), *SEER Survival Monograph: Cancer Survival Among Adults: U. S. SEER Program, 1988–2001, Patient and Tumor Characteristics* (Chapter 21, NIH publication no. 07-6215). Bethesda, MD: National Cancer Institute, SEER Program.

Billings, A. (1979). Conflict resolution in distressed and non-distressed married couples. *Journal of Consulting and Clinical Psychology, 47,* 368–376.

Binik, Y. M. (2005). Should dyspareunia be retained as a sexual dysfunction in *DSM-V?* A painful classification decision. *Archives of Sexual Behavior, 34,* 11–21.

Binik, Y. M., Bergeron, S., & Khalifé, S. (2007). Dyspareunia and vaginismus: So-called sexual pain. In S. Leiblum (Ed.), *Principles and practice of sex therapy* (4th ed., pp. 124–156). New York, NY: Guilford.

Bird, S. E. (1999). Gendered construction of the American Indian in popular media. *Journal of Communication, 49,* 61–83. doi:10.1111/j.1460-2466.1999.tb02805.x

Birnie, C., McClure, M. J., Lydon, J. E., & Holmberg, D. (2009). Attachment avoidance and commitment aversion: A script for relationship failure. *Personal Relationships, 16,* 79–97.

Bissell, M. (2000). Socio-economic outcomes of teen pregnancy and parenthood: A review of the literature. *Canadian Journal of Human Sexuality, 9,* 191–204.

Bivona, J., & Critelli, J. (2009). The nature of women's rape fantasies: An analysis of prevalence, frequency and contents. *Journal of Sex Research, 46,* 33–45.

Bixler, R. H. (1986). Of apes and men (including females). *Journal of Sex Research, 22,* 255–267.

Black, A., Bucio, A., Butt, C., Crangle, M., & Lalonde, A. (2009). *Improving sexual and reproductive health: Integrating women's empowerment and reproductive rights* (2nd ed.). Retrieved from http://iwhp.sogc.org/uploads/File/ISRH_booklet_web.pdf

Black, A., Yang, Q., Wu Wen, S., Lalonde, A. B., Guilbert, E., & Fisher, W. (2009). Contraceptive use among Canadian women of reproductive age: Results of a national survey. *Journal of Obstetrics and Gynaecology Canada, 31(7),* 627–640.

Black, M. C., et al. (2011). The National Intimate Partner and Sexual Violence Survey (NISVS): 2010 Summary Report. Atlanta, GA: Centers for Disease Control and Prevention. Retrieved from http://www.cdc.gov/violenceprevention

Blackless, M., et al. (2000). How sexually dimorphic are we? Review and synthesis. *American Journal of Human Biology, 12,* 151–166.

Blair, C. D., & Lanyon, R. I. (1981). Exhibitionism: Etiology and treatment. *Psychological Bulletin, 89,* 439–463.

Blake, J. (2004). *Words can work: When talking with kids about sexual health.* Gloucester, MA: Blake Works, Inc.

Blake, S., Ledsky, R., Goodenow, C., Sawyer, R., Lohrmann, D., & Windsor, R. (2003). Condom availability programs in Massachusetts high schools: Relationships with condom use and sexual behavior. *American Journal of Public Health, 93,* 955–962.

Blakemore, J., Berenbaum, S., & Liben, L. S. (2009). *Gender development.* New York, NY: Psychology Press.

Blanchard, R. (1997). Birth order and sibling sex ratio in homosexual versus heterosexual males and females. *Annual Review of Sex Research, 8,* 27–67.

Blanchard, R. (2004). Quantitative and theoretical analyses of the relation between older brothers and homosexuality in men. *Journal of Theoretical Biology, 230,* 173–187.

Blanchard, R., & Bogaert, A. F. (2004). Proportion of homosexual men who owe their sexual orientation to fraternal birth order: An estimate based on two national probability samples. *American Journal of Human Biology, 16,* 151–157.

Blanchard, R., Christensen, B. K., Strong, S. M., Cantor, J. M., Kuban, M. E., Klassen, P., et al. (2002). Retrospective self-reports of childhood accidents causing unconsciousness in phallometrically diagnosed pedophiles. *Archives of Sexual Behavior, 31,* 511–526.

Blanchard, R., Dickey, R., & Jones, C. (1995). Comparison of height and weight in homosexual versus nonhomosexual gender dysphorics. *Archives of Sexual Behavior, 24,* 543–554.

Blanchard, R., Kolla, N. J., Cantor, J. M., Klassen, P. E., Dickey, R., Kuban, M. E., & Blak, T. (2007). IQ, handedness, and pedophilia in adult male patients stratified by referral source. *Sexual Abuse: A Journal of Research and Treatment, 19,* 285–309.

Blanchard, R., Steiner, B. W., & Clemmenson, L. H. (1985). Gender dysphoria, gender reorientation and the clinical management of transsexualism. *Journal of Consulting & Clinical Psychology, 53(3),* 295–304.

Blanchard, R., Watson, M. S., Choy, A., Dickey, R., Klassen, P., Kuban, M., et al. (1999). Pedophiles: Mental retardation, maternal age, and sexual orientation. *Archives of Sexual Behavior, 28,* 111–127.

Blanchard, V., et al. (2009). Investigating the effects of marriage and relationship education on couples' communication skills: A meta-analytic study. *Journal of Family Psychology, 23,* 203–214.

Bleakley, A., Hennessy, M., & Fishbein, M. (2011). A model of adolescents' seeking of sexual content in their media choices. *Journal of Sex Research, 48,* 309–315

Bleakley, A., Hennessy, M., Fishbein, M., & Jordan, A. (2008). It works both ways: The relationship between exposure to sexual content in the media and adolescent sexual behavior. *Media Psychology, 11(4):* 443–461.

Blumberg, E. (2003). The lives and voices of highly sexual women. *Journal of Sex Research, 40,* 146–157.

Blumstein, P. W., & Schwartz, P. (1983). *American couples.* New York, NY: Morrow.

Boag, S. (2007). "Real processes" and the explanatory status of repression and inhibition. *Philosophical Psychology, 20,* 375–392.

Bockting, W. O. (1999, Oct. /Nov.). From construction to context: Gender through the eyes of the transgendered. *SIECUS Report,* 3–7.

Bockting, W. O. (2004). Plastic and reconstructive surgery for transgender and transsexual patients. In D. B. Sarwer et al. (Eds.), *Psychological aspects of plastic surgery.* Philadelphia, PA: Lippincott Williams & Wilkins.

Bodner, L. M., Markovic, N., Harger, G., & Roberts, J. M. (2004). Prepregnancy body mass index and the risk of preeclampsia. *Federation of American Societies for Experimental Biology Journal, 18(5),* A928.

Bogaert, A. F. (1993). *The sexual media: The role of individual differences.* Unpublished doctoral dissertation. University of Western Ontario, London, Ontario, Canada.

Bogaert, A. F. (1996). Volunteer bias in human sexuality research: Evidence for both sexuality and personality differences in males. *Archives of Sexual Behavior, 25(2),* 125–140.

Bogaert, A. F. (2001). Personality, individual differences, and preferences for the sexual media. *Archives of Sexual Behavior, 30,* 29–53.

Bogaert, A. F. (2003). Number of older brothers and sexual orientation: New tests and the attraction/behaviour distinction in two national probability samples. *Journal of Personality and Social Psychology, 84,* 644–652.

Bogaert, A. F. (2004). Asexuality: Prevalence and associated factors in a national probability sample. *Journal of Sex Research, 41,* 279–287.

Bogaert, A. F. (2005). Age at puberty and father absence in a national probability sample. *Journal of Adolescence, 28,* 541–546.

Bogaert, A. F., & Sadava, S. (2002). Adult attachment and sexual behavior. *Personal Relationships, 9,* 191–204.

Bogaert, A. F., Woodard, U., & Hafer, C. L. (1999). Intellectual ability and reactions to pornography. *Journal of Sex Research, 26(3),* 283–291.

Bogaert, A. F., & Skorska, M. (2011). Sexual orientation, fraternal birth order, and the maternal immune hypothesis: A review. *Frontiers in Neuroendocrinology, 32,*247–254.

Bogle, K. (2008). *Hooking up.* New York, NY: New York University Press.

Boies, S. C. (2002). University students uses of and reactions to online sexual information and entertainment: Links to online and offline sexual behaviour. *Canadian Journal of Human Sexuality, 11,* 77–89.

Boislard, M.-., & Poulin, F. (2011). Individual, familial, friends-related and contextual predictors of early sexual intercourse. *Journal of Adolescence, 34,* 289–300.

Bolton, M., McKay, A., & Schneider, M. (2010). Relational influences on condom use discontinuation: A qualitative study of young adult women in dating relationships. *Canadian Journal of Human Sexuality, 19,* 91–104.

Boon, S. L., & Alderson, K. G. (2009). A phenomenological study of women in same-sex relationships who were previously married to men. *Canadian Journal of Human Sexuality, 18,* 149–168.

Boonstra, H. (2001). Islam, women and family planning: A primer. *Guttmacher Report on Public Policy, 4,* 4–7.

Booth, C. L., & Meltzoff, A. N. (1984). Expected and actual experience in labour and delivery and their relationship to maternal attachment. *Journal of Reproductive and Infant Psychology, 2,* 79–91.

Bornstein, K. (1994). *Gender outlaw: On men, women, and the rest of us.* New York, NY: Routledge.

Bornstein, R. F. (1989). Exposure and affect: Overview and meta-analysis of research, 1968–1987. *Psychological Bulletin, 106,* 265–289.

Boroditsky, R., Fisher, W., & Sand, M. (1996, December). The 1996 Canadian contraceptive study. *Journal of the Society of Obstetricians and Gynaecologists of Canada.*

Boston Women's Health Book Collective. (2005). *Our bodies, ourselves for the new century.* New York, NY: Simon and Schuster.

Boswell, J. (1980). *Christianity, social tolerance, and homosexuality.* Chicago, IL: University of Chicago Press.

Boswell, J. (1994). *Same-sex unions in premodern Europe.* New York, NY: Villard Books.

Bouyer, J., Coste, J., Shojaei, T., Pouly, J. L., Fernandez, H., Gerbaud, L., et al. (2003). Risk factors for ectopic pregnancy: a comprehensive analysis based on a large case-control, population-based study in France. *American Journal of Epidemiology, 157,* 185–194.

Bowe, J. (2006, November 19). Gay donor or gay dad? *New York Times Magazine,* 66–73.

Bowen, A. (2005). Internet sexuality research with rural men who have sex with men: Can we recruit and retain them? *Journal of Sex Research, 42,* 317–323.

Bower, J., Gurevich, M., & Mathieson, C. (2002). (Con)tested identities: Bisexual women reorient sexuality. *Journal of Bisexuality, 2,* 23–52.

Boyarin, D. (1995). Are there any Jews in 'The History of Sexuality'? *Journal of the History of Sexuality, 5,* 333–355.

Boyce, W. F., Doherty-Poirier, M., Fortin, C., MacKinnon, D. (2003). *Canadian youth, sexual health and HIV/AIDS study.* Counsel of Ministers of Education, Canada.

Boyce, W. F., Doherty-Poirier, M., MacKinnon, D., Fortin, C., Saab, H., King, M., & Gallupe, O. (2006). Sexual health of Canadian youth: Findings from the Canadian youth, sexual health and HIV/AIDS Study. *Canadian Journal of Human Sexuality, 15,* 59–68.

Boyce, W. F., Gallupe, O., & Fergus, S. (2008). Characteristics of Canadian youth reporting a very early age of first sexual intercourse. *Canadian Journal of Human Sexuality, 17,* 97–108.

Boyce, W. F., King, A. J. C., & Warren, W. K. (2000). The effectiveness of a school-based HIV education program: A longitudinal comparative evaluation. *Canadian Journal of Program Evaluation, 15,* 93–116.

Boynton, P. M. (2003). "I'm just a girl who can't say no"? Women, consent, and sex research. *Journal of Sex & Marital Therapy, 29*(Suppl.), 23–32.

Brabant, M., Hébert, M., & Chagnon, F. (2013). Identification of sexually abused female adolescents at risk for suicidal ideations: A classification and regression tree analysis. *Journal of Child Sexual Abuse, 22,* 153–172.

Brabazon, C., Bercovitz, E., Dospital, L., Gunter, K., Mangat, S. S., Manson Singer, S., Tweedle, A., & West, J. (1993a) *Many voices: HIV/AIDS in the context of culture: Report for the Chinese communities. Ethnocultural communities facing AIDS: A national study.* Ottawa, Canada: National Health Research and Development Program (Health Canada)/AIDS Education and Prevention Unit (National AIDS Strategy), Health Canada.

Brabazon, C., Bercovitz, E., Dospital, L., Gunter, K., Mangat, S. S., Manson Singer, S., Tweedle, A., & West, J. (1993b) *Many voices: HIV/AIDS in the context of culture: Report for the South Asian communities. Report for the Chinese communities. Ethnocultural communities facing AIDS: A national study.* Ottawa, Canada: National Health Research and Development Program (Health Canada)/AIDS Education and Prevention Unit (National AIDS Strategy), Health Canada.

Bradford, J. M. W. (2000). The treatment of sexual deviation using a pharmacological approach. *Journal of Sex Research, 37,* 248–257.

Bradford, J. M. W., & Greenberg, D. M. (1996). Pharmacological treatment of deviant sexual behaviour. *Annual Review of Sex Research, 7,* 283–306.

Brassard, A., Shaver, P. R., & Lussier, Y. (2007). Attachment, sexual experience, and sexual pressure in romantic relationships: A dyadic approach. *Personal Relationships, 14,* 475–493.

Braun, V., & Kitzinger, C. (2001). "Snatch," "hole," or "honey-pot"? Semantic categories and the problem of nonspecificity in female genital slang. *Journal of Sex Research, 38,* 146–158.

Brecher, E. M. (1984). *Love, sex, and aging.* Mount Vernon, NY: Consumers Union.

Brecht M. L., O'Brien, A., von Mayrhauser, C., & Anglin, M. D. (2004). Methamphetamine use behaviors and gender differences. *Addictive Behaviors, 29,* 89–106.

Brecklin, L. R., & Ullman, S. E. (2005). Self-defense or assertiveness training and women's responses to sexual attacks. *Journal of Interpersonal Violence, 20,* 738–762.

Brennan, D. (2010). Sex tourism, and sex workers' aspirations. In R. Weitzer (Ed.), *Sex for sale: Prostitution, pornography, and the sex industry* (2nd ed., pp. 307–323). New York, NY: Routledge.

Brennan, P. A., & Zufall, F. (2006). Pheromonal communication in vertebrates. *Nature, 444,* 308–315.

Brenton, M. (1972). *Sex talk.* New York, NY: Stein and Day.

Breslow, N., Evans, L., & Langley, J. (1985). On the prevalence and roles of females in the sadomasochistic subculture: Report of an empirical study. *Archives of Sexual Behavior, 14,* 303–318.

Breton, S., Smith, P. J. S., Lut, B., & Brown, D. (1996). Acidification of the male reproductive tract by a proton pumping (H1)-ATPase. *Nature Medicine, 2,* 470–472.

Broad, K. D., & Keverne, E. B. (2011). Placental protection of the fetal brain during short-term food deprivation. *Proceedings of the National Academy of Science, 108,* 15237–15241.

Brock, G., McMahon, C. G., Chen, K K., Costigan, T., Shen, W., Watkins, V., et al. (2002). Efficacy and safety of tadalafil in men with erectile dysfunction: An integrated analysis of registration trials. *Journal of Urology, 167,* 178.

Brock, G., Nehra, A., Lipshultz, L. I., Karlin, G. S., Gleave, M. P., Seger, M., et al. (2003). Safety and efficacy of vardenafil for the treatment of men with erectile dysfunction after radical retropubic prostatectomy. *Journal of Urology, 170,* 1278–1283.

Brooke, C. L., Adam, B. D., McCauley, J., & Bortolin, S. (2010). Perceptions of HIV Risk Among Lesbian, Gay, and Bisexual Youth. *Our Schools/Our Selves, 19* (2), 39–54.

Brotman, H. (1984, Jan. 8). Human embryo transplants. *New York Times Magazine,* 42ff.

Brotto, L. A., & Gorzalka, B. B. (2002). Genital and subjective sexual arousal in postmenopausal women: Influence of laboratory-induced hyperventilation. *Journal of Sex & Marital Therapy, 28,* 39–53.

Brotto, L. A., & Heiman, J. R. (2007). Mindfulness in sex therapy: Applications for women with sexual difficulties following gynecologic cancer. *Sexual and Relationship Therapy, 22,* 3–11.

Brotto, L. A., & Klein, C. (2007). Sexual and gender identity disorders. In M. Hersen, S. M. Turner, & D. Beidel (Eds.) *Adult psychopathology and diagnosis* (5th ed., pp. 504–570). Hoboken, NJ: John Wiley & Sons.

Brotto, L. A., & Klein, C. (2010). Psychological factors involved in women's sexual dysfunctions. *Expert Reviews in Obstetrics and Gynecology, 5,* 93–104.

Brotto, L. A., & Luria, M. (2008). Menopause, aging, and sexual response in women. In D. L. Rowland, & L. Incrocci (Eds.), *Handbook of Sexual and Gender Identity Disorders* (pp. 251–283). Hoboken, NJ: John Wiley & Sons.

Brotto, L. A., & Yule, M. A. (2011). Physiological and subjective sexual arousal in self-identified asexual women. *Archives of Sexual Behavior, 40,* 699–712.

Brotto, L. A., Chik, H. M., Ryder, A. G., Gorzalka, B. B., & Seal, B. N. (2005). Acculturation and sexual function in Asian women. *Archives of Sexual Behaviour, 34,* 613–626.

Brotto, L. A., Chou, A. Y., Singh, T., & Woo, J. S. T. (2008). Reproductive health practices among Indian, Indo-Canadian, Canadian East Asian, and Euro-Canadian Women: The role of acculturation. *Journal of Obstetrics and Gynaecology Canada, 30,* 229–238.

Brotto, L. A., Heiman, J. R., Goff, B., Greer, B., Lentz, G., Swisher, E., Tamimi, H., & Van Blaricom, A. (2008). A psychoeducational intervention for sexual dysfunction in women with gynecologic cancer. *Archives of Sexual Behavior, 37,* 317–329.

Brotto, L. A., Knudson, G., Inskip, J., Rhodes, K., & Erskine, Y. (2010). Asexuality: A mixed-methods approach. *Archives of Sexual Behavior, 39,* 599–618.

Brotto, L. A., Mehak, L., & Kit, C. (2009). Yoga and sexual functioning: A review. *Journal of Sex & Marital Therapy, 35,* 378–390.

Brotto, L. A., Woo, J. S. T., & Ryder, A. G. (2007). Acculturation and sexual function in Canadian East Asian men. *Journal of Sexual Medicine, 4,* 72–82.

Brotto, L. A., Woo, J. S.T., & Gorzalka, B. B. (2011). Differences in sexual guilt and desire in East Asian and Euro-Canadian men. Journal of Sex Research, 49, 594–602.

Brotto, L., et al. (2009). Asexuality: A mixed-methods approach. *Archives of Sexual Behavior,* Retrieved from doi:10.1007/s10508-008-9434-x

Brousseau, M. M., Bergeron, S., Hébert, M., & McDuff, P. (2011). Sexual coercion victimization and perpetration in heterosexual couples: A dyadic investigation. *Archives of Sexual Behavior, 40, 363–372,* doi:10.1007/s10508-010-9617-0

Brown, G., Maycock, B., & Burns, S. (2005). Your picture is your bait: Use and meaning of cyberspace among gay men. *Journal of Sex Research, 42,* 63–73.

Brown, J. D. (2002). Mass media influences on sexuality. *Journal of Sex Research, 39,* 42–45.

Brown, J. D., & Bobkowski, P. S. (2011). Older and newer media: Patterns of use and effects on adolescents' health and well-being. *Journal of Research on Adolescence, 21,* 95–113.

Brown, J. D., L'Engle, K. L., Pardun, C. J., Guo, G., Kenneavy, K., & Jackson, C. (2006). Sexy media matter: exposure to sexual content in music, movies, television, and magazines predicts black and white adolescents' sexual behavior. *Pediatrics, 117*(4), 1018–1027.

Brown, J., & L'Engle, K. (2009). X-rated: Sexual attitudes and behaviors associated with U. S. early adolescents' exposure to sexually explicit media. *Communication Research, 36,* 129–151.

Brown, Z. A., et al. (2005). Genital herpes complicating pregnancy. *Obstetrics & Gynecology, 106,* 845–856.

Bruggemann, O., et al. (2007). Support to a woman by a companion of her choice during childbirth: A randomized controlled trial. *Reproductive Health, 4,*5.

Brym, R. J., & Lenton, R. L. (2001). Love online: A report on digital dating in Canada. Retrieved from http://www.nelson.com

Brym, R. J., & Lenton, R. L. (2003). Love at first byte: Internet Dating in Canada. Retrieved from http://www.societyinquestion4e.nelson.com/article2.html

Brzozowski, J. A. (2007). Family violence against children and youth. In L. Ogrodnik (Ed.) *Family Violence in Canada: A Statistical Profile, 2007.* (Catalogue no. 85-224-XIE). Ottawa, Canada: Canadian Centre for Justice Statistics.

Buchanan, K. M. (1986). *Apache women warriors.* El Paso, TX: Texas Western Press.

Buhi, E. R., et al. (2010). Quality and accuracy of sexual health information web sites visited by young people. *Journal of Adolescent Health, 47,* 206–208.

Bulik, C., Prescott, C., & Kendler, K. (2001). Features of childhood sexual abuse and the development of psychiatric and substance use disorders. *British Journal of Psychiatry, 179,* 444–449.

Bullivant, S. B., Sellergren, S. A., & Stern, K. (2004). Women's sexual experience during the menstrual cycle: Identification of the sexual phase by non-invasive measurement of luteinizing hormone. *Journal of Sex Research, 41,* 82–93.

Bullough, B., & Bullough, V. (1997). Are transvestites necessarily heterosexual? *Archives of Sexual Behavior, 26,* 1–12.

Bullough, V. L. (1994). *Science in the bedroom: A history of sex research.* New York, NY: Basic Books.

Bumpass, L. L., Sweet, J. A., & Cherlin, A. (1991). The role of cohabitation in declining rates of marriage. *Journal of Marriage and the Family, 53,* 913–927.

Burack, J. H., et al. (1993). Depressive symptoms and CD4 lymphocyte decline among HIV-infected men. *Journal of the American Medical Association, 270,* 2568–2573.

Burgess, A. W. (1984). *Child pornography and sex rings.* Lexington, MA: Lexington Books.

Burleson, B. R. (2003). The experience and effects of emotional support: What the study of cultural and gender differences can tell us about close relationships, emotion, and interpersonal communication. *Personal Relationships, 10,* 1–23.

Burleson, B., & Denton, W. (1997). The relationship between communication skill and marital satisfaction: Some moderating effects. *Journal of Marriage and the Family, 59,* 884–902.

Burleson, M. H., et al. (2007). In the mood for love or vice versa? Exploring the relations among sexual activity, physical affection, affect and stress in the daily lives of mid-aged women. *Archives of Sexual Behavior, 36,* 357–368.

Burnett, M., Aggarwal, A., Davis, V., Dempster, J., Fisher, W., . . .Wagner, M- (2011). SOGC policy statement: Sexual and reproductive health counselling by health care professionals. *Journal of Obstetrics and Gynaecology of Canada, 33,* 870–871.

Burrows, M., & Bird, S. R. (2005). Velocity at VO2 (max) and peak treadmill velocity are not influenced within or across the phases of the menstrual cycle. *European Journal of Applied Physiology, 93,* 575–580.

Burton, D. L. (2000). Were adolescent sexual offenders children with sexual behavior problems? *Sex Abuse, 12,* 37–48.

Burton, F. D. (1970). Sexual climax in *Macaca mulatta. Proceedings of the Third International Congress on Primatology, 3,* 180–191.

Busby, K. (1999). Not a victim until the conviction is entered: Sexual violence, prosecutions and legal "truth." In *Locating law: Race/class/gender connections.* Halifax, Canada: Fernwood Publishing.

Bushnik, T., Cook, J. L., Yuzpe, A. A., Tough, S., & Collins, J. (2012). Estimating the prevalence of infertility in Canada. *Human Reproduction, 27,* 738–746.

Buss, A. (1966). *Psychopathology.* New York, NY: Wiley.

Buss, D. M. (1988). The evolution of human intra-sexual competition: Tactics of mate attraction. *Journal of Personality and Social Psychology, 54,* 616–628.

Buss, D. M. (1989). Sex differences in human mate preferences: Evolutionary hypotheses tested in 37 cultures. *Behavioral and Brain Sciences, 12,* 1–49.

Buss, D. M. (1991). Evolutionary personality psychology. *Annual Review of Psychology, 45,* 459–491.

Buss, D. M. (1994). *The evolution of desire: Strategies of human mating.* New York, NY: Basic Books.

Buss, D. M. (2000). *The dangerous passion: Why jealousy is as necessary as love and sex.* New York, NY: The Free Press.

Buss, D. M. (2009). The great struggles of life: Darwin and the emergence of evolutionary psychology. *American Psychologist, 64,* 140–148.

Buss, D. M., & Schmitt, D. P. (1993). Sexual strategies theory: An evolutionary perspective on human mating. *Psychological Review, 100,* 204–232.

Buss, D., & Shackelford, T. (1997a). From vigilance to violence: Mate retention tactics in married couples. *Journal of Personality and Social Psychology, 72,* 346–361.

Buss, D., & Shackelford, T. (1997b). Susceptibility to infidelity in the first year of marriage. *Journal of Research in Personality, 31,* 193–221.

Butzer, B., & Campbell, L. (2008). Adult attachment, sexual satisfaction, and relationship satisfaction: A study of married couples. *Personal Relationships, 15,* 141–154.

Byard, R., Hucker, S., & Hazelwood, R. (1993). Fatal and near-fatal autoerotic asphyxial episodes in women. *The American Journal of Forensic Medicine and Pathology, 14,* 70–73.

Byers, E. S. (1996). How well does the traditional sexual script explain sexual coercion? Review of a program of research. *Journal of Psychology and Human Sexuality, 8,* 7–25.

Byers, E. S. (1999). The interpersonal exchange model of sexual satisfaction: Implications for sex therapy with couples. *Canadian Journal of Counselling, 33*(2), 95–111.

Byers, E. S. (2011). Beyond the birds and the bees and was it good for you?: Thirty years of research on sexual communication. *Canadian Psychology, 52,* 20–28.

Byers, E. S., & Demmons, S. (1999). Sexual satisfaction and sexual self disclosure within dating relationships. *Journal of Sex Research, 36,* 180–189.

Byers, E. S., & Glenn, S. A. (2012). Gender differences in cognitive and affective responses to sexual coercion. *Journal of Interpersonal Violence, 27,* 827–845.

Byers, E. S., & Grenier, G. (2003). Premature or rapid ejaculation: Heterosexual couples' perceptions of men's ejaculatory behavior. *Archives of Sexual Behavior, 32,* 261–270.

Byers, E. S., & Heinlein, L. (1989). Predicting initiation and refusals of sexual activities in married and cohabiting heterosexual couples. *Journal of Sex Research, 26,* 210–231.

Byers, E. S., & MacNeil, S. (2006). Further validation of the interpersonal exchange model of sexual satisfaction. *Journal of Sex & Marital Therapy, 32,* 53–69.

Byers, E. S., & O'Sullivan, L. F. (1998). Similar but different: Men's and women's experiences of sexual coercion. In P. B. Anderson & C. Strickman-Johnson (Eds.), *Sexually aggressive women.* New York, NY: Guilford Press.

Byers, E. S., & Rehman, U. (2013). Sexual well-being. In D. Tolman & L. Diamond (Eds.) *APA Handbook of sexuality and psychology.* Washington, DC: APA Books.

Byers, E. S., & Sears, H. A. (2012). Mothers who do and do not intend to discuss sexual health with their young adolescents. *Family Relations, 61,* 851–863.

Byers, E. S., & Slattery, G. (1997). Sexology in Russia and Estonia: Reflections on an exchange. *Canadian Journal of Human Sexuality, 6,* 53–64.

Byers, E. S., & Wang, A. (2004). Understanding sexuality in close relationships from the social exchange perspective. In J. H. Harvey, A. Wenzel, & S. Sprecher (Eds.), *The handbook of sexuality in close relationships* (pp. 203–234). Mahwah, NJ: Lawrence Erlbaum.

Byers, E. S., Crooks, R., Griffiths, B., Mackin, B., MacDonald, G., Mac-Donald, G., Marcoux-Galarneau, R., Renaud, C., Thomas, B., Thompson, B., & Yates, P. (1997). *The extent of sex offences and the nature of sex offenders in New Brunswick: A research project.* Submitted to the New Brunswick Department of the Solicitor General and Correctional Services Canada.

Byers, E. S., Demmons, S., & Lawrance, K.-A. (1998). Sexual satisfaction within dating relationships: A test of the interpersonal exchange model of sexual satisfaction. *Journal of Social and Personal Relationships, 15*(2), 257–267.

Byers, E. S., Henderson, J., & Hobson, K. (2009). University students' definitions of sexual abstinence and having sex. *Archives of Sexual Behavior, 38,* 665–674. doi:10.1007/s10508-007-9289-6

Byers, E. S., Nichols, S., & Voyer, S. D. (2013). Challenging stereotypes: Sexual functioning of single adults with high functioning autism spectrum disorder. *Journal of Autism and Developmental Disorders.* doi:10.1007/s10803-013-1813-z

Byers, E. S., Nichols, S., Voyer, S. D., & Reilly, G. (2012). Sexual well-being of a community sample of high-functioning adults on the autism spectrum who have been in a romantic relationship. *Autism.* doi:10.1177/1362631311431950

Byers, E. S., Purdon, C., & Clark, D. (1998). Sexual intrusive thoughts of college students. *Journal of Sex Research, 35,* 359–369.

Byers, E. S., Sears, H. A., & Foster, L. R. (2013). Factors associated with middle school students' perceptions of the quality of school-based sexual health education. *Sex Education, 13,* 214–227.

Byers, E. S., Sears, H. A., & Weaver, A. D. (2008). Parents' reports of sexual communication with children in kindergarten to grade 8. *Journal of Marriage and Family, 70*(1), 86–96.

Byers, E. S., Sears, H. A., Voyer, S. D., Thurlow, J. L., Cohen, J. N., & Weaver, A. D. (2003a). An adolescent perspective on sexual health education at school and at home: I. High school students. *Canadian Journal of Human Sexuality, 12,* 1–17.

Byers, E. S., Sears, H. A., Voyer, S. D., Thurlow, J. L., Cohen, J. N., & Weaver, A. D. (2003b). An adolescent perspective on sexual health education at school and at home: II. Middle school students. *Canadian Journal of Human Sexuality, 12,* 19–32.

Byers, L. J., Menzies, K. S., & W. L. O'Grady (2004). The impact of computer variables on the viewing and sending of sexually explicit material on the Internet: Testing Cooper's "triple-A engine." *Canadian Journal of Human Sexuality, 13,* 157–169.

Byers, M. E. (2005). *Growing up Degrassi.* Toronto, Canada: Sumach Press.

Byne, W., Lasco, M. S., Kemether, E., Shinwari, A., Edgar, M. A., & Morgello, S. (2000). The interstitial nuclei of the human anterior hypothalamus: Assessment for sexual variation in volume and neuronal size, density, and number. *Brain Research, 856,* 254–258.

Byrne, D. (1971). *The attraction paradigm.* New York, NY: Academic.

Byrne, D. (1983). Sex without contraception. In D. Byrne & W. A. Fisher (Eds.), *Adolescents, sex, and contraception.* Hillsdale, NJ: Lawrence Erlbaum.

Byrne, D. (1997). An overview (and underview) and research and theory within the attraction paradigm. *Journal of Social and Personal Relationships, 14,* 417–431.

Byrne, D., Ervin, C. E., & Lamberth, J. (1970). Continuity between the experimental study of attraction and real-life computer dating. *Journal of Personality and Social Psychology, 16,* 157–165.

Byun, S., et al. (2009). Internet addiction: Metasynthesis of 1996–2006 quantitative research. *CyberPsychology & Behavior, 12,* 203–207.

Cacioppo, S., et al. (2012a). The common neural bases between sexual desire and love: A multilevel kernel density fMRI analysis. *Journal of Sexual Medicine, 9,* 1048–1054.

Cacioppo, S., et al. (2012b). Social neuroscience of love. *Clinical Neuropsychiatry, 9,* 3–13

Cado, S., & Leitenberg, H. (1990). Guilt reactions to sexual fantasies during intercourse. *Archives of Sexual Behavior, 19,* 49–64.

Cahill, L. (2005). His brain, her brain. *Scientific American, 292,* 40–47.

Cahill, L. S. (1985). The "seamless garment": Life in its beginnings. *Theological Studies, 46,* 64–80.

Cairns, K. V. (1993). Sexual entitlement and sexual accommodations: implications for female and male experience of sexual coercion. *Canadian Journal of Human Sexuality, 2,* 203–213.

Calderwood, D. (1987, May). The male rape victim. *Medical Aspects of Human Sexuality,* 53–55.

Call, V., Sprecher, S., & Schwartz, P. (1995). The incidence and frequency of marital sex in a national sample. *Journal of Marriage and the Family, 57,* 639–652.

Callahan, D. (1986, February). How technology is reframing the abortion debate. *Hastings Center Report,* 33–42.

Calzavara, L. M., Burchell, A. N., Myers, T., Bullock, S. L., Escobar, M., & Cockerill, R. (1998). Condom use among Aboriginal people in Ontario, Canada. *International Journal of STD & AIDS, 9,* 272–279.

Calzo, J. P., & Ward, L. M. (2009). Media exposure and viewers' attitudes toward homosexuality: Evidence for mainstreaming or resonance? *Journal of Broadcasting and Electronic Media, 53,* 280–299.

Cameron, J. J., & Ross, M. (2007). In times of uncertainty: Predicting the survival of long-distance relationships. *Journal of Social Psychology, 147,* 581–606.

Camilleri, J. A., & Quinsey, V. L. (2008). Pedophilia: Assessment and treatment. In D. R. Laws & W. T. O'Donohue (Eds.), *Sexual deviance* (pp. 183–212). New York, NY: Guilford.

Campbell, A., Shirley, L., & Caygill, L. (2002). Sex-typed preferences in three domains: Do two-year-olds need cognitive variables? *British Journal of Psychology, 93,* 201–217.

Canadian AIDS Society. (2011). Rapid HIV testing in Canada. Retrieved from http://www.cdnaids.ca/rapidhivtestingincanada

Canadian Association for Adolescent Health. (2006). Teens face significant barriers seeking information about STIs and other sexual health matters. *Proteen, 15,* 12–16.

Canadian Association of Midwives. (2004). *Position statement on elective cesarean section.* Retrieved from http://www.canadianmidwives.org

Canadian Cancer Society. (2012). *Canadian cancer statistics 2012.* Toronto, Canada: Author.

Canadian Cancer Society. (2013a). *Risk factors for prostate cancer.* Toronto, Canada: Author.

Canadian Cancer Society. (2013b). What is breast cancer? Retrieved from http://www.cancer.ca/en/cancer-information/cancer-type/breast/breast-cancer/

Canadian Cancer Society. (2013c). *Risk factors for testicular cancer.* Retrieved from http://www.cancer.ca

Canadian Centre for Justice Statistics. (1999). Integration and analysis program: Sex offenders. *Juristat, 19*(3). Retrieved from http://publications.gc.ca/Collection-R/Statcan/85-002-XIE/0039985-002-XIE.pdf

Canadian Federation for Sexual Health (2007). *Sexual Health in Canada: Baseline 2007.* Ottawa, Canada: Author.

Canadian HIV/AIDS Legal Network. (2002). *HIV vaccines in Canada: Legal and ethical issues: An Overview.* Retrieved from http://www.aidslaw.ca/publications/publicationsdocEN.php?ref=368

Canadian HIV/AIDS Legal Network. (2009). *Canada's immigration policy as it affects people living with HIV/AIDS.* Retrieved from http://www.aidslaw.ca/publications/publicationsdocEN.php?ref=97

Canadian Institute for Health Information. (2010). Number of induced abortions reported in Canada Retrieved from http://www.cihi.ca/CIHI-ext-portal/pdf/internet/TA_08_ALLDATATABLES20101124_EN

Canadian Institute for Health Information. (2011). Number of induced abortions reported in Canada in 2011. Retrieved from http://www.cihi.ca/cihi-ext-portal/pdf/internet/ta_11_alldatatables20130221_en

Canadian Institute for Health Information. (2012). *Highlights of 2010–2011 selected indicators describing the birthing process in Canada.* Retrieved from http://www.cihi.ca

Canadian Midwifery Regulators Consortium. (2007). What is a Canadian registered midwife? Retrieved August 30, 2007 from http://cmrccosf.ca/node/18.

Canadian Paediatric Society. (2013, January 30). Reaffirmed position statement: Testing for HIV infection in pregnancy. *Paediatric Child Health 2008, 13,* 221–224.

Canadian Psychological Association. (1995). *Companion manual to the Canadian Code of Ethics for Psychologists, 1991.* Ottawa, Canada: Author.

Canadian Psychological Association. (2003, August 6). Gays and lesbians make bad parents: There is no basis in the scientific literature for this perception [Press Release]. Ottawa, Canada: Author.

Cantor, J. M., & Blanchard, R. (2012). White matter volumes in pedophiles, hebephiles, and teleiophiles [Letter to the Editor]. *Archives of Sexual Behavior, 41,* 749–752. doi:10.1007/s10508-012-9954-2

Cantor, J. M., Blanchard, R., & Barbaree, H. E. (2009). Sexual disorders. In P. H. Blaney & T. Millon (Eds.), *Oxford textbook of psychopathology* (2nd ed., pp. 527–548). New York, NY: Oxford University Press.

Cantor, J. M., Blanchard, R., Christensen, B. K., Dickey, R., Klassen, P. E., Beckstead, A. L., Blak, T., & Kuban, M. E. (2004). Intelligence, memory, and handedness in pedophilia. *Neuropsychology, 18,* 3–14.

Cantor, J. M., Blanchard, R., Paterson, A. D., & Bogaert, A. F. (2002). How many gay men owe their sexual orientation to fraternal birth order? *Archives of Sexual Behavior, 31,* 63–71.

Cantor, J. M., Blanchard, R., Robichaud, L., & Christensen, B. (2005). Quantitative reanalysis of aggregate data on IQ in sexual offenders. *Psychological Bulletin, 131,* 555–568.

Cantor, J. M., Kabani, N., Christensen, B. K., Zipursky, R. B., Barbaree, H. E., Dickey, R., Klassen, P. E., Mikulis, D. J., Kuban, M. E., Blak, T., Richards, B. A., Hanratty, M. K., & Blanchard, R. (2008). Cerebral white matter deficiencies in pedophilic men. *Journal of Psychiatric Research, 42,* 167–183.

Cantor, J. M., Klassen, P. E., Dickey, R., Christensen, B. K., Kuban, M. E., Blak, T., Williams, N. S., & Blanchard, R. (2005). Handedness in pedophilia and hebephilia. *Archives of Sexual Behavior, 34,* 447–459.

Cantor, J. M., Klein, C., Lykins, A., Rullo, J. E., Thaler, L., & Walling, B. R. (2013). A treatment-oriented typology of self-identified hypersexuality referrals. *Archives of Sexual Behavior, 42,* 883–893.

Caplan, P. (1995). *How do they decide who is normal?* Reading, MA: Addison-Wesley.

Cappon, P., Adrien, A., Godin, G., Manson Singer, S., Maticka-Tyndale, E., Willms, D., & Daus, T. (1996). HIV/AIDS in the context of culture: Selection of ethnocultural communities for study in Canada. *Canadian Journal of Public Health, 87*(1), S11–S25.

Caputo, T. (2000). *Hearing the voices of youth: Youth participation in selected Canadian municipalities.* Ottawa, Canada: ON: Health Canada.

CARAL (n. d.). *Historical biography of Henry Morgentaler,* Ottawa, Canada: CARAL.

Carani, C., et al. (1990). Effects of androgen treatment in impotent men with normal and low levels of free testosterone. *Archives of Sexual Behavior, 19,* 223–234.

Carnes, P. (1983). *The sexual addiction.* Minneapolis, MN: Compcare Publications.

Caron, A., Lafontaine, M-F., Bureau, J-F., Levesque, C., & Johnson, S. M. (2012). Comparisons of close relationships: An evaluation of relationship quality and patterns of attachment to parents, friends, and romantic partners in young adults. *Canadian Journal of Behavioural Science, 44,* 245–256.

Carpenter, L. M. (2001). The ambiguity of "having sex": The subjective experience of virginity loss in the United States. *Journal of Sex Research, 38,* 127–139.

Carter, C. S. (1992). Hormonal influences on human sexual behavior. In J. B. Becker et al. (Eds.), *Behavioral endocrinology* (pp. 131–142). Cambridge, MA: MIT Press.

Cashdan, E. (2008). Waist-to-hip ratio across cultures: Trade-offs between androgen- and estrogen-dependent traits. *Current Anthropology, 49,* 1099–1107.

Catania, J. A., Binson, D., Van Der Straten, A., & Stone, V. (1995). Methodological research on sexual behavior in the AIDS era. *Annual Review of Sex Research, 6,* 77–125.

Catania, J. A., Gibson, D., Marin, B., Coates, T., & Greenblatt, R. (1990). Response bias in assessing sexual behaviors relevant to HIV transmission. *Evaluation and Program Planning, 13,* 19–29.

Catellsagué, X., Bosch, F. X., Muñoz, N., Meijer, C. J. L. M., Shah, K. V., de Sanjosé, S., Eluf-Neto, J., Ngelangel, C. A., Chichareon, S., Smith, J. S., Herrero, R., Moreno, V., Franceschi, S., & International Agency for Research on Cancer Multicenter Cervical Cancer Study Group. (2002). Male circumcision, penile human papillomavirus infection, and cervical cancer in female partners. *New England Journal of Medicine, 346,* 1105–1112.

Causarano, N., Pole, Flicker, S., & the Toronto Teen Survey Team (2010). Exposure to and desire for sexual health eduation among urban youth: Associations with religion and other factors. *Canadian Journal of Human Sexuality, 19,* 169–184.

Centers for Disease Control. (2004). *Intimate partner violence: Fact sheet.* Retrieved from http://www.cdc.gov/ncipc/factsheets/ipvfacts.htm

Chalker, R. (1995, November/December) Sexual pleasure unscripted. *Ms,* 49–52.

Chalmers, B., & Hashi, K. O. (2000). 432 Somali women's birth experiences in Canada after earlier female genital mutilation. *Birth, 27,* 227–234.

Chan, C. S. (1995). Issues of sexual identity in an ethnic minority: The case of Chinese American lesbians, gay men, and bisexual people. In A. R. D'Augelli & C. J. Patterson (Eds.), *Lesbian, gay, and bisexual identities over the lifespan* (pp. 87–101). New York, NY: Oxford University Press.

Chan, D. K-S., et al. (2008). Examining the job related, psychological, and physical outcomes of workplace sexual harassment: A meta-analytic review. *Psychology of Women Quarterly, 32,* 362–376.

Chandra, A., Mosher, W., & Coopen, C. (2011). Sexual behavior, sexual attraction, and sexual identity in the United States: Data from the 2006–2008 National Survey of Family Growth. *National Health Statistics Reports, 36.*

Chang, S. C. H., Woo, J. S. T., Gorzalka, B. B., & Brotto, L. A. (2010). A questionnaire study of cervical cancer screening beliefs and practices of Chinese and Caucasian mother-daughter pairs living in Canada. *Journal of Obstetrics and Gynaecology Canada, 32,* 254–262.

Chapman, H., Hobfoll, S., & Ritter, C. (1997). Partners' stress underestimations lead to women's distress: A study of pregnant inner-city women. *Journal of Personality and Social Psychology, 73,* 418–425.

Charon, J. (1995). *Symbolic interactionism: An introduction, interpretation, and integration* (5th ed.). Englewood Cliffs, NJ: Prentice Hall.

Chavarro, J., et al. (2007). Diet and lifestyle in the prevention of ovulatory disorder infertility. *Obstetrics & Gynecology, 110,* 1050–1058.

Cheng, D., et al. (2009) Unintended pregnancy and associated maternal preconception, prenatal, and postpartum behaviors. *Contraception, 79,* 194–198.

Cheng, J., Elam-Evans, L. D., Berg, C. J., Herndon, J., Flowers, L., Seed, K. A., et al. (2003, February 21). Pregnancy-related mortality surveillance: United States, 1991–1999. *Morbidity & Mortality Weekly Report, 52,* 1–8.

Cheng, M. M., & Udry, J. R. (2003). How much do mentally disabled adolescents know about sex and birth control? *Adolescent & Family Health, 3,* 28–38.

Chesler, E. (1992). *Woman of valor: Margaret Sanger and the birth control movement.* New York, NY: Simon & Schuster.

Childbirth by Choice Trust. (2003). Contraceptive use in Canada. Retrieved from http://www.cbctrust.com

Chivers, M. L. (2005). A brief review and discussion of sex differences in the specificity of sexual arousal. *Sexual and Relationship Therapy, 20,* 377–390.

Chivers, M. L., & Bailey, J. M. (2000). Sexual orientation of female-to-male transsexuals: A comparison of homosexual and nonhomosexual types. *Archives of Sexual Behavior, 29,* 259–278.

Chivers, M. L., Rieger, G., Latty, E., & Bailey, J. M. (2004). A sex difference in the specificity of sexual arousal. *Psychological Science, 15,* 736–744.

Chivers, M. L., Seto, M. C., & Blanchard, R. (2007). Gender and sexual orientation differences in sexual response to sexual activities versus gender of actors in sexual films. *Journal of Personality and Social Psychology, 93,* 1108–1121. doi:10.1037/0022-351493.6.1108

Chivers, M. L., Seto, M. C., Lalumière, M. L., Laan, E., & Grimbos, T. (2010). Agreement of self-reported and genital measures of sexual arousal in men and women: A meta-analysis. *Archives of Sexual Behavior, 39,* 5–56.

Chivers, M., & Blanchard, R. (1996). Prostitution advertisements suggest association of transvestism and masochism. *Journal of Sex & Marital Therapy, 22*(2), 97–102.

Chivers, M., & Timmers, A. (2012). Effects of gender and relationship context in audio narratives on genital and subjective sexual response in heterosexual women and men. *Archives of Sexual Behavior, 41*(1), 185–197. doi:10.1007/s10508-012-9937-3

Choi, E. J, Ha, C. M, Choi, J., Kang, S. S., Choi, W. S., Park, S. K., et al. (2001). Low-density DNA array-coupled to PCR differential display identifies new estrogen-responsive genes during the postnatal differentiation of the rat hypothalamus. *Molecular Brain Research, 97,* 115–128.

Choi, Y., Bishai, D., & Minkovitz, C. (2009). Multiple birthe are a risk factor for postpartum maternal depression. *Pediatrics, 123,* 1147–1154.

Chrisler, J. C., et al. (2006). The PMS illusion: Social cognition maintains social construction. *Sex Roles, 54,* 371–376.

Christensen, C. V. (1971). *Kinsey: A biography.* Bloomington, IN: Indiana University Press.

Christopher, F. S., & Sprecher, S. (2000). Sexuality in marriage, dating, and other relationships: A decade review. *Journal of Marriage and the Family, 62,* 999–1017.

Chu, J. A., Frey, L. M., Ganzel, B., & Mattews, J. (1999). Memories of childhood abuse: Dissociation amnesia, and corroboration. *American Journal of Psychiatry, 156,* 749–755.

Chu, M., & Lobo, R. (2004). Formulations and use of androgens in women. *Journal of Family Practice, 53,* S3.

Church, S., Henderson, M., Barnard, M., & Hart, G. (2001). Violence by clients towards female prostitutes in different work settings: Questionnaire survey. *British Medical Journal, 322,* 524–525.

Cimbalo, R. S., Faling, B., & Mousaw, P. (1976). The course of love: A cross-sectional design. *Psychological Reports, 38,* 1292–1294.

Cizmar, M., Conklin, E., & Hinman, K. (2011). Real men get their facts straight. Retrieved from http://www.villagevoice.com/content/printVersion/2651144/

Clamen, J., Bruckert, C., & Mensah, M. N. (2013). Managing sex work: Information for third parties and sex workers in the incall and outcall sectors of the sex industry. Retrieved from http://www.sciences-sociales.uottawa.ca/gis-msi/eng/publications.asp

Clark, L., & Lewis, D. (1977). *Rape: The price of coercive sexuality.* Toronto, Canada: Women's Educational Press.

Clark, R. D., & Hatfield, E. (1989). Gender differences in receptivity to sexual offers. *Journal of Psychology & Human Sexuality, 2,* 39–45.

Clark, W., & Crompton, S. (2006). Till death do us part? The risk of first and second marriage dissolution. *Canadian Social Trends* (Catalogue no. 11-008E). Ottawa, Canada: Statistics Canada.

Clarke, J. N. (2006). Homophobia out of the closet in the media portrayal of HIV/AIDS 1991, 1996 and 2001: Celebrity, heterosexism and the silent victims. *Critical Public Health, 16,* 317–330.

Clark-Flory, T. (2011). I cross-dress and my wife doesn't know it. Retrieved from http://www.salon.com/2011/11/25/

Clausell, E., & Roisman, G. I. (2009). Outness, big five personality traits, and same-sex relationship quality. *Journal of Social and Personal Relationships, 26,* 211–226.

Cleland, K., et al. (2012). The efficacy of intrauterine devices for emergency contraception. *Human Reproduction, 27,* 1994–2000.

Clemente, C. D. (1987). *Anatomy: A regional atlas of the human body* (3rd ed.). Baltimore, MD: Urban & Schwarzenberg.

Clements-Schreiber, M. E., Rempel, J. K., & Desmarais, S. (1998). Women's sexual pressure tactics and adherence to related attitudes: A step towards prediction. *Journal of Sex Research, 35*(2), 197–205.

Clutton-Brock, T. (2007). Sexual selection in males and females. *Science, 318,* 1882–1885.

Cochran, S. D., et al. (2007). Mental health and substance use disorders among Latino and Asian American lesbian, gay, and bisexual adults. *Journal of Consulting and Clinical Psychology, 75,* 785–794.

Cochran, S., Sullivan, J. G., & Mays, V. (2003). Prevalence of mental disorders, psychological distress, and mental health services use among lesbian, gay, and bisexual adults in the United States. *Journal of Consulting and Clinical Psychology, 71,* 53–61.

Cochran, W. G., Mosteller, F., & Tukey, J. W. (1953). Statistical problems of the Kinsey report. *Journal of the American Statistical Association, 48,* 673–716.

Cohen, B. B., Zhang, Z., Nannini, A., Farr, S. L., Anderson, J. E., Jamieson, D. J., Tepper, N. K. (2009). Assisted reproductive technology and trends in low birthweight – Massachusetts, 1997–2004. *MMWR, 58,* 49–52.

Cohen, J. (1997). Exploiting the HIV-chemokine nexus. *Science, 275,* 1261–1264.

Cohen, J. (1998). Exploring how to get at-and eradicate-hidden HIV. *Science, 279,* 1854–1855.

Cohen, J. N., Byers, E. S., & Sears, H. A. (2012). Factors affecting Canadian teachers' willingness to teach sexual health education. *Sex Education, 12,* 299–316.

Cohen, J. N., Byers, E. S., & Walsh, L. P. (2008). Factors influencing the sexual relationships of lesbians and gay men. *International Journal of Sexual Health, 20,* 162–176.

Cohen, J. N., Byers, E. S., Sears, H. A., & Weaver, A. D. (2004). Sexual health education: Attitudes, knowledge, and comfort of teachers in New Brunswick schools. *Canadian Journal of Human Sexuality, 13,* 1–15.

Cohen, K. M. (2002). Relationships among childhood sex-atypical behavior, spatial ability, handedness, and sexual orientation in men. *Archives of Sexual Behavior, 31,* 129–144.

Cohen, M. S., Chen, Y. Q., McCauley, M., Gamble, T., Hosseinipour, M. C., Kumarasamy, N., . . . Fleming, T. R. (2011). Prevention of HIV-1 infection with early antiretroviral therapy. *New England Journal of Medicine, 365,* 493–505.

Cohn, L. (1983, November 16). Pix less able but porn is stable. *Variety, 313*(3), 1–2.

Colapinto, J. (2004, June 3). Gender gap: What were the real reasons behind David Reimer's Suicide? *Slate.* Retrieved from http://www.slate.com/id/2101678/

Cole, E. R. (2009). Intersectionality and research in psychology. *American Psychologist, 64,* 170–180.

Cole, L. (2011). The utility of six over-the counter(home) pregnancy tests. *Clinical Chemistry and Laboratory Medicine, 49,* 1317–1322.

Cole, L., Khantian, S., Sutton, J., Davies, S., & Rayburn, W. (2004). Accuracy of home pregnancy tests at the time of missed menses. *American Journal of Obstetrics and Gynecology, 190,* 100–105.

Coleman, E. (1991). Compulsive sexual behavior: New concepts and treatments. *Journal of Psychology and Human Sexuality, 4*(2), 37–51.

Coleman, E., Miner, M., Ohlerking, F., & Raymond, N. (2001). Compulsive Sexual Behavior inventory: A preliminary study of reliability and validity. *Journal of Sex and Marital Therapy, 27,* 325–332.

Coleman, E., Raymond, N., & McBean, A. (2003, July 2003). Assessment and treatment of compulsive sexual behaviour. *Minnesota Medicine, 86,* 42–47.

Collaborative Group on Hormonal Factors in Breast Cancer. (2002). Breast cancer and breast-feeding. *Lancet, 360,* 187–195.

Collins, N. L., & Miller, L. C. (1994). Self-disclosure and liking: A metaanalytic review. *Psychological Bulletin, 116,* 457–475.

Collins, R. L., Elliott, M. N., Berry, S. H., Kanouse, D. E., Kunkel, D., Hunter, S. B., Miu, A. (2004). Watching sex on television predicts adolescent initiation of sexual behavior. *Pediatrics, 114*(3), e280–e209.

Collins, R. L., et al. (2005). Isolating the nexus of substance use, violence and sexual risk for HIV infection among young adults in the United States. *AIDS and Behavior, 9,* 73–87.

Collins, W. A., Welsh, D. P., & Furman, W. (2009). Adolescent romantic relationships. *Annual Review of Psychology, 60,* 631–652.

Collin-Vézina, D., & Hébert, M. (2005). Comparing dissociation and PTSD in sexually abused school-aged girls. *Journal of Mental & Nervous Disease, 193,* 47–52.

Comet (Comparative Obstetric Mobile Epidural Trial) Study Group. (2001). Effect of low-dose mobile versus traditional epidural techniques on mode of delivery: A randomised controlled trial. *Lancet, 358,* 19–23.

Comfort, A. (1991). *The new joy of sex: A gourmet guide to lovemaking for the nineties.* New York, NY: Crown.

Compas Inc. (2005, February 14). Valentine's Day Poll for the National Post. Toronto, Canada: Author.

Compas, B. E., & Luecken, L. (2002). Psychological adjustment to breast cancer. *Current Directions in Psychological Science, 11,* 111–114.

Congregation for the Doctrine of the Faith. (1986). The pastoral care of homosexual persons. *Origins, 26,* 378–382.

Congregation for the Doctrine of the Faith. (1987). Instruction on respect for human life in its origin and on the dignity of procreation. *Origins, 16,* 198–211.

Congregation for the Doctrine of the Faith. (2008, September 8). Regarding the instruction dignitas personae. Retrieved from http://www.religiousinstitute.org/statement/regarding-the-instruction-dignitas-personaesummary

Conley, T. D. (2011). Perceived proposer personality characteristics and gender differences in acceptance of casual sex offers. *Journal of Personality and Social Psychology, 100,* 309–329.

Conley, T. D., et al. (2011). Women, men, and the bedroom: Methodological and conceptual insights that narrow, reframe, and eliminate gender differences in sexuality. *Current Directions in Psychological Science, 20,* 296–300.

Connell, E., & Hunt, A. (2006). Sexual ideology and sexual physiology in the discourses of sex advice literature. *Canadian Journal of Human Sexuality, 15,* 23–45.

Conrad, K., Dixon, T., & Zhang, Y. (2009). Controversial rap themes, gender portrayals and skin tone distortion: A content analysis of rap music videos. *Journal of Broadcasting & Electronic Media, 53,* 134–156.

Cook, K., & Rice, E. (2003). Social exchange theory. In J. DeLamater (Ed.), *The handbook of social psychology* (pp. 53–76). New York, NY: Kluwer-Plenum.

Cooper, A. (1998). Sexuality and the Internet: Surfing into the new millennium. *CyberPsychology & Behavior, 1,* 187–193.

Cooper, A., & Griffin-Shelley, E. (2002). Introduction. The Internet: The next sexual revolution. In A. Cooper (Ed.), *Sex and the internet: A guidebook for clinicians* (pp. 1–15). New York:Brunner-Routledge.

Cooper, A., Delmonico, D. L., Griffin-Shelley, E., & Mathy, R. M. (2004). Online sexual activity: An examination of potentially problematic behaviors. *Sexual Addiction & Compulsivity, 11,* 129–143.

Cooper, A., Delmonico, D., & Burg, R. (2000). Cybersex users, abusers, and compulsives: New findings and implications. In A. Cooper (Ed.), *Cybersex: The dark side of the force* (pp. 5–29). Philadelphia, PA: Brunner Routledge.

Cooper, A., Putnam, D. E., Planchon, L. A., & Boies, S. C. (1999a). Online sexual compulsivity: Getting tangled in the Net. *Sexual Addiction & Compulsivity: Journal of Treatment and Prevention, 6,* 79–104.

Cooper, A., Scherer, C. R., Gordon, B. L., & Boies, S. C. (1999b). Sexuality on the Internet: From sexual exploration to pathological expression. *Professional Psychology: Research & Practice, 30*(2), 154–164.

Cordova, M. J., Cunningham, L., Carlson, C., & Andrykowski, M. (2001). Posttraumatic growth following breast cancer: A controlled comparison study. *Health Psychology, 20,* 176–185.

Corey, L., & Wald, A. (2008). Genital herpes. In K. Holmes et al. (Eds.), *Sexually transmitted diseases.* (4th ed., pp. 399–438). New York, NY: McGraw-Hill.

Cortini, F., Hanson, R. K., & Coache, M. (2010). The recidivism rates of female sexual offenders are low: A meta-analysis. *Sex Abuse, 22,* 387–401

Coughlan, C. (2008). Surgical management of tubal disease and infertility. *Obstetrics, Gynaecology, and Reproductive Medicine, 11,* 013.

Countryman, L. W. (1987). The AIDS crisis: Theological and ethical reflections. *Anglican Theological Review, 69,* 125–134.

Countryman, L. W. (1994). New Testament sexual ethics and today's world. In J. B. Nelson & S. P. Longfellow (Eds.), *Sexuality and the sacred* (pp. 28–53). Louisville, KY: Westminster/ John Knox Press.

Coustan, D. (1995). Obstetric analgesia and anesthesia. In D. R. Coustan, R. V. Hunning, Jr., & D. Singer (Eds.), *Human reproduction: Growth and development* (pp. 327–340). Boston, MA: Little, Brown.

Coustan, D., & Angelini, D. (1995). The puerperium. In Donald R. Coustan, Ray V. Hunning, Jr., & Don Singer (Eds.), *Human reproduction: Growth and development* (pp. 341–358). Boston, MA: Little, Brown & Co.

Couzinet, B., et al. (1986). Termination of early pregnancy by the progesterone antagonist RU486 (mifepristone). *New England Journal of Medicine, 315,* 1565–1569.

Cowan, G., Chase, C. J., & Stahly, G. B. (1989). Feminist and fundamentalist attitudes toward pornography control. *Psychology of Women Quarterly, 13,* 97–112.

Cowley, J. J., & Brooksbank, B. W. L. (1991). Human exposure to putative pheromones and changes in aspects of social behavior. *Journal of Steroid Biochemistry and Molecular Biology, 39,* 647–659.

Cox, D. J. (1988). Incidence and nature of male genital exposure behavior as reported by college women. *Journal of Sex Research, 24,* 227–234.

Coyle, C. T., & Enright, R. D. (1997). Forgiveness intervention with post-abortion men. *Journal of Consulting and Clinical Psychology, 65,* 1042–1046.

Cramer, E. H., Jones, P., Keenan, N. L., & Thompson, B. L. (2003). Is naturopathy as effective as conventional therapy for treatment of menopausal symptoms? *Journal of Alternative and Complementary Medicine, 8,* 529–538.

Crawford, J., Kippax, S., & Waldby, C. (1994). Women's sex talk and men's sex talk: Different worlds. *Feminism and Psychology,* 571–587.

Crawford, M., & Popp, D. (2003). Sexual double standards: A review and methodological critique of two decades of research. *Journal of Sex Research, 40,* 13–26.

Craze, R. (2003). *Teach yourself tantric sex.* McGraw-Hill, Whitby, ON.

Creighton, J. (1992). *Don't go away mad.* New York, NY: Doubleday.

Creighton, S. M., & Minto, C. (2001). Managing intersex: Most vaginal surgery in childhood should be deferred. *British Medical Journal, 323,* 1264–1265.

Creighton, S. M., Minto, C., & Steele, S. (2001). Objective cosmetic and anatomical outcomes at adolescence of feminising surgery for ambiguous genitalia done in childhood. *Lancet, 358,* 124–125.

Crocker, D., & Kalemba, V. (1999). The incidence and impact of women's experiences of sexual harassment in Canadian workplaces. *Canadian Review of Sociology and Anthropology, 36,* 541–558.

Crompton, L. (2003). *Homosexuality and civilization.* Cambridge, MA: Harvard University Press.

Crompton, S. (2005). Always the bridesmaid: People who don't expect to marry. *Canadian Social Trends* (Catalogue no. 11-008E). Ottawa, Canada: Statistics Canada.

Cruess, S., Antoni, M. H., Hayes, A., Penedo, F. J., Ironson, G. H, Fletcher, M. A., et al. (2002). Changes in mood and depressive symptoms and related change processes during cognitive-behavioral stress management in HIV-infected men. *Cognitive Therapy & Research, 26,* 373–392.

Cunningham, F. G., MacDonald, P. C., Gant, N. F., Leveno, K. J., & Gilstrap, L. C., III. (1993). *Williams obstetrics* (19th ed.). Norwalk, CT: Appleton and Lange.

Cunningham, M., Roberts, A., Wu, C.-H., Burbee, A., & Druen, P. (1995). "Their ideas of beauty are, on the whole, the same as ours": Consistency and variability in the cross-cultural perception of female physical attractiveness. *Journal of Personality and Social Psychology, 68,* 261–279.

Curran, C. E. (1988). Roman Catholic sexual ethics: A dissenting view. *Christian Century, 105,* 1139–1142.

Curtis, J. T., & Wang, Z. X. (2003). The neurochemistry of pair bonding. *Current Directions in Psychological Science, 12,* 49–53.

Cutler, W. B. (1999). Human sex-attractant hormones. *Psychiatric Annals, 29,* 54–59.

Cyr, M. V., & Hébert, M. (2011). Analyse comparative des caractéristiques de l'agression sexuelle et des conséquences associées en function du sexe. *Service Social, 57,*15–30.

D'Augelli, A. (2002). Mental health problems among lesbian, gay, and bisexual youths ages 14 to 21. *Clinical Child Psychology and Psychiatry, 7,* 433–456.

D'Augelli, A. R. (2006). Developmental and contextual factors and mental health among lesbian, gay, and bisexual youths. In A. E. Omoto & H. M. Kurtzman (Eds.), *Recent research on sexual orientation.* Washington, DC: APA Books.

D'Souza, G., et al. (2007). Case-control study of human papillomavirus and oropharyngeal cancer. *New England Journal of Medicine, 356,* 1944–1956.

Da Costa D., Brender W., & Larouche J. (1998) A prospective study of the impact of psychosocial and lifestyle variables on pregnancy complications. *Journal of Psychosomatic Obstetrics and Gynaecology 19,* 28–37.

Dahl, B., Fylkesnes, A. M., Sørlie, V., & Malterud, K. (2013). Lesbian women's experiences with healthcare providers in the birthing context: A meta-ethnography. *Midwifery, 29,* 674–681.

Daigneault, I. Hébert, M., McDuff, P., & Frappier, J. (2012). Evaluation of a sexual abuse prevention workshop in a multicultural, impoverished urban area. *Journal of Child Sexual Abuse, 21,*521–542.

Dailard, C. (2006). The public health promise and potential pitfalls of the world's first cervical cancer vaccine. *Guttmacher Policy Review, 9,* 6–9.

Dalenberg, C. J., et al. (2012). Evaluation of the evidence for the trauma and fantasy models of dissociation. *Psychological Bulletin, 138,* 550–558.

Damsted-Petersen, C., Boyer, S. C., & Pukall, C. F. (2009). Current perspectives in vulvodynia. *Women's Health, 5,* 423–436.

Daneback, K., Cooper, A., & Månsson, S. (2005). An internet study of cybersex participants. *Archives of Sexual Behavior, 34,* 321–329.

Daniluk, J. C. (1999). When biology isn't destiny: Implications for the sexuality of women without children. *Canadian Journal of Counselling, 33,* 79–94.

Daniluk, J. C. (2001a). "If we had it to do over again…": Couples' reflections on their experiences of infertility treatments. *The Family Journal: Counseling and Therapy for Couples and Families, 9,* 122–133.

Daniluk, J. C. (2001b). Reconstructing their lives: A longitudinal, qualitative analysis of the transition to biological childlessness for infertile couples. *Journal of Counseling & Development, 79,* 439–449.

Darling, C. A., Davidson, J. K., & Conway-Welch, C. (1990). Female ejaculation: Perceived origins, the Gräfenberg spot/ area, and sexual responsiveness. *Archives of Sexual Behavior, 19,* 29–48.

Darroch, J. E., Frost, J. J., Singh, S., and the Study Team. (2001). *Teenage sexual and reproductive behavior in developed countries: Can more progress be made?* New York, NY: Alan Guttmacher Institute.

Darroch, J. E., Singh, S., Frost, J. J., & the Study Team. (2001). Differences in teenage pregnancy rates among five developed countries: The roles of sexual activity and contraceptive use. *Family Planning Perspectives, 33,* 244–250.

Darwich, L. et al. (2012). School avoidance and substance use among lesbian, gay, bisexual, and questioning youths: The impact of peer victimization and adult support. *Journal of Educational Psychology, 104,* 381–392.

Das, A., Waite, L., & Laumann, Ed. (2012). Sexual expression over the life course. In L. Carpenter & J. DeLamater (Eds.), *Sex for life: From virginity to Viagra, how sexuality changes throughout our lives* (pp. 236–259). New York, NY: New York University Press.

Davé, S., et al. (2010). Incidence of maternal and paternal depression in primary care. *Archives of Pediatric and Adolescent Medicine.* doi:10.1001/archpediatrics.2010.184

David, H. P., Dytrych, Z., & Matejcek, Z. (2003). Born unwanted: Observations from the Prague study. *American Psychologist, 58,* 224–229.

Davies, M. J., et al. (2012). Reproductive technologies and the risk of birth defects. *The New England Journal of Medicine, 366,* 1803–1813.

Davis, C. M., & Bauserman, R. (1993). Exposure to sexually explicit materials: An attitude change perspective. *Annual Review of Sex Research, 4,* 121–210.

Davis, D., Shaver, P. R., & Vernon, M. L. (2003). Physical, emotional, and behavioral reactions to breaking up: The roles of gender, age, emotional involvement, and attachment style. *Personality and Social Psychology Bulletin, 29(7),* 871–884.

Davis, D., Shaver, P. R., Widaman, K. F., Vernon, M. L., Follette, W. C., & Beitz, K. (2006). 'I can't get no satisfaction': Insecure attachment, inhibited sexual communication, and sexual dissatisfaction. *Personal Relationships, 13(4),* 465–483.

Dawson, S. J., Suschinsky, K. D., & Lalumière, M. L. (2012). Sexual fantasies and viewing times across the menstrual cycle: A diary study. *Archives of Sexual Behavior, 41,* 173–183.

De Cuypere, G., et al. (2005). Sexual and physical health after sex reassignment surgery. *Archives of Sexual Behavior, 34,* 679–690.

De Graaf, H., & Rademakers, J. (2006). Sexual behavior of prepubertal children. *Journal of Psychology & Human Sexuality, 18,* 1–21.

De Graaf, H., & Rademakers, J. (2011). The psychological measurement of childhood sexual development in western societies: Methodological challenges. *Journal of Sex Research, 48,* 118–129.

De Graaf, H., Vanwesenbeeck, I., Meijer, S., Woertman, L., & Meeus, W. (2009). Sexual trajectories during adolescence: Relation to demographic characteristics and sexual risk. *Archives of Sexual Behavior, 38(2),* 276–282.

De Jong, D. C. (2009). The role of attention in sexual arousal: Implications for treatment of sexual dysfunction. *Journal of Sex Research, 46,* 237–248.

De La Vega Salas, M. L., & Thériault, J. (2001). Sexualité parental et relation intime du couple parental: Conceptualisations des enfants âgés de dix et 11 ans. *Gynécologie, obstétrique, & fertilité, 29,* 226–233.

De Visser, R. O., et al. (2007). The impact of sexual coercion on psychological, physical, and sexual well-being in a representative sample of Australian women. *Archives of Sexual Behavior, 36,* 676–686.

De Waal, F. (2002). Evolutionary psychology: The wheat and the chaff. *Current Directions in Psychological Science, 11,* 187–191.

De Waal, F. B. M. (1995). The behavior of a close relative challenges assumptions about male supremacy in human evolution. *Scientific American,* 82–88.

DeBruine, L. M., Jones, B. C., Crawford, J. R., Welling, L. L. M., & Little, A. C. (2010). The health of a nation predicts their mate preferences: Crosscultural variation in women's preferences for masculinized male faces. *Proceedings of the Royal Society: Biological Sciences, 277,* 1692–2405.

DeKeseredy, W. S., & Kelly, K. (1993). Woman abuse in university and college dating relationships: The contribution of the ideology of familial patriarchy. *Journal of Human Justice, 4(2),* 25–52.

DeKeseredy, W. S., & Schwartz, M. D. (1998). *Women abuse on campus: Results from the Canadian national survey.* Thousand Oaks: Sage Publications.

Dekker, A., & Schmidt, G. (2002). Patterns of masturbatory behaviour: Changes between the sixties and the nineties. *Journal of Psychology & Human Sexuality, 14,* 35–48.

Del Giudice, M., Angeleri, R., & Manera, V. (2009). The juvenile transition: A developmental switch point in human life history. *Developmental Review, 29,* 1–3

DeLamater, J. (1987). A sociological perspective. In J. H. Geer & W. T. O'Donohue (Eds.), *Theories of human sexuality* (pp. 237–256). New York, NY: Plenum.

DeLamater, J., & Moorman, S. (2007). Sexuality and aging. In K. Markides (Ed.), *Encyclopedia of Health and Aging.* Thousand Oaks: Sage Publications.

DeLamater, J., Wagstaff, D. A., & Havens, K. K. (2000). The impact of a culturally appropriate STD/AIDS education intervention on Black male adolescents' sexual and condom use behavior. *Health Education and Behavior, 27,* 454–470.

Delemarre-van de Waal, H., & Cohen-Kettenis, P. (2006). Clinical management of gender identity disorder in adolescents: A protocol on psychological and paediatric endocrinology aspects. *European Journal of Endocrinology, 155,* S131–S137.

Deligeor-Oglov, E. (2000). Dysmenorrhea. *Annals of the New York Academy of Sciences, 900,* 237–244.

Dennerstein, L., Alexander, J. L., & Kotz, K. (2003). The menopause and sexual functioning: A review of the population-based studies. *Annual Review of Sex Research, 14,* 64–82.

Dennis, C. (2005). Psychosocial and psychological interventions for prevention of post-natal depression: Systematic review. *British Medical Journal, 331,* 15.

Denov, M. S. (2003). The myth of innocence: Sexual scripts and the recognition of child sexual abuse by female perpetrators. *Journal of Sex Research, 40,* 303–314.

Denzin, N. K., & Lincoln, Y. S. (1994). Introduction: Entering the field of qualitative research. In N. K. Denzin, & Y. S. Lincoln (Eds.), *Handbook of qualitative research* (pp. 1–17). Thousand Oaks, CA: Sage.

Denzin, N. K., & Lincoln, Y. S. (Eds.). (2005). *The Sage handbook of qualitative research* (3rd ed.). Thousand Oaks, CA: Sage.

DePaulo, B. (2006). *Singled out: How singles are stereotyped, stigmatized, and ignored, and still live happily ever after.* New York, NY: St. Martin's Press.

Derby, C. A., Mohr, B. A., Goldstein, I., Feldman, H. A., Johannes, C. B., & McKinlay, J. B. (2000). Modifiable risk factors and erectile dysfunction: Can lifestyle changes modify risk? *Urology, 56,* 302–306.

Desrochers, G., Bergeron, S., Khalifé, S., Dupuis, M., & Jodoin, M. (2009). Fear avoidance and self-efficacy in relation to pain and sexual impairment in women with provoked vestibulodynia. *Clinical Journal of Pain, 25,* 520–527.

Desrochers, G., Bergeron, S., Khalifé, S., Dupuis, M-., & Jodoin, M. (2010). Provoked vestibulodynia: Psychological predictors of topical and cognitive-behavioral treatment outcome. *Behaviour Research and Therapy, 48,* 106–115.

Desrochers, G., Bergeron, S., Landry, T., & Jodoin, M. (2008). Do psychosexual factors play a role in the etiology of provoked vestibulodynia? A critical review. *Journal of Sex & Marital Therapy, 34,* 198–226.

DeSteno, D., Valdesolo, P., & Bartlett, M. (2006). Jealousy and the threatened self: Getting to the heart of the green-eyed monster. *Journal of Personality and Social Psychology, 91,* 626–641.

Devor, A. H. (1989). *Gender blending: Confronting the limits of duality.* Bloomington, IN: Indiana University Press.

Devor, H. (1996). Female gender dysphoria in context: Social problem or personal problem? *Annual Review of Sex Research: An Integrative & Interdisciplinary Review, 7,* 44–89.

Devor, H. (1997a). *FTM: Female-to-male transsexuals in society.* Bloomington, IN: Indiana University Press.

Devor, H. (1997b). More than manly women: How female to male transsexuals reject lesbian identities. In B. Bullough, V. Bullough, & J. Elias (Eds.), *Gender blending.* Amherst, NJ: Prometheus.

Di Giulio, G. (2003). Sexuality and people living with physical or developmental disabilities: A review of key issues. *Canadian Journal of Human Sexuality, 12,* 53–68.

Di Giulio, G., & Reissing, E. D. (2006). Premenstrual dysphoric disorder: Prevalence, diagnostic considerations, and controversies. *Journal of Psychosomatic Obstetrics & Gynecology, 27,* 201–210.

Diamanti-Kandarakis, E., & Gore, A. C. (2009). Endocrine- disrupting chemicals: An Endocrine Society scientific statement. *Endocrine Review, 30,* 293–342.

Diamond, L. M. (2003). Was it a phase? Young women's relinquishment of lesbian/bisexual identities over a 5-year period. *Journal of Personality and Social Psychology, 84,* 352–364.

Diamond, L. M. (2004). Emerging perspectives on distinctions between romantic love and sexual desire. *Current Directions in Psychological Science, 13,* 116–119.

Diamond, L. M. (2005). A new view of lesbian subtypes: Stable versus fluid identity trajectories over an 8-year period. *Psychology of Women Quarterly, 29,* 119–128.

Diamond, L. M. (2008a). *Sexual fluidity: Understanding women's love and desire.* Cambridge, MA: Harvard University Press.

Diamond, L. M. (2008b). Female bisexuality from adolescence to adulthood: Results from a 10-year longitudinal study. *Developmental Psychology, 44,* 5–14.

Diamond, M. (1996). Prenatal predisposition and the clinical management of some pediatric conditions. *Journal of Sex and Marital Therapy, 22,* 139–147.

Diamond, M. (1999). Pediatric management of ambiguous and traumatized genitalia. *Journal of Urology, 162,* 1021–1028.

Diamond, M. (2009). Pornography, public acceptance, and sex-related crime: A review. *International Journal of Law and Psychiatry, 32,* 304–314.

Diamond, M., & Sigmundson, H. K. (1997). Sex reassignment at birth: Long-term review and clinical implications. *Archives of Pediatric and Adolescent Medicine, 151,* 298–304.

DiCenso, A., Gyatt, G., Willan, A., & Griffith, L. (2002). Interventions to reduce unintended pregnancies among adolescents: Systematic review of randomized controlled trials. *British Medical Journal, 324,* 1426.

Dickey, R. P. (2000). *Managing contraceptive pill patients* (10th ed.). Dallas, TX: EMIS.

Dickson, N., et al. (2003). Same-sex attraction in a birth cohort: Prevalence and persistence in early adulthood. *Social Science & Medicine, 56,* 1607–1615.

DiIorio, C., Kelley, M., & Hockenberry-Eaton, M. (1999). Communication about sexual issues: Mothers, fathers, and friends. *Adolescent Health, 24,* 181–189.

Dill, K. E., & Thill, K. (2007). Video game characters and the socialization of gender roles: Young people's perceptions mirror sexist media depictions. *Sex Roles, 57,* 851–864.

Dion, K. K. (1973). Young children's stereotyping of facial attractiveness. *Developmental Psychology, 9,* 183–188.

Dion, K. K., & Dion, K. L. (1993b). Individualistic and collectivistic perspectives on gender and the cultural content of love and intimacy. *Journal of Social Issues, 49,* 53–69.

Dion, K. L. (1977). The incentive value of physical attractiveness for young children. *Personality and Social Psychology Bulletin, 3,* 67–70.

Dion, K. L., & Dion, K. K. (1993a). Gender and ethnocultural comparisons in styles of love. *Psychology of Women Quarterly, 17,* 463–474.

Dixson, B. J., Grimshaw, G. M., Linklater, W. L., & Dixson, A. F. (2011). Eye-tracking of men's preferences for waist-to-hip ratio and breast size of women. *Archives of Sexual Behavior, 40,* 43–50.

Docter, R. F., & Prince, V. (1997). Transvestism: A survey of 1032 crossdressers. *Archives of Sexual Behavior, 26,* 589–606.

Dodge, B., Reece, M., Cole, S., & Sandfort, T. (2004). Sexual compulsivity among heterosexual college students. *Journal of Sex Research, 41,* 343–350.

Doing it and enjoying it. (1999, December 20). *Maclean's, 112*(51).

Donadio, R. (2010, December 21). Vatican adds nuance to Pope's condom remarks. *The New York Times*

Donahue, J. E., Stopa, E. G, & Chorsky, R. L. (2000). Cells containing immunoreactive estrogen receptor-a in the human basal forebrain. *Brain Research, 856,* 142–151.

Donnelly, D. A. (1993). Sexually inactive marriages. *Journal of Sex Research, 30,* 171–179.

Donnelly, D., Burgess, E., Anderson, S., Davis, R., & Dillard, J. (2001). Involuntary celibacy: A life course analysis. *Journal of Sex Research, 38,* 159–169.

Donnerstein, E., Linz, D., & Penrod, S. (1987). *The question of pornography: Research findings and policy implications.* New York, NY: Free Press.

Doran, T. A. (1990). Chorionic villus sampling as the primary diagnostic tool in prenatal diagnosis. *Journal of Reproductive Medicine, 35,* 935–940.

Douglas, M. (1970). *Purity and danger: An analysis of concepts of pollution and taboo.* Baltimore: Penguin.

Dreznick, M. T. (2003). Heterosocial competence of rapists and child molesters: A meta-analysis. *Journal of Sex Research, 40,* 170–178.

Driedger, S. D. (2002, September 30). What parents don't know (or won't admit). *Maclean's.*

Driscoll, R., Davis, K. E., & Lipetz, M. E. (1972). Parental interference and romantic love: The Romeo and Juliet effect. *Journal of Personality and Social Psychology, 24,* 1–10.

Drolet, M., Brisson, M., Maunsell, E., Franco, E. L., Coutlée, F., . . . Mansi, J. A. (2011). The impact of anogenital warts on health-related quality of life: A 6-month prospective study. *Sexually Transmitted Diseases, 38,* 949–956.

Dryer, P. C., & Horowitz, L. (1997). When do opposites attract? Interpersonal complementarity vs. similarity. *Journal of Personality and Social Psychology, 72,* 592–603.

du Mont, J., Macdonald, S., Rotbard, N., Asllani, E., Bainbridge, D., & Cohen M. M. (2009). Factors associated with suspected drug-facilitated sexual assault. *CMAJ, 180,* 513–519.

Duchesne, D. (1999). Street prostitution in Canada. In *The Juristat reader: A statistical overview of the Canadian justice system.* Toronto, Canada: Thomson Educational Publishing.

Duerr, A., et al. (2008). HIV vaccines. In K. Holmes et al. (Eds.), *Sexually transmitted diseases.* (4th ed., pp. 1937–1954). New York, NY: McGraw-Hill.

Duff, S. J., & Hampson, E. (2000). A beneficial effect of estrogen on working memory in postmenopausal women taking hormone replacement therapy. *Hormones and Behavior, 38,* 262–276.

Dugger, C. W. (2011, October 16). Senegal curbs a bloody rite, African-style. *The New York Times,* p. 1.

Dunbar, E. (2006). Race, gender, and sexual orientation in hate crime victimization: Identity politics or identity risk? *Violence and Victims, 21,* 323–337.

Dunmore, E., Clark, D. M., & Ehlers, A. (2001). A prospective investigation of the role of cognitive factors in persistent Posttraumatic Stress Disorder (PTSD) after physical or sexual assault. *Behaviour Research and Therapy, 39,* 1063–1084.

Dunn, L., Ross, B., Caines, T., & Howorth, P. (1998). A school-based HIV/AIDS prevention education program: Outcomes of peer-led versus community health nurse-led interventions. *Canadian Journal of Human Sexuality, 7,* 339–345.

Dunn, M. E., & Trost, J. E. (1989). Male multiple orgasms: A descriptive study. *Archives of Sexual Behavior, 18,* 377–388.

Dunn, S., & Guilbert, E. (2003). Emergency contraception. *SOGC Clinical Practice Guidelines, 131,* 1–7.

Dunne, M. P., Martin, N. G., Bailey, J. M., Heath, A. C., Bucholz, K. K., Madden, P. A. F., & Statham, D. J. (1997). Participation bias in a sexuality survey: Psychological and behavioural characteristics of responders and non-responders. *International Journal of Epidemiology, 26,* 844–854.

Dupras, A. (2001). Sexology as innovation. *Scandinavian Journal of Sexology, 4,* 139–148.

Durante, K. M., Griskevicius, V., Hill, S. E., Perilloux, C., & Li, N. P. (2011). Ovulation, female competition, and product choice. Hormonal influences on consumer behavior. *Journal of Consumer Research, 37,* 921–934.

Dutton, D. G., & Aron, A. P. (1974). Some evidence for heightened sexual attraction under conditions of high anxiety. *Journal of Personality and Social Psychology, 30,* 470–517.

Dwyer, V., & Farran, S. (1997, May 19). Class action: Fighting homophobia at school. *Maclean's.*

Earls, C. M., & David, H. (1989). A psychosocial study of male prostitution. *Archives of Sexual Behavior, 18,* 401–420.

Earls, C. M., & Lalumière, M. L. (2002). A case study of preferential bestiality (zoophilia). *Sexual Abuse: A Journal of Research and Treatment, 14,* 83–88.

Earls, C. M., & Lalumière, M. L. (2009). A case study of preferential bestiality. *Archives of Sexual Behavior, 38,* 605–609.

Eason, E., Labrecque, M., Wells, G., & Feldman P. (2000). Preventing perineal trauma during childbirth: A systematic review. *Obstetrics & Gynecology, 95,* 464–471.

Ebsworth, M., & Lalumière, M. L. (2012). Viewing time as a measure of bisexual sexual interest. *Archives of Sexual Behavior, 41,* 161–172.

Edgar, T., & Fitzpatrick, M. A. (1993). Expectations for sexual interaction: A cognitive test of the sequencing of sexual communication behaviors. *Health Communication, 5,* 239–261. doi:10.1207/s15327027hc0504_1

Edwards, W. M., & Coleman, E. (2004). Defining sexual health: A descriptive overview. *Archives of Sexual Behavior, 33,* 189–196.

Eisenberg, M. E., Wagenaar, A., Neumark-Sztainer, D. (1997). Viewpoints of Minnesota students on school-based sexuality education. *Journal of School Health, 67,* 322–326.

Elder, G. (1969). Appearance and education in marriage mobility. *American Sociological Review, 34,* 519–533.

Elias, J., & Gebhard, P. (1969). Sexuality and sexual learning in childhood. *Phi Delta Kappan, 50,* 401–405.

Eliot, L. (2009). *Pink brain, blue brain: How small differences grow into troublesome gaps–and what we can do about it.* Boston, MA: Houghton Mifflin.

Elliott, A. N., & O'Donohue, W. T. (1997). The effects of anxiety and distraction on sexual arousal in a nonclinical sample of heterosexual women. *Archives of Sexual Behavior, 26,* 607–624.

Elliott, S., Latini, D. M., Walker, L. M., Wasserug, R., Robinson, J. W., & the ADT Survivorship Working Group (2010). Androgen deprivation therapy for prostate cancer: Recommendations to improve patient and partner quality of life. *Journal of Sexual Medicine, 7*(9), 2996–3010.

Ellis, H. H. (1939). *My life.* Boston, MA: Houghton Mifflin.

Ellis, L. (1996). The role of perinatal factors in determining sexual orientation. In R. C. Savin-Williams & K. M. Cohen (Eds.), *The lives of lesbians, gays, and bisexuals* (pp. 35–70). Fort Worth, TX: Harcourt Brace.

Ellis, L., & Cole-Harding, S. (2001). The effects of prenatal stress, and of prenatal alcohol and nicotine exposure, on human sexual orientation. *Physiology & Behavior, 74,* 213–226.

Emmers-Sommer, T., Allen, M., Bourhis, J., Sahlstein, E., Laskowski, K., Falato, W., et al. (2004). A meta-analysis of the relationship between social skills and sexual offenders. *Communication Reports, 17,* 1–10.

Endocrine Society. (2009). Endocrine treatment of transsexual persons: An Endocrine Society clinical practice guideline. *Journal of Clinical Endocrinology and Metabolism, 94,* 3132–3154.

Enserink, M. (2002). The vanishing promises of hormone replacement. *Science, 297,* 325–326.

Epting, L. K., & Overman, W. H. (1998). Sex-sensitive tasks in men and women: A search for performance fluctuations across the menstrual cycle. *Behavioral Neuroscience, 112,* 1304–1317.

Erikson, E. H. (1950). *Childhood and society.* New York, NY: Norton.

Erikson, E. H. (1968) *Identity, youth and crisis.* New York, NY: Norton.

Eriksson, J., & Humphreys, T. P. (2013). Development of the Virginity Beliefs Scale. *Journal of Sex Research.* doi:10.1080/00224499.2012.724475

Ernulf, K. E., & Innala, S. M. (1995). Sexual bondage: A review and unobtrusive investigation. *Archives of Sexual Behavior, 24,* 631–654.

Espin, O. (1987). Issues of identity in the psychology of Latina lesbians. In Boston Lesbian Psychologies Collective, *Lesbian psychologies.* Urbana, IL: University of Illinois Press.

Esposito, K., et al. (2004). Effect of lifestyle changes on erectile dysfunction in obese men: A randomized controlled trial. *Journal of the American Medical Association, 291,* 2978–2984.

Euling SY, Herman-Giddens M. E., Lee P. A., Selevan S. G., Juul A., Sorensen, T. I., Dunkel L., Himes J. H., Teilmann G., & Swan S. H. (2008) Examination of US puberty-timing data from 1940 to 1994 for secular trends: Panel findings. *Pediatrics 121* (Suppl. 3), S172–S191.

Everett, G. M. (1975). Amyl nitrate ("poppers") as an aphrodisiac. In M. Sandler and G. L. Gessa (Eds.), *Sexual behavior: Pharmacology and biochemistry.* New York, NY: Raven.

Everitt, B. J., & Bancroft, J. (1991). Of rats and men: The comparative approach to male sexuality. *Annual Review of Sex Research, 2,* 77–118.

Exton, M. S., Bindert, A., Kruger, T., Scheller, F., Hartmann, U., & Schedlowski, M. (1999). Cardiovascular and endocrine alterations after masturbation-induced orgasm in women. *Psychosomatic Medicine, 61,* 280–289.

Eyler, A. E., & Wright, K. (1997, July–September). Gender identification and sexual orientation among genetic females with gender-blended self-perception in childhood and adolescence [Electronic version]. *The International Journal of Transgenderism, 1.* Retrieved from http://www.symposium.com

Ezzell, C. (1994). Breast cancer genes: Cloning BRCA1, mapping BRCA2. *Journal of NIH Research, 6*(10), 33–35.

Fallis, E. E., Purdon, C., & Rehman, U. S. (2013). Development and validation of the response to sexual difficulties scale. *Archives of Sexual Behavior, 42,*67–79.

Farley, M. A. (1994). Sexual ethics. In J. B. Nelson & S. P. Longfellow (Eds.), *Sexuality and the sacred* (pp. 54–67). Louisville, KY: Westminster/John Knox Press.

Farley, M., Lynne, J., & Cotton, A. J. (2005). Prostitution in Vancouver, Canada: Violence and the colonization of First Nations women. *Transcultural Psychiatry, 42,* 242–271.

Farr, R. H., Forssell, S., & Patterson, C. J. (2010). Parenting and child development in adoptive families: Does parental sexual orientation matter? *Applied Developmental Science, 14,* 164–176.

Farris, C., et al. (2006). Heterosocial perceptual organization: Application of the choice model to sexual coercion. *Psychological Science, 17,* 869–875.

Farris, C., et al. (2008). Perceptual mechanisms that characterize gender differences in decoding women's sexual intent. *Psychological Science, 19,* 348–354.

Fathy, A., et al. (2007). Experience with Tube® (Promedon) malleable penile implant. *Urologia Internationalis, 79,* 244–247.

Faulkner, E. (1997). *Anti-Gay/Lesbian Violence in Toronto, Canada: The Impact on Individuals and Communities.* Ottawa, Canada: Department of Justice Canada: Research and Statistics Division/Policy Sector. TR1997-5e. A Project of the 519

Church Street Community Centre Victim Assistance Programme, Toronto.

Fazekas, A., Senn, C. Y., & Ledgerwood, D. M. (2001). Predictors of intention to use condoms among university women: An application and extension of the theory of planned behaviour. *Canadian Journal of Behavioural Science, 33,* 103–117.

Federman, D. D. (2006). The biology of human sex differences. *New England Journal of Medicine, 354,* 1507–1514.

Federoff, J. P. (1995). Antiandrogens vs. serotonergic medications in the treatment of sex offenders: A preliminary compliance study. *Canadian Journal of Human Sexuality, 4,* 111–122.

Federoff, J. P., & Moran, B. (1997). Myths and misconceptions about sex offenders. *Canadian Journal of Human Sexuality, 6,* 263–276.

Federoff, J. P., Fishell, A., & Federoff, B. (1999). A case series of women evaluated for paraphilic sexual disorders. *Canadian Journal of Human Sexuality, 8,* 127–140.

Federoff, P. (2007, October). *The long and winding road: How the concept of "lovemap" has changed.* Paper presented at the meeting of the Canadian Sex Research Forum, Banff, AB.

Feinberg, L. (1996). *Transgender warriors: Making history from Joan of Arc to Dennis Rodman.* Boston, MA: Beacon Press Books.

Feingold, A. (1990). Gender differences in effects of physical attractiveness on romantic attraction. *Journal of Personality and Social Psychology, 59,* 981–993.

Feiring, C. et al. (2009). Childhood sexual abuse, stigmatization, internalizing symptoms, and the development of sexual difficulties and dating aggression. *Journal of Consulting and Clinical Psychology, 77,* 127–137.

Feldman, R., et al. (2007). Evidence for a neuroendocrinological foundation of human affiliation. *Psychological Science, 18,* 965–970.

Felmlee, D., Orzechowicz, D., & Fortes, C. (2010). Fairy tales: Attraction and sterotypes in same-gender relationships. *Sex Roles, 62,* 226–240.

Felton, G., & Segelman, F. (1978). Lamaze childbirth training and changes in belief about person control. *Birth and the Family Journal, 5,* 141–150.

Fenaughty, J., & Harré, N. (2003). Life on the seesaw: A qualitative study of suicide resiliency factors for young gay men. *Journal of Homosexuality, 45,* 1–22.

Ferguson, K. H., & Cespedes, R. D. (2003). Prospective long-term results and quality-of-life assessment after Dura-II penile prosthesis placement. *Urology, 61,* 437–441.

Fergusson, D. M., Horwood, L. J., & Boden, J. M. (2009). Reactions to abortion and subsequent mental health. *The British Journal of Psychiatry, 195,* 420–426.

Field, D., & Rabinovitch, J. (Eds.) (2003). *Stories from the margins: Writing by sex trade workers past and present.* Retrieved from http://www.peers.bc.ca/images/StoriesBookletWeb.pdf

Fielder, R. L., & Carey, M. P. (2010). Predictors and consequences of sexual "hookups" among college students: A short-term prospective study. *Archives of Sexual Behavior, 39,* 1105–1119.

Fields, R. D. (2007). Sex and the secret nerve. *Scientific American Mind, 18,* 20–27.

Filipp, D., et al. (2001). Soluble CD14 enriched in colostrums and milk induces B cell growth and differentiation. *Proceedings of the National Academy of Sciences, 98,* 603–608.

Findlay, M. W., Doldere, J., Trost, N., Craft, R., Cao, Y., Cooper-White, J., Stevens, G., & Morrison, W. (2011). Tissue-engineered breast reconstruction: Bridging the gap toward large-volume tissue engineering in humans. *Plastic and Reconstructive Surgery, 128,* 1206–1215.

Fink, H., et al. (2002). Sildenafi l for male erectile dysfunction: A systematic review and meta-analysis. *Archives of Internal Medicine, 162,* 1349–1360.

Finkel, E., et al. (2012). Online dating: A critical analysis from the perspective of psychological science. *Psychological Science in the Public Interest, 13,* 3–66.

Finkelhor, D., & Daro, D. (1997). Prevention of child sexual abuse. In M. E. Helfer & R. S. Kempe (Eds.), *The battered child* (5th ed., pp. 615–626). Chicago, IL: University of Chicago Press.

Finkelhor, D., & Russell, D. (1984). Women as perpetrators: Review of the evidence. In D. Finkelhor (Ed.), *Child sexual abuse: New theory and research.* New York, NY: The Free Press.

Finkelhor, D., Mitchell, K., & Wolak, J. (2000). *Online victimization: A report on the nation's youth.* Washington, DC: National Center for Missing & Exploited Children.

Firestone, P., Bradford, J. M., McCoy, M., Greenberg, D. M., Curry, S., & Larose, M. R. (2000). Prediction of recidivism in extrafamilial child molesters based on court-related assessments. *Sexual Abuse: A Journal of Research and Treatment, 12,* 203–221.

Firestone, P., Nunes, K. L., Moulden, H., Broom, I., & Bradford, J. M. (2005). Hostility and recidivism in sexual offenders. *Archives of Sexual Behavior, 34,* 277–283.

Fischtein, D. S., Herold, E. S., & Desmarais, S. (2005). Canadian attitudes toward female topless behaviour: A national survey. *Canadian Journal of Human Sexuality, 14,* 63–75.

Fisher, D., et al. (2007). Gay, lesbian, and bisexual content on television: A quantitative analysis across two season. *Journal of Homosexuality, 52,* 167–188.

Fisher, H. (1992). *Anatomy of love: The mysteries of mating, marriage and why we stray.* New York, NY: Ballantine Books.

Fisher, H., Aron, A., & Brown, L. (2006). Romantic love: A mammalian brain system for mate choice. *Philosophical Transactions of the Royal Society, B, 361,* 2173–2186.

Fisher, J. A., Bowman, M., & Thomas, T. (2003). Issues for South Asian Indian patients surrounding sexuality, fertility, and childbirth in the U. S. health care system. *Journal of the American Board of Family Medicine, 16*(2), 151–155.

Fisher, M., & Cox, A. (2009). The influence of male facial attractiveness on women's receptivity. *Journal of Social, Evolutionary, and Cultural Psychology, 3,* 49–61.

Fisher, T. D., et al. (2012). Sex on the brain? An examination of frequency of sexual cognitions as a function of gender, erotophilia, and social desirability. *Journal of Sex Research, 49,* 69–77.

Fisher, W. A., & Barak, A. (2000). Online sex shops: Phenomenological, psychological, and ideological perspectives on Internet sexuality. *Cyberpsychology & Behavior, 3,* 575–589.

Fisher, W. A., & Boroditsky, R. (2000). Sexual activity, contraceptive choice, and sexual and reproductive health indicators among single Canadian women aged 15–29: Additional findings from the Canadian contraception study. *Canadian Journal of Human Sexuality, 9,* 79–93.

Fisher, W. A., & Fisher, J. D. (1992). Understanding and promoting AIDS preventive behaviour: A conceptual model of educational tools. *Canadian Journal of Human Sexuality, 1,* 99–106.

Fisher, W. A., & Fisher, J. D. (1998). Understanding and promoting sexual and reporductive health behaviour: Theory and method. *Annual Review of Sex Research, 9,* 39–76.

Fisher, W. A., & Grenier, G. (1994). Violent pornography, antiwoman thoughts, and antiwoman acts: In search of reliable effects. *Journal of Sex Research, 31,* 23–38.

Fisher, W. A., Boroditsky, R., & Bridges, M. L. (1999a). Familiarity with opinions about and use of contraceptive methods among Canadian women. *Canadian Journal of Human Sexuality, 18,* 167–174.

Fisher, W. A., Boroditsky, R., & Bridges, M. L. (1999b). The 1998 contraception study. *Canadian Journal of Human Sexuality, 8,* 161–216.

Fisher, W. A., Boroditsky, R., & Morris, B. (2004). The 2002 Canadian contraception study: Part 2. *Journal of Obstetrics and Gynaecology Canada, 26,* 646–656.

Fisher, W. A., Byrne, D., & White, L. A. (1983). Emotional barriers to contraception. In D. Byrne and W. A. Fisher (Eds.), *Adolescents, sex, and contraception.* Hillsdale, NJ: Lawrence Erlbaum.

Fisher, W. A., Byrne, D., White, L. A., & Kelley, K. (1988). Eroto-phobiaerotophilia as a dimension of personality. *Journal of Sex Research, 25,* 123–151.

Fisher, W. A., Sukhbir, S. S., Shuper, P. A., Carey, M., Otchet, F., MacLean-Brine, D., Dal Bello, D., & Gunter, J. (2005). Characteristics of women undergoing repeat induced abortion. *Canadian Medical Association Journal, 172,* 637–641.

Fisher, W. A., & Holzapfel, S. (2014). Suppose they gave an epidemic and sex therapy didn't attend? Sexually transmitted infection concerns in the sex therapy context. In Y. M. Binik & K. S. K. Hall (Eds.), *Principles and Practice of Sex Therapy* (5th ed., ch. 22). New York, NY: Guilford.

Fisher, W. A., Kohut, T., & Fisher, J. D. (2009). AIDS exceptionalism: On the social psychology of HIV prevention research. *Social Issues and Policy Review, 3,* 45–77.

Fiske, S. T., & Glick, P. (1995). Ambivalence and stereotypes cause sexual harassment: A theory with implications for organizational change. *Journal of Social Issues, 51*(1), 97–115.

Fitch, R. H., & Bimonte, H. A. (2002). Hormones, brain, and behavior: Putative biological contributions to cognitive sex differences. In A. McGillicuddy-DeLisi & R. DeLisi (Eds.), *Biology, society, and behavior: The development of sex differences in cognition* (pp. 55–92). Westport, CT: Ablex.

Fitzgerald, L. F. (1993). Sexual harassment. *American Psychologist, 48,* 1070–1076.

Flack, William F., Jr., et al. (2007). Risk factors and consequences of unwanted sex among university students: Hooking up, alcohol, and stress response. *Journal of Interpersonal Violence, 22*(2), 139–157.

Flak, V., Beech, A., & Fisher, D. (2007). Forensic assessment of deviant sexual interests: The current position. *Issues in Forensic Psychology, 6,* 70–83.

Flaxman, S. M., & Sherman, P. W. (2000). Morning sickness: A mechanism for protecting mother and embryo. *Quarterly Review of Biology, 75,* 113–148.

Fleming, A., Ruble, D., Krieger, H., & Wong, P. Y. (1997). Hormonal and experiential correlates of internal responsiveness during pregnancy and the puerperium in human mothers. *Hormones and Behavior, 31,* 145–158.

Fleming, J., Mullen, P., Sibthorpe, B., & Bammer, G. (1999). The longterm impact of childhood sexual abuse in Australian women. *Child Abuse & Neglect, 23,* 145–159.

Fletcher, J. (1966). *Situation ethics: The new morality.* Philadelphia, PA: Westminster Press.

Foa, E. B., Steketee, G., & Olasov, B. (1989). Behavioral/cognitive conceptualization of post-traumatic stress disorder. *Behavior Therapy, 20,* 155–176.

Foldès, P., Cuzin, B., &Andro, A. (2012). Reconstructive surgery after female genital mutilation: A prospective cohort study. *The Lancet, 380,* 134–141.

Forbes, E. E., & Dahl, R. E. (2010). Pubertal development and behavior: Hormonal activation of social and motivational tendencies. *Brain and Cognition, 72,* 66–72.

Ford, C. S., & Beach, F. A. (1951). *Patterns of sexual behavior.* New York, NY: Harper & Row.

Ford, J. G. (2001). Healing homosexuals: A psychologist's journey through the ex-gay movement and the pseudo-science of reparative therapy. In A. Shidlo, M. Schroeder, & J. Drescher (Eds.), *Sexual conversion therapy: Ethical, clinical, and research perspectives* (pp. 69–86). New York, NY: Haworth.

Ford, K., & Norris, A. (1991). Methodological considerations for survey research on sexual behavior: Urban African American and Hispanic youth. *Journal of Sex Research, 28,* 539–555.

Fortenberry, J. D. (2002). Clinic-based service programs for increasing responsible sexual behavior. *Journal of Sex Research, 39,* 63–66.

Fortenberry, J. D., et al. (2005). Daily mood, partner support, sexual interest, and sexual activity among adolescent women. *Health Psychology, 24,* 252–257.

Forum Research Inc. (2012). Canada-wide abortion issues: Six in ten believe abortion should be legal in all circumstances. Retrieved from http://www.forumresearch.com

Foster, C. A., Witcher, B. S., Campbell, W. K., & Green, J. D. (1998). Arousal and attraction: Evidence for automatic and controlled processes. *Journal of Personality and Social Psychology, 74,* 86–101.

Foster, L. R., & Byers, E. S. (2008). Predictors of stigma and shame related to sexually transmitted infections: Attitudes, education, and knowledge. *Canadian Journal of Human Sexuality, 17,* 193–202.

Foster, L. R., Byers, E. S., & Sears, H. A. (2011). Middle school students' perceptions of the quality of the sexual health education received from their parents. *Canadian Journal of Human Sexuality, 20,* 55–65.

Fox, D. (2002). Gentle persuasion. *New Scientist, 173,* 32.

Fox, N., Gelber, S., & Chasen, S. (2008). Physical and sexual activity during pregnancy and near delivery. *Journal of Women's Health, 17,* 1431–1435

Fox, R. C. (1995). Bisexual identities. In A. R. D'Augelli & C. J. Patterson (Eds.), *Lesbian, gay, and bisexual identities over the lifespan.* New York, NY: Oxford University Press.

Frank, K. (2005). Exploring the motivations and fantasies of strip club customers in relation to legal regulations. *Archives of Sexual Behavior, 34,* 487–504.

Frank, K., & DeLamater, J. (2010). Deconstructing monogamy: Boundaries, identities, and fluidities across relationships. In M. Barker & D. Langdridge (Eds.), *Understanding non-monogamies* (pp. 9–22). New York, NY: Routledge.

Frappier, J.-Y., Kaufman, M., Baltzer, F., et al. (2008). Sex and sexual health: A survey of Canadian youth and mothers. *Pediatric and Child Health, 13,* 25–30.

Frayser, S. G. (1985). *Varieties of sexual experience: An anthropological perspective on human sexuality.* New Haven, CT: Human Relations Area Files Press.

Frayser, S. G. (1994). Defining normal childhood sexuality: An anthropological approach. *Annual Review of Sex Research, 5,* 173–217.

Frazier, P., Tashiro, T., Berman, M., Steger, M., & Long, J. (2004). Correlates of levels and patterns of positive life changes following sexual assault. *Journal of Consulting and Clinical Psychology, 72,* 19–30.

Frederick, D., Peplau, A., & Lever, J. (2008). The Barbie mystique: Satisfaction with breast size and shape across the lifespan. *International Journal of Sexual Health, 20,* 200–211.

Freese, J., & Meland, S. (2002). Seven-tenths incorrect: Heterogeneity and change in the waist-to-hip ratios of Playboy centerfold models and Miss America pageant winners. *Journal of Sex Research, 39,* 133–138.

Freud, S. (1924). *A general introduction to psychoanalysis.* New York, NY: Permabooks, 1953. (Boni & Liveright edition, 1924).

Freund, M., Lee, N., & Leonard, T. (1991). Sexual behavior of clients with street prostitutes in Camden, NJ. *Journal of Sex Research, 28,* 579–591.

Freyd, J. J. (1996). *Betrayal trauma theory.* Cambridge, MA: Harvard University Press.

Freyd, J. J., et al. (2005). The science of child sexual abuse. *Science, 308,* 501.

Frisch, R. E., & McArthur, J. W. (1974). Menstrual cycles: Fatness as a determinant of minimum weight for height necessary for their maintenance or onset. *Science, 185,* 949–951.

Frishman, G. (1995). Abortions, miscarriages, and ectopic pregnancies. In D. R. Carstrin, R. V. Hunning Jr., & E. D. B. Singer (Eds.), *Human reproduction: Growth and development.* Boston, MA: Little, Brown.

Frohlich, P., & Meston, C. (2002). Sexual functioning and self-reported depressive symptoms among college women. *Journal of Sex Research, 39,* 321–325.

Frühauf, S., Gerger, H., Schmidt, H. M., Munder, T., & Barth, J. (2013). Efficacy of psychological interventions for sexual dysfunction: A systematic review and meta-analysis. *Archives of Sexual Behavior, 42,* 6, 915–933.

Fryar, C., et al. (2007). Drug use and sexual behaviors reported by adults: United States, 1999–2002. *Advance Data from Vital and Health Statistics; 384.* Hyattsville, MD: National Center for Health Statistics.

Fryhofer, S. (2012). Preconception checklist for women planning pregnancy. *Medscape Internal Medicine.* http://www.medscape.com/viewarticle/762801

Fujimoto, V., et al. (2008). Racial and ethnic disparities in assisted reproductive technology outcomes in the United States. *Fertility and Sterility, 10,* 61.

Fullerton, T., Rye, B. J., Meaney, G. J., & Loomis, C. (2013). Condom and hormonal contraceptive use by young women: An information-motivation-behavioral skills assessment. *Canadian Journal of Behavioural Science, 45,* 196–209.

Furman, W. (2002). The emerging field of adolescent romantic relationships. *Current Directions in Psychological Science, 11,* 177–180.

Furnish, V. P. (1994). The Bible and homosexuality: Reading the texts in context. In J. S. Siker (Ed.), *Homosexuality in the church* (pp. 18–35). Louisville, KY: Westminster/John Knox Press.

Furstenberg, F. F., Brooks-Gunn, J., & Morgan, S. P. (1987). *Adolescent mothers in later life.* New York, NY: Cambridge University Press.

Future of Sex Education Initiative (2012). National sexuality education standards: Core content and skills, K-12 [a special publication of Journal of School Health]. Retrieved from http://www.future-ofsexeducation.org

Gager, C., & Yabiku, S. (2010). Who has the time? The relationship between household labor time and sexual frequency. *Journal of Family Issues, 31,* 135–163

Gagnon, J. H. (1977). *Human sexualities.* Glenview, IL: Scott, Foresman.

Gagnon, J. H. (1990). The explicit and implicit use of the scripting perspective in sex research. *Annual Review of Sex Research, 1,* 1–44.

Gagnon, J. H., & Simon, W. (1973). *Sexual conduct: The social origins of human sexuality.* Chicago, IL: Aldine.

Gaither, G. A., Sellbom, M., & Meier, B. P. (2003). The effect of stimulus content on volunteering for sexual interest research among college students. *Journal of Sex Research, 40,* 240–248.

Galbreath, N., Berlin, F., & Sawyer, D. (2002). Paraphilias and the Internet. In A. Cooper (Ed.), *Sex and the Internet: A guidebook for clinicians* (pp. 187–205). New York, NY: Brunner-Routledge.

Gallant, P. (2003). Count'em up. *DailyXtra.* Retrieved from http://dailyxtra.com/toronto/count-em

Gallant, S. J, Popiel, D. A., Hoffman, D. M., Chakraborty, P. K., & Hamilton, J. A. (1992). Using daily ratings to confirm premenstrual syndrome/late luteal phase dysphoric disorder: What makes a real difference? *Psychosomatic Medicine, 54,* 167–181.

Gallup Canada Inc. (1988). Canadian Gallup Poll, July 1988.

Galvani, A., & Slatkin, M. (2003). Evaluating plague and smallpox as historical selective pressures for the CCR5-Delta 32 HIV-resistance allele. *Proceedings of the National Academy of Sciences, 100,* 15276–15279.

Gangestad, S. W., & Buss, D. M. (1993). Pathogen prevalence and human mate preferences. *Ethology and Sociobiology, 14,* 89–96.

Gangestad, S. W., & Thornhill, R. (1997). Human sexual selection and developmental stability. In J. A. Simpson & D. T. Kenrick (Eds.), *Evolutionary social psychology* (pp. 169–195). Mahwah, NJ: Lawrence Erlbaum Associates.

Gannon, T. A., & Ward, T. (2008). Rape: Psychopathology and theory. In D. R. Laws & W. T. O'Donohue (Eds.), *Sexual deviance* (pp. 336–355). New York, NY: Guilford.

Ganz, T. (2002). Versatile defensins. *Science, 298,* 977–979.

Garcia, J., et al. (2010). Associations between dopamine D4 receptor gene variation with both infidelity and sexual promiscuity. Garcia, Justin, et al. (2010). Associations between

Garcia, M., & Fisher, W. A. (2007). Obstetrics and gynaecology residents' self-rated knowledge, motivation, skill, and practice patterns in counselling for contraception, STI prevention, sexual dysfunction, and intimate partner violence and sexual coercion. *Journal of Obstetrics and Gynaecology of Canada, 30,*59–65.

Garcia-Velasco, J., & Mondragon, M. (1991). The incidence of the vomeronasal organ in 1000 human subjects and its possible clinical significance. *Journal of Steroid Biochemistry and Molecular Biology, 39,* 561–563.

Garnets, L., & Peplau, L. A. (2006). Sexuality in the lives of adult lesbian and bisexual women. In D. C. Kimmel, T. Rose, & S. David (Eds.) *Research and clinical perspectives on lesbian, gay, bisexual, and transgender aging* (pp. 70–90). New York, NY: Columbia University Press.

Gartrell, N. K., et al. (2011). Adolescents of the U. S. National Longitudinal Lesbian Family Study: Sexual orientation, sexual behavior, and sexual risk exposure. *Archives of Sexual Behavior, 40,* 1199–1209.

Gartrell, N., et al. (2005). The National Lesbian Family Study: 4. Interviews with the 10-year-old children. *American Journal of Orthopsychiatry, 75,* 5181–5524.

Gathorne-Hardy, J. (2000). *Sex, the measure of all things: A life of Alfred C. Kinsey.* Bloomington, IN: Indiana University Press.

Gavey, N., Schmidt, J., Braun, V., Fenaughty, J., & Eremin, M. (2009). Unsafe, unwanted sexual coercion as a barrier to safer sex among men who have sex with men. *Journal of Health Psychology, 14,* 1021–1026.

Gay, P. (1984). *The bourgeois experience: Victoria to Freud.* New York, NY: Oxford University Press.

Gebhard, P. H. (1976). The Institute. In M. S. Weinberg (Ed.), *Sex research: Studies from the Kinsey Institute.* New York, NY: Oxford University Press.

Gemme, R. (1998). Legal and sexological aspects of adult street prostitution: A case for sexual pluralism. In J. Elias, V. J. Bullough, V. Elias, & G. Brewer (Eds.), *Prostitution: On whores, hustlers & johns.* Amherst, NY: Prometheus Books.

Gemme, R., Murphy, A., Bourque, A., Nemeh, M. A., & Payment, N. (1984). *A report on prostitution in Quebec* (Working Paper sec11). Ottawa, Canada: Department of Justice Canada.

Gender Identity Research and Education Society. (2006). Atypical gender development: A review. *International Journal of Transgenderism, 9,* 29–43.

Genel, M. (2000). Gender verification no more? *Medscape Women's Health, 5*(3).

Genovesi, V. J. (1987). *In pursuit of love: Catholic morality and human sexuality.* Wilmington, DE: Michael Glazier.

Gentilcore-Saulnier, E., McLean, L., Goldfinger, C., Pukall, C. F., & Chamberlain, S. (2010). Pelvic floor muscle assessment outcomes in women with and without provoked vestibulodynia and the impact of a physical therapy program. *Journal of Sexual Medicine, 7,* 1003–1022.

Gentile, D. A., et al. (2004). The effects of violent video game habits on adolescent attitudes and behaviors. *Journal of Adolescence, 27,* 5–22.

George, W. H., & Stoner, S. A. (2000). Understanding acute alcohol effects on sexual behavior. *Annual Review of Sex Research, 11,* 92–124.

George, W. H., et al. (2006). Postdrinking sexual perceptions and behaviors toward another person: Alcohol expectancy set and gender differences. *Journal of Sex Research, 43,* 282–291.

Georges, E. (1996). Abortion policy and practice in Greece. *Social Science & Medicine, 42,* 509–519.

Georgiadis, J. R., & Kringelbach, M. L. (2012). The human sexual response cycle: Brain imaging evidence linking sex to other pleasures. *Progress in Neurobiology, 98,* 49–81.

Gerbner, G., Gross, L., & Morgan, M. (2002). Growing up with television: Cultivation processes. In J. Bryant & D. Zillman (Eds.), *Media effects: Advances in theory and research* (2nd ed., pp. 43–67). Mahwah, NJ: Erlbaum.

Gerlach, N., et al. (2012). Promiscuous mating produces off spring with higher lifetime fitness. *Proceedings of the Royal Society B, 279* (1730), 860–866.

Gervais, S. J., Vescio, T., & Allen, J. (2011). When what you see is what you get: The consequences of the objectifying gaze for women and men. *Psychology of Women Quarterly, 35,* 5–17.

Gidycz, C. A., et al. (2011). Primary prevention of sexual violence. In J. White et al. (Eds.), *Violence against women and children* (vol. 2, pp. 159–180), Washington, DC: American Psychological Association.

Gilbert, L., Basso, O., Sampalis, J., Karp, I., Martins, C., Feng, J., Piedimonte, S., . . . DOvE Study Group. (2012). Assessment of symptomatic women for early diagnosis of ovarian cancer: Results from the prospective DOvE pilot project. *Lancet Oncology, 13*(3), 285–291.

Gillath, O., et al. (2008). When sex primes love: Subliminal sexual priming motivates relationship goal pursuit. *Personality and Social Psychology Bulletin, 34,* 1057–1069.

Gilligan, C. (1982). *In a different voice: Psychological theory and women's development.* Cambridge, MA: Harvard University Press.

Gilmore, M. R., Leigh, B. C., Hoppe, M. J., & Morrison, D. M. (2010). Comparison of daily and retrospective reports of vaginal sex in heterosexual men and women. *Journal of Sex Research, 47,* 279–284.

Ginsberg, T. B., Pomerantz, S. C., & Kramer-Feeley, V. (2005). Sexuality in older adults: Behaviours and preferences. *Age and Ageing, 34,* 475–480.

Ginsburg, F. (1989). *Contested lives: The abortion debate in an American community.* Berkeley, CA: University of California Press.

Giordano, P. et al. (2010). Affairs of the heart: Qualities of adolescent romantic relationships and sexual behavior. *Journal of Research on Adolescence, 20,* 983–1013.

Giraldi, A., & Kristensen, E. (2010). Sexual dysfunction in women with diabetes mellitus. *Journal of Sex Research, 47,* 199–211.

Girard, A. L., & Senn, C. Y. (2008). The role of the new "date rape drugs" in attributions about date rape. *Journal of Interpersonal Violence, 23,* 3–20.

Giuliano, F., & Clement, P. (2005). Neuroanatomy and physiology of ejaculation. *Annual Review of Sex Research, 15,* 190–216.

Gjerdingen, D. (2003). The effectiveness of various postpartum depression treatments and the impact of antidepressant drugs on nursing infants. *Journal of the American Board of Family Practice 16,* 372–382.

Glascock, J., & LaRose, R. (1993). Dial-a-porn recordings: The role of the female participant in male sexual fantasies. *Journal of Broadcasting & Electronic Media,* 313–324.

Glass, S. J., & Johnson, R. W. (1944). Limitations and complications of organotherapy in male homosexuality. *Journal of Clinical Endocrinology, 4,* 540–544.

Glenn, S. A., & Byers, E. S. (2009). The roles of situational factors, attributions, and guilt in the well-being of women who have experienced sexual coercion. *Canadian Journal of Human Sexuality, 18,* 201–219.

Gold, E. R. (1986). Long-term effects of sexual victimization in childhood: An attributional approach. *Journal of Consulting and Clinical Psychology, 54*(4), 471–475.

Gold, S. D., Marx, B. P., & Lexington, J. M. (2007). Gay male sexual assault survivors: The relations among internalized homophobia, experiential avoidance, and psychological symptom severity. *Behaviour Research and Therapy, 45,* 549–562.

Gold, S. N., Hughes, D., & Hohnecker, L. (1994). Degrees of repression of sexual abuse memories. *American Psychologist, 49,* 441–442.

Goldberg, M. (1987). Understanding hypersexuality in men and women. In G. R. Weeks & L. Hof (Eds.), *Integrating sex and marital therapy.* New York, NY: Brunner-Mazel.

Goldberg, S. (1983). Parent-infant bonding: Another look. *Child Development, 54,* 1355–1382.

Goldfarb, M. R., Trudel, G., Boyer, R., & Préville, M. (2007). Marital relationship and psychological distress: Its correlates and treatments. *Sexual and Relationship Therapy, 22,* 109–126.

Goldfinger, C., Pukall, C. F., Gentilcore-Saulnier, E., McLean, L., & Chamberlain, S. (2009). A prospective study of pelvic floor physical therapy: Pain and psychosexual outcomes in provoked vestibulodynia. *Journal of Sexual Medicine, 6,* 1955–1968.

Goldfoot, D. A., Westerberg-van Loon, W., Groeneveld, W., & Koos Slob, A. (1980). Behavioral and physiological evidence of sexual climax in the female stump-tailed macaque (*Macaca arctoides*). *Science, 208,* 1477–1478.

Golding, J. M. (1999). Sexual assault history and medical care seeking. *Psychology & Health, 14,* 949–957.

Goldstein, J. M, Seidman, L. J., Horton, N. J., Makris, N., Kennedy, D. N., Caviness, V., et al. (2001). Normal sexual dimorphism of the adult human brain assessed by in vivo magnetic resonance imaging. *Cerebral Cortex, 11,* 490–497.

Golub, S. (1992). *Periods: From menarche to menopause.* Newbury Park, CA: Sage.

Gonsiorek, J. C. (1996). Mental health and sexual orientation. In R. C. Savin-Williams & K. M. Cohen (Eds.), *The lives of lesbians, gays, and bisexuals* (pp. 462–478). Fort Worth, TX: Harcourt Brace.

Gonzaga, G., Turner, R., Keltner, D., Campos, B., & Altemus, M. (2006). Romantic love and sexual desire in close relationships. *Emotion, 6,* 163–179.

Gonzalez, F., & Espin, O. (1996). Latino men, Latina women, and homosexuality. In R. Cabaj & T. Stein (Eds.), *Textbook of homosexuality and mental health* (pp. 583–601). Washington, DC: American Psychiatric Association.

Goodson, P., & Edmundson, E. (1994). The problematic promotion of abstinence: An overview of Sex Respect. *Journal of School Health, 64,* 205–210.

Goodson, P., McCormic, D., & Evans, A. (2001). Searching for sexually explicit materials on the internet: An exploratory study of college students' behavior and attitudes. *Archives of Sexual Behavior, 30,*101–118.

Gooren, L. (2006). The biology of human psychosexual differentiation. *Hormones and Behavior, 50,* 589–601.

Gordon, B., & Schroeder, C. (1995). *Sexuality: A developmental approach to problems.* New York, NY: Plenum Press.

Gordts, S., et al. (2009). Clinical factors determining pregnancy outcome after microsurgical tubal reanastomosis. *Fertility and Sterility, 92,* 1198–1202

Gorzalka, B. B., & Hill, M. N. (2006). Cannabinoids, reproduction, and sexual behavior. *Annual Review of Sex Research, 17,* 132–161.

Gorzalka, B. B., et al. (2010). Male-female differences in the effects of cannabinoids on sexual behavior and gonadal hormone function. *Hormones and Behavior, 58,* 91–99.

Gosling, S. D., Vazire, S., Srivastava, S., & John, O. P. (2004). Should we trust web-based studies? A comparative analysis of six preconceptions about internet questionnaires. *American Psychologist, 59,* 93–104.

Gosselin, C., & Wilson, G. (1980). *Sexual variations: Fetishism, sadomasochism, transvestism.* New York, NY: Simon & Schuster.

Gottlieb, L. (2006, March). How do I love thee? *The Atlantic Monthly,* 58–70.

Gottman, J. M. (1994). *Why marriages succeed or fail.* New York, NY: Simon & Schuster.

Gottman, J. M., & Notarius, C. I. (2002). Marital research in the 20th century and a research agenda for the 21st century. *Family Process, 41,* 159–197.

Gottman, J., & Silver, N. (1999). *The seven principles for making marriage work.* Three Rivers/Random House.

Gottman, J., Conn, J., Carrere, S., & Swanson, C. (1998). Predicting marital happiness and stability from newlywed interactions. *Journal of Marriage and the Family, 60,* 5–22.

Gottman, J., Markman, H., & Notarius, C. (1977). The topography of marital conflict: A sequential analysis of verbal and nonverbal behavior. *Journal of Marriage and the Family, 39,* 461–478.

Gottman, J., Notarius, C., Gonso, J., & Markman, H. (1976). *A couple's guide to communication.* Champaign, IL: Research Press.

Gould, S. J. (1987). *An urchin in the storm.* New York, NY: Norton.

Gouliquer, L. (2000). Negotiation sexuality: Lesbians in the Canadian military. In B. Miedema, J. Stoppard, & V. Anderson (Eds.). *Women's bodies/women's lives: health, well-being and body image.* Toronto, Canada: Second Story Press.

Gower, D. B., & Ruparelia, B. A. (1993). Olfaction in humans with special reference to odorous 16-androstenes: Their occurrence, perception and possible social, psychological and sexual impact. *Journal of Endocrinology, 137,* 167–187.

Grabe, S., Ward, L. M., & Hyde, J. S. (2008). The role of the media in body image concerns among women: A meta-analysis of experimental and correlational studies. *Psychological Bulletin, 134,* 460–476.

Grace, A. P., & Wells, K. (2001). Getting an education in Edmonton, Alberta: The case of queer youth. *Journal of the Canadian Lesbian and Gay Studies Association, 3,* 137–151.

Grace, A. P., & Wells, K. (2006). The quest for a queer inclusive cultural ethics: Setting directions for teachers' preservice and continuing professional development. *New Directions for Adult and Continuing Education, 112,* 51–61.

Grace, A. P., & Wells, K. (2007). Gay and bisexual male youth as educator activists and cultural workers: The queer critical praxis of three Canadian high-school students. *International Journal of Inclusive Education,* 1–22.

Graham, C. A., Sanders, S. A., Milhausen, R. R., & McBride, K. R. (2004). Turning on and turning off: A focus group study of the factors that affect women's sexual arousal. *Archives of Sexual Behavior, 33,* 527–538.

Grau, I., & Kimpf, M. (1993). Love, sexuality, and satisfaction: Interventions of men and women. *Zeitschrift fur Sozial Psychologie, 24,* 83–93.

Gravel, E. E., Young, M., Olavarria-Turner, M., & Lee, A. M. S. (2011). Ethnic differences in sexual guilt between Anglo-Canadians and Franco-Québécois emerging adults: The mediating roles of family and religion. *Canadian Journal of Human Sexuality, 20,* 129–142.

Gray, N. S., et al. (2005). An implicit test of the associations between children and sex in pedophiles. *Journal of Abnormal Psychology, 114,* 304–308.

Grazian, D. (2008). *On the make: The hustle of urban nightlife.* Chicago, IL: University of Chicago Press.

Greeley, A. (1994). Review of the *Janus report on sexual behavior. Contemporary Sociology, 23,* 221–223.

Greely, H. (2011). Get ready for the flood of fetal gene screening. *Nature, 469,* 289–291.

Green, L. L., Fullilove, M. T., & Fullilove, R. E. (2005). Remembering the lizard: Reconstructing sexuality in the rooms of Narcotics Anonymous. *Journal of Sex Research, 42,* 28–34.

Green, R. (1975). Adults who want to change sex; adolescents who crossdress; and children called "sissy" and "tomboy." In R. Green (Ed.), *Human sexuality: A health practitioner's text.* Baltimore, MD: Williams & Wilkins.

Green, R. M. (1984). Genetic medicine in Jewish legal perspective. *The Annual of the Society of Christian Ethics,* 249–272.

Green, R. M. (2007). *Babies by design: The ethics of genetic choice.* New Haven, CT: Yale University Press.

Greenberg, D. M., Bradford, J., Firestone, P., & Curry, S. (2000). Relationships of child molesters: A study of victim relationship with the perpetrator. *Child Abuse and Neglect, 24,* 1485–1494.

Greenberg, S., Rabinowitz, R., Firestone, P., Bradford, J. M., & Greenberg, D. M. (2002). Prediction of recidivism in exhibitionists: Psychological, phallometric, and offence factors. *Sexual Abuse: A Journal of Research and Treatment* (329–347).

Gregersen, E. (1996). *The world of human sexuality: Behaviors, customs, and beliefs.* New York, NY: Irvington.

Gregor, T. (1985). *Anxious pleasures: The sexual lives of an Amazonian people.* Chicago, IL: University of Chicago Press.

Gregorian, R. S., Golden, K. A., Bahce, A., Goodman, C., Kwong, W. J., & Khan, Z. M. (2002). Antidepressant-induced sexual dysfunction. *The Annals of Pharmacotherapy, 36,* 1577–1589.

Grello, C. M., Welsh, D., & Harper, M. (2006). No strings attached: The nature of casual sex in college students. *Journal of Sex Research, 43,* 255–267.

Grenier, G., & Byers, E. S. (1995). Rapid ejaculation: A review of conceptual, etiological, and treatment issues. *Archives of Sexual Behavior, 24,* 447–474.

Grenier, G., & Byers, E. S. (1997). The relationships among ejaculatory control, ejaculatory latency, and attempts to prolong heterosexual intercourse. *Archives of Sexual Behavior, 26,* 27–48.

Grenier, G., & Byers, E. S. (2001). Operationalizing premature or rapid ejaculation. *Journal of Sex Research, 38,* 369–378.

Griffin, S. (1981). *Pornography and silence.* New York, NY: Harper & Row.

Griffiths, M. (2000). Excessive Internet use: Implications for sexual behavior. *CyberPsychology and Behavior, 3,* 537–552.

Griffiths, M. (2001). Sex on the Internet: Observations and implications for Internet sex addiction. *Journal of Sex Research, 38,* 333–342.

Grimbos, T., et al. (2010). Sexual orientation and the second to fourth finger length ratio: A meta-analysis in men and women. *Behavioral Neuroscience, 124,* 278–287.

Grimes D. A., Lopez L. M., Schulz K. F., Van Vliet H. A. A. M., Helmerhorst F. M. (2006) Triphasic versus monophasic oral contraceptives for contraception. *Cochrane Database of Systematic Reviews* 2006, Issue 3. Art. No.: CD003553. doi:10.1002/14651858.CD003553.pub2

Gruenbaum, E. (2000). *The female circumcision controversy: An anthropological perspective.* Philadelphia, PA: University of Pennsylvania Press.

Grumbach, M. M., & Styne, D. M. (1998). Puberty: Ontogeny, neuroendocrinology, physiology, and disorders. In J. D. Wilson et al. (Eds.), *Williams Textbook of Endocrinology* (9th ed., pp. 1509–1625). Philadelphia, PA: Saunders.

Guay, J.-P., Proulx, J., Cusson, M., & Ouimet, M. (2001). Victim-choice polymorphia among serious sex offenders. *Archives of Sexual Behavior, 30,* 521–534.

Guay, S., Boisvert, J., & Freeston, M. H. (2003). Validity of three measures of communication for predicting relationship adjustment and stability among a sample of young couples. *Psychological Assessment, 15,* 392–398.

Guéguen, N. (2011). Effects of solicitor sex and attractiveness on receptivity to sexual offers: A field study. *Archives of Sexual Behavior, 40,* 915–919.

Guerrero, L., Spitzberg, B., & Yoshimura, S. (2004). Sexual and emotional jealousy. In J. H. Harvey, A. Wenzel, & S. Sprecher (Eds.), *The handbook of sexuality in close relationships* (pp. 311–345). Mahwah, NJ: Lawrence Erlbaum.

Guidroz, K., & Rich, G. J. (2010). Commercial telephone sex: Fantasy and reality. In R. Weitzer (Ed.), *Sex for sale: Prostitution, pornography, and the sex* industry (2nd ed., pp. 139–159). New York, NY: Routledge.

Guise, J.-M., Palda, V., Westhoff, C., Chan, B. K. S., Helfand, K., & Lieu, T. A. (2003). The effectiveness of primary care-based interventions to promote breastfeeding: Systematic evidence review and meta-analysis for the US Preventive Services Task Force. *Annals of Family Medicine, 1,* 70–78.

Gunby, J., Bissonnette, F., Librach, C., & Cowan, L. (2011). Assisted reproductive technologies (ART) in Canada: 2007 results from the Canadian ART register. *Fertility and Sterility, 95,* 542–547.

Gunter K., Maticka-Tyndale E., Godin G., Manson-Singer S., & Bradet R. (1993a). *Beliefs and Behaviors related to HIV/AIDS: Report for the Caribbean Communities. Ethnocultural Communities Facing AIDS: A National Study.* Ottawa, Canada: National Health Research and Development Program Cross-Cultural Views of Disability and Sexuality (Health Canada)/AIDS Education and Prevention Unit (National AIDS Strategy) Health Canada.

Gunter K., Maticka-Tyndale E., Godin G., Manson-Singer S., & Bradet R. (1993b). *Beliefs and Behaviors related to HIV/AIDS: Report for the South Asian Communities. Ethnocultural Communities Facing AIDS: A National Study.* Ottawa, Canada: National Health Research and Development Program (Health Canada)/AIDS Education and Prevention Unit (National AIDS Strategy) Health Canada.

Gurevich, M., Mathieson, C. M., Bower, J., & Dhayanandhan, B. (2007). Disciplining bodies, desires and subjectivities: Sexuality and HIV-positive women. *Feminism & Psychology, 17,* 9–38.

Gurney, M. (2012, November 12). As debate heats up, Canadian support for unrestricted abortions skyrockets. *The National Post.*

Gursoy, A. (1996). Abortion in Turkey: A matter of state, family, or individual decision. *Social Science & Medicine, 42,* 531–542.

Gutek, B. A. (1985). *Sex and the workplace.* San Francisco: Jossey-Bass.

Guterman, M. A. (2008). Observance of the laws of family purity in modern-Orthodox Judaism. *Archives of Sexual Behavior, 37,* 340–345.

Hackney, A. C. (2008). Effects of endurance exercise on the reproductive system of men: The "exercise-hypogonadal male condition." *Journal of Endocrinological Investigation, 31,* 932–938.

Haig, D. (1996). Alteration of generations: Genetic conflicts of pregnancy. *American Journal of Reproductive Immunology, 35,* 226–232.

Halbreich, U., & Kahn, L. (2001). Role of estrogen in the aetiology and treatment of mood disorders. *CNS Drugs, 15,* 797–817.

Haldeman, D. C. (1994). The practice and ethics of sexual orientation conversion therapy. *Journal of Consulting and Clinical Psychology, 62,* 221–227.

Haldeman, D. C. (2001). Therapeutic antidotes: Helping gay and bisexual men recover from conversion therapies. In A. Shidlo, M. Schroeder, & J. Drescher (Eds.), *Sexual conversion therapy: Ethical, clinical, and research perspectives* (pp. 117–130). New York, NY: Haworth.

Hall, G. C. N. (1995). Sexual offender recidivism revisited: A meta-analysis of recent treatment studies. *Journal of Consulting and Clinical Psychology, 63,* 802–809.

Hall, G. C. N., & Barongan, C. (1997). Prevention of sexual aggression. *American Psychologist, 52,* 5–14.

Hall, G. C. N., et al. (2005). Ethnicity, culture, and sexual aggression: Risk and protective factors. *Journal of Consulting and Clinical Psychology, 73,* 830–840.

Hall, J. A. (1998). How big are nonverbal sex differences? The case of smiling and sensitivity to nonverbal cues. In D. Canary & K. Dindia (Eds.), *Sex differences and similarities in communication* (pp. 155–178). Mahwah, NJ: Erlbaum.

Hall, R. C. W., & Hall, R. C. W. (2007). A profile of pedophilia: Definition, characteristics of offenders, recidivism, treatment outcomes, and forensic issues. *Mayo Clinic Proceedings, 82,* 457–471.

Halldorsson, T., et al. (2010). Intake of artificially sweetened soft drinks and risk of preterm delivery: A prospective cohort study in 59,334 Danish pregnant women. *American Journal of Clinical Nutrition, 92,* 626–633.

Halpern, C. T. (2010). Reframing research on adolescent sexuality: Health sexual development as part of the life course. *Perspectives on Sexual and Reproductive Health, 42,* 6–7.

Hamilton, M. C., et al. (2006). Gender stereotypes and under-representation of female characters in 200 popular children's picture books: A twenty-first century update. *Sex Roles, 55,* 757–766.

Hampson, E., & Moffat, S. D. (2004). The psychobiology of gender: Cognitive effects of reproductive hormones in the adult nervous system. In A. H. Eagly, A. E. Beall, & R. J. Sternberg (Eds.). *The psychology of gender* (2nd ed.), New York, NY: Guilford Press.

Hampton, M. R., Jeffery, B., McWatters, B., & Smith, P. (2005). Influence of teens' perceptions of parental disapproval and peer behaviour on their initiation of sexual intercourse. *Canadian Journal of Human Sexuality, 14,* 105–121.

Hampton, M. R., McKay-McNabb, K., Racette, S. F., & Byrd, N. J. (2007). Aboriginal elders as healers: Saskatchewan elders speak about sexual health. In J. D. Pappas, W. E. Smythe, & A. Baydala (Eds.), *Cultural healing and belief systems* (pp. 236–259). Calgary, AB: Detselig Enterprises Ltd.

Hampton, M. R., McWatters, B., & Jeffery, B. (2000). Method-related experiences of Canadian women using Depo-Provera for contraception. *Canadian Journal of Human Sexuality, 9,* 247–257.

Handy, L. C., Valentich, M., Cammaert, L. P., & Gripton, J. (1985). Feminist issues in sex therapy. In M. Valentich & J. Gripton (Eds.), *Feminist perspectives on social work and human sexuality.* Hawthorne Press.

Hanson, R. K. (2000). Will they do it again? Predicting sex-offense recidivism. *Current Directions in Psychological Science, 9,* 106–109.

Hanson, R. K., & Bussière, M. T. (1998). Predicting relapse: A meta-analysis of sexual offender recidivism studies. *Journal of Consulting and Clinical Psychology, 66,* 348–362.

Hanson, R. K., Gordon, A., Harris, A. J. R., Marques, J. K., Murphy, W., Quinsey, V. L., & Seto, M. C. (2002). First report of the collaborative outcome data project on the effectiveness of psychological treatment for sex offenders. *Sexual Abuse: A Journal of Research and Treatment, 14,* 169–194.

Hardwick, D., & Patychuk, D. (1999) Geographic mapping demonstrates the association

Hardwick, D., McKay, A., & Ashem, M. (2007). Chlamydia screening of adolescent and young women by general practice physicians in Toronto, Canada: Baseline survey data from a physician

education campaign. *Canadian Journal of Human Sexuality, 16,* 63–75.

Hare, L., et al. (2008). Androgen receptor repeat length polymorphism associated with male-to-female transsexualism. *Biological Psychiatry, 65,* 93–96.

Harlow, H. F., Harlow, M. K., & Hause, F. W. (1963). The maternal affectional system of rhesus monkeys. In H. L. Rheingold (Ed.), *Maternal behavior in mammals.* New York, NY: Wiley.

Harper, C. C., et al. (2005). The effect of increased access to emergency contraception among young adolescents. *Obstetrics & Gynecology, 106,* 483–491.

Harrington, P. R., & Swanstrom, R. (2008). The biology of HIV, SIV, and other lentiviruses. In K. Holmes et al. (Eds.), *Sexually transmitted diseases.* (4th ed., pp. 323–339). New York, NY: McGraw-Hill.

Harris, C. R. (2002). Sexual and romantic jealousy in heterosexual and homosexual adults. *Psychological Science, 13,* 7–12.

Harris, G. (2004, February 28). Pfizer gives up testing Viagra on women. *New York Times,* pp. C1.

Harris, G. E., & Alderson, K. G. (2006). Gay men living with HIV/AIDS: The potential for empowerment. *Journal of HIV/AIDS & Social Services, 5,* 9–24.

Harris, G. W., & Levine, S. (1965). Sexual differentiation of the brain and its experimental control. *Journal of Physiology, 181,* 379–400.

Harris/Decima (2007).*The average Canadian is a 6.7 out of 10.* Press release. December 15, 2007.

Harte, C. B., & Meston, C. M. (2011). Recreational use of erectile dysfunction medications in undergraduate men in the United States: Characteristics and associated risk factors. *Archives of Sexual Behavior, 40,* 597–606.

Hartley, T., & Mazzuca, J. (2001, December 12). Fewer Canadians favour legalized abortion under any circumstance. *The Gallup Poll, 61* (85). Toronto, Canada: Gallup Canada Inc.

Hartman, W., & Fithian, M. (1984). *Any man can: The multiple orgasmic technique for every loving man.* New York, NY: St. Martin's Press.

Hartmann, K., Viswanathan, M., Palmieri, R., Gartlehner, G., Thorp, J., & Lohr, K. (2005). Outcomes of routine episiotomy: A systematic review. *Journal of the American Medical Association, 293,* 2141–2148.

Hartwick, C., Desmarais, S., & Hennig, K. (2007). Characteristics of male and female victims of sexual coercion. *Canadian Journal of Human Sexuality, 16,* 31–44.

Hatcher, R. A., et al. (2007). *Contraceptive Technology.* (19th ed.) New York, NY: Ardent Media.

Hatcher, R. A., et al. (2011). *Contraceptive technology* (20th ed.). New York, NY: Ardent Media.

Hatfield, E. (1978). Equity and extramarital sexuality. *Archives of Sexual Behavior, 7,* 127–141.

Hatfield, E., & Rapson, R. (1993a). Historical and cross-cultural perspectives on passionate love and sexual desire. *Annual Review of Sex Research, 4,* 67–97.

Hatfield, E., & Rapson, R. (1993b). *Love, sex, and intimacy.* New York, NY: HarperCollins.

Hatfield, E., & Sprecher, S. (1986). Measuring passionate love in intimate relations. *Journal of Adolescence, 9,* 383–410.

Hatfield, E., & Walster, G. W. (1978). *A new look at love.* Reading, MA: Addison-Wesley.

Hatfield, E., Walster, G. W., & Berscheid, E. (1978). *Equity theory and research.* Boston, MA: Allyn & Bacon.

Hatzichristou, D., Montorsi, F., Buvat, J., Laferriere, N., Bandel, T. J., & Porst, H. (2004). The efficacy and safety of flexible-dose vardenafil (Levitra) in a broad population of European men. *European Urology, 45*, 634–641.

Hawkins, A., et al. (2008). Does marriage and relationship education work? A meta-analytic study. *Journal of Consulting and Clinical Psychology, 76*, 723–734.

Hayashi, K., et al. (2012). Off spring from oocytes derived from in vitro primordial germ cell-like cells in mice. *Science.*

Hayes, T. B., et al. (2002). Hermaphroditic, demasculinized frogs after exposure to the herbicide atrazine at low ecologically relevant doses. *Processsdings of the National Academy of Sciences, 99*, 5476–5480.

Health Canada. (1994a). *Many voices: HIV/AIDS in the context of culture. Report for the communities from and the English-speaking Caribbean communities.* Ottawa, Canada: Author.

Health Canada. (1994b). *Many voices: HIV/AIDS in the context of culture. Report for the communities from the Horn of Africa.* Ottawa, Canada: Author.

Health Canada. (1994c). *Many voices: HIV/AIDS in the context of culture. Report for the South Asian communities.* Ottawa, Canada: Author.

Health Canada. (1994d). *Many voices: HIV/AIDS in the context of culture. Report for the Latin American community.* Ottawa, Canada: Author.

Health Canada. (1994e). *Many voices: HIV/AIDS in the context of culture. Report for the Chinese communities.* Ottawa, Canada: Author.

Health Canada. (1996a). *Breastfeeding.* Canadian Perinatal Surveillance System—Fact Sheets, 1–6.

Health Canada. (1996b). *HIV/AIDS and Aboriginal people in Canada.* Ottawa, Canada: Author.

Health Canada. (1996c) *HIV/AIDS Epidemiology among Aboriginal peoples in Canada. Epi Update.* Laboratory Centre for Disease Control. Ottawa, Canada: Health Canada.

Health Canada. (1998a). *Cervical cancer in Canada—cancer updates.* Laboratory Centre for Disease Control, 1–8.

Health Canada. (2000). What everyone should know about human papillomavirus (HPV): Questions and Answers. *Bureau of HIV/AIDS, STD and TB Update Series: Population and Public Health Branch, STD Epi Update.* Ottawa, Canada: Author.

Health Canada. (2001). HIV and AIDS in Canada, Surveillance Report to December 31, 2000. *Division of HIV/AIDS Epidemiology and Surveillance, Bureau of HIV/AIDS, STD and TB, Centre for Infectious Disease Prevention and Control.* Ottawa, Canada: Health Canada.

Health Canada. (2003). *Canadian guidelines for sexual health education.* Ottawa, Canada: Health Canada.

Health Canada. (2004). *Health Canada advises of potential adverse effects of SSRIs and other antidepressants on newborns.* [Advisory 2004-44]. Retrieved October 12, 2004 from http://www.hcsc.gc.ca

Hearn, K. D., O'Sullivan, L. F., & Dudley, C. D. (2003). Assessing reliability of early adolescent girls' reports of romantic and sexual behavior. *Archives of Sexual Behavior, 32*, 513–522.

Heatherington, L., & Lavner, J. A. (2008). Coming to terms with coming out: Review and recommendations for family systems-focused research. *Journal of Family Psychology, 22*, 329–343

Heaton, J. P. W. (2000). Central neuropharmacological agents and mechanisms in erectile dysfunction: The role of dopamine. *Neuroscience and Biobehavioral Reviews, 24*, 561–569.

Heaton, J. P. W. (2001). Key issues from the clinical trials of apomorphine SL. *World Journal of Urology, 19*, 25–31.

Hébert, M., & Tourigny, M. (2004). Child sexual abuse prevention: A review of evaluative studies and recommendations for program development. *Advances in Psychology Research, 32*, 109–142.

Hébert, M., & Tremblay, C. (2000). La prévention de l'agression sexuelle à l'égard des enfants. In F. Vitaro & C. Gagnon (Eds.), *Prévention des problèmes d'adaptation chez les enfants et les adolescents-*Tome 1 *Les problèmes internalisès* (pp. 429–503). Ste-Foy: Presses de l'Université du Québec.

Hébert, M., Lavoie, F., & Parent, N. (2002). An assessment of outcomes following parents' participation in a child abuse prevention program. *Victims and Violence, 17*, 355–372.

Hébert, M., Lavoie, F., Piché, C., & Poitras, M. (2001). Proximate effects of a child sexual abuse prevention program in elementary school children. *Child Abuse & Neglect, 25*, 505–522.

Hébert, M., Tourigny, M., Cyr, M., McDuff, P., & Joly, J. (2009). Prevalence of childhood sexual abuse and timing of disclosure in a representative sample of adults from Quèbec. *Canadian Journal of Psychiatry, 54*, 631–636.

Hébert, M., Tremblay, C., Parent, N., Daignault, I. V., & Piché, C. (2006). Correlates of behavioral outcomes in sexually abused children. *Journal of Family Violence, 21*, 287–299.

Heffron, R., et al. (2012). Use of hormonal contraceptives and risk of HIV-1 transmission: A prospective cohort study. *Lancet Infectious Diseases,12*, 19–26.

Heiman, J. R. (1975). The physiology of erotica: Women's sexual arousal. *Psychology Today, 8* (11), 90–94.

Heiman, J. R. (2007). Orgasmic disorders in women. In S. Leiblum (Ed.), *Principles and practice of sex therapy* (4th ed., pp. 84–123). New York, NY: Guilford.

Heiman, J. R., & LoPiccolo, J. (1988). *Becoming orgasmic: A sexual and personal growth program for women.* New York, NY: Simon & Schuster.

Heine, S. J., & Norenzayan, A. (2006). Toward a psychological science for a cultural species. *Perspectives in Psychological Science, 1*, 251–269.

Heino, A., & Gissler, M. (2013, March 20). "Pohjoismaiset raskaudenkeskytykset 2011 (Induced fs in the Nordic countries 2011)". Helsinki: Terveyden ja hyvinvoinnin laitos (National Institute for Health and Welfare), Finland.

Heldman, C., & Wade, L. (2010). Hook-up culture: Setting a new research agenda. *Sexuality Research and Social Policy, 7*, 323–333.

Hellerstedt, W. L., Peterson-Hickey, M., Rhodes, K. L., & Garwick, A. (2006). Environmental, social, and personal correlates of having ever had sexual intercourse among American Indian youths. *American Journal of Public Health, 96*, 2228–2234.

Hellstrom, W. (2003). Three-piece inflatable penile prosthesis components (surgical pearls on reservoirs, pumps, and rear-tip extenders). *International Journal of Impotence Research, 15*, S136–S138.

Hellstrom, W. J. G. (2011). Update on treatments for premature ejaculation. *International Journal of Clinical Practice, 65*, 16–26.

Hellstrom, W. J., Gittelman, M., Karlin, G., Segerson, T., Thibonnier, M., & Taylor, T. (2003b). Sustained efficacy and tolerability of vardenafil, a highly potent selective phosphodiesterase type 5 inhibitor, in men with erectile dysfunction: results of a randomized, double-blind, 26-week placebo-controlled pivotal trial. *Urology, 61*, 8–14.

Hellstrom, W., Overstreet, J. W., Yu, A. S., Saikali, K., Shen, W., Beasley, C. M., et al. (2003a). Tadalafil has no detrimental effect on human spermatogenesis or reproductive hormones. *Journal of Urology, 170*, 887–891.

Helminiak, D. A. (2001a). Sexual ethics in college textbooks: A survey. *Journal of Sex Education and Therapy, 26*, 106–114.

Helminiak, D. A. (2001b). Sexual ethics in college textbooks: A suggestion. *Journal of Sex Education and Therapy, 26*, 320–327.

Helminiak, D. A. (2004). The ethics of sex: A call to the gay community. *Pastoral Psychology, 52*, 259–267.

Hemels, M. E., Koren, G., & Einarson, T. R. (2002). Increased use of antidepressants in Canada: 1981-2000. *The Annals of Pharmacotherapy, 36*, 1375–1379.

Henderson, A. J. Z., Bartholomew, K., Trinke, S. J., & Kwong, M. J. (2005). When loving means hurting: An exploration of attachment and intimate abuse in a community sample. *Journal of Family Violence, 20*, 219–230

Hendrick, C., & Hendrick, S. (2004). Sex and romantic love: Connects and disconnects. In J. H. Harvey, A. Wenzel, & S. Sprecher (Eds.), *The handbook of sexuality in close relationships* (pp. 159–182). Mahwah, NJ: Lawrence Erlbaum.

Hendrick, S. S., Hendrick, C., & Adler, N. L. (1988). Romantic relationships: Love, satisfaction, and staying together. *Journal of Personality and Social Psychology, 54*, 980–988.

Hendrick, S., & Hendrick, C. (1992). *Liking, loving, and relating* (2nd ed.). Pacific Grove, CA: Brooks/Cole.

Henningsson, S., et al. (2005). Sex steroid-related genes and male-to-female transsexualism. *Psychoneuroendocrinology, 30*, 657–664.

Henrich, J., Boyd, R., & Richerson, P. J. (2012). The puzzle of monogamous marriage. *Philosophical transactions of the Royal Society, 367*, 657–669.

Henrich, J., Heine, S. J., & Norenzayan, A. (2010). The weirdest people in the world? *Behavioral and Brain Sciences, 33*, 61–135.

Herbenick, D., & Reece, M. (2010). Development and validation of the female genital self-image scale. *Journal of Sexual Medicine, 7*(5), 1822–1830. doi:10.1111/j.1743-6109.2010.01728.x

Herbenick, D., Reece, M., Sanders, S., Dodge, B., Ghassemi, A., & Fortenberry, J. D. (2009). Prevalence and characteristics of vibrator use by women in the United States: Results from a nationally representative study. *Journal of Sexual Medicine, 6*, 1857–1866.

Herbenick, D., Reece, M., Schick, V., Sanders, S. A., Dodge, B., & Fortenberry, J. D. (2010a). Sexual behavior in the United States: Results from a national probability sample of men and women ages 14-94. *Journal of Sexual Medicine, 7*(SS05), 255–265.

Herbenick, D., Reece, M., Schick, V., Sanders, S. A., Dodge, B., & Fortenberry, J. D. (2010b). Sexual behaviors, relationships and perceived health status among adult women in the United States.

Results from a national probability sample. *Journal of Sexual Medicine, 7*(SS05), 277-290

Herbenick, D., Reece, M., Schick, V., Sanders, S. A., Dodge, B., & Fortenberry, J. D. (2010c). An event-level analysis of the sexual characteristics and composition among adults ages 18 to 59: Results from a national probability sample in the United States. *Journal of Sexual Medicine, 7* (SS05), 346-361.

Herdt, G. (1990). Mistaken gender: 5-alpha reductase herma phroditism and biological reductionism in sexual identity reconsidered. *American Anthropologist, 92,* 433-446.

Herdt, G. H. (1984). *Ritualized homosexuality in Melanesia.* Berkeley, CA: University of California Press.

Herek, G. M. (2000). The psychology of sexual prejudice. *Current Directions In Psychological Science, 9,* 19-22.

Herek, G. M. (2002). Heterosexuals' attitudes toward bisexual men and women in the United States. *Journal of Sex Research, 39,* 264-274.

Hergenhahn, B. R. (2001). *An introduction to the history of psychology* (4th ed.). Toronto, Canada: Wadsworth/Thomas Learning.

Herold, E. (1981). Contraceptive embarrassment and contraceptive behaviour among young single women. *Journal of Youth & Adolescence, 10*(3), 233-242.

Herold, E. S., & Way, L. (1988). Sexual self disclosure among university women. *Journal of Sex Research, 24,* 1-14.

Heron, A. (1963). *Towards a Quaker view of sex.* London, England: Friends Home Service Committee.

Herrero, R., Castellsague, X., Pawlita, M., Lissowska, J., Kee, F., Balaram, P., Rajkumar, T., . . . IARC Multi-center Oral Cancer Study Group. (2003). Human papilloma virus and oral cancer: The International Agency for Research on Cancer multicenter study. *Journal of the National Cancer Institute, 95*(23), 1772-1783.

Hetherington, M. E., & Parke, R. D. (2003). *Child Psychology: A contemporary viewpoint updated* (5th ed.). McGraw-Hill.

Hewlett, B. S., & Hewlett, B. L. (2010). Sex and searching for children among Aka foragers and Ngandu farmers of Central Africa. *African Study Monographs, 31*(3), 107-125.

Hightower, M. (1997). Effects of exercise participation on menstrual pain and symptoms. *Women & Health, 26,* 15-27.

Hill, D. B. (2000). Categories of sex and gender: Either/or, both/and, and neither/nor. *History and Philosophy of Psychology Bulletin, 12,* 25-33.

Hill, D. B., et al. (2007). Gender identity disorders in childhood and adolescence: A critical inquiry. *International Journal of Sexual Health, 1,* 95-122.

Hill, M. (2002). Skin color and the perception of attractiveness among African Americans: Does gender make a difference? *Social Psychology Quarterly, 65,* 77-91.

Hines, A. L., & Jiang, H. J. (2102). Rates of obstetric trauma, 2009 (Statistical Brief #129). Agency for Healthcare Research and Quality. Retrieved from http://www.hcup-us.ahrq.gov/reports/statbriefs/sb129.pdf

Hines, D. A. (2007). Predictors of sexual coercion against women and men: A multilevel, multinational study of university students. *Archives of Sexual Behavior, 36,* 403-422.

Hines, A. L., & Jiang, H. J. (2102). Rates of obstetric trauma, 2009 (Statistical Brief #129). Agency for Healthcare Research and Quality. Retrieved from http://www.hcup-us.ahrq.gov/reports/statbriefs/sb129.pdf

Hinman, K. (2011). Lost boys. Retrieved from http://www.laweekly.com/content/printVersion/1535565/

Hirschenhauser, K., et al. (2002). Monthly patterns of testosterone and behavior in prospective fathers. *Hormones and Behavior, 42,* 172-181.

Hite, S. (1976). *The Hite report.* New York, NY: Macmillan.

Hite, S. (1981). *The Hite report on male sexuality.* New York, NY: Alfred Knopf.

Hobbs, M. M., et al. (2008). *Trichomonas vaginalis* and trichomoniasis. In K. Holmes et al. (Eds.), *Sexually transmitted diseases.* (4th ed., pp. 771-794). New York, NY: McGraw-Hill.

Hobfoll, S., Ritter, C., Lavin, J., Hulsizer, M., et al. (1995). Depression prevalence and incidence among inner-city pregnant and postpartum women. *Journal of Consulting and Clinical Psychology, 63,* 445-453.

Hoebeke, P. B., Decaestecker, K., Beysens, M., Opdenakker, Y., Lumen, N., & Monstrey, S. M. (2010). Erectile implants in female-to-male transsexuals: Our experience in 129 patients. *European Urology, 57,* 334-341.

Hoffmann, H., Janssen, E., & Turner, S. L. (2004). Classical conditioning of sexual arousal in women and men: Effects of varying awareness and biological relevance of the conditioned stimulus. *Archives of Sexual Behavior, 33,* 43-54.

Hollander, D. (1996). Programs to bring down cesarean section rate prove to be successful. *Family Planning Perspectives, 28,* 182-185.

Holman, A., & Sillars, A. (2012). Talk about "hooking up": The influence of college student social networks on nonrelationship sex. *Health Communication, 27,* 205-216.

Holmberg, D., & Blair, K. L. (2009). Sexual desire, communication, satisfaction, and preferences of men and women in same-sex versus mixed-sex relationships. *Journal of Sex Research, 46,* 57-66.

Holmberg, D., Blair, K. L., & Phillips, M. (2010). Women's sexual satisfaction as a predictor of well-being in same-sex versus mixed-sex relationships. *Journal of Sex Research, 47*(1), 1-11.

Holmes, M. (2002). Rethinking the meaning and management of intersexuality. *Sexualities, 5,* 159-180.

Holstege, G., Georgiadis, J. R., Paans, A. M., Meiners, L. C., van der Graaf, F. H., & Reinders, A. A. (2003). Brain activation during human male ejaculation. *Journal of Neuroscience, 23,* 9185-9193.

Holter, H., et al. (2006). First IVF treatment—short-term impact on psychological well-being and the marital relationship. *Human Reproduction, 21,* 3295-3302.

Homma, Y., Nicholson, D., & Saewyc, E. (2012). Profile of high school students exchanging sex for substances in rural Canada. *Canadian Journal of Human Sexuality, 21*(1), 29-40.

Homma, Y., Wang, N., Saewyc, E., & Kishor, N. (2012). The relationship between sexual abuse and risky sexual behavior among adolescent boys: A meta-analysis. *Journal of Adolescent Health, 51,* 18-24.

Hong, L. K. (1984). Survival of the fastest: On the origin of premature ejaculation. *Journal of Sex Research, 20,* 109-122.

Hook, E. W., & Handsfield, H. H. (2008). Gonococcal infections in the adult. In K. Holmes et al. (Eds.), *Sexually transmitted diseases.* (4th ed., pp. 627-646). New York, NY: McGraw-Hill.

Hopwood, N. J., et al. (1990). The onset of human puberty: Biological and environmental factors. In J. Bancroft & J. M. Reinisch (Eds.), *Adolescence and puberty.* New York, NY: Oxford University Press.

Horney, K. (1973). The flight from womanhood (1926). In K. Horney, *Feminine psychology.* New York, NY: Norton.

Horrocks, R. (1997). *An introduction to the study of sexuality.* New York, NY: St. Martin's Press.

Hou, F., & Myles, J. (2007). The changing role of education in the marriage market: Asortative marriage in Canada and the United States since the 1970s. *Analytical Studies Branch Research Paper Series* (Catalogue no. 11F0019MIE). Ottawa, Canada: Statistics Canada.

House, C. (1997). Navajo warrior women: An ancient tradition in a modern world. In S. Jacobs, et al. (Eds.), *Two-spirit people* (pp. 223-227). Urbana, IL: University of Illinois Press.

How big is porn? (2001, May 25). *Forbes.*

Hsiao, W., et al. (2011). Satisfaction profiles in men using intracavernosal injection therapy. *Journal of Sexual Medicine, 8,* 512-517.

Hubacher, D. (2002). The checkered history and bright future of intrauterine contraception in the United States. *Perspectives on Sexual and Reproductive Health, 34,* 98-103.

Huber, J. D., & Herold, E. S. (2006). Sexually overt approaches in singles bars. *Canadian Journal of Human Sexuality, 15,* 133-146.

Hucker, S. (2008). Sexual masochism: Psychopathology and theory. In D. Richard Laws & W. O'Donohue, (Eds.), *Sexual Deviance: Theory, Assessment, and Treatment.* (2nd ed. pp. 250-263). New York, NY: Guilford.

Hucker, S., & Blanchard, R. (1992). Death scene characteristics in 118 fatal cases of autoerotic asphyxia compared with suicidal asphyxia. *Behavioural Sciences and the Law, 10,* 509-523.

Huffstutter, P. J., & Frammolino, R. (2001). Lights, camera, Viagra: When the show must go on, sometimes a little chemistry helps. *Los Angeles Times,* July 6, A1.

Hughes, I. A., et al. (2006). Consensus statement on management of intersex disorders. *Archives of Disease in Childhood, 91,* 554-562.

Hughes, J. O., & Sandler, B. R. (1987). *"Friends" raping friends: Could it happen to you?* Washington, DC: Association of American Colleges.

Hugh-Jones, S., Gough, B., & Littlewood, A. (2005). Sexual exhibitionism as 'sexuality and individuality': A critique of the psycho-medical discourse from the perspectives of women who exhibit. *Sexualities, 8,* 259-281.

Huh, J., et al. (2008). Brain activation areas of sexual arousal with olfactory stimulation in men. A preliminary study using functional MRI. *Journal of Sexual Medicine, 5,* 619-625.

Hulshoff, H. E., et al. (2006). Changing your sex changes your brain: Influences of testosterone and estrogen on adult human brain structure. *European Journal of Endocrinology, 155,* S107-S114.

Humphreys, T. P (2007). Perceptions of sexual consent: The impact of relationship history and gender. *Journal of Sex Research, 44,* 307-315.

Humphreys, T. P., & Brousseau, M. M. (2010). The Sexual Consent Scale-Revised: Development, reliability, and preliminary validity. *Journal of Sex Research, 47*(5), 420–428.

Humphreys, T. P., & Herold, E. (2007). Sexual consent in heterosexual relationships: Development of a new measure. *Sex Roles, 57*, 305–315.

Humphreys, T. P., & Kennett, D. J. (2010). The reliability and validity of instruments supporting the sexual self-control model. *Canadian Journal of Human Sexuality, 19*(1–2), 1–13.

Humphreys, T. P. (2012). Cognitive frameworks of virginity and first intercourse. *Journal of Sex Research.* doi:10.1080/00224499.2012.677868

Hunt, M. (1974). *Sexual behavior in the 1970s.* Chicago, IL: Playboy Press.

Hust, S. J., Brown, J., & L'Engle, K. (2008). Boys will be boys and girls better be prepared: An analysis of the rare sexual health messages in young adolescents' media. *Mass Communication and Society, 11*, 3–23.

Hutchinson, K. A. (1995). Androgens and sexuality. *American Journal of Medicine, 98* (Suppl. 1A), 1A111S–1A115S.

Hyde, J. S., & Jaffee, S. R. (2000). Becoming a heterosexual adult: The experiences of young women. *Journal of Social Issues, 56*, 283–296.

Hyde, J. S., DeLamater, J., & Hewitt, E. (1998). Sexuality and the dualearner couple: Multiple rules and sexual functioning. *Journal of Family Psychology, 12*, 354–368.

Hyde, J. S., DeLamater, J., Plant, E. A., & Byrd, J. M. (1996). Sexuality during pregnancy and the year postpartum. *Journal of Sex Research, 33*, 143–151.

Hyde, J. S., & Else-Quest, N. (2012). *Half the human experience: The psychology of women* (8th ed.). Boston, MA: Houghton Mifflin.

Hynes, H. P., & Raymond, J. G. (2002). Put in harm's way: The neglected health consequences of sex trafficking in the United States. In J. Silliman, & A. Bhattacharjee (Eds.), *Policing the national body: Sex, race, and criminalization* (pp. 197–229). Cambridge, MA: South End Press.

Hynie, M., & Lydon, J. E. (1995). Women's perceptions of female contraceptive behaviour: Experimental evidence of the social double standard. *Psychology of Women Quarterly, 19*, 563–581.

Hynie, M., Lydon, J. E., & Taradash, A. (1997). Commitment, intimacy, and women's perceptions of premarital sex and contraceptive readiness. *Psychology of Women Quarterly, 21*, 447–464.

Hynie, M., Lydon, J. E., Cote, S., & Weiner, S. (1998). Relational sexual scripts and women's condom use: The importance of internalized norms. *Journal of Sex Research, 35*(4), 370–380.

Ibañez, G. E., et al. (2009). General and gay-related racism experienced by Latino gay men. *Cultural Diversity and Ethnic Minority Psychology, 15*, 215–222.

Idso, C. (2009). Sexually transmitted infection prevention in newly single older women: A forgotten health promotion need. *The Journal for Nurse Practitioners, 5*, 440–446

Ilies, R., et al. (2003). Reported incidence rates of work-related sexual harassment in the United States: Using meta-analysis to explain reported rate disparities. *Personnel Psychology, 56*, 607–631.

Ilkkaracan, P. (2001). Islam and women's sexuality. In P. B. Jung, M. E. Hunt, & R. Balakrishnan (Eds.), *Good sex: Feminist perspectives from the world's religions* (pp. 61–76). New Brunswick, NJ: Rutgers University Press.

Imperato-McGinley, J., et al. (1974). Steroid 5 reductase deficiency in man: An inherited form of male pseudohermaphroditism. *Science, 186*, 1213–1215.

Institute of Medicine. (2004). *New frontiers in contraceptive research.* Washington, DC: National Academies Press.

Ipsos. (2013, June). *A global advisory: Same-sex marriage.* Retrieved from http://ipsos-na.com/download/pr.aspx?id=12795

Irvine, J. M. (1995). *Sexuality education across cultures: Working with differences.* San Francisco: Jossey-Bass.

Isaacs, C. R., & Fisher, W. A. (2008). A computer-based educational intervention to address potential negative effects of Internet pornography. *Communication Studies, 59*, 1–18.

Israel, D. D., et al. (2012). Effects of leptin and melanocortin signaling interactions on pubertal development and reproduction. *Endocrinology, 153*, 2408–2419.

Iwaniuk, A. N., et al. (2006). The effects of environmental exposure to DDT on the brain of a songbird: Changes in structures associated with mating and song. *Behavioural Brain Research, 173*, 1–10.

Izugbara, C. O. (2008). Home-based sexuality education: Nigerian parents discussing sex with their children. *Youth & Society, 39*, 575–600.

Jaakkola, J., & Gissler, M. (2004). Maternal smoking in pregnancy, fetal development and childhood asthma. *American Journal of Public Health, 94*, 136–141.

Jackson, G. (2009). Sexual response in cardiovascular disease. *Journal of Sex Research, 46*, 233–236.

Jackson, T., Chen, H., et al. (2006). Stories we love by: Conceptions of love among couples from the People's Republic of China, and the United States. *Journal of Cross-Cultural Psychology, 37*, 446–464.

Jacobs, J. (2009). Have sex will travel: Romantic 'sex tourism' and women negotiating modernity in the Sinai. *Gender, Place, and Culture, 16*, 43–61.

Jacobs, S., Thomas, W., & Lang, S. (Eds.). (1997). *Two-spirit people.* Urbana: University of Illinois Press.

Jacobson, S. W., Jacobson, J. L., & Sokol, R. J. (1994). Effects of fetal alcohol exposure on infant reaction time. *Alcoholism: Clinical and Experimental Research, 18*, 1125–1132.

Jacobson, S. W., Jacobson, J. L., Sokol, R. J., Martier, S. S., & Ager, J. W. (1993). Prenatal alcohol exposure and infant information processing ability. *Child Development, 64*, 1706–1721.

Jamieson, D. J., Kaufman, S. C., Costello, C., Hillis, S. D., Marchbanks, P. A., & Peterson, H. B. (2002). A comparison of women's regret after vasectomy versus tubal sterilization. *Obstetrics and Gynecology, 99*, 1073–1079.

Janicek, M. F., & Averette, H. E. (2001). Cervical cancer: Prevention, diagnosis, and therapeutics. *CA: Cancer Journal for Clinicians, 51*, 92–114.

Janowsky, J. S., Chavez, B. Zamboni, B., & Orwoll, E. (1998). The cognitive neuropsychology of sex hormones in men and women. *Developmental Neuropsychology, 14*, 421–440.

Janssen, E., Vorst, H., Finn, P., & Bancroft, J. (2002a). The Sexual Inhibition (SIS) and Sexual Excitation (SES) Scales: I. Measuring sexual excitation proneness in men. *Journal of Sex Research, 39* (2), 114–126.

Janssen, E., Vorst, H., Finn, P., & Bancroft, J. (2002b). The Sexual Inhibition (SIS) and Sexual Excitation (SES) Scales: II. Predicting psychophysiological response patterns. *Journal of Sex Research, 39* (2), 127–132.

Janssen, P. A., Thiessen, P., Klein, M. C., Whitfield, M. F., MacNab, Y. C., & Cullis-Kuhl, S. C. (2007). Standards for the measurement of birth weight, length and head circumference at term in neonates of European, Chinese and South Asian ancestry. *Open Medicine, 1*, e74–88.

Janus, S. S., & Janus, C. L. (1993). *The Janus report on sexual behavior.* New York, NY: Wiley.

Jefferson, E. A. (2005). Grown up parties are turning up the heat. *Denver Post*, November 15.

Jeffrey, L. A., & MacDonald, G. (2006a). "It's the money, Honey": The economy of sex work in the Maritimes. *The Canadian Review of Sociology and Anthropology, 43*, 313–327.

Jeffrey, L. A., & MacDonald, G. (2006b). *Sex workers in the Maritimes talk back.* Vancouver, Canada: UBC Press.

Jemail, J. A., & Geer, J. (1977). Sexual scripts. In R. Gemme & C. C. Wheeler (Eds.), *Progress in sexology.* New York, NY: Plenum.

Jenkins, J. S., & Nussey, S. S. (1991). The role of oxytocin: Present concepts. *Clinical Endocrinology, 34*, 515–525.

Jenks, R. (1998). Swinging: A review of the literature. *Archives of Sexual Behavior, 27*, 507–521.

Jenks, R. J. (1985). Swinging: A replication and test of a theory. *Journal of Sex Research, 21*, 199–210.

Jenny, C., Roesler, T. A., & Poyer, K. A. (1994). Are children at risk for sexual abuse by homosexuals? *Pediatrics, 94*, 41–44.

Jensen, R. (2007). *Getting off: Pornography and the end of masculinity.* Cambridge: South End Press.

Jesperson, A. Lalumiere, M., & Seto, M. (2009). Sexual abuse history among adult sex offenders and non-sex offenders: A meta-analysis. *Child Abuse and Neglect, 33*, 179–192.

Jha, P., Kumar, R., Vasa, P., Dhingra, N., Thiruchelvam, D., & Maineddin, R. (2006). Low male-to-female sex ratio of children born in India: National survey of 1.1 million households. *The Lancet, 367*, 211–218.

Joel, D. (2011). Male or female? Brains are intersex. *Frontiers in Integrative Neuroscience, 5*, 57.

Johansmeyer, T. (2010). Even porn stars get the recession blues. Retrieved from http://www.dailyfinance.com/2010/01/08/even-porn-stars-get-the-recession-blues/

Johansson, A., et al. (2010). A five-year follow up study of Swedish adults with gender identity disorder. *Archives of Sexual Behavior, 39*, 1429–1437.

John, E. M., Savitz, D. A., & Sandler, D. P. (1991). Prenatal exposure to parents' smoking and childhood cancer. *American Journal of Epidemiology, 133*, 123–132.

Johnsdotter, S., & Essén, B. (2010). Genitals and ethnicity: The politics of genital modifications. *Reproductive Health Matters, 18*, 29–37.

Johnson, A. M., Mercer, C. H., Erens, B., Copas, A. J., McManus, S., Wellings, K., et al. (2001). Sexual behaviour in Britain: Partnerships, practices, and HIV risk behaviours. *Lancet, 358*, 1835–1842.

Johnson, A. M., Wadsworth, J., Wellings, K., Bradshaw, S., & Field, J. (1992). Sexual lifestyles and HIV risk. *Nature, 360*, 410–412.

Johnson, B. R., Horga, M., & Andronache, L. (1996). Women's perspectives on abortion in Romania. *Social Science & Medicine, 42,* 521–530.

Johnson, S. D., Phelps, D., & Cottier, L. (2004). The association of sexual dysfunction and substance use among a community epidemiological sample. *Archives of Sexual Behavior, 33,* 55–64.

Johri, A., Heaton, J., & Morales, A. (2001). Severe erectile dysfunction is a marker for hyperprolactinemia. *International Journal of Impotence Research, 13,* 176–182.

Joint Consortium for School Health. (2007). *Sexual health: Quick scan of activities and resources in Canadian schools.* Retrieved from http://www.jcsh-cces.ca/upload/Sexual/20Health.pdf

Joint SOGC-CFAS Guidelines. (2008). Guidelines for the number of embryos to transfer following in vitro fertilization. *International Journal of Gynecology and Obstetrics, 102,* 203–216.

Jonah, Metropolitan of All America and Canada. (2010, January 24). Sanctity of Life Sunday 2010. Retrieved from http://www.oca.org

Jonason, P. K., & Fisher, T. D. (2009). The power of prestige: Why young men report having more sex partners than young women. *Sex Roles, 60,* 151–159.

Jonason, P. K., Li, N. P., & Cason, M. J. (2009). The "booty call": A compromise between men's and women's ideal mating strategies. Journal of Sex Research, 46, 460–470.

Jonason, P. K., Li, N. P., & Richardson, J. (2011). Positioning the booty-call relationship on the spectrum of relationships: Sexual but more emotional than one-night stands. *Journal of Sex Research, 48,* 486–495.

Jones, C., Chan, C., & Farine, D. (2011). Sex in pregnancy. *Canadian Medical Association Journal.* doi:10:1503/cmaj.091580

Jones, J. H. (1997). *Alfred C. Kinsey: A public/private life.* New York, NY: Norton.

Jones, J., Pelham, B., Carvallo, M., & Mirenberg, M. (2004). How do I love thee? Let me count the Js: Implicit egotism and interpersonal attraction. *Journal of Personality and Social Psychology, 87,* 665–683.

Jones, L. M., et al. (2012). Trends in youth internet victimization: Findings from three youth internet safety surveys 2000–2010. *Journal of Adolescent Health, 50,* 179–186.

Jones, R. K., & Henshaw, S. K. (2002). Mifepristone for early medical abortion: Experiences in France, Great Britain and Sweden. *Perspectives on Sexual and Reproductive Health, 34,* 154–161.

Jones, R. K., & Kooistra, K. (2011). Abortion incidence and access to services in the United States, 2008. *Perspectives on Sexual and Reproductive Health, 43* (1): 41–50.

Joshi, S. P., et al. (2011). Scripts of sexual desire and danger in U. S. and Dutch teen girl magazines: A cross-national content analysis. *Sex Roles, 64,* 463–474.

Julien, D., Chartrand, E., Simard, M. C., Bouthillier, D., & Begin, J. (2003). Conflict, social support, and relationship quality: An observational study of heterosexual, gay male, and lesbian couples' communication. *Journal of Family Psychology, 17,* 419–428.

Julien, D., Jouvin, E., Jodoin, E., l'Archevêque, A., & Chartrand, E. (2008). Adjustment among mothers reporting same-gender sexual partners: A study of

a representative population sample from Quebec province (Canada). *Archives of Sexual Behavior, 37,* 864–876.

Kabir, A., Pridjian, G., Steinmann, W., Herrera, E., & Khan, M. (2005). Racial differences in cesareans: An analysis of U. S. 2001 national inpatient sample data. *Obstetrics and Gynecology, 195,* 710–718.

Kaestle, C. E., & Allen, K. R. (2011). The role of masturbation in healthy sexual development: Perceptions of young adults. *Archives of Sexual Behavior, 40,* 983–994.

Kafka, M., & Hennen, J. (2002). A DSM-IV Axis I comorbidity study of males (n 5 120) with paraphilias and paraphilia-related disorders. *Sex Abuse, 14,* 349–366.

Kahr, B. (2008). *Who's been sleeping in your head? The secret world of sexual fantasies.* New York, NY: Basic Books.

Kai, L., & Pourier, D. J. (2001). Using the National Longitudinal Study of Youth in the U. S. to study the birth process: A Bayesian approach. *Research in Official Statistics, 4,* 127–150.

Kaiser Family Foundation. (1998). *Sex in the 90s: 1998 national survey of Americans on sex and sexual health* (Publication No. 1430). Menlo Park, CA: Author.

Kaiser Family Foundation. (2001). *Biennial report on sex in the media: Executive summary.* Menlo Park, CA: Author.

Kaiser Family Foundation. (2003). *A biennial report of the Kaiser Family Foundation on Sex on TV3: Executive summary.* Menlo Park, CA: Author.

Kalichman, S. C., & Cain, D. (2004). The relationship between indicators of sexual compulsivity and high risk sexual practices among men and women receiving services from a sexually transmitted infection clinic. *Journal of Sex Research, 41,* 235–241.

Kalichman, S. C., Benotsch, E., & Simpson, D. (2001). Unwanted sexual experiences and sexual risks in gay and bisexual men: Associations among revictimization, substance use, and psychiatric symptoms. *Journal of Sex Research, 38,* 1–9.

Kalichman, S. C., & Rompa, D. (1995). Sexual sensation seeking and compulsivity scales: Reliability, validity, and predicting HIV risk behavior. *Journal of Personality Assessment, 62,* 586–601.

Kalick, S. M., Zebowitz, L., Langlois, J., & Johnson, R. (1998). Does human facial attractiveness honestly advertise health? Longitudinal data on an evolutionary question. *Psychological Science, 9,* 8–13.

Kalil, K., Gruber, J., Conley, J., & Sytniac, M. (1993). Social and family pressures on anxiety and stress during pregnancy. *Pre- and Perinatal Psychology Journal, 8,* 113–118.

Kallstrom-Fuqua, A. C., Weston, R., & Marshall, L. (2004). Childhood and adolescent sexual abuse of community women: Mediated effects on psychological distress and social relationships. *Journal of Consulting and Clinical Psychology, 72,* 980–992.

Kamel, H. K., Perry, H. M., & Morley, J. E. (2001). Hormone replacement therapy and fractures in older adults. *Journal of the American Geriatrics Society, 49,* 179–187.

Kaplan, H. S. (1974). *The new sex therapy.* New York, NY: Brunner/Mazel.

Kaplan, H. S. (1979). *Disorders of sexual desire.* New York, NY: Simon & Schuster.

Kaplan, H. S., & Sager, C. J. (1971, June). Sexual patterns at different ages. *Medical Aspects of Human Sexuality,* 10–23.

Kaplan, M., & Krueger, R. (2010). Diagnosis, assessment, and treatment of hypersexuality. *Journal of Sex Research, 47,* 181–198.

Karama, S., Lecours, A. R., Leroux, J. M., Bourgouin, P., Beaudoin, G., Joubert, S., et al. (2002). Areas of brain activation in males and females during viewing of erotic film excerpts. *Human Brain Mapping, 16,* 1–13.

Karraker, A., & DeLamater, J. (2013). Past year sexual inactivity among older married persons and their partners. *Journal of Marriage and Family.*

Karraker, A., DeLamater, J., & Schwartz, C. (2011). Sexual frequency decline from midlife to later life. *Journals of Gerontology Series B: Psychological Sciences & Social Sciences, 66B* (4), 502–512.

Katz-Wise, S. (2012). *Beyond labels: Sexual fluidity and sexual identity development in sexual minority young adults.* Doctoral dissertation, University of Wisconsin-Madison.

Kaufmann, J.-C. (2012). *Love online.* Cambridge, England: Polity Press.

Keefe, D. L. (2002). Sex hormones and neural mechanisms. *Archives of Sexual Behavior, 31,* 401–404.

Keelan, P. R., Dion, K. L., & Dion, K. K. (1994). Attachment style and heterosexual relationships among young adults: A short-term panel study. *Journal of Social and Personal Relationships, 11,* 201–214.

Keenan, T., & Ward, T. (2000). A theory of mind perspective on cognitive, affective, and intimacy deficits in child sex offenders. *Sex Abuse, 12,* 49–60.

Kegel, A. H. (1952). Sexual functions of the pubococcygeus muscle. *Western Journal of Surgery, 60,* 521–524.

Kelly, M. P., Strassberg, D. S., & Turner, C. M. (2006). Behavioral assessment of couples' communication in female orgasmic disorder. *Journal of Sex & Marital Therapy, 32*(2), 81–95.

Kempf, D. J., et al. (1995). ABT-538 is a potent inhibitor of human immunodeficiency virus protease. *Proceedings of the National Academy of Sciences, 92,* 2484.

Kempton, W., & Kahn, E. (1991). Sexuality and people with intellectual disabilities: A historical perspective. *Sexuality and Disability, 9,* 93–111.

Kendall-Tackett, K., Williams, L., & Finkelhor, D. (1993). Impact of sexual abuse on children: A review and synthesis of recent empirical studies. *Psychological Bulletin, 113,* 164–180.

Kendler, K. S., Bulik, C. M., Silberg, J., Hettema, J. M., Myers, J., Prescott, C. A., et al. (2000). Childhood sexual abuse and adult psychiatric and substance use disorders in women: An epidemiological and cotwin control analysis. *Archives of General Psychiatry, 57,* 953–959.

Kendler, K. S., Thornton, L., Gilman, S., & Kessler, R. (2000). Sexual orientation in a US national sample of twin and nontwin sibling pairs. *American Journal of Psychiatry, 157,* 1843–1846.

Kennedy, M. (2012, July 4). New poll shows most Canadians support abortion—with some restrictions. *The National Post.*

Kennedy, R., & Suttenfield, K. (2001). Postpartum depression. *Medscape Mental Health 6,* No. 4.

Kennett, D., Humphreys, T. P., & Schultz, K. E. (2012). Sexual resourcefulness and the impact of family, sex education, media and peers. *Sex Education, 12,* 351–368.

Kenny, M. C., & Wurtele, S. K. (2012). Child sexual behavior inventory: A comparison between Latino and normative samples of preschoolers. *Journal of Sex Research.* doi:10.1080/00224499.2011.652265

Kero, A., Lalos, A., Högberg, U., & Jacobssen, L. (1999). The male partner involved in legal abortion. *Human Reproduction, 14,* 2669–2675.

Keverne, E. B. (1999). The vomeronasal organ. *Science, 286,* 716–720.

Khan, A., & Pine, P. (2003). *Adolescent reproductive health in Pakistan: Status, policies, programs, and issues.* Washington, D. C., Futures Group International, POLICY Project (USAID Contract No. HRN-C-00-00-00006-00).

Kiefer, A. K., & Sanchez, D. T. (2007). Scripting sexual passivity: A gender role perspective. *Personal Relationships, 14,* 269–290.

Kikuras, A. (2004). An interview with Dave Cummings, Unchain the underground, http://www.unchain.com

Kim, J. L., et al. (2007). From sex to sexuality: Exposing the heterosexual script on primetime network television. *Journal of Sex Research, 44,* 145–157.

Kim, N., Stanton, B., Li, X., Dickersin, K., & Galbraith, J. (1997). Effectiveness of the 40 adolescent AIDS-risk reduction interventions: A quantitative review. *Journal of Adolescent Health, 20,* 204–215.

King, A. J. C., Beazley, R. P., Warren, W. K., Hankins, C. A., Robertson, A. S., & Radford, J. L. (1988). *Canada youth and AIDS study.* Kingston, ON: Social Program Evaluation Group, Queen's University.

King, D. B., DeCicco, T. L., & Humphreys, T. P. (2009). Investigating sexual dream imagery in relation to daytime sexual behaviours and fantasies among Canadian university students. *Canadian Journal of Human Sexuality, 18 (3),* 135–146.

King, M., et al. (2007). Women's views of their sexual difficulties: Agreement and disagreement with clinical diagnoses. *Archives of Sexual Behavior, 36,* 281–288.

King, M., et al. (2008). A systematic review of mental disorder, suicide, and deliberate self harm in lesbian, gay and bisexual people. *BMC Psychiatry, 8,* 70.

King, M., Marks, J., & Mandell, J. (2003). Breast and ovarian cancer risks due to inherited mutations in BRCA1 and BRCA2. *Science, 302,* 643–646.

Kingston, D. A., Malamuth, N. M., Federoff, P., & Marshall, W. L. (2009). The importance of individual differences in pornography use: Theoretical perspectives and implications for treating sexual offenders. *Journal of Sex Research, 46,* 216–232.

Kinnish, K. K., Strassberg, D., & Turner, C. (2005). Sex differences in the flexibility of sexual orientation: A multidimensional retrospective assessment. *Archives of Sexual Behavior, 34,* 173–184.

Kinsey, A. C., Pomeroy, W. B., & Martin, C. E. (1948). *Sexual behavior in the human male.* Philadelphia, PA: Saunders.

Kinsey, A. C., Pomeroy, W. B., Martin, C. E., & Gebhard, P. H. (1953). *Sexual behavior in the human female.* Philadelphia, PA: Saunders.

Kinsman, G. (1996). *The regulation of desire: Sexuality in Canada.* Montreal: Black Rose Books.

Kiragu, K., et al. (2001). Can we avoid catastrophe? Youth and HIV/AIDS. *Population Reports (Series L),*

No.12. Johns Hopkins University School of Public Health.

Kirby, D. (1992). School-based programs to reduce sexual risktaking behavior. *Journal of School Health, 62,* 281–287.

Kirby, D. (2002). Effective approaches to reducing adolescent unprotected sex, pregnancy, and childbearing. *Journal of Sex Research, 39,* 51–57.

Kirby, D., & Laris, B. A. (2009). Effective curriculum-based sex and STD/HIV education programs for adolescents. *Child Development Perspectives, 3,* 21–29.

Kirby, D., Short, L., Collins, J., Rugg, D., Kolbe, L., Howard, M., et al. (1994). School-based programs to reduce sexual risk behaviors: A review of effectiveness. *Public Health Reports, 109,* 339–360.

Kirk, K., Bailey, J., Dunne, M., & Martin, N. (2000). Measurement models for sexual orientation in a community twin sample. *Behavior Genetics, 30,* 345–356.

Kiselica, M., & Scheckel, S. (1995). The couvade syndrome (sympathetic pregnancy) and teenage fathers: A brief primer for counselors. *School Counselor, 43,* 42–51.

Klaus, M., & Kennell, J. (1976). Human maternal and paternal behavior. In M. Klaus & J. Kennell (Eds.), *Maternal infant bonding.* St. Louis, MO: Mosby.

Klebanov, P. K., & Jemmott, J. B. (1992). Effects of expectations and bodily sensations on self-reports of premenstrual symptoms. *Psychology of Women Quarterly, 16,* 289–310.

Klein, C., & Gorzalka, B. B. (2009). Sexual functioning in transsexuals following hormone therapy and genital surgery: A review. *Journal of Sexual Medicine, 6,* 2922–2939.

Kleinhaus, K., Perrin, M., Friedlander, Y., Paltiel, O., Malaspina, D., & Harlap, S. (2006). Paternal age and spontaneous abortion. *Obstetrics and Gynecology, 108,* 369–377.

Kleinplatz, P. J. (1992). The erotic experience and the intent to arouse. *Canadian Journal of Human Sexuality, 1*(3),133–139.

Kleinplatz, P. J. (1998). Sex therapy for vaginismus: A review, critique, and humanistic alternative. *Journal of Humanistic Psychology, 38*(2), 51–81

Kleinplatz, P. J. (2003a). Beyond sexual mechanics and hydraulics: Humanizing the discourse surrounding erectile dysfunction. *Journal of Humanistic Psychology, 43,* 1–29.

Kleinplatz, P. J. (2003b). What's new in sex therapy? From stagnation to fragmentation. *Sexual & Relationship Therapy, 18,* 95–106.

Kleinplatz, P. J. (2009). Consumer protection is the major purpose of sex therapy certification. *Archives of Sexual Behavior, 38,* 1031.

Kleinplatz, P. J. (2010). Lessons from great lovers. In S. Levine, S. Althof, & C. Risen, (Eds.), *Handbook of Clinical Sexuality for Mental Health Professionals* (2nd ed., pp. 57–72). New York, NY: Brunner-Routledge.

Kleinplatz, P. J., & Krippner, S. (2005). Spirituality and sexuality: Celebrating erotic transcendence and spiritual embodiment. In S. G. Mijares, & G. S. Khalsa (Eds.), *The psychospiritual clinician's handbook: Alternative methods for understanding and treating mental disorders.* Binghamton, NY: Haworth Press, Inc.

Kleinplatz, P. J., & Ménard, A. D. (2007). Building blocks toward optimal sexuality: Constructing a

conceptual model. *The Family Journal: Counseling and Therapy for Couples and Families, 15,* 72–78.

Kleinplatz, P. J., Ménard, A. D., Paquet, M.-P., Paradis, N., Campbell, M., Zuccarini, D., & Mehak, L. (2009). The components of optimal sexuality: A portrait of "great sex." *Canadian Journal of Human Sexuality, 18(1–2),* 1–13.

Kleinplatz, P. J., Ménard, A. D., Paradis, N., Campbell, M, Dalgleish, T., Segovia, A., & Davis, K. (2009). From closet to reality: Optimal sexuality among the elderly. *Irish Psychiatrist, 10 (1),* 15–18.

Kleinplatz, P. J., Ménard, A. D., & Campbell, M. (2013). Relational contributions to optimal sexual experiences. In A. C. Michalos (Ed.), *Encyclopedia of Quality of Life Research.* New York, NY: Springer.

Klemetti, R., Sevón, T., Gissler, M., & Hemminki, E. (2006, November). Health of children born as a result of in vitro fertilization. *Pediatrics, 118,* 1819–1827.

Kline, G., Stanley, S., Markman, H., Olmos-Gallo, P. A., St. Peters, M., Whitton, S., & Prado, L. (2004). Timing is everything: Pre-engagement cohabitation and increased risk for poor marital outcomes. *Journal of Family Psychology, 18,* 311–318.

Kloas, W., et al. (2009). Endocrine disruption in aquatic vertebrates. *Trends in Comparative Endocrinology and Neurobiology: Annals of the New York Academy of Sciences, 1163,* 187–200.

Knäuper, B., & Kornik, R. (2004). Perceived transmissibility of STIs: Lack of differentiation between HIV and chlamydia. *Sexually Transmitted Infections, 80,* 74–78.

Knäuper, B., Kornik, R., Atkinson, K., Guberman, C., & Aydin, C. (2005). Motivation influences the underestimation of cumulative risk. *Personality and Social Psychology Bulletin, 31,* 1511–1523.

Kniffin, K. M., & Wilson, D. S. (2004). The effect of nonphysical traits on perception of physical attractiveness: Three naturalistic studies. *Evolution and Human Behavior, 25,* 88–101.

Knobloch-Westerwick, S., & Hoplamazian, G. J. (2012). Gendering the self: Selective magazine reading and reinforcement of gender conformity. *Communication Research, 39,* 358–384.

Koch, P. B., Mansfield, P., Thurau, D., & Carey, M. (2005). "Feeling frumpy": The relationships between body image and sexual response changes in midlife women. *Journal of Sex Research, 42,* 215–223.

Koelman, C. A., Coumans, A. B., Nijman, H. W., Doxiadis, I. I., Dekker, G. A., & Claas, F. H. (2000). Correlation between oral sex and a low incidence of preeclampsia: A role for soluble HLA in seminal fluid? *Journal of Reproductive Immunology, 46,* 155–166.

Kolata, G. (2001, March 25). Researchers find grave defect risk in cloning animals. *New York Times,* p. 1ff.

Kolbenschlag, M. (1985). Abortion and moral consensus: Beyond Solomon's choice. *Christian Century, 102,* 179–183.

Kolker, A. (1989). Advances in prenatal diagnosis. *International Journal of Technology Assessment in Health Care, 5,* 601–617.

Komisaruk, B. R., & Whipple, B. (2005). Function MRI of the brain during orgasm in women. *Annual Review of Sex Research, 15,* 62–86.

Kong, R., Johnson, H., Beattie, S., & Cardillo, A. (2003). Sexual offences in Canada. *Juristat, 23,* 6.

Korff, J., & Geer, J. H. (1983). The relationship between sexual arousal experience and genital response. *Psychophysiology, 20,* 121–127.

Kosfeld, M., Heinrichs, M., Zak, P., Fischbacher, U., & Fehr, E. (2005). Oxytocin increases trust in humans. *Nature, 435* (June 2), 673–676.

Kosnick, A., et al. (1977). *Human sexuality: New directions in American Catholic thought.* New York, NY: Paulist Press.

Koss, M. P. (1993). Rape: Scope, impact, interventions, and public policy response. *American Psychologist, 48,* 1062–1063.

Koss, M. P., Koss, P. G., & Woodruff, W. J. (1991). Deleterious effects of criminal victimization on women's health and medical utilization. *Archives of Internal Medicine, 151,* 342–347.

Koss, M., & Figueredo, A. (2004). Change in cognitive mediators of rape's impact on psychosocial health across 2 years of recovery. *Journal of Consulting and Clinical Psychology, 72,* 1063–1072.

Kothari, P. (1984). For discussion: Ejaculatory disorders—a new dimension. *British Journal of Sexual Medicine, 11,* 205–209.

Kovacs, P. (2002a). Congenital anomalies and low birth weight associated with assisted reproductive technologies (Article 435963). *Medscape Women's Health 7,* No. 3.

Kovacs, P. (2002b). Preconception sex selection. *Medscape Ob/Gyn & Women's Health, 7,* No 2. Retrieved from http://www.medscape.com/viewarticle/441313

Krahé, B., et al. (2007). The role of sexual scripts in sexual aggression and victimization. *Archives of Sexual Behavior, 36,* 687–701.

Kramer, M. S., Platt, R. W., Wen, S. W., Joseph, K. S., Allen, A., Abrahamowicz, M., Blondel, B., & Breart, G. (2001). A new and improved population-based Canadian reference for birth weight for gestational age. *Pediatrics, 108,* e35.

Kraut, R., Olson, J., Banaji, M., Bruckman, A., Cohen, J., & Couper, M. (2004). Psychological research online: Report of the Board of Scientific Affairs' Advisory Group on the Conduct of Research on the Internet. *American Psychologist, 59,* 105–117.

Krings, F., & Facchin, S. (2009). Organizational justice and men's likelihood to sexually harass: The moderating role of sexism and personality. *Journal of Applied Psychology, 94,* 501–510.

Krippendorff, K. (2004). *Content analysis: An introduction to its methodology.* Thousand Oaks, CA: Sage.

Kroeber, A. L., & Kluckhohn, C. (1963). *Culture: A critical review of concepts and definitions.* New York, NY: Vintage Books.

Krueger, R. B., & Kaplan, M. S. (2001). Depo-leuprolide acetate for treatment of paraphilias: A report of twelve cases. *Archives of Sexual Behavior, 30,* 409–422.

Kruger, B. S. (2006). The post-orgasmic prolactin increase following intercourse is greater than following masturbation and suggests greater satiety. *Biological Psychology, 71,* 312–315.

Krüger, T. H., Haake, P., Hartmann, U., Schedlowski, M., & Exton, M. S. (2002). Orgasm-induced prolactin secretion: Feedback control of sexual drive? *Neuroscience and Biobehavioral Reviews, 26,* 31–44.

Kruijver, F., et al. (2000). Male-to-female transsexuals have female neuron numbers in a limbic nucleus. *Journal of Clinical Endocrinology and Metabolism, 85,* 2034–2041.

Krupa, C., & Esmail, S. (2010, June). Sexual health education for children with visual impairments: Talking about sex is not enough. *Journal of Visual Impairment & Blindness,* 327–337.

Kukkonen, T. M., Binik, Y. M., Amsel, R., & Carrier, S. (2007). Thermography as a physiological measure of sexual arousal in both men and women. *Journal of Sexual Medicine, 4,* 93–105.

Kukkonen, T. M., Binik, Y. M., Amsel, R., & Carrier, S. (2010). An evaluation of the validity of thermography as a physiological measure of sexual arousal in a non-university adult sample. *Archives of Sexual Behavior, 39,* 861–873.

Kunkel, D., Eyal, K., Finnerty, K., Biely, E., & Donnerstein, E. (2005). *Sex on TV 4.* Menlo Park, CA: Kaiser Family Foundation.

Kunkel, D., Farrar, K. M., Eyal, K., Biely, E., Donnerstein, E., Rideout, V. (2007). Sexual socialization messages on entertainment television: Comparing content trends 1997–2002. *Media Psychology, 9,* 595–622.

Kunzel, R. (2008). *Criminal intimacy: Prison and the uneven history of modern American sexuality.* Chicago, IL: University of Chicago Press.

Kuper, L. E., et al. (2012). Exploring the diversity of gender and sexual orientation identities in an online sample of transgender individuals. *Journal of Sex Research, 49,* 244–254.

Kurdek, L. A. (2005). What do we know about gay and lesbian couples? *Current Directions in Psychological Science, 14,* 251–254.

Kuyper, L. et al. (2012). Doing more good than harm? The effects of participation in sex research on young people in the Netherlands. *Archives of Sexual Behavior, 41,* 497–506

La Rocque, C. L., & Cioe, J. (2011). An evaluation of the relationship between body image and sexual avoidance. *Journal of Sex Research, 48,* 397–408.

Laan, E., et al. (1994). Women's sexual and emotional responses to male- and female-produced erotica. *Archives of Sexual Behavior, 23,* 153–170.

Labrecque, M., Eason, E., Marcoux, S., Lemieux, F., Pinault, J., Feldman, P., & Laperrière, L. (1999). Randomized controlled trial of prevention of perineal trauma by perineal massage during pregnancy. *American Journal of Obstetrics and Gynecology, 180,* 593–600.

Lacelle, C., Hébert, M., Lavoie F., Vitaro, F., & Tremblay, R. E. (2012a). Child sexual abuse and women's sexual health: The contribution of CSA severity and exposure to multiple forms of childhood victimization. *Journal of Child Sexual Abuse, 21,* 571–592.

Lacelle, C., Hébert, M., Lavoie F., Vitaro, F., & Tremblay, R. E. (2012b). Sexual health in women reporting a history of child sexual abuse. *Child Abuse & Neglect, 36,* 247–259.

Lacroix, N. (2003). *Kama Sutra: A modern guide to the ancient art of sex.* Hylas Publishing: New York.

LaFromboise, T. D., Heyle, A. M., & Ozer, E. J. (1990). Changing and diverse roles of women in American Indian cultures. *Sex Roles,* 455–476.

Lahey, K. A. (1999). *Are we "persons" yet? Law and sexuality in Canada.* Toronto, Canada: University of Toronto Press.

Laliberté, L. (2006). New vaginas for old. *National Review of Medicine, 3*(2).

Lalumière, M. L., & Quinsey, V. L. (1998). Pavlovian conditioning of sexual interests in human males. *Archives of Sexual Behavior, 27,* 241–252.

Lalumière, M. L., Blanchard, R., & Zucker, K. J. (2000). Sexual orientation and handedness in men and women: A meta-analysis. *Psychological Bulletin, 126,* 575–592.

Lalumière, M. L., Quinsey, V. L., Harris, G. T., Rice, M. E., & Trautrimas, C. (2003). Are rapists differentially aroused by coercive sex in phallometric assessments? *Annals of the New York Academy of Sciences, 989,* 211–224.

LaMarre, A. K., Paterson, L. Q., & Gorzalka, B. B. (2003). Breastfeeding and postpartum maternal sexual functioning: A review. *Canadian Journal of Human Sexuality, 12,* 151–168.

Lamb, M. E., & Hwang, C. (1982). Maternal attachment and mother-neonate bonding: A critical review. In M. E. Lamb & A. L. Brown (Eds.), *Advances in developmental psychology* (Vol. 2). Hillsdale, NJ: Lawrence Erlbaum.

Lambert, B., Bergeron, S., Desrosiers, M., & Lepage, Y. (2012). Introital primary and secondary dyspareunia: Multimodal clinical and surgical control. *Sexologies, 21,* 9–12.

Lambert, T. A., Kahn, A., & Apple, K. (2003). Pluralistic ignorance and hooking up. *Journal of Sex Research, 40,* 129–133.

Lamberts, S. W. J., et al. (1997). The endocrinology of aging. *Science, 278,* 419–424.

Lamont, J., Bajzak, K., Bouchard, C., Burnett, M., Byers, E. S., Cohen, T., Fisher, W., Holzapfel, S., & Senikas, V. (2012). Female sexual health consensus clinical guidelines. *Journal of Obstetrics & Gynaecology Canada, 34,* 769–775.

Landott, M. A., Bartholomew, K., Saffrey, C., Oram, D., & Perlman, D. (2004). Gender nonconformity, childhood rejection, and adult attachment: A study of Gay men. *Archives of Sexual Behavior, 33,* 117–128.

Landry, T., & Bergeron, S. (2009). How young does vulvo-vaginal pain begin? Prevalence and characteristics of dyspareunia in adolescents. *Journal of Sexual Medicine, 6*(4), 927–935.

Landry, T., & Bergeron, S. (2011). Biopsychosocial factors associated with dyspareunia in a community sample of adolescent girls. *Archives of Sexual Behavior, 40,* 877–889.

Landry, T., Bergeron, S., Dupuis, M-J., & Desrochers, G. (2008). The treatment of provoked vestibulodynia: A critical review. *Clinical Journal of Pain, 24,* 155–171.

Laner, M. R., & Ventrone, N. A. (2000). Dating scripts revisited. *Journal of Family Issues, 21,* 488–500.

Langfeldt, T. (1981). Childhood masturbation. In L. L. Constantine & F. M. Martinson (Eds.), *Children and sex* (pp. 63–74). Boston, MA: Little, Brown.

Langille, D. (2000). *Adolescent sexual health services and education: Options for Nova Scotia.* Maritime Centre of Excellence for Women's Health. Policy discussion Series Paper #8. Halifax, NS: Maritime Centre of Excellence for Women's Health.

Langille, D. B., Beazley, R., Shoveller, J., & Johnston, G. (1994). Prevalence of high risk sexual behaviour in adolescents attending school in a county in Nova Scotia. *Canadian Journal of Public Health, 85*(4), 227–230.

Langille, D. B., Murphy, G. T., Hughes, J., & Rigby, J. A. (2001). Nova Scotia high school students' interactions with physicians for sexual health information and services. *Canadian Journal of Public Health, 92,* 219–222.

Langille, D. B., Proudfoot, K., Rigby, J., Aquino-Russell, C., & Forward, K. (2008). A pilot project for chlamydia screening in adolescent females using self-testing: Characteristics of participants and non-participants. *Canadian Journal of Public Health, 99,* 117–120.

Langille, D., Beazley, R., & Doncaster, H. (1996). *Amherst parents' attitudes towards school-based sexual health education.* Amherst, NS: Amherst Initiative for Healthy Adolescent Sexuality.

Langille, D., Graham, J., Marshall, E., Blake, M., Chittey, C., & Doncaster-Scott, H. (1999). *Developing understanding from young women's experiences in obtaining sexual health services and education in a Nova Scotia community.* Maritime Centre of Excellence for Women's Health.

Långström, N., & Seto, M. (2006). Exhibitionistic and voyeuristic behavior in a Swedish national population survey. *Archives of Sexual Behavior, 35,* 427–435.

Långström, N., & Zucker, K. J. (2005). Tranvestic fetishism in the general population: Prevalence and correlates. *Journal of Sex & Marital Therapy, 31,* 87–95.

Lansford, J. E., Yu, T., Erath, S., Pettit, G. S., Bates, J. E., & Dodge, K. A. (2010). Developmental precursors of number of sexual partners from age 16 to 22. *Journal of Research on Adolescence, 20*(3), 651–677.

Larroque, B., Ancel, P-Y., Marret, S., et al. (2008). Neurodevelopmental disabilities and special care of 5-year-old children born before 33 weeks of gestation (the EPIPAGE study): A longitudinal cohort study. *The Lancet, 371,* 813–820.

Larsson, A., & Dykes, A. (2009). Care during pregnancy and childbirth in Sweden: Perspectives of lesbian women. *Midwifery, 25,* 682–690.

Larsson, I., & Svedin, C. G. (2002a). Teachers' and parents' reports on 3- to 6-year-old children's sexual behaviour: A comparison. *Child Abuse & Neglect, 26,* 247–266.

Larsson, I., & Svedin, C. G. (2002b). Sexual experiences in childhood: Young adults' recollections. *Archives of Sexual Behavior, 31,* 263–274.

Lassek, W. D., & Gaulin, S. (2007). Menarche is related to fat distribution. *American Journal of Physical Anthropology, 133,* 1147–1151.

Latty-Mann, H., & Davis, K. (1996). Attachment theory and partner choice: Preference and actuality. *Journal of Social and Personal Relationships, 13,* 5–23.

Lau, J. T. F., Tsui, H. Y., & Wang, Q. S. (2003). Effects of two telephone survey methods on the level of reported risk behaviours. *Sexually Transmitted Infections, 79,* 325–331.

Laughon, S. K., et al. (2012). Changes in labor patterns over 50 years. *American Journal of Obstetrics and Gynecology, 206,* 419 (e1–e9).

Laumann, E. O., Gagnon, J. H., Michael, R. T., & Michaels, S. (1994). *The social organization of sexuality: Sexual practices in the United States.* Chicago, IL: University of Chicago Press.

Laumann, E. O., Paik, A., & Rosen, R. (1999). Sexual dysfunction in the United States: Prevalence and predictors. *Journal of the American Medical Association, 281,* 537–544.

Laurenceau, J.-P., Feldman, B., & Pietromonaco, P. R. (1998). Intimacy as an interpersonal process: The importance of self-disclosure, partner disclosure, and perceived partner responsiveness in interpersonal exchanges. *Journal of Personality and Social Psychology, 74,* 1238–1251.

Lavin, M. (2008). Voyeurism: Psychopathology and theory. In D. R. Laws, & W. O'Donohue (Eds.), *Sexual Deviance: Theory, Assessment, and Treatment.* (2nd ed., pp. 305–319). New York, NY: Guilford.

Lavine, H., Sweeney, D., & Wagner, S. (1999). Depicting women as sex objects in television advertising: Effects on body dissatisfaction. *Personality and Social Psychology Bulletin, 25,* 1049–1058.

Lavoie, F., Thibodeau, C., Gagné, M., & Hébert, M. (2010). Buying and selling sex in Québec adolescents: A study of risk and protective factors. *Archives of Sexual Behavior, 39,* 1147–1160.

Law Reform Commission of Canada. (1992). *Medically assisted procreation working paper 65.* Ottawa, Canada: Canada Communication Group-Publishing, cat. #J32–1/65–1992.

Lawrance, K.-A., & Byers, E. S. (1995). Sexual satisfaction in long-term heterosexual relationships: The interpersonal exchange model of sexual satisfaction. *Personal Relationships, 2,* 267–285.

Lawrance, K.-A., Taylor, D., & Byers, E. S. (1996). Differences in men's and women's global, sexual and ideal-sexual expressiveness and instrumentality. *Sex Roles, 34*(5 & 6), 337–357.

Le Bourdais, C., & Lapierre-Adamcyk, E. (2004). Changes in conjugal life in Canada: Is cohabitation progressively replacing marriage? *Journal of Marriage and Family, 66,* 929–942.

Leader, A. (1999). New reproductive technologies: Why are we limiting choices for infertile couples? *Canadian Medical Association Journal, 161,* 1411–1412.

Leaper, C., & Ayres, M. M. (2007). A meta-analytic review of gender variations in adults' language use: Talkativeness, affiliative speech, and assertive speech. *Personality and Social Psychology Review, 11,* 328–363.

Leaper, C., & Friedman, C. (2007). The Socialization of Gender. *Handbook of socialization: Theory and research* (pp. 561–587). New York, NY, US: Guilford Press.

Leaver, J., & Dolnick, D. (2010). Call girls and street prostitutes: Selling sex and intimacy. In R. Weitzer (Ed.), *Sex for sale: Prostitution, pornography, and the sex industry* (2nd ed., pp. 187–203). New York, NY: Routledge.

Lebacqz, K. (1987). Appropriate vulnerability: A sexual ethic for singles. *Christian Century, 104,* 435–438.

Lebeque, B. (1991). Paraphilias in U. S. pornography titles: "Pornography made me do it" (Ted Bundy). *Bulletin of the American Academy of Psychiatry and Law, 19,* 43–48.

Lechner, S. C., Antoni, M. H., Lydston, D., LaPerriere, A., Ishii, M., Devieux, J., et al. (2003). Cognitive-behavioral interventions improve quality of life in women with AIDS. *Journal of Psychosomatic Research, 54,* 253–261.

Leclerc, B., Bergeron, S., Binik, Y. M., & Khalifé, S. (2010). History of sexual and physical abuse in women with dyspareunia: Association with pain, psychosocial adjustment, and sexual functioning. *Journal of Sexual Medicine, 7,* 971–980

Lederer, L. (Ed.). (1980). *Take back the night: Women on pornography.* New York, NY: Morrow.

Lee, J. A. (1979). The social organization of sexual risk. *Alternative Lifestyles, 2,* 69–100.

Lee, P. A., et al. (2006). Consensus statement on management of intersex disorders. Pediatrics, 118, e488–e500.

Lee, S., & Coates, J. (2007). *Sex trade research initiative, New Brunswick.* Report prepared for Provincial Government's Executive Council Office, Women's Issues Branch.

Leger Marketing (2012). Religiosity and atheism 2005–2012. Retrieved from http://www.leger360.com/admin/upload/publi_pdf/Religion_in_Canada_0812.pdf

Leifer, M. (1980). *Psychological effects of motherhood: A study of first pregnancy.* New York, NY: Praeger.

Leitenberg, H., & Henning, K. (1995). Sexual fantasy. *Psychological Bulletin, 117,* 469–496.

Lemieux, R., & Hale, J. (2002). Cross-sectional analysis of intimacy, passion, and commitment: Testing the assumptions of the triangular theory of love. *Psychological Reports, 90,* 1009–1014.

Lemieux, S. R., & Byers, E. S. (2008). The sexual well-being of women who have experienced child sexual abuse. *Psychology of Women Quarterly.*

Leonard, L. (2000). Interpreting female genital cutting: Moving beyond the impasse. *Annual Review of Sex Research, 11,* 158–190.

Leonard, L. M., & Follette, V. M. (2002). Sex functioning in women reporting a history of child sexual abuse: Clinical and empirical considerations. *Annual Review of Sex Research, 13,* 346–388.

Lerman, H. (1986). From Freud to feminist personality theory. *Psychology of Women Quarterly, 10,* 1–18.

LeTourneau, E., et al. (2009) Multisytemic therapy for juvenile sexual offenders: 1-Year results from a randomized effectiveness trial. *Journal of Family Psychology, 23:* 89–102.

Letts, C., Tamilyn, K., & Byers, E. S. (2010). Exploring the impact of prostate cancer on men's sexual well-being. *Journal of Psychosocial Oncology, 28,* 490–510.

LeVay, S. (1991). A difference in hypothalamic structure between heterosexual and homosexual men. *Science, 253,* 1034–1037.

LeVay, S. (1996). *Queer science: The use and abuse of research into homosexuality.* Cambridge, MA: MIT Press.

Lever, J. (1994, August). Sexual revelations. The 1994 Advocate Survey of Sexuality and Relationships: The Men. *The Advocate,* 17–24.

Lever, J. (1995, August). Lesbian sex survey. The 1995 Advocate Survey of Sexuality and Relationships: The Women. *The Advocate,* 22–30.

Lever, J., Frederick, D. A., & Peplau, L. (2006). Does size matter? Men's and women's views on penis size across the lifespan. *Psychology of Men & Masculinity, 7*(3), 129–143. doi:10. 1037/1524-9220.7.3.129

Lever, J., Grov, C., Royce, T., & Gillespie, B. J. (2008). Searching for love in all the "write" places: Exploring Internet personal use by sexual orientation, gender, and age. *International Journal of Sexual Health, 20,* 233–246.

Levin, D. (2009). So sexy, so soon: The sexualization of childhood. In Olfman, S. (Ed.), *The sexualization of childhood* (pp. 75–88). Westport, CT: Praeger.

Levin, I., & Trost, J. (1999). Living apart together. *Community, Work & Family 2*(3): 279–294.

Levin, R. J. (2003). Is prolactin the biological "off switch" for human sexual arousal? *Sexual and Relationship Therapy, 18,* 237–243.

Levin, R. J. (2005). Sexual arousal–its physiological roles in human reproduction. *Annual Review of Sex Research, 15,* 154–189.

Levine, R., Sato, S., Hashimoto, T., & Verma, J. (1995). Love and marriage in eleven cultures. *Journal of Cross-Cultural Psychology, 26,* 554–571.

Levitas, E., et al. (2003). Are semen parameters related to abstinence? Analysis of 7,233 semen samples. Paper presented at European Society for Human Reproduction and Embryology, Madrid.

Levitt, E., Moser, C., & Jamison, K. (1994). The prevalence and some attributes of females in the sadomasochistic subculture: A second report. *Archives of Sexual Behavior, 23,* 465–473.

Levy, J. J., Maticka-Tyndale, E., & Lew, V. A. (1992). Pratique contraceptives et preventive face au sida parmi un groupe de cegepiens de Montreal: Variations interethniques. *Novelles Pratique Sociale, 5*(2), 25–36.

Lewis, J., & Maticka-Tyndale, E. (1998). *Final report: Erotic/exotic dancing: HIV-related risk factors.* Ottawa, Canada: Health Canada.

Lewis, J., Maticka-Tyndale, E., Shaver, F., & Schramm, H. (2005). Managing risk and safety on the job: The experiences of Canadian sex workers. *Journal of Psychology and Human Sexuality, 17,* 147–167.

Lewis, R. W., et al. (2004). Definitions, classification, and epidemiology of sexual dysfunction. In T. F. Lue, R. Basson, R. Rosen, F. Giuliano, S. Khoury, & F. Montorsi (Eds.). *Sexual medicine* (pp. 39–72). Paris, France: Editions 21.

Lewis, R. W., et al. (2010). Definitions/epidemiology/risk factors for sexual dysfunction. *Journal of Sexual Medicine, 7,* 1598–1607.

Lewis, W. J. (1997). Factors associated with post-abortion adjustment problems: Implications for triage. *Canadian Journal of Human Sexuality, 6,* 9–16.

Liao, M., L., & Creighton, S. (2010). Labial surgery for well women: A review of the literature. *British Journal of Obstetrics and Gynecology, 117,* 20–25.

Libman, E. (1989). Sociocultural and cognitive factors in aging and sexual expression: Conceptual and research issues. *Canadian Psychology, 3*(3), 560–567.

Libman, E., & Fichten, C. S. (1987). Prostatectomy and sexual function. *Urology, 24*(5), 467–478.

Libman, E., Fichten, C. S., Creti, L., Weinstein, N., Amsel, R., & Brender, W. (1989). Transurethral prostatectomy: Differential effects of age category and presurgery sexual functioning on postprostatectomy sexual adjustment. *Journal of Behavioural Medicine, 12*(5), 469–485.

Liebmann-Smith, J. (1987). *In pursuit of pregnancy: How couples discover, cope with, and resolve their fertility problems.* New York, NY: Newmarket Press.

Lievore, D. (2003). *Non-reporting and hidden recording of sexual assault: An International literature review.* Canberra: Commonwealth Government of Australia.

Liljeros, F., Edling, C. R., Amaral, L. A., Stanley, H. E., & Aberg, Y. (2001). The web of human sexual contacts. *Nature, 411,* 907–908.

Lindgren, K. P., et al. (2008). Gender differences in perceptions of sexual intent: A qualitative review and integration. *Psychology of Women Quarterly, 32,* 423–439.

Linz, D., Donnerstein, E., & Penrod, S. (1987). The findings and recommendations of the Attorney General's Commission on pornography: Do the psychological "facts" fit the political fury? *American Psychologist, 42,* 946–953.

Lisak, D., & Miller, P. M. (2002). Repeat rape and multiple offending among undetected rapists. *Violence & Victims, 17,* 73–84.

Liskin, L., Kak, N., Rutledge A. H., Smit L. C., & Stewart, L. (1985, November–December). Youth in the 1980s: Social and health concerns. *Population Reports, XIII,* No. 5, M350–M388.

Liu, C. (2003). Does quality of marital sex decline with duration? *Archives of Sexual Behavior, 32,* 55–60.

Ljunger, E., Cnattingius, S., Lundin, C., & Anneren, G. (2005). Chromosomal anomalies in first-trimester miscarriages. *Acta Obstetrica et Gynecologica Scandinavica, 84,* 1103–1107.

Loeb, T. B., et al. (2002). Child sexual abuse: Associations with the sexual functioning of adolescents and adults. *Annual Review of Sex Research, 13,* 307–345.

Loffreda, B. (2000). *Losing Matt Shepard: Life and politics in the aftermath of anti-gay murder.* New York, NY: Columbia University Press.

Löfgren-Mårtenson, L., & Månsson, S. (2010). Lust, love, and life: A qualitative study of Swedish adolescents' perceptions and experiences with pornography. *Journal of Sex Research, 47*(6), 568–579.

Loftus, E. F. (1993). The reality of repressed memories. *American Psychologist, 48,* 518–537.

Logan, T. D. (2010). Personal characteristics, sexual behaviors, and male sex work: A quantitative approach. *American Sociological Review, 75,* 679–704.

Lombardi, E. L., Wilchins, R., Priesing, D., & Malouf, D. (2001). Gender violence: Transgender experiences with violence and discrimination. *Journal of Homosexuality, 42,* 89–101.

London Department of Health (2013, July 11). *Abortion statistics, England and Wales: 2012.* London: Department of Health, United Kingdom.

Longo, D. J., Clum, G. A., & Yaeger, N. J. (1988). Psychosocial treatment for recurrent genital herpes. *Journal of Consulting and Clinical Psychology, 56,* 61–66.

LoPiccolo, J., & Stock, W. E. (1986). Treatment of sexual dysfunction. *Journal of Consulting and Clinical Psychology, 54,* 158–167.

Lorius, C. (1999). *Tantric sex: Making love last.* London, England: Thorsons/Harper-Collins.

Los, M. (1994). The struggle to redefine rape in the early 1980s. In J. V. Roberts & R. M. Mohr (Eds.), *Confronting sexual assault: A decade of legal change.* Toronto, Canada: University of Toronto Press.

Lottes, I. L., & Alkula, T. (2011). An investigation of sexuality-related attitudinal patterns and characteristics related to those patterns for 32 European countries. *Sexuality Research and Social Policy, 8,* 77–92.

Lue, Y., et al. (2009). Levonorgestrel enhances spermatogenesis suppression by testosterone with greater alteration in testicular gene expression in men. *Biology of Reproduction, 80,* 484–492.

Luff, D. (2001). 'The downright torture of women': Moral lobby women, feminists, and pornography. *The Sociological Review, 49,* 78–99.

Luke, B. (1994). Nutritional influences on fetal growth. *Clinical Obstetrics and Gynecology, 37,* 538–549.

Luo, M., Fee, M., & Katz, L. (2003). Encoding pheromonal signals in the accessory olfactory bulb in behaving mice. *Science, 299,* 1196–1201.

Luo, S., & Klohnen, E. (2005). Assortative mating and marital quality in newly weds: A couple-centered approach. *Journal of Personality and Social Psychology, 88,* 304–326.

Luong, M. (2008). Life after teenage motherhood. *Perspectives* (Catalogue no. 75-001-X, p. 5–13). Ottawa, Canada: Statistics Canada.

Lussier, P., & Piché, L. (2008). Frotteurism: Psychopathology and theory. In D. R. Laws, & W. O'Donohue (Eds.), *Sexual Deviance: Theory, Assessment, and Treatment.* (2nd ed., pp. 131–149). New York, NY: Guilford.

Lydon-Rochelle, M., Holt, V., Easterling, T., & Martin, D. (2001). Risk of uterine rupture during labor among women with a prior cesarean delivery. *New England Journal of Medicine, 345,* 3–8.

Maass, A., Cadinu, M., Guarnieri, G., & Grasselli, A. (2003). Sexual harassment under social identity threat: The computer harassment paradigm. *Journal of Personality and Social Psychology, 85,* 853–870.

Maccoby, E. E. (2002). Gender and group process: A developmental perspective. *Current Directions in Psychological Science, 11,* 54–58.

MacCulloch, M., Gray, N., & Watt, A. (2000). Britain's sadistic murderer syndrome reconsidered: An associative account of the aetiology of sadistic sexual fantasies. *Journal of Forensic Psychiatry, 11:* 401–418.

MacDonald, G., & Jeffrey, L. (2000). The ethics of social control in researching the sex trade: Prostitutes and professors. Prepared for Gendering Ethics/Ethics of Gender Conference at the Centre for Interdisciplinary Gender Studies on June 21, 2000, at the University of Leeds, UK.

MacDonald, N., & Wong, T. (2007). Canadian guidelines on sexually transmitted infections, 2006. *Canadian Medical Association Journal, 176,* 175–176.

MacDonald, T. K., & Ross, M. (1999). Assessing the accuracy of predictions about dating relationships: How and why do lovers' predictions differ from those made by observers? *Personality and Social Psychology Bulletin, 25,* 1417–1429.

MacFarlane, G. R., Blomberg, S. P., & Vasey, P. L. (2010). Homosexual behaviour in birds: Frequency of expression is related to parental care disparity between the sexes. *Animal Behaviour, 80,* 375–390.

MacIntosh, H., Reissing, E. D., & Andruff, H. (2010). Same-sex marriage in Canada: The impact of legal marriage on the first cohort of gay and lesbian Canadians to wed. *Canadian Journal of Human Sexuality, 19*(3), 79–90.

Mackie, M. (1991). *Gender relations in Canada: Further explorations.* Toronto, Canada: Harcourt Brace Canada.

Maclean's/CTV Poll. (1994, Jan. 3). Canada under the covers. *Maclean's, 107*(1).

Maclean's/CTV Poll. (1995, Jan. 2). Looking inward. *Maclean's.*

Maclean's/Global Poll. (2000, December 25). Politics, social attitudes, and sex. *Maclean's, 113*(52), 52–54.

MacMillan, H. L., Fleming, J. E., Trocmé, N., Boyle, M. H., Wong, M., Racine, et al. (1997). Prevalence of child physical and sexual abuse in the community: Results from the Ontario Health Supplement. *Journal of the American Medical Association, 278,* 131–135.

MacNeil, S., & Byers, E. S. (1997). The relationship between sexual problems, communication and sexual satisfaction. *Canadian Journal of Human Sexuality, 6,* 277–283.

MacNeil, S., & Byers, E. S. (2005). Dyadic assessment of sexual self-disclosure and sexual satisfaction in heterosexual dating couples. *Journal of Social and Personal Relationships, 22,* 169–181.

MacNeil, S., & Byers, E. S. (2009). Role of sexual self-disclosure in the sexual satisfaction of long-term heterosexual couples. *Journal of Sex Research, 46,* 1–12. doi:10.1080/00224490802398399

Madden, M., & Lenhart, A. (2006). *Online dating.* Retrieved from http://www.pewinternet.org/pdfs/PIP_Online_Dating.pdf

Maddock, J. W. (1997). Sexuality education: A history lesson. In J. W. Maddock (Ed.), *Sexuality education in post-secondary and professional training settings* (pp. 1–22). Binghamton, NY: The Haworth Press.

Magaña, J. R., & Carrier, J. M. (1991). Mexican and Mexican American male sexual behavior and spread of AIDS in California. *Journal of Sex Research, 28,* 425–441.

Maguire, D. C. (2001). *Sacred choices: The right to contraception and abortion in ten world religions.* Minneapolis: Augsburg Fortress.

Mah, K., & Binik, Y. M. (2001). The nature of human orgasm: A critical review of major trends. *Clinical Psychology Review, 21,* 823–856.

Mah, K., & Binik, Y. M. (2002). Do all orgasms feel alike? Evaluating a two-dimensional model of the orgasm experience across gender and sexual context. *Journal of Sex Research, 39,* 104–113.

Mah, K., & Binik, Y. M. (2005). Are orgasms in the mind or the body? Psychosocial versus physiological correlates of orgasmic pleasure and satisfaction. *Journal of Sex and Marital Therapy, 31,* 187–200.

Mahoney, E. R. (1983). *Human sexuality.* New York, NY: McGraw-Hill.

Maines, R. P. (1999). *The technology of orgasm: "Hysteria," the vibrator, and women's sexual satisfaction.* Baltimore: Johns Hopkins University Press.

Major, B., Appelbaum, M., Beckman, L., Dutton M. A., Russo, N. F., & West, C. (2009). Abortion and mental health. *American Psychologist, 64*(9), 863–890.

Malamuth, N. M. (1998). The confluence model as an organizing framework for research on sexually aggressive men: Risk moderators, imagined aggression and pornography consumption. In R. Geen & E. Donnerstein (Eds.), *Aggression: Theoretical and empirical reviews.* New York, NY: Academic Press.

Malamuth, N. M., & Brown, L. M. (1994). Sexually aggressive men's perceptions of women's communications. *Journal of Personality and Social Psychology, 67,* 699–712.

Maltz, W., & Boss, S. (1997). *In the garden of desire. The intimate world of women's sexual fantasies.* New York, NY: Broadway Books.

Mandese, J. (2007). Feeling blue: Americans consume more adult content. *Media Post.* Retrieved from http://www.mediapost.com

Manson Singer, S., Willms, D. G., Adrien, A., Baxter, J., Brabazon, C., Leaune, V., Godin, G., Maticka-Tyndale, E., & Cappon, P. (1996). Many voices—Sociocultural results of the ethnocultural communities facing AIDS study in Canada. *Canadian Journal of Public Health, 8*(Supp. 1), S26–S32.

Mark, K., Janssen, E., & Milhausen, R. (2011). Infidelity in heterosexual couples: Demographic, interpersonal, and personality related predictors of extradyadic sex. *Archives of Sexual Behavior, 40,* 971–982.

Markman, H., & Kadushin, F. (1986). Preventive effects of human training for first-time parents: A short-term longitudinal study. *Journal of Consulting and Clinical Psychology, 54,* 872–874.

Markman, H., et al. (2010). The premarital communication roots of marital distress and divorce: The first five years of marriage. *Journal of Family Psychology, 24,* 289–298.

Marsan, C. D. (2008). (February 7). The hottest trends in online dating. Retrieved from http://www.networkworld.com/news/2008/020708-valentines-online-dating.html

Marshall, D. C. (1971). Sexual behavior on Mangaia. In D. S. Marshall & R. C. Suggs (Eds.), *Human sexual behavior* (pp. 103–162). New York, NY: Basic Books.

Marshall, T. C. (2008). Cultural differences in intimacy: The influence of gender-role ideology and individualism-collectivism. *Journal of Social and Personal Relationships, 25,* 143–168.

Marshall, W. L. (1993). A revised approach to the treatment of men who sexually assault adult females. In G. N. Hall, et al. (Eds.), *Sexual aggression* (pp. 143–165). Washington, DC: Taylor & Francis.

Marshall, W. L., & Barbaree, H. E. (1988). The long-term evaluation of a behavioural treatment program for child molesters. *Behaviour Research and Therapy, 6,* 499–511.

Marshall, W. L., Marshall, L. E., & Serran, G. A. (2006). Strategies in the treatment of paraphilias: A critical review. *Annual Review of Sex Research, 17,* 162–182.

Marshall, W. L., & Pithers, W. D. (1994). A reconsideration of treatment outcome with sex offenders. *Criminal Justice and Behavior, 21,* 10–27.

Marshall, W. L., Payne, K., Barbaree, H. E., & Eccles, A. (1991). Exhibitionists: Sexual preferences for exposing. *Behavioural Research Therapy, 20*(1), 37–40.

Martin, C. L., & Halverson, C. F. (1983). The effects of sex-typing schemas on young children's memory. *Child Development, 54,* 563–574.

Martin, C. L., & Ruble, D. (2004). Children's search for gender cues: Cognitive perspectives on gender development. *Current Directions in Psychological Science, 13,* 67–70.

Martin, C. L., Ruble, D., & Szkrybalo, J. (2002). Cognitive theories of early gender development. *Psychological Bulletin, 128,* 903–933.

Martin, S. L., Ray, N., Sotres-Alvarez, D., Kupper, L. L., Moracco, K. E., Dickens, P. A., Scandlin, D., & Gizlice, Z. (2006). Physical and sexual assault of women with disabilities. *Violence Against Women, 12,* 823–837.

Martin, S. L., et al. (2011). Health and economic consequences of sexual violence. In J. White et al. (Eds.), *Violence against women and children: Navigating solutions* (vol.1, pp. 173–196). Washington, DC: American Psychological Association.

Martins, Y., Preti, G., Crabtree, C. R., Runyan, T., Vainius, A. A., & Wysocki, C. (2005). Preference for human body odors is influenced by gender and sexual orientation. *Psychological Science, 16,* 694–701.

Martins, Y., Tiggemann, M, & Churchett, L. (2008). Hair today, gone tomorrow: A comparison of body hair removal practices in gay and heterosexual men. *Body Image, 5,* 312–316

Martinson, F. M. (1994). *The sexual life of children.* Westport, CT: Bergin & Garvey.

Masters, W. H., & Johnson, V. (1966). *Human sexual response.* Boston, MA: Little, Brown.

Masters, W. H., & Johnson, V. (1970). *Human sexual inadequacy.* Boston, MA: Little, Brown.

Masters, W. H., & Johnson, V. (1979). *Homosexuality in perspective.* Boston, MA: Little, Brown.

Masters, W. H., Johnson, V. E., & Kolodny, R. C. (1982). *Human sexuality.* Boston, MA: Little, Brown.

Mathieson, C., & Endicott, L. (1998). Lesbian and Bisexual Identity: Discourse of difference. *Atlantis, 23,* 38.

Mathy, R., & Cooper, A. (2003). The duration and frequency of Internet use in a nonclinical sample: Suicidality, behavioral problems, and treatment history. *Psychotherapy: Theory, Research, Practice, Training, 40,* 125–135.

Maticka-Tyndale, E. (1992). Social construction of HIV transmission and prevention among heterosexual young adults. *Social Problems, 39*(93), 238–252.

Maticka-Tyndale, E. (1997). Reducing the incidence of sexually transmitted disease through behavioural and social change. *Canadian Journal of Human Sexuality, 6,* 89–104.

Maticka-Tyndale, E. (2001). Sexual health and Canadian youth: How do we measure up? *Canadian Journal of Human Sexuality, 10,* 1–17.

Maticka-Tyndale, E. (2008). Sexuality and sexual health of Canadian adolescents: Yesterday, today and tomorrow. *Canadian Journal of Human Sexuality, 17,* 85–95.

Maticka-Tyndale, E., & Bicher, M. (1996). The impact of medicalization on women. In B. Schissel & L. Mahood (Eds.), *Social control in Canada: A reader on the social construction of deviance.* Toronto, Canada: Oxford University Press.

Maticka-Tyndale, E., & Smylie, L. (2008). Sexual rights: Striking a balance. *International Journal of Sexual Health, 20,* 7–24.

Maticka-Tyndale, E., Adams, B. D., & Cohen, J. (2002) Sexual desire and practice among people living with HIV and using combination anti-retroviral therapies. *Canadian Journal of Human Sexuality, 11,* 33–40.

Maticka-Tyndale, E., Barrett, M., & McKay, A. (2000). Adolescent sexual and reproductive health in Canada: A review of national data sources and their limitations. *Canadian Journal of Human Sexuality, 9,* 41–65.

Maticka-Tyndale, E., Godin, G., LeMay, G., Adrien, A., Manson-Singer, S., Willms, D., Cappon, P., & Bradet, R. (1996). Canadian ethnocultural communities facing AIDS: Overview and summary of survey results from phase III. *Canadian Journal of Public Health, 87*(Supp. 1), S38–S43.

Maticka-Tyndale, E., Herold, E., & Oppermann, M. (2003). Casual sex among Australian schoolies. *Journal of Sex Research, 40,* 158–169.

Maticka-Tyndale, E., Lewis, J., & Street, M. (2005). Making a place for escort work: A case study. *Journal of Sex Research, 42,* 46–53.

Maticka-Tyndale, E., Lewis, J., Clark, J. P., Zubick, J., & Young, S. (1999). Social and cultural vulnerability to sexually transmitted infection: The work of exotic dancers. *Canadian Journal of Public Health, 90*, 19–22.

Maticka-Tyndale, E., Lewis, J., Clark, J. P., Zubrick, J., & Young, S. (2000). Exotic dancing and health. *Women & Health, 31*, 87–108.

Matthews, J. E., Stephenson, R., & Sullivan, P. S. (2012). Factors associated with self-reported HBV vaccination among HIV-negative MSM participating in an online sexual health survey: A cross-sectional study. *PLoS ONE, 7*(2), e30609. doi:10.1371/journal.pone.0030609

Mattson, S., & Riley, E. (1998). A review of the neurobehavioral deficits in children with fetal alcohol syndrome or prenatal exposure to alcohol. *Alcoholism: Clinical and Experimental Research, 22*, 279–294.

Maurer, H. (1994). *Sex: Real people talk about what they really do.* New York, NY: Penguin Books.

Mayo Clinic. (2012a). Maximizing fertility. Retrieved from http://www.mayoclinic.com/health/how-to-get-pregnant/PR00103

Mayo Clinic. (2012b). Male infertility: Lifestyle and home remedies. Retrieved from http://www.mayoclinic.com/health/male-infertility/DSO1038/lifestyle-andhome-remedies

Mazer, D. B., & Percival, E. F. (1989). Students' experiences of sexual harassment at a small university. *Sex Roles, 20*(1&2), 1–22.

Mazzuca, J. (2004, November 2). Origin of homosexuality? Britons, Canadians say "nature." *Gallup News Service.* Washington DC: The Gallup Organization.

McCabe, M., et al. (2010). Psychological and interpersonal dimensions of sexual function and dysfunction. *Journal of Sexual Medicine, 7*, 327–336.

McCall, D., & McKay, A. (2004). SOGC policy statement: School-based and school-linked sexual health education and promotion in Canada. *Journal of Obstetrics and Gynaecology Canada, 146*, 596–600.

McCall, D., Beazley, R., Doherty-Poirier, M., Lovato, C., MacKinnon, D., Otis, J., & Shannon, M. (1999). *Schools, public health, sexuality and HIV: A status report.* Toronto, Canada: Council of Ministers of Education.

McCallum, E. B., & Peterson, Z. D. (2012). Investigating the impact of inquiry mode on self-reported sexual behavior: Theoretical considerations and review of the literature. *Journal of Sex Research, 49*, 212–226.

McCarthy, B. W. (1989). Cognitive-behavioral strategies and techniques in the treatment of early ejaculation. In S. R. Leiblum & R. C. Rosen (Eds.), *Principles and practice of sex therapy* (2nd ed.). New York, NY: Guilford.

McClelland, S. (1999, July 26). The bedroom and the new era of swing. *Maclean's.*

McClelland, S. (2001, December 3). Inside the sex trade. *Maclean's.*

McClintock, M. K. (1971). Menstrual synchrony and suppression. *Nature, 229*, 244–245.

McClintock, M. K. (1998). Whither menstrual synchrony? *Annual Review of Sex Research, 9*, 77–95.

McClintock, M. K. (2000). Human pheromones: Primers, releasers, signalers, or modulators? In K. Wallen & J. Schneider (Eds.), *Reproduction in context* (pp. 355–420). Cambridge, MA: MIT Press.

McClintock, M., & Herdt, G. (1996). Rethinking puberty: The development of sexual attraction. *Current Directions in Psychological Science, 5*, 178–183.

McClure, R., & Brewer, R. T. (1980). Attitudes of new parents towards child and spouse with Lamaze or non-Lamaze methods of childbirth. *Journal of Human Behavior, 17*, 45–48.

McCoy, N. L., & Pitino, L. (2002). Pheromonal influences on sociosexual behavior in young women. *Physiology & Behavior, 75*, 367–375.

McCoy, N. L. (1996). Menopause and sexuality. In M. K. Beard (Ed.), Optimizing hormone replacement therapy: Estrogen-androgen therapy in postmenopausal women (pp. 32–36). Minneapolis: McGraw-Hill Healthcare.

McCoy, N. L. (1997). Sexual issues for postmenopausal women. *Topics in Geriatric Rehabilitation, 12*, 28–39.

McCreary Centre Society (2007). *Not yet equal: The health of lesbian, gay, and bisexual youth in BC.* Vancouver, BC: Author.

McDermid, S. A., Zucker, K. J., Bradley, S. J., & Maing, D. M. (1998). Effects of physical appearance on masculine trait ratings of boys and girls with gender identity disorder. *Archives of Sexual Behavior, 27*(3), 253-267.

McDonagh, A., et al. (2005). Randomized trial of cognitive-behavioral therapy for chronic posttraumatic stress disorder in adult female survivors of childhood sexual abuse. *Journal of Consulting and Clinical Psychology, 73*, 515–524.

McEwen, B. S. (1997). Meeting report–Is there a neurobiology of love? *Molecular Psychiatry, 2*, 15–16.

McEwen, B. S. (2001). Estrogen effects on the brain: Multiple sites and molecular mechanisms. *Journal of Applied Physiology, 91*, 2785–2801.

McFarland, W. P. (2001). The legal duty to protect gay and lesbian students from violence in school. *Professional School Counseling, 4*, 171–180.

McFarlane, J. M., & Williams, T. M. (1994). Placing premenstrual syndrome in perspective. *Psychology of Women Quarterly, 18*, 339–374.

McFarlane, J., Martin, C. L., & Williams, T. M. (1988). Mood fluctuations: Women versus men and menstrual versus other cycles. *Psychology of Women Quarterly, 12*,201–224.

McGuire, J. K., & Barber, B. L. (2010). A person-centered approach to the multifaceted nature of young adult sexual behavior. *Journal of Sex Research, 47*, 301–313.

McKay, A. (1993). Research supports broadly-based sex education. *Canadian Journal of Human Sexuality, 2*, 89–98.

McKay, A. (1996). Rural parents' attitudes toward school-based sexual health education. *Canadian Journal of Human Sexuality, 5*, 15–29.

McKay, A. (2000). Common questions about sexual health education. *SIECCAN Newsletter, 35*, 129–137.

McKay, A. (2004). Oral sex among teenagers: Research, discourse and education. *Canadian Journal of Human Sexuality, 13*, 201–203.

McKay, A. (2005a). Sexuality and substance use: The impact of tobacco, alcohol, and selected recreational drugs on sexual function. *Canadian Journal of Human Sexuality, 14*, 47–56.

McKay, A. (2005b). *Sexual health education in the schools: Questions and answers.* Toronto, Canada: SIECCAN.

McKay, A. (2006a). Chlamydia screening programs: A review of the literature. Part 1. Issues in the promotion of chlamydia testing of youth by primary care physicians. *Canadian Journal of Human Sexuality, 15*, 1–11.

McKay, A. (2006b). Trends in teen pregnancy in Canada with comparisons to U. S.A. amd England/Wales. *Canadian Journal of Human Sexuality, 15*, 157–161.

McKay, A. (2007). The effectiveness of latex condoms for prevention of STI/HIV. *Canadian Journal of Human Sexuality, 16*, 57–61.

McKay, A. (2012). Trends in Canadian national and provincial/territorial teen pregnancy rates: 2001–2010. *Canadian Journal of Human Sexuality, 21*,161–175.

McKay, A., & Barrett, M. (1999). Pre-service sexual health education training of elementary, secondary, and physical health education teachers in Canadian faculties of education. *Canadian Journal of Human Sexuality, 8*, 91–101.

McKay, A., & Barrett, M. (2010). Trends in teen pregnancy rates from 1996–2006: A comparison of Canada, Sweden, U. S.A., and England/Wales. *Canadian Journal of Human Sexuality,19*, 43–52.

McKay, A., & Holowaty, P. (1997). Sexual health education: A study of adolescents' opinions, self-perceived needs, and current and preferred sources of information. *Canadian Journal of Human Sexuality, 6*, 29–38.

McKay, A., Pietrusiak, M.-A., & Holowaty, P. (1998). Parents' opinions and attitudes towards sexuality education in schools. *Canadian Journal of Human Sexuality, 7*, 139–145.

McKee, A. (2005). The objectification of women in mainstream pornographic videos in Australia. *Journal of Sex Research, 42*, 277–290.

McKenna, B., Hampton, M. R., Bourassa, C., McKay-McNabb, K., & Baydala, A. (2010). Voices from the moon lodge. In S. Geissler, L. Loutzenhiser, J. Praud, & L. Streifler (Eds.). *Mothering Canada: Interdisciplinary voices* (pp. 231–240). Toronto, Canada: Demeter Press.

McKenna, K. E. (2000). Some proposals regarding the organization of the central nervous system control of penile erection. *Neuroscience and Biobehavioral Reviews, 24*, 535–540.

McKenzie-Mohr, D., & Zanna, M. P. (1990). Treating women as sexual objects: Look to the (gender schematic) male who has viewed pornography. *Personality and Social Psychology Bulletin, 16*(2), 296–308.

McKinlay, S. M., Brambilla, D. J., & Posner, J. G. (1992). The normal menopause transition. *American Journal of Human Biology, 4*, 37–46.

McMahon, S., Hansen, L., Mann, J., Sevigny, C., Wong, T., & Roache, M. (2004). Contraception. *BMC Women's Health, 4* (Suppl 1), S25.

McManus, A. J., Hunter, L. P., & Renn, H. (2006). Lesbian experiences and needs during childbirth: Guidance for health care providers. *JOGNN, 35*, 13–23.

McMaster, L. E., Connolly, J., Pepler, D., & Craig, W. M. (2002). Peer to peer sexual harassment in early adolescence: A developmental perspective. *Development and Psychopathology, 14*, 91–105.

McNair, R., Dempsey, D., Wise, S., & Perlesz, A. (2002). Lesbian parenting: Issues, strengths and challenges. *Family Matters, 63*, 40–49.

McNeill, J. J. (1987). Homosexuality: Challenging the Church to grow. *Christian Century, 104*, 242–246.

Meana, M., Binik, Y. M., Khalife, S., & Cohen, D. R. (1997). Bio psychosocial profile of women with dyspareunia. *Obstetrics & Gynecology, 90*, 583–589.

Meaney, G. J., & Rye, B. J. (2010). Gendered egos: Attitude functions and gender as predictors of homonegativity. *Journal of Homosexuality, 57*, 1274–1302.

Meaney, G. J., Rye, B. J., Wood, E., & Solovieva, E. (2009). Satisfaction with school-based sexual health education in a sample of university students recently graduated from Ontario high schools. *Canadian Journal of Human Sexuality, 18*, 107–125.

Mehta, A., & Sheth, S. (2006). Postpartum depression: How to recognize and treat this common condition. *Medscape Psychiatry and Mental Health, 11*, article 529930.

Meischke, H. (1995). Implicit sexual portrayals in the movies: Interpretations of young women. *Journal of Sex Research, 32*, 29–36.

Ménard, A. D., & Kleinplatz, P. J. (2008). Twenty-one moves guaranteed to make his thighs go up in flames: Depictions of "great sex" in popular magazines. *Sexuality and Culture, 12*(1), 1–20.

Mercer, et al. (2008). Labor outcomes with increasing number of prior vaginal births after Caesarean delivery. *Obstetrics & Gynecology, 111*, 285–291.

Messenger, J. C. (1993). Sex and repression in an Irish folk community. In D. N. Suggs & A. W. Miracle (Eds.), *Culture and human sexuality* (pp. 240–261). Pacific Grove, CA: Brooks/Cole.

Messineo, M. J. (2008). Does advertising on Black Entertainment Television portray more positive gender representations compared to broadcast networks? *Sex Roles, 59*, 752–764.

Meston, C. M., & Buss, D. M. (2007). Why humans have sex. *Archives of Sexual Behavior, 36*, 477–507.

Meston, C. M., et al. (2004). Women's orgasm. *Annual Review of Sex Research, 15*, 173–257.

Meston, C. M., Rellini, A. H., & Heiman, J. R. (2006). Women's history of sexual abuse, their sexuality, and sexual self schemas. *Journal of Consulting and Clinical Psychology, 74*, 229–236.

Meston, C. M., Trapnell, P. D., & Gorzalka, B. B. (1996). Ethnic and gender differences in sexuality: Variations in sexual behavior between Asian and non-Asian university students. *Archives of Sexual Behavior, 25*, 33–72.

Meston, C. M., Trapnell, P., & Gorzlaka, B. (1998). Ethnic, gender, and length-of-residency influences on sexual knowledge and attitudes. *Journal of Sex Research, 35*, 176–188.

Metcalf, M. G., Skidmore, D. S. Lowry, G. F., & Mackenzie, J. A. (1983). Incidence of ovulation in the years after the menarche. *Journal of Endocrinology, 97*, 213–219.

Metz, M., & McCarthy, B. (2003). *Coping with premature ejaculation: How to overcome PE, please your partner and have great sex.* Oakland, CA: New Harbinger Publications, Inc.

Meyer, I. H. (2003). Prejudice, social stress, and mental health in lesbian, gay, and bisexual populations: Conceptual issues and research evidence. *Psychological Bulletin, 129*, 674–697.

Meyer-Bahlburg, H. F. L., Dolezal, C., Baker, S. W., Carlson, A. D., Obeid, J. S., & New, M. I. (2004). Prenatal androgenization affects gender-related behavior but not gender identity in 5–12-year-old girls with congenital adrenal hyperplasia. *Archives of Sexual Behavior, 33*, 97–104.

Meyer-Bahlburg, H. F. L., Dolezal, C., Baker, S. W., Ehrhardt, A. A., & New, M. I.. (2006). Gender development in women with congenital adrenal hyperplasia as a function of disorder severity. *Archives of Sexual Behavior, 35*, 667–684.

Mezzacappa, E., & Katkin, E. (2002). Breast-feeding is associated with reduced perceived stress and negative mood in mothers. *Health Psychology, 21*, 187–193.

Michael, R. T., Gagnon, J. H., Laumann, E. O., & Kolata, G. (1994) *Sex in America: A definitive survey.* Boston, MA: Little, Brown.

Miki, Y., Swensen, J., Shattuck-Eidens, D., Futreal, P. A., Harshman, K., Tavtigian, S., Liu, C., . . . Skolnick, M. H. (1994). A strong candidate for the breast and ovarian cancer susceptibility gene BRCA1. *Science, 266*, 66–71.

Miklos, J. R., & Moore, R. D. (2008). Labiaplasty of the labia minora: Patients' indications for pursuing surgery. *Journal of Sexual Medicine, 5*, 1492–1495.

Milam, J. (2006). Posttraumatic growth and HIV disease progression. *Journal of Consulting and Clinical Psychology, 74*, 817–827.

Milan, A., Maheux, H., & Chui, T. (2010). A portrait of couples in mixed unions. *Canadian Social Trends* (Catalogue no. 11-008). Ottawa, Canada: Statistics Canada.

Milan, R. J., & Kilmann, P. R. (1987). Interpersonal factors in premarital contraception. *Journal of Sex Research, 23*, 289–321.

Miller, B. B., Cox, D. N., & Saewyc, E. M. (2010). Age of sexual consent law in Canada: Population-based evidence for law and policy. *Canadian Journal of Human Sexuality, 19*,105–119.

Miller, E. M. (1986). *Street woman.* Philadelphia, PA: Temple University Press.

Miller, J., & Schwartz, M. (1995). Rape myths and violence against street prostitutes. *Deviant Behavior, 76*, 1–23.

Miller, L. C., & Fishkin, S. A. (1997). On the dynamics of human bonding and reproductive success: Seeking windows on the adapted-for-human-environmental interface. In J. A. Simpson & D. T. Kenrick (Eds.), *Evolutionary social psychology* (pp. 197–235). Mahwah, NJ: Lawrence Erlbaum.

Miller, N. (1992). *Out in the world: Gay and lesbian life from Buenos Aires to Bangkok.* New York, NY: Random House.

Miller, R. S., & Lefcourt, H. M. (1982). The assessment of social intimacy. *Journal of Personality Assessment, 46*, 514–518.

Miller, S. A., & Byers, E. S. (2004). Actual and desired duration of foreplay and intercourse: Discordance and misperceptions within heterosexual couples. *Journal of Sex Research, 41*, 301–309.

Miller, S. A., & Byers, E. S. (2009). Psychologists' continuing education and training in sexuality. *Journal of Sex & Marital Therapy, 35*, 206–219.

Miller, S. A., & Byers, E. S. (2010). Psychologists' sexual education and training in graduate school. *Canadian Journal of Behavioural Science, 42*, 93–100.

Miller, S. A., & Byers, E. S. (2012). Practicing psychologists' sexual intervention self-efficacy and willingness to treat sexual issues. *Archives of Sexual Behavior, 41*(4), 1041–1050.

Miller, S. L., & Maner, J. (2010). Scent of a woman: Men's testosterone responses to olfactory ovulation cues. *Psychological Science, 21*, 276–283.

Miller, S., Corrales, R., & Wachman, D. B. (1975). Recent progress in understanding and facilitating marital communication. *The Family Coordinator, 24*, 143–152.

Miller, W. J., Nair, C., & Wadhera, S. (1996). Declining cesarean section rates: A continuing trend? *Health Reports, 8*,17–24.

Milner, J., Dopke, C., & Crouch, J. (2008). Paraphilia not otherwise specified: Psychopathology and theory. In D. Richard Laws & William T. O'Donohue (Eds.), *Sexual Deviance: Theory, Assessment, and Treatment* (2nd ed., pp. 384–418). New York, NY: Guilford.

Miner, M., & Coleman, E. (2001). Advances in sex offender treatment and challenges for the future. *Journal of Psychology and Human Sexuality, 13*, 5–24.

Minkoff, H., & Chervenak, F. A. (2003). Elective primary cesarean delivery. *The New England Journal of Medicine, 348*, 946–950.

Minto, C. L., Liao, L. M., Woodhouse, C. R. J., Ransley, P. G., & Creighton, S. M. (2003). The effect of clitoral surgery on sexual outcome in individuals who have intersex conditions with ambiguous genitalia: A cross-sectional study. *Lancet, 361*, 1252–1257.

Misovich, S. J., Fisher, J. D., & Fisher, W. A. (1997). Close relationships and elevated HIV risk behavior: Evidence and possible underlying psychological processes. *Review of General Psychology, 1*, 72–107.

Mitchell, K. J., et al. (2007). Trends in youth reports of sexual solicitations, harassment and unwanted exposure to pornography on the Internet. *Journal of Adolescent Health, 40*, 116–126.

Mkumbo, K. A. K., & Ingham, R. (2010). What Tanzanian parents want (and do not want) covered in school-based sex and relationships education. *Sex Education, 10*, 67–78.

Moir, S., et al. (2008). Immunology and pathogenesis of Human Immunodeficiency Virus infection. In K. Holmes et al. (Eds.), *Sexually transmitted diseases.* (4th ed., pp. 341–358). New York, NY: McGraw-Hill.

Molitch, M. E. (1995). Neuroendocrinology. In P. Felig et al. (Eds.), *Endocrinology and metabolism.* New York, NY: McGraw-Hill.

Money, J. (1986). *Lovemaps: Clinical concepts of sexual/erotic health and pathology, paraphilia, and gender transposition in childhood, adolescence, and maturity.* New York, NY: Irvington Publishers.

Money, J. (1987). Sin, sickness, or status: Homosexual gender identity and psychoneuroendocrinology. *American Psychologist, 42*, 384–399.

Money, J., & Ehrhardt, A. (1972). *Man and woman, boy and girl.* Baltimore: Johns Hopkins. Reissued in a facsimile edition by Jason Aronson, Northvale, NJ, 1996.

Monro, S. (2000). Theorizing transgender diversity: Towards a social model of health. *Sexual and Relationship Therapy, 15*, 33–45.

Montazeri, A. (2008). Health-related quality of life in breast cancer patients: A bibliographic review of the literature from 1974 to 2007. *Journal of Experimental & Clinical Cancer Research, 27.*

Montesi, J., et al. (2010). The specific importance of communicating about sex to couples' sexual and overall relationship satisfaction. *Journal of Social and Personal Relationships, 28*, 591–609

Montorsi, F., & Althof, S. (2004). Partner responses to sildenafil citrate (Viagra) treatment of erectile dysfunction. *Urology, 63*, 762–767.

Montorsi, F., Perani, D., Anchisi, D., Salonia, A., Scifo, P., Rigiroli, P., et al. (2003a). Apomorphine-induced brain modulation during sexual stimulation: A new look at central phenomena related to erectile dysfunction. *International Journal of Impotence Research, 15,* 203–209.

Montorsi, F., Perani, D., Anchisi, D., Salonia, A., Scifo, P., Rigiroli, P., et al. (2003b). Brain activation patterns during video sexual stimulation following the administration of apomorphine. *European Urology, 43,* 405–411.

Montorsi, F., Verheyden, B., Meuleman, E., Junemann, K. P., Moncada, I., Valiquette, L., et al. (2004). Long-term safety and tolerability of tadalafil in the treatment of erectile dysfunction. *European Urology, 45,* 339–345.

Montoya, R. M. (2008) I'm hot, so I'd say you're not: The influence of objective physical attractiveness on mate selection. *Personality and Social Psychology Bulletin, 34,* 1315–1331.

Montoya, R. M., Horton, R., & Kirchner, J. (2008). Is actual similarity necessary for attraction? A meta-analysis of actual and perceived similarity. *Journal of Social and Personal Relationships, 25,* 889–922.

Moore, A. J. (1987). Teenage sexuality and public morality. *Christian Century, 104,* 747–750.

Moore, F., et al. (2006). The effects of female control of resources on sex-differentiated mate preferences. *Evolution and Human Behavior, 27,* 193–205.

Moore, T. (1994, January 3). Porn shop enjoys brisk business yearround. *The Capital Times,* pp. 5A–6A.

Morales, A., & Heaton, J. (2001). Hormonal erectile dysfunction: Evaluation and management. *Urologic Clinics of North America, 28,* 279.

Morales, A., et al. (1998). Clinical safety of oral sildenafil (Viagra) in the treatment of erectile dysfunction. *International Journal of Impotence Research, 10,* 69–74.

Morales, A., Heaton, J., & Carson, C. (2000). Andropause: A misnomer for a true clinical entity. *Journal of Urology, 163,* 705–712.

More women going from jobless to topless. (2009). Associated Press. Retrieved from http://www.today.com/id/29824663/

Morell, V. (1998). A new look at monogamy. *Science, 281,* 1982–1983.

Moreno, M., et al. (2009). Display of health risk behaviors on MySpace by adolescents: Prevalence and associations. *Archives of Pediatric and Adolescent Medicine, 163,* 27–34.

Morgan, E. M. (2011). Associations between young adults' use of sexually explicit materials and their sexual preferences, behaviors, and satisfaction. *Journal of Sex Research, 48,* 520–530.

Morgan, R. (1980). Theory and practice: Pornography and rape. In L. Lederer (Ed.), *Take back the night: Women on pornography.* New York, NY: Morrow.

Morrison, M. A., & Morrison, T. G. (2002). Development and validation of a scale measuring modern prejudice toward gay men and lesbians. *Journal of Homosexuality, 43,* 15–37.

Morrison, M. A., Morrison, T. G., & Franklin, R. (2009). Modern and old-fashioned homonegativity among samples of Canadian and American university students. *Journal of Cross-Cultural Psychology, 40,* 523–542.

Morrison, T. G. (2004). "He was treating me like trash, and I was loving it." Perspectives on gay male pornography. *Journal of Homosexuality, 47,* 167–183.

Morrison, T. G., & Tallack, D. (2005). Lesbian and bisexual women's interpretations of lesbian and ersatz lesbian pornography. *Sexuality & Culture, 9,* 3–30.

Morrison, T. G., Ellis, S. R., Morrison, M. A., Bearden, A., & Harriman, R. L. (2006). Exposure to sexually explicit material and variations in body esteem, genital attitudes, and sexual esteem among a sample of Canadian men. *Journal of Men's Studies, 14,* 209–222.

Morrison, T. G., Ryan, T. A., Fox, L., McDermott, D. T., & Morrison, M. A. (2008). Canadian university students' perception of the practices that constitute "normal" sexuality for men and women. *Canadian Journal of Human Sexuality, 17,* 161–171.

Morris-Rush, J., & Bernstein, P. (2002). Postpartum depression. *Medscape Women's Health, 7.*

Morry, M. M. (2007). The attraction-similarity hypothesis among crosssex friends: Relationship satisfaction, perceived similarities, and selfserving perceptions. *Journal of Social and Personal Relationships, 24,* 117–138.

Moser, C. (1998). S/M (Sadomasochistic) interactions in semi-public settings. *Journal of Homosexuality, 36,* 19–29.

Moser, C. (2001). Paraphilia: Another confused sexological concept. In P. J. Kleinpatz (Ed.), *New directions in sex therapy: Innovations and alternatives* (pp. 91–108.), Philadelphia, PA: W. B. Saunders Company.

Moser, C., & Kleinpatz, P. J. (2002). Transvestic fetishism: Psychopathology or iatrogenic artifact? *New Jersey Psychologist, 52,* 16–17.

Moser, C., & Kleinpatz, P. J. (2005). DSM-IV-TR and the paraphilias: An argument for removal. *Journal of Psychology and Human Sexuality, 17,* 91–109.

Moser, C., Kleinplatz, P. J., & Zuccarini, D. (2004). Situating unusual child and adolescent sexual behavior in context. *Child & Adolescent Psychiatric Clinics of North America, 13,* 569–589.

Moses, S., Bradley, J., Nagelkerke, N., Roland, A., Ndinya-Achola, J., & Plummer, F. (1990). Geographical patterns of male circumcision practices in Africa: Association with HIV seroprevalence. *International Journal of Epidemiology, 19,* 693–697.

Mosher, D., & MacIan, P. (1994). College men and women respond to X-rated videos intended for male or female audiences: Gender and sexual scripts. *Journal of Sex Research, 31,* 99–113.

Mosher, W. D., Chandra, A., & Jones, J. (2005). Sexual behavior and selected health measures: Men and women 15–44 years of age in the U. S., 2002. *Advance Data, 362,* 1–55.

Mosher, W. D., & Jones, J. (2010). Use of contraception in the United States: 1982–2008. National Center for Health Statistics, *Vital Health Statistics, 23* (29).

Moskovtsev, S. I., Dacanay, D., Baratz, A., Sharma, P., Glass, K., Librach, C. L., & CReATe Fertility Center (2013).*Significant increase in utilization of donor sperm by Lesbian couples after the legalization of same sex marriages in Ontario, Canada.* Presented at the International Federation of Fertility Societies and the American Society for Reproduction Medicine annual conference.

Moss, B. F., & Schwebel, A. I. (1993). Marriage and romantic relationships: Defining intimacy in romantic relationships. *Family Relations, 42,* 31–37.

Moulden, H. M., et al. (2009). Recidivism in pedophiles: An investigation using different diagnostic methods. *Journal of Forensic Psychiatry & Psychology, 20,* 680–701.

Mouritsen, A., Aksglaede, L., Sørensen, K., Sloth Mogensen, S., Leffers, H., Juul, A. (2010). Hypothesis: Exposure to endocrine-disrupting chemicals may interfere with timing of puberty. *International Journal of Andrology, 33,* 346–359.

Muehlenhard, C., & Skippee, S. (2010). Men's and women's reports of pretending orgasm. *Journal of Sex Research, 47,* 552–567.

Muller, J., Mittleman, M., Maclure, M., Sherwood, J., & Tofler, G. (1996). Triggering myocardial infarction by sexual activity. *Journal of the American Medical Association, 275,* 1405–1409.

Munk-Olsen, T., et al. (2011). Induced first trimester abortion and risk of mental disorder. *New England Journal of Medicine, 364,* 332–339.

Murnen, S. K., & Stockton, M. (1997). Gender and self-reported sexual arousal in response to sexual stimuli: A meta-analytic review. *Sex Roles, 37,* 135–154.

Murnen, S. K., Wright, C., & Kaluzny, G. (2002). If "boys will be boys," then girls will be victims? A meta-analytic review of the research that relates masculine ideology to sexual aggression. *Sex Roles, 46,* 359–376.

Murphy, L., Federoff, J. P., & Martineau, M. (2009). Canada's sex offender registries: Background, implementation, and social policy considerations. *Canadian Journal of Human Sexuality, 18,* 61–72.

Murray, S. L., & Holmes, J. G. (1997). A leap of faith? Positive illusions in romantic relationships. *Personality and Social Psychology Bulletin, 23,* 586–604.

Murray, S. L., Holmes, J. G., & Griffin, D. W. (1996). The benefits of positive illusions: Idealization and the construction of satisfaction in close relationships. *Journal of Personality and Social Psychology, 70*(1), 79–98.

Murray, S. O. (2000). *Homosexualities.* Chicago, IL: University of Chicago Press.

Mustanski, B. S., et al. (2005). A genomewide scan of male sexual orientation. *Human Genetics, 116,* 272–278.

Mustanski, B. S., et al. (2010). Mental health disorders, psychological distress, and suicidality in a diverse sample of lesbian, gay, bisexual, and transgender youths. *American Journal of Public Health, 100,* 2426–2432.

Myers, B. J. (1984). Mother-infant bonding: The status of this critical period hypothesis. *Developmental Review, 4,* 240–274.

Myers, K., & Raymond, L. (2010). Elementary school girls and heteronormativity: The girl project. *Gender & Society, 24,* 167–188.

Myers, P. N., & Biocca, F. A. (1992). The elastic body image: The effect of television advertising and programming on body image distortions in young women. *Journal of Communication, 42,* 108–133.

Myers, T., Bullock, S. L., Calzavara, L. M., Cockerill, R., Marshall, V. W., & George-Mandoka, C. (1999). Culture and sexual practices in response to HIV among Aboriginal people living on reserve in Ontario. *Culture, Health & Sexuality, 1*(1), 19–37.

Myers, T., Calzavara, L. M., Bullock, S., Cockerill, R., & Marshall, V. (1994). The Ontario First Nations AIDS and Healthy Lifestyle Survey: A model for community-based research in diverse reserve communities. *Arctic Medical Research, 53*(Suppl. 2), 726–731.

Myers, T., Godin, G., Calzavara, L., Lambert, J., & Locker, D. (1993). *The Canadian survey of gay and bisexual men and HIV infection: Men's survey.* Ottawa, Canada: Canadian Aids Society.

Nack, A. (2008). *Damaged goods: Women living with incurable STDs.* Philadelphia, PA: Temple University Press.

Najman, J. M., et al. (2005). Sexual abuse in childhood and sexual dysfunction in adulthood: An Australian population-based study. *Archives of Sexual Behavior, 34*, 517–526.

Narod, S. A., et al. (1988). Human mutagens: Evidence from paternal exposure? *Environmental and Molecular Mutagenesis, 11*, 401–415.

National Campaign to Prevent Teen and Unplanned Pregnancy. (2009). *Sex and tech: Results from a survey of teens and young adults.* http://www.thenationalcampaign.org/sextech/PDF/SexTech_Summary.pdf

Naz, R. K. (2011). Antisperm contraceptive vaccines: Where we are and where we are going. *American Journal of Reproductive Immunology, 66*, 5–12.

Ndovi, T. T., Parsons, T., Choi, L., Caffo, B., Rohde, C., & Hendrix, C. W. (2007). A new method to estimate quantitatively seminal vesicle and prostate gland contributions to ejaculate. *British Journal of Clinical Pharmacology, 63*, 404–420.

Nelson, A. L., & Purdon, C. (2011). Non-erotic thoughts, attentional focus, and sexual problems in a community sample. *Archives of Sexual Behavior, 40*, 395–406.

Nelson, J. B. (1978). *Embodiment: An approach to sexuality and Christian theology.* Minneapolis, MN: Augsburg.

Nelson, J. B. (1992). *Body theology.* Louisville, KY: Westminster/John Knox Press.

Nemeth, M. (1995, June 26). Nobody has the right to play God. *Maclean's.*

Neville, V. A., & Heppner, M. S. (1999). Contextualizing rape: Reviewing sequelae and proposing a culturally inclusive ecological model of sexual assault recovery. *Applied and Preventive Psychology, 8*, 41–62.

Newhouse, D. (1998). Magic & joy: Traditional aboriginal views of human sexuality. *Canadian Journal of Sexuality, 7*, 183–187.

Ngun, T. C., Ghahramani, N., Sanchez, F., Bocklandt, S., & Vilain, E. (2011). The genetics of sex differences in brain and behavior. *Frontiers in Neuroendocrinology, 32*, 227–246.

Ninomiya, M. M. (2010). Sexual health education in Newfoundland and Labrador schools: Junior high school teachers' experiences, coverage of topics, comfort levels and views about professional practice. *Canadian Journal of Human Sexuality, 19*, 15–26.

Noll, J., Trickett, P., & Putnam, F. (2003). A prospective investigation of the impact of childhood sexual abuse on the development of sexuality. *Journal of Consulting and Clinical Psychology, 71*, 575–586.

Norris, S. (2006). Reproductive technologies: Surrogacy, and egg and sperm donation (Report PRB 00–35E). Library of Parliament. Retrieved from http://www.parl.gc.ca/Content/LOP/ResearchPublications/prb0035-e.htm

Nosek, B. A., Banaji, M. R., & Greenwald, A. G. (2002). Math = male, me = female, therefore math me. *Journal of Personality and Social Psychology, 83*, 44–59.

Nosko, A., Wood, E., & Desmarais, S. (2007). Unsolicited online sexual material: What affects our attitudes and likelihood to search for more? *Canadian Journal of Human Sexuality, 16*, 1–10.

Noss, J. B. (1963). *Man's religions* (3rd ed.). New York, NY: Macmillan.

Nova Scotia Department of Community Services. (1991). *Mothers and children: One decade later.* Halifax, NS: Author.

Novembre, J., et al. (2005). The geographic spread of the CCR5 Delta 32 HIV-resistance allele. *PloS Biology, 3*, e339.

Nuttbrock, L. et al. (2010). Psychiatric impact of gender-related abuse across the life course of male-to-female transgender persons. *Journal of Sex Research, 47*, 12–23.

O'Byrne, P., & Dias, R. (2008). Urine drop-off testing: A self-directed method for STI screening and prevention. *Canadian Journal of Human Sexuality, 17*, 53–59.

O'Connell, H. E., & DeLancey, J. (2005). Clitoral anatomy in nulliparous, healthy, premenopausal volunteers using unenhanced magnetic resonance imaging. *Journal of Urology, 173*, 2060–2063.

O'Connor, A. (1987). Female sex offenders. *British Journal of Psychiatry, 150*, 615–620.

O'Hara, M. W., & Swain, A. M. (1996). Rates and risk of postpartum depression: A meta-analysis. *International Review of Psychiatry, 8*, 37–54.

O'Shea, P. A. (1995). Congenital defects and their causes. In D. R. Constan, R. V. Haning, Jr., & D. B. Singer (Eds.), *Human reproduction: Growth and development.* Boston, MA: Little, Brown.

O'Sullivan, L. F., & Byers, E. S. (1992). College students' incorporation of initiator and restrictor role in sexual dating interactions. *Journal of Sex Research, 29*, 435–446.

O'Sullivan, L. F., & Byers, E. S. (1996). Gender differences in responses to discrepancies in desired level of sexual intimacy. *Journal of Psychology & Human Sexuality, 8*(1&2), 49–67.

O'Sullivan, L. F., & Majerovich, J. (2008). Difficulties with sexual functioning in a sample of male and female late adolescent and young adult university students. *Canadian Journal of Human Sexuality, 17*, 109–121.

O'Sullivan, L. F., & Meyer-Bahlburg, H. (2003). African-American and Latina inner-city girls' reports of romantic and sexual development. *Journal of Social and Personal Relationships, 20*, 221–238.

O'Sullivan, L. F., Byers, E. S., & Finkelman, L. (1998). A comparison of male and female college students' experiences of sexual coercion. *Psychology of Women Quarterly, 22*, 177–195.

O'Sullivan, L. F. (2011, April). *Tweeting, texting, teens & chat: The Internet and sex in the lives of youth.* Ideas that matter, UNB Fredericton, New Brunswick.

O'Sullivan, L. F., & Ronis, S. T. (2013). Virtual cheating hearts: Extradyadic and poaching interactions among adolescents with links to online sexual activities. *Canadian Journal of Behavioural Science, 45*,175–184.

Ochs, E. P., Mah, K., & Binik, Y. (2002). Obtaining data about human sexual functioning from the Internet. In A. Cooper (Ed.), *Sex and the Internet: A guidebook for clinicians* (pp. 245–262). New York, NY: Routledge.

Ochs, E., & Binik, Y. M. (1999). The use of couple data to determine the reliability of self-reported sexual behaviour. *Journal of Sex Research, 36*, 374–384.

Offman, A., & Kleinplatz, P. J. (2004). Does PMDD belong in the DSM? Challenging the medicalization of women's bodies. *Canadian Journal of Human Sexuality, 13*, 17–27.

Offman, A., & Matheson, K. (2004). The sexual self-perceptions of young women experiencing abuse in dating relationships. *Sex Roles, 51*, 551–560.

Offman, A., & Matheson, K. (2005). Sexual compatibility and sexual functioning in intimate relationships. *Canadian Journal of Human Sexuality, 14*, 21–29.

Ogas, O., & Gaddam, S. (2011). *A billion wicked thoughts: What the world's largest experiment reveals about human desire.* New York, NY: Dutton Adult.

Ogletree, S. M., & Ginsburg, H. J. (2000). Kept under the hood: Neglect of the clitoris in common vernacular. *Sex Roles, 43*, 917–926.

Ogrodnik, L. (2010). *Child and youth victims of police-reported violent crime, 2008* (Catalogue no. 85F0033M). Ottawa, Canada: Statistics Canada.

Ogunjimi, L. O. (2006). Attitudes of students and parents towards the teaching of sex education in secondary schools in Cross Rivers States. *Education Research and Review, 1*, 347–349.

Okami, P., Olmstead, R., & Abramson, P. (1997). Sexual experiments in early childhood: 18-year longitudinal data from the UCLA Family Lifestyles Project. *Journal of Sex Research, 34*, 339–347.

Okoronkwo, C., Sieswerda, L. E., Cooper, R., Binette, D., & Todd, M. (2012). Parental consent to HPV vaccination for their daughters: The effects of knowledge and attitudes. *Canadian Journal of Human Sexuality, 21*, 117–126.

Olsson, S., & Möller, A. R. (2003). On the incidence and sex ratio of transsexualism in Sweden, 1972–2002. *Archives of Sexual Behavior, 32*(4), 381–386.

Olyan, S. M. (1994). And with a male you shall not lie the lying down of a woman: On the meaning and significance of Leviticus 18:22 and 20:13. *Journal of the History of Sexuality, 5*, 179–206.

Oosterhuis, H. (2000). *Step children of nature: Krafft-Ebing, psychiatry, and the making of sexual identity.* Chicago, IL: University of Chicago Press.

Options for Sexual Health. (2004). *An assessment of the effectiveness of sexual health education in BC schools.* Retrieved February 25, 2008, from http://www.optionsforsexualhealth.org

Ormond, G., et al. (2008). Endocrine disruptors in the workplace, hair spray, folate supplementation, and risk of hypospadias: Case-control study. *Environmental Health Perspectives, 117*, 303–307.

Ornstein, M. (1989). *AIDS in Canada: Knowledge, behaviour, and attitudes of adults.* Toronto, Canada: Institute for Social Research, York University.

Osman, S. L. (2003). Predicting men's rape perceptions based on the belief that "no" really means "yes." *Journal of Applied Social Psychology, 33*, 683–692.

Ott, M. A., Millstein, S. G., Ofner, S., & Halpern-Felsher, B. L. (2006). Greater expectations: Adolescents' positive motivations for sex. *Perspectives on Sexual and Reproductive Health, 38*(2), 84–89.

Owen, J. J., et al. (2010). "Hooking up" among college students: Demographic and psychosocial correlates. Archives of Sexual Behavior, 39, 653–663.

Owen, J., & Fincham, F. D. (2011a). Effects of gender and psychosocial factors on "friends with benefits" relationships among young adults. *Archives of Sexual Behavior, 40,* 311–320.

Owen, J., & Fincham, F. D. (2011b). Young adults' emotional reactions after hooking up encounters. *Archives of Sexual Behavior, 40,* 321–330.

Pachankis, J. E. (2007). The psychological implications of concealing a stigma: A cognitive-affective-behavioral model. *Psychological Bulletin, 133,* 328–345.

Padilla, M. (2007). *Caribbean pleasure industry: Tourism, sexuality, and AIDS in the Dominican Republic.* Chicago, IL: University of Chicago Press.

Padma-Nathan, H., McMurray, J. G., Pullman, W. E., Whitaker, J. S., Saoud, J. B., Ferguson, K. M., et al. (2001). On-demand IC351 (Cialis trade mark) enhances erectile function in patients with erectile dysfunction. *International Journal of Impotence Research, 13,* 2–9.

Page, S. T., et al. (2006). Testosterone gel combined with depomedroxyprogesterone acetate is an effective male hormonal contraceptive regimen and is not enhanced by the addition of a GnRH antagonist. *Journal of Clinical Endocrinology and Metabolism, 91,* 4374–4380.

Pakenham, K. I., Dadds, M. R., & Terry, D. J. (1994). Relationships between adjustment to HIV and both social support and coping. *Journal of Consulting and Clinical Psychology, 62,* 1194–1203.

Palace, E. M. (1995a). A cognitive-physiological process model of sexual arousal and response. *Clinical Psychology: Science and Practice, 2,* 370–384.

Palace, E. M. (1995b). Modification of dysfunctional patterns of sexual response through autonomic arousal and false physiological feedback. *Journal of Consulting and Clinical Psychology, 63,* 604–615.

Paras, M. L., et al. (2009). Sexual abuse and lifetime diagnosis of somatic disorders: A systematic review and meta-analysis. *Journal of the American Medical Association, 302,* 5, 550–561.

Parker, G. (1983). The legal regulation of sexual activity and the protection of females. *Osgoode Hall Law Journal, 21,* 187–244.

Parker, R., di Mauro, D., Filiano, B., Garcia, J., Munoz-Laboy, M., & Sember, R. (2004). Global transformations and intimate relations in the 21st century: Social science research on sexuality and the emergence of Sexual Health and Sexual Rights frameworks. *Annual Review of Sex Research, 15,* 362–398.

Parrinder, G. (1980). *Sex in the world's religions.* New York, NY: Oxford University Press.

Parrot, A., & Cummings, N. (2006). *Forsaken females: The global brutalization of women.* NY: Rowman & Littlefield.

Parrott, Y., & Esmail, S. (2010). Burn survivors' perceptions regarding relevant sexual education strategies. *Health Education, 110,* 84–97.

Parsons, J. T., et al. (2008). Explanations for the origins of sexual compulsivity among gay and bisexual men. *Archives of Sexual Behavior, 37,* 817–826.

Pasqualotto, F., et al. (2008). Effect of cigarette smoking on antioxidant levels and presence of leukocytospermia in infertile men: A prospective study. *Fertility and Sterility, 90:* 278–283.

Patrick, M. E., & Lee, C. M. (2010). Sexual motivations and engagement in sexual behaviour during the transition to college. *Archives of Sexual Behavior, 39,* 674–681

Patterson, C. J. (2000). Family relationships of lesbians and gay men. *Journal of Marriage and the Family, 62,* 1052–1069.

Patterson, C. J. (2006). Children of lesbian and gay parents. *Current Directions in Psychological Science, 15,* 241–244.

Patterson, C. J. (2009). Children of lesbian and gay parents: Psychology, law, and policy. *American Psychologist, 64,* 727–736.

Paul, B., & Linz, D. (2008). The effects of exposure to virtual child pornography on viewer cognitions and attitudes toward deviant sexual behavior. *Communication Research, 35,* 3–38.

Paul, C., Teng, S., & Saunders, P. T. K. (2008). A single, mild, transient scrotal heat stress causes DNA damage, subfertility and impairs formation of blastocysts in mice. *Reproduction, 136,* 73–84.

Payne, K. A., & Binik, Y. M (2006). Reviving the labial thermistor clip. *Archives of Sexual Behavior, 35,* 111–113.

Payne, K. A., Binik, Y. M., Amsel, R., & Khalifé, S. (2005). When sex hurts, anxiety and fear orient attention towards pain. *European Journal of Pain, 9,* 427–436.

Payne, K. A., Reissing, E. D., Lahaie, M., Binik, Y. M., Amsel, R., & Khalifé, S. (2005). What is sexual pain? A critique of DSM's classification of dyspareunia and vaginismus. *Journal of Psychology & Human Sexuality, 17,* 141–154.

Payne, K. A., Thaler, L., Kukkonen, T., Carrier S., & Binik, Y. (2007). Sensation and sexual arousal in circumcised and uncircumcised men. *Journal of Sexual Medicine, 4,* 667–674.

Pedersen, W., Miller, L. C., Putcha-Bhagavatula, A., & Yang, Y. (2002). Evolved sex differences in the number of partners desired: The long and short of it. *Psychological Science, 13,* 157–159.

Péloquin, K., Brassard, A., Lafontaine, M-F., & Shaver, P. R. (2013). Sexuality examined through the lens of attachment theory: Attachment, caregiving, and sexual satisfaction. *Journal of Sex Research,* doi:10.1080/00224499.2012.757281

Pennisi, E. (1996). Homing in on a prostate cancer gene. *Science, 274,* 1301.

Peplau, L. A. (2003). Human sexuality: How do men and women differ? *Current Directions in Psychological Science, 12,* 37–40.

Peplau, L. A., Fingerhut, A., & Beals, K. P. (2004). Sexuality in the relationships of lesbians and gay men. In J. Harvey, A. Wenzel & S. Sprecher (Eds.) *Handbook of Sexuality in Close Relationships* (pp. 349–369). New Jersey: Lawrence Erlbaum Associates, Inc.

Peplau, L. A., Garnets, L. D., Spalding, L. R., Conley, T. D., & Veniegas, R. C. (1998). A critique of Bem's "Exotic becomes erotic" theory of sexual orientation. *Psychological Review, 105,* 387–394.

Perel, E. (2006). *Mating in captivity: Unlocking erotic intelligence.* New York, NY: Harper.

Perelman, M. A., & Rowland, D. L. (2006). Retarded ejaculation. *World Journal of Urology.* doi:10.1007/s00345-006-0127-6

Perez, M. A., Skinner, E. C., & Meyerowitz, B. E. (2002). Sexuality and intimacy following radical prostatectomy: Patient and partner perspectives. *Health Psychology, 21,* 288–293.

Perilloux, C., et al. (2012). The misperception of sexual interest. *Psychological Science, 23,* 146–151.

Perlman, D., & Fehr, B. (1987). The development of intimate relationships. In D. Perlman & S. Duck (Eds.), *Intimate relationships: Development, dynamics, and deterioration.* Newbury Park, CA: Sage.

Perreault, S., & Brennan, S. (2010). Criminal victimization in Canada, 2009. *Juristat, 30*(2).

Perrott, S. (2012). Reforming policing of sex tourism in the Philippines and the Gambia: Can we avoid confusing messages? In Taylor, S. C., Torpy, D. J., & Das, D. K. (Eds.), *Policing global movement: Tourism, migration, human trafficking, and terrorism.* Boca Raton, FL: CRC Press.

Perry, J. D., & Whipple, B. (1981). Pelvic muscle strength of female ejaculators: Evidence in support of a new theory of orgasm. *Journal of Sex Research, 17,* 22–39.

Persson, G. (1980). Sexuality in a 70-year-old urban population. *Journal of Psychosomatic Research, 24,* 335–342.

Petersen, J. L., & Hyde, J. S. (2010). A meta-analytic review of research on gender differences in sexuality, 1993 to 2007. *Psychological Bulletin, 136,* 21–38.

Petkovich, A. (2004). From gonzo porn to mainstream? Porn starlet Sienna. *Spectator.* Retrieved from http://www.spectator.net

Pew Research (2013, June 4). *The global divide on homosexuality: Greater acceptance in more secular and affluent countries.* Retrieved from http://www.pewglobal.org/2013/06/04/the-global-divide-on-homosexuality/

Pew Research Center. (2010). The decline of marriage and the rise of new families. Pew Research Center Report.

Pfaus, J. (2009). Pathways of sexual desire. *Journal of Sexual Medicine, 6,* 1506–1533.

Pfaus, J. G., Kippin, T. E., & Coria-Avila, G. (2003). What can animal models tell us about human sexual response? *Annual Review of Sex Research, 14,* 1–63.

Pfaus, J. G., Kippin, T. E., Coria-Avila, G. A., Gelez, H., Afonso, V. M., Ismail, N., & Parada, M. (2012). Who, what, where, when (and maybe even why)? How the experience of sexual reward connects sexual desire, preference, and performance. *Archives of Sexual Behavior, 41,* 31–62.

Pfeiffer, E. (1975). Sex and aging. In L. Gross (Ed.), *Sexual issues in marriage.* New York, NY: Spectrum.

Pfeiffer, E., Verwoerdt, A., & Wang, H. S. (1968). Sexual behavior in aged men and women. *Archives of General Psychiatry, 19,* 753–758.

Phillips, P. (2012). Pregnancy test review. Retrieved from http://www.early-pregnancy-tests.com/compare.html

Phoenix, C. H., Goy, R. W., Gerall, A. A., & Young, W. C. (1959). Organizing action of prenatally administered testosterone propionate on the tissues mediating mating behavior in the female guinea pig. *Endocrinology, 65,* 369–382.

Pike, J. J., & Jennings, N. A. (2005). The effects of commercials on children's perceptions of gender appropriate toy use. *Sex Roles, 52,* 83–92.

Pilkington, N. W., & Lydon, J. E. (1997). The relative effect of attitude similarity and attitude dissimilarity and interpersonal attraction: Investigating the moderating roles of prejudice and group membership. *Journal of Personality and Social Psychology Bulletin, 23*(2), 107–122.

Pinheiro, R. C., Lambert, J., Benard, F., Mauffette, F., & Miron, P. (1999). Effectiveness of in vitro fertilization with intracytoplasmic sperm injection for severe male infertility. *Canadian Medical Association Journal, 161,* 1397–1442.

Pinkerton, J., Stovall, D., & Kightlinger, R. (2009). Advances in the treatment of menopausal symptoms. Medscape CME. http://cme.medscape.com/viewarticle/705445

Pithers, W. D. (1993). Treatment of rapists. In G. N. Hall, et al. (Eds.), *Sexual aggression* (pp. 167–196). Washington, D. C.: Taylor & Francis.

Pittenger, W. N. (1970). *Making sexuality human.* Philadelphia, PA: Pilgrim Press.

Pittman, F., III. (1993, May–June). Beyond betrayal: Life after infidelity. *Psychology Today,* 32–38, ff.

Pitts, M. K., Smith, A., Grierson, J., O'Brien, M., & Mission, S. (2004). Who pays for sex and why? An analysis of social and motivational factors associated with male clients of sex workers. *Archives of Sexual Behavior, 33,* 353–368.

Planned Parenthood Federation of Canada. (n.d.). *A history of birth control in Canada.*

Plaud, J. J., Gaither, G. A., Hegstadc, H. J., Rowan, L., & Devitt, M. K. (1999). Volunteer bias in human psychophysiological sexual arousal research: To whom do our research results apply? *Journal of Sex Research, 36,* 171–179.

Plaut, S. M. (2008). Sexual and nonsexual boundaries in professional relationships: Principles and teaching guidelines. *Sexual and Relationship Therapy, 23,* 85–94.

Ploem, C., & Byers, E. S. (1997). The effects of two AIDS risk-reduction interventions on heterosexual college women's AIDS-related knowledge and condom use. *Journal of Psychology & Human Sexuality, 9*(1), 1–24.

Plummer, K. (1975). *Sexual stigma: An interactionist account.* London, England: Routledge & Kegan Paul.

Poasa, K. H., Blanchard, R., & Zucker, K. J. (2004). Birth order in transgendered males from Polynesia: A quantitative study of Samoan *Fa'afa-fine. Journal of Sex & Marital Therapy, 30,* 13–23.

Polisois-Keating, A., & Joyal, C. C. (2013). Functional neuroimaging of sexual arousal: A preliminary meta-analysis comparing pedophilic to non-pedophilic men. *Archives of Sexual Behavior, 42,* 1111–1113.

Pollack, A., Dean, C., & Dreifus, C. (2004, February 13). Medical and ethical issues cloud plans to clone for therapy. *New York Times.*

Polzer, J. C., & Knabe, S. M. (2012). From desire to disease: Human papillomavirus (HPV) and the medicalization of nascent female sexuality. *Journal of sex Research, 49,* 344–352.

Pomeroy, W. B. (1972). *Dr. Kinsey and the Institute for Sex Research.* New York, NY: Harper & Row.

Poole, N. A. (2008). Fetal alcohol spectrum disorder (FASD) Prevention: Canadian Perspectives (2008). Retrieved from http://www.phac-aspc.gc.ca/fasd-etcaf/cp-pc-eng.php

Poon, M. K-L., Ho, Peter T-T, & Wong, J. P-H. (2001). Developing a comprehensive AIDS prevention outreach program: A needs assessment survey of MSM of East and Southeast Asian descent who visit bars and/or bath houses in Toronto. *Canadian Journal of Human Sexuality, 10,* 25–37.

Poon, M.K-L., Wong, J. P-H., Sutdhibhasilp, N., Ho, P.T-T., &Wong, B. (2011). HIV and STI testing among East and Southeast Asian men who have sex with men in Toronto. *Canadian Journal of Human Sexuality,20,* 157–166.

Pope John Paul II. (1995, March 25). *Evangelium Vitae:* Encyclical Letter on the Value and Inviolability of Human Life.

Pope Paul VI. (1968, July 30). *Humanae vitae.* (English text in the *New York Times,* p. 20.)

Pope, K. (2001). Sex between therapists and clients. In J. Worell (Ed.), *Encyclopedia of women and gender* (pp. 955–862). New York, NY: Academic Press.

Popenoe, D. (2009). Cohabitation, Marriage, and Child Wellbeing: A Cross-National Perspective. *Society, 46*(5), 429–436. doi:10.1007/s12115-009-9242-5

Posner, R. (1992). *Sex and reason.* Cambridge, MA: Harvard University Press.

Posner, R. B. (2006). Early menarche: A review of research on trends in timing, racial differences, etiology, and psychosocial consequences. *Sex Roles, 54,* 315–322.

Poteat, V. P., Kimmel, M. S., & Wilchins, R. (2011). The moderating effects of support for violence beliefs on masculine norms, aggression, and homophobic behavior during adolescence. *Journal of Research on Adolescence, 21,* 434–447.

Poteat, V. P., O'Dwyer, L. M., & Mereish, E. H. (2012). Changes in how students use and are called homophobic epithets over time: Patterns predicted by gender, bullying, and victimization status. *Journal of Educational Psychology, 104,* 393–406.

Potts, A., Gavey, N., Grace, V. M., & Vares, T. (2003). The downside of Viagra: Women's experiences and concerns. *Sociology of Health & Illness, 25,* 697–719.

Poulin, C., & Gouliquer, L. (2003). Part-time disabled lesbian passing on roller blades, or PMS, Prozac, and essentializing women's ailments. *Women & Therapy: A Feminist Quarterly, 26,* 95–108.

Powdermaker, H. (1933). *Life in Lesu.* New York, NY: Norton.

Practice Committee of the American Society for Reproductive Medicine. (2008). Obesity and reproduction: An educational bulletin. *Fertility and Sterility, 90* (Suppl. 3): S21–S29.

Prager, K. J. (1997). *The psychology of intimacy.* New York, NY: Guilford Press.

Prather, R. S. (2000). Pigs is pigs. *Science, 289,* 1886–1887.

Prause, N., & Graham, C. A. (2007). Asexuality: Classification and characterization. *Archives of Sexual Behavior, 36.*

Price, E. L., Byers, E. S., & the Dating Violence Research Team. (1999). The Attitudes Towards Dating Violence Scales: Development and initial validation. *Journal of Family Violence, 14,* 351–375.

Price, E. L., Byers, E. S., Sears, H., Whelan, J., & Saint-Pierre, M. (2000, January). Dating violence amongst New Brunswick adolescents: A summary of two studies. *Research Paper Series,* #2. Muriel McQueen Fergusson Centre for Family Violence Research.

Price, J., Allensworth, D., & Hillman, K. (1985). Comparison of sexual fantasies of homosexuals and heterosexuals. *Psychological Reports, 57,* 871–877.

Price, M., & Hyde, J. S. (2009). When two isn't better than one: Predictors of early sexual activity in adolescence using a cumulative risk model. *Journal of Youth and Adolescence, 38,* 1059–1071.

Price-Glynn, K. (2010). *Strip club: Gender, power and sex work.* New York, NY: New York University Press.

Prior, J., Hubbard, P., & Birch, P. (2012). Sex worker victimization, modes of working, and location in New South Wales, Australia: A geography of victimization. *Journal of Sex Research.* doi:10.1080/00224499.2012.668975

Propper, C. R. (2005). The study of endocrine-disrupting compounds: Past approaches and new directions. *Integrative and Comparative Biology, 45,* 194–200.

Proulx, J., Pellerin, B., Paradis, Y., McKibben, A., Aubut, J., & Ouimet, M. (1997). Static and dynamic predictors of recidivism in sexual aggressors. *Sexual Abuse: A Journal of Research and Treatment, 9,* 7–27.

Puar, J. K. (2001). Global circuits: Transnational sexualities and Trinidad. *Signs: Journal of Women in Culture and Society, 26,* 1039–1065.

Public Health Agency of Canada. (2005). *Fetal alcohol spectrum disorder (FASD).* Cat. No H124–4/2004. Available at http://www.phac-aspc.gc.ca/fasd-etcaf/pdf/faq_fasd_e.pdf

Public Health Agency of Canada. (2007a). *Frequently asked questions on emergency contraception.* Available at http://www.phac-aspc.gc.ca/stdmts/ec_cu_e.html

Public Health Agency of Canada. (2007b). *Sexually transmitted infections.* Retrieved from http://www.publichealth.gc.ca/sti

Public Health Agency of Canada. (2008a). *Canadian guidelines for sexual health education.* Ottawa, Canada: Author.

Public Health Agency of Canada. (2008b). *Canadian perinatal health report.* Ottawa, Canada: Author.

Public Health Agency of Canada. (2009a). *What mothers say: The Canadian maternity experiences survey.* Ottawa, Canada: Author.

Public Health Agency of Canada. (2009b). *HIV and AIDS in Canada. Surveillance report to December 31, 2008.* Surveillance and Risk Assessment Division, Centre for Infectious Disease Prevention and Control, Public Health Agency of Canada.

Public Health Agency of Canada. (2010a). Perinatal HIV transmission in Canada. *HIV/AIDS Epi Update.* Catalog HP40–56/8–2010E-PDF

Public Health Agency of Canada. (2010b). *Hepatitis B-Get the Facts.* Available at http://www.phac-aspc.gc.ca

Public Health Agency of Canada. (2010c). *Questions & answers: Sexual orrientaion in schools.* Ottawa, Canada: Author.

Public Health Agency of Canada. (2011a). Brief report: Hepatitis B infection in Canada. *Epi-Update.* Ottawa, Canada: Author.

Public Health Agency of Canada. (2011b). *What everyone should know about human papillomavirus (HPV): Questions and Answers.* Ottawa, Canada:Author.

Public Health Agency of Canada. (2012a). *Canadian hospitals maternity policies and practices survey.* Ottawa, Canada: Author.

Public Health Agency of Canada. (2012b). *The healthy pregnancy guide.* Ottawa, Canada: Author.

Public Health Agency of Canada. (2012c). Update on human papillomavirus (HPV) vaccines. *Canada Communicable Disease Report, 38,* ACS-1.

Public Health Agency of Canada. (2013). *Canadian guidelines on sexually transmitted infections.* Ottawa,

Canada: Author. http://www.phac-aspc.gc.ca/std-mts/sti-its/cgsti-ldcits/index-eng.php

Pukall, C. F., Payne, K. A., Binik, Y. M., & Khalifé, S. (2003). Pain measurement in vulvodynia. *Journal of Sex & Marital Therapy, 29*(Suppl.), 111–120.

Pukall, C. F., Reissing, E. D., Binik, Y. M., Khalifé, S., & Abbott, F. V. (2000). New clinical and research perspectives on the sexual pain disorders. *Journal of Sex Education and Therapy, 25,* 36–44.

Purdon, C., & Holdaway, L. (2006). Non-erotic thoughts: Content and relation to sexual functioning and sexual satisfaction. *Journal of Sex Research, 43,* 154–162.

Purdon, C., & Watson, C. (2011). Non-erotic thoughts and sexual functioning. *Archives of Sexual Behavior, 40,* 891–902.

Purnine, D., & Carey, M. (1997). Interpersonal communication and sexual adjustment: The roles of understanding and agreement. *Journal of Consulting & Clinical Psychology, 65,* 1017–1025.

Pyke, S. (1996). Sexual harassment and sexual intimacy in learning environments. *Canadian Psychology, 37*(1), 13–22.

Quadagno, D., et al. (1991). The menstrual cycle: Does it affect athletic performance? *Physician & Sports Medicine, 19,* 121–124.

Quas, J. A., et al. (2005). Childhood sexual assault victims: Long-term outcomes after testifying in criminal court. *Monographs of the Society for Research in Child Development, 70,* 1–127.

Quayle, E. (2008). Online sex offending: Psychopathology and theory. In D. R. Laws, & W. O'Donohue (Eds.), *Sexual Deviance: Theory, Assessment, and Treatment* (2nd ed., pp. 439–458). New York, NY: Guilford.

Quinn, T. C., Wawer, M. J., Sewankambo, N., Serwadda, D., Li, C., Wabwire-Mangen, F., Meehan, M. O., Lutalo, T., & Gray, R. H. (2000). Viral load and heterosexual transmission of human immunodeficiency virus type 1. *New England Journal of Medicine, 342,* 921–929.

Rabe, Thomas. (2007). Contraception—update and trends. *Journal Reproduktionsmed Endokrinol, 4,* 337–357.

Rachman, S. (1966). Sexual fetishism: An experimental analogue. *Psychological Record, 16,* 293–296.

Rako, S., & Friebely, J. (2004). Pheromonal influences on sociosexual behavior in postmenopausal women. *Journal of Sex Research, 41,* 372–380.

Ramchandani, P., Stein, A., Evans, J., O'Connor, T., & the ALSPAC Study Team. (2005). Paternal depression in the postnatal period and child development: A prospective population study. *Lancet, 365,* 2201–2205.

Rametti, G., et al. (2011). White matter microstructure in female to male transsexuals before cross-sex hormonal treatment: A diffusion tensor imaging study. *Journal of Psychiatric Research, 45,* 199–204.

Ramsey, S., Sweeney, C., Fraser, M., & Oades, G. (2009). Pubic hair and sexuality: A review. *Journal of Sexual Medicine, 6,* 2102–2110.

Randall, H. E., & Byers, E. S. (2003). What is sex?: Students' definitions of having sex, sexual partner, and unfaithful sexual behaviour. *Canadian Journal of Human Sexuality, 12,* 87–96.

Ratnam, S., Franco, E., & Ferenczy, A. (2000). Human papillomavirus testing for primary screening of cervical cancer precursors. *Cancer Epidemiology Biomarkers & Prevention, 9,* 945–951.

Ray, J. G., Henry, D. A., & Urquia, M. L. (2012). Sex ratios among Canadian liveborn infants of mothers from different countries. *CMAJ, 184,* E492–E496.

Raymond, N. C., Grant, J. E., Kim, S. W., & Coleman, E. (2002). Treatment of compulsive sexual behaviour with naltrexone and serotonin reuptake inhibitors: Two case studies. *International Clinical Psychopharmacology 127,* 201–205.

Reamy, K. J., & White, S. E. (1987). Sexuality in the puerperium: A review. *Archives of Sexual Behavior, 16,* 165–186.

Rederstorff, J. C., et al. (2007). The moderating roles of race and genderrole attitudes in the relationship between sexual harassment and psychological well-being. *Psychology of Women Quarterly, 31,* 50–61.

Reece, M., Herbenick, D., & Sherwood-Puzzello, C. (2004). Sexual health promotion and adult retail stores. *Journal of Sex Research, 41,* 173–180.

Reece, M., Herbenick, D., Sanders, S. A., Dodge, B., Ghassemi, A., & Fortenberry, J. D. (2009). Prevalence and characteristics of vibrator use by men in the United States. *Journal of Sexual Medicine, 6,* 1867–1874.

Reece, M., Herbenick, D., Schick, B., Sanders, S. A., Dodge, B., & Fortenberry, J. D. (2010a). Background and considerations on the National Survey of Sexual Health and Behavior (NSSHB) from the investigators. *Journal of Sexual Medicine, 7* (SS05), 243–246

Reece, M., Herbenick, D., Schick, V., Sanders, S. A., Dodge, B., & Fortenberry, J. D. (2010b). Sexual behaviors, relationships, and perceived health among adult men in the United States. *Journal of Sexual Medicine, 7* (SS05), 291–304.

Reefhuis, J., et al. (2009). Assisted reproductive technology and major structural birth defects in the United States. *Human Reproduction, 24,* 360–366.

Reeves, A., & Reading, C. (2013). Constructions of sexuality for First Nation women in Atlantic Canada: Results from a qualitative study. In D. Castaneda (Ed.), *The Essential handbook of women's sexuality* (pp. 93–114). Santa Barbara, CA: ABC-CLIO.

Regan, P. (2004). Sex and the attraction process: Lessons from science (and Shakespeare) on lust, love, chastity, and fidelity. In J. H. Harvey, A. Wenzel, & S. Sprecher (Eds.), *The handbook of sexuality in close relationships* (pp. 159–182). Mahwah, NJ: Lawrence Erlbaum.

Regnerus, M. (2007). *Forbidden fruit: Sex and religion in the lives of American teenagers.* New York, NY: Oxford University Press.

Rehman, U., Fallis, E., & Byers, E. S. (2013). Sexual satisfaction in heterosexual women. In D. Cataneda (Ed.). *The essential handbook of women's sexuality* (Vol. 1, pp. 25–45). Santa Barbara, CA: Praeger.

Reichert, T. (2002). Sex in advertising research: A review of content, effects, and functions of sexual information in consumer advertising. *Annual Review of Sex Research, 13,* 241–273.

Reichert, T., & Carpenter, C. (2004). An update on sex in magazine advertising: 1983 to 2003. *Journalism and Mass Communication Quarterly, 81,* 823–837.

Reid, R., Garos, S., & Carpenter, B. (2011). Reliability, validity, and psychometric development of the Hypersexual Behavior Inventory in an outpatient sample of men. *Sexual Addiction and Compulsivity, 18,* 30–51.

Reis, E. (2007). Divergence or disorder? The politics of naming intersex. *Perspectives in Biology and Medicine, 50,* 535–543.

Reisenzein, R. (1983). The Schachter theory of emotion: Two decades later. *Psychological Bulletin, 94,* 239–264.

Reiss, I. L. (1986). *Journey into sexuality: An exploratory voyage.* Englewood Cliffs, NJ: Prentice-Hall.

Reissing, E. D., & Di Giulio, G. (2010). Practicing clinical psychologists' provision of sexual health care services. *Professional Psychology: Research, and Practice, 41,* 57–63.

Reissing, E. D., Armstrong, H. L., & Allen, C. (2013). Pelvic floor physical therapy for lifelong vaginismus: A retrospective chart review and interview study. *Journal of Sex & Marital Therapy, 39,* 306–320.

Rellini, A. H., & Meston, C. M. (2011). Sexual self-schemas, sexual dysfunction, and the sexual responses of women with a history of childhood sexual abuse. *Archives of Sexual Behavior, 40,* 351–362.

Rempel, J. K., & Baumgartner, B. (2003). The relationship between attitudes towards menstruation and sexual attitudes, desires, and behavior in women. *Archives of Sexual Behavior, 32,* 155–163.

Rempel, L. A., & Rempel, J. K. (2004). Partner influence on health behavior decision-making: Increasing breastfeeding duration. *Journal of Social and Personal Relationships, 21,* 92–111.

Renaud, C. A., & Byers, E. S. (1999). Exploring the frequency, diversity, and content of university students' positive and negative sexual cognitions. *Canadian Journal of Human Sexuality, 8,* 17–30.

Renaud, C. A., & Byers, E. S. (2001). Positive and negative sexual cognitions: Subjective experience and relationships to sexual adjustment. *Journal of Sex Research, 38,* 252–262.

Renaud, C., Byers, E. S., & Pan, S. (1997). Sexual and relationship satisfaction in mainland China. *Journal of Sex Research, 34,* 399–410.

Renne, E. P. (1996). The pregnancy that doesn't stay: The practice and perception of abortion by Ekiti Yoruba women. *Social Science & Medicine, 42,* 483–494.

Repke, J. T. (1994). Calcium and vitamin D. *Clinical Obstetrics and Gynecology, 37,* 550–557.

Reppucci, N. D., Land, D., & Haugaard, J. J. (1999). Child sexual abuse prevention programs that target young children. In P. K. Trickett, & C. J. Schellenbach (Eds.), *Violence against children in the family and the community.* Washington, DC: American Psychological Association.

Resick, P. A., et al. (2012). Long-term outcomes of cognitive-behavioral treatments for posttraumatic stress disorder among female rape survivors. *Journal of Consulting and Clinical Psychology, 80,* 201–210.

Reuther, R. R. (1985). Catholics and abortion: Authority vs. dissent. *Christian Century, 102,* 859–862.

Rhoades, G. K., Stanley, S., & Markman, H. (2006). Pre-engagement cohabitation and gender asymmetry in marital commitment. *Journal of Family Psychology, 20,* 553–560.

Rhoades, G., et al. (2009). The pre-engagement cohabitation effect: A replication and extension of previous findings. *Journal of Family Psychology, 23,* 107–111.

Ribner, D. S., & Kleinplatz, P. J. (2007). The hole in the sheet and other myths about sexuality and Judaism. *Sex and Relationship Therapy, 22,* 445–456.

Rich, Frank. (2001, May 20). Naked capitalists. *New York Times Magazine.*

Richters, J., de Visser, R., Rissel, C., & Smith, A. (2006). Sexual practices at last heterosexual encounter and occurrence of orgasm in a national survey. *Journal of Sex Research, 43,* 217–226.

Rideout, V. J., Foehr, U. G., & Roberts, D. F. (2010). Generation M²: Media in the lives of 8- to 18-year-olds. Retrieved from Kaiser Family Foundation, http://www.kff.org

Ridley, C. A., et al. (2006). The ebb and flow of marital lust: A relational approach. *Journal of Sex Research, 43,* 144–153.

Ridley, C., et al. (2008). Sexual expression: Its emotional context in heterosexual, gay, and lesbian couples. *Journal of Sex Research, 45,* 305–314.

Rieger, G., et al. (2008). Sexual orientation and childhood gender nonconformity: Evidence from home videos. *Developmental Psychology, 44,* 46–58.

Riessing, E. D., Andruff, H. L., & Wentland, J. J. (2011). Looking back: the experience of first sexual intercourse and current sexual adjustment in young heterosexual adults. *Journal of Sex Research, 49*(1), 27–35.

Rigdon, S. M. (1996). Abortion law and practice in China: An overview with comparisons to the United States. *Social Science & Medicine, 42,* 543–560.

Rimm, M. (1995). Marketing pornography on the information superhighway: A survey of 917,410 images. *Georgetown Law Journal, 83,* 1849–1925.

Ringheim, K., & Gribble, J. (2009). *Expanding contraceptive choice: Five promising innovations.* New York, NY: Population Reference Bureau.

Rini, C., Dunkel Schetter, C., Hobel, C., Glynn, L., & Sandman, C. (2006). Effective social support: Antecedents and consequences of partner support during pregnancy. *Personal Relationships, 13,* 207–229.

Riportella-Muller, R. (1989). Sexuality in the elderly: A review. In K. McKinney & S. Sprecher (Eds.), *Human sexuality: The societal and interpersonal context* (pp. 210–236). New York, NY: Ablex.

Rissel, C. E., Richters, J., Grulich, A. E., de Visser, R. O., & Smith, A. M. A. (2003a). Sex in Australia: Attitudes towards sex in a representative sample of adults. *Australian and New Zealand Journal of Public Health, 27,* 118–123.

Rissel, C. E., Richters, J., Grulich, A. E., de Visser, R. O., & Smith, A. M. A. (2003b). Sex in Australia: First experiences of vaginal intercourse and oral sex among a representative sample of adults. *Australian and New Zealand Journal of Public Health, 27,* 131–137.

Rissel, C. E., Richters, J., Grulich, A. E., de Visser, R. O., & Smith, A. M. A. (2003c). Sex in Australia: Selected characteristics of regular sexual relationships. *Australian and New Zealand Journal of Public Health, 27,* 124–130

Ritchie, A., & Barker, M. (2006). There aren't words for what we do or how we feel so we have to make them up: Constructing polyamorous languages in a culture of compulsory monogamy. *Sexualities, 9,* 584–601.

Roach, K. (2000). *Criminal law* (2nd ed.). Toronto, Canada: Irwin.

Roberts, A. L., et al. (2010). Pervasive trauma exposure among U. S. sexual orientation minority adults and risk of posttraumatic stress disorder. *American Journal of Public Health, 100,* 2433–2441.

Roberts, J., & Gebotys, R. (1992). Reforming rape laws. *Law and Human Behaviour, 16,* 555–573.

Robertson, S., & Sharkey, D. (2001). The role of semen in induction of maternal immune tolerance to pregnancy. *Seminars in Immunology, 13,* 243.

Robinson, B. E., et al. (2011). Application of the Sexual Health Model in the long-term treatment of hypoactive sexual desire and female orgasmic disorder. *Archives of Sexual Behavior, 40,* 469–478.

Robinson, J. P., & Espelage, D. L. (2011). Inequities in educational and psychological outcomes between LGBTQ and straight students in middle and high school. *Educational Researcher, 40,* 315–330.

Roehr, B. (2007). Dramatic drop in HIV infections halts circumcision trials. *British Medical Journal, 334,* 11.

Rogen, S. (2008, July 20). Quoted in the *New York Times Sunday Magazine,* p. 49.

Romer, D., Hornik, R., Stanton, B., Black, M., Li, X., Ricardo, I., & Feigelman, S. (1997). "Talking computers": A reliable and private method to conduct interviews on sensitive topics with children. Journal of Sex Research, 34, 3–9.

Ronald, A., Pennell, C., & Whitehouse, A. (2011). Prenatal maternal stress associated with ADHD and autistic traits in early childhood. *Frontiers in Psychology, 1* (article 223), 1–7.

Ronis, S. T., & LeBouthillier, D. M. (2013). University students' attitudes toward purchasing condoms. *Canadian Journal of Human Sexuality, 22,* 86–94. doi:10.3138/CJHS.2013.2201

Rosaldo, M. A. (1974). Woman, culture, and society: A theoretical overview. In M. S. Rosaldo & L. Lamphere (Eds.), *Woman, culture, and society.* Stanford, CA: Stanford University Press.

Rosario, M., Meyer-Bahlburg, H., Hunter, J., Exner, T., Swadz, M., & Keller, A. (1996). The psychosexual development of urban lesbian, gay and bisexual youths. *Journal of Sex Research, 33,* 113–126.

Roscoe, B., Cavanaugh, L., & Kennedy, D. (1988). Dating infidelity: Behaviors, reasons, and consequences. *Adolescence, 89,* 36–43.

Roscoe, B., Kennedy, D., & Pope, T. (1987). Adolescents' views of intimacy: Distinguishing intimate from nonintimate relationships. *Adolescence, 22,* 511–516.

Rose, A. J., & Rudolph, K. D. (2006). A review of sex differences in peer relationship processes: Potential trade-off s for the emotional and behavioral development of girls and boys. Psychological Bulletin, 132, 89–131.

Roselli, C. E., Resko, J. A., & Stormshak, F. (2002). Hormonal influences on sexual partner preference in rams. *Archives of Sexual Behavior, 31,* 43–49.

Rosen, D. H. (1974). *Lesbianism: A study of female homosexuality.* Spring-field, IL: Charles C. Thomas.

Rosen, N. O., Knauper, B., Mozessohn, L., & Ho, M. R. (2005). Factors affecting knowledge of sexually transmitted infection transmissibility in healthcare providers: Results from a national survey. *Sexually Transmitted Diseases, 32,* 619–624.

Rosen, N. O., Bergeron, S., Glowacka, M., Delisle, I., & Baxter, M. L. (2012). Harmful or helpful: Perceived solicitous and facilitative partner responses are differentially associated with pain and sexual satisfaction in women with provoked vestibulodynia. *Journal of Sexual Medicine, 9,* 2351–2360.

Rosen, N. O., Bergeron, S., Lambert, B., & Steben, M. (2012). Provoked vestibulodynia: Mediators of the associations between partner responses, pain, and sexual satisfaction. *Archives of Sexual Behavior.* doi:10.1007/s10508-012-9905-y

Rosen, N. O., Bergeron, S., Leclerc, B., Lambert, B., & Steben, M. (2010). Woman and partner-perceived partner responses predict pain and sexual satisfaction in provoked vestibulodynia (PVD) couples. *Journal of Sexual Medicine, 7,* 3715–3724.

Rosen, R. C. (2007). Erectile dysfunction: Integration of medical and psychological approaches. In S. Leiblum (Ed.), *Principles and practice of sex therapy* (4th ed., pp. 277–312). New York, NY: Guilford.

Rosen, R. C., & Leiblum, S. R. (1995a). Hypoactive sexual desire. *Psychiatric Clinics of North America, 18,* 107–121.

Rosen, R. C., & Leiblum, S. R. (1995b). Treatment of sexual disorders in the 1990s: An integrated approach. *Journal of Consulting and Clinical Psychology, 63,* 877–890.

Rosen, R. C., & McKenna, K. E. (2002). PDE-5 inhibition and sexual response: Pharmacological mechanisms and clinical outcomes. *Annual Review of Sex Research, 13,* 36–88.

Rosen, R. C., Leiblum, S. R., & Spector, I. P. (1994). Psychologically based treatment for male erectile disorder: A cognitive-interpersonal model. *Journal of Sex & Marital Therapy, 20,* 67–85.

Rosen, R. C., Connor, M. K., Miyasato, G., Link, C., Shifren, J. L., Fisher, W. A., . . . Schobelock, M. J. (2012). Sexual desire problems in women seeking healthcare: A novel study design for ascertaining prevalence of hypoactive sexual desire disorder in clinic-based samples of U. S. women. *Journal of Women's Health, 21,* 505–515.

Rosenbaum, T. Y. (2005). Physiotherapy treatment of sexual pain disorders. *Journal of Sex & Marital Therapy, 31,* 329–340.

Rosenbaum, T. Y. (2007a). Pelvic floor involvement in male and female sexual dysfunction and the role of pelvic floor rehabilitation in treatment: A literature review. *Journal of Sexual Medicine, 4,* 4–13.

Rosenbaum, T. Y. (2007b). Physical therapy management and treatment of sexual pain disorders. In S. R. Leiblum (Ed.), *Principles and practice of sex therapy,* (4th ed., pp. 157–180). New York, NY: Guilford.

Rosenberg, Z. F., et al. (2008). Topical microbicides and other chemical barriers for the prevention of STD/HIV infection. In K. Holmes et al. (Eds.), *Sexually transmitted diseases.* (4th ed., pp. 1831–1848). New York, NY: McGraw-Hill.

Rosenblatt, K. A., Wicklund, K., & Stanford, J. (2001). Sexual factors and the risk of prostate cancer. *American Journal of Epidemiology, 153,* 1152–1158.

Rosner, F. (1983). In vitro fertilization and surrogate motherhood: The Jewish view. *Journal of Religion and Health, 22,* 139–160.

Ross, L. E., & Steiner, M. (2003). A biopsychosocial approach to premenstrual dysphoric disorder. *Psychiatric Clinics of North America, 26,* 529–546.

Ross, L. R., & Spinner, B. (2001). General and specific attachment representations in adulthood: Is there a relationship? *Journal of Social and Personal Relationships, 18,* 747–766.

Ross, M. N., Paulsen, J. A., & Stalstrom, O. W. (1988). Homosexuality and mental health: A cross-cultural review. *Journal of Homosexuality, 15,* 131–152.

Ross, M. W. (2005). Typing, being, and doing: Sexuality and the internet. *Journal of Sex Research, 42,* 342–354.

Ross, M. W. (2008). Psychological perspectives on sexuality and sexually transmissible diseases and HIV infection. In K. Holmes et al. (Eds.), *Sexually transmitted diseases.* (4th ed., pp. 137–148). New York, NY: McGraw-Hill.

Ross, M. W., et al. (2007). The advantages and limitations of seeking sex online: A comparison of reasons given for online and offline sexual liaisons by men who have sex with men. *Journal of Sex Research, 44,* 59–71.

Rossouw, J. E., et al. (2007). Postmenopausal hormone therapy and risk of cardiovascular diseases. *Journal of the American Medical Association, 297,* 1465–1477.

Rotello, G. (1997). *Sexual ecology: AIDS and the destiny of gay men.* New York, NY: Dutton.

Rotermann, M. (2005). Sex, condoms, and STDs among young people. *Health Reports, 16,* 39–45.

Rotermann, M. (2007a). Marital breakdown and subsequent depression. *Health Reports, 18*(2), 33–44.

Rotermann, M. (2007b). Second or subsequent births to teenagers. *Health Reports, 18,* 39–42.

Rotermann, M. (2008). Trends in teen sexual behaviour and condom use. *Health Reports, 19,* 1–5.

Rotermann, M. (2012). Sexual behaviour and condom use of 15- to 24-year-olds in 2003 and 2009/10. *Health Reports, 23,* 1–5.

Rotermann, M., Langlois, K. A., Severini, A., & Totten, S. (2013). Prevalence of chlamydia trachomatis and herpes simplex virus type 2: Results from the 2009 to 2011 Canadian Health Measures survey. *Health Reports, 24,*10–15.

Rothblum, E. D. (1994). "I only read about myself on bathroom walls": The need for research on the mental health of lesbians and gay men. *Journal of Consulting and Clinical Psychology, 62,* 213–220.

Rousseau, S., et al. (1983). The expectancy of pregnancy for "normal" infertile couples. *Fertility & Sterility, 40,* 768–772.

Rowland, D. A., & Slob, A. K. (1997). Premature ejaculation: Psychophysiological considerations in theory, research, and treatment. *Annual Review of Sex Research, 8,* 224–253.

Rowland, D. L., & Burnett, A. L. (2000). Pharmacotherapy in treatment of male sexual dysfunction. *Journal of Sex Research, 37,* 226–243.

Royal Commission on New Reproductive Technologies. (1993). *Proceed with care: Final report of the Royal Commission on New Reproductive Technologies.* Ottawa, Canada: Minister of Government Services Canada.

Rubin, Z., et al. (1980). Self-disclosure in dating couples: Sex roles and the ethic of openness. *Journal of Marriage and the Family, 42,* 305–317.

Ruble, D. N. (1977). Premenstrual symptoms: A reinterpretation. *Science, 197,* 291–292.

Ruble, D. N., & Stangor, C. (1986). Stalking the elusive schema: Insights from developmental and social-psychological analyses of gender schemas. *Social Cognition, 4,* 227–261.

Runtz, M. G., & Roche, D. N. (1999). Validation of the trauma symptom inventory in a Canadian sample of university women. *Child Maltreatment, 4*(1), 69–80.

Runtz, M. G., & Schallow, J. R. (1997). Social support and coping strategies as mediators of adult adjustment following childhood maltreatment. *Child Abuse & Neglect, 21,* 211–226.

Rupp, H. A., & Wallen, K. (2008). Sex differences in response to visual sexual stimuli: A review. *Archives of Sexual Behavior, 37,* 206–218.

Rusbult, C. (1983). A longitudinal test of the investment model: The development (and deterioration) of satisfaction and commitment in heterosexual involvements. *Journal of Personality and Social Psychology, 45,* 101–117.

Rusbult, C., Johnson, D. J., & Morrow, G. D. (1986). Predicting satisfaction and commitment in adult romantic involvements: An assessment of the generalizability of the investment model. *Social Psychology Quarterly, 49,* 81–89.

Russell, D. E. H. (1980). Pornography and violence: What does the new research say? In L. Lederer (Ed.), *Take back the night: Women on pornography.* New York, NY: Morrow.

Russell, D. E. H. (1990). *Rape in marriage.* (Rev. ed.). Bloomington, IN: Indiana University Press.

Russell, G. M., & Richards, J. A. (2003). Stressor and resilience factors for Lesbians, Gay men, and Bisexuals confronting antigay politics. *American Journal of Community Psychology, 31,* 313–328.

Rust, P. C. (2000a). Bisexuality: A contemporary paradox for women. *Journal of Social Issues, 56,* 205–221.

Rust, P. C. (2000b). *Bisexuality in the United States: A social science reader.* New York, NY: Columbia University Press.

Rust, P. C. (2001). Two many and not enough: The meaning of bisexual identities. *Journal of Bisexuality, 1,* 31–68.

Rust, P. C. (2002). Bisexuality: The state of the union. *Annual Review of Sex Research, 13,* 180–240.

Ruvalo, J. (2011). How much of the internet actually is for porn? Retrieved from http://www.forbes.com/sites/julieruvalo/2011/09/07/how-much-of-the-internet-is actuallyfor-porn

Ryan, C., et al. (2009). Family rejection as a predictor of negative health outcomes in White and Latino lesbian, gay, and bisexual young adults. *Pediatrics, 123,* 346–352.

Rye, B. J., & Meaney, G. J. (2007a). The pursuit of sexual pleasure. *Sexuality & Culture, 11,* 28–51.

Rye, B. J., & Meaney, G. J. (2007b). Voyeurism: It is good as long as we do not get caught. *International Journal of Sexual Health, 19,* 47–56.

Rye, B. J., & Meaney, G. J. (2009). Impact of a homonegativity awareness workshop on attitudes toward homosexuality. *Journal of Homosexuality, 56,* 31–55.

Rye, B. J., & Meaney, G. J. (2010). Measuring homonegativity: A psychometric analysis. *Canadian Journal of Behavioral Science, 42,*158–167.

Rye, B. J., Greatrix, S. A., & Enright, C. S. (2006). The case of the guilty victim: The effects of gender of victim and gender of perpetrator on attributions of blame and responsibility. *Sex Roles, 54,* 639–649.

Rylko-Bauer, B. (1996). Abortion from a cross-cultural perspective. *Social Science & Medicine, 42,* 479–482.

Sachs-Ericsson, N., et al. (2005). Childhood sexual and physical abuse and the 1-year prevalence of medical problems in the National Comorbidity Survey. *Health Psychology, 24,* 32–40.

Sacred Congregation for the Doctrine of the Faith (1976, January 16). Declaration on certain questions concerning sexual ethics. (English text in the *New York Times,* p. 2).

Saegert, S., Swap, W., & Zajonc, R. B. (1973). Exposure, context, and interpersonal attraction. *Journal of Personality and Social Psychology, 25,* 234–242.

Sáenz de Tejada, I., et al. (2004). Physiology of erectile dysfunction and pathophysiology of erectile dysfunction. In T. F. Lue, R. Basson, R. Rosen, F. Giuliano, S. Khoury, & F. Montorsi (Eds.), *Sexual medicine* (pp. 287–343). Paris, France: Editions 21.

Saewyc, E. M. (2007). Contested Conclusions: Claims That Can (and Cannot) Be Made from the Current Research on Gay, Lesbian, and Bisexual Teen Suicide Attempts. *Journal of LGBT Health Research, 3*(1), 79–87.

Saewyc, E. M., Taylor, D., Homma, Y., & Ogilvie, G. (2008). Trends in sexual health and risk behaviours among adolescent students in British Columbia. *Canadian Journal of Human Sexuality, 17,* 1–13.

Saewyc, E. M. (2011). Research on adolescent sexual orientation: Development, health disparities, stigma, and resilience. *Journal of Research on Adolescence, 21,* 256–272.

Sagarin, E. (1973). Power to the peephole. *Sexual Behavior, 3,* 2–7.

Saleh, F. M., & Berlin, F. S. (2003). Sex hormones, neurotransmitters, and psychopharmacological treatments in men with paraphilic disorders. *Journal of Child Sexual Abuse, 12,* 233–253.

Saleh, F. M., Niel, T., & Fishman, M. J. (2004). Treatment of paraphilia in young adults with leuprolide acetate: A preliminary case report series. *Journal of Forensic Science, 49,* 1343–1348.

Salehi, R., Flicker, S., & the Toronto Teen Survey Team (2010). Predictors of exposure to sexual health education among teens who are newcomers to Canada. *Canadian Journal of Human Sexuality, 19,* 157–168.

Salem, R. N. (2005). World Health Organization updates guidance on how to use contraceptives. *INFO Reports, 4,* Baltimore: Johns Hopkins University.

Salganik, M., & Heckathorn, D. (2004). Sampling and estimation in hidden populations using respondent-driven sampling. *Sociological Methodology, 34,* 193–239.

Salmon, C. (2012). The pop culture of sex: An evolutionary window on the worlds of pornography and romance. *Review of General Psychology, 16,* 152–160.

Samson, J.-M., Levy, J. J., Dupras, A., & Tessier, D. (1991). Coitus frequency among married or cohabiting heterosexual adults: A survey in French Canada. *Australian Journal of Marriage & Family, 12,* 103–109.

Samson, J.-M., Levy, J. J., Dupras, A., & Tessier, D. (1993). Active oralgenital sex among married and cohabiting heterosexual adults. *Sexological Review, 1,* 143–156.

Sanchez, D. T., Kiefer, A. K., & Ybarra, O. (2006). Sexual submissiveness in women: Costs for sexual autonomy and arousal. *Personality and Social Psychology Bulletin, 32,* 512–524.

Sanchez, D. T., et al. (2012). Eroticizing inequality in the United States: The consequences and determinants of traditional gender role adherence in intimate relationships. *Journal of Sex Research, 49,* 168–183.

Sand, M., & Fisher, W. A. (2007). Women's endorsement of models of female sexual response: The nurses' sexuality study. *Journal of Sexual Medicine, 4,* 708–719.

Sandberg, J. (2006). Infant mortality, social networks, and subsequent fertility. *American Sociological Review, 71,* 288–309.

Sanders, S., Graham, C. A., & Milhausen, R. (2008). Predicting sexual problems in women: The relevance of sexual excitation and sexual inhibition. *Archives of Sexual Behavior, 37,* 241–251.

Sandfort, T., & Ehrhardt, A. (2004). Sexual health: A useful public health paradigm or a moral imperative? *Archives of Sexual Behavior, 33,* 181–187.

Sanghavi, D. M. (2006, Oct. 17). Preschool puberty, and a search for the causes. *New York Times.*

Sansone, R. A., & Sansone, L. A. (2007). Cosmetic surgery and psychological issues. *Psychiatry, 4(12),* 65–68.

Santilla, P., Sandnabba, N., K., Laurence, A., & Nordling, N. (2002). Investigating the underlying structure in sadomasochistically oriented behavior. *Archives of Sexual Behavior, 31,* 185–196.

Sardell, R. et al. (2012). Are there indirect fitness benefits to female extra-pair reproduction? Lifetime reproductive success of within-pair and extra-pair off spring. *The American Naturalist, 179.* www.jstor.org/stable/10.1086/665665.

Sauvageau, A., & Racette, S. (2006). Autoerotic deaths in the literature from 1954 to 2004: A review. *Journal of Forensic Science, 51,* 140–146.

Savage, D. (2010, February 4). Gold star pedophiles. *The Stranger.* Retrieved from http://www.thestranger.com/seattle/SavageLove?oid=3347526

Savic, I., et al. (2005). Brain response to putative pheromones in homosexual men. *Proceedings of the National Academy of Sciences, 102,* 7456–7361.

Savin-Williams, R. C. (1995). An exploratory study of pubertal maturation timing and self-esteem among gay and bisexual male youths. *Developmental Psychology, 31,* 56–64.

Savin-Williams, R. C. (2001). Suicide attempts among sexual-minority youths: Population and measurement issues. *Journal of Consulting and Clinical Psychology, 69,* 983–991.

Savin-Williams, R. C. (2006). Who's gay? Does it matter? *Current Directions in Psychological Science, 15,* 40–44.

Savin-Williams, R. C., & Cohen, K. M. (2007). Development of same-sex attracted youth. In I. H. Meyer, & M. E. Northridge (Eds.), *The health of sexual minorities.* (pp. 27–47). NY: Springer. doi:10.1007/978-0-387-31334-4_2

Savin-Williams, R. C., & Ream, G. L. (2003). Suicide attempts among sexual-minority male youth. *Journal of Clinical Child and Adolescent Psychology, 32,* 509–522.

Sayle, A. E., Savitz, D. A., Thorpe, J. M., Jr., Hertz-Picciotto, L., & Wilcox, A. J. (2001). Sexual activity during late pregnancy and risk of preterm delivery. *Obstetrics and Gynecology, 97,* 283–289.

Schachter, S. (1964). The interaction of cognitive and physiological determinants of emotional state. In L. Berkowitz (Ed.), *Advances in experimental social psychology* (Vol. I). New York, NY: Academic.

Schaefer, M. T., & Olson, D. H. (1981). Assessing intimacy: The PAIR Inventory. *Journal of Marital and Family Therapy,* 47–60.

Schafer, G. (2008). Romantic love in heterosexual relationships: Women's experiences. *Journal of Social Science, 16,* 187–197.

Schaffir, J. (2006). Sexual intercourse at term and onset of labor. *Obstetrics and Gynecology, 107,* 1310–1314.

Scharfe, E., & Bartholomew, K. (1995). Accommodation and attachment representations in young couples. *Journal of Social and Personal Relationships, 12,* 389–401.

Schenck, C., Amulf, I., & Mahowald, M. (2007). Sleep and sex: What can go wrong? *Sleep, 30,* 683–702.

Schiavi, R. C., Mandeli, J., & Schreiner-Engel. (1994). Sexual satisfaction in healthy aging men. *Journal of Sex and Marital Therapy, 20,* 3–13.

Schick, V. R., Calabrese, S. K., Rima, B. N., & Zucker, A. N. (2010). Genital appearance dissatisfaction: Implications for women's genital image self-consciousness, sexual esteem, sexual satisfaction, and sexual risk. *Psychology of Women Quarterly, 34,* 394–404.

Schieffelin, E. L. (1976). *The sorrow of the lonely and the burning of the dancers.* New York, NY: St. Martin's Press.

Schmidt, L. (2006). Psychosocial burden of infertility and assisted reproduction. *The Lancet, 367,* 379–380.

Schmiege, S., & Russo, N. F. (2005). Depression and unwanted first pregnancy: Longitudinal cohort study. *British Medical Journal, 331,* 1303.

Schmitt, D. P. (2003). Universal sex differences in the desire for sexual variety: Tests from 52 nations, 6 continents, and 13 islands. *Journal of Personality and Social Psychology, 85,* 85–104.

Schmucker, M., & Losel, F. (2008). Does sexual offender treatment work? A systematic review of outcome evaluations. *Psicothema, 20:* 10–19.

Schneider, M. (1991). Developing service for lesbian and gay adolescents. *Canadian Journal of Community Mental Health, 10,* 133–151.

Schofield, A. T., & Vaughan-Jackson, P. (1913). *What a boy should know.* New York, NY: Cassell.

Schooler, D. et al. (2009). Beyond exposure: A person-oriented approach to adolescent media diets. *Journal of Research on Adolescence, 19,* 484–508.

Schroeder, A. (2000, Jan. 28). The money was great, risks were real. Student reflects on her year as a phone sex operator. *The Brunswickan.*

Schubach, G. (2002). The G-spot is the female prostate. *American Journal of Obstetrics and Gynecology, 186,* 850.

Schultz, W. C. M., Wiel, H. B. M., Klatter, J. A., Sturm, B. E., & Nauta, J. (1989). Vaginal sensitivity to electric stimuli: Theoretical and practical implications. *Archives of Sexual Behavior, 18*(2), 87–96.

Schultz, W. W., van Andel, P., Sabelis, I., & Mooyaart, E. (1999). Magnetic resonance imaging of male and female genitals during coitus and female sexual arousal. *British Medical Journal, 319,* 1596–1600.

Schwartz, L. B. (1997, December 20/27). Understanding human parturition. *The Lancet, 350,* 1792–1793.

Scott, J. P. (1964). The effects of early experience on social behavior and organization. In W. Etkin (Ed.), *Social behavior and organization among vertebrates.* Chicago, IL: University of Chicago Press.

Scott, V. M., Mottarella, K. E., & Lavooy, M. J. (2006). Does virtual intimacy exist? A brief exploration into reported levels of intimacy in online relationships. *Cyberpsychology & Behavior, 9,* 759–761.

Sears, H. A., & Byers, E. S. (2010). Adolescent girls' and boys' experiences of psychologically, physically and sexually aggressive behaviors in their dating relationships: Co-occurrence and emotional reaction. *Journal of Aggression, Maltreatment, & Trauma, 19,* 517–539.

Sears, H. A., Byers, E. S., & Price, E. L. (2007). The co-occurrence of adolescent boys' and girls' use of psychologically, physically, and sexually abusive behaviours in their dating relationships. *Journal of Adolescence, 30,* 487–504.

Sedgh, G., Henshaw, S. K., Singh, S., Bankole, A., & Drescher, J. (2007). Legal abortion worldwide: Incidence and recent trends. *Perspectives on Sexual and Reproductive Health, 39*(4), 216–225.

Segraves, R. T., & Balon, R. (2003). *Sexual pharmacology: Fast facts.* New York, NY: Norton.

Segraves, R. T., & Balon, R. (2010). Recognizing and reversing sexual side effects of medications. In S. Levine (Ed.), *Handbook of clinical sexuality for mental health professionals* (2nd ed., pp. 311–327). London, England: Routledge.

Sell, R. L. (1997). Defining and measuring sexual orientation: A review. *Archives of Sexual Behavior, 26,* 643–658.

Sell, R. L., Wells, J. A., & Wypij, D. (1995). The prevalence of homosexual behavior and attraction in the United States, the United Kingdom and France. *Archives of Sexual Behavior, 24,* 235–248.

Sellors, J. W., Mahoney, J. B., Kczorowski, J., Lytwyn, A., Bangura, H., Chong, S., et al. (2000). Prevalence and predictors of human papillomavirus infection in women in Ontario, Canada. *Canadian Medical Association Journal, 163,* 503–509.

Selvaggi, G., & Elander, A. (2008). Penile reconstruction/formation. *Current Opinion in Urology, 18,* 589–597.

Semple, S. J., et al. (2009). Sexual marathons and methamphetamine use among HIV positive men who have sex with men. *Archives of Sexual Behavior, 38,* 583–590.

Semple, S. J., Patterson, T. L., & Grant, I. (2004). The context of sexual risk behavior among heterosexual methamphetamine users. *Addictive Behaviors, 29,* 807–810.

Senn, C. Y. (2011). An imperfect feminist journey: Reflections on the process to develop an effective sexual assault resistance program for university women. *Feminism & Psychology, 21*(1), 121–137.

Senn, C. Y. (2013). Education on resistance to acquaintance sexual assault: Preliminary promise of a new program for young women in high school and university. *Canadian Journal of Behavioural Science, 45,* 24–33.

Senn, C. Y., & Desmarais, S. (2001). Are our recruitment practices for sex studies working across gender? The effect of topic and gender of recruiter on participation rates of university men and women. *Journal of Sex Research, 38,* 111–117.

Senn, C. Y., & Dzinas, K. (1996). Measuring fear of rape: A new scale. *Canadian Journal of Behavioural Science, 28,* 141–144.

Senn, C. Y., & Radtke, H. L. (1990). Women's evaluations of and affective reactions to mainstream violent pornography, nonviolent pornography and erotica. *Violence and Victims, 5,* 143–155.

Senn, C. Y., Desmarais, S., Verberg, N., & Wood, E. (2000). Predicting coercive sexual behaviour across the lifespan in a random sample of Canadian men. *Journal of Social and Personal Relationships, 17,* 95–113.

Senn, C. Y., Gee, S. S., & Thake, J. (2011). Emancipatory sexuality education and sexual assault resistance: Does the former enhance the latter? *Psychology of Women Quarterly, 35,* 72–91.

Seto, M. C. (2004). Pedophilia and sexual offenses against children. *Annual Review of Sex Research, 15,* 321–361.

Seto, M. C. (2009). Pedophilia. *Annual Review of Clinical Psychology, 5,* 391–407.

Seto, M. C., Cantor, J. M., & Blanchard, R. (2006). Child pornography offenses are a valid diagnostic indicator of pedophilia. *Journal of Abnormal Psychology, 115,* 610–615.

Seto, M. C., et al. (2010b). Sexual coercion experience and sexually coercive behavior: A population study of Swedish and Norwegian male youth. *Child Maltreatment, 15,* 219–228.

Seto, M. C., Lalumière, M. L., & Blanchard, R. (2000). The discriminative validity of a phallometric test for pedophilic interests among adolescent sex offenders against children. *Psychological Assessment, 12,* 319–327.

Seto, M. C., Maric, A., & Barbaree, H. E. (2001). The role of pornography in the etiology of sexual aggression. *Aggression and Violent Behavior, 6,* 35–53.

Seto, M. C., Murphy, W. D., Page, J., & Ennis, L. (2003). Detecting anomalous sexual interests in juvenile sex offenders. *Annals of the New York Academy of Sciences, 898,* 118–130.

Seto, M. C. (2009). Pedophilia. *Annual Review of Clinical Psychology, 5,* 391–407.

Seto, M. C., Lalumière, M. L., Harris, G. T., & Chivers, M. L. (2012). The sexual responses of sexual sadists. *Journal of Abnormal Psychology.* doi:10.1037/a0028714

Setty-Venugopal, V., & Upadhyay, U. D. (2002). Three to five saves lives. Population Reports, Series L, Number 13. Baltimore: Johns Hopkins University School of Public Health.

Sex Industry, The. (1998, February 14). *The Economist,* 21–23.

Sex survey results. (n.d.). *NOW* Toronto. Retrieved from http://www.nowtoronto.com/love/survey.cfm

Shabsigh, R., et al. (2000). Intracavernous alprostadil alfadex (Edex/viridal) is effective and safe in patients with erectile dysfunction after failing sildenafil (Viagra). *Urology, 55,* 477–480.

Shamloul, R. (2005). Treatment of men complaining of short penis. *Urology, 65,* 1183–1185.

Shapiro, C., Trajanovic, N., & Federoff, J. P. (2003). Sexsomnia–A new parasomnia? *Canadian Journal of Psychiatry, 48,* 311–317.

Shapiro, H. T. (1997). Ethical and policy issues in human cloning. *Science, 277,* 195–196.

Sharpstein, D. J., & Kirkpatrick, L. (1997). Romantic jealousy and adult romantic attachment. *Journal of Personality and Social Psychology, 72,* 627–640.

Shattock, R. J., et al. (2011). Turning the tide against HIV. *Science, 333,* 42–43.

Shattuck-Eidens, D., McClure, M., Simard, J., Labrie, F., Narod, S., Couch, F., Hoskins, K., Weber, B., Castilla, L., & Erdos, M. (1995). A collaborative survey of 80 mutations in the BRCA1 breast and ovarian cancer susceptibility gene. *JAMA, 273,* 535–541.

Shaughnessy, K., & Byers, E. S. (2013). Seeing the forest with the trees: Cybersex as a case study of single-item versus multi-item measures of sexual behaviour. *Canadian Journal of Behavioural Science, 45,* 220–229.

Shaughnessy, K., Byers, E. S., & Thornton, S. J. (2011). What is cybersex?: Heterosexual students' definitions. *International Journal of Sexual Health, 23,* 79–89.

Shaughnessy, K., Byers, E. S., & Walsh, L. (2011). Online sexual activity experience of heterosexual students: Gender similarities and differences. *Archives of Sexual Behavior, 40,* 419–427.

Shaver, F. M. (1993). Prostitution: A female crime? In E. Adelberg & C. Currie (Eds.), *In Conflict with the Law: Women and the Canadian Justice System* (pp. 153–173). Vancouver, Canada: Press Gang Publishers.

Shaver, F. M. (1994). The regulation of prostitution: Avoiding morality traps. *CHS/RCDS, 9*(1), 123–145.

Shaver, F. M. (1996a). Prostitution: On the dark side of the service industry. In Tom Fleming (Ed.), *Post critical criminology.* Scarborough, Canada: Prentice Hall.

Shaver, F. M. (1996b). Regulation of prostitution: Setting the morality trap. In B. Schissel & L. Mahood (Eds.), *Social control in Canada.* Toronto, Canada: Oxford University Press.

Shaver, F. M. (2005). Sex work research: Methodological and ethical challenges. *Journal of Interpersonal Violence, 20,* 296–319.

Shaw, J. (2006). *Reality check: A close look at accessing abortion services in Canadian hospitals.* Ottawa, Canada: Canadians for Choice.

Sheff, E. (2005). Polyamorous women, sexual subjectivity, and power. *Journal of Contemporary Ethnographics, 34,* 251–283.

Shell-Duncan, B. (2008). From health to human rights; Female genital cutting and the politics of intervention. *American Anthropologist, 110,* 225–236.

Sherwin, B. B. (1991). The psychoendocrinology of aging and female sexuality. *Annual Review of Sex Research, 2,* 181–198.

Shidlo, A., Schroeder, M., & Drescher, J. (2001). What needs fixing? An introduction. *Journal of Gay & Lesbian Psychotherapy, 5,* 1–4.

Shifren, J. L., Braunstein, G. D., Simon, J. A., Casson, P. R., Buster, J. E., & Redmond, G. P. (2000). Transdermal testosterone treatment in women with impaired sexual function after oophorectomy. *New England Journal of Medicine, 343,* 682–688.

Shifren, J. L., Nahum, R., & Mazer, N. A. (1998). Incidence of sexual dysfunction in surgically menopausal women. *Menopause, 5,* 189–190.

Shirpak, K. R., Maticka-Tyndale, E., & Chinichian, M. (2007). Iranian immigrants' perceptions of sexuality in Canada: A symbolic interactionist approach. *Canadian Journal of Human Sexuality, 16,* 113–128.

Shoveller, J. A., Johnson, J. L., Langille, D. B., & Mitchell, T. (2004). Sociocultural influences on young people's sexual development. *Social Sciences & Medicine, 59,* 473–487.

SIECCAN. (2004). Adolescent sexual and reproductive health in Canada: A report card in 2004. *Canadian Journal of Human Sexuality, 13,* 67–81.

SIECCAN. (2009). Sexual health education in the schools: Questions & answers (3rd ed.). *Canadian Journal of Human Sexuality, 18,* 47–60.

SIECUS. (1991). *Guidelines for comprehensive sexuality education.* New York, NY: Sexuality Information and Education Council of the United States.

Siegel, L. J., & McCormick, C. (1999). *Criminology in Canada: Theories, patterns and typologies.* Scarborough, Canada: ITP Nelson.

Signorile, M. (1997). *Life on the outside: The Signorile report on gay men.* New York, NY: HarperCollins.

Sik Ying Ho, P. (2006). The (charmed) circle game: Reflections on sexual hierarchy through multiple sexual relationships. *Sexualities, 9,* 547–564.

Siker, J. S. (Ed.). (1994). *Homosexuality in the church: Both sides of the debate.* Louisville, KY: Westminster/John Knox Press.

Silvera, M. (1990). Man royal and sodomites: Some thought on the invisibility of Afro-Caribbean lesbians. In S. D. Stone (Ed.), *Lesbians in Canada.* Toronto, Canada: Between the Lines.

Silverberg, C., & Odette, F. (2011). *Sexuality and access project: Survey summary.* Retrieved from http://sexuality-and-access.com

Simms, D. C., & Byers, E. S. (2013). Heterosexual daters' sexual initiation behaviors: Use of the theory of planned behavior. *Archives of Sexual Behavior, 42,* 105–116.

Simon, V., Ho, D., & Karim, Q. (2006). HIV/AIDS epidemiology, pathogenesis, prevention, and treatment. *The Lancet, 368,* 489–504.

Simpson, J. A. (1990). Influence of attachment styles on romantic relationships. *Journal of Personality and Social Psychology, 59,* 971–980.

Simpson, J., Collins, W. A., Tran, S., & Haydon, K. (2007). Attachment and the experience and expression of emotions in romantic relationships: A developmental perspective. *Journal of Personality and Social Psychology, 92,* 355–367.

Singh, D. (1993). Adaptive significance of female physical attractiveness: Role of waist-to-hip ratio. *Journal of Personality and Social Psychology, 65,* 293–307.

Singh, S., & Darroch, J. E. (2000). Adolescent pregnancy and childbearing: Levels and trends in developed countries. *Family Planning Perspectives, 32,* 14–23.

Singh, S., Darroch, J. E., Frost, J. J., & the Study Team. (2001). Socioeconomic disadvantage and adolescent women's sexual and reproductive behavior: The case of five developed countries. *Family Planning Perspectives, 33,* 251–258, 289.

Sinha, M. (2012). Family violence in Canada: A statistical profile, 2010. *Juristat* (Catalogue no. 85-002-X). Ottawa, Canada: Statistics Canada.

Sinha, M. (2013). Measuring violence against women: Statistical trends. *Juristat* (Catalogue no. 85-002-X). Ottawa, Canada: Statistics Canada.

Sipski, M. L., Alexander, C., & Rosen, R. (2001). Sexual arousal and orgasm in women: Effects of spinal cord injury. *Annals of Neurology, 49,* 35–44.

Skaletsky, H., Kuroda-Kawaguchi, T., Minx, P. J., Cordum, H. S., Hillier, L., Brown, L. G., et al. (2003). The male-specific region of the human Y chromosome is a mosaic of discrete sequence classes. *Nature, 423,* 825–837.

Small, M. F. (1993). *Female choices: Sexual behavior of female primates*. Ithaca, NY: Cornell University Press.

Smith, A. M. A., Rissel, C. E., Richters, J., Grulich, A. E., & de Visser, R. O. (2003). Sex in Australia: Sexual identity, sexual attraction and sexual experience among a representative sample of adults. *Australian and New Zealand Journal of Public Health, 27*, 138–145.

Smith, G., Frankel, S., & Yarnell, J. (1997). Sex and death: Are they related? Findings from the Caerphilly cohort study. *British Medical Journal, 315*, 1641–1645.

Smith, J. R., Smith, J. R., Freije, D., Carpten, J. D., Grönberg, H., Xu, J., Isaacs, S. D., Brownstein, M. J., . . . Isaacs, W. B. (1996). Major susceptibility locus for prostate cancer on chromosome 1 suggested by a genome-wide search. *Science, 274*, 1371–1373.

Smith, K. B., Pukall, C. F., Tripp, D. A., & Nickel, J. C. (2007). Sexual and relationship functioning in men with chronic prostatitis/chronic pelvic pain syndrome and their partners. *Archives of Sexual Behavior, 36*, 301–311.

Smith, M. (1999). *Lesbian and gay rights in Canada: Social movements and equality seeking, 1971–1995*. Toronto, Canada: University of Toronto Press.

Smith, T. (2003). *American sexual behavior: Trends, sociodemographic differences, and risk behavior*. University of Chicago, National Opinion Research Center, GSS Topical Report No. 25.

Smith, Y. L. S., van Goozen, S., Kuiper, A., & Cohen-Ketteris, P. (2005). Transsexual subtypes: Clinical and theoretical significance. *Psychiatry Research, 137*, 151–160.

Snowdon, C. T., et al. (2006). Social odours, sexual arousal and pairbonding in primates. *Philosophical Transactions of the Royal Society B, 361*, 2079–2089.

Snowdon, C. T., et al. (2010). Variation in oxytocin is related to variation in affiliative behaviour in monogamous, pair bonded tamarins. *Hormones and Behavior, 58*, 614–618.

Soble, A. (2009). A history of erotic philosophy. *Journal of Sex Research, 46*, 104–120.

Society of Obstetricians and Gynaecologists of Canada. (2013, February 19). Position Statement: *Hormonal Contraception and risk of venous thromboembolism (VTE)*. Ottawa, Canada: Author.

Society of Obstetricians and Gynaecologists of Canada. (2006). Canadian consensus conference on menopause, 2006 update. *Journal of Obstetrics and Gynaecology of Canada, 171*, S7–S10.

Society of Obstetricians and Gynaecologists of Canada. (2007a). Committee Opinion: Mid-trimester amniocentesis fetal loss rate. *Journal of Obstetrics and Gynaecology Canada, 194*, 586–590.

Society of Obstetricians and Gynaecologists of Canada. (2007b). Canadian consensus guideline on continuous and extended hormonal contraception, 2007. *Journal of Obstetrics and Gynaecology of Canada, 29* (7), Supplemental 2.

Society of Obstetricians and Gynaecologists of Canada. (2012). SOGC Committee Opinion: Delayed child-bearing. *Journal of Obstetrics and Gynaecology Canada, 34*, 80–93.

Society of Obstetricians and Gynaecologists of Canada. (2013). Alcohol and pregnancy. Retrieved from http://sogc.org/publications

Sokol, R. J., Delaney-Black, V., & Nordstrom, B. (2003). Fetal alchohol spectrum disorder. *Journal of the American Medical Association, 290*, 2996–2999.

Solms, M. (1997). *The neuropsychology of dreams: A clinico-anatomical study*. Mahwah, NJ: Erlbaum.

Solomon, S. E., Rothblum, E., & Balsam, K. (2005). Money, housework, sex, and conflict: Same-sex couples in civil unions, those not in civil unions, and heterosexual married siblings. *Sex Roles, 52*, 561–576.

Solursh, D. S., Ernst, I. L., Lewis, R. W., Prisant, L. M., Mills, T. M., Solursh, L. P., Jarvis, R. G., Salazar, W. H., & The Human Sexuality Multispecialty Group (2003). The human sexuality education of physicians in North American medical schools. *International Journal of Impotence Research, 15*, S41–S45.

Sommerville, D. M. (2004). *Rape and race in the nineteenth-century South*. Chapel Hill, NC: University of North Carolina Press.

Soon, J. A., Levine, M., Osmond, B. L., Ensom, M. H. H., & Fielding, D. W. (2005). Effects of making emergency contraception available without a physician's prescription: A population-based study. *Canadian Medical Association Journal, 172*, 878–883.

Special, W. P., & Li-Barber, K. T. (2012). Self- disclosure and student satisfaction with Facebook. *Computers in Human Behavior, 28*, 624–630.

Spehr, M., Gisselmann, G., Poplawski, A., Riffell, J. A., Wetzel, C. H., Zimmer, R. K., & Hatt, H. (2003). Identification of a testicular odorant receptor mediating human sperm chemotaxis. *Science, 299*, 2054–2058.

Spourk, R. F. (2002). Dehydroepiandrosterone: A springboard hormone for female sexuality. *Fertility and Sterility, 77*, S19–S25.

Sprecher, S. (1987). The effects of self-disclosure given and received on affection for an intimate partner and stability of the relationship. *Journal of Social and Personal Relationships, 4*, 115–127.

Sprecher, S., Sullivan, Q., & Hatfield, E. (1994). Mate selection preferences: Gender differences examined in a national sample. *Journal of Personality and Social Psychology, 66*, 1074–1080.

Springen, K., & Noonan, D. (2002). Sperm banks go online. MSNBC News 899016.

Sritharan, R., Heilpern, K., Wilbur, C. J., & Gawronski, B. (2010). I think I like you: Spontaneous and deliberate evaluations of potential romantic partners in an online dating context. *European Journal of Social Psychology, 40*(6), 1062–1077.

St. Augustine. (1950). *The city of God*. (Marcus Dods, Trans.). New York, NY: Modern Library.

Stack, S., & Gundlach, J. H. (1992). Divorce and sex. *Archives of Sexual Behavior, 21*, 359–368.

Stafford, L., & Merolla, A. J. (2007). Idealization, reunions, and stability in long distance dating relationships. *Journal of Social and Personal Relationships, 24*, 37–54.

Stamm, W. E. (2008). *Chlamydia trachomatis* infections. In K. Holmes et al. (Eds.), *Sexually transmitted diseases* (4th ed., pp. 575–594). New York, NY: McGraw-Hill.

Stanger-Hall, K., & Hall, D. (2011). Abstinence-only education and teen pregnancy rates: Why we need comprehensive sex education in the U. S. PLoS ONE, 6 (10), e24658. doi:10:1371/journal.pone.0024658

Stanley, S. M., Rhoades, G. K., & Markham, H. J. (2006). Sliding versus deciding: Inertia and the premarital cohabitation effect. *Family Relations, 55*, 499–509.

Stanton, A. L., Lobel, M., Sears, S., & DeLuca, R. (2002). Psychosocial aspects of selected issues in women's reproductive health: Current status and future directions. *Journal of Consulting and Clinical Psychology, 70*, 751–770.

Starks, K. J., & Morrison, E. S. (1996). *Growing up sexual* (2nd ed.). New York, NY: HarperCollins.

Statistics Canada. (1993). The violence against women survey. *The Daily*. Ottawa, Canada: Author.

Statistics Canada. (1995). Therapeutic abortions. *Statistical report on the health of Canadians: Conditions and diseases* (Catalogue no. 82-219-XPB). Ottawa, Canada: Author.

Statistics Canada. (2007, June 13). General Social Survey: Navigating family transitions. *The Daily*.

Statistics Canada. (2008a). Pregnancy Outcomes 2005. Catalogue no. 82-224-X. Ottawa: Author.

Statistics Canada. (2008b). Report on the demographic situatuation in Canada 2005 and 2006. Statistics Canada Catalogue no. 91-209-X. Ottawa, Canada: Industry Canada.

Statistics Canada. (2010, May 10). Canadian Internet use survey. *The Daily*. Retrieved from http://www.statcan.gc.ca/daily-quotidien/100510/dq100510a-eng.htm

Statistics Canada. (2011a). *Health fact sheets: Breast-feeding, 2009* (Catalogue no. 982-625-X). Ottawa, Canada: Author.

Statistics Canada. (2011b). *Conjugal status, Opposite/same-sex status and presence of children for the couple census families in private households of Canada, provinces, territories and census metropolitan areas, 2011 census* (Catalogue no. 98-312-XCB2011046). Ottawa, Canada: Author.

Statistics Canada. (2011c). *Family violence in Canada: A statistical profile* (Catalogue no. 85-224-X). Ottawa, Canada: Author.

Statistics Canada. (2012). Census: Families, households and marital status—Portrait of families and living arrangements in Canada, census year 2011, no. 1: Families, households and marital status, 2011 (Catalogue No. 98-312-X2011001). Ottawa, Canada: Author.

Statistics Canada. (2013). *National household survey, 2011: Immigration and ethnocultural diversity in Canada*. Ottawa, Canada: Author.

Steensma, T. D., et al. (2011). Desisting and persisting gender dysphoria after childhood: A qualitative follow-up study. *Clinical Child Psychology and Psychiatry, 16*, 499–516.

Steensma, T. D., et al. (2012). Gender variance in childhood and sexual orientation in adulthood: A prospective study. *Journal of Sexual Medicine*.

Steinberg, L. (2011). *Adolescence* (9th ed) New York, NY: McGraw-Hill.

Steiner, M. J., & Cates, W. (2006). Condoms and sexually-transmitted infections. *New England Journal of Medicine, 354*, 2642–2643.

Steiner, M. J., et al. (2008). Condoms and other barrier methods for prevention of STD/HIV infection and pregnancy. In K. Holmes et al. (Eds.), *Sexually transmitted diseases*. (4th ed., pp. 1821–1829). New York, NY: McGraw-Hill.

Steiner, M., et al. (2003). Hormones and mood: From menarche to menopause and beyond. *Journal of Affective Disorders, 74*, 67–83.

Stephure, R. J., Boon, S. D., MacKinnon, S. L., & Deveau, V. L. (2009). Internet initiated relationships: Associations between age and involvement in online dating. *Journal of*

Computer-Mediated Communication, 14(3), 658–681. doi:10.1111/j.1083-6101.2009.01457.x

Stern, K., & McClintock, M. K. (1998). Regulation of ovulation by human pheromones. *Nature, 392,* 177–179.

Sternberg, R. J. (1986). A triangular theory of love. *Psychological Review, 93,* 119–135.

Sternberg, R. J. (1987). Liking versus loving: A comparative evaluation of theories. *Psychological Bulletin, 102,* 331–345.

Sternberg, R. J. (1996). Love stories. *Personal Relationships, 3,* 59–79.

Sternberg, R. J. (1997). Construct validation of a triangular love scale. *European Journal of Social Psychology, 27,* 313–335.

Sternberg, R. J. (1998). *Love is a story: A new theory of relationships.* New York, NY: Oxford University Press.

Sternberg, R. J., Hojjat, M., & Barnes, M. L. (2001). Empirical tests of aspects of a theory of love as a story. *European Journal of Personality, 15,* 199–218.

Stevenson, M. R. (1995). Searching for a gay identity in Indonesia. *Journal of Men's Studies, 4,* 93–108.

Stevinson, C., & Ernst, E. (2001). Complementary/alternative therapies for premenstrual syndrome: A systematic review of randomized controlled trials. *American Journal of Obstetrics and Gynecology, 185,* 227–235.

Stobert, S., & Kemeny, A. (2003, Summer). *Childfree by choice* (Catalogue No. 11–008). Ottawa, Canada: Statistics Canada.

Stodghill, R., II. (1998, June 15). Where'd you learn that? *Time 151,* 52–59.

Stone, K. M. (1994). HIV, other STDs, and barriers. In C. Mauck et al. (Eds.), *Barrier contraceptives: Current status and future prospects* (pp. 203–212). New York, NY: Wiley.

Stoneburner, R. L., & Low-Beer, D. (2004). Population-level HIV declines and behavioral risk avoidance in Uganda. *Science, 304,* 714–718.

Storey, A. E., Walsh, C. J., Quinton, R. L., & Wynne-Edwards, K. E. (2000). Hormonal correlates of paternal responsiveness in new and expectant fathers. *Evolution and Human Behavior, 21,* 79–95.

Storms, M. D. (1980). Theories of sexual orientation. *Journal of Personality and Social Psychology, 38,* 783–792.

Stothard, K., et al. (2009). Maternal overweight and obesity and the risk of congenital abnormalities: A systematic review and meta-analysis. *Journal of the American Medical Association, 301,* 636–650.

Strachan, T., & Read, A. P. (2004). *Human molecular genetics* (3rd ed.). New York, NY: Garland Science.

Strandberg-Larsen, K. (2008). Binge drinking in pregnancy and risk of fetal death. *Obstet Gynecol, 111,* 602–609.

Stranges, E., Wier, L., & Elixhauser, A. (2011). *Complicating conditions of vaginal deliveries and Cesarean sections, 2009* (HCUP Statistical Brief #113). Rockville, MD: Agency for Healthcare Research and Quality. Retreive from http://www.hcup-us.ahrq.gov/reports/statbriefs/sb113.pdf

Streissguth, A. P., Barr, H. M., Bookstein, F. L., Sampson, P. D., & Olson, H. C. (1999). The long-term neurocognitive consequences of prenatal alcohol exposure: A 14-year study. *Psychological Science, 10,* 186–190.

Striepe, M. I., & Tolman, D. I. (2003). Mom, Dad, I'm straight: The coming out of gender ideologies in adolescent sexual-identity development. *Journal of Clinical Child and Adolescent Psychology, 32,* 523–530.

Strong, C. (1997). *Ethics in reproductive and perinatal medicine.* New Haven: Yale University Press.

Struckman-Johnson, C., et al. (1996). Sexual coercion reported by men and women in prison. *Journal of Sex Research, 33,* 67–76.

Struckman-Johnson, C., Struckman-Johnson, D., & Anderson, P. B. (2003). Tactics of sexual coercion: When men and women won't take no for an answer. *Journal of Sex Research, 40,* 76–86.

Stryker, S. (1987). The vitalization of symbolic interactionism. *Social Psychology Quarterly, 50,* 83–94.

Stubbs, M. L. (2008). Cultural perceptions and practices around menarche and adolescent menstruation in the United States. *Annals of the New York Academy of Sciences, 1135,* 58–66.

Štulhofer, A., Buško, V., & Landripet, I. (2010). Pornography, sexual socialization, and satisfaction among young men. *Archives of Sexual Behavior, 39*(1), 168–178. doi:10.1007/s10508-008-9387-0

Sun, S. S., et al. (2002). National estimates of the timing of sexual maturation and racial differences among US children. *Pediatrics, 110,* 911–919.

Suschinsky, K. D., Lalumière, M. L., & Chivers, M. L. (2009). Sex differences in patterns of genital sexual arousal: Measurement artifacts or true phenomena?. *Archives of Sexual Behavior, 38*(4), 559–573. doi:10.1007/s10508-008-9339-8

Suschinsky, K. D., & Lalumière, M. L. (2011). Category-specific and sexual concordance: The stability of sex differences in sexual arousal patterns. *Canadian Journal of Human Sexuality, 20,* 93–108.

Sutcliffe, P. A., et al. (2009). Evaluation of surgical procedures for sex reassignment: a systematic review. *Journal of Plastic, Reconstructive & Aesthetic Surgery, 62,* 294–308.

Sutton, K. S., Boyer, S. C., Goldfinger, C., Ezer, P., & Pukall, C. F. (2012). To lube or not to lube: Experiences and perceptions of lubricant use in women with and without dyspareunia. *Journal of Sexual Medicine, 9,* 240–250.

Swaab D. F., Gooren L. J., & Hofman M. A. (1995). Brain research, gender and sexual orientation. *Journal of Homosexuality, 28,* 283–301.

Swaab, D. F. (2005). The role of the hypothalamus and endocrine system in sexuality. In J. Hyde (Ed.), *Biological substrates of human sexuality.* Washington, DC: American Psychological Association.

Swami, V. (2009). An examination of the love-is-blind bias among gay men and lesbians. *Body Image, 6,* 149–151.

Swamy, G., Ostbye, T., & Skjaerven, R. (2008). Association of preterm birth with long-term survival, reproduction, and next generation preterm birth. *Journal of the American Medical Association, 299,* 1429–1436.

Swygard, H., Sena, A. C., Hobbs, M. M., & Cohen, M. S. (2004). Trichomoniasis: Clinical manifestations, diagnosis, and management. *Sexually Transmitted Infections, 80,* 91–95.

Symbalauk, D. G., & Jones, K. M. (1999). Prostitution offender programs: An educational alternative to sentencing. *Law Now, 23,* 38.

Szabo, R. (2000). How does male circumcision protect against HIV infection? *British Medical Journal, 320,* 1592.

Szasz, T. S. (1973). Sex. In *The second sin.* London, England: Routledge & Kegan Paul.

Szasz, T. S. (1980). *Sex by prescription.* Garden City, NY: Anchor Press/Doubleday.

Szielasko, A. L., Symons, D. K., & Price, E. L. (2013). Development of an attachment-informed measure of sexual behavior in late adolescence. *Journal of Adolescence.* doi:10.1016/j.adolescence.2012.12.008

Taberner, P. V. (1985). *Aphrodisiacs: The science and the myth.* Philadelphia, PA: University of Pennsylvania Press.

Tafoya, T., & Wirth, D. A. (1996). Native American two-spirit men. In J. F. Longres (Ed.), *Men of color* (pp. 51–67). New York, NY: Haworth.

Tag-Eldin, M. A., Gadallah, M. A., Al-Tayeb, M. N., Abdel-Aty, M., Mansour, E., & Sallema, M. (2008). Prevalence of female genital cutting among Egyptian girls. *Bulletin of the World Health Organization, 86,* 269–274.

Talamini, J. T. (1982). *Boys will be girls: The hidden world of the heterosexual male transvestite.* Washington, DC: University Press of America.

Talge, N. M., Neal, C., Glover, V., et al. (2007). Antenatal maternal stress and long-term effects on child neurodevelopment: How and why? *Journal of Child Psychology and Psychiatry, 48,* 245–261

Tannahill, R. (1980). *Sex in history.* New York, NY: Stein & Day.

Tannen, D. (1991). *You just don't understand: Women and men in conversation.* New York, NY: William Morrow.

Tanner, J. M. (1967). Puberty. In A. McLaren (Ed.), *Advances in reproductive physiology* (Vol. II). New York, NY: Academic.

Taylor, C., & Peter, T.,with McMinn, T. L., Schachter, K., Beldom, S., Ferry, A., Gross, Z., & Paquin, S. (2011). Every class in every school: The final report on the first national climate survey on homophobia, biphobia, and transphobia in Canadian schools. Toronto: EGALE Canada Human Rights Trust. Retrieved from http://www.egale.ca

Taylor, C., Peter, T., Schachter, K., Paquin, S., Beldom, S., Gross, Z., & McMinn, T. L. (2008). *Youth speak up about homophobia and transphobia: The first National Climate survey on homophobia in Canadian Schools. Phase one report.* Toronto, Canada: Egale Canada Human Rights Trust.

Taylor, D. (2006). From "It's all in your head" to "Taking back the month": Premenstrual syndrome (PMS) research and the contributions of the society for Menstrual Cycle Research. *Sex Roles, 54,* 377–392.

Taylor, L., et al. (2011). "Out of my league": A real-world test of the matching hypothesis. *Personality and Social Psychology Bulletin, 37,* 942–954.

Technical Working Group. (2002). Evaluation of abstinence education programs funded under Title V, Section 510: Interim Report. U. S. Department of Health and Human Services: Office of the Assistant Secretary for Planning and Evaluation.

Tedeschi, R. G., Park, C. L., & Calhoun, L. G. (Eds.). (1998). *Posttraumatic growth: Positive changes in the aftermath of crisis.* Mahwah, NJ: Erlbaum.

Templeman, T. L., & Stinnett, R. D. (1991). Patterns of sexual arousal and history in a "normal" sample of young men. *Archives of Sexual Behavior, 20,* 137–150.

Tennant, P. W. G., Rankin, J., & Bell, R. (2011). Maternal body mass index and the risk of fetal and infant death: A cohort study from the North of England. *Human Reproduction, 26,* 1501–1511.

Terasawa, E., et al. (2012). Body weight impact on puberty: Effects of high-calorie diet on puberty onset in female rhesus monkeys. *Endocrinology, 153,* 1696–1705.

Terman, L. M. (1948). Kinsey's *Sexual Behavior in the Human Male:* Some comments and criticisms. *Psychological Bulletin, 45,* 443–459.

Terman, L., et al. (1938). *Psychological factors in marital happiness.* New York, NY: McGraw-Hill.

Terry, L. L., & Vasey, P. L. (2010). Feederism in a woman. *Archives of Sexual Behavior.* doi:10.1007/s10508-009-9580-9

Tessler Lindau, S., Schumm, L. P., Laumann, E. O., Levinson, W., O'Muircheartaigh, C. A., & Waite, L. J. (2007). A study of sexuality and health among older adults in the United States. *The New England Journal of Medicine, 357,* 762–774.

Testa, M., VanZile-Tamsen, C., & Livingston, J. A. (2005). Childhood sexual abuse, relationship satisfaction, and sexual risk taking in a community sample of women. *Journal of Consulting and Clinical Psychology, 73,* 1116–1124.

Thakker, J., et al. (2008). Rape: Assessment and treatment. In D. R. Laws & W. T. O'Donohue (Eds.), *Sexual deviance* (pp. 356–383). New York, NY: Guilford.

Thibaut, F., et al. (2010). The World Federation of Societies for Biological Psychiatry (WFSBP) guidelines for the biological treatment of paraphilias. *The World Journal of Biological Psychiatry, 11,* 604–655.

Thompson, A. E., & O'Sullivan, L. F. (2012). Gender differences in associations of sexual and romantic stimuli: Do young men really prefer sex over romance? *Archives of Sexual Behavior, 41,* 949–957.

Thompson, A. P. (1983). Extramarital sex: A review of the research literature. *Journal of Sex Research, 19,* 1–22.

Thompson, S. K. (1975). Gender labels and early sex role development. *Child Development, 46,* 339–347.

Thorne, N., & Amrein, H. (2003). Vomeronasal organ: Pheromone recognition with a twist. *Current Biology, 13,* R220–R222.

Thorpe, L. P., Katz, B., & Lewis, R. T. (1961). *The psychology of abnormal behavior.* New York, NY: Ronald Press.

Tiefer, L. (1991). Historical, scientific, clinical, and feminist criticisms of "The Human Sexual Response Cycle" model. *Annual Review of Sex Research, 2,* 1–24.

Tiefer, L. (1994). Three crises facing sexology. *Archives of Sexual Behavior, 23,* 361–374.

Tiefer, L. (2000). Sexology and the pharmaceutical industry: The threat of co-optation. *Journal of Sex Research, 37,* 273–283.

Tiefer, L. (2001). Arriving at a "new view" of women's sexual problems: Background, theory, and activism. In E. Kachak & L. Tiefer (Eds.), *A new view of women's sexual problems* (pp. 63–98). New York, NY: Haworth Press.

Tiefer, L. (2004). *Sex is not a natural act and other essays* (2nd ed.). Boulder, CO: Westview Press.

Tiefer, L. (2008). Female genital cosmetic surgery: Freakish or inevitable? Analysis from medical marketing, bioethics, and feminist theory. *Feminism Psychology, 18,* 466–479.

Tiggemann, M., & Hodgson, S. (2008). The hairlessness norm extended: Reasons for and predictors of women's body hair removal at different body sites. *Sex Roles, 59,* 889–897.

Timmerman, G. (2003). Sexual harassment of adolescents perpetrated by teachers and by peers; An exploration of the dynamics of power, culture, and gender in secondary schools. *Sex Roles, 48,* 231–244.

Tjepkema, M. (2008). Health care use among gay, lesbian and bisexual Canadians. *Health Reports, 19,* 53–64.

Tobin, D. D., Menon, M., Menon, M., Spatta, B. C., Hodges, E. E., & Perry, D. G. (2010). The intrapsychics of gender: A model of self-socialization. *Psychological Review, 117*(2), 601–622.

Tolman, D. L., & McClelland, S. I. (2011). Normative sexuality development in adolescence: A decade in review, 2000–2009. *Journal of Research on Adolescence, 21,* 242–255.

Toppari, J., & Juul, A. (2010). Trends in puberty timing in humans and environmental modifiers. *Molecular and Cellular Endocrinology, 324,* 39–44.

Townsend, J. W. (2003). Reproductive behavior in the context of global population. *American Psychologist, 58,* 197–2004.

Traish, A. M., Kim, N. N., Munarriz, R., Moreland, R., & Goldstein, I. (2002). Biochemical and physiological mechanisms of female genital sexual arousal. *Archives of Sexual Behavior, 31,* 393–400.

Traven, S., Cuyllen, K., & Protter, B. (1990). Female sexual offenders: Severe victims and victimizers. *Journal of Forensic Sciences, 35,* 140–150.

Tremblay, C., Hébert, M., & Piché, C. (1999). Coping strategies and social support as mediators of consequences in child sexual abuse victims. *Child Abuse & Neglect, 23,* 929–945.

Tremblay, C., Hébert, M., & Piché, C. (2000). Type I and type II posttraumatic stress disorder in sexually abused children. *Journal of Child Sexual Abuse, 9,* 65–90.

Tremblay, L., & Frignon J. (2004). Biobehavioural and cognitive determinants of adolescent girls' involvement in sexual risk behaviours: A test of three theoretical models. *Canadian Journal of Human Sexuality, 13,* 29–43.

Trenholm, C., Devaney, B., Fortson, K., Quay, L., Wheeler, J., & Clark, M. (2007). *Impacts of four Title V section 510 abstinence education programs: Final report* (MPR Ref. No. 8549-110). Princeton, NJ: Mathematica Policy Research Inc.

Triandis, H. C., McCusker, C., & Hui, C. H. (1990). Multimethod probes of individualism and collectivism. *Journal of Personality and Social Psychology, 59,* 1006–1020.

Trocmé, N., MacLaurin, B., Fallon, B., Daciuk, J., Billingsley, D., Tourigny, M., et al. (2001). *Canadian Incidence Study of Reported Child Abuse and Neglect: Final Report.* Ottawa, Ontario: Minister of Public Works and Government Services Canada.

Trotter, E. C., & Alderson, K. G. (2007). University students' definitions of having sex, sexual partner, and virginity loss: The influence of participant gender, sexual experience, and contextual factors. *Canadian Journal of Human Sexuality, 16,* 11–29.

Trudel, G. (2002). Sexuality and marital life: Results of a survey. *Journal of Sex & Marital Therapy, 28,* 241–261.

Truitt, W. A., & Coolen, L. (2002). Identification of a potential ejaculation generator in the spinal cord. *Science, 297,* 1566–1569.

Trynka, S., & Tucker, N. (1995). Overview. In N. Tucker (Ed.), *Bisexual politics: Theories, queries, and visions.* New York, NY: Harrington Park Press.

Tsui, L., & Nicoladis, E. (2004). Losing it: Similarities and differences in first intercourse experiences of men and women. *Canadian Journal of Human Sexuality, 13,* 95–106.

Turkle, S. (1995). *Life on the screen: Identity in the age of the Internet.* New York, NY: Simon & Schuster.

Turner, P. K., Runtz, M. G., & Galambos, N. L. (1999). Sexual abuse, pubertal timing, and subjective age in adolescent girls: A research note. *Journal of Reproductive and Infant Psychology, 17*(2), 111–118.

Tutin, C. E. G., & McGinnis, P. R. (1981). Chimpanzee reproduction in the wild. In C. E. Graham (Ed.), *Reproductive biology of the great apes* (pp. 239–264). New York, NY: Academic Press.

Tutty, L. M. (1997). Child sexual abuse prevention programs: Evaluating who do you tell. *Child Abuse & Neglect, 21,* 869–881.

U.S. Bureau of the Census. (2004). Current population survey, Annual social and economic supplement. Table 2: Marital status of the population 15 years and older by age and gender. http://www.census.gov/population/socdemo/gender/2004gender_table2.xls

U.S. General Accounting Office. (1996). *Cycle of sexual abuse: Research inconclusive about whether child victims become adult abusers* (Report number GAO/GGD-96-178). Retrieved from http://www.gpo.gov/fdsys/pkg/GAOREPORTS-GGD-96-178/html/GAOREPORTS-GGD-96-178.htm

Udry, J. R. (1988). Biological predispositions and social control in adolescent sexual behavior. *American Sociological Review, 53,* 709–722.

Udry, J. R., & Eckland, B. K. (1984). Benefits of being attractive: Differential payoffs for men and women. *Psychological Reports, 54,* 47–56.

Udry, J. R., et al. (1985). Serum androgenic hormones motivate sexual behavior in adolescent boys. *Fertility and Sterility, 43,* 90–94.

Ueno, K. (2005). Sexual orientation and psychological distress in adolescence: Examining interpersonal stressors and social support processes. *Social Psychology Quarterly, 68,* 258–277.

Ulmann, A., Teutsch, G., & Philibert, D. (1990, June). RU-486. *Scientific American, 262,* 42–48.

UNAIDS. (2012a). *Fact sheet: Adolescents, young people and HIV.* Retrieved from http://www.unaids.org

UNAIDS. (2012b). *UNAIDS World AIDS Day Report 2012.* Retrieved from http://www.unaids.org/

UNAIDS. (2012c). *UNAIDS World AIDS Day Report 2012:* Global fact sheet. Retrieved from http://www.unaids.org/

UNAIDS. (1997). *Impact of HIV and sexual health education on the sexual behavior of young people.* Geneva, Switzerland: Author.

Underwood, M. K., et al. (2011). The BlackBerry project: Capturing the content of adolescents' text messaging. *Developmental Psychology, 48,* 295–302.

UNESCO. (2005). *Human cloning: Ethical Issues* (2nd ed.). Retrieved from http://unesdoc.unesco.org/images/0013/001359/135928e.pdf

Union for Reform Judaism. (2004). What is the Reform perspective on abortion? Retrieved from http://uahc.org

United Church of Canada, General Council 1980.

United Church of Canada, General Council 1989.

United Synagogue of Conservative Judaism. (1989). Retrieved from http://www.uscj.org

Upadhyay, U. D., et al. (2005). Microbicides: new potential for protection. *Inforeports, 3.* Baltimore: Johns Hopkins School of Public Health. http://www.infoforhealth.org

UPI. (1981, November 5). Toxicologist warns against butyl nitrite. *Delaware Gazette,* p. 3.

Urbina, A., & Jones, K. (2004). Crystal methamphetamine, its analogues, and HIV infection; Medical and psychiatric aspects of a new epidemic. *Clinical Infectious Diseases, 38,* 890–894.

Uy, J. M., Parsons, J. T., Bimbi, D. S., Koken, J. A., & Halkitis, P. N. (2004). Gay and bisexual male escorts who advertise on the Internet: Understanding reasons for and effects of involvement in commercial sex. *International Journal of Men's Health, 3,* 11–26.

Vaillancourt, T., & Aanchai, S. (2011). Intolerance of sexy peers: Intrasexual competition among women. *Aggressive Behavior, 37,* 569–577.

Valentich, M. (1994). Rape revisited: Sexual violence against women in the former Yugoslavia. *Canadian Journal of Human Sexuality, 3,* 53–64.

Valkenburg, P. M., et al. (2011). Gender differences in online and offline self-disclosure in pre-adolescence and adolescence. *British Journal of Developmental Psychology, 29,* 253–269.

Valkenburg, P., & Peter, J. (2009). Social consequences of the Internet for adolescents: A decade of research. *Current Directions in Psychological Science, 18,* 1–5.

Van Anders, S. M., & Watson, N. V. (2006). Menstrual cycle irregularities are associated with testosterone levels in healthy premenopausal women. *American Journal of Human Biology, 18,* 841–844.

Van Anders, S. M., Brotto, L., Farrell, J., & Yule, M. (2009). Associations among physiological and subjective sexual response, sexual desire, and salivary steroid hormones in healthy premenopausal women. *Journal of Sexual Medicine, 6,* 739–751.

Van Anders, S. M., Hamilton, L. D., & Watson, N. V. (2007). Multiple partners are associated with higher testosterone in North American men and women. *Hormones and Behavior, 51,* 454–459.

Van Dongen, S., & Gangestad, S. (2011). Human fluctuating asymmetry in relation to health and quality: A meta-analysis. *Evolution and Human Behavior, 32,* 380–396.

Van Goozen, S. H. M., et al. (1997). Psychoendocrinological assessment of the menstrual cycle: The relationship between hormones, sexuality, and mood. *Archives of Sexual Behavior, 26,* 359–382.

Van Horn, K. R., Arnone, A., Nesbitt, K., Desilets, L., Sears, T., Giffin, M., & Brudi, R. (1997). Physical distance and interpersonal characteristics in college students' romantic relationships. *Personal Relationships, 4,* 25–34.

Van Lankveld, J. (1998). Bibliotherapy in the treatment of sexual dysfunctions: A meta-analysis. *Journal of Consulting and Clinical Psychology, 66,* 702–708.

Van Lankveld, J. (2009). Self-help therapies for sexual dysfunction. *Journal of Sex Research, 46,* 143–155.

Van Lankveld, J., Everaerd, W., & Grotjohann, Y. (2001). Cognitive-behaviorial bibliotherapy for sexual dysfunctions in heterosexual couples: A randomized waiting-list controlled clinical trial in the Netherlands. *Journal of Sex Research, 38,* 51–67.

Van Lankveld, J., ter Kuile, M. M., de Groot, H. E., Melles, R., Nefs, J., & Zandbergen, M. (2006). Cognitive-behavioral therapy for women with lifelong vaginismus: A randomized waiting-list controlled trial of efficacy. *Journal of Consulting and Clinical Psychology, 74,* 168–178.

van Lankveld, J., Granot, M., Weijmar Schultz, W., Binik, Y., Wesselmann, U., . . . Achtrari, C. (2010). Women's sexual pain disorders. *Journal of Sexual Medicine, 7,* 615–631.

Van Lent, P. (1996). Her beautiful savage: The current sexual image of the Native American male. In S. E. Bird (Ed.), *Dressing in feathers: The construction of the Indian in American popular culture* (pp. 211–228). Boulder, CO: Westview.

Vance, E. B., & Wagner, N. N. (1976). Written descriptions of orgasm: A study of sex differences. *Archives of Sexual Behavior, 5,* 87–98.

Vancouver Coastal Health Authority (2009). Supporting sexual health and intimacy in care facilities: Guidelines for supporting adults living in long-term care facilities and group homes in British Columbia, Canada. Retrieved from http://www.sfu.ca

VanderLaan, D. P., & Vasey, P. L. (2008). Mate retention behavior of men and women in heterosexual and homosexual relationships. *Archives of Sexual Behavior, 37,* 572–585.

VanderLaan, D. P., Gothreau, L., Bartlett, N. H., & Vasey, P. L. (2011). Separation anxiety in feminine boys: Pathological or prosocial? *Journal of Gay and Lesbian Mental Health, 15,* 1–16.

Vannier, S. A., & O'Sullivan, L. F. (2008). The feasibility and acceptability of handheld computers in a prospective diary study of adolescent sexual behaviour. *Canadian Journal of Human Sexuality, 17,* 183–192.

Vannier, S. A., & O'Sullivan, L. F. (2011). Communicating interest in sex: Verbal and nonverbal initiation of sexual activity in young adults' romantic dating relationships. *Archives of Sexual Behavior, 40,* 961–969.

Vannier, S. A., & O'Sullivan, L. F. (2012). Who gives and who gets: Why, when, and with whom young people engage in oral sex. *Journal of Youth and Adolescence, 41,* 572–582.

Vanwesenbeeck, I. (1994). *Prostitutes' well-being and risk.* Amsterdam: VU University Press.

Vanwesenbeeck, I. (2001). Another decade of social scientific work on sex work: A review of research 1990–2000. *Annual Review of Sex Research, 12,* 242–289.

Vanwesenbeeck, I. (2005). Burnout among female indoor sex workers. *Archives of Sexual Behavior, 34,* 627–640.

Vanwesenbeeck, I. (2008). Sexual violence and the MDGs. *International Journal of Sexual Health, 20,* 25–49.

Varghese, B., Maher, J. E., Peterman, T. A., Branson, B. M., & Steketee, R. W. (2002). Reducing the risk of sexual HIV transmission: quantifying the per-act risk for HIV on the basis of choice of partner, sex act, and condom use. *Sexually Transmitted Diseases, 29,* 38–43.

Vasey, P. L. (2002). Sexual partner preference in female Japanese macaques. *Archives of Sexual Behavior, 31,* 51–62.

Vasey, P. L., & Bartlett, N. H. (2007). What can the Samoan "fa'afafine" teach us about the Western concept of gender identity disorder in childhood? *Perspectives in Biology and Medicine, 50,* 481–490.

Vasey, P. L., & Duckworth, N. (2008). Female-male mounting in Japanese macaques: The proximate role of sexual reward. *Behavioural Processes, 77,* 405–407. doi:10.1016/j.beproc.2007.07.004

Vasey, P. L., Foroud, A., Duckworth, N., & Kovacovsky, S. D. (2006). Male-female and female-female mounting in Japanese Macaques: A comparative study of posture and movement. *Archives of Sexual Behavior, 35,* 117–129.

Vasey, P. L., VanderLaan, D. P., Gothreau, L. M., & Bartlett, N. H. (2009). Traits of separation anxiety in childhood: A retrospective study of Samoan men, women and *Fa'afafine. Archives of Sexual Behavior.* doi:10.1007/s10508-9009-9589-0

Vasey, P. L., VanderLaan, D. P., Gothreau, L., & Bartlett, N. H. (2011). Traits of separation anxiety in childhood: A comparison of Samoan men, women and *fa'afafine. Archives of Sexual Behavior, 40,* 511–517.

Vasey, P. L., & Bartlett, N. H. (2007). What can the Samoan *fa'afafine* teach us about the Western concept of "Gender Identity Disorder in Childhood"? *Perspectives in Biology and Medicine, 50,* 481–490.

Ve Ard, C., & Veaux, F. (2003). Polyamory 101. Retrieved from http://www.xeromag.com/poly101.pdf

Venicz, L., & Vanwesenbeeck, I. (2000). *Something is going to change in prostitution: Social position and the psychological well being of indoor prostitutes before the law reform.* Utrecht/The Hague, The Netherlands: NISSO/Ministry of Justice.

Venkatesh, S. (2011). How tech tools transformed New York's sex trade. *Wired.* http://www.wired.com/magazine/2011/01/ff_sextrade/all

Vilain, E. (2000). The genetics of sexual development. *Annual Review of Sex Research, 11,* 1–25.

Vincent, J. P., Friedman, L. C., Nugent, J., & Messerly, L. (1979). Demand characteristics in observations of marital interaction. *Journal of Consulting and Clinical Psychology, 47,* 557–566.

Volbert, R. (2000). Sexual knowledge of preschool children. *Journal of Psychology and Human Sexuality, 12,* 5–26.

Volgsten, H., et al. (2008). Prevalence of psychiatric disorders in infertile women and men undergoing *in vitro* fertilization treatment. *Human Reproduction, 23:* 2056–2063.

Von Hertzen, H., Piaggio, G., Ding, J., Chen, J., Song, S., & Bartfai, G. (2002). Low dose mifepristone and two regimens of levonorgestrel for emergency contraception: A WHO multicentre randomised trial. *Lancet, 360,* 1803–1810.

Von Krafft-Ebing, R. (1886). *Psychopathia sexualis.* (Reprinted by Putnam, New York, 1965).

Von Kries, R., Koletzko, B., Sauerwald, T., von Mutius, E., Barnert, D., Grunert, V., von Voss, H. (1999). Breast feeding and obesity: Cross sectional study. *British Medical Journal, 319,* 147–150.

Wade, L., & DeLamater, J. (2002). Relationship dissolution as a life stage transition: Effects on sexual attitudes and behaviors. *Journal of Marriage and the Family, 64,* 898–914.

Waite, L., & Joyner, K. (2000). Emotional and physical satisfaction with sex in married, cohabiting, and dating sexual unions: Do men and women differ? In Edward Laumann & Robert Michael (Eds.), *Sex, love, and health in America: Private choices and public policy* (pp. 239–269). Chicago, IL: University of Chicago Press.

Wald, A., et al. (2005). The relationship between condom use and herpes simplex virus acquisition. *Annals of Internal Medicine, 143,* 707–713.

Walen, S. R., & Roth, D. (1987). A cognitive approach. In J. H. Geer & W. T. O'Donohue (Eds.), *Theories of human sexuality.* New York, NY: Plenum.

Walker, C. (2009). Lest we forget: The Tuskegee experiment. *Journal of Theory Construction & Testing, 13,* 5–6.

Walker, J., Archer, J., & Davies, M. (2005). Effects of rape on men: A descriptive analysis. *Archives of Sexual Behavior, 34,* 69–80.

Walker, L. M., Hampston, A. J., Wassersug, R. J., Thomas, B. C., & Robinson, J. W. (2013). Androgen deprivation therapy and maintenance of intimacy: A randomized controlled pilot study of an educational intervention for patients and their partners. *Contemporary Clinical Trials, 34,* 227–231.

Wallen, K. (2001). Sex and context: Hormones and primate sexual motivation. *Hormones and Behavior, 40,* 339–357.

Wallen, K., & Lloyd, E. (2011). Female sexual arousal: Genital anatomy and orgasm in intercourse. *Hormones and Behavior.* doi:10:1016/j.yhbeh.2010.12.004

Wallen, K., & Parsons, W. A. (1997). Sexual behavior in same-sexed nonhuman primates: Is it relevant to understanding human homosexuality? *Annual Review of Sex Research, 8,* 195–223.

Wallen, K., & Zehr, J. L. (2004). Hormones and history: The evolution and development of primate female sexuality. *Journal of Sex Research, 41,* 101–112.

Wallerstein, E. (1980). *Circumcision: An American health fallacy.* New York, NY: Springer.

Wallin, P. (1949). An appraisal of some methodological aspects of the Kinsey report. *American Sociological Review, 14,* 197–210.

Wallis, C. (2011). Performing gender: A content analysis of gender display in music videos. *Sex Roles, 64,* 160–172.

Walster, E., Walster, W., & Berscheid, E. (1978). *Equity: Theory and research.* Boston, MA: Allyn and Bacon.

Wang, P. J., McCarrey, J., Yang, F., & Page, D. (2001). An abundance of X-linked genes expressed in spermatogonia. *Nature Genetics, 27,* 422–426.

Ward, L. M., & Harrison, K. (2005). The impact of media use on girls' beliefs about gender roles, their bodies, and sexual relationships: A research synthesis. In E. Cole & J. H. Daniel (Eds.), *Featuring females: Feminist analyses of media* (pp. 3–24). Washington, DC: American Psychological Association

Ward, L. M., Hansbrough, E., & Walker, E. (2005). Contributions of music video exposure to Black adolescents' gender and sexual schemas. *Journal of Adolescent Research, 20,* 143–166.

Ward, O. B., Ward, I. L., Denning, J. H., Hendricks, S. E., & French, J. A. (2002). Hormonal mechanisms underlying aberrant sexual differentiation in male rats prenatally exposed to alcohol, stress, or both. *Archives of Sexual Behavior, 31,* 9–16.

Ward, T., Gannon, T., & Yates, P. (2008). The treatment of offenders: Current practice and new developments with an emphasis on sex offenders. *International Review of Victimology, 15:* 179–204.

Wassersug, R. J. (2010). On the invisibility of the emasculated. *Anthropology Today, 26,* 1–3.

Wassersug, R. J., McKenna, E., & Lieberman, T. (2012). Eunuch as a gender identity after castration. *Journal of Gender Studies, 21,* 253–270.

Wassersug, R. J., Zelenietz, S. A., & Squire, G. F. (2004). New age eunuchs: Motivation and rationale for voluntary castration. *Archives of Sexual Behavior, 33,* 433–442.

Waxman, S. E., & Pukall, C. F. (2009). Laser doppler imaging of genital blood flow: A direct measure of female sexual arousal. *Journal of Sexual Medicine, 6,* 2278–2285.

Waynforth, D., Hurtadoa, A. M., & Hillary, K. (1998). Environmentally contingent reproductive strategies in Mayan and Ache Males. *Evolution and Human Behavior, 19,* 369–385.

Weaver, A. D., & Byers, E. S. (2006). The relationships among body image, body mass index, exercise, and sexual functioning in heterosexual women. *Psychology of Women Quarterly, 30,* 333–339.

Weaver, A. D., Byers, E. S., Sears, H. A, Cohen, J. N., & Randall, H. E. S. (2002). New Brunswick parents' attitudes towards sexual health education at school and at home. *Canadian Journal of Human Sexuality, 11,* 19–31.

Weaver, A. D., & Byers, E. S. (2013). Eye of the beholder? Sociocultural factors in the body image and sexual well-being of heterosexual women. *International Journal of Sexual Health, 25,* 128–147.

Weaver, A. D., MacKeigan, K. L., & MacDonald, H. A. (2011). Experiences and perceptions of young adults in friends with benefits relationships: A qualitative study. *Canadian Journal of Human Sexuality, 20,* 41–53.

Weideger, P. (1976). *Menstruation and menopause.* New York, NY: Knopf.

Weinberg, M. S., Shaver, F. S., & Williams, C. J. (1999). Gendered sex work in the San Francisco tenderloin. *Archives of Sexual Behavior, 28,* 503–521.

Weinberg, M. S., Williams, C. J., & Pryor, D. W. (1994). *Dual attraction: Understanding bisexuality.* New York, NY: Oxford University Press.

Weinberg, M., Williams, C., & Calhan, C. (1995). "If the shoe fits . . . ": Exploring male homosexual foot fetishism. *Journal of Sex Research, 32,* 17–27.

Weinberg, T. S. (1987). Sadomasochism in the United States: A review of recent sociological literature. *Journal of Sex Research, 23,* 50–69.

Weinberg, T. S. (1994). Research in sadomasochism: A review of sociological and social psychological literature. *Annual Review of Sex Research, 5,* 257–279.

Weller, L., Weller, A., & Avinir, O. (1995). Menstrual synchrony: Only in roommates who are close friends? *Physiology and Behavior, 58,* 883–889.

Wellings, K., Collumbien, M., Slaymaker, E., Singh, S., Hodges, Z., Patel, D., & Bajos, N. (2006). Sexual and reproductive health 2: Sexual behaviour in context: A global perspective. *The Lancet, 368,* 1706–1728.

Wells, B. E., & Twenge, J. M. (2005). Changes in young people's sexual behavior and attitudes, 1943–1999: A cross-temporal meta-analysis. *Review of General Psychology, 9,* 249–261.

Wells, K. (2009). Research exploring the health, wellness, and safety concerns of sexual minority youth. *Canadian Journal of Human Sexuality, 18,* 221–229.

Wenk, M., & Nieschlag, E. (2006). Male contraception; A realistic option? *The European Journal of Contraception and Reproductive Health Care, 11,* 69–80.

Wentland, J. J., Herold, E. S., Desmarais, S., & Milhausen, R. R. (2009). Differentiating highly sexual women from less sexual women. *Canadian Journal of Human Sexuality, 18,* 169–182.

Wentland, J. J., & Reissing, E. D. (2011). Taking casual sex not too casually: Exploring definitions of casual sexual relationships. *Canadian Journal of Human Sexuality, 20,* 75–91.

Wheeler, G. D., et al. (1984). Reduced serum testosterone and prolactin levels in male distance runners. *Journal of the American Medical Association, 252,* 514–516.

Wheeler, J., Newring, K., & Draper, C. (2008). Transvestic fetishism: Psychopathology and theory. In D. R. Laws, & W. O'Donohue (Eds.), *Sexual Deviance: Theory, Assessment, and Treatment.* (2nd ed., pp. 272–284). New York, NY: Guilford.

Whipple, B., Ogden, G., & Komisanak, B. (1992). Physiological correlates of imagery-induced orgasm in women. *Archives of Sexual Behavior, 21,* 121–133.

Whitam, F. L. (1983). Culturally invariable properties of male homosexuality: Tentative conclusions from cross-cultural research. *Archives of Sexual Behavior, 12,* 207–226.

White, G. L., & Mullen, P. E. (1989). *Jealousy: Theory, research, and clinical strategies.* New York, NY: Guilford.

White, G. L., Fishbein, S., & Rutstein, J. (1981). Passionate love and the misattribution of arousal. *Journal of Personality and Social Psychology, 41,* 56–62.

White, L. J. (2001). Romans 1:26–27: The claim that homosexuality is unnatural. In P. Jung & J. Coray (Eds.), *Sexual diversity and Catholicism* (pp. 133–149). Collegeville, MN: The Liturgical Press.

Whitley, B., Jr. (1993). Reliability and aspects of the construct validity of Sternberg's Triangular Love Scale. *Journal of Social and Personal Relationships, 10,* 475–480.

Wibowo, E., Wassersug, R., Warkentin, K., Walker, L., Robinson, J., Brotto, L., & Johnson, T. (2012). Impact of androgen deprivation therapy on sexual function: a response. Asian Journal of Andrology, 14(5), 793–794.

Wichstrøm, L., & Hegna, K. (2003). Sexual orientation and suicide attempt: A longitudinal study of the general Norwegian adolescent population. *Journal of Abnormal Psychology, 112,* 144–151.

Wickler, W. (1973). *The sexual code.* New York, NY: Anchor Books.

Widmer, M., Villar, J., Benigni, A., Conde-Agudelo, A., Karumanchi, S. A., & Lindheimer, M. (2007). Mapping the theories of preeclampsia and the role of angiogenic factors: A systematic review. *Obstetrics & Gynecology, 109,* 168–180.

Wiederman, M. W., & Hurd, C. (1999). Extradyadic involvement during dating. *Journal of Social and Personal Relationships, 16,* 265–274.

Wiegel, M., Scepkowski, L., & Barlow, D. (2007). Cognitive-affective processes in sexual arousal and sexual dysfunction. In E. Janssen (Ed.), *The psychophysiology of sex* (pp. 143–165). Bloomington, IN: Indiana University Press.

Wierckx, K., Van Caenegem, E., Elaut, E., Dedecker, D., Van de Peer, F., Toye, K., . . . T'Sjoen, G. (2011). Quality of life and sexual health after sex reassignment surgery in Transsexual men. *Journal of Sexual Medicine, 8,* 3379–3388.

Wilcox, A. J., Weinberg, C. R., & Baird, D. D. (1995). Timing of sexual intercourse in relation to ovulation. *New England Journal of Medicine, 333,* 1517–1521.

Wilcox, B. L., & Wyatt, J. (1997). *Adolescent abstinence education programs: A meta-analysis.* Presented at the annual meeting, Society for the Scientific Study of Sexuality, Arlington, VA.

Wilkinson, Ross. (1995). Changes in psychological health and the marital relationship through child bearing: Transition or process as stressor. *Australian Journal of Psychology, 47,* 86–92.

Willetts, M., Sprecher, S., & Beck, F. (2004). Overview of sexual practices and attitudes within relational contexts. In J. H. Harvey, A. Wenzel, & S. Sprecher (Eds.), *The handbook of sexuality in close relationships* (pp. 57–85). Mahwah, NJ: Lawrence Erlbaum.

Williams, C., & Weinberg, M. (2003). Zoophilia in men: A study of sexual interest in animals. *Archives of Sexual Behavior, 32,* 523–535.

Williams, L. M. (1994). Recall of childhood trauma: A prospective study of women's memories of child sexual abuse. *Journal of Consulting and Clinical Psychology, 62,* 1167–1176.

Williams, S., & Lettieri, C. (2012). Sexsomnia: Clinical analysis of an underdiagnosed parasomnia. *Medscape.* Retrieved from http://www.medscape.com

Willness, C. R., et al. (2007). A meta-analysis of the antecedents and consequences of workplace sexual harassment. *Personnel Psychology, 60,* 127–162.

Willoughby, B. J., & Vitas, J. (2012). Sexual desire discrepancy: The effect of individual differences in desired and actual sexual frequency on dating couples. *Archives of Sexual Behavior, 41,* 477–486.

Wilson, G. (1997). Gender differences in sexual fantasy: An evolutionary analysis. *Personality and Individual Differences, 22,* 27–31.

Wilson, G. D. (1987). An ethological approach to sexual deviation. In G. D. Wilson (Ed.), *Variant sexuality: Research and theory.* Baltimore: Johns Hopkins University Press.

Wimpissinger, F., et al. (2009). Magnetic resonance imaging of female prostate pathology. *Journal of Sexual Medicine, 6,* 1704–1711

Wincze, J. P., & Carey, M. P. (2001). *Sexual dysfunction: A guide for assessment and treatment* (2nd ed.). New York, NY: The Guilford Press.

Winer, R. L., & Koutsky, L. A. (2008). Genital human papillomavirus infection. In K. Holmes et al. (Eds.), *Sexually transmitted diseases* (4th ed., pp. 489–508). New York, NY: McGraw-Hill.

Winer, R. L., et al. (2006). Condom use and the risk of genital human papillomavirus infection in young women. *New England Journal of Medicine, 354,* 2645–2654.

Winn, R. L., & Newton, N. (1982). Sexuality in aging: A study of 106 cultures. *Archives of Sexual Behavior, 11,* 283–298.

Winter, J. S. D., & Couch, R. M. (1995). Sexual differentiation. In P. Felig, J. D. Baxter, & L. A. Frohman (Eds.), *Endocrinology and metabolism* (3rd ed., pp. 1053–1104). New York, NY: McGraw-Hill.

Winters, J., Christoff, K., & Gorzalka, B. B. (2009). Conscious regulation of sexual arousal in men. *Journal of Sex Research, 46,* 330–343.

Wisborg, K., et al. (2008). Psychological stress during pregnancy and stillbirth: Prospective study. *BJOG, 115:* 882–885.

Wisniewski, A. B., et al. (2000). Complete androgen insensitivity syndrome: Long-term medical, surgical, and psychosexual outcome. *Journal of Clinical Endocrinology & Metabolism, 85,* 2664–2669.

Wisniewski, A. B., Migeon, C. J., Gearhart, J. P., Rock, J. A., Berkovitz, G. D., Plotnick, L. P., et al. (2001). Congenital micropenis: Long-term medical, surgical, and psychosexual follow-up of individuals raised male or female. *Hormone Research, 56,* 3–11.

Wiswell, T. E., Enzenauer, R. W., Cornish, J. D., & Hawkins, C. T. (1987). Declining frequency of circumcision: Implications for changes in the absolute incidence and male to female sex ratio of urinary tract infections in early infancy. *Pediatrics, 79,* 338–342.

Woertman, L., & van den Brink, F. (2012). Body image and female sexual functioning and behavior: A review. *Journal of Sex Research, 49,* 184–211.

Wohl, A. R., Johnson, D. F., Lu, S., Jordan, W., Beall, G., Currier, J., et al. (2002). HIV risk behaviors among African American men in Los Angeles County who self-identify as heterosexual. *Journal of Acquired Immune Deficiency Syndromes, 31,* 354–360.

Wolak, J., et al. (2008). Online "predators" and their victims. *American Psychologist, 63,* 111–128.

Wolak, J., Mitchell, K., & Finkelhor, D. (2007). Unwanted and wanted exposure to online pornography in a national sample of youth Internet users. *Pediatrics, 119,* 247–257.

Wolff, L., & Geissel, D. (1994). Street prostitution in Canada. *Canadian Social Trends* (Catalogue no. 11-008E). Ottawa, Canada: Statistics Canada.

Wonders, N. A., & Michalowski, R. (2001). Bodies, borders, and sex tourism in a globalized world: A tale of two cities—Amsterdam and Havana. *Social Problems, 48,* 645–571.

Wong, J. K., et al. (1997). Recovery of replication-competent HIV despite prolonged suppression of plasma viremia. *Science, 278,* 1291–1295.

Wong, J. P-H., Chan, K. B.K., Boi-Doku, R., & McWatt, S. (2012). Risk discourse and sexual stigma: Barriers to STI testing, treatment and care among young heterosexual women in disadvantaged neighbourhoods in Toronto. *Canadian Journal of Human Sexuality, 21,* 75–89.

Woo, J. S. T., & Brotto, L. A. (2008). Age of first sexual intercourse and acculturation: Effects on adult sexual responding. *Journal of Sexual Medicine, 5,* 571–582.

Woo, J. S. T., Brotto, L. A., & Gorzalka, B. B. (2009). The role of sexuality in cervical cancer screening among Chinese women. *Health Psychology, 28,* 598–604. doi:10.1037/a0015986

Woo, J. S. T., Brotto, L. A., & Gorzalka, B. B. (2010). Sex guilt and culture-linked barriers to testicular examinations. *International Journal of Sexual Health, 22,* 144–154.

Woo, J. S. T., Brotto, L. A., & Gorzalka, B. B. (2011). The role of sex guilt in the relationship between culture and women's sexual desire. *Archives of Sexual Behavior, 40,* 385–394.

Woo, J. S. T., Brotto, L. A., & Gorzalka, B. B. (2012). The relationship between sex guilt and sexual desire in a community sample of Chinese and Euro-Canadian women. *Journal of Sex Research, 49,* 290–298.

Wood, N. S., et al. (2000). Neurologic and developmental disability after extreme preterm birth. *New England Journal of Medicine, 343,* 378–384.

Woods, L. N., & Emery, R. E. (2002). The cohabitation effect on divorce: Causation or selection? *Journal of Divorce & Remarriage, 37,* 101–122.

Woods, N., et al. (2009). Is the menopausal transition stressful? Observations of perceived stress from the Seattle Midlife Women's Health Study. *Menopause, 16,* 90–97.

Woods, S., & Raju, U. (2001). Maternal smoking and the risk of congenital birth defects: A cohort study. *Journal of the American Board of Family Practice, 14,* 330–334.

Woodzicka, J. A., & LaFrance, M. (2005). The effects of subtle sexual harassment on women's performance in a job interview. *Sex Roles, 53,* 67–78.

Working Group for a New View of Women's Sexual Problems. (2001). Part I: A new view of women's sexual problems. In E. Kachak & L. Tiefer (Eds.), *A new view of women's sexual problems* (pp. 1–8). New York, NY: Haworth Press.

Workowski, K. A., & Berman, S. (2010). Sexually transmitted disease treatment guidelines, 2010. *Morbidity and Mortality Weekly Report, 59,* RR-12.

World Association for Transgender Health (2001). Standards of Care (6th ed.). Retrieved from http://www.wpath.org/publications_standards.cfm

World Health Organization. (1980). *International classification of Impairments, disabilities, and handicaps.* Geneva, Switzerland: Author.

World Health Organization. (2004). *Unsafe abortion: Global and regional estimates of incidence of unsafe abortion and associated mortality in 2000* (4th ed.). Retrieved from http://www.who.int

World Health Organization. (2006). *Defining sexual health: Report of a technical consultation on sexual health, 28–31 January 2002, Geneva.* Retrieved from http://www.who.int/reproductivehealth/topics/gender_rights/defining_sexual_health.pdf

World Health Organization. (2006). Defining sexual health: Report of a technical consultation on sexual health, 28–31 January 2002, Geneva. Retrieved from http://www.who.int/reproductivehealth/topics/gender_rights/defining_sexual_health.pdf

World Health Organization. (2007). *Male circumcision: Global trends and determinants of prevalence, safety and acceptability.* Geneva, World Health Organization. Retrieved from http://www.who.int

World Health Organization. (2009). *Epidemiological fact sheet on HIV and AIDS: 2008 Update.* Geneva SU. Retrieved from http://www.who.int

World Health Organization. (2012). *Female genital mutilation.* Fact sheet No. 241. Retrieved from http://www.who.int/mediacentre/factsheets/fs241/en/

World Professional Association for Transgender Health. (2012). Standards of care. Retrieved from http://www.wpath.org

Worthington, E., Martin, G., Shumate, M., & Carpenter, J. (1983). The effect of brief Lamaze training and social encouragement on pain endurance in a cold pressor task. *Journal of Applied Social Psychology, 13,* 223–233.

Wosick-Correa, K., & Joseph, L. (2008). Sexy ladies sexing ladies: Women as consumers in strip clubs. *Journal of Sex Research, 45,* 201–216.

Wright, J. L., Lin, D. W., & Stanford, J. L. l. (2012). Circumcision and the risk of prostate cancer. *Cancer, 118,* 4437–4443.

Wright, P. J. (2009). Sexual socialization messages in mainstream entertainment mass media: A review and synthesis. *Sexuality & Culture, 13,* 181–200.

Wright, P. J. (2011). Mass media effects on youth sexual behavior: Assessing the claim for causality. *Communication Yearbook, 35,* 343–385.

Wright, V., Schieve, L., Reynolds, M., & Jeng, G. (2005). Assisted reproductive technology surveillance–United States, 2002. *Morbidity and Mortality Weekly Report,54* (SS02), 1–24.

Wyatt, G. E. (1997). *Stolen women: Reclaiming our sexuality, taking back our lives.* New York, NY: Wiley.

Wyatt, G. E., Peters, S. D., & Guthrie, D. (1988). Kinsey revisited, Part I: Comparisons of the sexual socialization and sexual behavior of white women over 33 years. *Archives of Sexual Behavior, 17,* 201–240.

Wyatt, T. D. (2003). *Pheromones and animal behaviour.* New York, NY: Cambridge University Press.

Wylie, K. R., Jones, R., & Walters, S. (2003). The potential benefit of vacuum devices augmenting psychosexual therapy for erectile dysfunction: A randomized controlled trial. *Journal of Sex & Marital Therapy, 29,* 227–236.

Wynn, L. L., Foster, A., and Trussell, J. (2009). Can I get pregnant from oral sex? Sexual health misconceptions in emails to a reproductive health website. *Contraception, 71,* 91–97.

Yee, J. Apale, A. N., & Deleary, M. (2011). Sexual and reproductive health, rights and realities and access to services for First Nations, Inuit, and Métis in Canada. *Journal of Obstetrics & Gynaecology Canada, 33,* 633–637.

Yeh, Hsiu-Chen, Lorenz, F., Wickrama, K. A. S., Conger, R., and Elder, G. H. Jr. (2006). Relationships among sexual satisfaction, marital quality and marital instability at midlife. *Journal of Family Psychology, 20,* 336–343.

Yellowlees, P., & Marks, S. (2007). Problematic Internet use or Internet addiction? *Computers in Human Behavior, 23,* 1447–1453.

Yoder, P. S., Abderrahim, N., & Zhuzhuni, A. (2004). *Female genital cutting in the demographic and health surveys: A critical and comparative analysis.* DHS Comparative Reports No. 7. Calverton, MD: ORC Macro.

Yost, M. R., & Thomas, G. (2012). Gender and binegativity: Men's and women's attitudes toward male and female bisexuals. *Archives of Sexual Behavior, 41,* 691–702.

Yost, M. R., & Zurbriggen, E. L. (2006). Gender differences in the enactment of sociosexuality: An examination of implicit social motives, sexual fantasies, coercive sexual attitudes, and aggressive sexual behavior. *Journal of Sex Research, 43,* 163–173.

Young, A. (2008). The state is still in the bedrooms of the nation: The control and regulation of sexuality in Canadian criminal law. *Canadian Journal of Human Sexuality, 17,* 203–220.

Young, I. (1996). Education for sexuality–the role of the school. *Journal of Biological Education, 30,* 250–255.

Young, K., Griffin-Shelley, E., Cooper, A., O'Mara, J., & Buchananan, J. (2000). Online infidelity: A new dimension in couple relationships with implications for evaluation and treatment. *Sexual Addiction and Compulsivity, 7,* 59–74.

Yule, M. A. (2011) *Furthering our understanding of asexuality: An investigation into biological markers of asexuality, and the development of the Asexuality Identification Scale.* Masters Dissertation. University of British Columbia.

Zak, P. J., Kursban, R. O., & Matzner, W. L. (2004). The neurobiology of trust. *Annals of the New York Academy of Science, 1032,* 224–227.

Zala, S. M., & Penn, D. J. (2004). Abnormal behaviours induced by chemical pollution: A review of the evidence and new challenges. *Animal Behaviour, 68,* 649–664.

Zaviačič, M. (1994). Sexual asphyxiophilia (Koczwarism) in women and the biological phenomenon of female ejaculation. *Medical Hypotheses, 42,* 318–322.

Zaviačič, M., Ablin, R., Ružič, M. Štvrtina, S., Galbavý, S., Danihel, L., Pohlodek, K., Zaviačič, T., Holomáč, K. (2000). Immunohistochemical study of prostatespecific antigen in normal and pathological human tissues: Special reference to the male and female prostate and breast. *Journal of Histotechnology, 23,* 105–111.

Zaviačič, M., Zajíčková, M., Blažeková, J., Donárová, L., Stvrtina, S., Mikulecký, M., Zaviačič, T., Holomáč, K., & Breza, J. (2000). Weight, size, macroanatomy, and histology of the normal prostate in the adult human female: A minireview. *Journal of Histotechnology, 23,* 61–69.

Zax, M., Sameroff, A., & Farnum, J. (1975). Childbirth education, maternal attitude and delivery. *American Journal of Obstetrics and Gynecology, 123,* 185–190.

Zhou, J., Hogman, M., Gooren, L., & Swaab, D. (1995). A sex difference in the human brain and its relation to transsexuality. *Nature, 378,* 68–70.

Zilbergeld, B. (1992). *The new male sexuality.* New York, NY: Bantam Books.

Zilbergeld, B. (1999). *The new male sexuality* (rev. ed.). New York, NY: Bantam Books.

Zilbergeld, B. (1999). The truth about men, sex, and pleasure. In *The new male sexuality* (Rev. ed.). New York, NY: Bantam.

Zilbergeld, B., & Evans, M. (1980, August). The inadequacy of Masters and Johnson. *Psychology Today, 14,* 28–43.

Zillmann, D., Schweitzer, K. J., & Mundorf, N. (1994). Menstrual cycle variations of women's interest in erotica. *Archives of Sexual Behavior, 23,* 579–598.

Zlidar, Vera M., et al. (2003). The reproductive revolution continues. *Population Reports,* Series M, No. 17. Baltimore: Johns Hopkins University School of Public Health.

Zoucha-Jensen, J. M., & Coyne, A. (1993). The effects of resistance strategies on rape. *American Journal of Public Health, 83,* 1633–1634.

Zucker, K. J. (2000). Gender identity disorder. In A. J. Sameroff et al. (Eds.), *Handbook of developmental psychopathology* (2nd ed., pp. 671–686).

Zucker, K. J., Bradley, S. J., Kuksis, M., Pecore, K., Birkenfeld-Adams, A., Doering, R. W., & Wild, J. (1999). Gender constancy judgments in children with gender identity disorder: Evidence for a developmental lag. *Archives of Sexual Behavior, 28*(6), 475–502.

Zucker, K. J., Owen, A., Bradley, S. J., & Ameeriar, L. (2002). Gender-dysphoric children and adolescents: A comparative analysis of demographic characteristics and behavioral problems. *Clinical Child Psychology and Psychiatry, 7*(3), 398–411.

Zucker, K. J., Wilson-Smith, D. N., Kurita, J. A., & Stern, A. (1995). Children's appraisals of sex-typed behaviour in their peers. *Sex Roles, 33,* 703–725.

Zuger, A. (1987, June). AIDS on the wards: A residency in medical ethics. *Hastings Center Report,* 16–20.

Zumpe, D., & Michael, R. P. (1968). The clutching reaction and orgasm in the female rhesus monkey (*Macaca mulatta*). *Journal of Endocrinology, 40,* 117–123.

Zurbriggen, E. L. (2010). Rape, war, and the socialization of masculinity: Why our refusal to give up war ensures that rape cannot be eradicated. *Psychology of Women Quarterly, 34,* 538–549.

Zurbriggen, E. L., & Morgan, E. M. (2006). Who wants to marry a millionaire? Reality dating television programs, attitudes toward sex, and sexual behaviors. Sex Roles, 54, 1–17.

Zussman, L., Zussman, S., Sunley, R., & Bjornson, E. (1981). Sexual response after hysterectomy-oophorectomy. *American Journal of Obstetrics and Gynecology, 140,* 725–729.

Credits

Thinkstock; p. 357: Courtesy of J.R. Heiman; p. 364: MARK BLINCH/Reuters/Landov; p. 368 (both): Courtesy of Dr. Daniel Greenwald; p. 369 (all): Courtesy of Dr. Daniel Greenwald; p. 370: Courtesy of Dr. Daniel Greenwald; p. 372: AP Photo.

Chapter 14
p. 375: © Thinkstock; p. 377: © Scala/Art Resource, NY; p. 383: Camp Fyrefly, www.campfyrefly.ca; p. 384: MARK BLINCH/Reuters / Landov; p. 386: Frank Gunn/CP Images; p. 387: Funded by the Interior Community Services (IHA); p. 389: © Tetra Images/Getty Images; p. 391: Ian Willms/CP Images; p. 392: AP Photo/Chris Pizzello/CP Images; p. 393: © Plush Studios/Brand X Pictures/Getty; p. 394 (both): © Geoff Manasse/IPN/Aurora; p. 403: © Jeff Greenberg/PhotoEdit.

Chapter 15
p. 406: © Digital Vision/PunchStock; p. 408: dashek/iStock/Thinkstock; p. 410: © Eric Gay-Pool/Getty Images; p. 411: PBNJ Productions/Blend Images/Getty Images; p. 412: The Canadian Press/Michael Hudson; p. 419: © Joel Gordon; p. 420: © Alison Joyce; p. 422: © Peter Horree/Alamy; p. 427: Chris Turner/Stone/Getty Images; p. 431: David Harry Stewart/The Image Bank/Getty Images.

Chapter 16
p. 434: © Brand X Pictures/Punchstock; p. 438: © Photofusion Picture Library/Alamy; p. 445: J.T. Lewis/Welland Tribune/Sun Media; p. 446: © Colin McPherson/Corbis; p. 449 (top left): THE CANADIAN PRESS/Chris Young, (top right): CP Picture Archive/Jonathan Hayward, (bottom): © Yvonne Hemsey/ Gamma Liaison; p. 457: © Ryan McVay/Getty Images.

Chapter 17
p. 461: © Jonkmanns/laif/Aurora; p. 463: THE CANADIAN PRESS/Adrian Wyld; p. 465 (logo): Ingram Publishing, (left): © Jaroon Ittiwannapong/Dreamstime.com, (second from left): © Predrag Novakovic/Dreamstime.com, (second from right): Courtesy of KT/Free Range Stock, (right): RubberBall Productions; p. 466: The McGraw-Hill Companies, Inc./Christopher Kerrigan, photographer; p. 471: NB Photos/Alamy; p. 474: © Mats Bakken; p. 477: East News/Liason/Getty Images; p. 479: François Roy/La Presse; p. 481: Axel Koester for The *New York Times*; p. 482: © Kevin Mazur/AMA2012/WireImages; p. 483: © Gary Houlder/Corbis; p. 485: © Joel Gordon; p. 487: © Jack Hollingsworth/Corbis; p. 488: © Dan Callister/Online USA/Getty Images.

Chapter 18
p. 492: © Ryan McVay/Getty Images; p. 502 (left): © Jeff Greenberg/PhotoEdit (right): The McGraw-Hill Companies, Inc./Gary He, photographer; p. 505: © Royalty-free/Corbis; p. 512: Come As You Are Co-Operative; p. 513: © Larry Mulvehill/The Image Works.

Chapter 19
p. 519: © Creatas/Punchstock; p. 526: LEMOINE/SCIENCE PHOTO LIBRARY; p. 527: Fred Chartrand/CP Images; p. 529: Keith Dannemiller/Corbis; p. 530: Chuck Stoody/CP Images; p. 533: © Odilon Dimier/Getty Images; p. 537: Robert Nickelsberg/Getty Images; p. 539: Cusp and Flirt/Masterfile.

Chapter 20
p. 1: © Punchstock; p. 4: The Metropolitan Museum of Art/Art Resource; p. 6: © Hermitage Museum, St. Petersburg, Russia/Superstock; p. 7: Ognissanti Church, Florence, Italy/Bridgeman Art Library; p. 9: © Juliane Thiere/Alamy; p. 10: © Lauren Goodsmith/The Image Works; p. 11: © Sujoy Das/Stock Boston; p. 14: Tom Hanson/CP Images; p. 17: © National Gallery of Art, Washington, D.C./Superstock; p. 19: The United Church of Canada; p. 22: © Najlah Feanny/Stock Boston.

LINE ART AND TEXT

Chapter 1
p. 2: Debbi Rawlins. (2003). *Anything goes.* New York, NY: Harlequin Blaze.

First Person pp. 4–5: Based on an interview by Sandra Byers.

Figure 1.7: © Courtesy of Prof. Robert Gemme, Departement de sexologie, Université du Quebec.

Chapter 2
p. 23: Sigmund Freud. (1924). *A general introduction to psychoanalysis.* New York: Permabooks, 1953 (Boni & Liveright edition, 1924), pp. 26–27. and David Buss. (2000). *The dangerous passion: Why jealousy is as necessary as love and sex.* New York: Free Press, p. 10.

Table 2.1: Adapted by permission of Canada Law Book, a division of Thomson Reuters Canada Limited, from Martin's *Online Criminal Code*, eds. Edward L. Greenspan, The Honourable Justice Marc Rosenberg, and Marie Henein, (A91350-11) http://clb5.canadalawbook.ca/.

Chapter 3
Table 3.1: "Review of the Janus Report on Sexual Behavior" by Samuel S. Janus & Cynthia L. Janus in *Contemporary Sociology*, Vol. 23, no. 2 (March 1994), p. 222, table 1. Reprinted by permission of the American Sociological Association and Andrew M. Greeley.

Figure 3.4: PEARLS BEFORE SWINE © Stephen Pastis/Dist. By UNIVERSAL UCLICK. Reprinted with permission.

Chapter 4
p. 74: Jerry Seinfeld. (1993). *SeinLanguage.* New York: Bantam Books, p. 17.

First Person pp. 94–95: Richard J. Wassersug. (2014). "Prostate cancer, gonadal hormones, and my brain." *Journal of Sex & Marital Therapy*, 40 (5), 355–357. doi:10.1080/0092623X.2014.921477.

Chapter 5
p. 98: "This Way" by Sherri Groveman Morris in *Hermaphrodites with Attitude*, 1995, p. 2. Reprinted by permission of the author.

Chapter 6
p. 124: Boston Women's Health Book Collective. (1998). *Our bodies, ourselves for the new century.* New York: Simon and Schuster, pp. 443, 446.

Table 6.2: Adapted from E. Hetherington and R. Parke, *Child Psychology*, Table 4.2. c McGraw-Hill Companies, Inc. (2003).

First Person p. 145: Written by Trish McCourt.

Figure 6.14: Renault/Sacramento Bee, CA/Rothco. Reprinted by permission.

Chapter 7
p. 162: Paula Weideger. (1976). *Menstruation and menopause.* New York: Knopf, p. 42.

Figure 7.14: Councils of Ministers of Education, (2003). *Canadian Youth, Sexual Health and HIV/AIDS Study: Factors influencing knowledge, attitude, and behaviours.*

Table 7.4: Robert A. Hatcher et al., *Contraceptive technology* (18th ed.), 2007. Adapted by permission of Irvington Publishers.

Chapter 8
First Person pp. 202–203: As told to Krystelle Shaughnessy.

Chapter 9
p. 219: Eric Berne. (1970). *Sex in human loving.* New York: Simon & Schuster, p. 238.

Figure 9.3: Richard Jolley/Cartoon Stock.

First Person pp. 238–239: Written by Kaleigh Trace.

A Sexually Diverse World pp. 248–249: Written by Guy Grenier, PhD.

Chapter 10
p. 256: Sandra L. Bern, 1989, "Genital knowledge and gender consistency in preschool children." *Child Development*, 60, 649–662. Blackwell Publishing Ltd.

Milestones in Sex Research pp. 264–266: With updates and contributions from Erica Doty.

Table 10.1: Boyce et al., (2006). "Sexual health of Canadian youth: Findings from the Canadian youth, sexual health and HIV/AIDS Study." *The Canadian Journal of Human Sexuality*, 15, 59–68.

Figure 10.8: Brooke E. Wells & Jean M. Twenge, "Changes in young people's sexual behavior and attitudes, 1943–1999: A cross-temporal meta-analysis," *Review of General Psychology*, 9, 2005, 249–261 (Figure 2). Reprinted by permission of the American Psychological Association and the author.

Table 10.3: National Campaign to Prevent Teen and Unplanned Pregnancy, 2009. Reprinted with permission.

First Person on pp. 276–277: Kim McKay-McNabb, MA, who is originally from Sakimay First Nation. Her husband Patrick is from George Gordon First Nation.

Figure 10.13: Wentland, J.J. & Reissing, E.D., "Taking casual sex not too casually: Arriving at consensus definitions for different types of casual sexual relationships," *Canadian Journal of Human Sexuality*, 75–91, 2011. Used with permission.

Chapter 11
p. 282: Robert Browning. (1864). *Rabbi Ben Ezra.*

Table 11.3: Based on data from Albright, J. M. (2008). "Sex in America online: an Exploration of Sex, Marital Status, and Sexual Identity in Internet Sex-seeking and its Impacts." *Journal of Sex Research*, 45:2, 175–186.

Milestones in Sex Research pp. 298–299: Written by Krystelle Shaughnessy.

Milestones in Sex Research pp. 310–311: Kleinplatz, P., et al. (2009). The components of optimal sexuality: A portrait of "great sex." *The Canadian Journal of Human Sexuality*, 18, (1–2), 1–13.

Chapter 12
p. 315: Dr. Thomas Moore, "Soul Mates," *Psychology Today*, March–April 1994, downloaded from http://faculty.uccb.ns.ca/pmacintyre/psych365/quotes.htm.

Table 12.1: Edward O. Laumann, et al., *The Social Organization of Sexuality: Sexual Practices in the United States,* pp. 82, 98, 177, 305, 458. Copyright © 1994 University of Chicago Press. Reprinted with permission.

Figure 12.5: PEANUTS © United Feature Syndicate, Inc. Reprinted with permission.

First Person pp. 336–337: Faizal Sahukhan, Ph.D., couples counsellor, sex therapist, university instructor, advice columnist, author. wwwmulticulturalromance.com.

First Person p. 339: Fran Odette, Program Manager of the Women with Disabilities and Violence Program at Springtide Resources (formerly Education Wife Assault) in Toronto.

Figure 12.11: BLONDIE © 2010 King Features Syndicate, Inc. World Rights Reserved. Reprinted with permission.

Chapter 13
p. 349: Dr. William Acton. (1857). *The functions and disorders of the reproductive organs. and* Rogen, S. (2008, July 20). Quoted in the *New York Times Sunday Magazine*, p. 49.

First Person pp. 366–367: Based on an interview with Dr. Jacqueline Cohen.

Milestones in Sex Research pp. 370–371: Courtesy of Professor Paul Vasey, University of Lethbridge.

Chapter 14
p. 376: Pierre Trudeau, 1967, when defending his bill to overhaul the *Criminal Code of Canada,* including statutes that had criminalized consensual same-sex sexual activity. and Jennifer Egan. (2000). Lonely gay teen seeking same. *The New York Times Magazine,* December 10, 2000, p. 113.

Milestones in Sex Research pp. 380–381: Used with permission of Dr. Lori Brotto, University of British Columbia.

First Person p. 390: Lisa M. Diamond in *Sexual Fluidity: Understanding Women's Love and Desire,* pp. 155–158. Copyright © Harvard University Press. Reprinted with permission.

First Person p. 395: Based on an interview by Dr. Jacqueline Cohen.

Chapter 15
First Person pp. 416–417: © Courtesy of Trevor Jacques.

Figure 15.9b: Shoe-New Business © 1982 MacNelly. Distributed by King Features Syndicate. Reprinted by permission.

Chapter 16
p. 437: Hughes, J.O. & Sandler, B.R. (1987). "Friends" raping friends: Could it happen to you? Washington, DC: Association of American Colleges.

First Person p. 439: Based on an interview conducted by Janet Hyde.

Milestones in Sex Research pp. 452–453: Written by James M. Cantor, Ph.D., Centre for Addiction and Mental Health, Toronto, used by permission.

Chapter 17
p. 462: Chief Justice Beverley McLachlin, Supreme Court of Canada, December 20, 2013.

Milestones in Sex Research pp. 468–469: Written by Gayle MacDonald based on Leslie Ann Jeffrey and Gayle MacDonald (2006). *Sex Workers in the Maritimes Talk Back*. Vancouver: UBC Press. Used by permission.

Table 17.1: Martin Rimm, "Marketing Pornography on the Information Superhighway," in *Georgetown Law Journal,* Vol. 83, 1995, p. 1891. *Georgetown Law Journal* © 1995. Reprinted by permission of the publisher.

p. 484: Harry Maurer, *Sex: An Oral History.* Copyright © 1994 by Harry Maurer. Used by permission of Viking Penguin, a division of Penguin Group USA Inc., and by permission of International Creative Management.

Table 17.2: *Frontline,* courtesy of WGBH-TV Boston. Copyright © 1995–2010 WGBH Educational Foundation.

Chapter 18
p. 493: Margaret Avison. (1982). The Agnes Cleves Papers, *In Winter Sun/The Dumbfounding: Poems 1940–66,* Toronto: McClelland & Stewart.

First Person p. 509: Rosemary Basson, "Sexual Desire/Arousal Disorders in Women," in S. Leiblum (Ed.), *Principles and Practice of Sex Therapy* 4e, 2007, pp. 42–43. Reprinted by permission of the Guilford Press.

Chapter 19
p. 520: Michael Barrett (1990), Chair, Sex Information and Education Council of Canada (SIECCAN).

Table 19.1: Boyce, W., Doherty-Poirier, M., Fortin, C., MacKinnon, D. (2003). Canadian youth, sexual health and HIV/AIDS study. Council of Ministers of Education.

Figure 19.1: Reprinted with permission of Torstar Syndication Services. *Dennis the Menace* cartoon by T.M. 1983. *Dennis the Menace* ®: used by permission of Hank Ketcham and © North American Syndicate.

Figure 19.2: margulies/The Journal/Rothco. Used by permission.

Figure 19.7: *What Makes a Baby?* by Cory Silverberg. Used with permission.

Chapter 20
p. 2: James B. Nelson (1992), *Body theology,* Louisville, KY: Westminster/John Knox Press.

Index

F

G

T